# Metals Handbook® Ninth Edition

## Volume 9
## Metallography and Microstructures

*As-drawn hafnium crystal bar. Changes in grain orientation produce different colors when viewed under polarized light. Some twinning is also evident. Specimen was attack polished and heat tinted at ~425 °C (800 °F). 180×. Courtesy of Paul E. Danielson, Teledyne Wah Chang Albany. Additional color micrographs can be found in the article "Color Metallography," which begins on page 135.*

# Metals Handbook® Ninth Edition

## Volume 9
## Metallography and Microstructures

Prepared under the direction of
the ASM Handbook Committee

**Kathleen Mills,** Manager of Editorial Operations
**Joseph R. Davis,** Senior Technical Editor
**James D. Destefani,** Technical Editor
**Deborah A. Dieterich,** Production Editor
**George M. Crankovic,** Assistant Editor
**Heather J. Frissell,** Assistant Editor
**Diane M. Jenkins,** Word Processing Specialist

**William H. Cubberly,** Director of Publications
**Robert L. Stedfeld,** Assistant Director of Publications

Editorial Assistance
**Robert T. Kiepura**
**Bonnie R. Sanders**

AMERICAN SOCIETY FOR METALS
METALS PARK, OHIO 44073

First printing, December 1985

Metals Handbook is a collective effort involving thousands of technical specialists. It brings together in one book a wealth of information from world-wide sources to help scientists, engineers, and technicians solve current and long-range problems.

Great care is taken in the compilation and production of this volume, but it should be made clear that no warranties, express or implied, are given in connection with the accuracy or completeness of this publication, and no responsibility can be taken for any claims that may arise.

Nothing contained in the Metals Handbook shall be construed as a grant of any right of manufacture, sale, use, or reproduction, in connection with any method, process, apparatus, product, composition, or system, whether or not covered by letters patent, copyright, or trademark, and nothing contained in the Metals Handbook shall be construed as a defense against any alleged infringement of letters patent, copyright, or trademark, or as a defense against any liability for such infringement.

Comments, criticisms, and suggestions are invited, and should be forwarded to the American Society for Metals.

Library of Congress Cataloging in Publication Data

American Society for Metals

Metals handbook.

Includes bibliographies and indexes.
Contents: v. 1. Properties and selection—v. 2.
Properties and selection—nonferrous alloys and pure
metals—[etc.]—v. 9. Metallography and microstructures.
1. Metals—Handbooks, manuals, etc. I. American
Society for Metals. Handbook Committee.
TA459.M43    1978      669      78-14934
ISBN 0-87170-007-7 (v. 1)

SAN 204-7586

Printed in the United States of America

# Foreword

*Metallography and Microstructures* is a comprehensive and convenient reference source—and an outstanding example of the special commitment of the American Society for Metals to the field of metallography and recognition of its continued growth and sophistication. In the early 1970s, ASM published Volumes 7 and 8 of the 8th Edition of *Metals Handbook*. The *Atlas of Microstructures of Industrial Alloys* was essentially a picture book, designed to provide a meaningful sampling of normal and abnormal structures and to illustrate the effects of major processing variables and service conditions. *Metallography, Structures and Phase Diagrams* covered metallographic laboratory practices, metallographic structures, and phase diagrams of binary and ternary alloys. When the time came to plan the revision of these Volumes for the 9th Edition, it was decided to combine them into one book (excluding the phase diagrams, which will be published by ASM next year as a two-volume set entitled *Binary Alloy Phase Diagrams*; volumes on ternary and higher order phase diagrams are also planned).

In this latest addition to the prestigious *Metals Handbook* series, the reader will find detailed treatments of every aspect of metallography, from advances in standard specimen preparation methods to the latest computerized color imaging techniques. Coverage has been significantly expanded to encompass more materials and representative microstructures, including information on metallographic techniques associated with metal-matrix and resin-matrix fiber composites. There are brand-new articles written by internationally recognized authorities on etching, on optical, scanning electron, and transmission electron microscopy, and on color metallography.

We would like to express our appreciation for the hard work and dedication of the Handbook staff, the ASM Handbook Committee, and the hundreds of authors, reviewers, and other contributors listed in the next several pages. Many of the more than 3,000 micrographs in this Volume were contributed over the years by friends of ASM and carry no specific attribution in their captions. To these anonymous metallographers we extend special thanks.

John W. Pridgeon
President

Edward L. Langer
Managing Director

The Ninth Edition of Metals Handbook
is dedicated to the memory of
TAYLOR LYMAN, A.B. (Eng.), S.M., Ph.D.
(1917—1973)
Editor, Metals Handbook, 1945—1973

# Preface

Metallography is one of the metallurgist's most valuable tools. Since the pioneering work of Henry Clifton Sorby in petrography and metallography in the 1860s, a multitude of techniques has been developed (particularly during the past 40 years) and applied to the study and characterization of metals and other engineering materials, such as ceramics and polymers. In addition to the conventional optical microscope, the materials scientist can utilize electron microscopes and deploy characterization techniques such as x-ray diffraction, electron microprobe analysis, and field ion microscopy. This Volume examines the development and applicability of optical and electron microscopy as related to the study of metals. A subsequent Volume in this Handbook series (*Materials Characterization*) will detail alternate methods for crystallographic analysis, as well as methods for examining atomic/molecular structure and determining chemical composition.

Metallography is as much an art as a science. The artistry lies in the techniques used to prepare a specimen—sectioning, mounting, grinding, polishing, and etching—and to photograph a specimen. When properly carried out, these techniques result in a micrograph that is both a true representation of the microstructure of a material and a beautifully executed photograph. Five articles in the first Section of this Volume, "Metallographic Techniques," review the methods used to prepare metallographic specimens for optical microscopy. Attention is given to problems that may be encountered and methods for their control and elimination. These are followed by articles explaining the principles and applicability of optical microscopy, scanning electron microscopy, transmission electron microscopy, and quantitative metallography. The final article in this Section, "Color Metallography," is perhaps the most vivid example of the art and beauty of metallography, as evidenced by the eight-page atlas of color micrographs that showcases the work of a number of metallographer/artists.

Detailed specimen preparation procedures for various materials are given in the 34 articles in the Section "Metallographic Techniques and Microstructures: Specific Metals and Alloys." Recommended specimen preparation guidelines, information on the characteristics and constituents of various alloy systems, and a series of representative micrographs are presented in each article. Also included in this Section is an in-depth discussion of the metallography of metal-matrix and resin-matrix fiber composite materials.

The science of metallography lies in the interpretation of structures, which is thoroughly reviewed in the final Section, "Structures." Following an introductory overview of the subject, 18 articles deal with the principles underlying metallographic structures. Among the microstructural features of metals discussed are:

- *Solidification structures,* including those of pure metals, solid solutions, eutectic alloys, steels, aluminum alloy ingots, and copper alloy ingots
- *Transformation structures,* including structures resulting from precipitation from solid solution, spinodal structures, massive transformation structures, eutectoid structures, bainitic structures, martensitic structures, peritectic structures, and ordered structures
- *Deformation and annealing structures,* including structures resulting from plastic deformation, from plastic deformation at elevated temperature, and from recovery, recrystallization, and grain growth
- *Textured structures*
- *Crystal structures*

By virtue of its comprehensive coverage of metallographic techniques and the representation and interpretation of microstructures, metallurgical engineers and technicians should find this Volume a valuable reference work. Undergraduate and graduate students involved in physical metallurgy and/or microscopy coursework should also find it useful.

ASM is grateful to the many authors and reviewers who gave freely of their time and knowledge and to the dozens of engineers and metallographers who contributed the thousands of micrographs published in this Volume. Special thanks are due to Robert J. Gray, George F. Vander Voort, and Paul E. Danielson for their extraordinary efforts and assistance throughout this project. Publication of this Volume would not have been possible without the valuable contributions of all these individuals.

The Editors

# Policy on Units of Measure

By a resolution of its Board of Trustees, the American Society for Metals has adopted the practice of publishing data in both metric and customary U.S. units of measure. In preparing this Handbook, the editors have attempted to present data primarily in metric units based on Système International d'Unités (SI), with secondary mention of the corresponding values in customary U.S. units. The decision to use SI as the primary system of units was based on the aforementioned resolution of the Board of Trustees, the widespread use of metric units throughout the world, and the expectation that the use of metric units in the United States will increase substantially during the anticipated lifetime of this Handbook.

For the most part, numerical engineering data in the text and in tables are presented in SI-based units with the customary U.S. equivalents in parentheses (text) or adjoining columns (tables). For example, pressure, stress, and strength are shown both in SI units, which are pascals (Pa) with a suitable prefix, and in customary U.S. units, which are pounds per square inch (psi). To save space, large values of psi have been converted to kips per square inch (ksi), where one kip equals 1000 pounds. Some strictly scientific data are presented in SI units only.

On graphs and charts, grids correspond to SI-based units, which appear along the left and bottom edges; where appropriate, corresponding customary U.S. units appear along the top and right edges.

Data pertaining to a specification published by a specification-writing group may be given in only the units used in that specification or in dual units, depending on the nature of the data. For example, the typical yield strength of aluminum sheet made to a specification written in customary U.S. units would be presented in dual units, but the thickness specified in that specification might be presented only in inches.

Data obtained according to standardized test methods for which the standard recommends a particular system of units are presented in the units of that system. Wherever feasible, equivalent units are also presented.

Conversions and rounding have been done in accordance with ASTM Standard E 380, with careful attention to the number of significant digits in the original data. For example, an annealing temperature of 1575 °F contains three significant digits. In this instance, the equivalent temperature would be given as 855 °C: the exact conversion to 857.22 °C would not be appropriate. For an invariant physical phenomenon that occurs at a precise temperature (such as the melting of pure silver), it would be appropriate to report the temperature as 961.93 °C or 1763.5 °F. In many instances (especially in tables and data compilations), temperature values in °C and °F are alternatives rather than conversions.

The policy on units of measure in this Handbook contains several exceptions to strict conformance to ASTM E 380; in each instance, the exception has been made to improve the clarity of the Handbook. The most notable exception is the use of $MPa\sqrt{m}$ rather than $MPa \cdot m^{-3/2}$ as the SI unit of measure for fracture toughness. Other examples of such exceptions are the use of "L" rather than "l" as the abbreviation for liter, the use of $g/cm^3$ rather than $kg/m^3$ as the unit of measure for density (mass per unit volume), and the use of $A/cm^2$ rather than $A/m^2$ as the unit of measure for electric current density.

SI practice requires that only one virgule (diagonal) appear in units formed by combination of several basic units. Therefore, all of the units preceding the virgule are in the numerator and all units following the virgule are in the denominator of the expression; no parentheses are required to prevent ambiguity.

# Authors and Reviewers

**Hubert I. Aaronson**
Carnegie-Mellon University
**John K. Abraham**
LTV-Republic Steel Research Center
**N.R. Adsit**
Rohr Industries, Inc.
**Samuel M. Allen**
Massachusetts Institute of Technology
**P. Ambalal**
Lawrence Livermore National Laboratory
**R.J. Barnhurst**
Noranda, Inc. (Canada)
**Edmund F. Baroch**
Consultant
**Charles S. Barrett**
University of Denver
**Charles E. Bates**
Southern Research Institute
**R. Batich**
Brush Wellman Inc.
**Alan M. Bayer**
Teledyne VASCO
**Arlan O. Benscoter**
Bethlehem Steel Corporation
**Michael L. Bess**
Eastern Alloys, Inc.
**Michael B. Bever**
Massachusetts Institute of Technology
**C.R. Bird**
Stainless Foundry & Engineering, Inc.
**George A. Blann**
Buehler Ltd.
**Arne Boe**
Struers, Inc.
**William J. Boettinger**
National Bureau of Standards
**T.F. Bower**
Chase Brass & Copper Company
**Rodney R. Boyer**
Boeing Commercial Airplane Company
**B.L. Bramfitt**
Bethlehem Steel Corporation
**Richard Bratt**
Colt Industries
**John F. Breedis**
Olin Corporation
**Robert J. Brennan**
E.F. Houghton & Company

**Harold Brody**
University of Pittsburgh
**Ronald A. Bulwith**
Alpha Metals, Inc.
**Michael E. Burnett**
The Timken Company
**J.G. Byrne**
University of Utah
**R.L. Caton**
Carpenter Technology Corporation
**Robert Chaney**
Wellman Furnaces, Inc.
**Henry J. Chapin**
Abex Corporation
**James C. Chesnutt**
Rockwell International
**G.Y. Chin**
AT&T Bell Laboratories
**Kenneth J. Clark**
Wellman Dynamics Corporation
**Linda Clements**
San Jose State University
**Hans Conrad**
North Carolina State University
**Richard Corle**
Rockwell International
**L.R. Cornwell**
Texas A&M University
**Carl E. Cross**
Colorado School of Mines
**Robert S. Crouse**
Oak Ridge National Laboratory
**N.J. Culp**
Carpenter Technology Corporation
**Donald S. Dabkowski**
United States Steel Corporation
**Craig B. Dallam**
Colorado School of Mines
**Brian K. Damkroger**
Colorado School of Mines
**Frank Danek**
Cleveland Refractory Metals
**Paul E. Danielson**
Teledyne Wah Chang Albany
**Robert T. DeHoff**
University of Florida
**John A. DeVore**
General Electric Company

**Thomas Diebold**
Colorado School of Mines
**Lee Dillinger**
Leco Corporation
**Carl DiMartini**
ASARCO, Inc.
**David Dozer**
Lockheed Missiles & Space
Company, Inc.
**T.E. Dwyer**
National Steel Corporation
**James Early**
National Bureau of Standards
**Kenneth H. Eckelmeyer**
Sandia National Laboratories
**D.V. Edmonds**
University of Oxford (England)
**G. Elssner**
Max-Planck-Institut für Metallforschung
(West Germany)
**J.D. Embury**
McMaster University
(Canada)
**H.E. Exner**
Max-Planck-Institut für Metallforschung
(West Germany)
**D. Eylon**
Metcut-Materials Research Group
**E.W. Filer**
Cabot Corporation
**M.C. Flemings**
Massachusetts Institute of Technology
**D.Y. Foster**
Carpenter Technology Corporation
**Fred A. Foyle**
Rhenium Alloys, Inc.
**Aaron Freeman**
Kennametal, Inc.
**Paul B. Gallagher**
Columbia Tool Steel Company
**Michael Gigliotti, Jr.**
General Electric Company
**Claus G. Goetzel**
Stanford University
**R.C. Gower**
Carpenter Technology Corporation
**Douglas A. Granger**
Aluminum Company of America

Robert J. Gray
Unitron Inc.
R. Gronsky
University of California at Berkeley
Gary W. Grube
Abex Corporation
Amitava Guha
Brush Wellman Inc.
Richard B. Gundlach
Amax Research & Development Center
Martin N. Haller
Kennametal, Inc.
William B. Hampshire
Tin Research Institute, Inc.
John Harkness
Brush Wellman Inc.
E. Harper
Systems Research Laboratories
Walter T. Haswell
Colt Industries
R.M. Hemphill
Carpenter Technology Corporation
John A. Hendrickson
Wyman-Gordon Company
Helen Henson
Oak Ridge National Laboratory
Tommy Henson
Oak Ridge National Laboratory
Dennis W. Hetzner
The Timken Company
James Hoag
Abex Corporation
William F. Hosford
University of Michigan
Helmut Hoven
Institut für Reaktorwerkstoffe
(West Germany)
Norman S. Hoyer
Westinghouse Electric Corporation
Hsun Hu
University of Pittsburgh
James Lee Hubbard
Georgia Institute of Technology
Paul L. Huber
Seco/Warwick Corporation
Glenn S. Huppi
Colorado School of Mines
K.A. Jackson
AT&T Bell Laboratories
Mitchell A. Jacobs
Taussig Associates, Inc.
Hughston M. James
Carpenter Technology Corporation
N.C. Jessen
Martin Marietta Energy Systems
Wilbur Johns
Rockwell International
Mark J. Johnson
Allegheny Ludlum Steel Corporation
E.A. Jonas
Consulting Metallurgical Engineer
John J. Jonas
McGill University (Canada)
Jerald E. Jones
Colorado School of Mines
Frederick W. Kern
U.S. Steel Corporation

Jon A. Kish
Rhenium Alloys, Inc.
Michael Kim
Rhenium Alloys, Inc.
Roger W. Koch
Ladish Company
Karl Koizlik
Institut für Reaktorwerkstoffe
(West Germany)
T. Kosa
Carpenter Technology Corporation
J.A. Kowalik
Lehigh University
R. Wayne Kraft
Lehigh University
George Krauss
Colorado School of Mines
John B. Lambert
Fansteel
John A. Larson
Ingersoll-Rand Company
David E. Laughlin
Carnegie-Mellon University
James L. Laverick
The Timken Company
Harvie H. Lee
Inland Steel Company
Peter W. Lee
The Timken Company
Franklin D. Lemkey
United Technologies Research Center/
Dartmouth College
William C. Leslie
University of Michigan
Jochen Linke
Institut für Reaktorwerkstoffe
(West Germany)
Stephen Liu
Pennsylvania State University
Ken Lloyd
D.A.B. Industries, Inc.
Richard F. Lynch
Zinc Institute, Inc.
William L. Mankins
Huntington Alloys International
M.J. Marcinkowski
University of Maryland
A.R. Marder
Bethlehem Steel Corporation
James M. Marder
Brush Wellman Inc.
T.B. Massalski
Carnegie-Mellon University
M.S. Masteller
Carpenter Technology Corporation
John E. Masters
American Cyanamid Company
Daniel J. Maykuth
Tin Research Institute, Inc.
James L. McCall
Battelle Columbus Laboratories
George McClary
H. Cross Company
E.J. Minarcik
Lead Industries Association, Inc.
T.E. Mitchell
Case Western Reserve University

L. Mondolfo
Rensselaer Polytechnic Institute
L. Mongeon
Noranda, Inc. (Canada)
Jeremy P. Morse
Huntington Alloys International
William M. Mueller
Colorado School of Mines
Michael S. Nagorka
Colorado School of Mines
James A. Nelson
Buehler Ltd.
Hubertus Nickel
Institut für Reaktorwerkstoffe
(West Germany)
B. Oliver
University of Tennessee
Oliver E. Olsen
Lead Industries Association, Inc.
T. Palomaki
Honeywell Inc.
W.B. Pearson
University of Waterloo (Canada)
Leander F. Pease III
Powder-Tech Associates, Inc.
John H. Perepezko
University of Wisconsin at Madison
A. Jeffrey Perkins
Naval Postgraduate School
Robert N. Peterson
Enduro Stainless, Inc.
G. Petzow
Max-Planck-Institut für Metallforschung
(West Germany)
Mark Podob
Abar Ipsen Industries
Larry E. Pope
Sandia National Laboratories
C.E. Price
Oklahoma State University
S.M. Purdy
National Steel Corporation
Dennis T. Quinto
Kennametal, Inc.
M.R. Randlett
Chase Brass & Copper Company
W.P. Rehrer
Carpenter Technology Corporation
R. Ricksecker
Chase Brass & Copper Company
N. Ridley
University of Manchester (England)
H.C. Rogers
Drexel University
Kempton Roll
Metal Powder Industries Federation
Alton D. Romig, Jr.
Sandia National Laboratories
Charles R. Roper, Jr.
Lukens Steel Company
H.W. Rosenberg
Alta Group
M. Rühle
Max-Planck-Institut für Metallforschung
(West Germany)
Moy Ryvola
Alcan International, Ltd. (Canada)

N. Saenz
  Battelle Pacific Northwest
    Laboratories
Anant V. Samudra
  LTV Steel Company
L.E. Samuels
  Samuels Consulting (Australia)
Ernest A. Schoefer
  Technical Consultant
J. Schruers
  Westinghouse Electric
    Corporation
D.D. Schwemmer
  Rockwell International
Brian Scott
  International Tin Research Institute
    (England)
J. Self
  Colorado School of Mines
Jerome F. Smith
  Lead Industries Association, Inc.
William A. Soffa
  University of Pittsburgh
Peter D. Southwick
  Inland Steel Company
R.E. Spear
  Aluminum Company of
    America
G.R. Speich
  Illinois Institute of Technology

D.L. Sponseller
  Amax Research & Development
    Center
E.E. Stansbury
  University of Tennessee
J.H. Steele, Jr.
  Armco, Inc.
Richard H. Stevens
  Aluminum Company of
    America
Patricia Stumpff
  Air Force Wright Aeronautical
    Laboratories
Dilip K. Subramanyam
  Abex Corporation
C.J. Thwaites
  International Tin Research Institute
    (England)
Milton W. Toaz
  Imperial Clevite, Inc.
H.E. Townsend
  Bethlehem Steel Corporation
Frank J. Toye, Jr.
  Leco Corporation
Rohit Trivedi
  Iowa State University
George B. Tyler
  Reynolds Metals Company
Ervin E. Underwood
  Georgia Institute of Technology

Roy A. Vandermeer
  Naval Research Laboratory
George F. Vander Voort
  Carpenter Technology Corporation
John D. Verhoven
  Iowa State University
Rajat Verma
  Abar Ipsen Industries
Steven E. Wall
  Bendix Corporation
Francis J. Warmuth
  Special Metals Corporation
M.E. Warwick
  International Tin Research Institute
    (England)
D.M. Wayman
  University of Illinois
Elisabeth Weidmann
  Struers, Inc.
William E. White
  Petro-Canada Resources
    (Canada)
C.R. Whitney
  Carpenter Technology Corporation
David B. Williams
  Lehigh University
W.A. Yahraus
  Imperial Clevite, Inc.
J.N. Zgonc
  National Steel Corporation

# Other Contributors

*The following individuals supplied micrographs for this Volume, as did many authors, reviewers, and other anonymous contributors.*

R.L. Anderson
  Westinghouse Research Laboratories
G.L. Armstrong
  U.S. Reduction Company
R.J. Asaro
  Brown University
F. Assmus
  Vacuumschmelze Siemens
    (West Germany)
F.A. Badia
  International Nickel Company, Inc.
R.W. Balluffi
  Cornell University
P. Bania
  Timet
J. Bartholomew
  Chase Brass & Copper Company, Inc.
P.I. Basalyk
  Chase Brass & Copper Company, Inc.
B. Bay
  Danish Academy of Mechanical
    Engineering (Denmark)
C. Brady
  National Bureau of Standards
L.L. Bright
  American Steel Foundries
R.D. Buchheit
  Battelle Columbus Laboratories

M.G. Burke
  University of Pittsburgh
B.C. Buzek
  NASA Lewis Research Center
J.W. Cahn
  Massachusetts Institute of
    Technology
R. Carbonara
  Battelle Columbus Laboratories
D.A. Chatfield
  National Steel Corporation
J.B. Clark
  University of Missouri—Rolla
R.S. Cline
  U.S. Steel Corporation
T. Cobb
  Chase Brass & Copper Company, Inc.
J. Cornie
  Massachusetts Institute of
    Technology
M.H. Cornell
  NLO Inc.
J.E. Costa
  Carnegie-Mellon University
S.L. Couling
  Battelle Columbus Laboratories
A. Datta
  University of Pittsburgh

L.W. Davis
  NETCO
L. Delaey
  Katholieke Universiteit
    (Belgium)
K. Detert
  Vacuumschmelze Siemens
    (West Germany)
J. Dibee
  Chase Brass & Copper Company, Inc.
J.E. Gatehouse
  Bethlehem Steel Corporation
J.J. Gilman
  Allied Chemical Corporation
R.C. Glenn
  U.S. Steel Corporation
S.R. Goodman
  U.S. Steel Corporation
F.E. Goodwin
  International Lead Zinc Research
    Organization
N. Grant
  Massachusetts Institute of Technology
G. Grosse
  Chase Brass & Copper Company, Inc.
N. Hansen
  Riso National Laboratory
    (Denmark)

W.C. Harrigan
DWA Composite Specialties
M. Hatherly
University of New South Wales
(Australia)
M. Henry
General Electric Research &
Development
D. Hull
University of Liverpool (England)
J. Humphries
University of Oxford (England)
M.S. Hunter
Alcoa Research Laboratories
F.I. Hurwitz
NASA Lewis Research Center
G. Ibe
Vacuumschmelze Siemens
(West Germany)
S. Jin
AT&T Bell Laboratories
A.R. Jones
Riso National Laboratory (Denmark)
Anwar-ul Karim
Engineering University (Bangladesh)
R.S. Karz
University of Illinois
T.J. Kelly
International Nickel Company, Inc.
J.R. Kilpatrick
Bethlehem Steel Corporation
M. Kitada
Hitachi Ltd. (Japan)
J.W. Koger
Martin Marietta
M.M. Lappin
Sandia National Laboratories
P.K. Lattari
Texas Instruments, Inc.
M. Lee
San Jose State University
P.R. Lee
NASA Ames Research Center
I. Lefever
Katholieke Universiteit
(Belgium)
D.S. Lieberman
University of Illinois
J.D. Livingston
General Electric Research &
Development
A.C. Lon
Phillips Petroleum Company
T. Long
Boeing Commercial Airplane Company
D.M. Maher
AT&T Bell Laboratories
A.S. Malin
University of New South Wales
(Australia)
J.J. Manganello
Chrysler Corporation
M.E. McAllaster
Sandia National Laboratories

H. McQueen
Sir George Williams University (Canada)
D. Metzler
University of Pittsburgh
J.T. Michalak
U.S. Steel Corporation
M.K. Miller
Oak Ridge National Laboratory
P.N. Mincer
Battelle Columbus Laboratories
L.R. Morris
Alcan Kingston Laboratories
(Canada)
R. Moss
Ford Aerospace and Communications
Corporation
A.W. Mullendore
Sandia Corporation
G. Müller
Struers GmbH (West Germany)
A. Needleman
Brown University
J.R. Patel
AT&T Bell Laboratories
N.E. Paton
North American Rockwell Corporation
H.W. Paxton
U.S. Steel Corporation
J.F. Peck
Massachusetts Institute of Technology
L. Penn
Midwest Research Institute
R.L. Perry
Bethlehem Steel Corporation
W.G. Pfann
AT&T Bell Laboratories
V.A. Phillips
General Electric Company
K.M. Prewo
United Technologies Research Center
S.V. Ramani
NASA Ames Research Center
B.B. Rath
U.S. Steel Corporation
T. Redden
General Electric Company
W. Reinsch
Timet
W.H. Rowley, Jr.
The Stackpole Corporation
M.A. Scherling
University of Illinois
C. Scholl
Wyman-Gordon Company
M. Scott
Bethlehem Steel Corporation
G. Shaw
Midwest Research Institute
D. Shechtman
Technion, Israel Institute of Technology
M.J. Shemanski
AT&T Bell Laboratories
H.M. Shih
NASA Ames Research Center

J.W. Shilling
Allegheny Ludlum Steel Corporation
V.L. Shultes
Boeing Vertol Company
J.R. Sims
Square D Company
D.P. Skinner
Princeton Gamma-Tech, Inc.
E. Snell
Lawrence Livermore National
Laboratory
R.L. Snyder
Bendix Aircraft Brake and Strut Division
C.N. Su
The Aerospace Corporation
D.A. Thomas
Massachusetts Institute of Technology
G. Thomas
University of California—Berkeley
D. Tyler
Olin Corporation Metals Research
Laboratories
J.L. Uvira
Steel Company of Canada, Ltd.
J.M. Van Orden
Lockheed Corporation
G.B. Wadsworth
Boeing Vertol Company
E. Walden
Lockheed Corporation
H. Warlimont
Max-Planck-Institut für Metallforschung
(West Germany)
B. Weinberger
Struers, Inc.
J. Williams
North American Rockwell Corporation
J.C. Williams
Carnegie-Mellon University
D.J. Willis
Broken Hill Proprietary Company, Ltd.
(Australia)
P. Wingert
GTE Products Corporation
W.N. Wise
NLO Inc.
G.J. Wiskow
Falk Corporation
D.A. Witmer
University of Denver
W.A. Wong
McGill University (Canada)
J.H. Wood
General Electric Company
S.A. Wright
Bethlehem Steel Corporation
P. Yaffe
Chase Brass & Copper Company, Inc.
K.P. Young
ITT Engineered Metal Processes
A. Zeltser
University of Pittsburgh
J.E. Zimmer
Acurex Corporation, Aerotherm Division

# Contents

# Terms and Definitions

## A

**aberration.** Any error that causes image degradation. Such an error may be chromatic, spherical, astigmatic, or comatic and can result from design, execution, or both. See also *astigmatism, chromatic aberration, coma,* and *spherical aberration.*

**abrasion.** The process of grinding or wearing away through the use of abrasives; a roughening or scratching of a surface due to abrasive wear.

**abrasion artifact.** A false structure introduced during an abrasion stage of a surface-preparation sequence.

**abrasion fluid.** A liquid added to an abrasion system. The liquid may act as a lubricant, as a coolant, or as a means of flushing abrasion debris from the abrasion track.

**abrasion process.** An abrasive machining procedure in which the surface of the workpiece is rubbed against a two-dimensional array of abrasive particles under approximately constant load.

**abrasion rate.** The rate at which material is removed from a surface during abrasion. It is usually expressed in terms of the thickness removed per unit of time or distance traversed.

**abrasive.** A substance capable of removing material from another substance in machining, abrasion, or polishing that usually takes the form of several of small, irregularly shaped particles of a hard material.

**abrasive machining.** A machining process in which the points of abrasive particles are used as machining tools. Grinding is a typical abrasive machining process.

**abrasive wear.** The removal of material from a surface when hard particles slide or roll across the surface under pressure. The particles may be loose or may be part of another surface in contact with the surface being abraded. Contrast with *adhesive wear.*

**accelerating potential.** A relatively high voltage applied between the cathode and anode of an electron gun to accelerate electrons.

**achromatic.** Free of color. A lens or objective is achromatic when corrected for longitudinal chromatic aberration for two colors. See also *achromatic objective.*

**achromatic objective.** Objectives are achromatic when corrected chromatically for two colors, generally red and green, and spherically for light of one color, usually in the yellow-green portion of the spectrum.

**acicular alpha.** A product of nucleation and growth from $\beta$ to the lower temperature allotrope $\alpha$ phase. It may have a needlelike appearance in a photomicrograph and may have needle, lenticular, or flattened bar morphology in three dimensions. See also *alpha.*

**acid extraction.** Removal of phases by dissolution of the matrix metal in an acid. See also *extraction.*

**adhesive wear.** The removal of material from a surface by the welding together and subsequent shearing of minute areas of two surfaces that slide across each other under pressure. Contrast with *abrasive wear.*

**age hardening.** Hardening by aging, usually after rapid cooling or cold working. See also *aging.*

**aging.** A change in properties that occurs at ambient or moderately elevated temperatures after hot working, heat treating, or cold working (strain aging). The change in properties is often due to a phase change (precipitation), but does not alter chemical composition. See also *age hardening, artificial aging, interrupted aging, natural aging, overaging, precipitation hardening, precipitation heat treatment, progressive aging, quench aging, step aging,* and *strain aging.*

**alignment.** A mechanical or electrical adjustment of the components of an optical device so that the path of the radiating beam coincides with the optical axis or other predetermined path in the system. See also *magnetic alignment, mechanical alignment,* and *voltage alignment.*

**allotriomorphic crystal.** A crystal having a normal lattice structure but an outward shape that is imperfect, because it is determined to some extent by the surroundings. The grains in a metallic aggregate are allotriomorphic crystals. Compare with *idiomorphic crystal.*

**allotropy.** The property by which certain elements may exist in more than one crystal structure. See also *polymorphism.*

**alloying element.** An element added to and remaining in a metal that changes structure and properties.

**alloy system.** A complete series of compositions produced by mixing in all proportions any group of two or more components, at least one of which is a metal.

**alpha, α.** The low-temperature allotrope of titanium with a hexagonal close-packed crystal structure that occurs below the $\beta$ transus.

**alpha-beta structure.** A microstructure containing $\alpha$ and $\beta$ as the principal phases at a specific temperature. See also *beta.*

**alpha brass.** A solid-solution phase of one or more alloying elements in copper having the same crystal lattice as copper.

**alpha case.** The oxygen-, nitrogen-, or carbon-enriched, $\alpha$-stabilized surface resulting from elevated temperature exposure. See also *alpha stabilizer.*

**alpha double prime (orthorhombic martensite).** A supersaturated, nonequilibrium orthorhombic phase formed by a diffusionless transformation of the $\beta$ phase in certain alloys.

**alpha iron.** Solid phase of pure iron that is stable below 910 °C (1670 °F), possesses the body-centered cubic lattice, and is ferromagnetic below 768 °C (1415 °F).

**alpha prime (hexagonal martensite).** A supersaturated, nonequilibrium hexagonal $\alpha$ phase formed by a diffusionless transformation of the $\beta$ phase. It is often difficult to distinguish from acicular $\alpha$, although the latter is usually less well defined and frequently has curved, instead of straight, sides.

**alpha stabilizer.** An alloying element that dissolves preferentially in the $\alpha$ phase and raises the $\alpha$-$\beta$ transformation temperature.

**alpha transus.** The temperature that designates the phase boundary between the $\alpha$ and $\alpha + \beta$ fields.

**amplifier.** A negative lens used instead of an eyepiece to project under magnification the image formed by an objective. The amplifier is designed for flatness of field and should be used with an apochromatic objective.

**analyzer.** An optical device capable of producing plane-polarized light. It is used f⟨ detecting the effect of the object on p'⟨ polarized light produced by the ⟨

**angle of reflection.** (1) Reflectio⟨ between the reflected beam⟨ to the reflecting surfac⟨ (2) Diffraction: the⟨ fracted beam a⟨

**angstrom unit** (Å⟨ equal to $10^{-10}$ n⟨ an accepted SI un⟨ for small distances, ⟨ tances, and some wav⟨

**angular aperture.** In optical microscopy, the angle between the most divergent rays that can pass through a lens to form the image of an object. See also *aperture (optical)*.

**anisotropy.** Characterized by having different values of a property in different directions.

**annealing.** A generic term denoting a treatment—heating to and holding at a suitable temperature followed by cooling at a suitable rate—used primarily to soften metallic materials, but also to produce desired changes simultaneously in other properties or in microstructure. When applied only for the relief of stress, the process is called stress relieving or stress-relief annealing. In ferrous alloys, annealing is carried out above the upper critical temperature, but the time-temperature cycles vary widely in maximum temperature attained and cooling rate used, depending on composition, material condition, and desired results. See also *black annealing, blue annealing, box annealing, bright annealing, cycle annealing, flame annealing, graphitizing, isothermal annealing, malleablizing, process annealing, quench annealing, spheroidizing,* and *subcritical annealing.* In nonferrous alloys, annealing cycles are designed to remove part or all the effects of cold working (recrystallization may or may not be involved), cause complete coalescence of precipitates from the solid solution in relatively coarse form, or both, depending on composition and material condition. See also *anneal to temper, final annealing, intermediate annealing, recrystallization annealing,* and *stress relieving.*

**annealing carbon.** See *temper carbon.*

**annealing twin.** A twin formed in a crystal during recrystallization.

**annealing twin bands.** See *twin bands.*

**anneal to temper.** A final partial anneal that softens a cold-worked nonferrous alloy to a specified level of hardness or tensile strength.

**anode aperture.** In electron microscopy, the opening in the accelerating voltage anode shield of an electron gun through which the electrons must pass to illuminate or irradiate the specimen.

**anodic etching.** Development of microstructure by selective dissolution of the polished surface under application of a direct current. Variation with layer formation: anodizing.

**aperture (electron).** See *anode aperture, condenser aperture,* and *physical objective aperture.*

**aperture (optical).** In optical microscopy, the working diameter of a lens or a mirror. See also *angular aperture.*

**[ap]lanatic.** Corrected for spherical aberration [a]nd coma.

**[ac]hromatic objective.** Objectives corrected [achr]omatically for three colors and spheri[cally] for two colors are called apochro[mats.] These corrections are superior to [those of] the achromatic series of lenses. Be[cause apo]chromats are not well corrected

for lateral color, special eyepieces are used to compensate. See also *achromatic.*

**artifact.** A feature of artificial character, such as a scratch or a piece of dust on a metallographic specimen, that can be erroneously interpreted as a real feature. See also *abrasion artifact, mounting artifact,* and *polishing artifact.*

**artificial aging.** Aging above room temperature. Compare with *natural aging.*

**astigmatism.** A defect in a lens or optical system that causes rays in one plane parallel to the optical axis to focus at a distance different from those in the plane at right angles to it.

**ASTM grain size number.** See *grain size.*

**athermal.** Not isothermal. Changing rather than constant temperature conditions.

**atomic replica.** A thin replica devoid of structure on the molecular level. It is prepared by the vacuum or hydrolytic deposition of metals or simple compounds of low molecular weight. See also *replica.*

**atomic scattering factor, $f$.** The ratio of the amplitude of the wave scattered by an atom to that scattered by a single electron.

**attack-polishing.** Simultaneous etching and mechanical polishing.

**austempering.** Cooling (quenching) an austenitized steel at a rate high enough to suppress formation of high-temperature transformation products, then holding the steel at a temperature below that for pearlite formation and above that for martensite formation until transformation to an essentially bainitic structure is complete.

**austenite.** Generally, a solid solution of one or more alloying elements in a face-centered cubic polymorph of iron ($\gamma$-iron). Specifically, in carbon steels, the interstitial solid solution of carbon in $\gamma$-iron.

**austenitic grain size.** The size attained by the grains in steel when heated to the austenitic region. This may be revealed by appropriate etching of cross sections after cooling to room temperature.

**austenitizing.** Forming austenite by heating a ferrous alloy into the transformation range (partial austenitizing) or above the transformation range (complete austenitizing).

**average grain diameter.** The mean diameter of an equiaxed grain section whose size represents all the grain sections in the aggregate being measured. See also *grain size.*

**axial ratio.** The ratio of the length of one axis to that of another, for example, $c/a$, or the continued ratio of three axes, such as $a:b:c$.

**axis (crystal).** The edge of the unit cell of a space lattice. Any one axis of any one lattice is defined in length and direction relative to other axes of that lattice.

## B

**back reflection.** The diffraction of x-rays at a Bragg angle approaching 90°.

**backing film.** A film used as auxiliary support for the thin replica or specimen-supporting film.

**bainite.** A eutectoid transformation product of ferrite and a fine dispersion of carbide generally formed below 450 to 500 °C (840 to 930 °F). Upper bainite is an aggregate that contains parallel lath-shape units of ferrite, produces the so-called "feathery" appearance in optical microscopy, and is formed above approximately 350 °C (660 °F). Lower bainite, which has an acicular appearance similar to tempered martensite, is formed below approximately 350 °C (660 °F).

**banding.** Inhomogeneous distribution of alloying elements or phases aligned in filaments or plates parallel to the direction of working. See also *ferrite-pearlite banding* and *segregation banding.*

**barrel distortion.** See *negative distortion.*

**basal plane.** That plane of a hexagonal or tetragonal crystal perpendicular to the axis of highest symmetry. Its Miller indices are (001).

**basketweave.** Alpha platelets with or without interleaved $\beta$ platelets that occur in colonies in a Widmanstätten structure.

**beta, $\beta$.** The high-temperature allotrope of titanium with a body-centered cubic crystal structure that occurs above the $\beta$ transus.

**beta eutectoid stabilizer.** An alloying element that dissolves preferentially in the $\beta$ phase, lowers the $\alpha$-$\beta$ to $\beta$ transformation temperature, and results in $\beta$ decomposition to $\alpha$ plus a compound. This eutectoid reaction can be sluggish for some alloys.

**beta fleck.** Alpha-lean region in the $\alpha$-$\beta$ microstructure significantly larger than the primary $\alpha$ width. This $\beta$-rich area has a $\beta$ transus measurably below that of the matrix. Beta flecks have reduced amounts of primary $\alpha$ that may exhibit a morphology different from the primary $\alpha$ in the surrounding $\alpha$-$\beta$ matrix.

**beta isomorphous stabilizer.** An alloying element that dissolves preferentially in the $\beta$ phase, lowers the $\alpha$-$\beta$ to $\beta$ transformation temperature without a eutectoid reaction, and forms a continuous series of solid solutions with $\beta$-titanium.

**beta structure.** Structurally analogous body-centered cubic phases (similar to $\beta$-brass) or electron compounds that have ratios of three valence electrons to two atoms.

**beta transus.** The minimum temperature above which equilibrium $\alpha$ does not exist. For $\beta$ eutectoid additions, the $\beta$ transus ordinarily is applied to hypoeutectoid compositions or those that lie to the left of the eutectoid composition.

**bifilar eyepiece.** A filar eyepiece with motion in two mutually perpendicular directions.

**binary alloy.** Any specific composition in a binary system.

**binary system.** The complete series of compositions produced by mixing a pair of components in all proportions.

**binodal curve.** In a two-dimensional phase diagram, a continuous line consisting of both of the pair of conjugate boundaries of a two-phase equilibrium that join without inflection at a critical point. See also *miscibility gap*.

**birefringence.** A double-refraction phenomenon in anisotropic materials in which an unpolarized beam of light is divided into two beams with different directions and relative velocities of propagation. The amount of energy transmitted along an optical path through a crystal that exhibits birefringence becomes a function of crystalline orientation.

**bivariant equilibrium.** A stable state among several phases equal to the number of components in a system and in which any two of the external variables of temperature, pressure, or concentration may be varied without necessarily changing the number of phases. Sometimes termed divariant equilibrium.

**black annealing.** Box annealing of ferrous alloy sheet, strip, or wire.

**blackbody.** A hypothetical "body" that completely absorbs all incident radiant energy, independent of wavelength and direction, that is, that neither reflects nor transmits any of the incident radiant energy.

**blocky alpha.** Alpha phase that is considerably larger and more polygonal in appearance than the primary $\alpha$ in the sample. It may arise from extended exposure high in the $\alpha$-$\beta$ phase field or by slow cooling through the $\beta$ transus during forging or heat treating. It may be removed by $\beta$ recrystallization, or all-$\beta$ working, followed by further $\alpha$-$\beta$ work, and may accompany grain-boundary $\alpha$.

**blowholes.** A hole produced in a casting or weld by gas trapped during solidification.

**blue annealing.** Heating hot-rolled ferrous sheet in an open furnace to a temperature within the transformation range, then cooling in air to soften the metal. A bluish oxide surface layer forms.

**body-centered.** Having an atom or group of atoms separated by a translation of $1/2$, $1/2$, $1/2$ from a similar atom or group of atoms. The number of atoms in a body-centered cell must be a multiple of 2.

**boundary grain.** In the Jeffries' method for grain size measurement, a grain that is intersected by the boundary of the standard area and is therefore counted only as one half of a grain.

**box annealing.** Annealing of a metal or alloy in a sealed container under conditions that minimize oxidation. See also *black annealing*.

**Bragg angle.** The angle between the incident beam and the lattice planes considered.

**Bragg equation.** $n\lambda = 2d \sin \theta$, where $n$ is the order of reflection, $\lambda$ the wavelength of x-rays, $d$ the distance between lattice planes, and $\theta$ the Bragg angle. See also *order (in x-ray reflection)*.

**Bragg method.** A method of x-ray diffraction in which a single crystal is mounted on a spectrometer with a crystal face parallel to the axis of the instrument.

**bright annealing.** Annealing in a protective medium to prevent discoloration of the bright surface.

**bright-field illumination.** For reflected light, the form of illumination that causes specularly reflected surfaces normal to the axis of the microscope to appear bright. For transmission electron microscopy, the illumination of an object so that it appears on a bright background.

**brittle fracture.** Rapid fracture preceded by little or no plastic deformation.

**brittleness.** The tendency of a material to fracture without first undergoing significant plastic deformation.

**buffer.** A substance added to aqueous solutions to maintain a constant hydrogen-ion concentration even in the presence of acids or alkalis.

**burning.** (1) During austenitizing, permanent damage of a metal or alloy by heating to cause incipient melting or intergranular oxidation. See also *overheating*. (2) During subcritical annealing, particularly in continuous annealing, production of a severely decarburized and grain-coarsened surface layer that results from excessively prolonged heating to an excessively high temperature. (3) In grinding, sufficient heating of the workpiece to cause discoloration or to change the microstructure by tempering or hardening.

**burnishing.** Smoothing surfaces through frictional contact between the workpiece and some hard pieces of material, such as hardened steel balls.

## C

**capping (of abrasive particles).** A mechanism of deterioration of abrasive points in which the points become covered by caps of adherent abrasion debris.

**carbide.** A compound of carbon with one or more metallic elements.

**carbon potential.** A measure of the capacity of an environment containing active carbon to alter or maintain, under prescribed conditions, the carbon concentration in a steel.

**carbon restoration.** Replacing the carbon lost in the surface layer during previous processing by carburizing this layer to the original carbon level.

**carbonitriding.** A case-hardening process in which a suitable ferrous material is heated above the lower transformation temperature in a gaseous atmosphere having a composition that results in simultaneous absorption of carbon and nitrogen by the surface and, by diffusion, creates a concentration gradient. The process is completed by cooling at a rate that produces the desired properties in the workpiece.

**carburizing.** A case-hardening process in which an austenitized ferrous material contacts a carbonaceous atmosphere having sufficient carbon potential to cause absorption of carbon at the surface and, by diffusion, to create a concentration gradient.

**case.** That portion of a ferrous alloy, extending inward from the surface, whose composition has been altered during case hardening. Typically considered to be the portion of an alloy (a) whose composition has been measurably altered from the original composition, (b) that appears dark when etched, or (c) that has a higher hardness value than the core. Contrast with *core*.

**case hardening.** A generic term covering several processes applicable to steel that change the chemical composition of the surface layer by absorption of carbon, nitrogen, or both and, by diffusion, create a concentration gradient. See also *carbonitriding*, *carburizing*, *cyaniding*, *nitriding*, *nitrocarburizing*, and *quench hardening*.

**cast replica.** A reproduction of a surface in plastic made by the evaporation of the solvent from a solution of the plastic or by polymerization of a monomer on the surface. See also *replica*.

**cast structure.** The metallographic structure of a casting evidenced by shape and orientation of grains as well as segregation of impurities.

**cathodic etching.** See *ion etching*.

**cementite.** A very hard and brittle compound of iron and carbon corresponding to the empirical formula $Fe_3C$ and commonly known as iron carbide. It is characterized by its orthorhombic crystal structure. Its occurrence as a phase in steels alters chemical composition by the presence of manganese and other carbide-forming elements.

**chemical polishing.** A process that produces a polished surface by the action of a chemical etching solution. The etching solution is compounded so that peaks in the topography of the surface are dissolved preferentially.

**Chinese-script eutectic.** A configuration of eutectic constituents, found particularly in some cast alloys of aluminum containing iron and silicon and in magnesium alloys containing silicon, that resembles the characters in Chinese script.

**chlorine extraction.** Removal of phases by formation of a volatile chloride. See also *extraction*.

**chromatic aberration.** A defect in a lens or lens system that results in different focal lengths of the lens for radiation of diverse wavelengths. The dispersive power of a simple positive lens focuses light from the blue end of the spectrum at a shorter distance than light from the red end. An image produced by such a lens will exhibit color fringes around the border of the image. The difference in position along the axis for the focal points of light is called longitudinal chromatic aberration. The difference in magnification due to variations in position of the principal points for light of different wavelengths, also a difference in focal length, is known as lateral chromatic aberration.

**cleavage.** Fracture of a crystal by crack propagation across a crystallographic plane of low index.

**cleavage crack.** A crack that extends along a plane of easy cleavage in a crystalline material.

**cleavage fracture.** A fracture, usually of a polycrystalline metal, in which most of the grains have failed by cleavage, resulting in bright reflecting facets. See also *crystalline fracture*.

**cleavage plane.** A characteristic crystallographic plane or set of planes in a crystal on which cleavage fracture occurs easily.

**close-packed.** A geometric arrangement in which a collection of equally sized spheres (atoms) may be packed together in a minimum total volume.

**coalescence.** Growth of grains at the expense of the remainder by absorption or the growth of a phase or particle at the expense of the remainder by absorption or reprecipitation.

**coarse grains.** Grains larger than normal for the particular wrought metal or alloy or of a size that produces a surface roughening known as orange peel or alligator skin.

**coated abrasive product.** A two-body abrasion device in which a backing paper or cloth is coated with a layer of abrasive grits, which are cemented to the backing.

**coherent precipitate.** A precipitated particle of a second phase whose lattice maintains registry with the matrix lattice. Because the lattice spacings are usually different, strains often exist at the interface.

**coherent scattering.** A type of x-ray or electron scattering in which the phase of the scattered beam has a definite (not random) relationship to the phase of the incident beam. Also termed unmodified scattering. See also *incoherent scattering*.

**cold etching.** Development of microstructure at room temperature and below.

**cold-worked structure.** A microstructure resulting from plastic deformation of a metal or alloy below its recrystallization temperature.

**collimation.** The operation of controlling a beam of radiation so that its rays are as nearly parallel as possible.

**collodian replica.** A replica of a surface cast in nitrocellulose.

**colonies.** Regions within prior-$\beta$ grains with $\alpha$ platelets having nearly identical orientations. In commercially pure titanium, colonies often have serrated boundaries. Colonies arise as transformation products during cooling from the $\beta$ field at cooling rates that induce platelet nucleation and growth.

**color filter.** A device that transmits principally a predetermined range of wavelengths. See also *contrast filter* and *filter*.

**color temperature.** The temperature in degrees Kelvin at which a blackbody must be operated to provide a color equivalent to that of the source in question. See also *blackbody*.

**columnar structure.** A coarse structure of parallel, elongated grains formed by unidirectional growth that is most often observed in castings, but sometimes seen in structures. This results from diffusional growth accompanied by a solid-state transformation.

**coma.** A lens aberration occurring in the part of the image field that is some distance from the principal axis of the system. It results from different magnification in the various lens zones. Extra-axial object points appear as short, cometlike images, with the brighter small head toward the center of the field (positive coma) or away from the center (negative coma).

**combined carbon.** That part of the total carbon in steel or cast iron present as other than free carbon.

**comet tails (on a polished surface).** A group of comparatively deep unidirectional scratches that form adjacent to a microstructural discontinuity during mechanical polishing. They have the general shape of a comet tail. Comet tails form only when a unidirectional motion is maintained between the surface being polished and the polishing cloth.

**comparison standard.** A standard micrograph or a series of micrographs, usually taken at 75 to 100$\times$, used to determine grain size by direct comparison with the image.

**compensating eyepiece.** An eyepiece designed for use with apochromatic objectives. They are also used to advantage with high-power (oil-immersion) achromatic objectives. Because apochromatic objectives are undercorrected chromatically, these eyepieces are overcorrected. See also *apochromatic objective*.

**complex silicate inclusions.** A general term describing silicate inclusions containing visible constituents in addition to the silicate matrix. An example is corundum or spinel crystals occurring in a silicate matrix in steel.

**condenser.** A system of lenses or mirrors designed to collect, control, and concentrate light.

**condenser aperture.** In electron microscopy, an opening in the condenser lens controlling the number of electrons entering the lens and the angular aperture of the illuminating beam.

**condenser lens.** A device used to focus radiation in or near the plane of the object.

**conjugate phases.** Those states of matter of unique composition that coexist at equilibrium at a single point in temperature and pressure. For example, the two coexisting phases of a two-phase equilibrium.

**conjugate planes.** Two planes of an optical system such that one is the image of the other.

**constituent.** A phase or combination of phases that occurs in a characteristic configuration in a microstructure.

**constitutional diagram.** See *phase diagram*.

**continuous phase.** The phase that forms the background or matrix in which the other phase or phases may be dispersed.

**continuous spectrum (x-rays).** The polychromatic radiation emitted by the target of an x-ray tube. It contains all wavelengths above a certain minimum value, known as the short wavelength limit.

**contrast enhancement (electron optics).** An improvement in electron image contrast by the use of an objective aperture diaphragm, shadow casting, or other means. See also *shadowing*.

**contrast filter.** A color filter, usually with strong absorption, that uses the special absorption bands of the object to control the contrast of the image by exaggerating or diminishing the brightness difference between differently colored areas.

**contrast perception.** The ability to differentiate various components of the object structure by various intensity levels in the image.

**controlled etching.** Electrolytic etching with selection of suitable etchant and voltage resulting in a balance between current and dissolved metal ions.

**controlled rolling.** A hot-rolling process in which the temperature of the steel is closely controlled, particularly during the final rolling passes, to produce a fine-grain microstructure.

**cooling curve.** A graph showing the relationship between time and temperature during the cooling of a material. It is used to find the temperatures at which phase changes occur. A property or function other than time may occasionally be used—for example, thermal expansion.

**cooling rate.** The average slope of the time-temperature curve taken over a specified time and temperature interval.

**core.** (1) In a ferrous alloy that has undergone case hardening, that portion of the alloy structure not part of the case. Typically considered to be the portion that (a) appears light when etched, (b) has an unaltered chemical composition, or (c) has a hardness value lower than that of the case. (2) A specially formed material inserted in a mold to shape the interior or other part of a casting that cannot be shaped as easily by the pattern.

**coring.** A variation in composition between the center and surface of a unit of structure, such as a dendrite, a grain, or a carbide particle, that results from nonequilibrium growth over a temperature range.

**corundum.** A naturally occurring, impure $\alpha$-aluminum oxide. A purer form of the oxide than emery.

**critical cooling rate.** The minimum rate of continuous cooling for preventing undesirable transformations. For steel, unless otherwise specified, it is the slowest rate at which austenite can be cooled from above critical temperature to prevent its transformation above the martensite start temperature.

**critical curve.** In a binary or higher order phase diagram, a line along which the phases of a heterogeneous equilibrium become identical.

**critical illumination.** The formation of an image of the light source in the object field.

**critical point.** (1) The temperature or pressure at which a change in crystal structure, phase, or physical properties occurs. Also termed *transformation temperature*. (2) In an equilibrium diagram, that combination of composition, temperature, and pressure at which the phases of an inhomogeneous system are in equilibrium.

**critical pressure.** That pressure above which the liquid and vapor states are no longer distinguishable.

**critical rake angle.** The rake angle at which the action of a V-point tool changes from cutting to plowing.

**critical strain.** That strain resulting in the formation of very large grains during recrystallization.

**critical surface.** In a ternary or higher order phase diagram, the area upon which the phases in equilibrium become identical.

**critical temperature.** That temperature above which the vapor phase cannot be condensed to liquid by an increase in pressure. Synonymous with *critical point* if pressure is constant.

**cross direction.** See *transverse direction*.

**cross rolling.** A hot-rolling process in which rolling reduction proceeds perpendicular to and parallel to the length of the original slab.

**crystal.** A solid composed of atoms, ions, or molecules arranged in a pattern that is periodic in three dimensions.

**crystal analysis.** A method for determining crystal structure, for example, the size and shape of the unit cell and the location of all atoms within the unit cell.

**crystal-figure etching.** Discontinuity in etching depending on crystal orientation. Distinctive sectional figures form at polished surfaces. Closely related to *dislocation etching*.

**crystal system.** One of seven groups into which all crystals may be divided: triclinic, monoclinic, orthorhombic, hexagonal, rhombohedral, tetragonal, and cubic.

**crystalline fracture.** A pattern of brightly reflecting crystal facets on the fracture surface of a polycrystalline metal resulting from cleavage fracture of many individual crystals. Contrast with *fibrous fracture*.

**crystallite.** A crystalline grain not bounded by habit planes.

**cube texture.** A texture found in wrought metals in the cubic system in which nearly all the crystal grains have a plane of the type (100) parallel or nearly parallel to the plane of working and a direction of the type [001] parallel or nearly parallel to the direction of elongation.

**cubic.** Having three mutually perpendicular axes of equal length.

**cupping.** The condition sometimes occurring in heavily cold-worked rods and wires in which the outside fibers remain intact and the central zone has failed in a series of cup-and-cone fractures.

**curvature of field.** A property of a lens that causes the image of a plane to be focused into a curved surface instead of a plane.

**cyaniding.** A case-hardening process in which a ferrous material is heated above the lower transformation temperature range in a molten salt containing cyanide to cause simultaneous absorption of carbon and nitrogen at the surface and, by diffusion, create a concentration gradient. Quench hardening completes the process.

**cycle annealing.** An annealing process that uses a predetermined and closely controlled time-temperature cycle to produce specific properties or microstructures.

# D

**dark-field illumination.** The illumination of an object such that it appears bright and the surrounding field dark. This results from illuminating the object with rays of sufficient obliquity so that none can enter the objective directly. In electron microscopy, the image is formed using only electrons scattered by the object.

**Debye-Scherrer method.** A method of x-ray diffraction using monochromatic radiation and a polycrystalline specimen mounted on the axis of a cylindrical strip of film. See also *powder method*.

**Debye ring.** A continuous circle, concentric about the undeviated beam, produced by monochromatic x-ray diffraction from a randomly oriented crystalline powder. An analogous effect is obtained using electron diffraction.

**decarburization.** Loss of carbon from the surface of a ferrous alloy as a result of heating in a medium that reacts with carbon.

**decoration (of dislocations).** Segregation of solute atoms to the line of a dislocation in a crystal. In ferrite, the dislocations may be decorated with carbon or nitrogen atoms.

**deep etching.** Macroetching, especially for steels, to determine the overall character of the material, that is, the presence of imperfections, such as seams, forging bursts, shrinkage-void remnants, cracks, and coring.

**define (x-rays).** To limit a beam of x-rays by passage through apertures to obtain a parallel, divergent, or convergent beam.

**definition.** The clarity or sharpness of a microscopic image.

**deformation bands.** Parts of a crystal that have rotated differently during deformation to produce bands of varied orientation within individual grains.

**deformation lines.** Thin bands or lines produced by cold working in grains of some metals, particularly those of face-centered cubic structure. They are not removed by repolishing and re-etching.

**degrees of freedom.** The number of independent variables, such as temperature, pressure, or concentration, within the phases present that may be adjusted independently without causing a phase change in an alloy system at equilibrium.

**delta-ferrite.** Designation commonly assigned to δ-iron that indicates inclusion of elements in solid solution. Small amounts of carbon and large amounts of other alloying elements markedly affect the high- and low-temperature limit of equilibrium.

**delta iron.** Solid phase of pure iron that is stable from 1400 to 1539 °C (2550 to 2800 °F) and possesses the body-centered cubic lattice.

**dendrite.** A crystal with a treelike branching pattern. It is most evident in cast metals slowly cooled through the solidification range.

**dendritic segregation.** Inhomogeneous distribution of alloying elements through the arms of dendrites.

**deoxidation products.** Those nonmetallic inclusions that form as a result of adding deoxidizing agents to molten metal.

**depletion.** Selective removal of one component of an alloy, usually from the surface or preferentially from grain-boundary regions.

**depth of field.** The depth in the subject over which features can be seen to be acceptably in focus in the final image produced by a microscope.

**deviation (x-ray).** The angle between the diffracted beam and the transmitted incident beam. It is equal to twice the Bragg angle $\theta$.

**devitrification.** Crystallization of an amorphous substance.

**dezincification.** A type of corrosion in which zinc is selectively leached from zinc-containing alloys. This occurs most commonly in copper-zinc alloys.

**differential interference contrast illumination.** A microscopic technique using a beam-splitting double-quartz prism, that is, a modified Wollaston prism placed ahead of the objective together with a polarizer and analyzer in the 90° crossed positions. The two light beams are made to coincide at the focal plane of the objective, revealing height differences as variations in color. The prism can be moved, shifting the interference image through the range of Newtonian colors.

**diffraction.** (1) A modification that radiation undergoes, for example, in passing by the edge of opaque bodies or through narrow slits, in which the rays appear to be deflected. (2) Coherent scattering of x-rays by the atoms of a crystal that necessarily results in beams in characteristic directions. Sometimes termed reflection. (3) The scattering of electrons by any crystalline material through discrete angles depending only on the lattice spacings of the material and the velocity of the electrons.

**diffraction grating.** An artificially produced periodic array of scattering centers capable of producing a pattern of diffracted energy, such as accurately ruled lines on a plane surface.

**diffraction pattern (x-rays).** The spatial arrangement and relative intensities of diffracted beams.

**diffraction ring.** The diffraction pattern produced by a given set of planes from randomly oriented crystalline material. See also *Debye ring*.

**diffusion.** (1) Spreading of a constituent in a gas, liquid, or solid that tends to make the composition of all parts uniform. (2) The spontaneous movement of atoms or molecules to new sites within a material.

**diffusion zone.** The zone of variable composition at the junction between two different materials, such as in welds or between the surface layer and the core of clad materials or sleeve bearings, in which interdiffusion between the various components has taken place.

**dislocation.** A linear imperfection in a crystalline array of atoms. The two basic types recognized are (a) an edge dislocation that corresponds to the row of mismatched atoms along the edge formed by an extra, partial plane of atoms within the body of a crystal and (b) a screw dislocation that corresponds to the axis of a spiral structure in a crystal and is characterized by a distortion joining normally parallel lines together to form a continuous helical ramp (with a pitch of one interplanar distance) winding about the dislocation. A mixed dislocation, which is any combination of a screw dislocation and an edge dislocation, is prevalent.

**dislocation etching.** Etching of exit points of dislocations on a surface. Depends on the strain field ranging over a distance of several atoms. Crystal figures (etch pits) are formed at exit points. For example, etch pits for cubic materials are cube faces.

**disordered structure.** The crystal structure of a solid solution in which the atoms of different elements are randomly distributed relative to the available lattice sites. Contrast with *ordered structure*.

**dispersoid.** Finely divided particles of relatively insoluble constituents visible in the microstructure of certain alloys.

**dissociation.** As applied to heterogeneous equilibria, the transformation of one phase into two or more new phases of different composition.

**dissociation pressure.** At a designated temperature, the pressure at which a phase will transform into two or more new phases of different composition.

**dissolution etching.** Development of microstructure by surface removal.

**divariant equilibrium.** See *bivariant equilibrium*.

**divorced eutectic.** A structure in which the components of a eutectic appear to be entirely separate.

**double etching.** Use of two etching solutions in sequence. The second etchant emphasizes a particular microstructural feature.

**drift.** In electron optics, motion of the electron beam or image due to current, voltage, or specimen instabilities or to charging of a projection, such as dirt in or near the electron beam.

**drop etching.** Placing of a drop of etchant on the polished surface.

**dry etching.** Development of microstructure under the influence of gases.

**dry objective.** Any microscope objective designed for use without liquid between the cover glass and the objective or, in the case of metallurgical objectives, in the space between objective and specimen.

**duplex grain size.** The simultaneous presence of two grain sizes in substantial amounts, with one grain size appreciably larger than the others. Also termed mixed grain size.

**duplex microstructure.** A two-phase structure.

# E

**edge-trailing technique.** A unidirectional motion perpendicular to and toward one edge of the specimen during abrasion or polishing used to improve edge retention.

**elastic electron scatter.** The scatter of electrons by an object without loss of energy, usually an interaction between electrons and atoms.

**electric-discharge machining.** Removal of stock from an electrically conductive material by rapid, repetitive spark discharge through a dielectric fluid flowing between the workpiece and a shaped electrode.

**electrochemical (chemical) etching.** General expression for all developments of microstructure through reduction and oxidation (redox reactions).

**electrolytic etching.** See *anodic etching*.

**electrolytic extraction.** Removal of phases by using an electrolytic cell containing an electrolyte that preferentially dissolves the metal matrix. See also *extraction*.

**electrolytic polishing.** An electrochemical polishing process in which the metal to be polished is made the anode in an electrolytic cell where preferential dissolution at high points in the surface topography produces a specularly reflective surface.

**electromagnetic focusing device.** See *focusing device*.

**electromagnetic lens.** An electromagnet designed to produce a suitably shaped magnetic field for the focusing and deflection of electrons or other charged particles in electron-optical instrumentation.

**electromechanical polishing.** An attack-polishing method in which the chemical action of the polishing fluid is enhanced or controlled by the application of an electric current between the specimen and the polishing wheel.

**electron.** An elementary particle that is the negatively charged constituent of ordinary matter. The electron is the lightest known particle possessing an electric charge. Its rest mass is $m_e \cong 9.1 \times 10^{-28}$ g, approximately $^1/_{1836}$ of the mass of the proton or neutron, which are, respectively, the positively charged and neutral constituents of ordinary matter. The charge of the electron is $-e \cong -4.8 \times 10^{-10}$ esu $= -1.6 \times 10^{-19}$ C.

**electron beam.** A stream of electrons in an electron-optical system.

**electron diffraction.** The phenomenon, or the technique of producing diffraction patterns through the incidence of electrons upon matter.

**electron gun.** A device for producing and accelerating a beam of electrons.

**electron image.** A representation of an object formed by a beam of electrons focused by an electron-optical system. See also *image*.

**electron lens.** A device for focusing an electron beam to produce an image of an object.

**electron micrograph.** A reproduction of an image formed by the action of an electron beam on a photographic emulsion.

**electron microscope.** An electron-optical device that produces a magnified image of an object. Detail may be revealed by selective transmission, reflection, or emission of electrons by the object. See also *scanning electron microscope* and *transmission electron microscope*.

**electron microscope column.** The assembly of gun, lenses, specimen, and viewing and plate chambers.

**electron microscopy impression.** See *impression*.

**electron microscopy.** The study of materials by means of an electron microscope.

**electron optical axis.** The path of an electron through an electron-optical system, along which it suffers no deflection due to lens fields. This axis does not necessarily coincide with the mechanical axis of the system.

**electron optical system.** A combination of parts capable of producing and controlling a beam of electrons to yield an image of an object.

**electron probe.** A narrow beam of electrons used to scan or illuminate an object or screen.

**electron trajectory.** The path of an electron.

**electron velocity.** The rate of motion of an electron.

**electron wavelength.** The wavelength necessary to account for the deviation of electron rays in crystals by wave-diffraction theory. It is numerically equal to the quotient of Planck's constant divided by the electron momentum.

**electropolishing.** See *electrolytic polishing*.

**electrostatic focusing device.** See *focusing device*.

**electrostatic immersion lens.** See *immersion objective*.

**electrostatic lens.** A lens producing a potential field capable of deflecting electron rays to form an image of an object.

**elongated alpha.** A fibrous structure brought about by unidirectional metalworking. It may be enhanced by the prior presence of blocky and/or grain-boundary α.

**elongated grain.** A grain with one principal axis significantly longer than either of the other two.

**embedded abrasive.** Fragments of abrasive particles forced into the surface of a workpiece during grinding, abrasion, or polishing.

**emery.** A naturally occurring, impure α-aluminum oxide. A less pure form of the oxide than corundum.

**enantiotropy.** The relation of crystal forms of the same substance in which one form is stable above a certain temperature and the other form is stable below that temperature. For example, ferrite and austenite are enantiotropic in ferrous alloys.

**end-centered.** Having an atom or group of atoms separated by a translation of the type $1/2$, $1/2$, 0 from a similar atom or group of atoms. The number of atoms in an end-centered cell must be a multiple of 2.

**epitaxy.** Oriented growth of a crystalline substance on a substrate with the same crystal orientation.

**epsilon, ε.** Designation generally assigned to intermetallic, metal-metalloid, and metal-nonmetallic compounds found in ferrous alloy systems, for example, $Fe_3Mo_2$, $FeSi$, and $Fe_3P$.

**epsilon carbide.** Carbide with hexagonal close-packed lattice that precipitates during the first stage of tempering of primary martensite. Its composition corresponds to the empirical formula $Fe_{24}C$.

**epsilon structure.** Structurally analogous close-packed phases or electron compounds that have ratios of seven valence electrons to four atoms.

**equiaxed grain structure.** A structure in which the grains have approximately the same dimensions in all directions.

**equilibrium diagram.** A graph of the temperature, pressure, and composition limits of phase fields in an alloy system as they exist under conditions of thermodynamical equilibrium. In metal systems, pressure is usually considered constant. Compare with *phase diagram*.

**equilibrium.** A state of dynamic balance between the opposing actions, reactions, or velocities of a reversible process.

**etch cracks.** Shallow cracks in hardened steel containing high residual surface stresses, produced by etching in an embrittling acid.

**etch figures.** Characteristic markings produced on crystal surfaces by chemical attack, usually having facets parallel to low-index crystallographic planes.

**etchant.** A chemical solution used to etch a metal to reveal structural details.

**etching.** Subjecting the surface of a metal to preferential chemical or electrolytic attack to reveal structural details for metallographic examination.

**etch rinsing.** Pouring etchant over a tilted surface until the desired degree of attack is achieved. Used for etchants with severe gas formation.

**eutectic.** (1) An isothermal reversible reaction in which a liquid solution is converted into two or more intimately mixed solids upon cooling; the number of solids formed equals the number of components in the system. (2) An alloy having the composition indicated by the eutectic point on an equilibrium diagram. (3) An alloy structure of intermixed solid constituents formed by a eutectic reaction.

**eutectic arrest.** In a cooling or heating curve, an approximately isothermal segment corresponding to the time interval during which the heat of transformation from the liquid phase to two or more solid phases is evolving.

**eutectic carbides.** Carbide formed during freezing as one of the mutually insoluble phases participating in the eutectic reaction of a hypereutectic tool steel. See also *hypereutectic alloy*.

**eutectic point.** The composition of a liquid phase in univariant equilibrium with two or more solid phases; the lowest melting alloy of a composition series.

**eutectic-cell etching.** Development of eutectic cells (grains).

**eutectoid.** (1) An isothermal, reversible transformation in which a solid solution is converted into two or more intimately mixed solids. The number of solids formed equals the number of components in the system. (2) An alloy having the composition indicated by the eutectoid point on an equilibrium diagram. (3) An alloy structure of intermixed solid constituents formed by a eutectoid transformation.

**eutectoid point.** The composition of a solid phase that undergoes univariant transformation into two or more other solid phases upon cooling.

**evaporation.** The vaporization of a material by heating, usually in a vacuum. In electron microscopy, this process is used for shadowing or to produce thin support films by condensation of the vapors of metals or salts.

**Ewald sphere.** A geometric construction, of radius equal to the reciprocal of the wavelength of the incident radiation, with its surface at the origin of the reciprocal lattice. Any crystal plane will reflect if the corresponding reciprocal lattice point lies on the surface of this sphere.

**exogenous inclusions.** Nonmetallic inclusions generally large in size and representing accidental contamination from materials, such as fireclay refractories.

**extinction coefficient.** The ratio of the diffracted beam intensity when extinction is present to the diffracted beam intensity when extinction is absent. It applies to primary or secondary extinction.

**extinction.** A decrease in the intensity of the diffracted beam caused by perfection or near perfection of crystal structure. See also *primary extinction* and *secondary extinction*.

**extraction.** A general term denoting chemical methods of isolating phases from the metal matrix.

**eyepiece.** A lens or system of lenses for increasing magnification in a microscope by magnifying the image formed by the objective.

## F

**face (crystal).** An idiomorphic plane surface on a crystal.

**face-centered.** Having atoms or groups of atoms separated by translations of $1/2$, $1/2$, 0; $1/2$, 0, $1/2$; and 0, $1/2$, $1/2$ from a similar atom or group of atoms. The number of atoms in a face-centered cell must be a multiple of 4.

**ferrite.** Generally, a solid solution of one or more elements in body-centered cubic iron. In plain carbon steels, the interstitial solid solution of carbon in α-iron.

**ferrite-pearlite banding.** Inhomogeneous distribution of ferrite and pearlite aligned in filaments or plates parallel to the direction of working.

**ferritic grain size.** The grain size of the ferritic matrix of a steel.

**ferritizing anneal.** The process of producing a predominantly ferritic matrix in a ferrous alloy through an appropriate heat treatment.

**fiber.** (1) The characteristic of wrought metal that indicates directional properties. It is revealed by etching a longitudinal section or manifested by the fibrous appearance of a fracture. It is caused chiefly by extension of the metallic and nonmetallic constituents of the metal in the direction of working. (2) The pattern of preferred orientation of metal crystals after a given deformation process.

**fiber texture.** A texture characterized by having only one preferred crystallographic direction.

**fibrous fracture.** A fracture whose surface is characterized by a dull gray or silky appearance. Contrast with *crystalline fracture*.

**fibrous structure.** (1) In forgings, a structure revealed as laminations, not necessarily detrimental, on an etched section or as a ropy appearance on a fracture. (2) In wrought iron, a structure consisting of slag fibers embedded in ferrite. (3) In rolled steel plate stock, a uniform, lamination-free fine-grained structure on a fractured surface.

**filar eyepiece.** An eyepiece having in its focal plane a fiducial line that can be moved using a calibrated micrometer screw. Useful for accurate determination of linear dimensions. Also termed filar micrometer.

**filter.** A device that modifies the light from the light source.

**final annealing.** The last anneal given a non-ferrous alloy before shipment.

**final polishing.** A polishing process in which the primary objective is to produce a final surface suitable for microscopic examination.

**flake graphite.** An irregularly shaped body, usually appearing as long, curved plates of graphitic carbon, such as that found in gray cast irons.

**flakes.** Short, discontinuous internal cracks in ferrous metals attributed to stresses produced by localized transformation and hydrogen-solubility effects during cooling after hot working. In fracture surfaces, flakes appear as bright, silvery areas with a coarse texture. In deep acid-etched transverse sections, they appear as discontinuities that are usually in the midway to center location of the section. Also termed hairline cracks and shatter cracks.

**flame annealing.** Annealing in which the heat is applied directly by a flame.

**flow lines.** Texture showing the direction of metal flow during hot or cold working. Flow lines often can be revealed by etching the surface or a section of a metal part.

**focal length.** The distance from the second principal point to the point on the axis at which parallel rays entering the lens will converge or focus.

**focal spot.** That area on the target of an x-ray tube that is bombarded by electrons.

**focus.** A point at which rays originating from a point in the object converge or from which they diverge or appear to diverge under the influence of a lens or diffracting system.

**focusing (x-rays).** The operation of producing a convergent beam in which all rays meet in a point or line.

**focusing device (electrons).** A device that effectively increases the angular aperture of the electron beam illuminating the object, rendering the focusing more critical.

**forged structure.** The macrostructure through a suitable section of a forging that reveals direction of working.

**Formvar.** A plastic material used for the preparation of replicas or for specimen-supporting membranes.

**Formvar replica.** A reproduction of a surface in a plastic Formvar film. See also *replica*.

**fractography.** Descriptive treatment of fracture, especially in metals, with specific reference to photography of the fracture surface.

**fracture grain size.** Grain size determined by comparing a fracture of a specimen with a set of standard fractures. For steel, a fully martensitic specimen is generally used, and the depth of hardening and the prior austenitic grain size are determined.

**fragmentation.** The subdivision of a grain into small, discrete crystallite outlined by a heavily deformed network of intersecting slip bands as a result of cold working. These small crystals or fragments differ in orientation and tend to rotate to a stable orientation determined by the slip systems.

**freckling.** A type of segregation revealed as dark spots on a macroetched specimen of a consumable-electrode vacuum-arc-remelted alloy.

**free carbon.** The part of the total carbon content in steel or cast iron present in elemental form as graphite.

**free-energy diagram.** A graph of the variation with concentration of the Gibbs free energy at constant pressure and temperature.

**free-energy surface.** In a ternary or higher order free-energy diagram, the locus of points representing the Gibbs free energy as a function of concentration, with pressure and temperature constant.

**free ferrite.** See *proeutectoid ferrite*.

**freezing point.** See *melting point*.

**frequency (x-ray).** The number of alternations per second of the electric vector of the x-ray beam. It is equal to the velocity divided by the wavelength.

**Fresnel fringes.** A class of diffraction fringes formed when the source of illumination and the viewing screen are at a finite distance from a diffracting edge. In the electron microscope, these fringes are best seen when the object is slightly out of focus.

# G

**gamma iron.** Solid nonmagnetic phase of pure iron that is stable from 910 to 1400 °C (1670 to 2550 °F) and possesses the face-centered cubic lattice.

**gamma structure.** Structurally analogous phases or electron compounds having ratios of 21 valence electrons to 13 atoms. This is generally a large, complex cubic structure.

**gelatin replica.** A reproduction of a surface prepared in a film composed of gelatin. See also *replica*.

**general precipitate.** A precipitate that is dispersed throughout the matrix.

**Gibbs free energy.** The maximum useful work obtainable from a chemical system without net change in temperature or pressure.

**Gibbs triangle.** An equilateral triangle used for plotting composition in a ternary system.

**glancing angle.** The angle (usually small) between an incident x-ray beam and the surface of the specimen.

**glide.** See *slip*.

**graded abrasive.** An abrasive powder in which the sizes of the individual particles are confined to certain specified limits.

**grain.** An individual crystal in a polycrystalline metal or alloy, including twinned regions or subgrains if present.

**grain boundary.** An interface separating two grains at which the orientation of the lattice changes from that of one grain to that of the other. When the orientation change is very small the boundary is sometimes referred to as a *sub-boundary structure*.

**grain-boundary etching.** Development of intersections of grain faces with the polished surface. Because of severe, localized crystal deformation, grain boundaries have higher dissolution potential than grains themselves. Accumulation of impurities in grain boundaries increases this effect.

**grain-boundary liquation.** An advanced stage of overheating in which material in the region of austenitic grain boundaries melts. Also termed *burning*.

**grain-boundary sulfide precipitation.** An intermediate stage of overheating in which sulfide inclusions are redistributed to the austenitic grain boundaries by partial solution at the overheating temperature and reprecipitation during subsequent cooling.

**grain coarsening.** A heat treatment that produces excessively large austenitic grains.

**grain-contrast etching.** Development of grain surfaces lying in the polished surface of the microsection. These become visible through differences in reflectivity caused by reaction products on the surface or by differences in roughness.

**grain fineness number.** A weighted average grain size of a granular material. The American Foundrymen's Society grain fineness number is calculated with prescribed weighting factors from the standard screen analysis.

**grain flow.** Fiberlike lines on polished and etched sections of forgings caused by orientation of the constituents of the metal in the direction of working during forging. Grain flow produced by proper die design can improve required mechanical properties of forgings.

**grain growth.** An increase in the grain size of a metal usually as a result of heating at an elevated temperature.

**grain size.** (1) A measure of the areas or volumes of grains in a polycrystalline metal or alloy, usually expressed as an average when the individual sizes are fairly uniform. In metals containing two or more phases, the grain size refers to that of the matrix unless otherwise specified. Grain size is reported in terms of number of grains per unit area or volume, average diameter, or as a number derived from area measurements. (2) For grinding wheels, see the preferred term *grit size*.

**granular fracture.** An irregular surface produced when metal fractures. This fracture is characterized by a rough, grainlike appearance. It can be subclassified into transgranular and intergranular forms. This fracture is frequently called crystalline fracture, but the implication that the metal failed because it crystallized is misleading, because all metals are crystalline in the solid state.

**graphite.** The polymorph of carbon with a hexagonal crystal structure. See also *flake graphite, nodular graphite, rosette graphite*, and *spheroidal graphite*.

**graphitization.** Formation of graphite in iron or steel. Primary graphitization refers to formation of graphite during solidification; secondary graphitization, later formation during heat treatment.

**graphitizing.** Annealing a ferrous alloy such that some or all the carbon precipitates as graphite.

**grinding.** Removing material from a workpiece using a grinding wheel or abrasive belt.

**grit size.** Nominal size of abrasive particles in a grinding wheel, corresponding to the number of openings per linear inch in a screen through which the particles can pass.

**Guinier-Preston (G-P) zone.** A small precipitation domain in a supersaturated metallic solid solution. A G-P zone has no well-defined crystalline structure of its own and contains an abnormally high concentration of solute atoms. The formation of G-P zones constitutes the first stage of precipitation and is usually accompanied by a change in properties of the solid solution in which they occur.

# H

**habit plane.** The plane or system of planes of a crystalline phase along which some phenomenon, such as twinning or transformation, occurs.

**hairline cracks.** See *flakes*.

**hardenability.** The relative ability of a ferrous alloy to form martensite when quenched from a temperature above the upper critical temperature. Hardenability is commonly measured as the distance below a quenched surface at which the metal exhibits a specific hardness—50 HRC, for example—or a specific percentage of martensite in the microstructure.

**hardening.** Increasing hardness by suitable treatment, usually involving heating and cooling. See also *age hardening*, *case hardening*, *induction hardening*, *precipitation hardening*, and *quench hardening*.

**heat-affected zone.** That portion of the base metal that was not melted during brazing, cutting, or welding, but whose microstructure and mechanical properties were altered by the heat.

**heat tinting.** Coloration of a metal surface through thermal oxidation by heating to reveal details of structure.

**heterogeneous equilibrium.** In a chemical system, a state of dynamic balance among two or more homogeneous phases capable of stable coexistence in mutual or sequential contact.

**hexagonal (lattices for crystals).** Having two equal coplanar axes, $a_1$ and $a_2$, at 120° to each other and a third axis, $c$, at right angles to the other two; $c$ may or may not equal $a_1$ and $a_2$.

**hexagonal close-packed.** (1) A structure containing two atoms per unit cell located at $(0, 0, 0)$ and $(1/3, 2/3, 1/2)$ or $(2/3, 1/3, 1/2)$. (2) One of the two ways in which spherical objects can be most closely packed together so that the close-packed planes are alternately staggered in the order A-B-A-B-A-B.

**high aluminum defect.** An $\alpha$-stabilized region in titanium containing an abnormally large amount of aluminum that may span a large number of $\beta$ grains. It contains an inordinate fraction of primary $\alpha$, but has a microhardness only slightly higher than the adjacent matrix. Also termed type II defects.

**high interstitial defect.** Interstitially stabilized $\alpha$-phase region in titanium of substantially higher hardness than surrounding material. It arises from very high local nitrogen or oxygen concentrations that increase the $\beta$ transus and produce the high-hardness, often brittle $\alpha$ phase. Such a defect is often accompanied by a void resulting from thermomechanical working. Also termed type I or low-density interstitial defects, although they are not necessarily low density.

**homogenizing.** Holding at high temperature to eliminate or decrease chemical segregation by diffusion.

**hot cathode gun.** See *thermionic cathode gun*.

**hot crack.** See *solidification shrinkage crack*.

**hot etching.** Development and stabilization of the microstructure at elevated temperature in etchants or gases.

**hot quenching.** An imprecise term for various quenching procedures in which a quenching medium is maintained at a prescribed temperature above 70 °C (160 °F).

**hot-worked structure.** The structure of a material worked at a temperature higher than the recrystallization temperature.

**hot working.** Deformation under conditions that result in recrystallization.

**hydride phase.** The phase $TiH_x$ formed in titanium when the hydrogen content exceeds the solubility limit, generally locally due to some special circumstance.

**hypereutectic alloy.** In an alloy system exhibiting a eutectic, any alloy whose composition has an excess of alloying element compared with the eutectic composition and whose equilibrium microstructure contains some eutectic structure.

**hypereutectoid alloy.** In an alloy system exhibiting a eutectoid, any alloy whose composition has an excess of alloying element compared with the eutectoid composition and whose equilibrium microstructure contains some eutectoid structure.

**hypoeutectic alloy.** In an alloy system exhibiting a eutectic, any alloy whose composition has an excess of base metal compared with the eutectic composition and whose equilibrium microstructure contains some eutectic structure.

**hypoeutectoid alloy.** In an alloy system exhibiting a eutectoid, any alloy whose composition has an excess of base metal compared with the eutectoid composition and whose equilibrium microstructure contains some eutectoid structure.

# I

**identification etching.** Etching to expose particular microconstituents; all others remain unaffected.

**idiomorphic crystal.** Single crystals that have grown without restraint so that the habit planes are clearly developed.

**illumination.** See *bright-field illumination*, *dark-field illumination*, *differential interference contrast illumination*, and *polarized light illumination*.

**image.** A representation of an object produced by radiation, usually with a lens or mirror system.

**image rotation.** In electron optics, the angular shift of the electron image of an object about the optic axis induced by the tangential component of force exerted on the electrons perpendicular to the direction of motion in the field of a magnetic lens.

**immersion etching.** Method in which a microsection is dipped face up into etching solution and is moved around during etching. This is the most common etching method.

**immersion lens.** See *immersion objective*.

**immersion objective.** An objective in which a medium of high refractive index is used in the object space to increase the numerical aperture and therefore the resolving power of the lens.

**immersion objective (electron optics).** A lens system in which the object space is at a potential or in a medium of index of refraction different from that of the image space.

**imperfection.** In crystallography, any deviation from an ideal space lattice.

**impression replica.** A surface replica made by impression. See also *impression* and *replica*.

**impression.** (1) In electron microscopy, the reproduction of the surface contours of a specimen formed in a plastic material after the application of pressure, heat, or both. (2) In hardness testing, the imprint or dent made in the specimen by the indenter of a hardness-measuring device.

**impurities.** Undesirable elements or compounds in a material.

**inclusion count.** Determination of the number, kind, size, and distribution of nonmetallic inclusions.

**inclusions.** Particles of foreign material in a metallic matrix. The particles are usually compounds, such as oxides, sulfides, or silicates, but may be any substance foreign to and essentially insoluble in the matrix.

**incoherent scattering.** The deflection of electrons by electrons or atoms that results in a loss of kinetic energy by the incident electron. See also *coherent scattering*.

**indentation.** See *impression*.

**indices.** See *Miller indices*.

**indigenous inclusions.** See *deoxidation products*.

**induction hardening.** A surface-hardening process in which only the surface layer of a suitable ferrous workpiece is heated by electrical induction to above the upper transformation temperature and immediately quenched.

**induction heating.** Heating by electrical induction.

**inelastic electron scatter.** See *incoherent scattering*.

**inflection point.** Position on a curved line, such as a phase boundary, at which the direction of curvature is reversed.

**intensity (x-rays).** The energy per unit of time of a beam per unit area perpendicular to the direction of propagation.

**intensity of scattering.** The energy per unit time per unit area of the general radiation diffracted by matter. Its value depends on the scattering power of the individual atoms of the material, the scattering angle, and the wavelength of the radiation.

**intercept method.** A quantitative metallographic technique in which the desired quantity, such as grain size or amount of precipitate, is expressed as the number of times per unit length a straight line on a metallographic image crosses particles of the feature being measured.

**intercrystalline.** Between crystals, or between grains. Also termed intergranular.

**intercrystalline cracks.** Cracks or fractures that occur between the grains or crystals in a polycrystalline aggregate.

**interdendritic.** Located within the branches of a dendrite or between the boundaries of two or more dendrites.

**interdendritic porosity.** Voids occurring between the dendrites in cast metal.

**interference.** The effect of a combination of wave trains of various phases and amplitudes.

**interference filter.** A combination of several thin optical films to form a layered coating for transmitting or reflecting a narrow band of wavelengths by interference effects.

**intergranular.** See *intercrystalline*.

**intergranular beta.** Beta phase situated between α grains. It may be at grain corners, as in the case of equiaxed α-type microstructures in alloys having low β-stabilizer contents.

**intermediate annealing.** Annealing wrought metal at one or more stages during manufacture and before final thermal treatment.

**intermediate phase.** In a chemical system, a distinguishable homogeneous substance whose composition range of existence does not extend to any of the pure components of the system.

**intermetallic compound.** An intermediate phase in an alloy system having a narrow range of homogeneity and relatively simple stoichiometric proportions. Nearly all are brittle and of stoichiometric composition.

**intermetallic phases.** Compounds, or intermediate solid solutions, containing two or more metals, which usually have compositions, characteristic properties, and crystal structures different from those of the pure components of the system.

**internal oxidation.** Preferential *in situ* oxidation of certain components of phases within the bulk of a solid alloy accomplished by diffusion of oxygen into the body. This is commonly used to prepare electrical contact materials.

**interplanar distance.** The perpendicular distance between adjacent parallel lattice planes.

**interrupted aging.** Aging at two or more temperatures by steps and cooling to room temperature after each step. Compare with *progressive aging* and *step aging*.

**interrupted quenching.** Quenching in which the metal object being quenched is removed from the quenching medium while the object is at a temperature substantially higher than that of the quenching medium.

**interstitial solid solution.** A type of solid solution that sometimes forms in alloy systems having two elements of widely different atomic sizes. Elements of small atomic size, such as carbon, hydrogen, and nitrogen, often dissolve in solid metals to form this solid solution. The space lattice is similar to that of the pure metal, and the atoms of carbon, hydrogen, and nitrogen occupy the spaces or interstices between the metal atoms.

**intracrystalline.** Within or across crystals or grains. Same as transcrystalline and transgranular.

**intracrystalline cracking.** See *transcrystalline cracking*.

**inverse segregation.** A concentration of low-melting constituents in those regions in which solidification first occurs.

**inverted microscope.** A microscope arranged so that the line of sight is directed upward through the objective to the object.

**ion etching.** Surface removal by bombarding with accelerated ions in vacuum (1 to 10 kV).

**isometric.** A crystal form in which the unit dimension on all three axes is the same.

**isomorphous system.** A complete series of mixtures in all proportions of two or more components in which unlimited mutual solubility exists in the liquid and solid states.

**isomorphous.** Having the same crystal structure. This usually refers to intermediate phases that form a continuous series of solid solutions.

**isothermal annealing.** Austenitizing a ferrous alloy, then cooling to and holding at a temperature at which austenite transforms to a relatively soft ferrite-carbide aggregate. See also *austenitizing*.

**isothermal transformation (IT) diagram.** A diagram that shows the isothermal time required for transformation of austenite to begin and to finish as a function of temperature. Same as time-temperature-transformation (TTT) diagram or S-curve.

**isothermal transformation.** A change in phase at any constant temperature.

**isotropic.** Having equal values of properties in all directions. Quasi-isotropic refers to material in which statistical uniformity exists, such as polycrystalline metals.

**isotropy.** The condition of having the same values of properties in all directions.

**J**

**Jeffries' method.** A method for determining grain size based on counting grains in a prescribed area.

**K**

**K (abbreviation), x-rays.** See *K radiation*.

**K radiation.** Characteristic x-rays produced by an atom when a vacancy in the K shell is filled by one of the outer electrons.

**K series.** The set of x-ray wavelengths comprising K radiation.

**Kikuchi lines.** Light and dark lines superimposed on the background of a single-crystal electron-diffraction pattern caused by diffraction of diffusely scattered electrons within the crystal; the pattern provides information on the structure of the crystal.

**kink band (deformation).** In polycrystalline materials, a volume of crystal that has rotated physically to accommodate differential deformation between adjoining parts of a grain while the band itself has deformed homogeneously. This occurs by regular bending of the slip lamellae along the boundaries of the band.

**L**

**lamellar tear.** A system of cracks or discontinuities aligned generally parallel to the worked surface of a plate. This is usually associated with a fusion weld in thick plate.

**lamination.** An abnormal structure resulting in a separation or weakness aligned generally parallel to the worked surface of the metal.

**lap.** (1) A flat surface that holds an abrasive for polishing operations. (2) A surface imperfection on worked metal caused by folding over a fin overfill or similar surface condition, then impressing this into the surface by subsequent working without welding it.

**lath martensite.** Martensite formed partly in steels containing less than approximately 1.0% C and solely in steels containing less than approximately 0.5% C as parallel arrays of packets of lath-shape units 0.1 to 0.3 μm thick.

**lattice constants.** See *lattice parameter*.

**lattice parameter.** The length of any side of a unit cell of a given crystal structure. The term is also used for the fractional coordinates $x, y, z$ of lattice points when these are variable.

**lattice.** (1) A space lattice is a set of equal and adjoining parallelopipeds formed by dividing space by three sets of parallel planes, the planes in any one set being equally spaced. There are seven ways of so dividing space, corresponding to the seven crystal systems. The unit parallelopiped is usually chosen as the unit cell of the system. See also *crystal system*. (2) A point lattice is a set of points in space located so that each point has identical surroundings. There are

14 ways of so arranging points in space, corresponding to the 14 Bravais lattices. See the article "Crystal Structure of Metals" in this Volume.

**Laue equations.** The three simultaneous equations that state the conditions to be met for diffraction from a three-dimensional network of diffraction centers.

**Laue method (for crystal analysis).** A method of x-ray diffraction using a beam of white radiation, a fixed single crystal specimen, and a flat photographic film usually normal to the incident beam. If the film is located on the same side of the specimen as the x-ray source, the method is known as the back reflection Laue method; if on the other side, as the transmission Laue method.

**ledeburite.** A eutectic structure formed below 1148 °C (2098 °F) consisting of austenite and cementite in metastable equilibrium in alloys of iron and carbon containing greater than 2% but less than 6.67% C. Further slow cooling causes decomposition of the austenite into ferrite and cementite (pearlite) as a result of the eutectoid reaction.

**lever rule.** A method that can be applied to any two-phase field of a binary phase diagram to determine the amounts of the different phases present at a given temperature in a given alloy. A horizontal line, referred to as a tie line, represents the lever, and the alloy composition its fulcrum. The intersection of the tie line with the boundaries of the two-phase field fixes the compositions of the coexisting phases, and the amounts of the phases are proportional to the segments of the tie line between the alloy and the phase compositions.

**levigation.** A process by which a powder is separated into a fraction with a restricted range of particle sizes.

**light filter.** See *color filter.*

**light-field illumination.** See *bright-field illumination.*

**limited solid solution.** A crystalline miscibility series whose composition range does not extend all the way between the components of the system; that is, the system is not isomorphous.

**line (in x-ray diffraction patterns).** An array of small diffraction spots arranged so that they appear to form a continuous line on the film.

**line indices.** The Miller indices of the set of planes producing a diffraction line.

**lineage structure.** (1) Deviations from perfect alignment of parallel arms of a columnar dendrite as a result of interdendritic shrinkage during solidification from a liquid. This type of deviation may vary in orientation from a few minutes to as much as two degrees of arc. (2) A type of substructure consisting of elongated subgrains.

**liquation.** Partial melting of an alloy, usually as a result of coring or other compositional heterogeneities.

**liquidus.** In a phase diagram, the locus of points representing the temperatures at which various components begin to freeze during cooling or finish melting during heating. See also *solidus.*

**long-term etching.** Etching times of a few minutes to hours.

**longitudinal direction.** That direction parallel to the direction of maximum elongation in a worked material. See also *normal direction* and *transverse direction.*

**Lüders lines or bands.** Elongated surface markings or depressions caused by localized plastic deformation that results from discontinuous (inhomogeneous) yielding.

# M

**macroetching.** Etching a metal surface to accentuate gross structural details, such as grain flow, segregation, porosity, or cracks, for observation by the unaided eye or at magnifications to $25\times$.

**macrograph.** A graphic reproduction of a prepared surface of a specimen at a magnification not exceeding $25\times$.

**macroscopic.** Visible at magnifications to $25\times$.

**macrostructure.** The structure of metals as revealed by macroscopic examination of the etched surface of a polished specimen.

**magnetic alignment.** An alignment of the electron-optical axis of the electron microscope so that the image rotates about a point in the center of the viewing screen when the current flowing through a lens is varied. See also *alignment.*

**magnetic lens.** A device for focusing an electron beam using a magnetic field.

**magnetic shielding.** In electron microscopy, shielding for the purpose of preventing extraneous magnetic fields from affecting the electron beam in the microscope.

**magnetite.** The oxide of iron of intermediate valence that has a composition close to the stoichiometric composition $Fe_3O_4$.

**magnification.** The ratio of the length of a line in the image plane, for example, ground glass or photographic plate, to the length of the same line in the object. Magnifications are usually expressed in linear terms and in units called diameters.

**malleablizing.** Annealing white cast iron so that some or all of the combined carbon is transformed into graphite or, in some instances, so that part of the carbon is removed completely.

**martempering.** (1) A hardening procedure in which an austenitized ferrous material is quenched into an appropriate medium at a temperature just above the martensite start temperature of the material, held in the medium until the temperature is uniform throughout, although not long enough for bainite to form, then cooled in air. The treatment is frequently followed by tempering. (2) When the process is applied to carburized material, the controlling martensite start temperature is that of the case.

This variation of the process is frequently called marquenching.

**martensite.** A generic term for microstructures formed by diffusionless phase transformation in which the parent and product phases have a specific crystallographic relationship. Martensite is characterized by an acicular pattern in the microstructure in ferrous and nonferrous alloys. In alloys in which the solute atoms occupy interstitial positions in the martensitic lattice, such as carbon in iron, the structure is hard and highly strained; however, if the solute atoms occupy substitutional positions, such as nickel in iron, the martensite is soft and ductile. The amount of high-temperature phase that transforms to martensite upon cooling depends to a large extent on the lowest temperature attained, there being a distinct starting temperature ($M_s$) and a temperature at which the transformation is essentially complete ($M_f$), which is the martensite finish temperature. See also *transformation temperature.*

**martensite range.** The interval between the martensite start ($M_s$) and martensite finish ($M_f$) temperatures.

**martensitic.** A platelike constituent having an appearance and a mechanism of formation similar to that of martensite.

**matrix.** The continuous or principal phase in which another constituent is dispersed.

**McQuaid-Ehn grain size.** The austenitic grain size developed in steels by carburizing at 927 °C (1700 °F) followed by slow cooling. Eight standard McQuaid-Ehn grain sizes rate the structure, from No. 8, the finest, to No. 1, the coarsest.

**mechanical alignment.** A method of aligning the geometrical axis of the electron microscope by relative physical movement of the components, usually as a step preceding magnetic or voltage alignment. See also *alignment.*

**mechanical polishing.** A process that yields a specularly reflecting surface entirely by the action of machining tools, which are usually the points of abrasive particles.

**mechanical stage.** A device provided for adjusting the position of a specimen, usually by translation in two directions at right angles to each other.

**mechanical twin.** A twin formed in a metal during plastic deformation by simple shear of the structure.

**melting point.** The temperature at which a pure metal, compound, or eutectic changes from solid to liquid; the temperature at which the liquid and the solid are in equilibrium.

**melting pressure.** At a stated temperature, the pressure at which the solid phases of an element or congruently melting compound may coexist at equilibrium with liquid of the same composition.

**melting temperature.** See *melting point.*

**membrane.** Any thin sheet or layer.

**metallograph.** An optical instrument designed for visual observation and photomicrography of prepared surfaces of opaque materials at magnifications of 25 to approximately $2000\times$. The instrument consists of a high-intensity illuminating source, a microscope, and a camera bellows. On some instruments, provisions are made for examination of specimen surfaces using polarized light, phase contrast, oblique illumination, dark-field illumination, and bright-field illumination.

**metallography.** The science dealing with the constitution and structure of metals and alloys as revealed to the unaided eye or by using such tools as low-power magnification, optical microscopy, electron microscopy, and diffraction or x-ray techniques.

**metal shadowing.** The enhancement of contrast in a microscope by vacuum depositing a dense metal onto the specimen at an angle generally not perpendicular to the surface of the specimen. See also *shadowing*.

**metastable.** Possessing a state of pseudoequilibrium that has a free energy higher than that of the true equilibrium state.

**metastable beta.** A $\beta$-phase composition that can be partially or completely transformed to martensite, $\alpha$, or eutectoid decomposition products with thermal or strain-energy activation during subsequent processing or service exposure.

**microbands.** Thin, sheetlike volumes of constant thickness in which cooperative slip occurs on a fine scale. They are an instability that carry exclusively the deformation at medium strains when normal homogeneous slip is precluded. The sheets are aligned at $\pm55°$ to the compression direction and are confined to individual grains, which usually contain two sets of bands. Compare with *shear bands*.

**microcrack.** A crack of microscopic proportions.

**microetching.** Development of microstructure for microscopic examination. The usual magnification exceeds $25\times$ ($50\times$ in Europe).

**microfissure.** See *microcrack*.

**micrograph.** A graphic reproduction of the prepared surface of a specimen at a magnification greater than $25\times$.

**microporosity.** Extremely fine porosity in castings.

**microscope.** An instrument capable of producing a magnified image of a small object.

**microscopic.** Visible at magnifications above $25\times$.

**microsegregation.** Segregation within a grain, crystal, or small particle. See also *coring*.

**microstructure.** The structure of a prepared surface of a metal as revealed by a microscope at a magnification exceeding $25\times$.

**Miller-Bravais indices.** Indices used for the hexagonal system. They involve use of a fourth axis, $a_3$, coplanar with and at $120°$ to $a_1$ and $a_2$.

**Miller indices (for lattice planes).** The reciprocals of the fractional intercepts a plane makes on the three axes. The symbols are $(hkl)$.

**mirror illuminator.** A thin, half-round opaque mirror interposed in a microscope for directing an intense oblique beam of light to the object. The light incident on the object passes through one half of the aperture of the objective, and the light reflected from the object passes through the other half aperture of the objective.

**miscibility gap.** A region of multiphase equilibrium. It is commonly applied to the specific case in which an otherwise continuous series of liquid or solid solutions is interrupted over a limited temperature range by a two-phase field terminating at a critical point. See also *binodal curve*.

**mixed grain size.** See *duplex grain size*.

**monochromatic (homogeneous).** Of the same wavelength.

**monochromatic objective.** An objective, usually of fused quartz, that has been corrected for use with monochromatic light only.

**monoclinic.** Having three axes of any length, with two included angles equal to $90°$ and one included angle not equal to $90°$.

**monotropism.** The ability of a solid to exist in two or more forms (crystal structures), but in which one form is the stable modification at all temperatures and pressures. Ferrite and martensite are a monotropic pair below the temperature at which austenite begins to form, for example, in steels. Alternate spelling is monotrophism.

**mosaic crystal.** An imperfect single crystal composed of regions that are slightly disoriented relative to each other.

**mosaic structure.** In crystals, a substructure in which adjoining regions have only slightly different orientations.

**mounting.** A means by which a specimen may be held during preparation of a section surface. The specimen can be embedded in plastic or secured mechanically in clamps.

**mounting artifact.** A false structure introduced during the mounting stages of a surface-preparation sequence.

**multiple etching.** Sequential etching of a microsection, with specific reagents attacking distinct microconstituents.

## N

**napped cloth.** A woven cloth in which some fibers are aligned approximately normal to one of its surfaces.

**natural aging.** Spontaneous aging of a supersaturated solid solution at room temperature. See also *aging*.

**negative distortion.** The distortion in the image that occurs when the magnification in the center of the field exceeds that in the edge of the field. Also termed barrel distortion. Contrast with *positive distortion*.

**negative eyepiece.** An eyepiece in which the real image of the object forms between the lens elements of the eyepiece.

**negative replica.** A method of reproducing a surface obtained by the direct contact of the replicating material with the specimen. Using this technique, the contour of the replica surface is reversed with respect to that of the original. See also *replica*.

**network etching.** Formation of networks, especially in mild steels, after etching in nitric acid. These networks relate to subgrain boundaries.

**network structure.** A structure in which one constituent occurs primarily at the grain boundaries, partially or completely enveloping the grains of the other constituents.

**Neumann band.** A mechanical twin in ferrite.

**neutral filter.** (1) A color filter that reduces the intensity of the transmitted illumination without affecting its hue. (2) A color filter having identical transmission at all wavelengths throughout the spectrum. Such an ideal filter does not exist in practice.

**Nicol prism.** A prism used for polarizing or analyzing light made by cementing together two pieces of calcite using Canada balsam so that the extraordinary ray from the first piece passes through the second piece while the ordinary ray is reflected to the side into an absorbing layer of black paint. No light passes through when two Nicol prisms are crossed.

**nitride-carbide inclusion types.** A compound with the general formula $M_x(C,N)_y$ observed generally as colored idiomorphic cubic crystals, where M includes titanium, niobium, tantalum, and zirconium.

**nitriding.** A case-hardening process that introduces nitrogen into the surface layer of a ferrous material by holding it at a suitable temperature in a nitrogenous atmosphere, usually ammonia or molten cyanide of appropriate composition. Quenching is not required to produce a hard case.

**nitrocarburizing.** Any of several case-hardening processes in which nitrogen and carbon are absorbed into the surface layers of a ferrous material at temperatures below the lower critical temperature and, by diffusion, create a concentration gradient. Compare with *carbonitriding*.

**nodular graphite.** Rounded clusters of tempered carbon, such as that obtained in malleable cast iron as a result of the thermal decomposition of cementite.

**nodular pearlite.** Pearlite that has grown as a colony with an approximately spherical morphology.

**nonmetallic inclusions.** See *inclusions*.

**normal.** An imaginary line forming right angles with a surface or other lines sometimes called the perpendicular. It is used as a basis for determining angles of incidence reflection and refraction. See also *angle of reflection*.

**normal direction.** That direction perpendicular to the plane of working in a worked material. See also *longitudinal direction* and *transverse direction*.

**normalizing.** Heating a ferrous alloy to a suitable temperature above the transformation

range, then cooling in air to a temperature substantially below the transformation range. See also *transformation temperature*.

**normal segregation.** A concentration of alloying components or constituents having lower melting points in those regions that are the last to solidify.

**nucleation.** Initiation of a phase transformation at discrete sites, the new phase growing from nuclei. See also *nucleus*.

**nucleus.** (1) The first structurally stable particle capable of initiating recrystallization of a phase or the growth of a new phase. It is separated from the matrix by an interface. (2) The heavy central core of an atom in which most of the mass and the total positive electrical charge are concentrated.

**numerical aperture (NA).** The product of the lowest index of refraction in the object space multiplied by the sine of half the angular aperture of the objective.

## O

**objective.** The primary magnifying system of a microscope. A system, generally of lenses and less frequently of mirrors, that forms a real, inverted, and magnified image of the object.

**objective aperture.** See *aperture (electron)* and *aperture (optical)*.

**oblique evaporation shadowing.** The condensation of evaporated material onto a substrate that is inclined to the direct line of the vapor stream to produce shadows. See also *shadowing*.

**oblique illumination.** Illumination from light inclined at an oblique angle to the optical axis.

**ocular.** See *eyepiece*.

**omega phase.** A nonequilibrium, submicroscopic phase that forms as a nucleation growth product; often thought to be a transition phase during the formation of α from β. It occurs in metastable β alloys and can lead to severe embrittlement. It typically occurs during aging at low temperature, but can also be induced by high hydrostatic pressures.

**optical etching.** Development of microstructure under application of special illumination techniques, such as dark-field illumination, phase contrast illumination, differential interference contrast illumination, and polarized light illumination.

**order (in x-ray reflection).** The factor *n* in the Bragg equation. In x-ray reflection from a crystal, the order is an integral number that is the path difference measured in wavelengths between reflections from adjacent planes.

**order-disorder transformation.** A phase change among two solid solutions having the same crystal structure, but in which the atoms of one phase (disordered) are randomly distributed; in the other, the different kinds of atoms occur in a regular sequence upon the crystal lattice, that is, in an ordered arrangement.

**ordered structure.** That crystal structure of a solid solution in which the atoms of different elements seek preferred lattice positions. Contrast with *disordered structure*.

**orientation (crystal).** Arrangements in space of the axes of the lattice of a crystal with respect to a chosen reference or coordinate system. See also *preferred orientation*.

**orthochromatic filter.** A color filter that modifies the illumination quality reaching the film so that the brightness of colored objects will be relatively the same in the resultant black-and-white positive.

**orthorhombic.** Having three mutually perpendicular axes of unequal lengths.

**overaging.** Aging under conditions of time and temperature greater than those required to obtain maximum change in a certain property. See also *aging*.

**overheating.** (1) In ferrous alloys, heating to an excessively high temperature so that the properties/structure undergo modification. The resulting structure is very coarse grained. Unlike burning, it may be possible to restore the original properties/structure by further heat treatment, mechanical working, or both. (2) In aluminum alloys, overheating produces structures that show areas of resolidified eutectic or other evidence indicating the metal has been heated within the melting range.

**oxidation grain size.** (1) Grain size determined by holding a specimen at a suitably elevated temperature in a mildly oxidizing atmosphere. The specimen is polished before oxidation and etched afterwards. (2) Refers to the method involving heating a polished steel specimen to a specified temperature, followed by quenching and repolishing. The grain boundaries are sharply defined by the presence of iron oxide.

**oxide film replica.** A thin film of an oxide of the specimen to be examined. The replica is prepared by air, oxygen, chemical, or electrochemical oxidation of the parent metal and is subsequently freed mechanically or chemically for examination. See also *replica*.

**oxide-type inclusions.** Oxide compounds occurring as nonmetallic inclusions in metals, usually as a result of deoxidizing additions. In wrought steel products, they may occur as a stinger formation composed of distinct granular or crystalline-appearing particles.

## P

**pancake grain structure.** A structure in which the lengths and widths of individual grains are large compared to their thicknesses.

**parameter (in crystals).** See *lattice parameter*.

**parfocal eyepiece.** Eyepieces, with common focal planes, that are interchangeable without refocusing.

**pattern.** See *diffraction pattern*.

**pearlite.** A metastable eutectoid-transformation product consisting of alternating lamellae of ferrite and cementite resulting from the transformation of austenite at temperatures above the bainite range.

**pearlitic structure.** A microstructure resembling that of the pearlite constituent in steel. Therefore, it is a lamellar structure of varying degrees of coarseness.

**peritectic.** An isothermal reversible reaction in which a liquid phase reacts with a solid phase to produce another solid phase.

**peritectic equilibrium.** A reversible univariant transformation in which a solid phase stable only at lower temperature decomposes into a liquid and a solid phase that are conjugate at higher temperature, or conversely.

**peritectoid equilibrium.** A reversible univariant transformation in which a solid phase stable only at low temperature decomposes with rising temperature into two or more conjugate solid phases.

**perpendicular section.** A section cut perpendicular to a surface of interest in a specimen. Compare with *taper section*.

**petrography.** The study of nonmetallic matter under suitable microscopes to determine structural relationships and to identify the phases or minerals present. With transparent materials, the determination of the optical properties, such as the indices of refraction and the behavior in transmitted polarized light, are means of identification. With opaque materials, the color, hardness, reflectivity, shape, and etching behavior in polished sections are means of identification.

**phase.** A physically homogeneous and distinct portion of a material system.

**phase contrast illumination.** A special method of controlled illumination ideally suited to observing thin, transparent objects whose structural details vary only slightly in thickness or refractive index. This can also be applied to the examination of opaque materials to determine surface elevation changes.

**phase diagram.** A graph of the temperature and composition limits of phase fields in an alloy system as they actually exist under the specific conditions of heating or cooling (synonymous with constitutional diagram). A phase diagram may be an equilibrium diagram, an approximation to an equilibrium diagram, or a representation of metastable conditions of phases. Compare with *equilibrium diagram*.

**phase rule.** The maximum number of phases (P) that may coexist at equilibrium is two, plus the number of components (C) in the mixture, minus the number of degrees of freedom (F): $P + F = C + 2$.

**photomicrograph.** A micrograph made by photographic means.

**physical etching.** Development of microstructure through removal of atoms from the surface or lowering the grain-surface potential.

**physical objective aperture.** In electron microscopy, a metal diaphragm centrally pierced with a small hole used to limit the cone of electrons accepted by the objective lens. This improves image contrast, because highly scattered electrons are prevented from arriving at the Gaussian image plane and therefore cannot contribute to background fog.

**pincushion distortion.** See *positive distortion.*

**pinhole eyepiece.** An eyepiece, or a cap to place over an eyepiece, that has a small central aperture instead of an eye lens. It is used in adjusting or aligning microscopes.

**pinhole ocular.** See *pinhole eyepiece.*

**pinhole system.** A group of two or more pinholes arranged to define a beam.

**pinholes.** (1) Very small holes that are sometimes found as a type of porosity in a casting because of the microshrinkage or gas evolution during solidification. In wrought products, due to removal of inclusions or microconstituents during macroetching of transverse sections. (2) In photography, a very small circular aperture.

**plane (crystal).** An idiomorphic face of a crystal. Any atom-containing plane in a crystal.

**plane glass illuminator.** A thin, transparent, flat glass disk interposed in a microscope or a lens imaging system to direct light to the object without reducing the useful aperture of the lens system.

**plane of working.** The plane of maximum area extension.

**planimetric method.** See *Jeffries' method.*

**plastic deformation.** Deformation that remains or will remain permanent after release of the stress that caused it.

**plasticity.** The capacity of a metal to deform nonelastically without rupturing.

**plastic replica.** A reproduction in plastic of the surface to be studied. It is prepared by evaporation of the solvent from a solution of plastic, polymerization of a monomer, or solidification of a plastic on the surface. See also *replica.*

**platelet alpha structure.** Acicular alpha of a coarser variety, usually with low aspect ratios. This microstructure arises from cooling $\alpha$ or $\alpha$-$\beta$ alloys from temperatures at which a significant fraction of $\beta$ phase exists.

**plate martensite.** Martensite formed partly in steel containing more than approximately 0.5% C and solely in steel containing more than approximately 1.0% C as lenticular-shape plates on irrational habit planes near $\{225\}_A$, or $\{259\}_A$ in high-carbon steels (>0.9% C).

**polarized light illumination.** A method of illumination in which the incident light is plane polarized before it impinges on the specimen.

**polarizer.** A Nicol prism, polarizing film, or similar device into which normal light passes and from which polarized light emerges.

**pole figure (crystalline aggregates).** A graph of the crystal orientations present in an aggregate.

**polished surface.** A surface that reflects a large proportion of the incident light in a specular manner.

**polishing.** A mechanical, chemical, or electrolytic process or combination thereof used to prepare a smooth, reflective surface suitable for microstructural examination that is free of artifacts or damage introduced during prior sectioning or grinding.

**polishing artifact.** A false structure introduced during a polishing stage of a surface-preparation sequence.

**polishing rate.** The rate at which material is removed from a surface during polishing. It is usually expressed in terms of the thickness removed per unit of time or distance traversed.

**polycrystalline.** Comprising an aggregate of more than one crystal and usually a large number of crystals.

**polymorphism.** A general term of the ability of a solid to exist in more than one form. In metals, alloys, and similar substances, this usually means the ability to exist in two or more crystal structures, or in an amorphous state and at least one crystal structure. See also *allotropy, enantiotropy,* and *monotropism.*

**porosity.** Holes in a solid, not necessarily connected.

**positive distortion.** The distortion in the image that results when the magnification in the center of the field is less than that at the edge of the field. Also termed pincushion distortion. Contrast with *negative distortion.*

**positive eyepiece.** An eyepiece in which the real image of the object is formed below the lower lens elements of the eyepiece.

**positive replica.** A replica whose contours correspond directly to the surface being replicated. Contrast with *negative replica.*

**potentiometer.** An instrument that measures electromotive force by balancing against it an equal and opposite electromotive force across a calibrated resistance carrying a definite current.

**potentiostat.** An instrument that automatically maintains an electrode in an electrolyte at a constant potential or controlled potentials relative to a suitable reference electrode.

**potentiostatic etching.** Anodic development of microstructure at a constant potential. Adjusting the potential makes possible a defined etching of singular phases.

**powder method.** Any method of x-ray diffraction involving a polycrystalline and preferably randomly oriented powder specimen and a narrow beam of monochromatic radiation.

**precipitation etching.** Development of microstructure through formation of reaction products at the surface of the microsection. See also *staining.*

**precipitation.** Separation of a new phase from solid or liquid solution, usually with changing conditions of temperature, pressure, or both.

**precipitation hardening.** Hardening caused by precipitation of a constituent from a supersaturated solid solution. See also *age hardening* and *aging.*

**precipitation heat treatment.** Artificial aging in which a constituent precipitates from a supersaturated solid solution.

**preferred orientation.** A condition of a polycrystalline aggregate in which the crystal orientations are not random, but tend to align in a specific direction in the bulk material that is completely related to the direction of working. Also termed *texture.*

**preshadowed replica.** A replica formed by the application of shadowing material to the surface to be replicated. It is formed before the thin replica film is cast or otherwise deposited on the surface. See also *shadowing.*

**primary (x-ray).** The beam incident on the specimen.

**primary alpha.** Alpha phase in a crystallographic structure that is retained from the last high-temperature $\alpha$-$\beta$ working or heat treatment. The morphology of $\alpha$ is influenced by the prior thermomechanical history.

**primary crystals.** The first type of crystals that separate from a melt during solidification.

**primary etching.** Development of cast structures including coring.

**primary extinction.** A decrease in intensity of a diffracted x-ray beam caused by perfection of crystal structure extending over such a distance (approximately 1 $\mu$m or greater) that interference between multiply reflected beams inside the crystal decreases the intensity of the externally diffracted beam.

**printing.** A method in which a carrier material is saturated with an etchant and pressed against the surface of the specimen. The etchant reacts with one of the phases, and substances form that react with the carrier material, leaving behind a life-size image. Used for exposing particular elements—for example, sulfur (sulfur prints).

**prior-beta grain size.** Size of $\beta$ grains established during the most recent $\beta$-field excursion. Grains may be distorted by subsequent subtransus deformation. Beta grain boundaries may be obscured by a superimposed $\alpha$-$\beta$ microstructure and detectable only by special techniques.

**process annealing.** A heat treatment used to soften metal for further cold working. In ferrous sheet and wire industries, heating to a temperature close to but below the lower limit of the transformation range and subsequently cooling for working. In the nonferrous industries, heating above the recrystallization temperatures at a time and temperature sufficient to permit the desired subsequent cold working.

**proeutectoid carbide.** Primary crystals of cementite formed directly from the decomposition of austenite exclusive of that cementite resulting from the eutectoid reaction.

**proeutectoid ferrite.** Primary crystals of ferrite formed directly from the decomposition of austenite exclusive of that ferrite resulting from the eutectoid reaction.

**proeutectoid (phase).** Particles of a phase that precipitate during cooling after austenitizing but before the eutectoid transformation takes place.

**progressive aging.** Aging by increasing the temperature in steps or continuously during the aging cycle. Compare with *interrupted aging* and *step aging*.

**projection distance.** Distance from the eyepiece to the image screen.

**projection lens.** The final lens in the electron microscope corresponding to an ocular or projector in a compound optical microscope. This lens forms a real image on the viewing screen or photographic film.

**P-T diagram.** A two-dimensional graph of phase relationships in a system of any order by means of the pressure and temperature variables.

**P-T-X diagram.** A three-dimensional graph of the phase relationships in a binary system by means of the pressure, temperature, and concentration variables.

**P-X diagram.** A two-dimensional graph of the isothermal phase relationships in a binary system; the coordinates of the graph are pressure and concentration.

**P-X projection.** A two-dimensional graph of the phase relationships in a binary system produced by making an orthographic projection of the phase boundaries of a P-T-X diagram upon a pressure-concentration plane.

## Q

**quadrivariant equilibrium.** A stable state among several conjugate phases equal to two less than the number of components, that is, having four degrees of freedom.

**quantitative metallography.** Determination of specific characteristics of a microstructure by quantitative measurements on micrographs or metallographic images. Quantities so measured include volume concentration of phases, grain size, particle size, mean free path between like particles or secondary phases, and surface area to volume ratio of microconstituents, particles, or grains.

**quasi-isotropic.** See *isotropic.*

**quaternary system.** The complete series of compositions produced by mixing four components in all proportions.

**quench aging.** Aging induced from rapid cooling after solution heat treatment.

**quench annealing.** Annealing an austenitic ferrous alloy by solution heat treatment followed by rapid quenching.

**quench hardening.** (1) Hardening suitable α-β alloys—most often certain copper or titanium alloys—by solution treating and quenching to develop a martensite-like structure. (2) In ferrous alloys, hardening by austenitizing, then cooling at a rate so that a substantial amount of austenite transforms to martensite.

**quenching crack.** Cracks formed as a result of thermal stresses produced by rapid cooling from a high temperature.

## R

**random orientation.** A condition of a polycrystalline aggregate in which the orientations of the constituent crystals are completely random relative to each other. Contrast with *preferred orientation.*

**recalescence.** The increase in temperature that occurs after undercooling, because the rate of liberation of heat during transformation of a material exceeds the rate of dissipation of heat.

**recarburizing.** (1) Increasing the carbon content of molten cast iron or steel by adding carbonaceous material, high-carbon pig iron, or a high-carbon alloy. (2) Carburizing a metal part to return surface carbon lost in processing.

**reciprocal lattice.** A lattice of points, each representing a set of planes in the crystal lattice, so that a vector from the origin of the reciprocal lattice to any point is normal to the crystal planes represented by that point and has a length that is the reciprocal of the plane spacing.

**recovery.** Reduction or removal of strain-hardening effects, without motion of large-angle grain boundaries.

**recrystallization.** (1) A change from one crystal structure to another, such as that occurring upon heating or cooling through a critical temperature. (2) Formation of a new, strain-free grain structure from the structure existing in cold-worked metal.

**recrystallization annealing.** Annealing cold-worked metal to produce a new grain structure without a phase change.

**recrystallization temperature.** The approximate minimum temperature at which recrystallization of a cold-worked metal occurs within a specified time.

**recrystallized grain size.** (1) The grain size developed by heating cold-worked metal. The time and temperature are selected so that, although recrystallization is complete, essentially no grain growth occurs. (2) In aluminum and magnesium alloys, the grain size after recrystallization, without regard to grain growth or the recrystallization conditions.

**reflection (x-ray).** See *diffraction.*

**reflection method.** The technique of producing a diffraction pattern by x-rays or electrons that have been reflected from a specimen surface.

**refractive index (electrons).** The ratio of electron wavelength in free space to its wavelength in a material medium.

**regular reflection.** See *specular reflection.*

**replica.** A reproduction of a surface in a material. It is usually accomplished by depositing a thin film of suitable material, such as plastic, onto the specimen surface. This film is subsequently extracted and examined by transmission electron microscopy. See also *atomic replica, cast replica, collodion replica, Formvar replica, gelatin replica, impression replica, negative replica, oxide film replica, plastic replica, positive replica,*

*preshadowed replica, tape replica method (faxfilm),* and *vapor-deposited replica.*

**replicate.** In electron microscopy, to reproduce using a replica.

**residual elements.** Small quantities of elements unintentionally present in an alloy.

**resolution.** The capacity of an optical or radiation system to separate closely spaced forms or entities; in addition, the degree to which such forms or entities can be discriminated. Resolution is usually specified as the minimum distance by which two lines or points in the object must be separated before they can be revealed as separate lines or points in the image. See also *resolving power* and *shape resolution.*

**resolving power.** The ability of a given lens system to reveal fine detail in an object. See also *resolution.*

**retardation plate.** A plate placed in the path of a beam of polarized light for the purpose of introducing a difference in phase. Usually quarter-wave or half-wave plates are used, but if the light passes through them twice, the phase difference is doubled.

**rhombohedral.** Having three equal axes, with the included angles equal to each other, but not equal to 90°.

**rolling direction (in rolled metals).** See *longitudinal direction.*

**rosette.** (1) Rounded configuration of microconstituents arranged in whorls or radiating from a center. (2) Strain gages arranged to indicate at a single position strains in three different directions.

**rosette graphite.** Arrangement of graphite flakes in which the flakes extend radially from the center of crystallized areas in gray cast iron.

**rough-polishing process.** A polishing process having the primary objective of removing the layer of significant damage produced during earlier machining and abrasion stages of a preparation sequence. A secondary objective is to produce a finish of such quality that a final polish can be produced easily.

## S

**saturated gun.** A self-biased electron gun in which electron emission is limited by space charge rather than filament temperature.

**scale.** A layer of oxidation products formed on a metal at high temperature.

**scanning electron microscope.** An electron microscope in which the image is formed by a beam operating in synchronism with an electron probe scanning the object. The intensity of the image-forming beam is proportional to the scattering or secondary emission of the specimen where the probe strikes it.

**scattering (x-ray).** A general term including *coherent scattering* and *incoherent scattering.*

**scoring.** Marring or scratching of a smooth surface. It is most often caused by sliding contact with a mating member having a hard projection or embedded particle on its surface.

**scratch trace.** A line of etch markings produced on a surface at the site of a pre-existing scratch, the physical groove of the scratch having been removed. The scratch trace develops when the deformed material extending beneath the scratch has not been removed with the scratch groove and when the residual deformed material is attacked preferentially during etching.

**scratch.** A groove produced in a surface by an abrasive point.

**seam.** An unwelded fold or lap on the surface of metal that appears as a crack. This is usually the result of defects in casting or working that have not welded shut.

**secondary x-rays.** The x-rays emitted by a specimen irradiated by a primary beam.

**secondary etching.** Development of microstructures deviating from primary structure through transformation and heat treatment in the solid state.

**secondary extinction.** A decrease in the intensity of a diffracted x-ray beam caused by parallelism or near-parallelism of mosaic blocks in a mosaic crystal; the lower blocks are partially screened from the incident radiation by the upper blocks, which have reflected some of it.

**segregation.** Nonuniform distribution of alloying elements, impurities, or phases.

**segregation banding.** Inhomogeneous distribution of alloying elements aligned in filaments or plates parallel to the direction of working.

**segregation (coring) etching.** Development of segregation (coring) mainly in macrostructures and microstructures of castings.

**sensitive tint plate.** A gypsum plate used in conjunction with polarizing filters to provide very sensitive detection of birefringence and double refraction.

**serial sectioning.** A technique in which an identified area on a section surface is observed repeatedly after successive layers of known thickness have been removed from the surface. It is used to construct a three-dimensional morphology of structural features.

**shadow angle.** The angle between the line of motion of the evaporated atoms and the surface being shadowed. The angle analogous to the angle of incidence in optics. It may be specified as arc tangent *a* so that *a* is in the ratio between the height of the object casting the shadow over the length of the shadow. See also *shadowing*.

**shadow cast replica.** A replica that has been shadowed. See also *shadowing*.

**shadow microscope.** An electron microscope that forms a shadow image of an object using electrons emanating from a point source located close to the object.

**shadowing.** A process by which a metal or salt is deposited on a specimen at an angle from a heated filament in a vacuum to enhance image contrast by inhibiting the deposition of the shadowing material behind projections. See also *shadow angle*, *metal shadowing*, and *oblique evaporation shadowing*.

**shales.** Abrasive particles of platelike shape. The term is applied particularly to diamond abrasives.

**shape resolution.** An electron image exhibits shape resolution when a polygon can be recognized as such in the image. Roughly, the particle diameter—defined as the diameter of a circle of the same area as the particle—must exceed the resolution by a factor equal to the number of sides on the polygon.

**shatter cracks.** See *flakes*.

**shear bands.** Bands in which deformation has been concentrated inhomogeneously in sheets that extend across regional groups of grains. Only one system is usually present in each regional group of grains, different systems being present in adjoining groups. The bands are noncrystallographic and form on planes of maximum shear stress (55° to the compression direction). They carry most of the deformation at large strains. Compare with *microbands*.

**shelling.** A mechanism of deterioration of coated abrasive products in which entire abrasive grains are removed from the cement coating that held the abrasive to the backing layer of the product.

**shielding.** In an electron-optical instrument, the protection of the electron beam from distortion due to extraneous electric and magnetic fields. Because the metallic column of the microscope is at ground potential, it provides electrostatic shielding. Magnetic shields may be made of a high-permeability material.

**shortness.** A form of brittleness in metal. It is designated as "cold," "hot," and "red" to indicate the temperature range in which the brittleness occurs.

**short-term etching.** Etching times of seconds to a few minutes.

**shrink etching.** Precipitation on grain surfaces. Shrinkage takes place during drying, which cracks the layer formed during etching. Crack orientation depends on the underlying structure.

**sigma, σ.** Solid phase found originally in binary iron-chromium alloys that is in stable equilibrium below 820 °C (1510 °F). It is now used to identify any structure having the same complex body-centered crystal structure.

**silicate-type inclusions.** Inclusions composed essentially of silicate glass, normally plastic at forging and hot-rolling temperatures, that appear in steel in the wrought condition as small elongated inclusions usually dark in color under reflected light as normally observed.

**simple (lattices).** Having similar atoms or groups of atoms separated by integral translations only.

**skid-polishing process.** A mechanical polishing process in which the surface to be polished is made to skid across a layer of paste, consisting of the abrasive and the polishing fluid, without contacting the fibers of the polishing cloth.

**slag.** A nonmetallic product resulting from mutual dissolution of flux and nonmetallic impurities in smelting and refining operations.

**slip.** Plastic deformation by the irreversible shear displacement (translation) of one part of a crystal relative to another in a definite crystallographic direction and usually on a specific crystallographic plane. Sometimes termed glide.

**slip band.** A group of parallel slip lines so closely spaced as to appear as a single line when observed under an optical microscope. See also *slip line*.

**slip direction.** The crystallographic direction in which the translation of slip takes place.

**slip line.** The trace of the slip plane on the viewing surface; the trace is usually observable only if the surface has been polished before deformation. The usual observation on metal crystals (under an optical microscope) is of a cluster of slip lines known as a slip band.

**slip plane.** The crystallographic plane in which slip occurs in a crystal.

**slivers.** Abrasive particles of rodlike shape with an aspect ratio greater than 3. The term is applied particularly to diamond abrasives.

**solid solution.** A solid crystalline phase containing two or more chemical species in concentrations that may vary between limits imposed by phase equilibrium.

**solidification range.** The temperature range between the liquidus and the solidus.

**solidification shrinkage crack.** A crack that forms, usually at elevated temperature, because of the shrinkage stresses accumulating during solidification of a metal casting. Also termed hot crack.

**solidus.** In a phase diagram, the locus of points representing the temperatures at which various components finish freezing on cooling or begin to melt on heating.

**solute.** The component of a liquid or solid solution that is present to the lesser or minor extent; the component that is dissolved in the solvent.

**solution.** In a chemical system, a phase existing over a range of composition.

**solution heat treatment.** A heat treatment in which an alloy is heated to a suitable temperature, held at that temperature long enough to cause one or more constituents to enter into solid solution, then cooled rapidly enough to hold these constituents in solution.

**solvent.** The component of a liquid or solid solution that is present to the greater or major extent; the component that dissolves the solute.

**solvus.** In a phase or equilibrium diagram, the locus of points representing the temperature at which solid phases with various compositions coexist with other solid phases, that is, the limits of solid solubility.

**sorbite** (obsolete). A fine mixture of ferrite and cementite produced by regulating the rate of cooling of steel or by tempering steel after hardening. The former is very fine pearlite that is difficult to resolve under the microscope; the latter is tempered martensite.

**source (x-rays).** The area emitting primary x-rays in a diffraction experiment. The actual source is always the focal spot of the x-ray tube, but the virtual source may be a slit or pinhole, depending on the conditions of the experiment.

**space-charge aberration.** An aberration resulting from the mutual repulsion of the electrons in a beam. This aberration is most noticeable in low-voltage, high-current beams. This repulsion acts as a negative lens, causing rays, which were originally parallel, to diverge.

**space lattice.** See *lattice.*

**spacing (lattice planes).** See *interplanar distance.*

**spatial grain size.** The average size of the three-dimensional grains, as opposed to the more conventional grain size determined by a simple average of observations made on a cross section of the material.

**specimen chamber (electron optics).** The compartment located in the column of the electron microscope in which the specimen is placed for observation.

**specimen charge (electron optics).** The electrical charge resulting from the impingement of electrons on a nonconducting specimen.

**specimen contamination (electron optics).** The contamination of the specimen caused by the condensation upon it of residual vapors in the microscope under the influence of electron bombardment.

**specimen distortion (electron optics).** A physical change in the specimen caused by desiccation or heating by the electron beam.

**specimen grid.** See *specimen screen.*

**specimen holder (electron optics).** A device that supports the specimen and specimen screen in the correct position in the specimen chamber of the microscope.

**specimen screen (electron optics).** A disk of fine screen, usually 200-mesh stainless steel, copper, or nickel, that supports the replica or specimen support film for observation in the microscope.

**specimen stage.** The part of the microscope that supports the specimen holder and specimen in the microscope and can be moved in a plane perpendicular to the optic axis from outside the column.

**specimen strain.** A distortion of the specimen resulting from stresses occurring during preparation or observation. In electron metallography, strain may be caused by stretching during removal of a replica or during subsequent washing or drying.

**specular reflection.** The condition in which all the incident light is reflected at the same angle as the angle of the incident light relative to the normal at the point of incidence.

The reflection surface then appears bright, or mirrorlike, when viewed with the naked eye. Sometimes termed regular reflection.

**spherical aberration.** The zonal aberrations of a lens referred to an axial point. When rays from a point on the axis passing through the outer lens zones are focused closer to the lens than rays passing the central zones, the lens suffers positive spherical aberration. If the condition is reversed, that is, the outer zones have a longer focal length than the inner zones, the lens has negative spherical aberration. In the first instance, the lens is uncorrected or undercorrected; in the second, overcorrected.

**spherical projection.** A projection in which the orientation of a crystal plane is represented by the point at which the plane normal intersects a sphere drawn with the crystal as the center.

**spheroidal graphite.** Graphite of spheroidal shape with a polycrystalline radial structure. This structure can be obtained, for example, by adding cerium or magnesium to the melt.

**spheroidite.** An aggregate of iron or alloy carbides of essentially spherical shape dispersed throughout a matrix of ferrite.

**spheroidized structure.** A microstructure consisting of a matrix containing spheroidal particles of another constituent.

**spheroidizing.** Heating and cooling to produce a spheroidal or globular form of carbide in steel.

**spinodal curve.** A graph of the realizable limit of the supersaturation of a solution.

**spinodal structure.** A fine, homogeneous mixture of two phases that form by the growth of composition waves in a solid solution during suitable heat treatment. The phases of a spinodal structure differ in composition from each other and from the parent phase, but have the same crystal structure as the parent phase.

**sputtering.** The production of specimens in the form of thin films by deposition from a cathode subjected to positive-ion bombardment.

**stage.** A device for holding a specimen in the desired position in the optical path.

**staining.** Precipitation etching that causes contrast by distinctive staining of microconstituents; different interference colors originate from surface layers of varying thickness.

**standard grain-size micrograph.** A micrograph taken of a known grain size at a known magnification that is used to determine grain size by direct comparison with another micrograph or with the image of a specimen.

**steadite.** A hard structural constituent of cast iron that consists of a binary eutectic of ferrite, containing some phosphorus in solution, and iron phosphide ($Fe_3P$). The eutectic consists of 10.2% P and 89.8% Fe. The melting temperature is 1050 °C (1920 °F).

**step aging.** Aging at two or more temperatures by steps, without cooling to room temperature after each step. Compare with *interrupted aging* and *progressive aging.*

**stepdown test.** A test involving the preparation of a series of machined steps progressing inward from the surface of a bar for the purpose of detecting by visual inspection the internal laminations caused by inclusion segregates.

**stereo angle.** One half of the angle through which the specimen is tilted when taking a pair of stereoscopic micrographs. The axis of rotation lies in the plane of the specimen.

**stereoscopic micrographs.** A pair of micrographs of the same area, but taken from different angles so that the two micrographs when properly mounted and viewed reveal the structures of the objects in their three-dimensional relationships.

**stereoscopic specimen holder.** A specimen holder designed for the purpose of making stereoscopic micrographs. It makes possible the tilting of the specimen through the stereo angle.

**strain aging.** Aging induced by cold work.

**strain etching.** Etching that provides information on deformed and undeformed areas if present side by side. In strained areas, more compounds are precipitated.

**strain hardening.** An increase in hardness and strength caused by plastic deformation at temperatures below the recrystallization range.

**strain markings.** Manifestations of prior plastic deformation visible after etching of a metallographic section. These markings may be referred to as slip strain markings, twin strain markings, and so on, to indicate the specific deformation mechanism of which they are a manifestation.

**stress relieving.** Heating to a suitable temperature, holding long enough to reduce residual stresses, then cooling slowly enough to minimize the development of new residual stresses.

**stretcher strains.** Elongated markings that appear on the surfaces of some materials when they are deformed just past the yield point. These markings lie approximately parallel to the direction of maximum shear stress and are the result of localized yielding. See also *Lüders lines.*

**stringer.** A microstructural configuration of alloy constituents or foreign nonmetallic material lined up in the direction of working.

**structure factor, *F*.** The ratio of the amplitude of the wave scattered by all the atoms of a unit cell to the amplitude of the wave scattered by a single electron.

**structure.** As applied to a crystal, the shape and size of the unit cell and the location of all atoms within the unit cell. As applied to microstructure, the size, shape, and arrangement of phases.

**sub-boundary structure (subgrain structure).** A network of low-angle boundaries, usually with misorientations less than 1° within the main grains of a microstructure.

**subcritical annealing.** An annealing treatment in which a steel is heated to a temperature below the $A_1$ temperature, then cooled slowly to room temperature. See also *transformation temperature.*

**subgrain.** A portion of a crystal or grain slightly different in orientation from adjoining portions of the same crystal. Generally, adjoining subgrains are separated by low-angle boundaries.

**submicroscopic.** Below the resolution of the microscope.

**substitutional element.** An alloying element with an atomic size and other features similar to the solvent that can replace or substitute for the solvent atoms in the lattice and form a significant region of solid solution in the phase diagram.

**substitutional solid solution.** A solid solution in which the solvent and solute atoms are located randomly at the atom sites in the crystal structure of the solution.

**substrate.** The layer of metal underlying a coating, regardless of whether the layer is base metal.

**sulfide spheroidization.** A stage of overheating in which sulfide inclusions are partly or completely spheroidized.

**sulfide-type inclusions.** In steels, nonmetallic inclusions composed essentially of manganese iron sulfide solid solutions (Fe,Mn)S. They are characterized by plasticity at hot-rolling and forging temperatures and, in the hot-worked product, appear as dove-gray elongated inclusions varying from a threadlike to oval outline.

**sulfur print.** A macrographic method of examining distribution of sulfide inclusions. See also *printing.*

**supercooling.** Cooling to a temperature below that of an equilibrium phase transformation without the transformation taking place. Also termed undercooling.

**superheating.** (1) Heating a phase to a temperature above that of a phase transformation without the transformation taking place. (2) Heating molten metal to a temperature above the normal casting temperature to obtain more complete refining or greater fluidity.

**superlattice.** See *ordered structure.*

**swabbing.** Wiping of the specimen surface with a cotton ball saturated with etchant to remove reaction products simultaneously.

**syntectic equilibrium.** A reversible univariant transformation in which a solid phase that is stable only at lower temperature decomposes into two conjugate liquid phases that remain stable at higher temperature.

**system (crystal).** See *crystal system.*

**T**

**tape replica method (faxfilm).** A method of producing a replica by pressing the softened surface of tape or plastic sheet material onto the surface to be replicated.

**taper section.** A section made at an acute angle to a surface of interest, achieving a geometrical magnification of depth. A sectioning angle of 5° 43' achieves a depth magnification of 10:1.

**target (x-ray).** That part of an x-ray tube the electrons strike and from which x-rays are emitted.

**temper carbon.** Clusters of finely divided graphite, such as that found in malleable iron, that are formed as a result of decomposition of cementite, for example, by heating white cast iron above the ferrite-austenite transformation temperature and holding at these temperatures for a considerable period of time. Also termed annealing carbon. See also *nodular graphite.*

**tempered layer.** A surface or subsurface layer in a steel specimen that has been tempered by heating during some stage of the preparation sequence. When observed in a section after etching, the layer appears darker than the base material.

**tempered martensite.** The decomposition products that result from heating martensite below the ferrite-austenite transformation temperature. Under the optical microscope, darkening of the martensite needles is observed in the initial stages of tempering. Prolonged tempering at high temperatures produces spheroidized carbides in a matrix of ferrite. At the higher resolution of the electron microscope, the initial stage of tempering is observed to result in a structure containing a precipitate of fine $\varepsilon$ iron carbide particles. At approximately 260 °C (500 °F), a transition occurs to a structure of larger and elongated cementite particles in a ferrite matrix. With further tempering at higher temperatures, the cementite particles become spheroidal, decreased in number, and increased in size.

**tempering.** In heat treatment, reheating hardened steel to some temperature below the eutectoid temperature to decrease hardness and/or increase toughness.

**temper rolling.** Light cold rolling of sheet steel to improve flatness, to minimize the formation of stretcher strains, and to obtain a specified hardness or temper.

**terminal solid solution.** In a multicomponent system, any solid phase of limited composition range that includes the composition of one of the components of the system.

**ternary system.** The complete series of compositions produced by mixing three components in all proportions.

**tetragonal.** Having three mutually perpendicular axes, two equal in length and unequal to the third.

**texture.** In a polycrystalline aggregate, the state of distribution of crystal orientations. In the usual sense, it is synonymous with *preferred orientation*, in which the distribution is not random.

**thermal etching.** Annealing of the specimen in vacuum or inert atmosphere. Used primarily in high-temperature microscopy.

**thermionic cathode gun.** An electron gun that derives its electrons from a heated filament, which may also serve as the cathode. Also termed hot cathode gun.

**thermionic emission.** The ejection of a stream of electrons from a hot cathode, usually under the influence of an electrostatic field.

**thermocouple.** Two dissimilar electrical conductors so joined as to produce a thermal electromotive force when the junctions are at different temperatures.

**time-temperature curve.** A curve produced by plotting time against temperature.

**time-temperature-transformation (TTT) diagram.** See *isothermal transformation (IT) diagram.*

**tinting.** See *heat tinting.*

**transcrystalline.** See *intracrystalline.*

**transcrystalline cracking.** Cracking or fracturing that occurs through or across a crystal. Also termed intracrystalline cracking.

**transformation ranges.** Those ranges of temperature within which austenite forms during heating and transforms during cooling. The two ranges are distinct, sometimes overlapping but never coinciding. The limiting temperatures of the ranges depend on the composition of the alloy and on the rate of change of temperature, particularly during cooling. See also *transformation temperature.*

**transformation temperature.** The temperature at which a change in phase occurs. The term is sometimes used to denote the limiting temperature of a transformation range. The following symbols are used for iron and steels:

$Ac_{cm}$. In hypereutectoid steel, the temperature at which the solution of cementite in austenite is complete during heating.

$Ac_1$. The temperature at which austenite begins to form during heating.

$Ac_3$. The temperature at which transformation of ferrite to austenite is complete during heating.

$Ac_4$. The temperature at which austenite transforms to δ-ferrite during heating.

$Ae_1$, $Ae_3$, $Ae_{cm}$, $Ae_4$. The temperatures of phase changes at equilibrium.

$Ar_{cm}$. In hypereutectoid steel, the temperature at which precipitation of cementite begins during cooling.

$Ar_1$. The temperature at which transformation of austenite to ferrite or to ferrite plus cementite is complete during cooling.

$Ar_3$. The temperature at which austenite begins to transform to ferrite during cooling.

$Ar_4$. The temperature at which δ-ferrite transforms to austenite during cooling.

$M_s$. The temperature at which transformation of austenite to martensite begins during cooling.

$M_f$. The temperature, during cooling, at which transformation of austenite to martensite is substantially complete.

**transformed beta.** A local or continuous structure consisting of decomposition products arising by nucleation and growth processes during cooling from above the local or overall $\beta$ transus. Primary and re-growth $\alpha$ may be present. Transformed $\beta$ typically consists of $\alpha$ platelets that may or may not be separated by $\beta$ phase.

**transgranular.** See *intracrystalline*.

**transition phase.** A nonequilibrium state that appears in a chemical system in the course of transformation between two equilibrium states.

**transition structure.** In precipitation from solid solution, a metastable precipitate that is coherent with the matrix.

**transmission method.** A method of x-ray or electron diffraction in which the recorded diffracted beams emerge on the same side of the specimen as the transmitted primary beam.

**transmission electron microscope.** A microscope in which the image-forming rays pass through (are transmitted by) the specimen being observed.

**transverse direction.** Literally, across, usually signifying a direction or plane perpendicular to the direction of working. In rolled plate or sheet, the direction across the width is often called long transverse, and the direction through the thickness, short transverse. See also *longitudinal direction* and *normal direction*.

**triclinic.** Having three axes of any length, none of the included angles being equal to one another or equal to 90°.

**triple curve.** In a P-T diagram, a line representing the sequence of pressure and temperature values along which two conjugate phases occur in univariant equilibrium.

**triple point.** The intersection of the boundaries of three adjoining grains, as observed in a section.

**troostite.** A previously unresolvable, rapidly etching, fine aggregate of carbide and ferrite produced by tempering martensite at approximately 400 °C (750 °F). The term is variously and erroneously applied to bainite and nodular fine pearlite. Confusion arose because of the similarity in appearance among the three structures before the advent of high-power microscopy. With reference to tool steels, synonymous with upper bainite.

**twin.** Two portions of a crystal with a definite orientation relationship; one may be regarded as the parent, the other as the twin. The orientation of the twin is a mirror image of the orientation of the parent across a twinning plane or an orientation that can be derived by rotating the twin portion about a twinning axis. See also *annealing twin* and *mechanical twin*.

**twin bands.** Bands across a crystal grain, observed on a polished and etched section, where crystallographic orientations have a mirror-image relationship to the orientation of the matrix grain across a composition plane that is usually parallel to the sides of the band.

**T-X diagram.** A two-dimensional graph of the isobaric phase relationships in a binary system; the coordinates of the graph are temperature and concentration.

# U

**ultramicroscopic.** See *submicroscopic*.

**unary system.** Composed of one component.

**undercooling.** See *supercooling*.

**unit cell.** A parallelepiped element of crystal structure, containing a certain number of atoms, the repetition of which through space will build up the complete crystal. See also *lattice*.

**univariant equilibrium.** A stable state among several phases equal to one more than the number of components, that is, having one degree of freedom.

# V

**vacancy.** A structural imperfection in which an individual atom site is temporarily unoccupied.

**vapor-deposited replica.** A replica formed of a metal or a salt by the condensation of the vapors of the material onto the surface to be replicated.

**variability.** The number of degrees of freedom of a heterogeneous phase equilibrium. Also termed variance.

**variance.** See *variability*.

**veining.** A sub-boundary structure that can be delineated because of the presence of a greater than average concentration of precipitate or solute atoms.

**vertical illumination.** Light incident on an object from the objective side so that smooth planes perpendicular to the optical axis of the objective appear bright.

**vibratory polishing.** A mechanical polishing process in which the specimen is made to move around the polishing cloth by imparting a suitable vibratory motion to the polishing system.

**voltage alignment.** A condition of alignment of an electron microscope so that the image expands or contracts symmetrically about the center of the viewing screen when the accelerating voltage is changed. See also *alignment*.

**V-X diagram.** A graph of the isothermal or isobaric phase relationships in a binary system, the coordinates of the graph being specific volume and concentration.

# W

**wavelength (x-rays).** The minimum distance between points at which the electric vector of an electromagnetic wave has the same value. It is measured along the direction of propagation of the wave, and it is equal to the velocity divided by the frequency. See also *electron wavelength*.

**weld structure.** The microstructure of a weld deposit and heat-affected base metal. See also *heat-affected zone*.

**wet etching.** Development of microstructure with liquids, such as acids, bases, neutral solutions, or mixtures of solutions.

**white-etching layer.** A surface layer in a steel that, as viewed in a section after etching, appears whiter than the base metal. The presence of the layer may be due to a number of causes, including plastic deformation induced by machining or surface rubbing, heating during a preparation stage to such an extent that the layer is austenitized and then hardened during cooling, and diffusion of extraneous elements into the surface.

**Widmanstätten structure.** A structure characterized by a geometrical pattern resulting from the formation of a new phase along certain crystallograhic planes of the parent solid solution. The orientation of the lattice in the new phase is related crystallographically to the orientation of the lattice in the parent phase. The structure was originally observed in meteorites, but is readily produced in many alloys, such as titanium, by appropriate heat treatment.

**wipe etching.** See *swabbing*.

**work hardening.** See *strain hardening*.

**working distance.** The distance between the surface of the specimen being examined and the front surface of the objective lens.

# X

**x-radiation.** Electromagnetic radiation of the same nature as visible light, but having a wavelength approximately $1/1000$ that of visible light. Commonly referred to as x-rays.

**x-rays.** See *x-radiation*.

**x-ray tube.** A device for the production of x-rays by the impact of high-speed electrons on a metal target.

# Z

**zone.** Any group of crystal planes that are all parallel to one line, which is called the zone axis.

## SELECTED REFERENCES

- *Glossary of Metallurgical Terms and Engineering Tables*, American Society for Metals, 1979
- G. Petzow, *Metallographic Etching*, American Society for Metals, 1978, p 31-34
- W.A. Reinsch, Terminology for Titanium Microstructure, *Met. Prog.*, Feb 1982, p 51-54
- L.E. Samuels, *Metallographic Polishing by Mechanical Methods*, 3rd ed., American Society for Metals, 1982, p 373-377
- L.E. Samuels, *Optical Microscopy of Carbon Steels*, American Society for Metals, 1980, p 563-574
- "Standard Definitions of Terms Relating to Heat Treatment of Metals," E 44, *Annual Book of ASTM Standards*, Vol 03.03, ASTM, Philadelphia, 1984, p 54-60
- "Standard Definitions of Terms Relating to Metallography," E 7, *Annual Book of ASTM Standards*, Vol 03.03, ASTM, Philadelphia, 1984, p 12-48

# Metallographic Techniques

# Sectioning

SECTIONING, the removal of a conveniently sized, representative specimen from a larger sample, is one of five major operations in the preparation of metallographic specimens. The other operations are mounting (optional), grinding, polishing, and etching. In many ways, sectioning is the most important step in preparing specimens for physical or microscopic analysis.

Incorrect preparation techniques may alter the true microstructure and lead to erroneous conclusions. Because the microstructure should not be altered, conditions that may cause microstructural changes ideally should be avoided. However, hot and cold working accompany most sectioning methods.

The damage to the specimen during sectioning depends on the material being sectioned, the nature of the cutting device used, the cutting speed and feed rate, and the amount and type of coolant used. On some specimens, surface damage is inconsequential and can be removed during subsequent grinding and polishing. The depth of damage varies with material and sectioning method (Fig. 1).

Sectioning methods discussed in this article include fracturing, shearing, sawing (using hacksaws, band saws, and wire saws), abrasive cutting, and electric discharge machining. Additional information can be found in Ref 1 to 4.

## Fracturing

Fracture surfaces can be obtained by breaking specimens with blows of a hammer or by steadily applying pressure. Controlled fractures can be produced by impact or tension testing, and the location of the fracture can be controlled by nicking or notching the material. Less brittle materials can be cooled in liquid nitrogen before breaking to obtain a flatter surface. Fracturing has also been used on other brittle materials, such as carbides and ceramics.

Fracturing is not recommended, because it seldom follows desired directions, unless the sample is prenotched. Also, the fracture surface is the one usually prepared, and lengthy coarse grinding may be required to obtain a flat surface. Moreover, damage from fracturing can mask inherent features, obscuring the outside surface from microscopic examination.

## Shearing (Ref 1)

Low-carbon sheet steel and other thin, reasonably soft materials can be cut to size by shearing, a fast, simple, effective sectioning technique. Although little heat is generated, shearing produces substantial deformation and is not recommended for materials sensitive to mechanical twin formation. The area affected by shearing must be removed by grinding.

## Sawing

Sawing, perhaps the oldest sectioning method, can be performed using a hand-held hacksaw, a band saw, or an oscillating power hacksaw. Hand-held hacksaws or band saws, either vertical or horizontal, generally do not generate enough frictional heat to alter the microstructure; however, frictional heat can temper the blades enough to eliminate their cutting ability.

Power hacksaws are not appropriate in the metallographic laboratory. This type of sectioning equipment can irreparably damage a material, particularly if it is prone to deformation. A power hacksaw should be used only to cut a larger piece down so that a smaller piece can be subsequently sectioned by some other means. Saw-cut surfaces are rough, and coarse grinding is required to obtain a flat surface prior to fine grinding.

Although coolants should be used in any type of sectioning, band saw cutting can be performed without a coolant; the speed is slow enough that frictional heat is not detrimental to the material. In the case of power hacksaws, with their thicker and coarser blades, a coolant must be used, because the depth of deformation introduced by this severe method of sectioning can be quite deep.

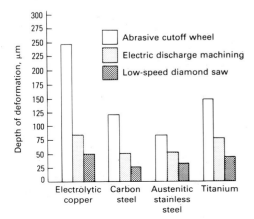

**Fig. 1** Depth of deformation in different metals due to cutting method. (Ref 1)

**Fig. 2** Typical abrasive cutter. (Buehler Ltd.)

## Abrasive Cutting (Ref 2)

Abrasive cutting is the most widely used method of sectioning materials for microscopic examination and other material investigations. Conventional abrasive cutting using consumable wheels is the most popular method for routine metallographic sectioning, because it is fast, accurate, and economical.

The quality of the cut surface obtained is often superior to that obtained by other means, and fewer subsequent steps may be required. Metal-matrix diamond blades handle such specialized applications as ceramics, rocks, very hard metallics, and printed circuit boards. Methods of abrasive cutting offer various cutting characteristics useful for most material sectioning situations. Figure 2 illustrates a typical abrasive cutting machine.

### Consumable-Abrasive Cutting

Abrasive cutting is the sectioning of material using a relatively thin rotating disk composed of abrasive particles supported by a suitable medium. The thousands of particles contacting the material in rapid succession and at very high speeds section the material.

Consumable-wheel abrasive cutting is often performed using a coolant, ensuring an almost plane surface without serious mechanical or thermal damage. In selecting a wheel for a particular application, the abrasive, bonding material, bond hardness, and density must be considered. Coolant, wheel speed, applied pressure, and wheel edge wear affect the quality of the cut. Table 1 lists problems and solutions of abrasive cutoff sectioning.

**Wheel Selection.** Abrasive wheels afford more control over the conditions used than do other types of specimen sectioning. Many factors determine the suitability of a particular wheel when cutting a given material:

- The nature of the abrasive
- The size of the abrasive grains
- The nature of the bond
- The hardness of the bond
- The porosity of the wheel

Silicon carbide is preferred for cutting nonferrous metals and nonmetals. Alumina ($Al_2O_3$) is recommended for ferrous metals. Coarse-grain wheels generally cut heavier sections faster and cooler, but fine-grain wheels produce smoother cuts with less burring. Fine-grain wheels are therefore recommended for cutting delicate materials, such as thin-wall tubing. Cutoff wheels with grit sizes from 60 to 120 are recommended for sectioning metallographic specimens. The surface finish does not require coarse grinding, and the grinding sequence usually can begin with a 180-grit silicon carbide.

Resin-bonded wheels, which have very high cutting rates, are generally used for dry cutting and find application in plant production cutting. Wet cutting wheels require a rubber or rubber-resin bond and are used in metallographic laboratories.

The rate of wheel deterioration depends on the type of bond used. Resin- and resinoid-bonded wheels generally break down more rapidly than rubber-bonded wheels. The rubber bond retains abrasive particles more tenaciously, resulting in slower wheel wear and more cuts per wheel. In addition, the rubber forms a solid bond; that is, there are no pores. However, resin used as a bond sets up in a polymerization process and there are extremely small pores throughout the wheel that may or may not be near abrasive grains. Therefore, resin-bonded wheels wear away faster, but always present a fresh cutting surface, because each abrasive grain is ejected before it becomes dull. The abrasive used is more important than the bond. Selection of bond is usually based on objections to the odor of burning rubber as the wheel degrades.

Two terms used in selecting abrasive cutoff wheels are "hard" and "soft." These terms do not refer to the hardness of the abrasive grains but to how the wheel breaks down. Silicon carbide (approximately 9.4 on the Mohs scale) and $Al_2O_3$ (approximately 9.0) differ only slightly in hardness. A hard wheel (one made with hard bonding material) is usually best for cutting soft stock, but a soft wheel is preferred for cutting hard materials. A good general-purpose cutoff wheel is a medium-hard silicon carbide abrasive wheel.

In rubber-resin wheels, the amount of bonding material and the percentage of free space determine the hardness or wheel grade. A more porous, less dense (softer) wheel breaks down faster because the abrasive particles are held more loosely. Softer wheels are used because fresh, sharp abrasive grains are more frequently exposed. Less porous, more dense wheels are harder, break down slower, and are better for softer materials.

**Coolants.** Water alone should not be used as a coolant for wet sectioning. A coolant should contain a water-soluble oil with a rust-inhibitor additive, which protects the moving parts of the cutoff machine, minimizes the possibility of burning, and produces better cuts. Some foaming of the coolant is desirable.

The preferred cooling condition is submerged sectioning, in which the entire piece

**Table 1  Solutions for problems encountered in abrasive cutoff sectioning**

| Problem | Possible cause | Solution |
|---|---|---|
| Burning (bluish discoloration) | Overheated specimen | Increase coolant rate; lessen cutting pressure; choose softer wheel. |
| Rapid wheel wear | Wheel bond breaking down too rapidly | Choose harder wheel; lessen cutting pressure. |
| Frequent wheel breakage | Uneven coolant distribution, loose specimen fixturing | Distribute coolant uniformly; fix specimen rigidly. |
| Resistance to cutting | Slow wheel breakdown | Choose softer wheel; reduce coolant flow; use oscillating stroke. |
| Cutter stalls | Cutter too light for the work | Use heavier cutter; limit sample size. |

Source: Ref 2

**Fig. 3** Typical low-speed diamond saw. (Leco Corp.)

**Fig. 4** Three pieces of honeycomb cut with a diamond wire saw. Note the absence of burrs and breakout. From left: titanium; section from helicopter rotor blade consisting of plastic, paper honeycomb, epoxy, stainless steel screws, and Kevlar; extruded ceramic honeycomb used in automotive catalytic converters. (Laser Technology, Inc.)

**Fig. 5** Kevlar honeycomb cut with a wire saw. (Laser Technology, Inc.)

is under water. Submerged sectioning is recommended for heat-sensitive materials that undergo microstructural changes at low temperatures. For example, as-quenched alloy steels with an untempered martensitic microstructure can readily transform to tempered martensite with the frictional heat developed.

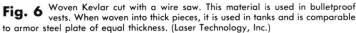

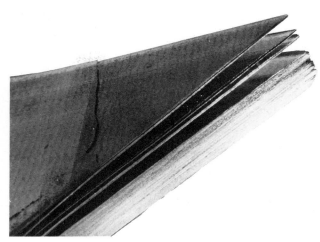

**Fig. 6** Woven Kevlar cut with a wire saw. This material is used in bulletproof vests. When woven into thick pieces, it is used in tanks and is comparable to armor steel plate of equal thickness. (Laser Technology, Inc.)

**Fig. 7** Amorphous iron (Metglas) cut with a wire saw. Each laminate is 0.1 mm (0.004 in.) thick. (Laser Technology, Inc.)

The quality of a submerged cut is excellent, and the specimens produced will not require extensive grinding. Section size, material, and hardness dictate whether submerged cutting can be employed. Submerged cutting will tend to make a wheel bond act harder.

**Wheel speed** must be carefully considered in the design of a cutter and the selection of wheels for a given cutter. In the interest of safety, maximum operating speeds printed on the specific blade or wheel should never be exceeded. Also, increased wheel speed may introduce frictional heat, which damages the microstructure.

**Wheel edge wear** may be used to determine whether the correct wheel has been selected. Abrasive wheels that show little or no wear are not performing satisfactorily. Controlled wheel loss indicates that the wheel bond is breaking down, exposing fresh abrasive grains for faster, more effective, and cooler cutting. Wheels that do not deteriorate fast enough may become glazed with specimen material, resulting in poor cutting and excessive specimen heating. Exerting additional pressure will most likely cause overheating.

The acceptable rate of wheel loss is:

$$LR = \frac{M}{W}$$

where $LR$ is wheel life ratio, $M$ is area of material cut, and $W$ is area of abrasive wheel consumed. In plant production cutting, resin-bonded wheels are commonly used without a coolant. Rate of cutting is the main concern, because this step probably precedes heat treating. In this application, an $M/W$ ratio of 1.5:1 is acceptable. In other words, 1.5 times more material should be cut as wheel area consumed.

**Shelf Life.** Rubber-bonded wheels have a definite shelf life, which ranges from 12 to 18 months, depending on storage and climatic conditions. The rubber has a tendency to harden and become brittle. Storing abrasive wheels in an extremely warm area hastens the degradation of the rubber, further reducing shelf life. Abrasive wheels should be removed from their shipping containers and laid flat on a rigid surface in a relatively dry environment; they should never be hung on a wall or stored on edge, because warpage can occur. Resin-bonded wheels should be stored in the same manner as rubber-bonded wheels; a dry atmosphere is particularly important. Storage in a high-humidity area can lead to early disintegration of the resin bond, because resin can absorb moisture, which eventually weakens the bond.

**Surface Damage.** Abrasive-wheel sectioning can produce damage to a depth of 1 mm (0.04 in.). However, control of cutting speed, wheel pressure, and coolant application minimizes damage.

## Nonconsumable Abrasive Cutting

The exceptional hardness and resistance to fracturing of diamond make it an ideal choice as an abrasive for cutting. Because of its high cost, however, diamond must be used in nonconsumable wheels. Diamond bort (imperfectly crystallized diamond material unsuitable for gems) that has been crushed, graded, chemically cleaned, and properly sized is attached to a metal wheel using resin, vitreous, or metal bonding in a rimlock or a continuous-rim configuration.

**Metal-bonded rimlock wheels** consist of metal disks with hundreds of small notches uniformly cut into the periphery. Each notch contains many diamond particles, which are held in place with a metal bond. The sides of the wheel rim are serrated and are considerably thicker than the core itself, a construction that does not lend itself to delicate cutting. When cutting more ductile materials, the blades will require more frequent dressing.

Rimlock blades are recommended for the bulk cutting of rocks and ceramics where considerable material loss may be tolerated. Kerosene or mineral spirits are used as the coolant/lubricant, and a constant cutting pressure or feed must be maintained to avoid damaging the rim.

**Continuous-rim resin-bonded wheels** consist of diamond particles attached by resin bonding to the rim of a metal core. These blades are suitable for cutting very hard metallics, such as tungsten carbide, and nonmetals, such as high-alumina ceramics, dense-fired refractories, and metal-ceramic composites. Water-base coolants are used.

**Wafering Blades.** For precision cutting of metallographic specimens or thin-foil specimens for transmission electron microscopy, very thin, small-diameter wafering blades are used. These blades are usually constructed of diamond, metal powders, and fillers that are pressed, sintered, and bonded to a metal core. Wafering blades are available in high and low diamond concentrations. Lower concentrations are better for harder materials, particularly the nonmetals; higher concentrations are preferred for softer materials.

Wafering blades may be used with diamond saws. Unlike some other methods of sectioning, the diamond saw uses relatively low speeds (300 rpm maximum) and a thin, continuous-rim diamond-impregnated blade to accomplish true cutting of nearly all solid materials. Applications include cutting of hard and soft materials, brittle and ductile metals, composites, cermets, laminates, miniature devices, and honeycombs. The as-cut surface is generally free of damage and distortion and is ready for microscopic examination with minimum polishing or other preparation. Figure 3 illustrates a typical low-speed diamond saw.

## Wire Saws (Ref 3)

The need to produce damage-free, single-crystal semiconductor surfaces for the electronics industry has generated interest in using the wire saw in the metallographic laboratory. Applications include:

• Removing samples from the bulk material

**Fig. 8** Wire saw with an endless loop. (South Bay Technology, Inc.)

- Cutting electronic assemblies for failure analysis
- Cutting thin-wall tubing
- Cutting fiber-reinforced and laminated composite materials
- Cutting honeycomb structural materials (Fig. 4, 5)
- Cutting polymers (Fig. 6)
- Cutting metallic glasses (Fig. 7)
- Preparing thin specimens for transmission electron microscopy, electron probe microanalysis, ion probe analysis, and x-ray diffraction analysis

In principle, a fine wire is continuously drawn over the sample at a controlled force. Cutting is accomplished using an abrasive slurry applied to the wire, a chemical solution (generally acidic) dripped onto the wire, or electrolytic action. Although cutting rates are much lower than those of abrasive cutoff wheels, hacksaws, or band saws, the deformation produced is negligible, and subsequent grinding and polishing is often not necessary.

Wire saws are available in a variety of designs. Some move the specimen into the wire, some move the wire into the specimen, some run horizontal, and some run vertical. A saw in which the wire runs vertical is advantageous if a specimen is to be removed from bulk material. In this case, the material is attached to an x-y table and is moved into the saw.

Various methods have been devised for drawing the wire across the specimen. The endless-wire saw consists of a loop of wire fastened together at its ends and driven in one direction (Fig. 8). The oscillating wire saw passes a wire back and forth across the sample, usually with a short stroke. A variation of this technique employs a 30-m (100-ft) length of wire that is fed from a capstan across the workpiece and back onto the capstan. The direction of the capstan is reversed at the end of each stroke. The capstan is further shuttled back and forth to maintain the alignment of the wire regarding the pulleys.

**Abrasives.** Any crystalline material can be used as an abrasive in wire sawing if the abrasive is harder than the specimen to be cut. Although natural abrasives, such as emery and garnet, have been used extensively,

the best overall abrasive currently available is synthetic diamond. There are two methods for applying abrasives to the wire. Loose abrasive can be mixed with a liquid vehicle as a slurry to be applied at the kerf behind the wire, or the abrasive can be bonded to a stainless steel wire core.

In the first method, part of the abrasive remains with the specimen and erodes the wire. Furthermore, much of the abrasive is wasted, which precludes using diamond in a slurry. In the second method, all the abrasive moves with the wire to cut the specimen. Therefore, only a fixed quantity of abrasive is employed; diamond then becomes economically feasible. Figure 9 illustrates typical diamond-impregnated wires.

**Lubricants.** Water is used in wire sawing with diamond-impregnated wire. This is not used to lubricate the cut, nor is it used to prevent heat buildup. The amount of heat generated is negligible, and lubrication of the wire is unnecessary. Water is used to wash out the debris that would accumulate above the wire and prevent the easy exit of the wire when the cut is complete.

**Force.** As force is increased between the wire and the specimen, the bow in the wire increases, even though the wire is under maximum tension. Little is gained in cutting time by increasing the force. When the force is increased excessively, the bow becomes so great that the wire has a tendency to wander, which increases the kerf. When wandering occurs, more material is being cut away, and cutting time increases. This also shortens wire life. Therefore, high force with the resulting wider kerf is a poor alternative to lighter force with a straighter wire and a more accurate cut. Lighter force also yields a better finish. If the cut is to be flat at the bottom, the saw should be allowed to dwell for a short time with no force.

The force between the wire and the specimen ranges from 10 to 500 gf. As an example, for a specimen that is in limited supply, fragile, high priced, and/or delicate, a 0.08-mm (0.003-in.) diam wire impregnated with 8-μm diamonds would be selected. The force between the wire and the crystal would range from 10 to 35 gf. The tension on the wire

would be 500 to 750 gf, and the wire would travel 20 to 30 m/min (60 to 100 ft/min).

When a firm, hard, tough specimen is to be cut and when surface damage poses little or no problem, the fastest and most economical method of cutting usually is best. For example, a 0.4-mm (0.015-in.) diam wire impregnated with 60-μm diamonds would be chosen. The tension on the wire would be approximately 6000 to 8000 gf. The machine would operate at 60 m/min (200 ft/min). The force between the wire and the specimen would range from 200 to 500 gf.

## Electric Discharge Machining (Ref 4)

Electric discharge machining (EDM), or spark machining, is a process that uses sparks in a controlled manner to remove material from a conducting workpiece in a dielectric fluid (usually kerosene or transformer oil). A spark gap is generated between the tool and the sample, and the material is removed from the sample in the form of microscopic craters. The material produced by the disintegration of the tool and workpiece as well as by the decomposition of the dielectric is called "swarf." Sparking is done while the sample and tool are immersed in the dielectric.

The dielectric must be kept clean to achieve the full accuracy capability of the instrument, and this is routinely accomplished by using a pump and filter attachment. Depending on the polarity of discharge, type of generator, and particularly the relative hardness of the sample and tool, material can be removed effectively and accurately. No contact is required between the tool and workpiece.

The initial preparation of metallographic specimens for optical and transmission electron microscopy can be performed on EDM

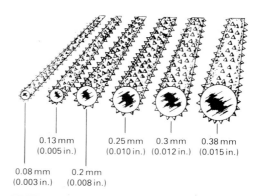

0.13 mm (0.005 in.)   0.25 mm (0.010 in.)   0.3 mm (0.012 in.)   0.38 mm (0.015 in.)

0.08 mm (0.003 in.)   0.2 mm (0.008 in.)

| Wire size | | Diamond | Kerf size | |
|---|---|---|---|---|
| mm | in. | size, μm | mm | in. |
| 0.08 | 0.003 | 8 | 0.08 | 0.00325 |
| 0.13 | 0.005 | 20 | 0.14 | 0.0055 |
| 0.2 | 0.008 | 45 | 0.23 | 0.009 |
| 0.25 | 0.010 | 60 | 0.29 | 0.0115 |
| 0.3 | 0.012 | 60 | 0.34 | 0.0135 |
| 0.38 | 0.015 | 60 | 0.42 | 0.0165 |

**Fig. 9** Diamond-impregnated wires

machines. Resulting samples have a surface finish of 0.13 $\mu$m (5 $\mu$in.), exhibit excellent edge definition, and can be less than 0.13-mm (0.005-in.) thick. A typical EDM setup is shown in Fig. 10.

**Depth of Damage.** Electric discharge machining will damage the specimen to several millimeters or more in depth if precautions are not taken. Two criteria for assessing depth of damage are, first, depth of detectable damage, which is the depth at which the structure is altered as measured by the most sensitive process available, and, second, the depth of significant damage, which is the depth to which damage can be tolerated for the application intended.

Four zones can be defined in the spark-affected surface layer. The most strongly affected layer is the melted zone, which can extend from fractions of a micron to hundreds of microns, depending on the instrumentation used. In electric discharge machining, sparks melt a shallow crater of metal in the melted zone. Most of this is ejected at the end of the spark. Some residual liquid material remains and freezes epitaxially onto the solid below, leaving the melted layer in tension and the layer beneath in compression. Deep melted layers can cause cracking.

The second layer is the chemically affected zone, in which the chemical composition has

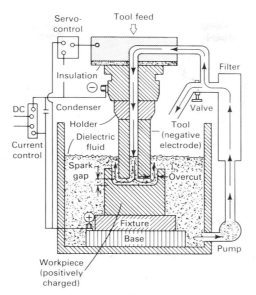

**Fig. 10** Typical setup for electric discharge machining

changed perhaps because of reaction with the dielectric and the tool and diffusion of impurities. This zone is generally very small due to the time involved. The third layer is the microstrained zone, which is subjected to large compressive forces during the heating cycle

and later during the shrinkage of the rapidly frozen molten layer. This zone can be detected by optical microscopy and is characterized by the presence of twins, slip, phase changes, and, sometimes, microcracks. The fourth layer is the submicrostrained zone. Damage in this layer can be detected only by counting dislocations. Slip, twinning, or cracking does not occur.

## REFERENCES

1. G.F. Vander Voort, *Metallography: Principles and Practice*, McGraw-Hill, 1984
2. J.A. Nelson and R.M. Westrich, Abrasive Cutting in Metallography, in *Metallographic Specimen Preparation—Optical and Electron Microscopy*, J.L. McCall and W.M. Mueller, Ed., Plenum Press, 1974, p 41-54
3. H.B. McLaughlin, The Use of Wire Saws for Metallographic Sectioning, in *Metallographic Specimen Preparation—Optical and Electron Microscopy*, J.L. McCall and W.M. Mueller, Ed., Plenum Press, 1974, p 55-68
4. J. Barrett, Electric Discharge Machining, in *Metallographic Specimen Preparation—Optical and Electron Microscopy*, J.L. McCall and W.M. Mueller, Ed., Plenum Press, 1974, p 69-76

# Mounting of Specimens

MOUNTING is often necessary in the preparation of specimens for metallographic study. Although bulk samples may not require mounting, small or oddly shaped specimens should be mounted to facilitate handling during preparation and examination. Sharp edges and corners are eliminated, increasing safety for the metallographer and avoiding damage to the papers and cloths used in preparation. Some automatic preparation devices require mounted specimens of a specific size and shape. Proper mounting of specimens also aids edge retention when such features as surface coatings are to be examined. In addition, uniformly sized and shaped specimens are convenient to prepare, view, and store.

Standard mounts usually measure 25 mm (1 in.), 32 mm (1.25 in.), or 38 mm (1.5 in.) in diameter; mount thickness is often approximately one half the mount diameter. Thickness is important in proper metallographic preparation, because thin mounts are difficult to handle, and very thick mounts are difficult to hold flat during grinding and polishing.

Mount size and shape are sometimes influenced by the size and shape of the specimen to be mounted as well as by the type of metallographic examination to be performed. For example, square or rectangular mounts are often used in x-ray diffraction examination, which requires a relatively large surface. Mounting of wire, tubing, sheet, and powder specimens requires special techniques that will be discussed below.

## Cleaning

Prior to mounting, it is often necessary to clean specimens. Cleaning may also be indicated before plating for edge retention. With certain samples, such as those in which surface oxide layers are to be examined, cleaning must be limited to very simple treatments, or the detail to be examined may be lost.

A distinction can be made between physically and chemically clean surfaces. Physical cleanliness implies freedom from solid dirt, grease, or other debris; chemical cleanliness, freedom from any contaminant. In metallographic work, physical cleanliness is usually adequate and nearly always necessary.

Vapor degreasing is frequently used to remove oil and grease left on metal surfaces from machining operations, but ultrasonic cleaning is usually the most effective method for routine use. Specimens that require cleaning may be placed directly in the tank of the ultrasonic cleaner, but the cleaning solution must be changed frequently. This can be avoided by placing approximately 1 in. of water in the tank, then placing inside the tank a beaker containing the cleaning solution and the specimen. Cleaning times are usually 2 to 5 min, but very soft specimens can be damaged by the cavitation; therefore, ultrasonic cleaning should be limited to 30 s or less for these materials (Ref 1).

## Selection of Mounting Materials

The first concern in selecting a mounting material and technique must be the protection and preservation of the specimen. Fragile or delicate specimens are subject to physical damage. The heat and pressure required for some mounting materials can alter microstructures. Shrinkage stresses can be high enough to pull a protective plating from the specimen, thus limiting edge retention.

Moreover, the mount must have sufficient hardness, although hardness is not always an indication of abrasion characteristics. Grinding and polishing characteristics should ideally be similar to those of the specimen. The mount must also resist physical distortion caused by the heat generated during grinding and polishing as well as withstand exposure to lubricants, solvents, and etchants.

The mounting material should be able to penetrate small pores, crevices, and other surface irregularities in the specimen. For some types of metallographic examination, such as scanning electron microscopy, and for electrolytic polishing, an electrically conductive mount is desirable.

The mounting medium should be simple and fast to use and convenient to store. It should not be prone to formation of defects in the cured mount, such as cracks or voids. Transparent mounts are often advantageous. The mount material should present no health hazards, and it should be readily available at a reasonable cost.

Because one mounting material or technique cannot fulfill every requirement, a variety of materials and methods are available. Proper selection will yield a mount that meets the most critical requirements.

## Mechanical Mounting Devices

Mechanical clamping devices facilitate mounting and can be very effective, particularly in preparing transverse or longitudinal sheet surfaces. Clamps for this type of work are usually fabricated from approximately 6-mm (0.25-in.) thick plate stock, which can be cut into blocks of various sizes. A common size is approximately 12 mm by 38 mm (0.5 in. by 1.5 in.). Holes are drilled into each end of the clamp halves, and one half is threaded to receive a bolt of suitable length. Mating holes in the other half are drilled just large enough to clear the bolt threads. Specimens are then cut or sheared to a length that will fit between the bolts and sandwiched between the clamp halves. The clamp is placed in a vise, and the clamp bolts are tightened.

The pressure used to hold the specimens within a mechanical clamp can be important. Insufficient pressure can result in seepage and abrasive entrapment. Too much pressure could damage the specimens.

Spacers, often used with this type of mechanical mount, especially if specimen surfaces are rough, are thin sheets of such materials as copper, lead, or plastic. Specimens can also be coated with a layer of epoxy or lacquer before being placed in the clamp. For maximum edge retention, a spacer should have abrasion and polishing rates similar to those of the specimen. Material for the spacer and the clamp should be selected to avoid galvanic effects that would inhibit etching of the specimen. If the etchant more readily attacks the clamp or spacer, the specimen will not etch properly.

Another common mechanical mount is a cylinder or other convenient shape in which the specimen is held by a set screw. Again, abrasion and polishing rates should approximate those of the specimen, and the mount should be inert to any solvents and etchants used or have the same reactivity as the speci-

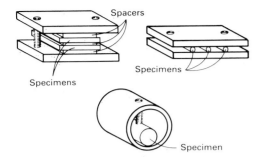

**Fig. 1** Typical examples of clamps used for mechanical mounting. (Ref 2)

Spacers

Specimens

Specimens

Specimens

Specimen

men. Figure 1 illustrates three mechanical mounting devices.

## Plastic Mounting Materials

The various plastics used for metallographic mounting can be classified in several different ways, according to the technique used and the properties of the material. Plastics may be divided into one group that requires the application of heat and pressure and another group that is castable at room temperature. The former group is usually obtained as powders; the latter group, which requires blending of two components, may be obtained as two liquids or as a liquid and a solid.

Plastics that require heat and pressure for curing are known as compression-mounting materials. These can be further divided into thermosetting resins and thermoplastic resins.

**Thermosetting resins** require heat and pressure during molding, but can be ejected from the mold at the molding temperature. The two most widely used thermosetting resins are Bakelite and diallyl phthalate. Melamine, although rather brittle when used alone, and the recently developed compression-mounting epoxies have also been used.

Bakelite, popular because of its low cost and convenience, is available as red, green, or black powders or as "premolds," which are already formed to standard mount sizes. Premolds can be used if the specimen is a uniform shape and if the initial application of pressure will not damage the specimen. Bakelite normally contains wood flour fillers but is also available as 100% resin (Bakelite amber).

Depending on mold diameter, curing times for Bakelite vary from 5 to 9 min at 29 MPa (4200 psi) and 150 °C (300 °F). Curing times for premolds range from 3 to 7 min at the same pressure and temperature. Bakelite, however, exhibits relatively low hardness, limited abrasion resistance, significant linear shrinkage upon cooling, and limited edge protection. Typical properties of Bakelite and diallyl phthalate are given in Table 1.

Diallyl phthalate is available as a powder with mineral or glass filler. In glass-filled form, it will provide harder mounts and better edge retention than Bakelite. Although mineral-filled diallyl phthalate does not have specific edge retention properties, it and glass-filled diallyl phthalate exhibit good resistance to chemical attack, which is useful when using powerful etchants or etching at elevated temperatures. Depending on mold diameter, curing times for diallyl phthalate vary from 7 to 12 min at approximately 22 MPa (3200 psi) and 150 °C (300 °F). Copper- or aluminum-filled diallyl phthalate can be used as a conductive mount for electrolytic polishing or scanning electron microscopy.

Compression-mounting epoxies provide low shrinkage and produce excellent edge retention. Molding time, pressure, and temperature are similar to those used for diallyl

### Table 1 Typical properties of thermosetting molding resins

| Resin | Molding conditions Temperature °C | °F | Pressure MPa | psi | Time, min | Heat distortion temperature °C | °F | Coefficient of thermal expansion in./in.°C(a) | Abrasion rate, μm/min(b) | Polishing rate, μm/min(c) | Transparency | Chemical resistance |
|---|---|---|---|---|---|---|---|---|---|---|---|---|
| Bakelite (wood-filled) | 135-170 | 275-340 | 17-29 | 2500-4200 | 5-12 | 140 | 285 | $3.0\text{-}4.5 \times 10^{-5}$ | 100 | 2.9 | Opaque | Attacked by strong acids and alkalies |
| Diallyl phthalate (asbestos-filled) | 140-160 | 285-320 | 17-21 | 2500-3000 | 6-12 | 150 | 300 | $3.5 \times 10^{-5}$ | 190 | 0.8 | Opaque | Attacked by strong acids and alkalies |

(a) Determined by method ASTM D 648. (b) Specimen 100 mm² (0.15 in.²) in area abraded on slightly worn 600-grit silicon carbide under load of 100 g at rubbing speed of 10⁵ mm/min (4 × 10³ in./min). (c) 25-mm (1-in.) diam mount on a wheel rotating at 250 rpm covered with synthetic suede cloth and charged with 4 to 8 μm diamond paste.
Source: Ref 1

### Table 2 Typical properties of thermoplastic molding resins

| Resin | Molding conditions Heating Temperature °C | °F | Pressure MPa | psi | Time (min) | Cooling Temperature °C | °F | Pressure MPa | psi | Time (min) | Transparency | Heat distortion temperature(a) °C | °F | Coefficient of thermal expansion, in./in.°C | Abrasion rate, μm/min(b) | Polishing rate, μm/min(c) | Chemical resistance |
|---|---|---|---|---|---|---|---|---|---|---|---|---|---|---|---|---|---|
| Methyl methacrylate | 140-165 | 285-330 | 17-29 | 2500-4200 | 6 | 75-85 | 165-185 | max | max | 6-7 | Water, white to clear | 65 | 150 | $5\text{-}9 \times 10^{-5}$ | ... | 7.5 | Not resistant to strong acids and some solvents, especially ethanol |
| Polystyrene | 140-165 | 285-330 | 17 | 2500 | 5 | 85 | 185-212 | max | ... | 6 | ... | 65 | 150 | ... | ... | ... | ... |
| Polyvinyl formal | 220 | 430 | 27 | 4000 | ... | ... | ... | ... | ... | ... | Light brown, clear | 75 | 165 | $6\text{-}8 \times 18^{-5}$ | 20 | 1.1 | Not resistant to strong acids |
| Polyvinyl chloride | 120-160 | 250-320 | 0.7 | 100 | nil | 60 | 140 | 27 | 4000 | ... | Opaque | 60 | 140 | $5\text{-}18 \times 10^{-5}$ | 45 | 1.3 | Resistant to most acids and alkalies |

(a) Determined by method ASTM D 648 (b) Specimen 100 mm² (0.15 in.) in area abraded on a slightly worn 600-grit silicon carbide paper under load of 100 g at rubbing speed of 10⁵ mm/min (c) 25-mm (1-in.) diam mount on a wheel rotating at 250 rpm covered with a synthetic suede cloth and charged with 4-8 μm diamond paste
Source: Ref 1

phthalate, but molding defects are less common. A mold release agent is generally required to prevent the mount from adhering to the ram.

**Thermoplastic resins** also require heat and pressure during molding, but must be cooled to ambient temperature under pressure. These materials can be used with delicate specimens, because the required molding pressure can be applied after the resin is molten. Transparent methyl methacrylate (Lucite or Transoptic), polystyrene, polyvinyl chloride (PVC), and polyvinyl formal are some of the thermoplastic resins. Properties are listed in Table 2.

Because they must be cooled under pressure, thermoplastic resins are more difficult to use than thermosetting materials. Methyl methacrylate and polyvinyl formal have become prevalent because of their transparency, which can be a useful property when grinding and polishing must be controlled to locate a particular defect or area of interest.

Other properties of thermoplastic resins are similar to those of thermosetting materials. Linear shrinkage upon cooling is high.

Abrasion and polishing rates are generally lower than those of thermosetting materials, and fairly low heat distortion temperatures can result in softening of the mount if frictional heat generated during grinding and polishing is not controlled. Of the thermoplastics, PVC and polyvinyl formal display the best polishing characteristics (Ref 2). The chemical resistance of thermoplastics is good, although most are attacked by strong acids. Some are at least partially soluble in organic solvents, but all show good resistance to dilute acids and to alcohol except methyl methacrylate, which is partially soluble in alcohol.

To use thermoplastic powders, an initial pressure of 0.7 MPa (100 psi) must be applied while heating to approximately 150 °C (300 °F). Once that temperature is reached, pressure is increased to 29 MPa (4200 psi). The mount must be held at this pressure until it has cooled to approximately 40 °C (105 °F). This operation may require 40 min, but coolers (see below) can reduce this time significantly.

Use of thermosetting or thermoplastic materials requires a heated press. These devices

range from very basic to highly automated and share a general configuration. A high-capacity heater is placed around the mold for rapid heating. Radiator coolers, copper chill blocks, or water-cooled jackets are used for cooling after the heater is removed or turned off. Some presses incorporate heating and cooling devices in the same enclosure around the mold. Common problems in using compression-mounting materials are shown in Table 3.

**Castable resins,** or cold-mounting materials, offer certain advantages over compression-mounting materials and possess properties that add flexibility to the mounting capabilities of metallographic laboratories. These plastics are usually classified as acrylics, polyesters, or epoxies. Various mold shapes can be used, but standard, cylindrical mount sizes are the most common. Castable materials usually consist of the resin and the hardener. Because hardening is based on the chemical reaction of the components, resin and hardener must be carefully measured and thoroughly mixed, or the mount may not harden. Table 4 lists common mold defects of castable materials.

Acrylic materials require curing times of only approximately 30 min. They are simple to use and relatively foolproof. However, acrylics do not provide good edge retention. In addition, although referred to as cold-mounting materials, acrylics generate considerable heat during curing, which can be minimized by using mold materials with good heat conduction. Figure 2 shows how molding method can influence the magnitude of the exotherm of an acrylic material. Temperature versus time curves for Bakelite and for a castable epoxy are included.

Polyesters generally require slightly longer curing times than acrylics and are not very sensitive to slight variations in the mixture. They exhibit less shrinkage than acrylics and show good chemical resistance to typical metallographic reagents.

Epoxies have the lowest shrinkage of the castable resins. They adhere well to most other materials and are chemically resistant, except in concentrated acids. The epoxies are sensitive to variations in the resin-hardener mixture; however, premeasured packets are available. Curing times vary according to the specific formula used. Epoxies generate significant stresses during curing, which may damage delicate specimens.

Various materials can be used as molds for castable plastics, including glass, disposable Bakelite or aluminum rings, aluminum foil, and silicone rubber cups. If the mold is to be reclaimed, a mold release agent, such as silicone oil or vacuum grease, should be used. Release agents are not necessary if flexible silicone rubber molds are employed; however, rubber molds tend to deteriorate when exposed to the epoxy hardener.

One simple procedure begins by covering a flat plate with aluminum foil. Rubber cement is applied to one end of a disposable Bakelite

**Table 3  Typical problems of compression-mounting materials**

| Problem | Cause | Solution |
|---|---|---|
| **Thermosetting resins** | | |
| Radial split | Too large a section in the given mold area; sharp cornered specimens | Increase mold size; reduce specimen size. |
| Edge shrinkage | Excessive shrinkage of plastic away from sample | Decrease molding temperature; cool mold slightly prior to ejection. |
| Circumferential splits | Absorbed moisture; entrapped gasses during molding | Preheat powder or premold; momentarily release pressure during fluid state. |
| Burst | Too short a cure period; insufficient pressure | Lengthen cure period; apply sufficient pressure during transition from fluid state to solid state. |
| Unfused | Insufficient molding pressure; insufficient time at cure temperature; increased surface area of powdered materials | Use proper molding pressure; increase cure time. With powders, quickly seal mold closure and apply pressure to eliminate localized curing. |
| **Thermoplastic resins** | | |
| Cottonball | Powdered media did not reach maximum temperature; insufficient time at maximum temperature | Increase holding time at maximum temperature. |
| Crazing | Inherent stresses relieved upon or after ejection | Allow cooling to a lower temperature prior to ejection; temper mounts in boiling water. |

**Table 4  Typical problems of castable mounting materials**

| Problem | Cause | Solution |
|---|---|---|
| **Acrylics** | | |
| Bubbles | Too violent agitation while blending resin and hardener | Blend mixture gently to avoid air entrapment. |
| **Polyesters** | | |
| Cracking | Insufficient air cure prior to oven cure; oven cure temperature too high; resin-to-hardener ratio incorrect | Increase air cure time; decrease oven cure temperature; correct resin-to-hardener ratio. |
| Discoloration | Resin-to-hardener ratio incorrect; resin has oxidized | Correct resin-to-hardener ratio; keep containers tightly sealed. |
| Soft mounts | Resin-to-hardener ratio incorrect; incomplete blending of resin-hardener mixture | Correct resin-to-hardener ratio; blend mixture completely. |
| Tacky tops | Resin-to-hardener ratio incorrect; incomplete blending of resin-hardener mixture | Correct resin-to-hardener ratio; blend mixture completely. |
| **Epoxies** | | |
| Cracking | Insufficient air cure prior to oven cure; oven cure temperature too high; resin-to-hardener ratio incorrect | Increase air cure time; decrease oven cure temperature; correct resin-to-hardener ratio. |
| Bubbles | Too violent agitation while blending resin and hardener mixture | Blend mixture gently to avoid air entrapment. |
| Discoloration | Resin-to-hardener ratio incorrect; oxidized hardener | Correct resin-to-hardener ratio; keep containers tightly sealed. |
| Soft mounts | Resin-to-hardener ratio incorrect; incorrect blending of resin-hardener mixture | Correct resin-to-hardener ratio; blend mixture completely. |

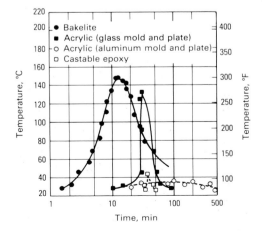

**Fig. 2** Heat generated during curing of various mounting materials. Note how the choice of mold material affects the temperature versus time curve of the acrylic resin. (Ref 3)

ring form of the desired mount diameter, and this end is pressed against the foil. The specimen is placed inside the ring form with the side to be polished against the foil, and the mixed mounting material is poured around the specimen after the rubber cement hardens. After curing, the mount, permanently enclosed by the ring, can be easily removed from the foil.

Because all castable resins produce vapors, mounting under a ventilation hood is preferred. Skin damage can also result from frequent contact with some materials, but these hazards are minimal if reasonable care is taken.

## Special Techniques

Some specimens require special methods, such as mechanical mounting of thin-sheet specimens. Vacuum-impregnation mounting, mounting of small-diameter wire and tube specimens, mounting for edge retention, and electrically conductive mounting will be discussed.

**Vacuum impregnation** techniques take full advantage of the good adherence and fluidity of castable epoxies and are frequently used with powdered specimens, in corrosion or failure analysis, and in mounting porous or fragile specimens. Vacuum impregnation removes air from pores, cracks, and crevices, allowing the epoxy to enter. This ensures complete bonding. Best results are obtained by adding the epoxy to the mold under vacuum, but the resin can be added under atmospheric pressure and the entire mold placed into the vacuum chamber until all air bubbles are removed. This generally takes approximately 10 min. When air is admitted to the vacuum chamber, the epoxy flows into any openings created by the vacuum. Cycling from air to vacuum to air several times aids in impregnation. Alternatively, the epoxy can be subjected to vacuum before it is added to the mold. The filled mold is then placed in the vacuum chamber.

In one procedure for mounting metal powders using vacuum impregnation, a small amount of powder is placed in the center of the mold. Epoxy is poured around the powder, taking care not to disturb the specimen or cause it to segregate. The mold is then evacuated for approximately 10 min, repressurized, and allowed to cure at room temperature. Metal powders can also be blended with a small amount of epoxy to form a thick, pasty mixture. This mixture is poured into the mold, epoxy is added, and the mold is evacuated. For more information on mounting of metal powders, see the article "Powder Metallurgy Materials" in this Volume.

**Mounting of wire and tube** can be a challenge, and several methods have been used. Holes or slots just large enough to hold the specimen can be machined into a preformed blank of cured or uncured resin into which the specimen is then inserted. For thermoplastic resins, simply repeating the molding cycle will hold the specimen in place. Thermosetting resins require more resin before the molding cycle is repeated. Another technique involves mounting the specimen horizontally in any plastic mounting material. This mount is then cut to reveal the cross section of the specimen, and the sectioned mount is remounted with the specimen in the desired position.

One simple technique for mounting wire includes coiling the specimen into a spring, which is placed longitudinally in the mold. Polishing reveals transverse and longitudinal sections of the specimen. Wire specimens can also be fused inside pyrex glass capillary tubing. The tubing is heated until it collapses around the wire. If the specimen cannot be heated, it can be placed inside a capillary tube and vacuum impregnated with epoxy to produce a tight bond.

**Edge retention,** often necessary in metallographic examinations, depends on the mounting material, the preparation technique used, and the use of fillers or plating. Mold filler materials include ground glass, cast iron grit, metal flakes, and pelletized alumina ($Al_2O_3$). Black or white pelletized $Al_2O_3$, available in three hardness grades and several sizes, is the most widely used. Use of black pelletized $Al_2O_3$ with a black mounting resin can reduce reflected light from the specimen surface and improve contrast between the specimen and the mount. Pelletized $Al_2O_3$ also effectively distributes the curing stresses in castable epoxies and protects delicate specimens from damage. Because of the very high hardness of $Al_2O_3$, grinding and polishing are slowed, and additional abrasive is often required.

One of the most effective methods of edge preservation is plating, which can be carried out electrolytically or with electroless solutions. Nickel, copper, iron, chromium, and zinc are often used to electroplate specimens. The primary problem in electroplating is obtaining a clean specimen. Many of the cleaning methods used for industrial plating are too harsh for metallographic work, and plating can pull away from the surface of a contaminated sample. Internal stresses in the plating also influence adhesion.

Electroless plating, therefore, is preferred for metallography. The specimen is dipped into the heated plating solution, and deposition proceeds at about the same rate as in electroplating. Penetration of rough or porous surfaces is usually better than electroplating, and internal stresses are low. Moreover, any type of metal or alloy can be plated using this method, regardless of electrical conductivity. In addition to enhancing edge retention, metallic coatings enhance contrast between the sample and the mounting material.

**Conductive mounts** are useful for electrolytic polishing of specimens or for scanning electron microscopy. Plastic mounting materials are electrical insulators, but several methods are available that allow electricity to flow to the specimen. The most common is use of a metal filler material in the mount itself. Iron, aluminum, carbon, and copper have been used for this purpose; copper diallyl phthalate is a widely known conductive mounting material. Good conductivity can be achieved with approximately 10 vol% metal mixed with mounting plastic; however, coating the individual plastic particles with a conductor yields more reliable results. For example, PVC can be milled with carbon black to produce a conductive mounting material.

## Mount Marking and Storage

After mounting, specimens are usually identified using hand scribers or vibrating-point engravers. Markings made with these tools can then be inked over to increase their visibility.

If a transparent mounting material is used, a small metal tag or piece of paper bearing the identification can be included in the mount. An indelible ink must be used, but identification is then permanently visible and protected with the specimen.

Specimens are usually stored in a dessicator to minimize surface oxidation during preparation and examination. Surfaces can also be coated with clear lacquer for preservation. The microstructure can be viewed through the lacquer, or the coating can be removed with acetone.

## REFERENCES

1. G.F. Vander Voort, *Metallography: Principles and Practice*, McGraw-Hill, 1984, p 71-93
2. D.V. Miley and A.E. Calabra, A Review of Specimen Mounting Methods for Metallography, in *Metallographic Specimen Preparation*, J.L. McCall and W.M. Mueller, Ed., Plenum Press, 1974, p 1-40
3. J.A. Nelson, "Heating of Metallographic Specimens Mounted in 'Cold Setting' Resins," *Prakt. Metallogr.*, Vol 7, 1970, p 510-521

# Mechanical Grinding, Abrasion, and Polishing

By L.E. Samuels
Consultant

INVESTIGATIONS OF THE STRUCTURES of metals are generally carried out on sections that have been cut from a bulk specimen. Frequently, only a single section surface is prepared, and the structural features exposed on this surface may be investigated using various techniques. All these techniques involve the reflection of some form of radiation from the section surface; an image of the surface is formed from the reflected radiation that allows variations in crystal structure or composition over the surface to be discerned.

Visible light is commonly used for this purpose. The surface is examined by the human eye with or without magnification. Optical macrography and microscopy are examples. It is usually necessary first to treat the section surface by some chemical or physical process

that alters the way light is reflected by the various structural constituents that have been exposed.

Alternatively, a section surface may be investigated by probing with a beam of electrons in a high vacuum. Structures are revealed that in effect depend on how electrons are reflected off the surface; this may be determined by variations in topography or composition. Scanning electron microscopes and electron probe microanalyzers are examples of investigative techniques operating on these principles. It is possible also to use x-rays to determine variations in composition, as in x-ray fluorescent analysis, or to determine structural features that depend on crystal lattice spacing and orientation, as in x-ray microscopy and x-ray methods of determining internal stresses.

Another group of techniques requires preparation of section surfaces on two parallel planes in close proximity. The radiation used is transmitted through the thin slice so formed. Transmission electron microscopy and diffraction are important examples of techniques that require this type of specimen.

Three operations are generally involved in determining the structures of metals: (1) the preparation of a section surface, (2) the development of features on the surface that are related to the structure and can be detected by the examinational technique used, and (3) the examination itself. The overall effectiveness of the examination often is determined by the operation carried out least effectively, which too frequently is the preparation of the section surface.

A preparation procedure must produce a

**Fig. 1, 2, 3** Annealed 70-30 brass. Fig. 1: taper section (horizontal magnification 600×, vertical magnification 4920×) of surface layers that were abraded on 220-grit silicon carbide paper. Fig. 2 and 3: results of abrading on 220-grit silicon carbide paper and then polishing until about 5 μm (Fig. 2) and 15 μm (Fig. 3) of metal are removed. The banded markings in Fig. 2 are false structures (abrasion artifacts). Figure 3 shows the true structure. Aqueous ferric chloride. 250×

Some of the information and micrographs presented in this article originally appeared in Ref 1. Reference should be made to that publication for full details of the mechanical abrasion processes, the mechanisms by which they operate, their effects on the surfaces being produced, and the most efficient methods of carrying them out.

**Fig. 4, 5, 6** Austenitic stainless steel (18Ni-8Cr). Fig. 4: taper section (horizontal magnification 600×, vertical magnification 6060×) of surface layers that were abraded on 220-grit silicon carbide paper. Fig. 5 and 6: results of abrading on 600-grit silicon carbide paper and then polishing until about 1 μm (Fig. 5) and 3 μm (Fig. 6) of metal are removed. Figure 5 shows abrasion artifacts. Figure 6 shows the true structure. Electrolytic: oxalic acid. 500×

**Fig. 7, 8, 9, 10** Annealed zinc. Fig. 7: taper section (horizontal magnification 150×, vertical magnification 2040×) of surface layers that were abraded on 220-grit silicon carbide paper. Note recrystallization at the top. Polarized light was used. Fig. 8, 9, and 10: results of abrading on 220-grit silicon carbide paper and polishing until about 2.5 μm (Fig. 8), 15 μm (Fig. 9), and 45 μm (Fig. 10) of metal are removed. The small grains in Fig. 8 and the twins in Fig. 9 are artifact structures. The true structure is shown in Fig. 10. As-polished. 150×

surface that accurately represents the structure as it existed in the metal before sectioning. All structural features that should be detected by the particular examination technique being used must be detectable, and false structures must not be introduced. This is a more demanding requirement.

Successful specimen preparation requires information based on systematic and objective experiments. Therefore, this article will illustrate how objective experiments and comparisons can be used to develop procedures that not only give better results, but also are simpler and less laborious. Principles useful as guidelines in the development of practical preparation procedures will be emphasized, rather than the details of those procedures.

The other investigative techniques mentioned earlier are doubtless crucial in many research investigations and have pushed the frontiers of metallography far beyond what would have been possible by optical metallography alone. Nevertheless, most metallography in industry and in general investigations is still carried out by optical microscopy, so this article will also consider the preparation of surfaces for examination by optical microscopy.

Because it is possible to deal here with only a limited number of concepts involved in preparing fully representative surfaces, the concepts selected illustrate the types of problems that arise and how their solutions may be approached systematically.

## Surface Preparation

Any classification of the numerous processes used to cut a section, then to prepare the cut surface suitably for metallographic examination, inevitably is arbitrary and argu-able. One convenient system, however, is to classify the processes as machining, grinding and abrasion, or polishing.

**Machining** involves the use of tools having cutting edges of controlled shape, as in conventional machine shop practice. Examples are sawing, lathe turning, milling, and filing. These processes normally are used only for the preliminary stages of preparation and do not require particular attention here.

**Grinding and abrasion** employ an array of fixed abrasive particles whose projecting points act as the cutting tools. In some of these processes, the particles are in effect cemented together into a block whose exposed surface is the working surface. This surface is "dressed" by fracturing the exposed abrasive particles to form an array of sharp points. Examples are abrasive cutoff wheels, grinding wheels, abrasive laps, and abrasive stones. In other processes, a layer of abrasive particles

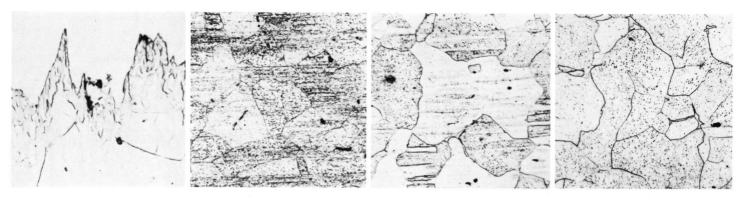

**Fig. 11, 12, 13, 14** Ferritic steel. Fig. 11: taper section (horizontal magnification 1000×, vertical magnification 10 000×) of surface layers that were abraded on 220-grit silicon carbide paper. Note the outer fragmented layer. Fig. 12: results of abrading on 000 emery paper and then polishing only long enough to remove abrasion scratches. Fig. 13: results of abrading on 600-grit silicon carbide paper and polishing only long enough to remove abrasion scratches. Fig. 12 and 13: banded markings and generally artifact-dominated structure. Fig. 14: results of abrading on 600-grit silicon carbide paper and polishing for a longer time than for Fig. 13; it shows the true structure of the steel. Nital. 250×

is cemented onto a cloth or paper backing, creating coated abrasive products such as papers, cloths, or belts. In still other processes, the abrasive particles are forced into a flat surface of a comparatively soft material where they are held as an array similar to that in a coated abrasive product.

A range of surface speeds may be employed in any of these processes; it is convenient, therefore, to distinguish between grinding and abrasion. The term "grinding" denotes processes that employ high surface speeds with the possibility that significant heating of the surface layers of the specimen may occur. The term "abrasion" refers to processes that use low surface speeds and copious liquid coolant; significant heating of the specimen surface cannot occur.

**Polishing** uses abrasive particles that are not firmly fixed but suspended in a liquid among the fibers of a cloth. The objective is to produce a bright mirrorlike, or specularly reflecting, surface, commonly referred to as a polished surface.

**Typical metallographic preparation procedures** employ a sequence of machining or grinding stages of increasing fineness, then a sequence of abrasion processes of increasing fineness, followed by a sequence of polishing processes of increasing fineness until the desired surface finish has been achieved. Increasing fineness refers to the use of finer grades of abrasive to produce finer grooves or scratches in the surface.

Therefore, metallographic preparation processes employ abrasive particles to remove material and to improve surface finish, two objectives that are not always compatible. It is not possible to discuss in detail how the processes operate (see Ref 1 for a more detailed treatment). Briefly, in grinding and abrasion, the abrasive points that contact the surface may be regarded as V-point cutting tools. The rake angles of these tools vary widely. Only a small proportion of the points have a configuration suitable for removing metal by cutting a chip, as in normal machining. The others plough a groove in the surface, displacing material laterally. Both processes produce scratches and impose severe plastic deformations on the outer layers of the surface.

Most mechanical polishing procedures are similar to those for abrasion, except that only

small forces are applied to individual abrasive particles by the fibers of the cloth that supports them. They therefore produce comparatively shallow, narrow scratches. Some very fine polishing procedures, however, remove material by less drastic mechanical processes that remove very small flakes of material. Some others occur largely by chemical dissolution processes. Barring these exceptions, the processes involved in grinding, abrasion, and polishing differ in degree rather than in kind. This is why any classification of preparation processes necessarily is arbitrary.

Sections to be prepared are usually no larger than about 5 cm² (0.78 in.²), although larger areas can be prepared if necessary. The specimen is mounted to facilitate handling; it is often molded into a plastic cylinder. Various plastics are available for this purpose, each with advantages and disadvantages in particular applications. A simple phenolic resin is often used when the sole requirement is to facilitate handling.

At the simplest level the section surface, after preliminary machining, is rubbed by hand against the working surface of an abrasive paper supported on a flat backing surface. The working surface of the paper is flooded with a liquid. Waterproof abrasive papers, usually those coated with silicon carbide abrasive, are convenient because their working surfaces can be flushed continuously with water to remove the abrasion debris as it forms. The section surface is treated in this way, using successively finer grades of abrasive paper, usually to the finest available. The surface is then polished by rotating it by hand against a cloth that has been charged with a fine abrasive and an appropriate liquid, and then has been stretched across a flat backing surface. Several stages of polishing employing increasingly finer abrasives usually are necessary. Diamond, alumina ($Al_2O_3$), and magnesium oxide (MgO) are the abrasives most commonly used for polishing; colloidal silica is sometimes used.

**Mechanized processes** are less time consuming and laborious than manual operations. The first step in mechanization is to drive the abrasive paper or polishing cloth.

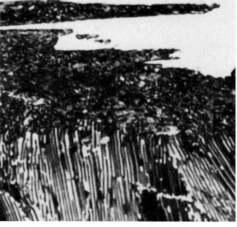

**Fig. 15, 16** Pearlitic steel. Longitudinal taper sections of surface layers that were belt abraded on 100-mesh $Al_2O_3$, showing that cementite plates of pearlite are merely bent adjacent to some scratches (Fig. 15) and are completely fragmented adjacent to others (Fig. 16). Picral. Horizontal: 2000×; vertical: 20 000×

The paper or cloth is attached to the surface of a wheel that is rotated at a comparatively low speed in a horizontal plane. The specimen is held against the working surface of a wheel and rotated slowly in a direction opposite that of the wheel.

The next step involves handling the specimen. This is more difficult because the specimen must be held and rotated so that the section surface is maintained precisely in a horizontal plane against the working surface of the abrasive or polishing wheel. The full surface must maintain contact with the working surface. The specimen should be rotated counter to the direction of wheel rotation. Several commercially available devices can perform this procedure. Most of them handle a batch of specimens that must be processed through the full preparation cycle on the machine. Some of these machines are highly automated, providing control of rotation speeds, pressure applied to the specimen, and polishing time.

Mechanization is particularly useful when a large number of specimens must be handled. In addition, once optimum preparation parameters are established, they can be reproduced exactly without having to rely on the operator. Moreover, flatter surfaces are produced. Nevertheless, only the mechanics of the preparation procedure are affected, not the mechanisms or principles involved. The various steps proposed for an automated preparation sequence should be judged on this basis.

## Abrasion Damage and Abrasion Artifacts

The obvious result of abrasion is a system of comparatively fine, uniform scratches on the surface of the specimen. Abrasion also produces a plastically deformed surface layer (disturbed metal) of considerable depth. The microstructure of this layer may be recognizably different from the true structure of the specimen.

The general pattern of a surface layer that has been plastically deformed is shown in Fig. 1,* which depicts abraded 70-30 brass, an alloy in which the effects of prior plastic deformation can be easily revealed by a range of etchants. Also illustrated in Fig. 1 is a shallow, dark-etching, unresolved band contouring the surface scratches that is known as the outer fragmented layer; here the strains have been very large and the crystal structure has been altered as a result. Beneath this extends a layer in which the strains have been comparatively small and in which they tend to concentrate in rays extending beneath individual surface scratches. This is shown by the

bands of etch markings, which develop at the sites of slip bands, and by the more diffuse rays, which indicate the presence of kink bands. These effects extend for many times the depth of the surface scratches.

The importance of the surface damage in Fig. 1 is illustrated in Fig. 2 and 3. A sample of annealed 70-30 brass was abraded on 220-grit silicon carbide paper, then polished to remove a surface layer about 5 µm thick. Although all traces of the abrasion scratches were removed and what appeared to be a satisfactory surface was produced, the bands of deformation etch markings shown in Fig. 2 appeared when the surface was etched. When layers of greater thickness were removed during polishing, these bands were gradually reduced in number and intensity; they eventually were eliminated, as can be seen in Fig. 3, which shows the true structure.

The bands of deformation etch markings in Fig. 2 are false structures introduced by the preparation process, or artifact structures. They clearly are related to the rays of deformation produced during abrasion, as shown in Fig. 1. Because the artifacts are the result of deformation introduced into the surface during abrasion, they may be called abrasion artifacts.

Detectable microstructural changes in the abrasion-damaged layer are potential sources of abrasion artifacts in the final surface. Metals vary markedly in their susceptibility to the formation of abrasion artifacts. Highly alloyed copper alloys such as 70-30 brass, for example, are among the most sensitive. Etchants also vary in their ability to delineate abrasion damage. Because a major objective of metallographic preparation is to ensure that unrepresentative structures are not present in the surface to be examined, the metallographer must recognize abrasion artifacts, understand how these artifacts originate, and eliminate them when they are found.

Each successive abrasion stage should remove the artifact-containing layer produced by the preceding abrasion stage. This takes longer than the time required simply to remove existing scratches, and places a premium on obtaining maximum possible material removal rates. The effectiveness of an abrasion stage must be judged on how quickly it removes the preexisting deformed layer. Also considered are the depths of the damaged layer and the scratches that abrasion produces. Similarly, the first objective of rough polishing must be effective removal of abrasion damage. This necessitates obtaining maximum material removal rates. The polishing processes with fast cutting rates usually produce comparatively coarse finishes. They must be followed by polishing processes that produce finer finishes. Only after the abrasion damage has been removed effectively by a rough-polishing process should attention be given to producing a final polish.

The depth of the artifact-containing layer generally decreases as specimen hardness increases. It also decreases with increasing fine-

ness of the abrasion stage until the working surface of the abrasion device clogs with metallic abrasion debris. Deep artifact-containing layers are then produced. The material removal rate achieved by an abrasion stage depends on many factors, and of those factors, specimen hardness is only marginally important. The most important parameter is often how the specimen material causes the abrasion device to deteriorate; this can be established only by experimentation.

The material removal rates achieved by conventional polishing stages can vary more than those of abrasion. Diamond abrasives produce the highest removal rates, but the removal rate even with this abrasive varies by several orders of magnitude, depending on the nature of the specimen material and how the abrasive is used. Many of the commonly recommended methods of using this abrasive yield far from optimum removal rates. Quantitative, or at least semiquantitative, data on the material removal rates of the abrasion and polishing stages proposed for a preparation system should be obtained to ensure optimum conditions and that abrasion and polishing artifacts are removed effectively.

**Abrasion Artifacts in Austenitic Steels.** Austenitic steels generally are susceptible to abrasion artifacts, and the common etchants reveal effects due to prior deformation with considerable sensitivity. The structure of a typical abrasion-damaged layer (see Fig. 4) is comparable to that for brass. A shallow, unresolved layer contours the surface scratches, and deep rays of deformation etch markings extend beneath the surface scratches. Bands of these deformation etch markings may appear in a final-polished surface as abrasion artifacts (see Fig. 5). Good abrasion practice and efficient polishing will remove the abrasion artifacts in an acceptable polishing time (see Fig. 6).

When a surface contains artifacts of the type shown in Fig. 5, it can be assumed that a deep surface layer will have to be removed to obtain an artifact-free surface. Therefore, the specimen must be returned to rough polishing to attain a sufficiently high cutting rate. Alternate polishing and etching at the final-polishing stage, as is sometimes recommended, is not likely to be effective.

**Abrasion Artifacts in Zinc.** Metals of noncubic crystal structure, such as zinc, characteristically form large mechanical twins during plastic deformation. This is reflected in the abrasion-damaged layer in Fig. 7, where deformation twins are present to considerable depth. In metals with low melting points, such as tin and zinc, recrystallization of the outer layers of the deformed structure may also occur at ambient temperature; this accounts for the recrystallization of the outermost portion of the abrasion-damaged layer in Fig. 7. The grain size of a recrystallized layer usually is fine and becomes finer as the surface is approached; only by coincidence will the grain size be similar to that of the parent metal.

---

*Figure 1 shows a taper section in which the apparent magnification in depth (vertically in the micrograph) is 8.2 times the nominal magnification. Here, the section line is perpendicular to a set of unidirectional abrasion scratches. Similar taper sections are shown in Fig. 4, 7, 11, 20, 38, 52, and 53. When the section line is parallel to the abrasion scratches (as in Fig. 15, 16, and 26 to 28), the section is referred to as a longitudinal taper section.

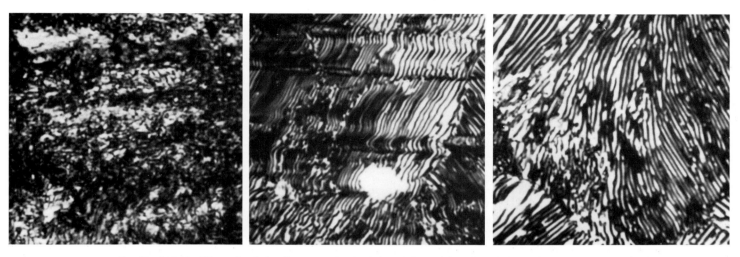

**Fig. 17, 18, 19** Pearlitic steel. Fig. 17: results of abrading on an abrasive belt and then polishing for only long enough to remove abrasion scratches; structure contains abrasion-deformation artifacts. Fig. 18: results of abrading on 600-grit silicon carbide paper and then polishing only long enough to remove abrasion scratches; kinking of cementite plates is an abrasion-deformation artifact. Fig. 19: results of abrading on 600-grit silicon carbide paper and polishing for a longer time than for Fig. 18. Figure 19 shows the true structure. Picral. 2000×

**Fig. 20, 21, 22** Plain carbon steel, hardened but not tempered. Fig. 20: taper section (horizontal magnification 1200×, vertical magnification 13080×) of surface layers that were abusively ground, producing martensite (white-etching constituent) and tempering (dark-etching bands). Fig. 21: dark-etching bands of tempered structure that originated from dry belt grinding. Fig. 22: the true structure. Picral. 250×

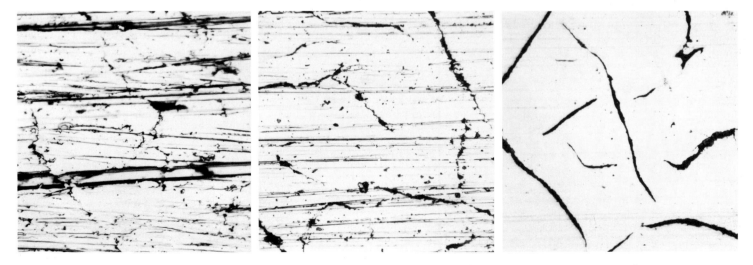

**Fig. 23, 24, 25** Effects of abrasion on flake graphite in gray iron. Fig. 23: results of abrading on 220-grit silicon carbide paper. Fig. 24: results of abrading on 600-grit silicon carbide paper. Fig. 25: results of abrading on a fine fixed-abrasive lap. See also the taper section in Fig. 26 to 28. As-polished. 500×

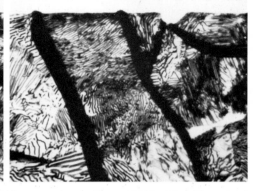

**Fig. 26, 27, 28** Longitudinal taper sections of abraded surfaces in gray iron (horizontal magnification 1000×, vertical magnification 10000×). Fig. 26: results of abrading on 220-grit silicon carbide paper. Fig. 27: results of abrading on 600-grit silicon carbide paper. Fig. 28: results of abrading on a fine fixed-abrasive lap. Picral

The following range of artifact structures may be observed if an abraded surface of zinc is polished for progressively longer times:

- A fully recrystallized structure of different grain size than the parent metal (Fig. 8)
- A mixed structure of recrystallized grains and parent-metal grains containing deformation twins
- Parent-metal grains containing deformation twins that are likely to be aligned in bands in the direction of the initiating abrasion scratches (Fig. 9)

When polishing has been continued long enough for removal of the abrasion-damaged layer, the true structure may be observed (Fig. 10). Efficient preparation procedures depend on avoiding the production of deep abrasion-damaged layers prior to polishing, eliminating the need for removing them by excessive polishing.

**Abrasion Artifacts in Ferritic Steels.** The deep abrasion-damage effects discussed so far cause difficulties in a limited range of alloys, but effects due to an outer fragmented layer are likely to be found in all metals. For example, a section of the outer fragmented layer in a ferritic steel is shown in Fig. 11. The structure of the fragmented layer cannot be properly resolved by optical microscopy, but it is clearly different from that of the parent-metal ferrite grains. The types of artifacts that may be found in final-polished surfaces of ferritic steel are illustrated in Fig. 12 and 13. These artifacts obscure the true structure, shown in Fig. 14; they can be developed in virtually all metals. However, as shown in Fig. 11, the damaged layer is quite thin, and a polishing treatment continued for twice the time it takes to remove the abrasion scratches will eliminate the abrasion artifacts. Therefore, abrasion artifacts are usually the result of inadequate preparation procedures.

**Abrasion Artifacts in Pearlitic Steels.** Distinctive artifacts caused by disturbance in the outer fragmented layer are observed in pearlitic steels. Taper sections of abraded surfaces of these steels show that the cementite plates of pearlite may simply be bent adjacent to some scratches (Fig. 15) and may be completely fragmented adjacent to others (Fig. 16). As a result, artifact structures of the types shown in Fig. 17 and 18 may be observed in surfaces after final polishing. The cementite plates in Fig. 17 have been so fragmented that the pearlite structure is unrecognizable; the appearance, in fact, is more like that found after hardening and tempering. The structure in Fig. 18 is recognizable as lamellar pearlite, but the kinking of the cementite plates represents an artifact structure. The true pearlite structure, free of artifacts, is shown in Fig. 19. The affected layer in Fig. 17 and 18 is quite shallow, and the artifacts shown are likely to be found only after inefficient preparation procedures.

**Tempering Artifacts in Steel.** When steels with medium to high carbon content are ground abusively, especially with inadequate coolant, the surface may be heated sufficiently to develop a rehardened martensitic surface layer, such as the outer white-etching layer shown in Fig. 20. A martensitic layer is likely to be quite thin. If the steels initially are in the hardened-and-untempered condition, the rehardened layer will be accompanied by a tempered layer that is much deeper and highly variable in depth; the tempered layer is dark etching. The bands of tempered structure (see Fig. 21) are much more likely to produce artifact structures than the martensitic layer. The artifact structure is banded, because the grinding that caused the damage produced unidirectional scratches. When compared to the true structure in Fig. 22, it is apparent that artifact banding could be mistaken for segregation banding in steel. Similar effects may occur in any alloy system in which structural changes can result from reheating.

Tempering artifacts can be avoided by ensuring that the specimen is continuously flooded with liquid coolant during abrasive machinings, particularly those involving high speeds. Dry, mechanized abrasion processes should be avoided.

**Abrasion Damage in Gray Iron.** Cast irons are an important group of alloys for which a purpose of metallographic examination often is the determination of the true size

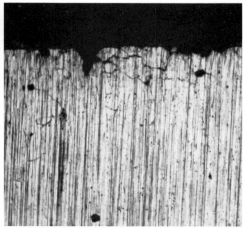

**Fig. 29, 30** Comparison of abrasives for preservation of corroded surface of aluminum alloy. Fig. 29: results of abrading on 600-grit silicon carbide paper. Fig. 30: improvement in finish and edge preservation obtained by abrading on a fine fixed-abrasive lap. As-polished. 100×

and shape of the particles of free graphite that are present. The apparent size and shape of the graphite can be severely altered at several stages of the preparation sequence, causing false structures.

The true graphite form for a particular gray iron is most closely represented in Fig. 25. This can be confirmed by examining a taper section of the surface (Fig. 28), which shows that most of the graphite flakes are accurately sectioned. Those few that were acutely aligned to the section surface are slightly enlarged. On the other hand, the majority of flakes on a coarsely abraded surface appear much narrower than their true width (Fig. 23), because the graphite has been removed from its cavity for a considerable depth and the empty portion of the cavity has collapsed (Fig. 26). An intermediate abrasion treatment gives an intermediate result (Fig. 24); the flakes in some areas are of true width and in others are greatly contracted. On the other hand, the flakes appear to be much wider than their true width at occasional areas in Fig. 23 and 24, because the graphite has been removed from its cavity, then the cavity has been enlarged (Fig. 27), presumably by erosion.

Because problems in preserving graphite correctly also arise during polishing, it is unwise to rely on subsequent polishing to correct damage introduced by abrasion. The graphite should be retained as fully as possible during abrasion; elimination of water lubrication during fine grinding steps (400- and 600-grit abrasives) is beneficial.

**Other Effects of Abrasion Damage.** The effects of abrasion damage discussed so far represent those that can be recognized by optical microscopy. Other indirect effects are also noticeable. For example, a hardness measurement made on the prepared surface may be unusually high if the depth of the damage layer is comparable to that of the hardness indentation and if the strains in the layer are large enough to increase detectably the hardness of the material. True hardness values are obtained only after sufficient material has been removed during polishing to ensure that the strains in the residual layer are not high enough to affect hardness. This usually is achieved, because small deformations often do not greatly affect hardness. At the other extreme, surfaces prepared for examination by transmission electron microscopy must be free of residual abrasion strains. Small strains introduce crystal defects detectable by transmission electron microscopy.

**Flatness of Abraded Surfaces.** Finishing abrasion on a fixed-abrasive lap often yields more satisfactory results than those obtained by finishing on abrasive papers. In general, a flatter surface is obtained from a dressed lap or stone, resulting, for example, in improved preservation of edges (compare Fig. 29 and 30), improved retention of nonmetallic inclusions (compare Fig. 31 and 32), and reduction in the difference in level between different phases (compare Fig. 33 and 34). A

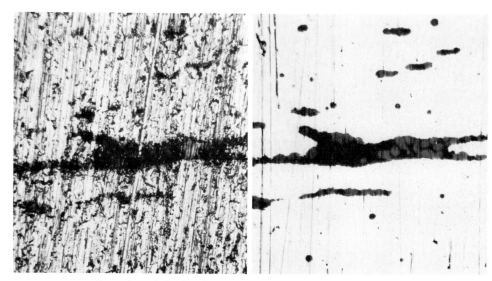

**Fig. 31, 32** Comparison of abrasives for preservation of a nonmetallic inclusion in wrought iron. Fig. 31: results of abrading on 600-grit silicon carbide paper. Fig. 32: improved results obtained by abrading on a fine fixed-abrasive lap. As-polished. 500×

slightly finer finish is also obtained. However, because fixed-abrasive laps clog easily, producing deep, damaged layers, and are more difficult to use than abrasive paper, it is necessary to decide if the improvement in finish justifies the additional effort.

**Embedding of Abrasive.** The points of the contacting abrasive particles of an abrasive paper fracture readily during abrasion. These fragments may become embedded in the surface of a very soft metal, such as lead or annealed high-purity aluminum, where they are difficult to discern by optical microscopy. However, a surface with a high concentration of embedded abrasive characteristically has a rough, torn appearance (Fig. 35), quite different from the regular grooves of a normal abraded surface. It is difficult to prepare such a surface through subsequent stages.

Embedding of abrasive fragments can be avoided by filling the surface of the abrasive paper with a soft wax; the fragments will then embed in the wax rather than in the specimen. The result of finishing high-purity lead on a silicon carbide paper lubricated with wax is shown in Fig. 36. The surface of soft metals may also be prepared by cutting with a heavy microtome. This produces the highest quality surface, as shown in Fig. 37.

## Polishing Damage

The mechanical polishing procedures most commonly used in metallography remove metal by mechanical cutting processes analogous to those of abrasion. This type of mechanical polishing produces a series of scratch grooves on the surface of the specimen that are difficult to detect by optical microscopy, particularly with bright-field illumination, but are readily detected by scanning electron microscopy. Moreover, a

plastically deformed, damaged layer is also introduced. The layer is much shallower than that produced by abrasion, but its structure is similar.

The damaged layer produced on the surface of annealed 70-30 brass by polishing (Fig. 38) can be compared with that produced by abrading (Fig. 1). A layer, analogous to the outer fragmented layer in abraded surfaces, can be recognized contouring the surface scratches, and occasional rays of deformed metal extend to depths many times that of the polishing scratches. The gradient of plastic strains on the layer is the same as for the fragmented layer in abraded surfaces, but the layer is shallower by one or two orders of magnitude. The presence of this damaged layer affects the response of the surface to etching.

This damaged layer cannot be avoided in a polishing that removes material primarily by chip cutting. Several fine polishing processes, however, do not operate in this way. In the first group of these processes, polishing occurs by detaching small flakes of material from the surface. The surface strains introduced by this polishing are so small and the strained layer so shallow that often it would be removed by etching.

The second group consists of polishing processes in which, intentionally or otherwise, the liquid in which the polishing abrasive is suspended is chemically active with respect to the specimen material. The function of the abrasive then appears to be that of continuously removing protective films, ensuring more rapid and more uniform dissolution of the surface by chemical attack. This combination of actions may be referred to as a chemical-mechanical polishing mechanism. The surface produced is damage-free when the chemical component is large enough.

However, an excessive chemical component in a mechanical-chemical process may

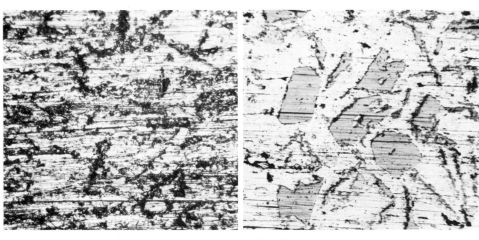

**Fig. 33, 34** Comparison of abrasives for reduction of the differences in level of different phases in Al-13Si alloy. Fig. 33: results of abrading on 600-grit silicon carbide paper. Fig. 34: improved results obtained by abrading on a fine fixed-abrasive lap. As-polished. 250×

cause such detrimental effects as severe etch pitting. Proper balance between the mechanical and chemical components can preserve most of the benefits provided by mechanical polishing and yet produce a damage-free surface—a most desirable combination in a final polishing.

**Degradation of Etching Contrast.** The orientation of the grain sectioned in Fig. 38 is such that it should have appeared white on the original polished surface under the etching conditions indicated, as it does in the middle portions of this micrograph. However, it is covered by a fragmented layer that etches darkly. Therefore, this grain would have appeared much darker than it should have if the original surface had been etched and examined. Consequently, the contrast between this grain and the others would have been less than it should have been. This is why the grain contrast in Fig. 39 is poor compared to that in Fig. 41. This phenomenon can be expected whenever an etchant develops contrast by differential coloring; it may be described as a polishing artifact.

**Scratch Traces.** If a surface is subjected to coarse polishing, followed by finer polishing until the first series of scratches but not all the rays of deformation in the layer damaged by polishing have been removed, the residuals of the rays of deformation left in the surface may be preferentially attacked during etching, as shown in Fig. 40, giving the impression that some of the first series of scratches have reappeared. These effects can be avoided by continuing finer polishing long enough to remove all the preexisting polishing damage, as shown in Fig. 41.

This phenomenon, common in metallography, is frequently ascribed to the reappearance of the scratches themselves. However, the features developed should be thought of as "ghosts" of the original scratches; they are not the grooves of the original scratches. They may more properly be termed scratch traces, another type of polishing artifact.

**Enlargement of Polishing Scratches by Etching.** A surface that appeared to be free of scratches when examined as-polished under bright-field illumination often appears severely scratched after etching (see Fig. 42 to 44). The numerous fine scratches were not detected on the unetched specimen; they were enlarged, or shown in greater contrast, by etching.

Scratches are attacked preferentially during etching because of the disturbed metal, or damaged layer, associated with them. Severity of attack varies directly with the ability of the etchant to reveal deformation. The appearance of scratches also depends on the etching time. A certain minimum etching time is necessary to develop the scratches to maximum visibility, after which the scratches recede with increasing etching time, because etching progressively removes the damaged layer.

Metals vary in their susceptibility to this effect; the greater the sensitivity of the metal-etchant combination to plastic deformation, the more likely that enlargement of scratches during etching will be troublesome. On the other hand, the phenomenon becomes less troublesome when the depth of the damaged layer is less than that of the layer removed during etching. Polishing processes that do not introduce a damaged layer cause no such problems.

It may be difficult to distinguish scratches enlarged by the final polishing stages from scratch traces introduced during the previous polishing stage. This can be resolved by making the earlier set of scratches unidirectional and parallel to a known direction in the specimen surface. The originating system of scratches can then be recognized. This technique was used in preparing the specimen for Fig. 40.

**Flatness.** Surfaces should be adequately free of confusing polishing scratches and should be sufficiently flat for examination of all constituents and local regions. Two examples of how markedly the choice of polishing

abrasive and polishing cloth can affect surface flatness in specimens of duplex structure are given in Fig. 45 to 48. These micrographs show that $Al_2O_3$ abrasive on billiard cloth produced a result inferior to diamond abrasive on synthetic suede cloth in polishing wrought iron and an aluminum alloy. The $Al_2O_3$ on billiard cloth produced marked relief between the silicon constituent and the aluminum matrix of the aluminum alloy (Fig. 47) and removed a portion of the silicate inclusion in the wrought iron (Fig. 45). These are not the only types of polishing cloths available, but the examples demonstrate the wide variation in quality of results that is possible and the type of systematic experiment that can be carried out to compare polishing processes.

**Retention of Graphite in Gray Iron.** Earlier in this article it was demonstrated that although the graphite in cast iron can be damaged severely by abrasion, it is possible by suitable choice of abrasion process to obtain a reasonably true representation of the structure. However, there is the problem of retaining the graphite during polishing. The solution to the problem depends heavily on the length of the nap of the polishing cloth.

Graphite flakes in a gray iron invariably look much larger when a long-nap cloth is used for polishing, as demonstrated in Fig. 49. This apparent enlargement is caused by erosion, which occurs at the interface between graphite and matrix, producing an enlarged cavity from which the flake itself eventually is removed (see Fig. 52). With a cloth of reasonably short nap, many of the flakes are well retained, although some appear slightly larger (see Fig. 50 and 53). Examination of sections of such a surface indicates that flakes aligned perpendicular to the surface are not eroded (flakes at right in Fig. 53), but that slight erosion occurs around flakes that happen to be acutely aligned at the section surface (flake at left in Fig. 53). Correct representation of the graphite flakes is obtained after polishing with a napless cloth, as shown in Fig. 51.

Only certain abrasives, notably diamond abrasives, produce satisfactory results on napless cloths. Even then, a moderately heavily scratched polish is obtained. If this finish is unacceptable, a finishing treatment with a fine abrasive on a napped cloth is necessary. The treatment must be brief to avoid enlargement of the cavities.

## Final-Polishing Processes

Only rarely must final-polished surfaces be totally free of scratches. Rather, no scratches should be detectable under the particular conditions of examination. Attaining this will depend, therefore, on the specimen material (more difficult with soft materials), the etching conditions (more difficult with etchants that are sensitive to deformed structures), and the optical conditions of examination. In general, high-standard polishing processes

**Fig. 35, 36, 37** Fig. 35: results obtained by finishing high-purity lead on 600-grit silicon carbide paper using water as the fluid. Fig. 36: results obtained on 600-grit silicon carbide paper using wax on the abrasion surface. Fig. 37: results obtained using a sledge microtome. As-polished. 250×

**Fig. 38, 39, 40, 41** Effect of polishing damage on response to etching for annealed 70-30 brass. Fig. 38: taper section (horizontal magnification 2000×, vertical magnification 21 800×) of surface layers that were polished on 1-μm diamond abrasive. Fig. 39: results of etching immediately after polishing on a 1-μm diamond abrasive. Fig. 40: fine polishing for a short time before etching. Fig. 41: fine polishing for a longer time before etching. The fine polishing process is skid polishing on magnesium oxide abrasive, a chemical-mechanical polishing process that does not produce a damaged layer. Aqueous FeCl₃. 250×

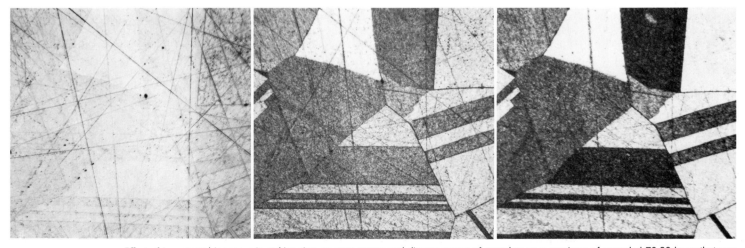

**Fig. 42, 43, 44** Effect of incremental increases in etching time on appearance and disappearance of scratches on a specimen of annealed 70-30 brass that was polished on fine Al₂O₃. Fig. 44: longer etching time removes scratches and the damaged layer. Aqueous FeCl₃. 250×

**Fig. 45, 46** Comparison of polishing methods for showing inclusions in wrought iron. Fig. 45: specimen was polished on 10- to 20-μm Al₂O₃ on billiard cloth. Fig. 46: specimen was polished on 4- to 8-μm diamond on synthetic suede cloth. Both specimens were abraded on a fixed-abrasive lap before polishing. As-polished. 350×

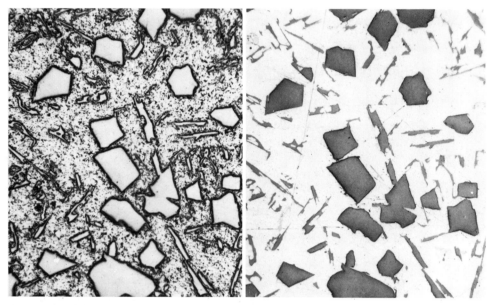

**Fig. 47, 48** Comparison of polishing methods for showing phases in Al-13Si alloy. Fig. 47: specimen was polished on 10- to 20-μm Al₂O₃ on billiard cloth. Fig. 48: specimen was polished on 4- to 8-μm diamond on a synthetic suede cloth. Both specimens were abraded on a fixed-abrasive lap before polishing. As-polished. 250×

are more laborious and require greater operator skill. A variety of final-polishing processes should be available that can produce increasingly higher qualities of finish from which to select the most suitable and simplest for a particular need.

**Skid Polishing.** The nap of the polishing cloth is filled with a thick paste of a fine polishing abrasive and an appropriate polishing fluid, and the specimen is rotated lightly against the surface of the paste so that it skids over the paste without touching the fibers of the polishing cloth. Alternatively the nap is filled with an abrasive-free paste of an appropriate material, and the polishing abrasive is sprinkled onto the surface of the paste. These procedures should eliminate the scratches that would ordinarily result from contact with the fibers of the polishing cloth. In addition, because the abrasive particles are more lightly supported than usual, they produce finer scratches. Processes carried out in

this way can also involve a chemical-mechanical mechanism of material removal, particularly if active chemicals are added to the abrasive paste. They sometimes operate entirely by such a mechanism. The skidding technique with MgO abrasive used for Fig. 41 is an example. Skid-polishing methods, however, are tedious and difficult.

**Vibratory polishing methods,** in which the specimen is made to track automatically around the polishing cloth by imparting a suitable vibratory motion to the polishing head, are useful for final polishing because they operate automatically and permit accurate control of polishing conditions. Results are highly reproducible once the controlling variables have been identified and optimized. A further advantage of vibratory polishing is that it can be adapted to chemical-mechanical polishing. The important variables in vibratory polishing are the abrasive, the nature of the liquid in which the abrasive is sus-

pended, and the load applied to the specimen.

The results of varying the suspending liquid are illustrated in Fig. 54 to 56. The polishing rate with straight glycol as the suspending liquid was so low that scratch traces from the previous polishing stage were retained even after a protracted polishing time (Fig. 54). Water as the suspending liquid provided fast polishing, but caused severe etch pitting (Fig. 56). A suitable mixture of the two provided an adequate polishing rate and a satisfactory polish (Fig. 55).

Some etch attack occurs with the glycol-water suspending liquid, even with optimum adjustment of the liquid; the etching varies directly with the load applied to the specimen, increasing with increasing load, as shown in Fig. 57 to 59. This behavior offers evidence that the polishing process is occurring by a chemical-mechanical mechanism, with the water acting as the active ingredient and the glycol (a chelating agent) acting as a modifier.

The most appropriate suspending fluid varies with the specimen material. Sometimes it is also necessary to add a more aggressive etching reagent to the suspending liquid to ensure an adequate chemical component in the polishing mechanism. For example, the mechanism for an $\alpha$-$\beta$ brass that was polished with the use of a straight glycol-water mixture had an excessive mechanical component, and final-polishing scratches became apparent as a result (Fig. 60). The addition of a large amount of ammonium hydroxide ($NH_4OH$) caused the chemical mechanism to predominate, and an unacceptable degree of relief developed between the two phases of the microstructure (Fig. 62). Adjustment of the $NH_4OH$ addition balanced the two mechanisms to give an acceptable result (Fig. 61).

The optimum polishing conditions are arrived at largely by experimentation, guided by a few broad principles. However, highly reproducible results have been achieved once the optimum conditions have been determined.

**Etch-Attack and Electromechanical Polishing.** The material removal rate obtained with some metals, particularly the refractory metals, is very small with conventional polishing methods. This inhibits the removal of preexisting abrasion and polishing damage as well as the production of adequately scratch-free final surfaces. It is possible in many cases to increase the polishing rate acceptably by adding an active chemical etchant to the abrasive slurry. Unfortunately, because the reagents necessary are frequently very aggressive to other metals and human tissue, they require the use of special corrosion-resistant equipment and specimen-handling arrangements. Less than ideal results, however, often are obtained, as shown in Fig. 63.

Less aggressive reagents can be employed if an electrical potential is applied between the specimen and the polishing wheel; the two act as electrodes of an electrolytic cell.

**Fig. 49, 50, 51** Comparison of polishing methods for retention of graphite in gray iron. Fig. 49: results of polishing on 10- to 20-μm Al₂O₃ on long-nap billiard cloth. Fig. 50: results of polishing on 1-μm diamond on a synthetic suede short-nap cloth. Fig. 51: results of polishing on 1-μm diamond on cotton drill. All specimens were abraded on a fixed-abrasive lap before polishing. As-polished. 250×

**Fig. 52, 53** Taper sections (horizontal magnification 1000×, vertical magnification 10 000×) comparing polishing methods for retention of graphite in gray iron. Fig. 52: results of polishing on 10- to 20-μm Al₂O₃ on long-nap billiard cloth. Fig. 53: results of polishing on 1-μm diamond on short-nap synthetic suede. Picral. 1000 and 10 000×

soft materials, when used conventionally. Apparently, the improved results are obtained because these abrasives act by different mechanisms than conventional fine polishing processes. For example, 0- to ¼-μm grade of polycrystalline diamond used conventionally as a carrier paste added to a short-nap cloth produces a surface with a shallow low-strain-damaged layer.

Another example is a proprietary material that is a colloidal suspension of silica (SiO₂). This material is widely used for polishing silicon in the semiconductor industry. A number of precautions are essential for its use; the solution must not be allowed to freeze or to dry out on the polishing cloth, and it may be necessary to adjust its pH for particular types of specimens. This polishing process appears to act largely by a chemical-mechanical mechanism. Although some relief is produced between the grains and constituents, it is usually well within acceptable limits.

Suitable electromechanical processes of this type have been developed for various difficult metals and alloys. Only minor modifications to standard polishing equipment are required to use these techniques, and a more uniform polish is achieved than by straight etch-attack techniques (compare Fig. 63 and 64).

**Polishing With Special Abrasives.** Two fine abrasives are available that produce unusually scratch-free surfaces, particularly in

**Fig. 54, 55, 56** Effect of type of suspending liquid used in vibratory polishing of low-carbon steel. Specimens were rough polished on 1-μm diamond and finish polished for 4 h on 0.1-μm Al₂O₃. Fig. 54: using propylene glycol; scratches have not been removed. Fig. 55: using a 2:1 mixture of propylene glycol and water; results are satisfactory. Fig. 56: as-polished; using water; large corrosion pits have developed. Nital. 500×

**Fig. 57, 58, 59** Effect of load applied to the specimen in vibratory polishing of low-carbon steel. Specimens were rough polished on 1-μm diamond and finish polished for 4 h on 0.1-μm $Al_2O_3$ suspended in a 2:1 mixture of propylene glycol and water. Fig. 57: using a 40-g load. Fig. 58: using a 70-g load. Fig. 59: using a 380-g load. Etch relief develops during polishing, being greater the larger the applied load. As-polished. 100×

## Edge Retention

For metallographic examination, the surface produced should be flat up to an edge of the specimen. The criterion is that the regions adjacent to the edge should all be focused sharply by the particular microscope system that is used for the examination of the section. This may require adopting special procedures during specimen preparation, because unsupported edges of a section normally round off slightly when the specimen rocks during preparation, particularly during manual operations. Special procedures may be required also because of the elasticity of the working surfaces on the abrasion and polishing devices. An acceptable degree of rounding and therefore the extent of the precautions necessary during specimen preparation depend on the depth of field of the microscope system to be used. Comparatively large degrees of rounding are acceptable in scanning electron microscopy, but much lesser degrees are acceptable in optical microscopy. The higher the magnification in use in optical microscopy, the lesser the degree of rounding that is acceptable.

Many techniques, which usually require a degree of operator skill, have been devised to improve edge retention, yet few have general application. The basic problems involved and methods by which they may be overcome by the simplest possible modifications of standard procedures are discussed below. Although the difficulties involved in edge retention are alleviated by the use of mechanized preparation machines, the same principles apply to manual operations. Additional information on edge retention (or preservation) can be found in the article "Mounting of Specimens" in this Volume.

With few exceptions, the abrasion rates of the plastics in which metallographic specimens are mounted greatly exceed those of metals. The plastic abrades to a lower general level than the metal, and rounding of the specimen edge occurs to blend in the differences in level. The degree of edge rounding may be increased or decreased during polishing; long-nap polishing cloths increase edge rounding.

However, the abrasion rates of different types of plastic differ significantly, and edge retention can be improved by choosing a mounting plastic that has an abrasion rate matching as closely as possible that of the specimen. For example, progressively improved edge retention is obtained, as shown in Fig. 65 to 67, with the change from a phenolic (Fig. 65) to an allyl (Fig. 66) to a polyvinyl formal (Fig. 67) mounting plastic. Metals such as chromium and tungsten, which have very low abrasion rates, show poorer edge retention than that illustrated in Fig. 67, even when mounted in a polyvinyl formal plastic. Metals such as copper and aluminum, which have high abrasion rates, show good edge retention, even when mounted in phenolic or epoxy plastics.

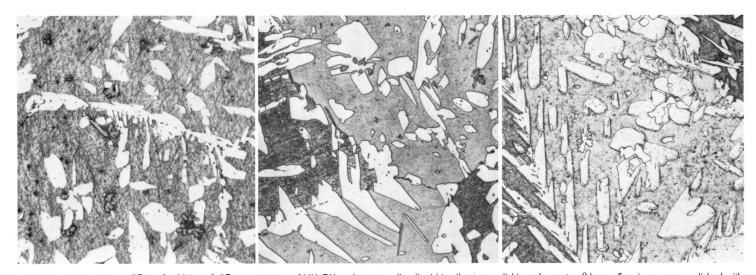

**Fig. 60, 61, 62** Effect of addition of different amounts of $NH_4OH$ to the suspending liquid in vibratory polishing of a cast α-β brass. Specimens were polished with magnesia suspended in a 3:1 mixture of propylene glycol and water. Fig. 60: using no addition of $NH_4OH$; note numerous polishing scratches. Fig. 61: using an optimum addition of $NH_4OH$. Fig. 62: using excessive $NH_4OH$; note excessive relief between the two phases. As-polished (etched during polishing). 500×

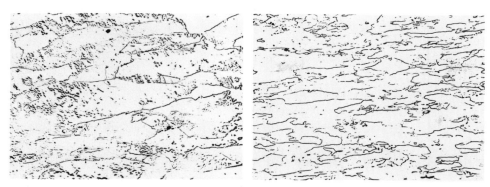

**Fig. 63, 64** Comparison of etch-attack and electrochemical methods of polishing tungsten, a representative refractory metal. Fig. 63: polishing by an etch-attack technique using $Al_2O_3$ abrasive suspended in an aqueous solution of potassium ferricyanide (KCN) and sodium hydroxide (NaOH). Fig. 64: polishing by an electromechanical technique using $Al_2O_3$ abrasive suspended in a saturated aqueous solution of NaOH. The etch-attack technique produced some grain relief and many wiping marks. The electromechanical technique produced a surface in which no structure could be seen before etching. A satisfactory artifact-free result was obtained on etching. 100×

Reducing the difference in abrasion rate between the specimen and mount improves edge retention. This may be accomplished by incorporating chips or pellets of a metal similar to the specimen in the mount face (see Fig. 68). Any included material that reduces the abrasion rate of the plastic will also be effective. Plastics are available to which a substantial volume fraction of mineral or ceramic (for example, mica, $SiO_2$, or $Al_2O_3$) has been added as a filler. They are effective for edge retention, but cause rapid deterioration of abrasive papers. The potential for removing preexisting damaged layers is therefore considerably reduced, an important factor when considering mineral- or ceramic-filled plastics.

The polishing rates of plastics are small compared to their abrasion rates. They can now be either less than or greater than that of the metal specimen itself. If the former, any edge rounding that developed during abrasion will increase during polishing; if the latter, it will decrease to a degree that also depends on the elasticity of the polishing cloth. Consequently, it is easier to achieve good edge retention with some metals than with others using standard procedures. If the polishing ratio of metal and plastic is adverse, anything that reduces the polishing rate of the plastic will improve edge retention, such as adding a mineral or ceramic filler. However, the overall polishing rate of the metal-plastic combination is then reduced correspondingly, with an attendant increase in the difficulty of removing the abrasion-damaged layer.

The napped cloths used in standard polish-

ing procedures are likely to worsen the edge rounding developed during abrasion, because these soft cloths tend to conform locally to the contour of the abraded surface. If polishing is done on a fairly rigid pad so that contact is made during polishing only with high spots on the abraded surface, the specimen surface can be polished down to the level of the plastic. Edge retention, therefore, will be improved. Results obtained by this procedure are shown in Fig. 70. When polishing on a rigid pad, careful selection of the polishing abrasive and cloth will prevent the development of excessive polishing scratches.

A high standard of edge retention is achieved ideally by depositing on the surface concerned, before sectioning, a layer of material with abrasion and polishing removal rate characteristics similar to those of the specimen material. This is illustrated in Fig. 69. In addition, the deposited layer sometimes must have electrochemical characteristics similar to those of the specimen material so that it does not interfere with etching of the specimen material. Good adhesion between deposit and base metal is also essential. Electrodeposition is the most common method of forming the protective layer, but the number of metals that can be deposited in this way is limited. A similar result is achieved by clamping a pack of like specimens together, but this applies only to specimens in the form of thin sheet.

## Special Techniques for Unusual Materials

**Very Hard Materials.** An abrasive particle generally will not embed in a specimen material and remove material by machining a chip unless it is at least two times and prefer-

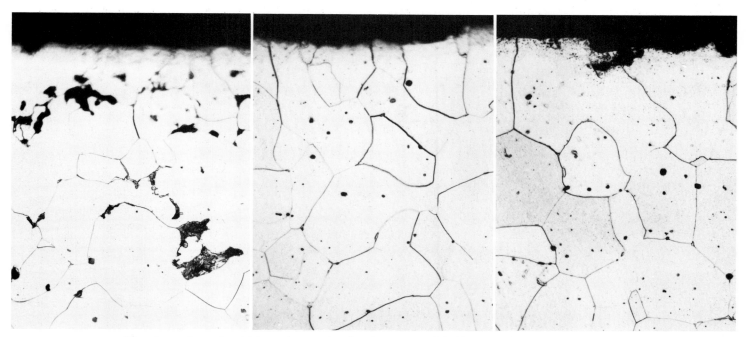

**Fig. 65, 66, 67** Effect of type of mounting plastic on edge retention of steel specimens polished by standard technique. Fig. 65: specimen mounted in a phenolic plastic; also representative of edge retention using an epoxy. Fig. 66: specimen mounted in an allyl plastic. Fig. 67: specimen mounted in a polyvinyl formal plastic; also representative of edge retention using polyvinyl chloride plastic. Nital. 500×

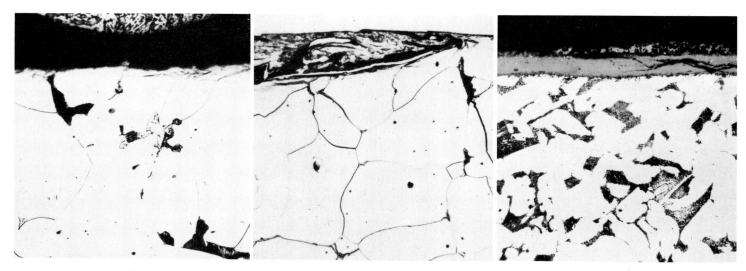

**Fig. 68, 69, 70** Effect of special techniques for improving edge retention of steel specimens mounted in an epoxy resin. Fig. 68: Steel shot incorporated in the mount; specimen finish polished by a standard technique. Fig. 69: Edge protected by an electrodeposited coating of nickel; specimen finish polished by a standard technique. Fig. 70: specimen finish polished using a fairly rigid napless pad and diamond abrasive. Nital. 500×

**Fig. 71, 72, 73** Sintered WC-15Ti. Fig. 71: Dark, angular areas are artifacts due to chipping during abrasion of 6-μm diamond-plastic lap. Fig. 72: Result of polishing the abraded surface for comparatively short period on a cotton drill cloth charged with 6-μm diamond abrasive. Many of the deeper pits produced during abrasion remain and might be mistaken for sintering pores. They are abrasion artifacts. Fig. 73: Result obtained after polishing further. The chipping artifacts have been removed, and the true distribution of the sintering pores can now be seen. As-polished. 500×

ably three times harder than the specimen material. This applies also to individual constituents in an alloy when their size is comparable to that of the scratches being produced. The hardnesses of the commonly used abrasives are 2500 HV (silicon carbide), 2000 HV ($Al_2O_3$), and 8000 HV (diamond). In practice for example, very little material can be removed by silicon carbide and $Al_2O_3$ abrasives from materials with a hardness of about 1000 HV. Such materials usually are cermets or ceramics, such as tungsten carbide or $Al_2O_3$. Diamond abrasives clearly are desirable for all stages of the preparation of materials of these types and are mandatory for the hardest of them.

Diamond abrasive laps suitable for the abrasion stages of preparation are available commercially in a range of grades. In the most common form, the abrasive is held onto a metal disk by a covering layer of metallic material, often an electrodeposit of nickel. Very hard materials are invariably brittle. Abrasion then occurs by irregular blocky chips fracturing out of the surface. This leaves deep pits on the surface (see Fig. 71), with systems of cracks extending beneath the pits. These pits and chips become the arti-

facts that must be removed during polishing (compare Fig. 71, 72, and 73). This is important, because the pits may be mistaken for the porosity often present in hard materials when they have been fabricated by sintering, as is commonly the case.

Polishing of these materials occurs by the normal mechanisms, but the rates of material removal obtained even with diamond abrasives are low. The polishing times required to remove abrasion artifacts consequently may be long—much longer than for soft materials. It is important, therefore, to establish the polishing parameters that achieve maximum removal rates. Automated polishing also becomes useful. Even then, long polishing times will still be necessary, and it becomes desirable to check using the experiment illustrated in Fig. 71 to 73 that the true result will be obtained. Final polishing must be carried out on the finest diamond abrasive available.

**Surface Oxide Layers.** Determination of the structure of a surface layer of oxide, or scale, on a specimen is sometimes the principal reason for metallographic examination. A specimen with such a surface layer presents a problem in edge retention. The oxide is usually brittle and friable, being therefore sus-

ceptible to chipping and cracking during preparation. Because the detection of porosity or cracking in the layer is usually an important feature of the examination, it is essential to avoid the development of preparation artifacts that might be mistaken for such features. The development of such artifacts during abrasion is likely, because treatment on standard abrasive papers often results in extensive chipping of the oxide layer (see Fig. 74). Even a fixed-abrasive lap produces some artifact chipping (see Fig. 75), but a special diamond-abrasive leadfoil lap produces a satisfactorily artifact-free result (see Fig. 76). Then polishing with diamond abrasive on a hard napless cloth ensures that a high degree of surface flatness will be maintained and that no polishing damage will be introduced (see Fig. 77).

**Very Soft Materials.** Metals and alloys with a hardness of less than about 20 HV require special treatments, because many abrasive particles can embed in the section during abrasion and because it is difficult to obtain an adequately scratch-free final polish (see Fig. 78). These materials are also sensitive to abrasion artifact of the types illustrated in Fig. 7 to 10.

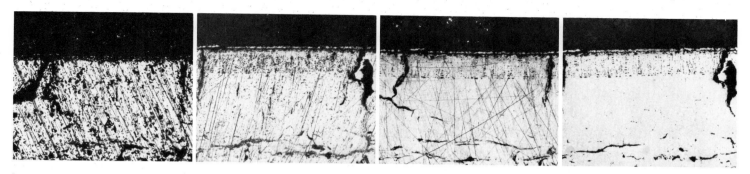

**Fig. 74, 75, 76, 77** Effect of different abrading and polishing techniques on the appearance of oxide scale on high-purity iron. Fig. 74: Specimen abraded on 400-grit silicon carbide paper; numerous chipping artifacts are present in the oxide. Fig. 75: Specimen abraded on a fine fixed-abrasive lap; minor chipping artifacts are present in the oxide. Fig. 76: Specimen abraded on a leadfoil lap coated with 1-$\mu$m diamond paste; oxide and metal are free from chipping artifacts, but are badly scratched. Fig. 77: Specimen polished on 1-$\mu$m diamond abrasive on a cotton drill cloth after being abraded as described for Fig. 76; oxide is free from chipping artifacts, and the surface of the specimen has an adequately scratch-free finish. As-polished. 70$\times$

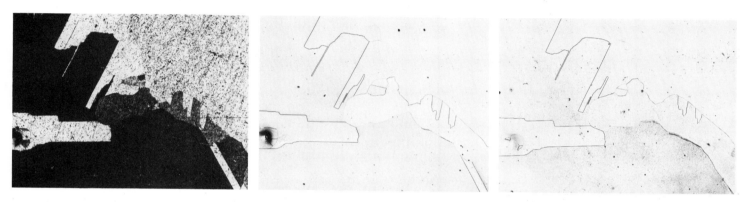

**Fig. 78, 79, 80** Comparison of three methods of final polishing commercially pure lead. Fig. 78: Final polishing by a conventional method using fine $Al_2O_3$. Many polishing artifacts, principally in the form of polishing scratches enlarged by etching, are present. Dark grain contrast has been developed by etching after polishing. Fig. 79: Final polishing by a vibratory method using a proprietary colloidal silica solution. No polishing artifacts are present, and a lighter, clearer grain contrast has been developed by etching. Fig. 80: Final polishing by chemical polishing. No artifacts and clear etching grain contrast, but some etch pitting and grain relief was developed during chemical polishing. 10% ammonium molybdate, 10% citric acid. 55$\times$

Methods of preventing the embedment of abrasive during conventional abrasion were discussed previously. As an alternative, the preliminary surface preparation of these soft metals can be carried out by machining in a heavy microtome. Rough polishing can be carried out conventionally, but final polishing is most effectively performed by special methods. Polishing with a colloidal silica solution using very low pressures is effective (Fig. 79). A number of chemical polishing methods are also available that can be used as brief treatments after polishing by conventional methods (Fig. 80).

**Electrochemical Differences.** Some specimens contain phases or areas whose electrochemical characteristics are quite different from those of the main areas of the section surface. The electrochemically negative phase or area may then dissolve preferentially during conventional polishing processes and thus will not be obtained in a properly polished condition. This is most likely to occur during a final polish using an electrolytic polishing fluid. For example, marked electrochemical differences arise between the zinc-rich coating and the steel base of galvanized steels. Severe etching of the coating occurs when a section is polished using water, even normal distilled water, as the suspending liquid for the polishing abrasive, as shown in Fig. 81. The effect in this instance can be eliminated by using a suspending liquid that has a pH close to 7.0. This pH can be conveniently achieved by using a standard pH 7 buffer solution to prepare the slurry of polishing abrasive; results are shown in Fig. 82. Liquids with other pH values may be necessary with other types of specimens.

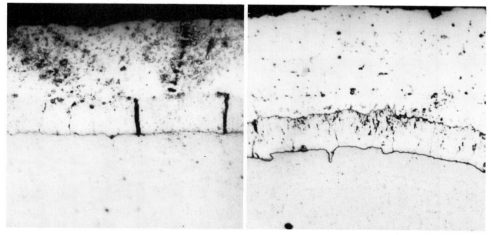

**Fig. 81, 82** Effect of pH of suspending liquid in the final polishing of specimens of galvanized iron. Fig. 81: using a good-quality tap water. Fig. 82: using a buffer solution with a pH of 7. The severe etching of the coating in Fig. 81 occurred as the result of electrochemical differences between the zinc coating and the steel base. As-polished. 700$\times$

**REFERENCE**

1. L.E. Samuels, *Metallographic Polishing by Mechanical Methods*, 3rd ed., American Society for Metals, 1982

# Electrolytic Polishing

ELECTROLYTIC POLISHING, or electropolishing, is used widely in the metallography of stainless steels, copper alloys, aluminum alloys, magnesium, zirconium, and other metals that are difficult to polish by conventional mechanical methods. Electrolytic polishing can completely remove all traces of worked metal remaining from mechanical grinding and polishing operations used in specimen preparation. When electropolishing is used in metallography, it is preceded by mechanical grinding (and sometimes polishing), and followed by etching.

## Mechanism

Although the mechanism of electropolishing is not completely understood, the process is generally considered to include both a leveling (or smoothing) action and a brightening action. Current-voltage relations also affect the polishing results and vary with electrolytes and metals.

**Smoothing** is accomplished by preferential solution of the "hills" or ridges on a rough surface, which commonly results from mechanical grinding (Ref 1). When such a rough surface is made the anode of a suitable electrolytic cell, a viscous liquid layer immediately adjacent to this surface is produced by the reaction between the metal and electrolyte. This layer of solution, known as the polishing film (Fig. 1), has a greater electrical resistance than the remainder of the solution. As such, it controls the smoothing action.

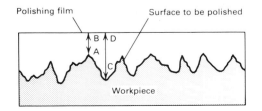

**Fig. 1** Mechanism of electrolytic polishing

Revised by Elisabeth Weidmann, Laboratory Manager, Struers, Inc.

The resistance at a peak A, represented by the distance A-B, will be lower than at depression C, represented by the distance C-D, because the film is thinner at A-B. The current at A will be much higher than at C, causing metal to dissolve faster at A than at C, and producing a nearly level, gently undulating surface by removing asperities 1-$\mu$m or more in size. More rapid ionic and molecular diffusion through the thinner polishing film at A, as well as differences in anodic polarization phenomena at A and C, may also contribute to the leveling or smoothing action.

**The brightening action** is related to the elimination of irregularities as small as about 0.01 $\mu$m and to the suppression of etching on the metal surface. This behavior is generally attributed to the formation of a thin, partly passivating film directly on the surface of the metal and following its contours.

Optimum brightening conditions are related to local differences in anodic passivation at heterogeneities and between secondary peaks and crevices, as well as to the effects of passivation inhibitors that influence oxide-film formation and gas evolution. Similar factors may also contribute to the primary leveling or smoothing action in electropolishing (Ref 2).

**Current-voltage relations** in electropolishing vary in different electrolytes and for different metals. The simple relation, wherein polishing occurs over an extensive continuous range of currents and voltages, is shown in Fig. 2. At low voltages, a film forms on the surface, and little or no current passes. Thus, etching occurs, but not polishing. At higher voltages, polishing occurs. The perchloric acid ($HClO_4$) electrolytes used for aluminum conform to this relation.

A more complex relation that is frequently encountered is illustrated in Fig. 3. Cell voltage is depicted as a function of anode current density for electropolishing copper in an aqueous solution of orthophosphoric acid (ortho-$H_3PO_4$), using a potentiometric circuit.

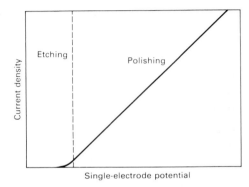

**Fig. 2** Relationship between current density and single-electrode potential for electrolytes possessing polishing action over a wide range of voltages and currents

Five distinct regions can be distinguished on the cell-voltage curve. In the region A-B, current density increases with potential, some metal dissolves, and the surface has a dull etched appearance. The region B-C reflects an unstable condition, while region C-D indicates a stable plateau. At this stage, the previously formed polishing film reaches equilibrium, and polishing occurs. During the polishing stage, current density remains constant.

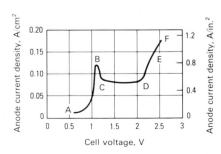

**Fig. 3** Cell voltage as a function of anode current density for electropolishing copper in ortho-$H_3PO_4$ (900 g per 1000 mL $H_2O$), using a potentiometric circuit

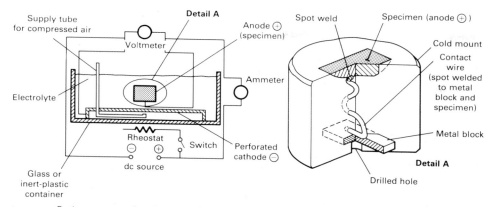

**Fig. 4** Equipment setup for electropolishing. Air agitation of electrolyte is provided through a perforated cathode. Detail at right shows an indirect electrical connection to a mounted specimen.

Optimum polishing conditions occur along C-D near D. In the region D-E, gas bubbles evolve slowly, breaking the polishing film and causing severe pitting. Polishing with rapid evolution of gas is represented by the region E-F.

Electrolytes of the sulfuric-phosphoric acid ($H_2SO_4$ + $H_3PO_4$) and chromic-acetic acid ($CrO_3$ + $CH_3COOH$) types used for stainless steels also typify the complex, multistage relationship shown in Fig. 3.

In establishing voltage-current curves, electrolysis must be allowed to proceed under fixed conditions until enough metal has dissolved to produce a steady-state condition at the anode.

## Mounting Specimens

To properly conduct metallography studies involving electropolishing techniques, only the portion of the specimen to be polished should be in contact with the electrolyte. Small specimens may be hot mounted using conductive or nonconductive resins. On nonconductive mounts, electrical contact can be made via a small hole drilled through the back of the mount into the metal specimen, or by an indirect connection, as shown in Fig. 4.

When specimens are mounted in plastic, violent reactions may occur between the plastic and some electrolytes. For example, phenol-formaldehyde and acrylic-resin mounting materials and cellulose-base insulating lacquers and materials should not be used in solutions containing $HClO_4$ because of the danger of explosion. However, polyethylene, polystyrene, epoxy resins, and polyvinyl chloride can be used as mounting materials in $HClO_4$ solutions without danger.

Mounting of specimens in dissimilar metals is undesirable, because the metal in contact with the electrolyte is likely to interfere with polishing and also because fusible mounting alloys containing bismuth may be dangerously reactive in certain electrolytes that contain oxidizing agents. Bismuth-containing alloys may form explosive compounds in $HClO_4$ solutions.

In preparing an unmounted specimen for electropolishing, a suitable chemically inert, electrically insulating coating can be applied to all surfaces of the specimen and specimen holder, except the surface to be polished. Plastic electrical tape is also an effective stop-off, because it is impervious to most electrolytes and is readily removable from the specimen after electropolishing.

Most commercially available equipment features plastic tops with different sized apertures that are placed over the polishing cell. The surface to be polished is clamped face down over the aperture.

## Apparatus and Procedure

Electrical equipment used for electropolishing can vary from the simplest arrangement of dry cells to complex arrays of rectifiers and electronic control devices. Various types of apparatus are available commercially. Selection of equipment depends on the number and type of specimens to be treated and the versatility and control desired.

**Current Source.** Direct current usually is used in electropolishing. The current source may consist of a battery, a direct-current generator, or a rectifier. Generally, a battery supply is used for low voltages only, because a bank of batteries is required to produce higher voltages.

**Electrical Circuits.** Figure 5 illustrates two typical circuits—one for low and one for high current densities. For solutions in which a small drop in potential occurs across the cell, a potentiometric circuit for low current densities is more suitable (Fig. 5a). Conversely, when the drop in potential across the cell is large, a series circuit for high current densities should be used (Fig. 5b). Provision must be made for controlling voltage and current.

Alternating current is used for electropolishing and electroetching metals of the platinum group (platinum, iridium, palladium, rhodium, osmium, and ruthenium), in conjunction with a series circuit and test setup similar to that shown in Fig. 5(b) with an alternating-current source.

**The electrolytic cell** is simply a container for the electrolyte, in which the cathode and anode are suspended. The cell usually is made of glass, but polyethylene or polypropylene may be used for solutions containing fluoride ions. Sometimes a stainless steel cell is used, which may also serve as the cathode. Frequently, the cell is surrounded by water or an ice bath, or is cooled in another manner.

The specimen to be polished (anode) should be arranged to facilitate rapid removal from the electrolyte. The electrical connection to the specimen should be simple and easily broken so that the specimen can be rinsed immediately after polishing.

The cathode should be made of a metal that is inert in the electrolyte being used. Generally, stainless steel is satisfactory for most applications.

For many applications, stirring or air agitation of the electrolyte is necessary. During electropolishing under steady-state conditions, the anodic reaction products accumulate on the surface of the polished metal. Frequently, natural diffusion and convection processes cannot remove these products from the anode surface into the bulk of the electrolyte rapidly enough, and excessive accumulation of reaction products interferes with the electropolishing process. Stirring or air agita-

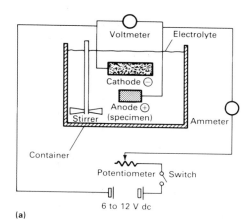

(a)

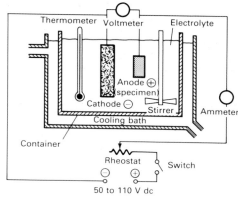

(b)

**Fig. 5** Typical electrical circuits and equipment setups used for electropolishing. (a) Potentiometric circuit (for low current densities). (b) Series circuit (for high current densities)

tion hastens the removal of these products, prevents localized heating of the surface, maintains a uniform bath temperature, and removes gas bubbles that may adhere to the surface and cause pitting. However, the use of agitation usually requires an increase in the current density to maintain a sufficiently thick polishing film.

In some applications, vibratory motion of the specimen can be substituted for stirring. In other applications, agitation of the electrolyte in the cell and simultaneous control of the electropolishing temperature can be accomplished by circulating the electrolyte with a pump and an external cooling bath or device. To prevent "furrowing" of the surface being electropolished, the movement of the electrolyte (and gas) across the metal surface should be gentle and nondirectional.

**Anode and Cathode.** Figure 5 illustrates two methods of positioning the specimen (anode) and cathode. In each arrangement, only the portion of the specimen to be polished is exposed to the electrolyte.

In Fig. 5(a), the surface to be polished is horizontal and facing upward, toward the cathode. This arrangement helps to maintain a stable layer near the surface being polished and is used when polishing occurs under a viscous layer.

In Fig. 5(b), the surface to be polished is vertical and facing toward the cathode. This arrangement is sometimes used when polishing occurs with gas evolution, because it allows the gas bubbles to escape easily. However, unless special attention is given to positioning and agitation, directional streaming can cause furrowing of the surface being polished. Reciprocating movement of the specimen helps prevent furrowing.

Pitting and furrowing are prevented in the cell arrangement shown in Fig. 4, in which gentle, nondirectional movement of the electrolyte at the surface being polished is provided by introduction of air through perforations in a horizontal cathode at the bottom of the cell. Although the electrical circuit shown in Fig. 4 (a series circuit, same as in Fig. 5b) is ordinarily used, the potentiometric circuit shown in Fig. 5(a) can also be used.

The electrical connection to the specimen is made indirectly through a metal block and a contact wire that is spot welded to the back of the specimen and the metal block before the assembly is mounted in epoxy resin or other suitable material (see detail A in Fig. 4). After mounting, a hole is drilled through the back of the mount to the metal block to permit attachment of the electrical connector wire. The indirect connection lessens the danger of loosening the bond of specimen to mount that would exist with a direct connection through a hole drilled into the specimen.

The arrangement shown in Fig. 4 is particularly well suited for electropolishing at medium to high current densities. The mount is conveniently held in an alligator clip with stainless steel extensions welded to the jaws. The clip is attached to a hook that can be

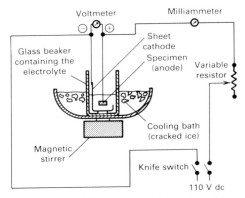

**Fig. 6** Basic laboratory setup for electropolishing and electrolytic etching

supported on a horizontal anode bar for ease of manipulation.

By placing the hook on the bar, electrical contact to the specimen is made almost simultaneously with immersion in the electrolyte. Contact is broken almost simultaneously with removal from the electrolyte when the hook is lifted from the anode bar, thus allowing immediate rinsing to prevent staining of the polished surface. A similar setup, in which the cathode is an L-shaped strip and agitation is provided by means of a magnetic stirrer below the cathode is illustrated in Fig. 6.

For electropolishing at low current densities, agitation is not ordinarily used. Any of the cell arrangements described above can be used in these applications. However, when low current densities are used, it is advantageous to place the specimen horizontally at the center of a circular, vertical-walled cell of glass or inert plastic, in which the cathode is a vertical stainless steel sheet that has been formed into a circular shape slightly smaller than the cell.

## Developing an Electropolishing Procedure

In developing a suitable procedure for electropolishing a metal or alloy, it is generally helpful to compare the position of the major component of the alloy with elements of the same general group in a periodic table and to study the phase diagram, if available, to predict the number of phases and their characteristics. Single-phase alloys generally are easy to electropolish, whereas multiphase alloys are likely to be difficult or impossible to polish with electrolytic techniques. Even minor alloying additions to a metal may significantly affect the response of the metal to polishing in a given electrolyte.

The possibility of polishing a metal and the conditions for polishing metal in a given electrolyte can sometimes be ascertained by plotting current density versus electrode potential. The curve illustrated in Fig. 2 is typical of electrolytes that polish over a very wide range or that will not polish at all. The curve depicted in Fig. 3 is characteristic of electro-

lytes that form an ionic film; polishing will occur between points C and D on this curve and is usually best near point D.

In a cell designed so that the anode is clearly visible during electrolysis, the polishing plateau can be determined by observing the anode while gradually increasing the current. For stable and reproducible results, current is passed for 30 min before recording data, and the current is increased slowly.

In working with radioactive metals, the specimen is held close to a thin, transparent window in a special cell, and the polishing action is observed using an external optical system that has a focal length of 5 mm (0.2 in.) or more, while circulating electrolyte between the specimen and the window.

After the polishing range is determined, other constants such as preparation, agitation, and time can be determined experimentally. The amount of preparation required depends on the nature of the specimen and on the results desired.

**Specimen Preparation.** Prior to electropolishing, the specimen must be ground with 600-grit abrasive paper. With some materials, such as beryllium and lithium, it may be necessary to polish to a finer finish, for example, 6-μm diamond, before beginning the electropolishing procedure.

The surface to be polished should be clean to allow uniform attack by the electrolyte. To avoid contamination with hand oil, the specimen should be handled with forceps or tongs after final preparation for electropolishing.

**Test Cells.** A simple method to determine optimum electropolishing conditions after a suitable polishing solution has been selected involves the use of test cells, as shown in Fig. 7. In Fig. 7(a), the rod anode, the 360° glass insulating cylinder surrounding it, and the 360° circular cathode rest on the bottom of the cell, and the liquid level is maintained some distance above the upper end of the cathode and the glass cylinder.

In the cell shown in Fig. 7(b), the cathode consists of two opposing circular segments. The rod anode does not extend to the bottom of the cell, and the liquid level is maintained

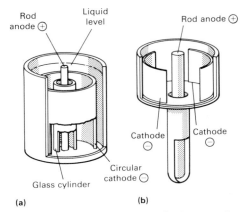

(a)                    (b)

**Fig. 7** Test cells for use in evaluating operating conditions in electropolishing over a range of anode current densities

slightly below the upper end of the anode and the two-segment cathode.

In each cell, the anode current density is greater near the liquid level and is progressively lower at greater depths. In operation, when a constant current is passed through the cell, the finish at any depth on the anode is related to the current density at that depth.

If the electrolyte is of a composition that makes it suitable for electropolishing, the optimum ranges of current density can be estimated roughly from the positions and lengths of the polished zones. Additional information can be obtained from such cells by measurements of anode potential.

The cell shown in Fig. 7(b) allows accurate temperature control and observation of the anode during the passage of current. Similar results can be obtained in a Hull cell, which is widely used for evaluating operating conditions in electroplating.

## Electrolytes

Table 1 lists the formulas of several groups of electrolytes and conditions for their use in electropolishing various metals and alloys. Table 2 summarizes the applicability of these electrolytes to electropolishing specific metals.

Generally, an electrolyte should be somewhat viscous. It must be a good solvent for the anode metal (specimen) during electrolysis conditions and should preferably not attack the anode metal when current is not flowing.

An electrolyte should contain one or more ions of large radii, such as $(PO_4)^{-3}$, $(ClO_4)^{-1}$, or $(SO_4)^{-2}$, and sometimes large organic molecules. It should be simple to mix, stable, and safe to handle; many effective electrolytes are deficient in these respects. It should function effectively at room temperature and should not be sensitive to temperature changes.

## Advantages and Limitations

When properly applied, electropolishing can be a useful tool for the metallographer and offers several advantages. For some metals, electropolishing can produce a high-quality surface finish that is better than or equivalent to the best surface finish obtained by mechanical methods. Once a procedure has been established, good results can be obtained with less operator skill than required for mechanical polishing.

A significant saving of time can be achieved if many specimens of the same material are to be polished sequentially. Electropolishing is particularly well suited to softer metals, which may be difficult to polish by mechanical methods. Scratching does not occur in electrolytic polishing. The absence of scratches is advantageous in viewing high-quality electropolished surfaces of optically active materials under polarized light.

Artifacts resulting from mechanical deformation, such as disturbed metal or mechanical twins, which are produced on the surface even by careful grinding and mechanical polishing, do not occur in electropolishing. Surfaces are completely unworked by the polishing procedure, which is particularly beneficial in low-load hardness testing, x-ray studies, and electron microscopy.

In some applications, etching can be accomplished by reducing the voltage to approximately one tenth the potential required for polishing and then continuing electrolysis for a few seconds. In general, electropolishing is frequently useful in electron microscopy, in which high resolution is important, because it can produce clean, undistorted metal surfaces.

Metallographic preparation by electropolishing is subject to several limitations, which should be recognized to prevent misapplication of the method and inappropriate results (Ref 3).

Generally, the chemicals and combinations of chemicals used in electropolishing are poisonous; many are highly flammable or potentially explosive. Only well-trained personnel who are thoroughly familiar with chemical laboratory procedures should be permitted to handle or mix the chemicals, or to operate the polishing baths (see the article "Etching" in this Volume).

The conditions and electrolytes required to obtain a satisfactorily polished surface differ for different alloys. Consequently, considerable time may be required to develop a procedure for a new alloy, if it can be developed at all. This limitation does not apply if appropriate procedures exist.

In multiphase alloys, the rates of polishing of different phases often are not the same. Polishing results depend significantly on whether the second or third phases are strongly cathodic or anodic with respect to the matrix. The matrix is dissolved preferentially if the other phases are relatively cathodic, thus causing the latter to stand in relief.

Preferential attack may also occur at the interface between two phases. These effects are most pronounced when phases other than the matrix are virtually unattacked by the polishing bath. The effects are reversed when the matrix phase is relatively cathodic.

A large number of electrolytes may be needed to polish the variety of metals encountered by a given laboratory. Plastic or metal mounting materials may react with the electrolyte.

Electropolished surfaces exhibit an undulating rather than a plane surface and, in some cases, may not be suited for examination at all magnifications. Under some conditions, furrowing and pitting may be produced. Also, edge effects limit applications involving small specimens, surface phenomena, coatings, interfaces and cracks.

Attack around nonmetallic particles and adjacent metal, voids, and various inhomogeneities may not be the same as that of the matrix, thus exaggerating the size of the voids and inclusions. Additionally, electropolished surfaces of certain materials may be passive and difficult to etch.

## Safety Precautions

Many electrolytes used for electropolishing can be dangerous if improperly handled. Although general safety precautions are discussed below, the bulk of the following discussion relates directly to the electrolyte groups listed in Table 1 (Groups I to VIII). *It is essential that the following instructions be read before any electrolyte is mixed or used.*

Mixtures of $HClO_4$ and acetic anhydride are extremely dangerous to prepare and are even more unpredictable to use. Many industrial firms and research laboratories forbid their use. Some municipalities also have ordinances prohibiting the use of such potentially explosive mixtures, which have caused fatalities and property damage in some accidents. These mixtures are highly corrosive to the skin, and the vapors of acetic anhydride can cause severe damage by inhalation. These hazards are considered sufficient reason for recommending that mixtures of $HClO_4$ and acetic anhydride not be used, despite their effectiveness as electropolishing electrolytes.

Mixtures of oxidizable organic compounds and powerful oxidizing agents are always potentially dangerous. After some use, any electrolyte will become heavily laden with ions of the metals polished. These ions may catalyze the decomposition of the electrolyte, and the metallic salts that can crystallize from some reagents may be explosive. Electrolytes must be discarded immediately after use by flushing down a chemical waste drain with a large amount of water.

Mixing, storing, and handling of electrolytes should be done using containers and equipment made of materials suitable for the chemicals used. Glass is resistant to nearly all chemicals.

Polyethylene, polypropylene, and similarly inert plastics are resistant to hydrofluoric (HF), fluosilicic ($H_2SiF_6$), and fluoboric ($HBF_4$) acids, as well as to solutions containing salts of these acids. These materials are also recommended for prolonged storage of strongly alkaline solutions and strong solutions of phosphoric acid ($H_3PO_4$), both of which attack glass (particularly ordinary grades of glass).

Electrolytes must not be allowed to become heavily laden with dissolved metals in use. They must never be allowed to become more concentrated by evaporation during storage or use.

The electrolytes listed in Table 1 are classified by chemical type (Ref 4). Their chemical components are listed in the order of mixing. Although contrary to common practice, listing in this order is done to prevent possibly dangerous mistakes. Unless other instructions are given, the electrolytes are intended to be used in the temperature range of 20 to 40 °C (65 to 100 °F). The use of a stainless

**Table 1  Electrolytes for electropolishing of various metals and alloys**

| Class | Formula | Use | Cell voltage | Time | Notes |
|---|---|---|---|---|---|
| **Group I: Electrolytes composed of HClO₄ and alcohol with or without organic additions(a)** | | | | | |
| I-1 . . . . . . . . . | 800 mL ethanol (absolute), 140 mL distilled H₂O (optional), 60 mL HClO₄ (60%) | Aluminum and aluminum alloys with less than 2% Si | 30-80 | 15-60 s | . . . |
| | | Carbon, alloy, and stainless steels | 35-65 | 15-60 s | . . . |
| | | Lead, lead-tin, lead-tin-cadmium, lead-tin-antimony | 12-35 | 15-60 s | . . . |
| | | Zinc, zinc-tin-iron, zinc-aluminum-copper | 20-60 | . . . | . . . |
| | | Magnesium and high-magnesium alloys | . . . | . . . | (b) |
| I-2 . . . . . . . . . | 800 mL ethanol (absolute), 200 mL HClO₄ (60%) | Stainless steel; aluminum | 35-80 | 15-60 s | . . . |
| I-3 . . . . . . . . . | 940 mL ethanol (absolute), 6 mL distilled H₂O, 54 mL HClO₄ (70%) | Stainless steel | 30-45 | 15-60 s | . . . |
| | | Thorium | 30-40 | 15-45 s | . . . |
| I-4 . . . . . . . . . | 700 mL ethanol (absolute), 120 mL distilled H₂O, 100 mL 2-butoxyethanol, 80 mL HClO₄ (60%) | Steel, cast iron, aluminum, aluminum alloys, nickel, tin, silver, beryllium, titanium, zirconium, uranium, heat-resistant alloys | 30-65 | 15-60 s | (c) |
| I-5 . . . . . . . . . | 700 mL ethanol (absolute), 120 mL distilled H₂O, 100 mL glycerol, 80 mL HClO₄ (60%) | Stainless, alloy, and high-speed steels; aluminum, iron, iron-silicon alloys, lead, zirconium | 15-50 | 15-60 s | (d) |
| I-6 . . . . . . . . . | 760 mL ethanol (absolute), 30 mL distilled H₂O, 190 mL ether, 20 mL HClO₄ (60%) | Aluminum, aluminum-silicon alloys, iron-silicon alloys | 35-60 | 15-60 s | (e) |
| I-7 . . . . . . . . . | 600 mL methanol (absolute), 370 mL 2-butoxyethanol, 30 mL HClO₄ (60%) | Molybdenum, titanium, zinc, zirconium, uranium-zirconium alloy | 60-150 | 5-30 s | . . . |
| I-8 . . . . . . . . . | 840 mL methanol (absolute), 4 mL distilled H₂O, 125 mL glycerol, 31 mL HClO₄ (70%) | Aluminum, aluminum-silicon alloys, iron-silicon alloys | 50-100 | 5-60 s | . . . |
| I-9 . . . . . . . . . | 590 mL methanol (absolute), 6 mL distilled H₂O, 350 mL 2-butoxyethanol, 54 mL HClO₄ (70%) | Germanium | 25-35 | 30-60 s | . . . |
| | | Titanium | 58-66 | 45 s | (f) |
| | | Vanadium | 30 | 3 s | (g) |
| | | Zirconium | 70-75 | 15 s | (h) |
| I-10 . . . . . . . . | 950 mL methanol (absolute), 15 mL HNO₃, 50 mL HClO₄ (60%) | Aluminum | 30-60 | 15-60 s | . . . |
| **Group II: Electrolytes composed of HClO₄ (60%) and glacial acetic acid** | | | | | |
| II-1 . . . . . . . . | 940 mL acetic acid, 60 mL HClO₄ | Chromium, titanium, uranium, zirconium, iron, cast iron, carbon, alloy, and stainless steels | 20-60 | 1-5 min | (j) |
| II-2 . . . . . . . . | 900 mL acetic acid, 100 mL HClO₄ | Zirconium, titanium, uranium, steels, superalloys | 12-70 | ½-2 min | . . . |
| II-3 . . . . . . . . | 800 mL acetic acid, 200 mL HClO₄ | Uranium, zirconium, titanium, aluminum, steels, superalloys | 40-100 | 1-15 min | . . . |
| II-4 . . . . . . . . | 700 mL acetic acid, 300 mL HClO₄ | Nickel, lead, lead-antimony alloys | 40-100 | 1-5 min | . . . |
| II-5 . . . . . . . . | 650 mL acetic acid, 350 mL HClO₄ | 3% silicon iron | . . . | 5 min | (k) |
| **Group III: Electrolytes composed of H₃PO₄ (85%) in water or organic solvent** | | | | | |
| III-1 . . . . . . . . | 1000 mL H₃PO₄ | Cobalt | 1.2 | 3-5 min | . . . |
| III-2 . . . . . . . . | 175 mL distilled H₂O, 825 mL H₃PO₄ | Pure copper | 1.0-1.6 | 10-40 min | (m) |
| III-3 . . . . . . . . | 300 mL H₂O, 700 mL H₃PO₄ | Stainless steel, brass, copper, and copper alloys except tin-bronze | 1.5-1.8 | 5-15 min | (m) |
| III-4 . . . . . . . . | 600 mL H₂O, 400 mL H₃PO₄ | α or α + β brass, copper-iron, copper-cobalt, cobalt, cadmium | 1-2 | 1-15 min | (n) |
| III-5 . . . . . . . . | 1000 mL H₂O, 580 g H₄P₂O₇ (pyrophosphoric acid) | Copper, copper-zinc | 1-2 | 10 min | (m) |
| III-6 . . . . . . . . | 500 mL diethylene glycol monoethyl ether, 500 mL H₃PO₄ | Steel | 5-20 | 5-15 min | (p) |
| III-7 . . . . . . . . | 200 mL H₂O, 380 mL ethanol (95%), 400 mL H₃PO₄ | Aluminum, magnesium, silver | 25-30 | 4-6 min | (q) |
| III-8 . . . . . . . . | 300 mL ethanol (absolute), 300 mL glycerol (cp), 300 mL H₃PO₄ | Uranium | . . . | . . . | . . . |
| III-9 . . . . . . . . | 500 mL ethanol (95%), 250 mL glycerol, 250 mL H₃PO₄ | Manganese, manganese-copper alloys | 18 | . . . | . . . |
| III-10 . . . . . . . | 500 mL distilled H₂O, 250 mL ethanol (95%), 250 mL H₃PO₄ | Copper and copper-based alloys | . . . | 1-5 min | . . . |
| III-11 . . . . . . . | Ethanol (absolute) to make 1000 mL of solution; 400 g H₄P₂O₇ | Stainless steel, all austenitic heat-resistant alloys | . . . | 10 min | (r) |
| III-12 . . . . . . . | 625 mL ethanol (95%), 375 mL H₃PO₄ | Magnesium-zinc | 1.5-2.5 | 3-30 min | . . . |
| III-13 . . . . . . . | 445 mL ethanol (95%), 275 mL ethylene glycol, 275 mL H₃PO₄ | Uranium | 18-20 | 5-15 min | (s) |
| **Group IV: Electrolytes composed of H₂SO₄ in water or organic solvent** | | | | | |
| IV-1 . . . . . . . . | 250 mL H₂O, 750 mL H₂SO₄ | Stainless steel | 1.5-6 | 1-2 min | . . . |
| IV-2 . . . . . . . . | 400 mL H₂O, 600 mL H₂SO₄ | Stainless steel, iron, nickel | 1.5-6 | 2-6 min | . . . |
| IV-3 . . . . . . . . | 750 mL H₂O, 250 mL H₂SO₄ | Stainless steel, iron, nickel | 1.5-6 | 2-10 min | . . . |
| | | Molybdenum | 1.5-6 | ⅓-1 min | (t) |
| IV-4 . . . . . . . . | 900 mL H₂O, 100 mL H₂SO₄ | Molybdenum | 1.5-6 | ⅓-2 min | (t) |
| IV-5 . . . . . . . . | 70 mL H₂O, 200 mL glycerol, 720 mL H₂SO₄ | Stainless steel | 1.5-6 | ½-5 min | . . . |
| IV-6 . . . . . . . . | 220 mL H₂O, 200 mL glycerol, 580 mL H₂SO₄ | Stainless steel, aluminum | 1.5-12 | 1-20 min | . . . |
| IV-7 . . . . . . . . | 875 mL methanol (absolute), 125 mL H₂SO₄ | Molybdenum | 6-18 | ½-1½ min | (u) |
| **Group V: Electrolytes composed of CrO₃ in water** | | | | | |
| V-1 . . . . . . . . . | 830 mL H₂O, 620 g CrO₃ | Stainless steel | 1.5-9 | 2-10 min | . . . |
| V-2 . . . . . . . . . | 830 mL H₂O, 170 g CrO₃ | Zinc, brass | 1.5-12 | 10-60 s | . . . |

(continued)

**Table 1**  (continued)

| Class | Formula | Use | Cell voltage | Time | Notes |
|---|---|---|---|---|---|
| **Group VI: Electrolytes composed of mixed acids or salts in water or organic solution** | | | | | |
| VI-1 . . . . . . . . | 600 mL $H_3PO_4$ (85%), 400 mL $H_2SO_4$ | Stainless steel | . . . | . . . | . . . |
| VI-2 . . . . . . . . | 150 mL $H_2O$, 300 mL $H_3PO_4$ (85%), 550 mL $H_2SO_4$ | Stainless steel | . . . | 2 min | (v) |
| VI-3 . . . . . . . . | 240 mL $H_2O$, 420 mL $H_3PO_4$ (85%), 340 mL $H_2SO_4$ | Stainless and alloy steels | . . . | 2-10 min | (w) |
| VI-4 . . . . . . . . | 330 mL $H_2O$, 550 mL $H_3PO_4$ (85%), 120 mL $H_2SO_4$ | Stainless steel | . . . | 1 min | (x) |
| VI-5 . . . . . . . . | 450 mL $H_2O$, 390 mL $H_3PO_4$ (85%), 160 mL $H_2SO_4$ | Bronze (to 9% Sn) | . . . | 1-5 min | (y) |
| VI-6 . . . . . . . . | 330 mL $H_2O$, 580 mL $H_3PO_4$ (85%), 90 mL $H_2SO_4$ | Bronze (to 6% Sn) | . . . | 1-5 min | (y) |
| VI-7 . . . . . . . . | 140 mL $H_2O$, 100 mL glycerol, 430 mL $H_3PO_4$ (85%), 330 mL $H_2SO_4$ | Steel | . . . | 1-5 min | (z) |
| VI-8 . . . . . . . . | 200 mL $H_2O$, 590 mL glycerol, 100 mL $H_3PO_4$ (85%), 110 mL $H_2SO_4$ | Stainless steel | . . . | 5 min | (aa) |
| VI-9 . . . . . . . . | 260 mL $H_2O$, 175 g $CrO_3$, 175 mL $H_3PO_4$ (85%), 580 mL $H_2SO_4$ | Stainless steel | . . . | 30 min | (bb) |
| VI-10 . . . . . . . . | 175 mL $H_2O$, 105 g $CrO_3$, 460 mL $H_3PO_4$ (85%), 390 mL $H_2SO_4$ | Stainless steel | . . . | 60 min | (cc) |
| VI-11 . . . . . . . . | 245 mL $H_2O$, 80 g $CrO_3$, 650 mL $H_3PO_4$ (85%), 130 mL $H_2SO_4$ | Stainless and alloy steels | . . . | 5-60 min | (dd) |
| VI-12 . . . . . . . . | 100 mL HF, 900 mL $H_2SO_4$ | Tantalum | . . . | 9 min | (ee) |
| VI-13 . . . . . . . . | 210 mL $H_2O$, 180 mL HF, 610 mL $H_2SO_4$ | Stainless steel | . . . | 5 min | (ff) |
| VI-14 . . . . . . . . | 800 mL $H_2O$, 100 g $CrO_3$, 46 mL $H_2SO_4$ 310 g sodium dichromate, 96 mL acetic acid (glacial) | Zinc | . . . | . . . | (gg) |
| VI-15 . . . . . . . . | 260 mL $H_2O_2$ (30%), 240 mL HF, 500 mL $H_2SO_4$ | Stainless steel | . . . | 5 min | (hh) |
| VI-16 . . . . . . . . | 520 mL $H_2O$, 80 mL HF, 400 mL $H_2SO_4$ | Stainless steel | . . . | 1/2-4 min | (jj) |
| VI-17 . . . . . . . . | 600 mL $H_2O$, 180 g $CrO_3$, 60 mL $HNO_3$, 3 mL HCl, 240 mL $H_2SO_4$ | Stainless steel | . . . | . . . | . . . |
| VI-18 . . . . . . . . | 750 mL glycerol, 125 mL acetic acid (glacial), 125 mL $HNO_3$ | Bismuth | 12 | 1-5 min | (kk) |
| VI-19 . . . . . . . . | 900 mL ethylene glycol monoethyl ether, 100 mL HCl | Magnesium | 50-60 | 10-30 s | (mm) |
| VI-20 . . . . . . . . | 685 mL methanol (absolute), 225 mL HCl, 90 mL $H_2SO_4$ | Molybdenum, sintered and cast | 19-35 | 20-35 s | (nn) |
| VI-21 . . . . . . . . | 885 mL ethanol (absolute), 100 mL $n$-butyl alcohol, 109 g $AlCl_3 \cdot 6 H_2O$ (hydrated aluminum chloride), 250 g $ZnCl_2$ (zinc chloride) (anhydrous) | Titanium | 30-60 | 1-6 min | . . . |
| VI-22 . . . . . . . . | 750 mL acetic acid (glacial), 210 mL distilled $H_2O$, 180 g $CrO_3$ | Uranium | 80 | 5-30 min | (pp) |
| VI-23 . . . . . . . . | 720 mL ethanol (95%), 90 g $AlCl_3 \cdot 6H_2O$, 225 g ZnCl (anhydrous), 120 mL distilled $H_2O$, 80 mL $n$-butyl alcohol | Pure zinc | 25-40 | 1/2-3 min | (qq) |
| VI-24 . . . . . . . . | 870 mL glycerol, 43 mL HF, 87 mL $HNO_3$ | Zirconium(h) | 9-12 | 1-10 min | (rr) |
| VI-25 . . . . . . . . | 980 mL saturated solution of KI (potassium iodide) in distilled $H_2O$, 20 mL HCl | Bismuth | 7 | 30 s | (ss) |
| **Group VII: Alkaline electrolytes** | | | | | |
| VII-1 . . . . . . . . | Water to make 1000 mL, 80 g KCN (potassium cyanide), 40 g $K_2CO_3$ (potassium carbonate), 50 g $AuCl_3$ (gold chloride) | Gold, silver | 7.5 | 2-4 min | (tt) |
| VII-2 . . . . . . . . | Water to make 1000 mL, 100 g NaCN (sodium cyanide), 100 g potassium ferricyanide | Silver | 2.5 | To 1 min | (tt) |
| VII-3 . . . . . . . . | Water to make 1000 mL, 400 g KCN, 280 g silver cyanide, 280 g $K_2CrO_7$ (potassium dichromate) | Silver | . . . | To 9 min | (uu) |
| VII-4 . . . . . . . . | Water to make 1000 mL, 160 g $Na_3PO_4 \cdot 12 H_2O$ (trisodium phosphate) | Tungsten | . . . | 10 min | (vv) |
| VII-5 . . . . . . . . | Water to make 1000 mL, 100 g NaOH | Tungsten, lead | . . . | 8-10 min | (ww) |
| VII-6 . . . . . . . . | Water to make 1000 mL, 200 g KOH | Zinc, tin | 2-6 | 15 min | (xx) |
| **Group VIII: Electrolyte composed of methanol and $HNO_3$** | | | | | |
| VIII-1 . . . . . . . | 600 mL methanol (absolute), 300 mL $HNO_3$ | Nickel, copper, zinc, Monel, brass, Nichrome, stainless steel | 40-70 | 10-60 s | (yy) |

Note: Chemical components of electrolytes are listed in the order of mixing. Except where otherwise noted, the electrolytes are intended for use at ambient temperatures, in the approximate range of 18 to 38 °C (65 to 100 °F), and with stainless steel cathodes.
(a) In electrolytes I-1 through I-6, absolute SD-3A or SD-30 ethanol can be substituted for absolute ethanol. (b) Nickel cathode. (c) One of the best electrolytes for universal use. (d) Universal electrolyte comparable to I-4. (e) Particularly good with Al-Si alloys. (f) Polish only. (g) 3-s cycles repeated at least seven times to prevent heating. (h) Polish and etch simultaneously. (j) Good general-purpose electrolyte. (k) 0.06 A/cm² (0.4 A/in.²). (m) Copper cathode. (n) Copper or stainless steel cathode. (p) 49 °C (120 °F). (q) Aluminum cathode; 38 to 43 °C (100 to 110 °F). (r) 38 °C (100 °F) plus. (s) 0.03 A/cm² (0.2 A/in.²). (t) Particularly good for sintered molybdenum; 0 to 27 °C (32 to 80 °F). (u) 0 to 27 °C (32 to 80 °F). (v) 0.3 A/cm² (1.9 A/in.²). (w) 0.1 to 0.2 A/cm² (0.65 to 1.3 A/in.²). (x) 0.05 A/cm² (0.3 A/in.²). (y) 0.1 A/cm² (0.65 A/in.²). (z) 1 to 5 A/cm² (6.5 to 32 A/in.²); 38 °C (100 °F) plus. (aa) 1 A/cm² (6.5 A/in.²); 27 to 49 °C (80 to 120 °F). (bb) 0.6 A/cm² (3.9 A/in.²); 27 to 49 °C (80 to 120 °F). (cc) 0.5 A/cm² (3.2 A/in.²); 27 to 49 °C (80 to 120 °F). (dd) 0.5 A/cm² (3.2 A/in.²); 38 to 54 °C (100 to 130 °F).
(ee) Graphite cathode: 0.1 A/cm² (0.65 A/in.²); 32 to 38 °C (90 to 100 °F). (ff) 0.5 A/cm² (3.2 A/in.²); 21 to 49 °C (70 to 120 °F). (gg) 0.002 A/cm² (0.013 A/in.²); 21 to 38 °C (70 to 100 °F). (hh) 0.5 A/cm² (3.2 A/in.²). Caution: This mixture will decompose vigorously after a short time; do not try to keep. (mm) Bath should be stirred. Cool below 2 °C (35 °F) with cracked ice. (nn) Mix slowly. Heat is developed. Avoid contamination with water. Use below 2 °C (35 °F). (pp) Chromic acid is dissolved in the water, and this solution is then added to the acetic acid. Electrolyte is used below 2 °C (35 °F). (qq) Electrolyte is used below 16 °C (60 °F). (rr) Caution: Electrolyte will decompose on standing, and is dangerous if kept too long. (ss) Polish 30 s, but allow to remain in electrolyte until brown film is dissolved. (tt) Graphite cathode. (uu) Graphite cathode; 0.003 to 0.009 A/cm² (0.02 to 0.06 A/in.²). (vv) Graphite cathode; 0.09 A/cm² (0.58 A/in.²). 38 to 49 °C (100 to 120 °F). (ww) Graphite cathode; 0.03 to 0.06 A/cm² (0.02 to 0.4 A/in.²). (xx) Copper cathode; 0.1 to 0.2 A/cm² (0.65 to 1.3 A/in.²). (yy) An extremely useful electrolyte for certain applications, but dangerous; see text.

steel cathode with these electrolytes is also presumed unless otherwise stipulated.

**Use of Perchloric Acid.** Electrolytes of Groups I and II contain $HClO_4$ because of its unique effectiveness in electropolishing many metals. No attempt should be made to store, handle, or prepare mixtures of $HClO_4$ without a thorough understanding of all the precautions that must be observed to avoid accidents.

Some highly concentrated mixtures of $HClO_4$ can be exploded by detonation; others that are not detonatable can be ignited by sparks or by general heating, and the ensuing fire may result in an explosion. Perchloric acid solutions should not be used in contact with organic materials; polyethylene, polystyrene, epoxy resins, and polyvinyl chloride are

**Table 2  Applicability of electrolytes in Table 1 to electropolishing of various metals and alloys**

| Metal | Electrolyte |
|---|---|
| Aluminum | I-1, I-2, I-4, I-5, I-6, I-8, I-10, II-3, III-7, IV-6 |
| Aluminum-silicon alloys | I-6, I-8 |
| Antimony | II-4 |
| Beryllium | I-4 |
| Bismuth | VI-18, VI-25 |
| Cadmium | III-4 |
| Cast iron | I-4, II-1 |
| Chromium | II-1, VIII-1 |
| Cobalt | I-5, III-1, III-4 |
| Copper | III-2, III-3, III-4, III-5, III-10, VIII-1 |
| Copper-nickel alloys | III-3, III-10, VIII-1 |
| Copper-tin alloys | III-10, VI-5, VI-6, VIII-1 |
| Copper-zinc alloys | III-3, III-4, III-5, III-10, V-2, VIII-1 |
| Germanium | I-9 |
| Gold | VII-1 |
| Iron, pure | I-5, II-1, IV-2, IV-3 |
| Iron-copper alloys | III-3, III-4 |
| Iron-nickel alloys | I-5, II-1, II-2, II-4, IV-3, VIII-1 |
| Iron-silicon alloys | I-5, I-6, I-8, II-5 |
| Lead | I-1, I-5, II-4, VII-5 |
| Magnesium | I-1, III-7, III-12, VI-19 |
| Manganese | III-9 |
| Molybdenum | I-7, IV-3, IV-4, IV-7, VI-20 |
| Nickel | I-4, II-4, IV-2, VII-1 |
| Nickel-chromium alloys | II-4, VIII-1 |
| Silver | I-4, III-7, VII-1, VII-2, VII-3 |
| Steel: austenitic stainless and superalloys | I-1, I-2, I-3, I-4, I-5, II-1, II-2, II-3, III-3, III-6, III-11, IV-1, IV-2, IV-3, IV-5, V-6, V-1, VI-1, VI-2, VI-3, VI-4, VI-7, VI-8, VI-9, VI-10, VI-11, VI-13, VI-15, VI-16, VI-17, VIII-1 |
| Steel: carbon and alloy | I-1, I-4, I-5, II-1, II-2, II-3, III-6, VI-3, VI-7, VI-11 |
| Tantalum | VI-12 |
| Thorium | I-3 |
| Tin | I-4, VI-5, VI-6, VII-6 |
| Titanium | I-4, I-7, I-9, II-1, II-2, II-3, VI-21 |
| Tungsten | VII-4, VII-5 |
| Uranium | I-4, I-7, II-1, II-2, II-3, III-8, III-13, VI-22 |
| Vanadium | I-9 |
| Zinc | I-1, I-5, III-12, VI-2, VI-14, VI-23, VII-6, VII-1 |
| Zirconium | I-4, I-5, I-7, I-9, II-1, II-2, II-3, VI-24 |

among the mounting materials considered safe for use with $HClO_4$. For a detailed discussion of the hazards of $HClO_4$ solutions and the precautions that must be observed in their use, see Ref 4 and 5.

**Group I electrolytes** (composed of $HClO_4$ and alcohol with or without organic additions) are believed to be safe to mix and use, provided the following precautions are observed:

- The baths should be made up only in small quantities and should be stored in glass-stoppered bottles that are filled completely with the electrolyte.
- Any evaporated solvents should be promptly replaced by refilling the bottle.

- Spent or exhausted baths should be promptly discarded.
- No departure should be allowed from the prescribed formula, the method of mixing, or the strength of the acid used.
- The electrolytes should always be protected from heat or fire.

**Group II electrolytes** are composed of $HClO_4$ and glacial acetic acid in varying proportions. Very little heat is developed when $HClO_4$ is mixed with glacial acetic acid. In mixing, $HClO_4$ should be added to the acetic acid while stirring. Although these mixtures are considered safe to mix and use, great care should be exercised in their use. Temperatures should not exceed 30 °C (85 °F).

These electrolytes are flammable and must be guarded against fire or the evaporation of the acetic acid. Plastic parts are likely to be damaged quickly by exposure to such mixtures.

**Group III electrolytes** (composed of $H_3PO_4$ in water or organic solvent) are generally quite easy to prepare. In mixing, the acid must be slowly poured into the water or solvent with constant stirring to prevent the formation of a heavy layer of acid at the bottom of the vessel. Pyrophosphoric acid reacts vigorously when dissolved in water. It hydrolyzes slowly in water at room temperature and rapidly in hot water to form ortho-$H_3PO_4$.

**Group IV electrolyes** are composed of $H_2SO_4$ in water or organic solvent. Dilution of $H_2SO_4$ with water is somewhat difficult, because it is accompanied by an extremely exothermic reaction. The acid must always be poured into the water slowly and with constant stirring to prevent violent boiling. Great care should be taken to prevent spattering.

Mixing should be done in an exhaust hood, and a face shield and protective laboratory apron should be worn. Even dilute solutions of $H_2SO_4$ strongly attack the skin or clothing. Such solutions are also very hygroscopic.

These solutions vigorously attack most plastics; only certain mounting materials, such as polyvinyl chloride, provide satisfactory resistance. Mixtures of $H_2SO_4$ with other inorganic acids are generally more useful as electrolytes.

**Group V electrolytes** are composed of chromic acid in water*. Dissolving of crystalline chromic acid or chromium trioxide ($CrO_3$) in water is not hazardous, because very little heat is developed. Chromic acid, however, is a powerful oxidant and, under certain conditions, reacts violently with organic matter or other reducing substances.

Chromic acid generally is dangerous and may be incendiary in the presence of oxidizable materials. It cannot be safely mixed with most organic liquids. It generally can be mixed with saturated organic acids. Chromic

*Chromic acid ($H_2CrO_4$) exists only in solution. It is the hydrate of chromium trioxide ($CrO_3$).

acid solutions cannot be used in contact with plastic parts without eventually destroying them. Care should be taken to prevent contact of these solutions with the skin, as repeated exposure to even dilute solutions of $CrO_3$ or chromates in acidic solutions causes persistent and painful ulcers that are difficult to heal.

**Group VI electrolytes** (mixed acids or salts in water or organic solutions) are safe to mix and use, provided the mixing is done carefully and in the specified sequence. In all cases, the acid must be added to the solvent slowly and with constant stirring. If $H_2SO_4$ is contained in the formula, it should be added last and with extreme care, after cooling the initially prepared mixture to room temperature if necessary.

If HF or fluorides are contained in the electrolyte formula, the vessels used should be made of polyethylene or other material that is resistant to HF. Particular care should be taken to avoid skin contact with acid fluorides; exposure, which may pass unnoticed at the time of occurrence, may result in serious burns.

In mixing electrolytes containing anhydrous aluminum chloride ($AlCl_3$), extreme care must be exercised. The reaction between this compound and water is almost explosive. Chromic acid cannot be safely mixed with most organic liquids, but can be mixed with saturated organic acids. Care should be taken to prevent contact with the skin.

**Group VII (alkaline) electrolytes** are classified into two general groups: those that contain cyanide and those that do not. Use of cyanide by untrained personnel is extremely dangerous. Cyanides are among the most rapid acting and most potent poisons encountered in the laboratory, and lethal concentrations of hydrogen cyanide gas may not be detected readily by odor or irritant action. Cyanide is so quick-acting and deadly that the administration of an antidote is usually ineffective.

Extreme care must be taken that neither a droplet of the solution nor a crystal of the salt is left where it can be accidentally picked up and carried to the mouth. If any spillage occurs, as much as possible should be mopped up with a sponge and water. The remainder can then be destroyed by washing the area with very dilute nitric acid ($HNO_3$).

Solutions of the alkali hydroxides are very useful for the polishing of certain amphoteric metals, such as lead, tin, tungsten, and zinc. The attack of these solutions on the skin is drastic, so great care should be exercised in their use.

These solutions evolve considerable amounts of heat in contact with water and should be dissolved with constant stirring, using cooling and adding the hydroxide in small portions when preparing concentrated solutions. Incomplete mixing can cause layering, with danger of a delayed violent reaction.

**Group VIII electrolyte** is a mixture of methanol and $HNO_3$. With careful handling,

$HNO_3$ can be safely mixed with methanol. The acid should be added gradually to the alcohol, with constant stirring. Nitric acid cannot be safely mixed with ethanol or higher alcohols, except in solutions not stronger than about 5 vol% $HNO_3$.

If pure chemicals are used, the mixture of $HNO_3$ and methanol is quite stable, provided it is never heated or confined in any way. Consequently, it must not be stored in a closed container.

Under certain conditions, extremely unstable or explosive nitro compounds, azides, or fulminates can be formed. The spontaneous decomposition of the mixture can also be catalyzed by impurities or heat. The electrolyte should be discarded immediately after use.

For some applications, Group VIII electrolyte is extremely useful, but because of its dangerous nature, it should be used only when necessary.

## Local Electropolishing

Special techniques for local polishing extend the application of electropolishing from use on conventional small metallographic specimens to the examination of selected regions on large objects, and to almost any metal. Several types of portable cathode probes for *in situ* local electropolishing (complete with current sources and controls) are available commercially. These devices vary in design and complexity.

In one type of unit, electrolyte is circulated from an external container through a replaceable pencil-type plastic polishing chamber that can be clamped against the area (about 7 mm, or ¼ in., in diameter) to be polished. Both conventional and proprietary electrolytes are used, and polishing is conveniently followed by electrolytic etching at greatly reduced current, or by chemical etching where needed.

A typical simple unit for local electropolishing is the portable, handheld tampon-type probe (Fig. 8). In this application, it is used to polish a recessed portion of a large roll. The probe consists of an austenitic stainless steel head (cathode) attached to the end of an electrically insulating plastic body.

The stainless steel head is cooled by internal circulation of water to maintain the tip and the electrolyte at a predetermined optimum temperature for electropolishing, usually between 0 and 10 °C (32 and 50 °F). The head is covered by a removable sheath made of an inner layer of fiberglass and an outer layer of chemically resistant woven synthetic fabric. The sheath is flexible, electrically insulating, and spongy enough to retain the electrolyte.

In use, a small amount of electrolyte is retained by capillarity between the specimen and the cathode by keeping the sheath saturated with electrolyte. The sheath tip is held at about 1.6 mm (¹⁄₁₆ in.) from the specimen (see section A-A in Fig. 8).

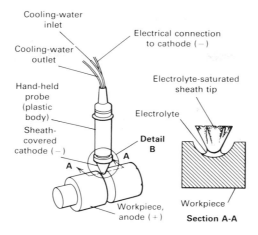

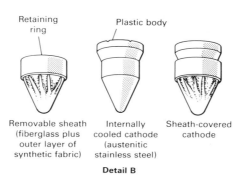

**Fig. 8** Arrangement for nondestructive local electropolishing on a recessed portion of a large object, using a small-radius tampon-type portable probe. Cathode shown has a radius of about 1.6 mm (¹⁄₁₆ in.); for polishing flat surfaces or larger areas, a cathode with a more rounded tip (radius of about 9.5 mm, or ³⁄₈ in.) is used.

Conical stainless steel cathodes with tips having radii of about 9.5 and 1.6 mm (³⁄₈ and ¹⁄₁₆ in.) are available; the sharper tip is used where access is difficult and where high current densities are needed. The diameter of the spot on the specimen covered by the drop of electrolyte is about 9.5 mm (³⁄₈ in.) when the sharper tip is used and about 19 mm (¾ in.) with the more rounded tip.

The electrolyte held by the sheath is renewed about once a minute by dipping the sheath in a beaker of electrolyte. To polish larger areas, the probe is moved in a circular pattern and back and forth, as desired. Polishing usually takes about 3 min. The sheath

is removed and washed after each use and can be used 20 to 50 times.

**Specimen Preparation.** Before electropolishing, specimen surfaces usually are mechanically ground with 220-, 320-, 400-, and 600-grit papers in sequence and then polished with 6- and 1-μm diamond paste. A portable mechanical grinding/polishing machine is well suited for this purpose.

**Electrolytes and Recommended Voltages.** Not all conventional electrolytes are suitable for local electropolishing by the tampon method, and special electrolytes are available for this purpose. Recommended electrolytes and voltages for polishing various metals are listed in Table 3.

**Examination.** After polishing, the surface can be observed under a metallographic microscope. However, the range of the technique can be extended considerably by the use of plastic replicas.

After removal, the replica can be examined by transmission in an ordinary microscope, by reflection in a metallographic microscope, or in an electron microscope after coating with carbon and metal (two-stage replica).

**Advantages and Applications.** The polishing current used is usually lower than that used in a conventional cell. Convex and concave surfaces with small radii can be examined, and voltage and current density can be controlled accurately.

With the aid of replication techniques, the fine structure on large objects or parts for which removal of a conventional specimen would be costly or impractical can be examined with an optical or electron microscope. The surface changes during fatigue of parts in service can be followed, and structures of highly radioactive specimens can be examined (with special precautions).

The surface macrostructure, microstructure, and submicrostructure of parts as large as a ship propeller and a crankshaft and a connecting rod of a diesel engine have been inspected during manufacture, in service, and after damage. The tampon method can also be used for laboratory metallographic work and is particularly useful for examining thin sheets and tubes.

Another use has been the study of crack growth in fatigue and fracture toughness specimens—polishing areas about 50 by 125

**Table 3 Electrolytes and voltages for tampon-type local electropolishing of various metals**

| Electrolyte composition | Metal | Voltage |
|---|---|---|
| 9 mL HClO₄ (60%), 91 mL butyl cellosolve | Steel, iron, and iron-base alloys | 35-40 |
| | Aluminum and aluminum alloys | 30-45 |
| | Beryllium and beryllium alloys | 43-46 |
| 10 mL HClO₄ (60%), 45 mL acetic acid (glacial), 45 mL butyl cellosolve | Steel | 30-35 |
| | Chromium-base alloys | 32-37 |
| | Nickel and nickel-base alloys | 30-40 |
| | Cobalt-base alloys | 30-60 |
| 54 mL H₃PO₄ (85%), 22 mL ethanol (absolute), 3 mL H₂O, 21 mL butyl cellosolve | Copper and copper alloys | 4-6 |
| 11 mL HClO₄ (60%), 65 mL methanol (absolute), 24 mL butyl cellosolve | Titanium alloys | 26-28 |

mm (2 by 5 in.) to measure crack length and optically examining deformation markings related to the plastic zone at the tip of a crack. In addition, longitudinal sections of fatigue and fracture toughness specimens have been locally electropolished for measurement of plastic zone sizes by microhardness indentations, using special edge-retention techniques. The equipment, procedures, and applications of local electropolishing by the tampon technique are discussed in Ref 7 and 8.

## Electrolytic Etching

Immediately after an electropolishing operation is completed, electrolytic etching can be accomplished in some applications by reducing the voltage to approximately one tenth the potential required for electropolishing and then continuing electrolysis for a few seconds. For more information on the procedures, apparatus, and applications of electrolytic etching, see the article "Etching" in this Volume and Ref 5 and 6. Specific applications of electrolytic etching are also described in the Section "Metallographic Techniques and Microstructures: Specific Metals and Alloys." Information on anodizing, an electrolytic etch process for depositing an oxide film on a metal surface, and electrolytic-potentiostatic etching can be found in the article "Color Metallography" in this Volume.

### REFERENCES

1. P.A. Jacquet, Electrolytic Polishing of Metallic Surfaces, *Metal Finishing*, May 1949, p 48-54; June 1949, p 83-92; July 1949, p 58-64; Sept 1949, p 60-67; Oct 1949, p 68-73; Jan 1950, p 56-62; Feb 1950, p 55-62

2. P.V. Schigolev, *Electrolytic and Chemical Polishing of Metals*, Freund, Holon, Israel, 1970

3. L.E. Samuels, "A Critical Comparison Between Mechanical and Electrolytic Methods of Metallographic Polishing," *Metallurgia*, Vol 66 (No. 396), 1962, p 187-199

4. R.L. Anderson, "Electrolytic Polishing of Metallographic Specimens," Westinghouse Research Laboratories, Research Report 60-94402-11-R2, April 20, 1955

5. G.F. Vander Voort, *Metallography: Principles and Practice*, McGraw-Hill, 1984

6. G. Petzow, *Metallographic Etching*, American Society for Metals, 1978

7. C. Bathias and R.M.N. Pelloux, Electropolishing System Ideal for Small Areas of Large Structures, *Met. Prog.*, Aug 1972, p 69

8. W.J.McG. Tegart, *The Electrolytic and Chemical Polishing of Metals in Research and Industry*, 2nd ed., Pergamon Press, 1959

# Etching*

By G. Petzow
Director, College for Metallography
Max-Planck-Institut für Metallforschung
Institut für Werkstoffwissenschaften

and

G. Elssner
Senior Scientist
Max-Planck-Institut für Metallforschung
Institut für Werkstoffwissenschaften

ETCHING is used in metallography primarily to reveal the microstructure of a specimen under the optical (light) microscope. A specimen suitable for etching must include a carefully polished plane area of the material free of changes caused by surface deformation, flowed materials (smears), pullout, and scratches. The edges of the specimens often must be preserved.

Although some information may be obtained from as-polished specimens, the microstructure is usually visible only after etching. Only features that exhibit a 10% or greater difference in reflectivity can be viewed without etching. This is true of microstructural features with strong color differences or with large differences in hardness that cause relief formation. Crack, pores, pits, and nonmetallic inclusions may be observed in the as-polished condition.

A polished specimen frequently will not exhibit its microstructure, because light is uniformly reflected. The eye cannot discern small differences in reflectivity; therefore, image contrast must be produced. Although this has become known as etching, it does not always refer to the selective chemical dissolution of various structural features. Metallographic contrasting methods include electrochemical, optical, and physical etching techniques. These can be subdivided into methods based on processes that alter the surface or leave it in intact, as discussed in the section "Methods of Metallographic Etching" in this article. Details of etching to specific aspects of structure are also discussed, and attention is given to some general principles. This article is also supplemented by two appendices (see "Appendix I: Magnetic Etching" and "Appendix II: Procedures and Precautions for the Preparation and Handling of Etchants").

This article primarily discusses etching in conjunction with optical examination, although polished and etched sections are increasingly examined using the scanning electron microscope with magnifications between those of the optical and transmission electron microscopes. For scanning electron microscopy (SEM), polished specimens are electrochemically etched as for optical examination. However, the depth of etching will generally be quite different, depending on the microstructural features to be examined and the large depth of field characterizing the scanning electron microscope. Fine microstructures from polished surfaces can often be contrasted in secondary electron images when they are selectively coated with chemical layers or when the surface is uniformly coated with a thin physically deposited film. For additional information, see the article "Scanning Electron Microscopy" in this Volume.

## Etching Nomenclature

The most commonly used metallographic etching terms can be classified on the basis of distinctive features. Optical, electrochemical, and physical etching may be differentiated by kinetic phenomena occurring at the specimen surface. Further distinctions are changes in microsection surface, such as dissolution and precipitation etching; the state of aggregation of etchant, for example, wet and dry etching; etching conditions, such as time and temperature; magnifications used; etching methods and techniques; and etching phenomena dependent on microstructure. Terms are often used that refer to the major component of the etchant, for example, dilute nitric acid, aqua regia, and sodium thiosulfate; to the originator of the etchant, such as Vilella, Murakami,

and Beraha; or to alloys of chief constituents for which the etchant is intended, for example, carbide, phosphide, and steel etchant.

Several terms may apply to the same phenomenon, which can be named according to different viewpoints, without converse limitation or exclusion of notation. For example, steels may be etched chemically or electrochemically. The microstructure may be revealed by dissolution or precipitation phenomena; it may display distinct grain boundaries and/or colored grains, microstructures and/or macrostructures. Combinations of etching procedures may be used, usually in increasing severity. Therefore, steel etching can be accomplished by practically any of the etching methods, using one of the many suitable etchants under one of the many suitable conditions. All have one ultimate goal: to produce a structure with sufficient contrast to delineate as much detail as possible. The most commonly used etching terms are explained in the "Terms and Definitions" section in this Volume.

## Methods of Metallographic Etching

The metallographic etching procedures for achieving contrast can be classified as nondestructive techniques, which do not alter the surface of the microsection, and destructive methods, which induce surface changes. Both methods will be discussed.

### Nondestructive Etching

Nondestructive metallographic etching encompasses optical etching and the development of structural contrast by interference layers physically deposited on the surfaces of polished specimens.

---

*This article is a revision of parts of Chapter 1 of *Metallographic Etching* by G. Petzow, American Society for Metals, 1978. The section on optical etching has been expanded.

**Optical Etching.** Special illumination techniques used in reflected light microscopy can be applied to reveal details of the microstructure even in the as-polished condition. These optical etching techniques are dark-field illumination, polarized light microscopy, phase contrast microscopy, and differential interference contrast, all of which use the Köhler illumination principle known from the most common bright-field illumination mode.

The Köhler principle (Fig. 1) provides the uniform illumination of the microsection necessary for obtaining optimum contrast by optical etching. The collector lens forms an image of the light source at the first condenser lens or at the illumination condenser aperture. The second condenser lens reproduces the image of the light source in the back focal plane of the objective lens after reflection of the light at the reflector (plane glass, half-silvered mirror, or prism). Therefore, the surface of the specimen is uniformly illuminated. The condenser lenses and the objective form an image of the radiant field stop in the plane of the specimen surface.

The illumination modes for optical etching are available in many commercially produced metallurgical microscopes. The mode often may be put into operation with a few simple manipulations; in other cases, accessories must be added. Illumination modes and their microscopic techniques are discussed in the article "Optical Microscopy" in this Volume.

**Dark-Field Illumination.** If the difference between the angle of incidence and half the aperture of the cone of light is larger than half the aperture angle of the objective, no regularly reflected light passes through the objective. This is realized in dark-field illumination (Fig. 2). Only those light rays deflected by diffuse scattering from their original direction toward the optical axis of the microscope are used for image formation. Therefore, surface regions perpendicular to the optical axis will appear dark, and angled surfaces will appear light. Dark-field illumination produces contrast completely reversed from that obtained using bright-field illumination.

Optical etching by dark-field illumination is applied to reveal cracks, pores, voids, and inclusions. Nonmetallic inclusions often undergo an intensive brightening by dark-field illumination. The surface quality of polished microsections can also be controlled using this method, because even very fine scratches and indications of relief formation are revealed.

**Polarized Light.** The basic arrangement for optical etching by polarized light is shown in Fig. 3. The incident light on the specimen is plane polarized by placing a polarizer in front of the condenser lens. The reflected light is analyzed by a polarizing unit placed behind the eyepiece of the microscope. This analyzer is normally in a crossed relationship regarding the polarizer, with the plane of polarization of the analyzer perpendicular to that of the polarizer.

Application of this optical etching technique is based on the fact that optically anisotropic metals and phases reflect plane-polarized light as elliptically polarized light with a rotation of the plane of polarization. However, plane-polarized light reflected from the surface of an optically isotropic cubic metal remains unchanged if it strikes at normal incidence. Under this condition, as-polished cubic metals will appear uniformly dark under crossed polars, because an analyzer in the crossed position will extinguish the unchanged reflected beam. By contrast, anisotropic metals and phases react to polarized light and exhibit a grain contrast effect under crossed polars as a variation in brightness and color.

Examination under polarized light requires well-polished microsections, because surface irregularities, smudges, and surface layers influence the state of polarization and may suppress anisotropic effects. Chemical and electrolytic polishing, because they avoid plastic deformation of the surface regions, are more successful than mechanical polishing.

Optical etching by polarized light is applied to anisotropic metals and to metal alloys containing anisotropic phases. Anisotropic metals include:

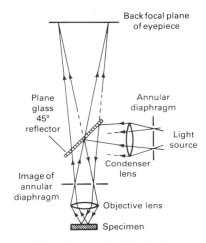

**Fig. 2** Principles of dark-field illumination. Basic components of an opaque-stop microscope

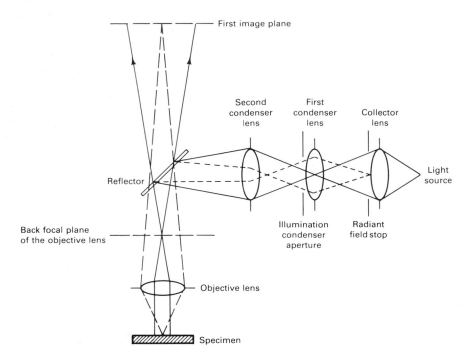

**Fig. 1** The Köhler illumination principle in incident light microscopy

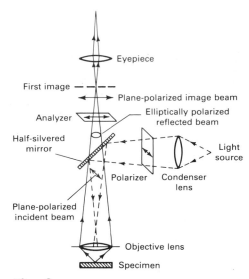

**Fig. 3** Principles of polarized light microscopy

- Beryllium*
- Bismuth
- Cadmium
- Magnesium*
- Antimony
- Tin*
- α-Titanium*
- α-Uranium*
- Zinc*
- α-Zirconium*

Polarized light is used primarily for revealing grain structure (Fig. 4) and for distinguishing and identifying phases in multiphase alloys. Other uses include detecting preferred orientation in polycrystalline materials and identifying nonmetallic anisotropic inclusions in optically isotropic metal-matrix materials.

Anisotropic surface layers produced by chemical etching or by anodic oxidation of isotropic metals and metal alloys provide a stronger grain contrast when polarized light is used. For anisotropic material, an increase in grain contrast is observed when the surface of the polished microsection is coated with interference layers before examination under polarized light. A special application is the examination of polished cross sections of transparent resin, glass, or ceramic layers. Under polarized light, the inherent colors of these layers can be determined, and cracks or other flaws are revealed.

**Phase Contrast.** Slight differences in height on polished microsections are invisible in bright-field illumination, because they produce only phase differences between the reflected light waves. Optical etching using the phase-contrast technique transforms these phase differences into detectable variations in brightness. To achieve phase contrast, an angular disk is inserted at the front focal plane of the condenser lens, and a transparent phase plate of suitable size is placed in the back focal plane of the objective, as shown in Fig. 5. Depending on the type of transparent

*Asterisk indicates that an article on metallographic techniques and microstructures for that particular metal system can be found in this Volume.

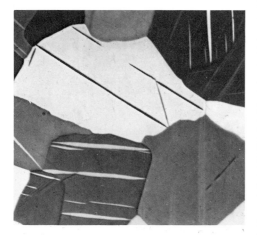

**Fig. 4** Grains and deformation twins revealed by polarized light on an as-polished section of cast bismuth. 50×

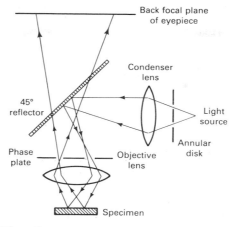

**Fig. 5** Principles of phase contrast microscopy

phase plate used, positive or negative phase contrast results. In positive phase contrast, higher areas of the specimen appear bright, and depressions dark. In negative phase contrast, lower areas on the specimen are brighter, and higher areas are darker than the background. Minimal differences in height of 1 to 5 nm (10 to 50 Å) are disclosed using this method. The optimum range of differences in surface level is approximately 20 to 50 nm (200 to 500 Å).

The phase-contrast technique can be applied to reveal the microstructure of metals and alloys after polishing or light etching of the microsections. Examples are the identification of carbide and σ phase in ferritic chromium steel and the identification of σ phase in austenite. Other applications of phase-contrast microscopy include the study of cleavage surfaces and the observation of twins and slip lines. Phase contrast is also useful as an optical etching method in high-temperature (hot-stage) microscopy.

**Differential Interference Contrast.** Among the various techniques of interference contrast microscopy, differential interference contrast after Nomarski has found broad application in metallography. The basic arrangement for this optical etching method is shown in Fig. 6. A ray of light emitted from the light source is linearly polarized after it passes through the polarizer. It then enters the Nomarski biprism (Wollaston prism), which consists of two optically uniaxially doubly refracting crystals and is divided into two rays of linearly polarized light. The planes of vibration of these rays are perpendicular to each other. Upon passing through the objective, the rays become parallel and impinge on the specimen. After reflection from the specimen surface, they are recombined by the biprism. Interference is produced when these recombined rays pass through the analyzer.

As with normal polarized light microscopy, the analyzer is in a crossed relationship with respect to the polarizer. Phase differences resulting from the two spatially separated beams reflecting from the specimen are due

to differences in height of the surface relief, which are modified by the optical properties of the specimen. These phase differences cause the light-dark or color interference contrast. Lateral displacement of the biprism allows an additional phase difference to be superimposed that varies color contrast. The achievable contrast depends on the local gradient of the phase difference. Therefore, this type of contrast is termed differential interference contrast. Images produced using this optical etching technique are characterized by their three-dimensional appearance, as illustrated in Fig. 7.

Differential interference contrast can be used to reveal phases of different hardness in polished microsections of metal alloys, layered materials, and materials joints. Good results have been obtained in visualizing carbide particles in roller bearing and high-speed steels. A special field of application is the study of coherent phase transformations, which produce surface reliefs. Surface and subsurface defects of thin films evaporated or sputtered on metallic or nonmetallic substrates are also detectable using differential interference contrast. See the article "Color Metallography" in this Volume for additional information on the advantages and applications of differential interference contrast.

**Contrasting by Interference Layers.** The method of revealing the microstructure with the aid of physically deposited interference layers (films) is based on an optical-contrast mechanism without chemical or morphological alteration of the specimen surface. The specimen is coated with a transparent layer whose thickness is small compared to the resolving power of the optical microscope. In interference layer microscopy, light that is incident on the deposited film is reflected at the air/layer and layer/specimen interfaces (Fig. 8). Phases with different optical constants appear in various degrees of brightness and colors. The color of a phase is determined by its optical constants and by the thickness and optical constants of the interference layer.

For contrasting by interference layers, reactively sputtered and vapor-deposited films are used. Both of these processes are explicated in the article "Color Metallography" in this Volume. A commercially available con-

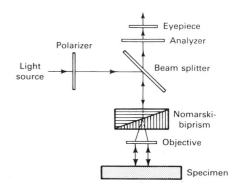

**Fig. 6** Principles of differential interference contrast after Nomarski

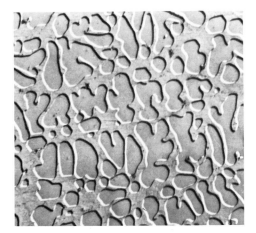

**Fig. 7** Differential interference contrast after Nomarski showing the two-phase structure of a U-33Al-25Co (at.%) alloy. Electrolytically etched. 250×

trasting chamber greatly simplifies determination of the optimum contrasting conditions, because the results of reactive sputtering can be directly observed by placing the coated specimen under a microscope without removing the specimen from the chamber (see Fig. 9). The chamber consists of an atomizer with interchangeable cathodes, a high-voltage supply, and an electron gun to ionize the reactive gas (oxygen).

The most frequently used cathode materials are iron, lead, and platinum, although gold, copper, indium, nickel, and palladium have also been used. The oxide layers formed by reactive sputtering of these metals have refractive indices, $n_s$, of 1.8 to 2.8 and absorption coefficients, $k_s$, of 0.01 to 0.5. The values of the optical constants are a function of the light wavelength $\lambda$. The composition of the reactively sputtered interference layers is determined only by the cathode material and the reactive gas. The vapor deposition of interference layers is carried out in a vacuum at approximately $10^{-3}$ Pa ($10^{-5}$ torr). Commonly used evaporated layer materials are zinc telluride ($n_s = 3.25$, $k_s = 0.4$ at $\lambda = 550$ nm, or 5500 Å) and the nonabsorbing materials zinc selenide ($n_s = 2.65$ at $\lambda = 550$ nm, or

5500 Å) and zinc sulfide ($n_s = 2.36$ at $\lambda = 550$ nm, or 5500 Å).

In interference layer metallography, special attention must be paid to the preparation of the polished microsection. The reproducibility of the results can be guaranteed only if the surface quality of the specimen is maintained. Contrasting by physically deposited interference layers is applied to various metal alloys, composite materials, coatings, and joined materials. For example, good contrast is obtained for aluminum alloys, high-temperature nickel and cobalt alloys, cemented carbides, plasma-sprayed layers, brazed joints, and sintered metals.

Typical results of contrasting by interference layers are illustrated in Fig. 10; four phases can be differentiated on the polished microsection of a cast tin-silver-copper alloy coated with a platinum oxide layer. If the contrast requirements are given, the optimum optical constants of the coating materials can be calculated from the optical constants of the phases present. However, contrasting calculations are often empirically or semiempirically formulated, because of the lack of knowledge of the optical constants of the phases. Measurement of the missing values is hampered because the composition of the phases changes with heat treatment and specimen composition, with the optical constants varying accordingly.

Contrasting by physically deposited interference layers is particularly useful in quantitative metallography, because the size and shape of the different phases can be reproduced more accurately than is possible using the destructive physical and chemical etching techniques described below. Additional information on contrasting by physically deposited interference layers can be found in Ref 1 to 3.

## Destructive Etching

The methods of destructive etching can be classified as electrochemical and physical etching. Of the two methods, the classical electrochemical etching procedures, including conventional etching, are utilized more fre-

quently. Physical etching methods are used primarily when other techniques fail.

**Electrochemical (Chemical) Etching.** During the electrochemical etching of metallic specimens, reduction (cathodic reactions) and oxidation (anodic reactions) take place. All metals contacting the etching solutions tend to become ionized by releasing electrons. The extent of this reaction can be recorded by measuring the electrochemical potential. This is performed by comparing the potential of metal versus the standard potential of a reference electrode. The tabulation of various metals results in the electromotive series of elements: $Li^+$, $Na^+$, $K^+$, $Ca^{++}$, $Ba^{++}$, $Be^{++}$, $Mg^{++}$, $Al^{+++}$, $Mn^{++}$, $Zn^{++}$, $Cr^{+++}$, $Cd^{++}$, $Ti^+$, $Co^{++}$, $Ni^{++}$, $Pb^{++}$, $Fe^{+++}$, $H^+$, $Sn^{++++}$, $Sb^{+++}$, $Bi^{+++}$, $As^{+++}$, $Cu^{++}$, $Ag^+$, $Mg^{++}$, $Au^{+++}$, $Pt^{+++}$.

The elements are listed in decreasing electroaffinity. Acids attack all elements preceding hydrogen ($H_2$) as it evolves. All elements following hydrogen cannot be attacked without the addition of an oxidizing agent. Therefore, microstructural elements of different electrochemical potential are attacked at varying rates, producing differential etching, which results in microstructural contrast.

Electrochemical etching can be considered "forced corrosion." The difference in potential of the microstructural elements causes a subdivision into a network of miniature cells consisting of small, adjoining anodic and cathodic regions. These local elements cannot originate from differences in phase composition only, but also must derive from irregularities in the crystal as present, for example, at grain boundaries, as well as from other inhomogeneities such as:

- Inhomogeneities resulting from deformation (deformed zones), which are less resistant to attack than undeformed material
- Unevenness in the formation of oxidation layers (regions free of oxides are preferentially etched)
- Concentration fluctuation in the electrolyte (low concentration is less resistant)

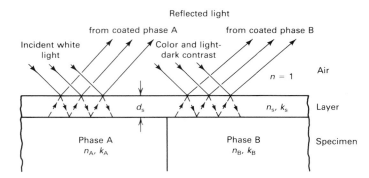

**Fig. 8** The function of a physically deposited interference layer. Contrast between phase A and B is achieved by optimizing the optical constants ($n_s$, $k_s$) of the layer with respect to the optical constants of the phases ($n_A$, $k_A$, $n_B$, $k_B$) and adjusting the layer thickness $d_s$.

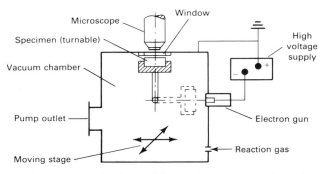

**Fig. 9** Gas contrasting chamber used for reactive sputtering and optical examination of interference layers on polished specimens. The results of the reactive sputtering process can be monitored through the viewing window.

- Differences in electrolyte velocity (higher circulation rates reduce resistance to attack)
- Differences in the oxygen content of the electrolyte (aerated solutions are more resistant)
- Differences in the illumination intensity, which can initiate differences in potential

Because of differences in potential among microstructural features, dissolution of the surface proceeds at various rates, producing contrast.

*Precipitation (Deposit) Etching.* Contrast can also originate from layers formed simultaneously with material dissolution. In precipitation etching, the material is dissolved at the surface; it then reacts with certain components of the etchant to form insoluble compounds. These compounds precipitate selectively on the surface, causing interference

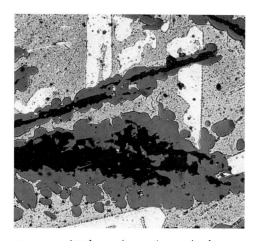

**Fig. 10** Interference-layer micrograph of a cast Sn-18Ag-15Cu alloy. Polished specimen coated with a platinum oxide layer by reactive sputtering. Structure consists of Ag₃Sn (white), Sn (light gray), Cu₆Sn₅ (medium gray), and Cu₃Sn (dark gray). 300×

colors or heavy layers of an inherent color. Additional information on precipitation etching can be found in Ref 4.

*Heat Tinting.* Oxide films can be formed by heat tinting. The polished specimen is heated in an oxidizing atmosphere. Coloration of the surface takes place at different rates according to the reaction characteristics of different microstructural elements under the given conditions of atmosphere and temperature. The observed interference colors allow the differentiation of phases and grains. Additional information on heat tinting can be found in the article "Color Metallography" in this Volume.

*Chemical etching* is the oldest and most commonly applied technique for producing microstructural contrast. In this technique, the etchant reacts with the specimen without the use of an external current supply. Etching proceeds by selective dissolution according to the electrochemical characteristics of the microstructural constituents. The articles in the Section "Metallographic Techniques and Microstructures: Specific Metals and Alloys" in this Volume provide detailed information on selection and uses of various chemical etchants.

*Electrolytic Etching.* In electrolytic (anodic) etching, electrical potential is applied to the specimen using an external circuit. Figure 11 shows a typical setup consisting of the specimen (anode) and its counterelectrode (cathode) immersed in an electrolyte (etchant). During electrolytic etching, positive metal ions leave the specimen surface and diffuse into the electrolyte; an equivalent number of electrons remain in the material. This results in direct etching, shown as segment A-B of the current density versus voltage curve in Fig. 12. Specimen dissolution without formation of a precipitated layer occurs in this instance. However, if the metal ions leaving the material react with nonmetal ions from the

electrolyte and form an insoluble compound, precipitated layers will form on the specimen surface whose thicknesses are a function of the composition and orientation of the microstructural features exposed to the solution.

*Anodizing* is the formation of layers by electrolytic etching that reveal interference colors due to variations in thickness determined by the underlying microstructure. See the articles "Zirconium and Hafnium and Their Alloys" and "Color Metallography" in this Volume for additional information on anodizing.

*Potentiostatic etching* is an advanced form of electrolytic etching that produces the ultimate etching contrast through highly controlled conditions. The potential of the specimen, which usually changes with variations in electrolytic concentration, is maintained at a fixed level through the use of a potentiostat and suitable reference electrodes. The principle of this technique is shown in Fig. 13. In some cases, the cell current can be maintained with a coulombmeter to determine the extent of etching (controlled etching). Additional information on potentiostatic etching can be found in the article "Color Metallography" in this Volume and in Ref. 5.

*Magnetic etching* can be used to examine domain structures of magnetic materials to relate metallographic and domain structures to properties (see Appendix I of this article for more information).

**Physical etching** leaves the surface free of chemical residues and offers advantages where electrochemical etching is difficult—for example, when there is an extremely large difference in electrochemical potential between microstructural elements or when chemical etchants cause stains or residues that could produce false microstructures. Ion and thermal etching are physical etching techniques that alter the morphology of the polished specimen surface. Some probable

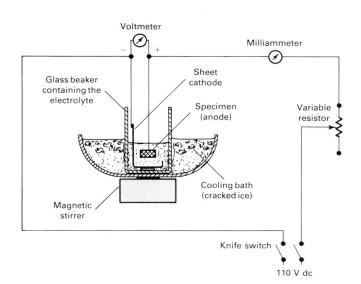

**Fig. 11** Basic laboratory setup for electrolytic etching and polishing

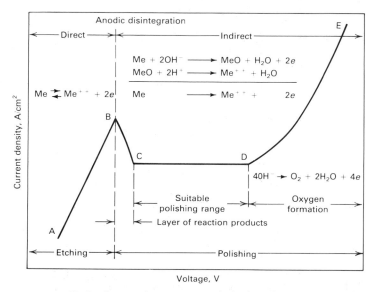

**Fig. 12** Idealized current density versus applied voltage for many common electrolytes. Regions for electrolytic etching and polishing are indicated.

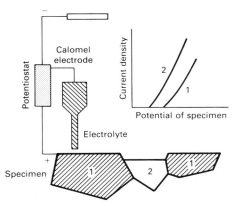

**Fig. 13** Principles of electrolytic potentiostatic etching

applications of these methods are ceramic materials, plated layers, welds joining dissimilar materials, and porous materials.

*Ion etching*, or cathodic vacuum etching, produces structural contrast by selective removal of atoms from the specimen surface. This is accomplished by using high-energy ions, such as argon, accelerated by voltages of 1 to 10 kV. Individual atoms are removed at various rates, depending on their atomic number, their bonding state, and the crystal orientation of the individual grains. Ion beam etching and cathodic sputtering are the ion etching techniques used in metallography and ceramography. Additional information on ion etching can be found in Ref 6 and 7.

*Thermal etching* is used in high-temperature microscopy and to etch polished surfaces of ceramic materials well below their sintering or hot-pressing temperature. Thermal etching is also partially based on atoms leaving the material surface as a result of additional energy. However, the predominant force in thermal etching is the formation of slightly curved equilibrium surfaces having individual grains with minimum surface tension. Thermal etching of ceramic materials in air, vacuum, or inert gases is often better than conventional chemical etching. Figure 14 shows as an example the grain structure of a diffusion-welded ceramic joint revealed by thermal etching. Additional information on thermal etching can be found in Ref 8.

## Etching for Effect

Etching techniques are developed in practical metallography by optimizing the effects they produce regarding the intended examination of the specimens. Considering the size of structural details revealed by etching as a distinguishing feature, metallographic etching can be subdivided into microetching and macroetching. Among the various microetching procedures, etch pitting and line etching are two typical examples of etching for special effects.

**Macroetching** is based on conventional chemical etching methods. Macroetching re-

veals the structure of a section or displays surface imperfections of a workpiece to magnifications of $25\times$ ($50\times$ in Europe). These low magnifications enable examination of surface regions having large differences in height produced by very aggressive macroetchants (deep etching). However, many macroetching procedures, which are based on the application of modified or regular microetchants, may be used for macrostructural and microstructural observations if a coarse structure prevails and the surface irregularities due to etching are within the depth of field at higher magnifications.

Typical macrostructural details revealed are variations in grain size, solidification structure, segregation, inclusions, voids, porosity, flow lines, and cracks. Macroetching is used extensively for quality control and failure analysis of weld structures, heat-treated parts, extrusions, forgings, and castings. Because macroetching yields an overall view of the inhomogeneity of the structure under examination, it also provides the necessary information about the location of sections to be used for subsequent microstructural investigations. Specimen preparation need not be elaborate. Wet grinding on silicon carbide papers is normally sufficient. When examining surface imperfections, etching is performed directly.

**Microetching** is based on electrochemical, physical, or optical etching methods and is used mainly to reveal microstructural features under the optical microscope at magnifications exceeding $25\times$ and up to $1500\times$. This approximate practical limit of magnification is dictated by the resolving power of the optical microscope. It can be shifted to higher values if microetched sections are examined with the scanning electron microscope. Most commonly used magnifications of secondary electron and backscattered electron images taken from microsections are from 300 to $10\,000\times$.

Microetching techniques reveal the shape, size, and arrangement of such structural com-

ponents as phases, inclusions, and pores. Although grain and phase boundaries will clearly be revealed if proper chemical, electrolytic, potentiostatic, or physical microetching procedures are used, contrasting by physically deposited interfaces uncovers phase boundaries only because of the light-dark or color contrast of the adjacent phases. Microetching is particularly useful for disclosing structural changes caused by chemical, mechanical, and/or thermal treatments rendered during manufacture or service.

**Etch Pitting.** Suitable etchants produce etch pits on polished surfaces of single crystalline or polycrystalline metals. The geometric shape of these pits depends on the crystallographic orientation of the examined grain or crystal. The etchant first attacks local defects, such as dislocations, vacancies, inclusions, or impurities. The ratio of the dissolution rates at the specimen plane and at the facets of etch pits governs the observed variety of the shapes of the etch pits.

Quantitative evaluation of etch pits having geometrically well-defined facets yields information on the crystallographic position of the sectioning plane of the examined grain, the crystallographic directions in the sectioning plane, and the orientation of the examined grain relative to a fixed reference direction. Etch pitting can also be applied to investigate the crystallographic correlation of a precipitated phase and the matrix as well as to study the orientation effect of domain structures. The dislocation density of single crystals can be estimated from the number of etch pits when surfaces of the crystals are oriented parallel to low-index planes and when proper etchants are used. Additional information on etch pitting can be found in Ref 9 and 10.

**Line Etching.** The technique for line etching presupposes a reaction layer formed on the surface of the specimen by precipitation (deposit) etching. With extended etching and upon subsequent drying, shrinking stresses crack the layer. Under certain experimental conditions, the crack formation leads to a pattern of lines visible on the individual grain surfaces that relates to their crystallographic orientation (Fig. 15).

Line etching is used to determine preferred directions and to study recrystallization effects. Suitable etching procedures exist for copper and copper alloys ($\alpha$-brass and $\alpha$-bronze), aluminum alloys containing copper, low-carbon steels, and austenitic stainless steels. Etchants based on sodium thiosulfate ($Na_2S_2O_3$) are preferentially used (Ref 11). They form sulfur-containing layers whose nature depends on the chemical composition of the reagent and the specimen.

A modified line-etching technique is used to carry out metallographic texture control on silicon steel transformer sheets. In this double-etch procedure, precipitation etching using sodium picrate is followed by a brief etch in dilute nitric acid ($HNO_3$). This solution penetrates the crack, attacks the metal surface, and lifts off the layer. The exposed

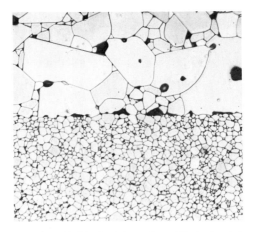

**Fig. 14** Polished section of a diffusion-bonded joint between a coarse-grained and a fine-grained alumina ceramic (99.7% $Al_2O_3$) thermally etched in air at 1400 °C (2550 °F) for 1 h. $500\times$

**Fig. 15** Line-etched grains of α-brass (Cu-33Zn). 200×

surface exhibits parallel lines on grains oriented at or near {110}. The relationship between the deviation of the direction of the parallel lines from the rolling direction of transformer sheets and the magnitude of the coercive force has been demonstrated (Ref 12).

## Etchants and Etching Practice

A variety of etchants are available, including acids, bases, neutral solutions, mixtures of solutions, molten salts, and gases. Many examples are provided in the articles in the Section "Metallographic Techniques and Microstructures: Specific Metals and Alloys" in this Volume. Most of these formulas were derived empirically. Because their composition and mode of application are easily varied and modified, they are useful for materials other than the ones mentioned in these articles. The rate of attack is determined chiefly by the degree of dissociation of the etchant and its electrical conductivity. Both are often influenced by small additions of other chemicals. This may explain why many formulas contain small amounts of substances whose significance is not immediately apparent. The stability of many etching solutions is limited; oxidation-reduction (redox) potentials vary with time. Changes that necessitate discarding after a limited time may also occur while the etchant is in use.

**Etching times** range from several seconds to several hours. When no instructions are given, progress is judged by the appearance of the surface during etching. The surface will usually become less reflective (duller) as etching proceeds.

**Etching temperature** and etching time are closely related; increasing the temperature usually allows the duration to be decreased. However, this may not be advisable, because the contrast could become uneven when the rate of attack is too rapid. Most etching is performed at room temperature.

**Errors.** Sources of error are numerous, especially in electrochemical etching. Etching errors may lead to microstructural misinterpretation. For example, precipitates from etching or washing solutions could be interpreted as additional phases.

**Cleaning.** Upon completion of any chemical or electrochemical etching, the specimen should be rinsed in clean water to remove the chemicals and halt any reactions. For example, etching to reveal segregations in irons and steels using copper-containing compounds sometimes requires rinsing in alcohol first, or copper could precipitate on the specimen surface because of the change in the degree of dissociation. After specimens are water rinsed, they should be rinsed in alcohol and dried in a stream of warm air.

Alcohol hastens drying and prevents the formation of water spots. If etching produces water-soluble layers, water must be avoided in rinsing. Mounted specimens must be cleaned thoroughly to avoid the destructive effects of etchants and solvents seeping from pores, cracks, or mounting clamp interfaces. An ultrasonic cleaner will help avoid these problems. If specimens are highly porous or if highly concentrated acids are used for etching—for example, as in deep etching—the chemicals should be neutralized before rinsing and drying the specimen.

**Specimen Storage.** When polished and etched specimens are to be stored for long periods of time, they must be protected from atmospheric corrosion. Desiccators and desiccator cabinets are the most common means of specimen storage, although plastic coating and cellophane tape are sometimes used.

**Reproducibility in Etching.** For the most part, metallographic etching continues to be an empirical method. This condition results from the abundance of etching methods, nonuniform nomenclature, and, frequently, the lack of knowledge of etchant mechanisms. For these reasons, it is difficult to present a clear view of etching.

Conventional etching in particular is difficult to reproduce, regardless of its simplicity. During the electrochemical processes, numerous side effects must be considered. For example, changes in the electrolyte and inhibiting reactions at the specimen surface that cause polarization phenomena, overpotential, and so on, must be appraised.

To achieve more reproducibility and dependable structural contrast, various new methods have been developed in recent years. Electrolytic potentiostatic etching, ion etching, and contrasting by physically deposited interference layer are gradually gaining acceptance.

The development of more reproducible etching methods is of particular importance for quantitative image analysis. These instruments are used to determine automatically the area fraction of various phases and are not sensitive to subtle differences. Therefore, sharply reproducible etching contrast is necessary to obtain accurate information.

# Appendix I: Magnetic Etching

By Robert J. Gray
Senior Program Manager of Metallography
American Society for Metals
Metallographic Consultant
Unitron, Inc.

MAGNETIC ETCHING uses magnetism to reveal specific features in the microstructure of fully or partially magnetic materials. The atoms in most materials have electrons that are paired; both electrons spin in opposite directions, canceling net magnetism. However, some materials have atoms with one or more unpaired electrons that produce a net magnetic moment. All materials are classified in one of four types as related to magnetism. Materials exhibiting strong magnetism are classified as ferromagnetic; if the material displays significant magnetism, it is classified as ferrimagnetic. If the magnetic response is weak, it is paramagnetic, or if there is no net magnetism, it is antiferromagnetic (diamagnetic).

In 1931, a rather crude application of magnetic etching was established (Ref 13, 14). This technique, which originated the identity of "Bitter patterns," involved sprinkling magnetic powder on the surface of a material in a magnetic field and observing the distribution of the particles. This basic concept remains today, although with many refinements. Improvements to this technique began in 1932 (Ref 15). However, the major advance occurred two years later (Ref 16) with the utilization of magnetic particles in a colloidal suspension in the successful observation of the well-defined magnetic domain patterns on the faces of iron crystals. The magnetization of a ferromagnetic or a ferrimagnetic material tends to break up into regions called domains, which are separated by the transition regions called domain walls (Ref 17). Domain patterns usually must be observed using the microscope and are the basis for magnetic etching. Although the domain patterns are visible on some materials, the use of this technique to reveal ferromagnetic conditions can serve a more practical role. An example is the distribution of strain-induced martensite in a paramagnetic matrix of austenite of a type 300 stainless steel. This application will be discussed.

Although some problems impeded the progress of magnetic etching, further developments in the use of the colloid technique were reported in the observation of magnetic domain patterns, ferromagnetic phases, and constituents in the microstructure (Ref 18-23). Some difficulties continued in the lack of stability of the laboratory-prepared colloid solution. Although many reports included procedures for preparing the colloid along with the description of the technique, a satisfactory colloid never materialized. In addition, the laboratory-prepared suspension corroded the specimens.

Another problem was that the small magnetic coil just fit the 32-mm (1.25-in.) diam cylindrical specimen mount (Ref 24) and generated sufficient heat to evaporate the aqueous carrier of the colloid during prolonged examinations. These problems have been corrected (Ref 25-29). The laboratory-prepared colloid was replaced with commercially available Ferrofluid (Ref 30), and a much larger coil was used to separate the heat from the specimen.

## Laboratory Procedures

**Ferrofluid and Its Application.** Ferrofluid is an extremely stable and reliable colloid suspension. The water-base Ferrofluid with saturated magnetization of 200 G is recommended as a stock solution. The particle density is two to four times that which is suitable for magnetic etching. A 50- to 100-G concentration work solution is obtained by diluting the stock solution with distilled water. Only approximately 1 mL of the stock solution should be diluted, because the less dense solution may not remain in the suspension, although experience has shown that the particles remain in suspension for several months, and accidental contamination or loss could occur. The fluid is used sparingly; a 1-mL working supply is adequate.

Ferrofluid is applied as shown in Fig. 16. Specimen size should range from 0.5 to 2 cm² (0.08 to 0.3 in.²). The specimen should be mounted in a dense material, such as epoxy resin. Bakelite contains a porous binder and is therefore unsuitable because it absorbs the carrier (water) from the colloid. The mounted specimen should be mechanically polished to a scratch-free finish; however, even the best mechanically polished specimen surface will contain some superficially disturbed metal, which is usually removed, at least in part, in conventional metallographic procedures by chemical or electrolytic etching. This amount of chemical or electrolytic etching is not desirable before magnetic etching, because a microscopically flat surface must be maintained. A light electropolish to the specimen surface is more useful.

A mechanically polished surface usually is slightly in relief to the surrounding mount; therefore, electropolishing must be restricted to 15 to 20 s to remove most of the induced relief effect and the superficially cold-worked layer caused by mechanical polishing. However, if the specimen profile is lower than the surrounding mount due to longer electropolishing, the colloid layer will be too thick to relate the magnetic etch pattern to the substrate. To relate the epitaxial magnetic etch to the microstructure of the substrate, a color or light etch should follow the electropolish.

A small-volume dispensing syringe should be used. A plastic tuberculin syringe of 0.5- or 1-mL capacity is easily controlled when dispensing the approximately 5 μL of fluid. The cover glass, or cover slip, should be No. 0 (22 mm² × 0.12 mm, or 0.35 in.² × 0.005 in., thick) and should be cleaned of grease and fingerprints with a household liquid detergent. Both surfaces of the cover glass are usually coated with detergent while holding the glass with tweezers. The detergent is then removed using distilled water in an ultrasonic

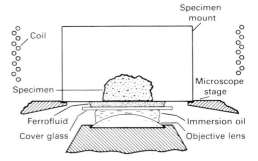

**Fig. 17** Components in place for magnetic etching on an inverted microscope

cleaner. Finally, the cover glass is rinsed in distilled water, then absolute alcohol, and dried with hot air. Cleaning should be repeated to remove residue. This care is essential for complete wetting of the bottom surface of the glass by the colloid solution. When the colloid solution is confined within the outer edges of the cover glass, the fluid surface tension secures the glass to the specimen surface and forms the desired thin layer of colloid between the cover glass and the specimen surface.

## Optical Examination

Examinations have been performed on an inverted-stage metallograph, although its use is not essential. Resolving the minute features in the microstructure may require magnifications of 1000× or higher as well as immersion oil. The drop of immersion oil can be placed on the outer surface of the cover glass. With the specimen in place on the metallograph, the objective lens and the specimen can then be positioned at the required working distance, allowing the oil to fill the gap between the cover glass and the lens normally. Figure 17 shows the respective components in place. The magnet coil with a display of the flux pattern and the coil and specimen in place on the metallograph stage are depicted in Fig. 18. The flux pattern (Fig. 18a) was obtained with iron filings sprinkled on white cardboard. The pattern developed after activation of the direct current.

The conventional approach in the examination of metallographic specimens is to tint or to produce a microtopographical surface from which the light can reflect to reveal the etched surface. The structure remains static. Considerable difference is apparent in the use of magnetic etching. The size of the iron oxide particles in the suspension is less than 30 nm (300 Å) and cannot be resolved using the optical microscope.

Motion of the particles is detected by viewing at 1000× or above. This motion is due to Brownian movement, which is the random thermal agitation produced by impact of the colloid particles with molecules of the liquid. This movement can be observed with the magnetic coil off. When the coil is energized, the particles collect at ferromagnetic features

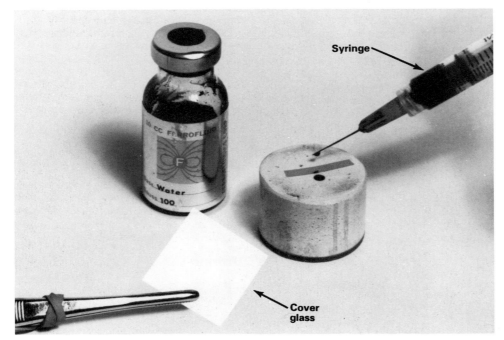

**Fig. 16** The application of Ferrofluid. Less than ¼ drop (approximately 5 μL) of the colloid is applied to the specimen using a syringe. The cover glass is then positioned over the colloid and the specimen to form a thin fluid layer.

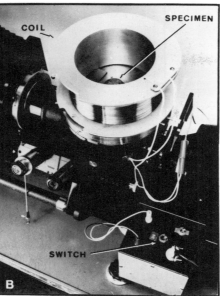

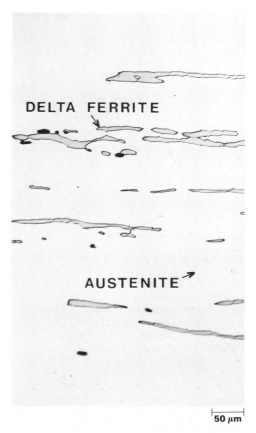

**Fig. 18** Coils used for magnetic etching. Fig. 18(a): iron filings have formed a flux pattern (caused by the magnetic field of the coil) on white cardboard. Fig. 18(b): magnetic etching equipment ready for use. A rectifier at 4.0 A, 37 V supplies direct current.

**Fig. 19** Type 304 stainless steel, with δ-ferrite stringers in an austenite matrix. The ferrite is ferromagnetic; the austenite, paramagnetic. 200×

in the microstructure. Breaking the current to the coil causes the particles to disperse again, with some residual attraction to the ferromagnetic features.

If the partial drop of colloid is placed on a paramagnetic austenitic material with microscopic ferromagnetic islands, as shown in Fig. 19, a unique pattern appears (Fig. 20 and 21). These domain patterns are analog patterns of the substrate. This field is illustrated in Fig. 20 and 21 with the polarity of the direct current to the coil reversed. If the current to the coil is broken, some attraction of the particles is evident in a faint domain pattern. Most of the particles move freely by Brownian movement. Only a certain number of particles is

required to form the domain patterns with the current activated. Excess colloid particles are visible around the ferrite islands in Fig. 20 and 21.

Magnetic etching is also useful in studying δ-ferrite in type 304 stainless steel after a 10 000-h heat treatment at 650 °C (1200 °F). This heat treatment partially transforms the metastable, ductile ferrite to brittle σ phase. The combined use of magnetic and tint etching demonstrated in Fig. 22 to 24 more completely explains this occurrence. Sigma phase is paramagnetic. If the specimen is etched using alkaline potassium ferricyanide (10 g KOH, 10 g $K_3Fe(CN)_6$, and 100 mL $H_2O$) at 95 °C (205 °F), the microstructure appears as

shown in Fig. 22. The σ phase is tinted reddish brown (dark in a black-and-white print). This field is shown in Fig. 23 with the colloid added and the magnet off. Figure 24 depicts the field with the magnet activated. This illustrates the transformation resulting from heat treatment.

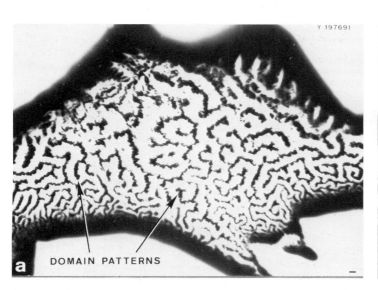

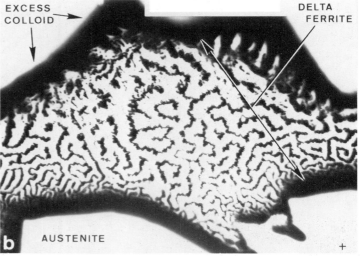

**Fig. 20, 21** Magnetic domain patterns on δ-ferrite in an austenite matrix. The colloid particles (less than 30 nm, or 300 Å, in diameter) form analog patterns over the ferromagnetic δ-ferrite; paramagnetic austenite does not attract the particles. Patterns reverse when the polarity of the direct current is reversed. 650×

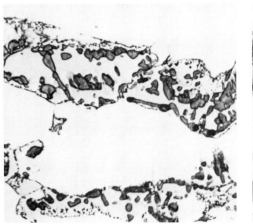
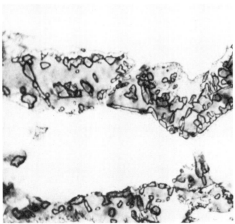
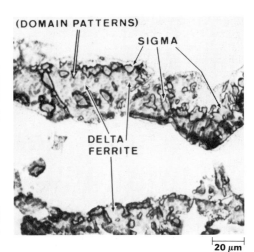

**Fig. 22, 23, 24** Type 304 stainless steel, heat treated 10000 h at 650 °C (1200 °F). Delta-ferrite was partially transformed during heat treatment to σ phase and austenite. Fig. 22: microstructure after electropolishing and chemical tinting. Fig. 23: Ferrofluid has been added. Fig. 24: The magnet has been activated, and colloid particles are attracted to the retained, ferromagnetic δ-ferrite. 1000×

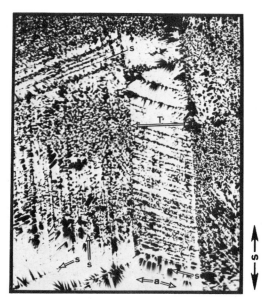

# Appendix II: Procedures and Precautions for the Preparation and Handling of Etchants

**Fig. 25, 26** Type 304 stainless steel fatigue specimens, showing strain-induced martensite. Fig. 25: The magnet is off. Note the regions of high-density slip (s) and the twin area (T). Clear areas are untransformed austenite (a). Fig 26: The magnet is on, and colloid particles are attracted to the ferromagnetic α-martensite that formed along slip planes in the grains. Note the changes in the slip direction between the grains and the twin. 650×

PROCEDURES AND PRECAUTIONS for etchants, which include reagents used in metallography for microetching, macroetching, electropolishing, chemical polishing, and similar operations, are discussed in this Appendix. Applications and compositions of the reagents are described in articles in this Volume that discuss metallographic techniques for specific metals and alloys.

The formulations of etchants given in articles in this Volume are adequate for most applications, but may require modification. Adjustments in etchant composition, time, and technique, based on the experience and skill of the metallographer and depending on the specific application and the magnification to be used, are frequently indicated for satisfactory results. Details of etching to reveal specific aspects of structure are discussed in the articles on metallographic techniques for specific metals and alloys.

## Expression of Composition

Etchants are generally aqueous or alcoholic solutions containing one or more active chemicals (acids, bases, or salts). Liquids other than water or alcohol are used as solvents in some formulations. Compositions of most etchants described in this Volume are expressed in terms of the amounts of the substances to be used in preparing small quantities of these reagents.

For etchants that are solutions of solid substances in liquids, the amounts of the

Martensite can be formed in some stainless steels by strains that are generated when the material is plastically deformed. This strain-induced martensitic transformation will occur at a temperature, $M_d$, above the martensite start temperature, $M_s$. No amount of deformation will induce the martensite transformation in austenite if the temperature exceeds $M_d$ (Ref 31). The types of strain-induced martensite that can form in 300 series stainless steels having less than 0.08% C are α and ε. Alpha-martensite is a ferromagnetic, body-centered cubic (bcc) structure; ε-martensite is a nonferromagnetic, hexagonal close-packed (hcp) structure (Ref 32).

The amount of α-martensite normally increases with increasing strain in austenitic stainless steel. The amount of ε-martensite increases with plastic strain to a maximum, then gradually decreases due to its transformation to α-martensite (Ref 33). Magnetic etching accurately detects α (ferromagnetic) martensite but not nonferromagnetic ε-martensite. The use of magnetic etching on a type 304 stainless steel fatigue specimen is exemplified in Fig. 25 and 26. The stress axis (← S →) is identified, and the bands of martensite are perceptible. Some cross slip is evident. A twin (T) is identified. Some residual magnetic attraction is illustrated in Fig. 25 with the magnet off; however, the collection of the colloid particles at the slip lines is evident with the magnet on, as shown in Fig. 26.

solid substances are usually expressed in grams, and the amounts of liquids (or the total volumes of solution) are expressed in milliliters. The liquids may be individual commercially available substances or stock solutions containing two or more substances.

To prepare large quantities, as for some macroetching, kilograms and liters may be taken instead of grams and milliliters, or the amounts specified may be converted to pounds (1 kg = 2.2 lb) and gallons (1 L = 0.264 gal).

Other generally accepted methods for expressing composition are also used where appropriate. Compositions of some etchants prepared by mixing together two or more liquids are given in parts by volume or percentage by volume. Compositions of some etchants consisting of solutions of solid substances in liquids are described in terms of percentage by weight.

In long-established, although nonstandard, usage in metallography, such terms as 1%, 2%, and 4% have been used to describe the approximate strength of picral and are understood to mean 1, 2, and 4 g, respectively, of picric acid per 100 mL alcohol. These approximate expressions are used in this sense in many articles in this Volume.

## Purity of Chemicals

In the preparation of solutions for microetching and electropolishing, recommended practice is to use chemicals meeting the requirements of NF (National Formulary), USP (U.S. Pharmacopoeia), "laboratory," or "purified" grades or grades of still higher purity, such as reagent, ACS (American Chemical Society), or "certified" grades. The commercial or technical grades of certain special-purpose industrial chemicals, such as chromium trioxide ($CrO_3$) and synthetic methanol. These grades are extremely pure and are equivalent to reagent, ACS, or "certified" grades for use in microetching and electropolishing.

Where water is specified, distilled water is preferred because of wide variations in the purity of tap water. For macroetching, technical grades of chemicals are satisfactory, unless specifications indicate otherwise, and potable water of good quality is generally acceptable.

## Identification of Chemicals

The practices generally followed in the technical literature on metallography are used in this Volume to identify the chemicals used in the preparation of etchants.

**Aqueous Acids.** In identification of aqueous acids, the name or formula alone, sometimes followed by "conc" or "concentrated," refers to the common commercially available concentrated laboratory grade (see Table 1). Where more than one concentration is commonly available, the percentage by weight of the active constituent follows the name or formula.

An acid designated "tech" indicates the technical grade having the same concentration as the common laboratory grade. The concentration of technical grades is sometimes expressed by suppliers in terms of specific gravity, as shown in Table 1. Most technical-grade chemicals are available in several concentrations.

**Miscellaneous aqueous chemicals,** such as ammonium hydroxide ($NH_4OH$) and hydrogen peroxide ($H_2O_2$) (see Table 1), which are used in various etchants, are identified similarly to aqueous acids (see above). Concentration must always be specified for $H_2O_2$, which is available in several widely differing concentrations.

**The alcohols** most frequently used in etchants are methanol and ethanol, which are described in Table 2. It is important to use alcohol that has the desired water content—anhydrous or "95%" alcohol, whichever is specified—in etchants that contain a small percentage of water. However, either grade can be used when the etchant is a dilute aqueous solution. Practice regarding the substitution of methanol for ethanol (or conversely) and the use of some grades of denatured ethanol in etchants varies greatly.

Although many etchant formulations show the use of methanol or ethanol as alternate materials, caution should be exercised in substituting one for the other in formulations where their equivalence is not indicated. Safety precludes changing accepted formulations for electropolishing without a thorough chemical study (see the article "Electrolytic Polishing" in this Volume). In addition, ethanol or higher alcohols should not be substi-

tuted for methanol in nital containing more than 5% by volume concentrated nitric acid ($HNO_3$) or in other methanol-base etchants that contain strong oxidants and only a small percentage of water.

In a variety of applications for which the etchant is specified to contain ethanol, excluding electropolishing electrolytes, a proprietary solvent or denatured "reagent" alcohol having suitable water content (see Table 3) may substitute for pure "anhydrous" or "absolute" (99.5%) ethanol and for pure 95% ethanol (see Table 2). These substitutes are available without permit from suppliers of laboratory chemicals. These grades have been formulated in accordance with U.S. government regulations to be suitable for general laboratory purposes and have been denatured with small percentages of volatile solvents; they may substitute for pure ethanol having the same water content, except where pure ethanol is required.

### Table 1 Characteristics of aqueous liquid chemicals used in metallographic etchants
Except for $H_2SO_4$, all data apply to laboratory and technical or commercial grades of chemicals

| Name | Active constituent | Nominal composition, % by weight(a) | Specific gravity |
|---|---|---|---|
| **Aqueous acids** | | | |
| Acetic acid, glacial | $HC_2H_3O_2$ | 99.5 | 1.05 |
| Fluoboric acid | $HBF_4$ | 48 | 1.32 |
| Hydrochloric acid(b) | $HCl$ | 37 | 1.18 |
| Hydrofluoric acid | $HF$ | 48 | 1.15 |
| Lactic acid | $HC_3H_5O_3$ | 85 | 1.20 |
| Nitric acid | $HNO_3$ | 70 | 1.42 |
| Perchloric acid | $HClO_4$ | 70 | 1.67 |
| | | 60 | 1.53 |
| Phosphoric acid (ortho) | $H_3PO_4$ | 85 | 1.70 |
| Sulfuric acid | $H_2SO_4$ | 96(c) | 1.84 |
| **Miscellaneous aqueous chemicals** | | | |
| Ammonium hydroxide | $NH_4OH$ | 28(d) | 0.90 |
| Hydrogen peroxide | $H_2O_2$ | 3(e) | 1.01 |
| | | 30(f) | 1.11 |
| | | 50(g) | 1.20 |

(a) Nominal percentage of the active constituent; remainder is water. Reagents made by different manufacturers may differ slightly in nominal concentration and allowable range of concentration. (b) Technical grade is also called muriatic acid. (c) Laboratory grade. Technical grade has concentration of 93%. (d) Percent $NH_3$. (e) Sometimes called 10 volume. (f) Sometimes called 100 volume. (g) Sometimes called 170 volume

### Table 2 Characteristics of pure methanol and ethanol

| Name | Active constituent | Nominal composition, % by weight(a) |
|---|---|---|
| Methanol | $CH_3OH$ | 99.5(b) |
| Methanol, 95% | $CH_3OH$ | 95(c) |
| Ethanol, anhydrous | $C_2H_5OH$ | 99.5(d)(e) |
| Ethanol, 95% | $C_2H_5OH$ | 95(e) |

(a) Nominal percentage of the active constituent; remainder is $H_2O$, unless otherwise specified. (b) Synthetic methanol; the commercial grade is of high purity and is satisfactory for use in all ordinary metallographic etchants where methanol is specified; wood alcohol has not been manufactured commercially in the United States since 1969. Methanol is available only as an anhydrous, or absolute, grade containing less than 0.1 or 0.2% $H_2O$ as packaged, and usually not more than approximately 0.5% $H_2O$ at time of use, depending on storage and handling. (c) Where methanol, 95%, is called for, the ordinary anhydrous grade must be diluted with 5% $H_2O$ by volume. (d) The anhydrous, or absolute, grade of ethanol is ordinarily used only where no significant amount of $H_2O$ can be tolerated. It contains less than 0.1 or 0.2% $H_2O$ as packaged and usually not more than approximately 0.5% $H_2O$ at time of use, depending on storage and handling. (e) Available only with special governmental permit

**Table 3  Nominal compositions of various grades of denatured alcohol (ethanol) used in some metallographic etchants(a)**

| Component | Parts by volume in specially denatured alcohol(b) | | | | | |
|---|---|---|---|---|---|---|
| | Formula SD-1(c) | | Formula SD-3A | | Formula SD-30 | |
| | Anhydrous | 95%(d) | Anhydrous | 95%(d) | Anhydrous | 95%(d) |
| Ethanol, anhydrous | 100 | 95 | 100 | 95 | 100 | 95 |
| Water | ... | 5 | ... | 5 | ... | 5 |
| Methanol | 4 | 4 | 5 | 5 | 10 | 10 |
| Methyl isobutyl ketone | 1 | 1 | ... | ... | ... | ... |

| Component | Parts by volume in proprietary solvent(e) | | Parts by volume in "reagent" alcohol(e) | |
|---|---|---|---|---|
| | Anhydrous | 95%(d) | Anhydrous | 95%(d) |
| SD-1, anhydrous(c) | 100 | ... | ... | ... |
| SD-1, 95%(c)(d) | ... | 100 | ... | ... |
| SD-3A, anhydrous | ... | ... | 95 | ... |
| SD-3A, 95%(d) | ... | ... | ... | 95 |
| Methyl isobutyl ketone | 1 | 1 | ... | ... |
| Hydrocarbon solvent or gasoline | 1 | 1 | ... | ... |
| Ethyl acetate | 1 | 1 | ... | ... |
| Isopropyl alcohol | ... | ... | 5 | 5 |

(a) See text for discussion of suitability of the various grades for use in etchants. (b) Specially denatured alcohol is available only with special governmental permit. (c) The formula shown here has replaced the obsolete SD-1 formula in which wood alcohol was specified; wood alcohol has not been manufactured commercially in the United States since 1969. (d) The designation of type of denatured alcohol as "95%" means that the denatured product contains 5 parts H₂O for every 95 parts anhydrous (absolute) ethanol, plus denaturants as specified. (e) Available without governmental permit from suppliers of laboratory chemicals for scientific and general laboratory purposes

The specially denatured (SD) alcohols described in Table 3 are generally suitable for use in etchants. However, SD alcohol is obtainable only with special governmental permits and usually can be purchased only in larger quantities than the proprietary solvent and "reagent" alcohol in Table 3 and only from major suppliers. The metallographic laboratories of at least one large governmental scientific and engineering facility denature all the pure ethanol they use by adding less than 1% by volume isopropyl alcohol.

**Water of Hydration.** With some exceptions, it has been common practice to identify solid salts and acids used in etchants only by name and abbreviated formula, without indicating the presence or absence of water of hydration (see Table 4). Historically, in developing and preparing etchants, the most stable hydrate, which was the common commercial form, was ordinarily used, except for salts that do not form hydrates. Current practice varies.

Using the specified amount of the anhydrous or a hydrated form of a solid salt or acid in preparing an etchant will in most cases produce essentially the same etching behavior; any difference in results will usually be small compared to the effects of normal differences in technique and other variables in specimen preparation. Exceptions are the preparation of etchants that must be anhydrous or must contain only a small and fairly critical percentage of water for proper etching activity; for such etchants, the need to use specific anhydrous or hydrated forms of each component should be clearly stated.

Some salts, such as ferric nitrate ($Fe(NO_3)_3 \cdot 9H_2O$), do not exist in an anhydrous form. Conversely, some nominally water-free compounds contain a substantial percentage of water. One of these is picric acid, for which

the 10 to 15% $H_2O$ content found in laboratory grades is necessary for satisfactory performance of etchants based on it (see Table 4).

**Miscellaneous chemicals** may be difficult to identify because of similarity in names of different chemicals or because of misleading or nonstandard nomenclature and trade names. The chemicals are described in Table 4. Also included are certain chemicals for which some aspects of composition or behavior are important.

## Safety Precautions

All chemicals are potentially dangerous; formulating and using etchants requires thorough knowledge of the chemicals involved and the proper procedures for handling and mixing. The discussion that follows indicates many of the potential hazards of using chemicals and describes precautions and safe practice.

**Ventilation.** Etchants should be mixed, handled, and used in a well-ventilated area, preferably under an exhaust hood, to prevent exposure to or inhalation of toxic and corrosive fumes. Use of an exhaust hood is mandatory whenever large quantities of chemicals are handled or large areas of metal are etched (as in macroetching), when executing lengthy electropolishing operations, or when electropolishing large areas.

**Protection of Personnel.** Pouring, mixing, handling, and use of chemicals and etchants necessitates the wearing of suitable protective equipment and clothing, such as glasses, face shield, gloves, apron, and so on, to prevent contact of chemicals with the eyes, skin, or clothing.

Chemicals that contact the skin should be washed off promptly using water and soap. Medical attention should be sought immediately for chemical burns, especially if at cuts or abrasions in the skin. If chemicals contact

**Table 4  Description of miscellaneous chemicals used in metallographic etchants**

**aluminum chloride, anhydrous.** Solid; $AlCl_3$; reacts violently with water, evolving HCl gas; use of hydrated form, $AlCl_3 \cdot 6H_2O$, is preferred

**ammonium molybdate.** Crystals; also called ammonium paramolybdate or heptamolybdate; $(NH_4)_6Mo_7O_{24} \cdot 4H_2O$; can be used interchangeably with "molybdic acid, 85%"

**benzalkonium chloride.** Crystals; essentially alkyl-dimethyl-benzyl-ammonium chloride. May not be readily avilable in this form; see zephiran chloride

**1-butanol.** See n-butyl alcohol

**2-butoxyethanol.** See butyl cellosolve

**n-butyl alcohol.** Liquid; normal butyl alcohol; also called butyl alcohol and 1-butanol

**butyl carbitol.** Liquid; diethylene glycol monobutyl ether

**butyl cellosolve.** Liquid; ethylene glycol monobutyl ether; also called 2-butoxyethanol

**carbitol.** Liquid; diethylene glycol monoethyl ether

**cellosolve.** Liquid; ethylene glycol monoethyl ether

**chromic acid.** Dark-red crystals or flakes; $CrO_3$; also called chromic anhydride, chromic acid anhydride, and chromium trioxide; see chromic oxide

**chromic anhydride.** See chromic acid

**chromic oxide.** Fine green powder; $Cr_2O_3$; a polishing abrasive; do not confuse with $CrO_3$, which is a strong acid and a component of many etchants

**cupric ammonium chloride.** Crystals; a double salt, $CuCl_2 \cdot 2NH_4Cl \cdot 2H_2O$; if not available, substitute 0.6 g $CuCl_2 \cdot 2H_2O$ plus 0.4 g $NH_4Cl$ for each gram of the double salt

**diethylene glycol.** Syrupy liquid; also called 2,2'-oxydiethanol and dihydroxydiethyl ether; $(HOCH_2CH_2)_2O$; more viscous than ethylene glycol—otherwise similar in behavior

**diethylene glycol monobutyl ether.** See butyl carbitol

**diethylene glycol monoethyl ether.** See carbitol

**diethyl ether.** See ether

**ether.** Liquid; also called ethyl ether and diethyl ether; very low flash point, highly explosive; boiling point is 34.4 °C (94 °F)

**ethylene glycol.** Syrupy liquid; also called 1,2-ethanediol and dihydroxyethane; $(CH_2)_2/(OH)_2$. Less viscous than diethylene glycol; otherwise similar in behavior

**ethylene glycol monobutyl ether.** Liquid; also called 2-butoxyethanol or butyl cellosolve

**ethylene glycol monoethyl ether.** See cellosolve

**ethyl ether.** See ether

**ferric nitrate.** Crystals; $Fe(NO_3)_3 \cdot 9H_2O$; there is no anhydrous form of this salt

**fluoboric acid, 48%.** Liquid; $HBF_4$; if not readily available in small quantities, substitute 10.3 mL HF (48%) plus 4.4 g $H_3BO_3$ for each 10 mL 48% $HBF_4$ specified

**glycerol.** Syrupy liquid; also called glycerin or glycerine; $C_3H_5(OH)_3$; contains to 5% (by weight) $H_2O$

**molybdic acid, 85%.** Crystals or powder containing the equivalent of 85% $MoO_3$. This misnamed chemical consists mostly of ammonium molybdate, or paramolybdate, which is $(NH_4)_6Mo_7O_{24} \cdot 4H_2O$; the two chemicals can be used interchangeably; see ammonium molybdate

**muriatic acid.** Liquid; technical grade HCl; see Table 1

**picric acid.** Crystals; 2,4,6-trinitrophenol; crystals of laboratory chemical contain 10 to 15% $H_2O$; its crystalline metallic salts are even more explosive; do not use grades that do not have the 10 to 15% $H_2O$ content

**pyrophosphoric acid.** Crystals or viscous liquid; $H_4P_2O_7$, anhydrous; hydrolyzes to $H_3PO_4$ slowly in cold $H_2O$ and rapidly in hot $H_2O$

**zephiran chloride.** Aqueous solution; a proprietary material produced in grades containing approximately 12% and 17% (by weight) benzalkonium chloride (alkyl-dimethyl-benzyl-ammonium chloride) as the active constituent, plus some ammonium acetate; also called sephiran chloride; available from pharmacies or pharmaceutical distributors; see benzalkonium chloride

the eyes, the eyes should be flushed at once with large quantities of water, and medical attention should be obtained without delay. A face-and-eye fountain should be available for use where chemicals or etchants are stored or handled. A safety shower is also required where quantities large enough to be hazardous are stored or handled. This washing equipment should be readily available, and should be tested at scheduled intervals to ensure dependable performance in an emergency.

Hydrofluoric acid (HF) and fluosilicic acid ($H_2SiF_6$) can cause painful and serious ulcers upon contacting the skin, unless washed off immediately. Also especially harmful to the skin are concentrated $HNO_3$, sulfuric acid ($H_2SO_4$), $CrO_3$, 30 or 50% $H_2O_2$, sodium hydroxide (NaOH), potassium hydroxide (KOH), bromine ($Br_2$), and anhydrous aluminum chloride ($AlCl_3$). Inhalation of vapors or mist from these chemicals or etchants containing them can also cause irritation or serious damage to the respiratory system.

**Container Material and Design.** Preparation, storage, and handling of etchants dictates using containers and equipment made of materials suitable for the chemicals used. Glass resists nearly all chemicals. Polyethylene, polypropylene, and similarly inert plastics resist HF, $H_2SiF_6$, and fluoboric acid ($HBF_4$), as well as solutions containing salts of these acids. These inert plastics are also recommended for prolonged storage of strongly alkaline solutions and strong solutions of phosphoric acid ($H_3PO_4$), both of which attack glass, especially ordinary grades of glass.

Certain mixtures of chemicals can generate gaseous reaction products over a period of time or if inadvertently exposed to heat and can build up dangerous pressures if stored in tightly sealed containers. One example is the methanol-$HNO_3$ solution used for electropolishing. The use of vented or pressure-relief stoppers instead of tightly sealed screw caps or conventional stoppers on bottles of etchants that are prepared in quantity and stored is recommended.

**Heat Evolution in Preparing Etchants.** Caution should be exercised and accepted laboratory procedures followed when mixing chemicals. In general, heat is evolved, sometimes in large amounts, when strong acids (particularly $H_2SO_4$), alkalis (NaOH and KOH), anhydrous $AlCl_3$, or their concentrated solutions are added to water, alcohols, or solutions of other chemicals and when combining acidic with alkaline substances or solutions.

The acid, alkali, or anhydrous $AlCl_3$ should always be added to the water, alcohol, or solution. These chemicals should be introduced slowly while stirring continuously to avoid local overheating. Incomplete mixing can permit layering, with danger of a delayed violent reaction. Special attention and special cooling procedures may be necessary when large quantities of etchants are prepared and large areas of metal are etched, as in some macroetching, and when high currents are used in electropolishing.

**Mixing of Oxidizing Agents With Reducing Agents.** Mixing oxidizing agents, such as $HNO_3$, $H_2SO_4$, perchloric acid ($HClO_4$), $CrO_3$, salts of these acids, persulfates, $Br_2$, and $H_2O_2$, with reducing agents—for example, alcohols and other organic solvents, acetic acid, acetic anhydride [$(CH_3CO)_2O$] and most organic compounds—requires special care. Failure to follow accepted safe procedures can result in violent or explosive reactions. The use of $(CH_3CO)_2O$ is not safe in electropolishing solutions, except in limited ranges of composition and water content, and is therefore not recommended. The article "Electrolytic Polishing" in this Volume contains special precautions for procedures and the reagents used in electropolishing.

**Care With Cyanides.** Etchants containing cyanides present special toxicity hazards, because poisoning can result from inhaling hard-to-detect small amounts of HCN gas evolved from acidic solutions, from ingesting small amounts of cyanides, and from absorbing cyanides through the skin or exposed body tissues. Careful handling and the use of an effective exhaust hood are especially important. Used cyanide-containing solutions should be rendered slightly alkaline with ammonia and poured into a chemically resistant waste-disposal drain, and the drain flushed thoroughly with copious water.

**Disposal of Etchants.** Spent etchant solutions should be individually poured slowly into a chemically resistant waste-disposal drain in an exhaust hood promptly after use while running a substantial flow of tap water down the drain. The drain should then be flushed thoroughly with abundant water. Strongly acidic, strongly alkaline, corrosive, or toxic solutions should be handled with extra care during disposal, because of the hazards described in the section "Protection of Personnel" in this article. The safe disposal of used solutions containing substantial amounts of volatile solvents requires special attention to avoid the creation of toxicity, fire, or explosion hazards from vapors of the solvents.

## REFERENCES

1. H.-E. Bühler and H.P. Hougardy, Atlas of Interference Layer Metallography, *Dtsch. Ges. Metallkd. Fachber.*, Oberursel, 1980
2. H.E. Exner and J. Roth, Metallographic Contrasting by Reactively Sputtered Interference Layers, *Pract. Metallog.*, Vol 18, 1980, p 365
3. H. Zogg, S. Weber, and H. Warlimont, Optical Enhancement for Al-Alloys by Vacuum Deposited ZnTe Interference Layers, *Pract. Metallog.*, Vol 14, 1977, p 553
4. H. Gahm, F. Jeglitsch, and E.M. Hörl,

Investigations of the Structure of Chemically Deposited Films Produced by Precipitation Etching, *Pract. Metallog.*, Vol 19, 1982, p 369
5. G. Hertsleb and P. Schwaab, Fundamentals of the Potentiostatic Development of Structures Using High-Alloy Steels as an Example, *Pract. Metallog.*, Vol 15, 1978, p 213
6. M. Pohl and W.-G. Burchard, Ion Etching in Metallography, *Pract. Metallog.*, Special Edition 11, Dr. Riederer-Verlag, 1980, p 42 (in German)
7. R.C. Sanwald and D.J. Gould, Ion Etching Metallographic Samples, *Metallography*, Vol 7, 1974, p 73
8. G. Willmann and G. Heimke, Thermal Etching of α-Alumina and Na-β-Alumina, *Pract. Metallog.*, Vol 15, 1978, p 11
9. J.D. Livingstone, Etch Pits at Dislocations in Copper, *J. Appl. Phys.*, Vol 31, 1960, p 1071
10. Luo Yang, Wang Zhen-chin, and Li Wen-chen, Forming Conditions and Geometric Variety of Etch Pits, *Pract. Metallog.*, Vol 20, 1980, p 194, 232
11. H. Klemm, Uses of Thiosulphate (Klemm's Reagent) as an Etchant, *Pract. Metallog.*, Vol 5, 1968, p 163
12. W. Schatt, Control of Textured Sheet by Means of Line Etching, *Pract. Metallog.*, Vol 4, 1967, p 620
13. F. Bitter, On Inhomogeneities in the Magnetization of Ferromagnetic Materials, *Phys. Rev.*, Vol 38, 1931, p 1903
14. L. von Hamos and P.A. Thiessen, Uber die Sicharmachung von Bezirken verschiedemen ferromagnetersehen Zustanden festen Korpen, *Z. Phys.*, Vol 71, 1931, p 442
15. F. Bitter, Experiments on the Nature of Ferromagnetism, *Phys. Rev.*, Vol 41, 1932, p 507
16. L.W. McKeehan and W.C. Elmore, Surface Magnetization in Ferro Magnetic Crystals, *Phys. Rev.*, Vol 46, 1934, p 226
17. *Handbook of Chemistry and Physics*, 48th ed., The Chemical Rubber Co., 1967-68
18. H.S. Avery, V.O. Homerberg, and E. Cook, Metallographic Identification of Ferro Magnetic Phases, *Met. Alloys*, Vol 10, 1935, p 353-355
19. W.C. Elmore, Ferromagnetic Colloid for Studying Magnetic Phases, *Phys. Rev.*, Vol 32, 1938, p 309-310
20. E.A.M. Harvey, Metallographic Identification of Ferro-Magnetic Phases, *Metallurgia*, Vol 32, June 1945, p 71-72
21. P.F. Weinrich, Microferrographic Technique, *Australas. Engr.*, Nov 1948, p 42-44
22. G.F. Fisinai, Magnetic Oxide Etchant, *Met. Prog.*, Vol 17, Oct 1956, p 120-122
23. R. Carey and E.D. Isaac, Ed., *Magnetic Domains and Techniques for Their Observation*, Academic Press, 1966
24. *Metallography, Structures and Phase Diagrams*, Vol 8, 8th ed., *Metals Handbook*, American Society for Metals, 1973

25. R.J. Gray, Revealing Ferromagnetic Microstructures With Ferrofluids, in *Proceedings of the International Microstructural Analysis Society*, International Microstructural Analysis Society, Northglenn, CO, 1971

26. R.J. Gray, "Revealing Ferromagnetic Microstructures With Ferrofluids," ORNL-TM-368, Oak Ridge National Laboratory, Oak Ridge, TN, March 1972

27. R.J. Gray, The Detection of Ferromagnetic Phases in Types 304 and 301 Stainless Steels by Epitaxial Ferromagnetic Etching, in *Microstructural Science*, R.J. Gray and J.L. McCall, Ed., American Elsevier, 1973

28. R.J. Gray, Detection of Ferromagnetic Phases in Types 304 and 301 Stainless Steels by Epitaxial Ferromagnetic Etching, in *Metallog. Rev.*, Vol 2, 1973, p 2

29. R.J. Gray, Magnetic Etching With Ferrofluid, in *Metallographic Specimen Etching*, J.L. McCall and W.M. Mueller, Ed., Plenum Press, 1974, p 155-177

30. Ferrofluid, Ferrofluidics Corp., Nashua, NH

31. P.G. Shewmon, *Transformation in Metals*, McGraw-Hill, 1969, p 394

32. D.T. Read, R.P. Read, and R.E. Schamm, Low Temperature Deformation of Fe-18Cr-8Ni Steel, *Materials Studies for Magnetic Fusion Energy Applications at Low Temperature*, 1979, p 149-172

33. V. Seetharaman and R. Krishnan, Influence of the Martensitic Transformation on the Deformation Behavior of an AISI 316 Stainless Steel at Low Temperatures, *J. Mater. Sci.*, Vol 16, 1981, p 523-530

## SELECTED REFERENCES

- M. Beckert and H. Klemm, *Handbook of Metallographic Etching Techniques*, VEB Deutscher Verlag für Grundstoffindustrie, 1976 (in German)

- G. Elssner and G. Petzow, Modern Ceramographic Preparation and Etching Methods for Incident Light and Scanning Electron Microscopy, in *Microstructural Science*, Vol 9, American Elsevier, 1981, p 83

- P.M. French and J.L. McCall, Ed., *Interpretive Techniques for Microstructural Analysis*, Plenum Press, 1977

- J.L. McCall and W.M. Mueller, Ed., *Metallographic Specimen Preparation*, Plenum Press, 1971

- J.L. McCall and W.M. Mueller, Ed., *Microstructural Analysis, Tools and Techniques*, Plenum Press, 1973

- G. Petzow, *Metallographic Etching*, American Society for Metals, 1978

- G.F. Vander Voort, *Metallography: Principles and Practice*, McGraw-Hill, 1984

# Optical Microscopy

By George F. Vander Voort
Supervisor
Applied Physics Research & Development
Carpenter Technology Corporation

THE OPTICAL (LIGHT) MICROSCOPE remains the most important tool for the study of microstructure, despite the evolution of sophisticated electron metallographic instruments. Scanning electron microscopy (SEM) and transmission electron microscopy (TEM) are invaluable tools as well; however, they should be used in conjunction with optical microscopy, rather than as a substitute. For more information on these methods, see the articles "Scanning Electron Microscopy" and "Transmission Electron Microscopy" in this Volume.

All examinations of microstructure should begin with use of the optical microscope, starting at low magnification, such as 100×, followed by progressively higher magnifications to assess the basic characteristics of the microstructure efficiently. Most microstructures can be observed with the optical microscope and identified based on their characteristics. Identification of questionable or unknown constituents may be aided by ob-

servation of their hardness relative to the matrix, by their natural color, by their response to polarized light, and by their response to selective etchants. These observations are compared to known details about the physical metallurgy of the material being examined. If doubt still remains or if the structure is too fine to observe, more sophisticated techniques must be implemented.

The optical microscope can be used to examine as-polished or etched metallographic specimens. Certain constituents are more readily observed as-polished, because they are not obscured by etching detail. Inclusions, nitrides, certain carbides, and intermetallic phases can be readily observed without etching. Except for inclusions, the other phases may be more easily examined if some relief is introduced during final polishing. The specimen must be adequately prepared to ensure correct observation and interpretation of the microstructure without complications from artifacts. Specimens that respond

to polarized light, such as materials with non-cubic crystal structures, are generally examined without etching.

However, in most cases etching must be performed to observe the microstructure. A general-purpose etchant is normally used first to reveal the grain structure and the phases present, followed by selective etchants that attack or color specific phases of interest. Selective etchants are widely used for quantitative metallography, particularly if performed using an automated device. In either case, etching must be carefully carried out to reveal the microstructure with clarity. General reviews on the use of the optical microscope in metallography are given in Ref 1 to 9.

## Microscope Components

Optical microscopes vary considerably in cost and capability. Reflected light is used for the study of metals. Transmitted-light microscopes are used to study minerals and poly-

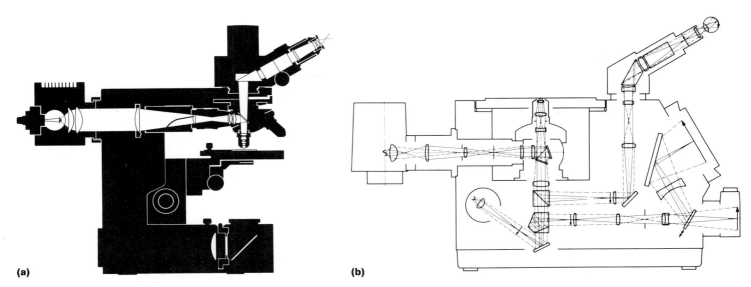

**Fig. 1** Light paths in (a) an upright incident-light microscope and (b) an inverted incident-light microscope. (E. Leitz, Inc.; C. Zeiss, Inc.)

mers, which can also be examined using reflected light. Optical microscopes are also classified as "upright" or "inverted"; these terms refer to the orientation of the plane of polish of the specimen during observation. Figure 1 illustrates the light path in the two designs. Because each configuration has certain advantages and disadvantages, selection generally is based on personal preference. The simplest optical microscope is the bench type (usually upright). Photographic capabilities can be added to some units depending on the rigidity of the stand. Figure 2 illustrates basic bench microscopes, and Figure 3 shows

**(a)**

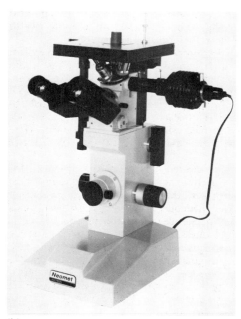

**(b)**

**Fig. 2** (a) Upright bench microscope. (b) Inverted bench microscope (Nikon, Inc.; Unitron Instruments, Inc.)

research-quality bench microscopes suitable for photographic work.

Various metallographs suitable for observation and photomicroscopy are available. These can be rather simple units or full-scale research metallographs with assorted illumination modes, light sources, microhardness attachments, hot stages, and so on. Figure 4 shows a typical example of a medium-priced metallograph; Figure 5 illustrates a full-scale research metallograph. Basic components of the optical microscope are described below.

**Illumination System.** A variety of light sources for optical microscopy are available. The low-voltage tungsten-filament lamp used primarily with bench microscopes has adequate intensity for observation, but not for photography. Altering the current to the bulb controls light intensity.

Carbon-arc illumination systems, once common on metallographs, have been replaced by arc or filament light sources. The xenon-arc light source is prevalent because of its high intensity and daylight color characteristics. Light intensity, however, can be adjusted only by the use of neutral-density filters. Tungsten-halogen filament lamps are also widely used for their high intensity and high color temperature. Light intensity can be controlled by varying the current or by use of neutral-density filters. Other light sources, such as the zirconium-arc, sodium-arc, quartz-iodine, or mercury-vapor lamps, are less common.

**Condenser.** An adjustable lens free of spherical aberration and coma is placed in front of the light source to focus the light at the desired point in the optical path. A field diaphragm is placed in front of this lens to minimize internal glare and reflections within the microscope. The field diaphragm is stopped down to the edge of the field of view.

A second adjustable-iris diaphragm, the aperture diaphragm, is placed in the light path before the vertical illuminator. Opening or closing this diaphragm alters the amount of light and the angle of the cone of light entering the objective lens. The optimum setting for this aperture varies with each objective lens and is a compromise among image contrast, sharpness, and depth of field. As magnification increases, the aperture diaphragm is stopped down. Opening this aperture increases image sharpness, but reduces contrast; closing the aperture increases contrast, but impairs image sharpness. The aperture diaphragm should not be used for reducing light intensity. It should be adjusted only for contrast and sharpness.

**Light filters** are used to modify the light for ease of observation, for improved photomicroscopy, or to alter contrast. Neutral-density filters are used to reduce the light intensity uniformly across the visible spectrum. Various neutral-density filters from approximately 85 to 0.01% transmittance are available. Most optical microscopes offer selection of at least two such filters.

Selective filters are used to balance the color temperature of the light source to that of the film. This is often necessary for faithful reproduction of color images, depending on the light source used and the film type. A green or yellow-green filter is widely used in black-and-white photography to reduce the effect of lens defects on image quality. Most objectives, particularly the lower cost achromats, require such filtering for best results.

Polarizing filters are used to produce plane-polarized light (one filter) or crossed-polarized light (two filters rotated to produce extinction) for examination of noncubic (crystallographic) materials. Materials that are optically anisotropic, such as beryllium, zirconium, $\alpha$-titanium, and uranium, can be examined in the crossed-polarized condition without etching. A sensitive-tint plate may also be used with crossed-polarized light to enhance coloration.

**The objective lens** forms the primary image of the microstructure and is the most important component of the optical microscope. The objective lens collects as much light as possible from the specimen and combines this light to produce the image. The numerical aperture ($NA$) of the objective, a measure of the light-collecting ability of the lens, is defined as:

$$NA = n \sin \alpha \qquad \text{(Eq 1)}$$

where $n$ is the minimum refraction index of the material (air or oil) between the specimen and the lens, and $\alpha$ is the half-angle of the most oblique light rays that enter the front lens of the objective. Light-collecting ability increases with $\alpha$. The setting of the aperture diaphragm will alter the $NA$ of the condenser and therefore the $NA$ of the system.

Objective lenses are usually mounted on a nosepiece turret that can accept four to six objectives. Some metallographs do not use nosepiece turrets, and only one objective at a time can be placed on the vertical illuminator using a bayonet mount. The vertical illuminator contains a reflector or prism that deflects the light down the objective onto the specimen surface. It usually holds the aperture and field diaphragms and filters as well. The vertical illuminator usually provides only one or two types of illumination, such as bright-field and dark-field illumination or bright-field and polarized light illumination. However, universal vertical illuminators are now available that provide all types of illumination with one vertical illuminator and one set of objectives.

The tube length is the length of the body tube from the eye line of the eyepiece to the objective thread. This length is not standardized and can vary. Most objectives are designed for use with a certain tube length, generally 160 to 250 mm, and generally cannot be interchanged.

The most commonly used objective is the achromat, which is corrected spherically for one color (usually yellow-green) and for lon-

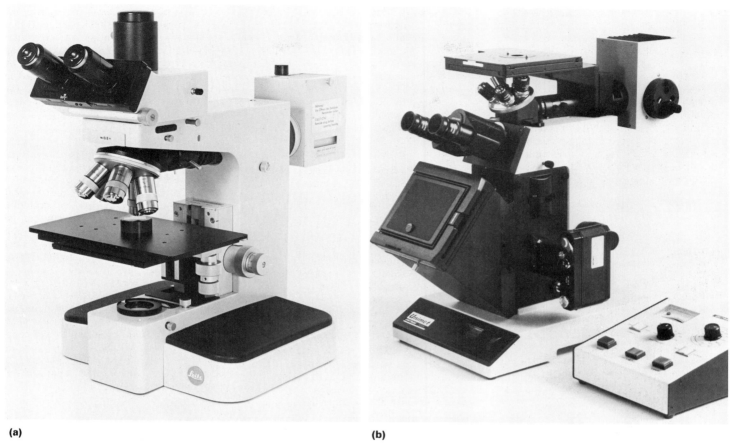

**(a)**

**(b)**

**Fig. 3** Research-quality optical microscopes. (a) Upright. (b) Inverted. (E. Leitz, Inc.; Unitron Instruments, Inc.)

gitudinal chromatic aberration for two colors (usually red and green). Therefore, achromats are not suitable for color photomicroscopy. Use of a yellow-green filter and orthochromatic film yields optimum results. However, achromats do provide a relatively long working distance, that is, the distance from the front lens of the objective to the specimen surface. Working distance decreases as magnification of the objective increases. Most manufacturers make long-working-distance objectives for special applications, for example, in hot-stage microscopy. Achromats are strain free, which is important for polarized light examinations. Because they contain fewer lenses than other more highly corrected lenses, internal reflection losses are minimized.

Semiapochromatic or fluorite objectives provide a higher degree of correction of spherical and chromatic aberration. Therefore, they produce higher quality images than achromats. The apochromatic objectives have the highest degree of correction, produce the best results, and are more expensive. Plano objectives have extensive correction for flatness of field, which reduces eyestrain, and are often found on modern microscopes. Figure 6 illustrates three plano-type objectives. Each is coded as to the type of objective, its magnification, and numerical aperture.

With parfocal lens systems, each objective on the nosepiece turret will be nearly in focus when the turret is rotated, preventing the objective front lens from striking the specimen when lenses are switched. Many objectives also are spring loaded, which helps prevent damage to the lens. This is more of a problem with high-magnification objectives, because the working distance can be very small.

Certain objectives are designed for use with oil between the specimen and the front lens of the objective. However, oil-immersion lenses are rarely used, because the specimen and lens must be cleaned after use. However, they do provide higher resolutions than can be achieved when air is between the lens and specimen. In the latter case, the maximum possible $NA$ is 0.95; oil-immersion lenses produce a 1.3 to 1.45 $NA$, depending on the lens and the oil used. Magnifications from 25 to $160\times$ are available. Use of oil also sharpens the image, which is valuable when examining low-reflectivity specimens, such as coal or ceramics.

**The eyepiece,** or ocular, magnifies the primary image produced by the objective; the eye can then use the full resolution capability of the objective. The microscope produces a virtual image of the specimen at the point of most distinct vision, generally 250 mm (10 in.) from the eye. The eyepiece magnifies this

image, permitting achievement of useful magnifications. The standard eyepiece has a 24-mm-diam field of view; wide-field eyepieces for plano objectives have a 30-mm-diam field of view (Fig. 7), which increases the usable area of the primary image.

The simplest eyepiece is the Huygenian, which is satisfactory for use with low- and medium-power achromat objectives. Compensating eyepieces are used with high $NA$ achromat and the more highly corrected objectives. Because some lens corrections are performed using these eyepieces, the eyepiece must be matched with the type of objective used.

Eye clearance is the distance between the eye lens of the ocular and the eye. For most eyepieces, the eye clearance is 10 mm or less—inadequate if the microscopist wears glasses. Simple vision problems, such as nearsightedness, can be accommodated using the fine focus adjustment. Vision problems such as astigmatism cannot be corrected by the microscope, and glasses must be worn. High-eyepoint eyepieces are available to provide the eye clearance of approximately 20 mm necessary for glasses (Fig. 8).

Eyepieces are commonly equipped with various reticles or graticules for locating, measuring, counting, or comparing microstructures. The eyepiece enlarges the reticle

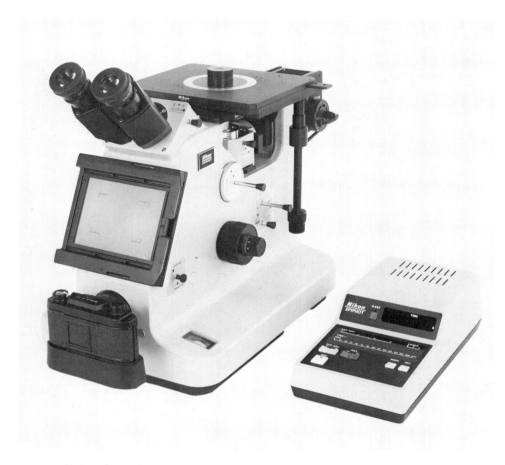

**Fig. 4** Moderately priced inverted metallograph. The small box to the right is an automatic exposure control. (Nikon, Inc.)

**Fig. 5** Research-quality metallograph with a projection screen for group viewing. (E. Leitz, Inc.)

A $10\times$ magnification eyepiece is usually used; to obtain standard magnifications, some systems require other magnifications, such as $6.3\times$. Higher power eyepieces, such as $12\times$, $15\times$, $20\times$, or $25\times$, are also useful in certain situations. The overall magnification is found by multiplying the objective magnification, $M_o$, by the eyepiece magnification, $M_e$. If a zoom system or bellows is also used, the magnification should be altered accordingly.

**Stage.** A mechanical stage is provided for focusing and moving the specimen, which is placed on the stage and secured using clips. The stage of an inverted microscope has replaceable center-stage plates with different size holes. The polished surface is placed against the hole for viewing. However, the entire surface cannot be viewed, and at high magnifications it may not be possible to focus the objective near the edge of the hole due to the restricted working distance.

Using the upright microscope, the specimen is placed on a slide on the stage. Because the polished surface must be perpendicular to the light beam, clay is placed between the specimen bottom and the slide. A piece of lens tissue is placed over the polished surface, and the specimen is pressed into the clay using a leveling press. However, pieces of tissue may adhere to the specimen surface. An alternative, particularly useful with mounted specimens, is to use a ring instead of tissue to flatten the specimen. Aluminum or stainless steel ring forms of the same size as the mounts (flattened slightly in a vise) will seat on the mount rather than the specimen.

The upright microscope allows viewing of the entire surface with any objective, and the operator can see which section of the specimen is being viewed—a useful feature when examining specific areas on coated specimens, welds, and other specimens where specific areas are to be examined. For mounted specimens, an autoleveling stage holder for mounts can eliminate leveling specimens on clay.

The stage must be rigid to eliminate vibrations. Stage movement, controlled by $x$- and $y$-micrometers, must be smooth and precise; rack and pinion gearing is normally used. Many stages have scales for measuring the distances in the $x$- and $y$-directions. The focusing controls often contain rulings for estimating vertical movement. Some units have motorized stages and focus controls.

A circular rotatable stage plate may facilitate polarized light examination. Such stages, common for mineralogical or petrographic studies, are graduated to permit measuring the angle of rotation. A rectilinear stage is generally placed on top of the circular stage.

**Stand.** Bench microscopes require a rigid stand, particularly if photomicroscopy is performed on the unit. The various pieces of the microscope are attached to the stand when assembled. In some cases, the bench microscope is placed on a separate stand that also holds the photographic system.

or graticule image and the primary image. Both images must be in focus simultaneously. Special eyepieces are also produced to permit more accurate measurements than can be made with a graticule scale. Examples are the filar-micrometer ocular or screw-micrometer ocular. Such devices can be automated to produce a direct digital readout of the measurement (Fig. 9), which is accurate to approximately 1 $\mu$m.

**Fig. 6** Plano-type objective lenses and cross sections through each. The lens shown in (c) is a 14-element oil-immersion objective, with a numerical aperture (NA) of 1.32. Because the lens and specimen must be cleaned between each use, oil immersion is rarely used; it does provide higher resolution and a crisper image, which is valuable for examining low-reflectivity specimens. (E. Leitz, Inc.)

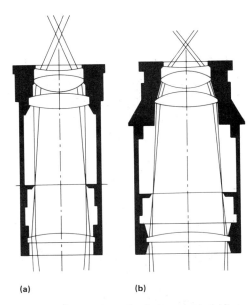

**Fig. 7** Cross sections of typical eyepieces. (a) Standard (24-mm) field of view. (b) Wide (30-mm) field of view. The wide-field eyepiece increases the usable area of the primary image. (E. Leitz, Inc.)

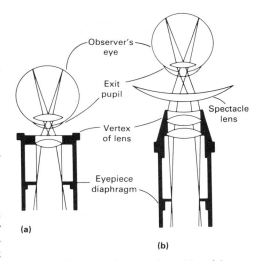

**Fig. 8** Comparison between the position of the eye with (a) a standard eyepiece and (b) a high-point eyepiece. Eye clearance with a standard eyepiece is approximately 10 mm (0.4 in.); a high-point eyepiece allows clearances of approximately 20 mm (0.8 in.) (E. Leitz, Inc.)

## Lens Defects

Many lens defects result from the laws of reflection and refraction. The refractive index of a lens varies with the wavelength of light, and the focal length of the lens varies with the refractive index. Therefore, focal length will change for different colors of light. A separate image for each wavelength present is focused at different distances from the lens (Fig. 10). This is longitudinal chromatic aberration. Moreover, magnification varies with focal length, altering the size of the image. This is lateral chromatic aberration (Fig. 11). These differences must be eliminated to produce color photographs. Because achromats have limited corrections for these problems, they must be used with yellow-green light filtering to obtain sharp images.

Spherical aberration (Fig. 12) occurs when light from a point object on the optical axis is more strongly refracted at the center or at the periphery of the lens, producing a series of focal positions in which the point image appears as a circle of finite area. This can be minimized by using an aperture that restricts use of the objective to the central portion. Lens design also can correct part of this problem.

Because the image surface of optimum focus is curved, compensating eyepieces with equal but opposite curvature are used to produce a flat image (Fig. 13). Other problems, such as coma and astigmatism, can impair image quality unless corrected.

## Resolution

To see microstructural detail, the optical system must produce adequate resolution, or resolving power, and adequate image contrast. If resolution is acceptable but contrast is lacking, detail cannot be observed. In general, the ability to resolve two points or lines separated by a distance $d$ is a function of the wavelength, $\lambda$, of the incident light and the numerical aperture, $NA$, of the objective.

$$d = \frac{k\lambda}{NA} \qquad \text{(Eq 2)}$$

where $k$ is 0.5 or 0.61. Figure 14 illustrates this relationship for $k = 0.61$ and four light wavelengths. Other formulas have also been reported (Ref 10). Equation 2 does not include other factors that influence resolution, such as the degree of correction of the objectives and the visual acuity of the microscopist. It was based on the work of Abbe under conditions not present in metallography, such as self-luminous points, perfect black-white contrast, transmitted-light examination, an ideal point-light source, and absence of lens defects (Ref 11).

Using Eq 2, the limit of resolution for an objective with an $NA$ of 1.4 is approximately 0.2 $\mu$m. To see lines or points spaced 0.2 $\mu$m apart, the required magnification must be determined by dividing the resolving power of the objective by the resolving power of the human eye, which is difficult to determine under observation conditions. Abbe used a value of 0.3 mm at a distance of 250 mm—the distance from the eye for optimum vision. For light with a mean wavelength of 0.55 $\mu$m, the required magnification is 1100 times the $NA$ of the objective. This is the origin of the 1000 $NA$ rule for the maximum useful magnification. Any magnification above 1000 $NA$ is termed "empty," or useless.

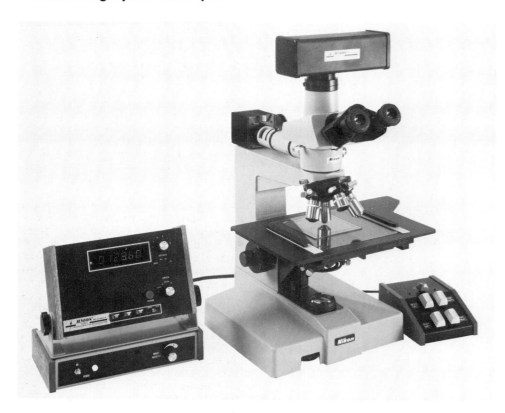

**Fig. 9** Electronic digital filar eyepiece system. This device allows measurements on the microstructure with less error and eye fatigue than an eyepiece equipped with reticles or graticules. (Nikon, Inc.)

Strict adherence to the 1000 *NA* rule should be questioned, considering the conditions under which it was developed, which are certainly far different from those encountered in metallography. According to the Abbe analysis, for a microscopist with optimum 20/20 vision and for optimum contrast conditions and a mean light wavelength of 550 nm, the lowest magnification that takes full advantage of the *NA* of the objective is 550 times the *NA*. This establishes a useful minimum magnification to use with a given objective. It has been suggested that the upper limit of useful magnification for the average microscopist is 2200 *NA*, not 1000 *NA* (Ref 11).

## Depth of Field

Depth of field is the distance along the optical axis over which image details are observed with acceptable clarity. Those factors that influence resolution also affect depth of field, but in the opposite direction. Therefore, a compromise must be reached between these two parameters, which becomes more difficult as magnification increases. This is one reason light etching is preferred for high-magnification examination. The depth of field, $T_f$, can be estimated from:

$$T_f = \frac{\lambda \sqrt{n^2 - NA^2}}{NA^2} \qquad \text{(Eq 3)}$$

where *n* is the refractive index of the medium between the specimen and the objective ($n \approx$ 1.0 for air), $\lambda$ is the wavelength of light, and *NA* is the numerical aperture. Equation 3 shows that depth of field increases as the *NA* decreases and when longer wavelength light is used, as shown in Fig. 15.

## Examination Modes

To achieve the resolution capability of the selected objective, image contrast must be adequate. Image contrast depends on specimen preparation and optics. Differences in light reflectivity from the specimen surface produce amplitude features visible to the eye after magnification. Phase differences created by light reflection must be rendered visible by the use of phase-contrast or interference-contrast attachments to the microscope.

**Bright-Field Illumination.** Bright-field vertical illumination, the most widely used method of observation, accounts for the vast majority of micrographs taken. In operation, light passes through the objective and strikes the specimen surface perpendicularly. Surface features normal to the incident light reflect light back through the objective to the eyepieces, where the surface features appear bright. Surfaces oblique to the light beam reflect less light to the objective and appear darker, depending on their angle.

**Oblique Illumination.** With some microscopes, it is possible to decenter the condenser assembly or the mirror so that the light passing through the objective strikes the specimen surface at a nonperpendicular angle. Roughness on the specimen surface will cast shadows, producing a three-dimensional appearance. This allows determination of features that are in relief or are recessed. However, very little obliqueness can be introduced, because this technique causes lighting to become nonuniform and reduces resolution.

**In dark-field illumination,** the light reflected from obliquely oriented features is collected, and the rays reflected from features normal to the incident beam are blocked. Therefore, the contrast is essentially reversed from that of bright-field illumination; that is, features that are bright in bright-field illumination appear dark, and features normally dark appear bright. This produces very strong image contrast, with the oblique features appearing luminous. Under such conditions, it is often possible to see features not visible using bright-field illumination. This method is particularly useful for studying grain structures. However, the low light intensity makes photomicroscopy more difficult, a problem lessened by the use of automatic exposure-control devices.

Figures 16 to 18 illustrate the value of dark-field illumination for examining grain structure. Figures 19 to 21 show the eutectic in the copper-phosphorus system in bright-field, dark-field, and interference-contrast illumination. Note the strong contrast at the lamellae in dark-field. Figures 22 to 25 show martensite formed in a copper-aluminum alloy using bright-field, dark-field, polarized light, and interference-contrast illumination. Note how the latter three illumination modes produce greater detail of the structure than bright-field illumination (even if the specimen is etched).

**Polarized light** (Ref 12-14), as used in metallography, has generally been limited to observation of certain optically anisotropic metals, such as beryllium, α-titanium, zirconium, and uranium, that are difficult to etch but respond well to polarized light when properly polished. Before development of the electron microprobe analyzer (EMPA) and energy-dispersive spectroscopy (EDS), polarized light examination was an integral part of the procedure for identifying inclusions. Since the development of these instruments, polarized light has been used less frequently for this purpose, because identification with the EMPA or EDS techniques is more definitive.

Most metallurgical microscopes now use synthetic Polaroid filters. The "polarizer" is placed in the light path before the objective, and the "analyzer" is placed in the light path after the objective, generally just below the eyepiece. Figure 26 shows the light path in the incident-light polarizing microscope.

Light consists of transverse waves vibrating in all directions at right angles to the direction of propagation. These vibrations occur

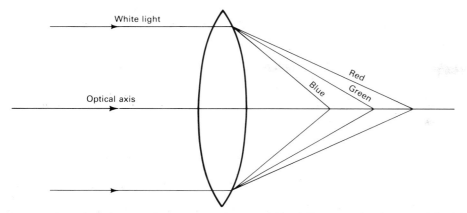

**Fig. 10** Longitudinal chromatic aberration in an uncorrected lens. Different wavelengths cause each of the three primary colors to be focused at a different point along the optical axis.

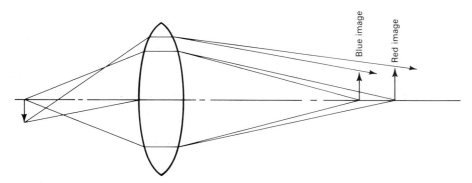

**Fig. 11** Lateral chromatic aberration. As focal length is varied, magnification changes, altering image size.

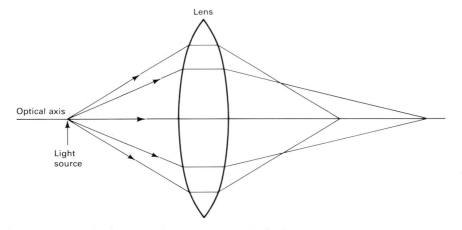

**Fig. 12** Spherical aberration. Light rays passing through the outer portion of the lens are more strongly refracted than those passing through the central portion and are focused at a different point along the optical axis. This problem can be minimized by using an aperture to restrict the light path to the central part of the objective.

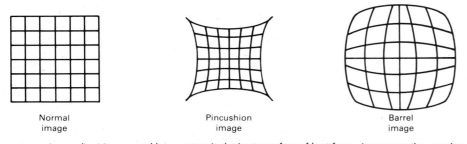

**Fig. 13** Image distortions caused by curvature in the image surface of best focus. A compensating eyepiece, with a curvature equal to but opposite of that of the image surface, must be used to produce a normal image.

symmetrically around the direction of propagation and are unpolarized. When light passes through a polarizing filter, the vibrations occur in only one plane in the direction of propagation, and the light is termed plane-polarized. This plane will change as the filter is rotated. When the analyzer filter is placed in the light path, plane-polarized light will pass through it if the plane of vibration of the light is parallel to the plane of vibration of the analyzer. If the plane of vibration of the analyzer is perpendicular to that of the light, the light will not pass through, and extinction results.

When plane-polarized light is reflected from the surface of an isotropic metal (any metal with a cubic crystallographic structure, such as iron), then passes through the analyzer in the crossed position (plane of vibration perpendicular to that of the plane-polarized light), the image is extinguished, or dark. However, in practice, because the metallurgical microscope will not produce perfectly plane-polarized light, complete extinction will not occur. This is not a serious problem, because polarized light is used only in a qualitative manner in metallography. Strain-free objectives, usually achromats, must be used. Fluorite or apochromatic objectives are unsuitable. A strong white-light source is required to produce accurate color effects.

If an optically anisotropic, polished metal is placed under the light beam with the polarizer and analyzer crossed, the microstructure will be revealed (Fig. 27 and 28). The quality of specimen preparation is very important, and the surface must be perpendicular to the light path. Rotation of the specimen under the beam changes light intensity and color. Because it may be difficult to set the polarizer and analyzer in the crossed position accurately when an anisotropic specimen is in place unless the crossed positions are marked on the polarizer and the analyzer, it is best to find this position first using an isotropic specimen.

When plane-polarized light strikes an anisotropic metal surface, reflection occurs as two plane-polarized components at right angles to each other. The directions vary with crystal structure. The strength of these two perpendicular reflections can change, and a phase difference exists between them. These differences vary with each metal and depend on the crystal orientation. No reflection is obtained when the basal plane of hexagonal or tetragonal crystals is perpendicular to the light beam. Maximum reflectance occurs when the principal symmetry axis of the crystal is perpendicular to the light beam. The resultant image is predominantly influenced by these orientation effects; phase differences are of little significance.

When the analyzer is crossed with respect to the polarizer, rotation of plane-polarized light from the anisotropic surface allows the light to pass through the analyzer, producing an image in which each grain has a different light intensity and color, depending on its

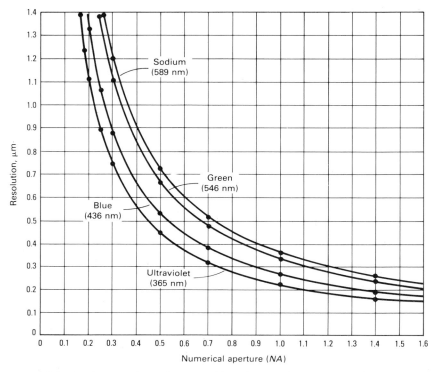

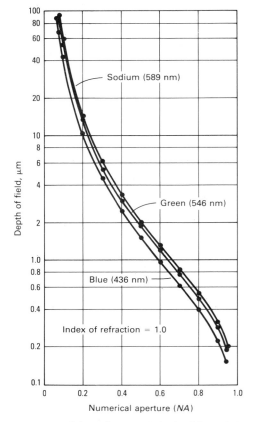

**Fig. 14** Relationship between the resolution possible with an incident-light microscope and the numerical aperture of the objective lens used for four wavelengths of light

**Fig. 15** Relationship among depth of field of the image produced, numerical aperture of the objective used, and wavelength of light employed

crystal orientation relative to the light beam. As the stage is rotated, each grain changes four times in intensity from light to dark during a 360° rotation. If the phase difference is appreciable, the light will be elliptically polarized, the difference in intensity in each grain with rotation will be less, and extinction will not be observed. Color images are obtained when the reflected plane-polarized light varies with wavelength. When little color is present, a sensitive tint plate inserted between the polarizer and the objective will enhance coloration.

Isotropic metals can be examined using crossed-polarized light if the surface can be rendered optically active by etching, staining, or anodizing. Procedures have been devel-

oped for several metals (Ref 9); however, all etched surfaces do not respond to polarized light. Generally, the etch must produce etch pits or facets in each grain to cause double reflection at these features. Grains with different crystal orientations produce differently oriented pits or facets, yielding different degrees of elliptical polarization and therefore varying light intensity.

Anodizing produces a thick oxide film on the specimen surface; irregularities in the film lead to double reflection. Although the polarization response of anodized specimens has been attributed to optical anisotropy of the film, experimentation has shown that the effect is due to film surface irregularities (Ref 15). Tint etchants produce surface films that

result in interference colors that can be enhanced using polarized light. In general, best results are obtained when the analyzer is shifted slightly from the crossed position.

In addition to its use in examining inclusions, anisotropic metals (antimony, beryllium, bismuth, cadmium, cobalt, magnesium, scandium, tellurium, tin, titanium, uranium, zinc, and zirconium, for example), and etched/anodized/tint-etched cubic metals, polarized light is useful for examination of coated or deformed metals. Phase identifica-

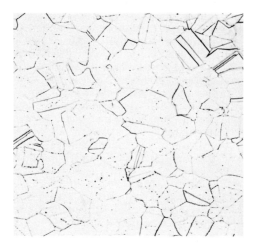

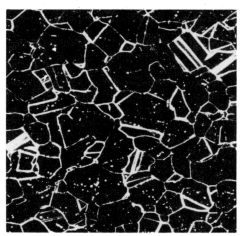

**Fig. 16, 17, 18** Austenitic stainless steel (Fe-20Cr-33Ni-2.5Mo-3.5Cu and Nb + Ta), solution annealed. Fig. 16: bright-field illumination. Fig. 17: dark-field illumination. Fig. 18: differential interference-contrast illumination. 15 mL HCl, 10 mL acetic acid, 10 mL HNO₃, and 2 drops glycerol. 400×

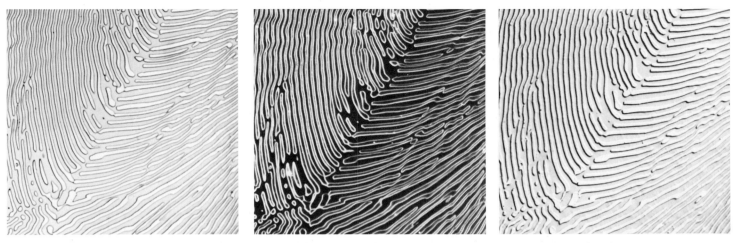

**Fig. 19, 20, 21** Cu-8.9P sand cast alloy showing the $\alpha$ + Cu$_3$P eutectic. Fig. 19: bright-field illumination. Fig. 20: dark-field illumination. Fig. 21: differential interference-contrast illumination. Swab etched using an aqueous solution of 3% (NH$_4$)$_2$S$_2$O$_8$ and 1% NH$_4$OH. 1000×

**Fig. 22, 23, 24, 25** Cu-11.8Al (aluminum bronze), heat treated, with martensite in the microstructure. Fig. 22: bright-field illumination. Fig. 23: dark-field illumination. Fig. 24: differential interference-contrast illumination. Fig. 25: crossed polarized light illumination. As-polished. 200×

tion may also be aided in some cases. The internal structure of graphite nodules in cast iron is vividly revealed using polarized light (Fig. 29 to 31). Martensitic structures are frequently better revealed using polarized light, as shown in Fig. 32 and 33, which illustrate lath martensite in a high-strength iron-base alloy, AF 1410.

**Phase contrast illumination** (Ref 16) permits examination of subtle phase variations in microstructures with little or no amplitude contrast from differences in the optical path at the surface (reflected light) or from differences in the optical path through the specimen (transmitted light). Height differences as small as 0.005 $\mu$m can be detected. Application of phase-contrast illumination in metallography has been limited. The technique requires a separate set of objectives and a special vertical illuminator.

**Interference-Contrast Illumination.** Differential interference-contrast (DIC) illumination (Ref 17-19) produces images with emphasized topographic detail similar to those observed using oblique illumination. Detail that is invisible or faintly visible using bright-

field illumination may be revealed vividly with interference-contrast illumination.

Figure 34 shows the light path in the incident light interference contrast mode using the Nomarski-modified Wollaston prism. When light passes through the double-quartz prism, it is split into two wave fronts with a path difference of T$_1$; that is, one wave front is slightly ahead of the other. When this light is reflected from the specimen surface, the path difference T$_1$ changes due to the height differences on the surface. The split wave fronts also cause phase jumps resulting from different refractive indices of the specimen phases. The change in path difference after reflection is T$_0$. When the reflected light re-enters the prism, the path difference is T$_2$. These wave fronts are recombined without interference, because they are still linearly polarized perpendicular to each other. The path difference before the analyzer is T$_{total}$ (T$_{Ges}$):

$$T_{total} = T_1 \pm T_0 \pm T_2 \qquad \text{(Eq 4)}$$

Only those split wavefronts of T$_{total}$ = (2$k$ + 1) $\lambda$/2 where $k$ = 0, 1, 2, and so on, pass

through the analyzer. If the prism is symmetrical to the microscope axis, T$_1$ = T$_2$ and the image intensity in the field of view is a function of T$_0$ because of geometric height differences and phase jumps. Therefore, the intensity differences produce relief effects resembling unilateral, oblique illumination.

Examples of the topographic detail that can be revealed using differential interference-contrast illumination are illustrated in Fig. 18, 21, 24, and 30. This detail shows the relative hardness of the constituents or the nature of the etching process, that is, which areas or constituents were attacked by the etchant. In some instances, other aspects of the structure may be revealed that are invisible or faintly visible in bright-field illumination. Figures 35 to 37 show the microstructure of solution-annealed and aged Waspaloy, a nickel-base superalloy, etched in glyceregia. Interference-contrast better reveals the austenitic twin structure and shows the roughness in the austenite matrix due to the presence of very fine $\gamma'$ phase. Figures 38 and 39 depict the structure of Inconel 718 after extended high-temperature exposure that has produced orthorhombic platelets of

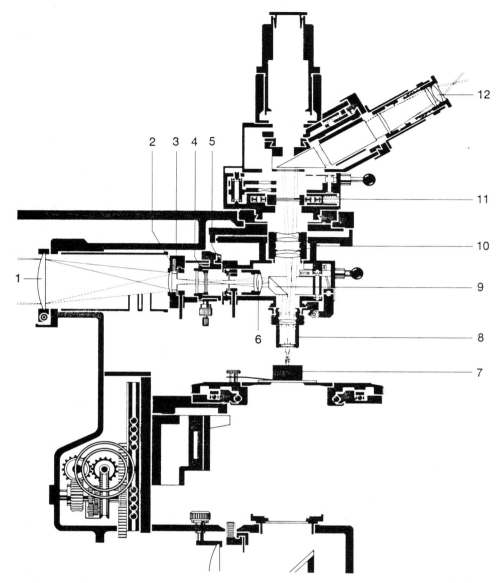

**Fig. 26** Light path in an incident-light polarizing microscope. 1, Hinged lens; 2, half stop; 3, aperture diaphragm; 4, filter or prism polarizer; 5, field diaphragm; 6, centrable lens, used to center the field diaphragm; 7, polished section; 8, objective; 9, compensating prism, with switchover against optical-flat reflector; 10, tube lens (intermediate optical system); 11, rotating analyzer; 12, eyepiece with focusing eyelens. (E. Leitz, Inc.)

$\delta$-Ni$_3$Nb. Differential interference-contrast illumination clearly shows this phase and the massive MC-type carbides in relief.

**Interference Techniques.** Several interference techniques (Ref 20, 21) are used to measure height differences on specimens. Interference fringes on a perfectly flat surface appear as straight, parallel lines of equal width and spacing. Height variations cause these fringes to appear curved or jagged, depending on the unit used. The interference microscope divides the light from a single point source into two or more waves that are superimposed after traveling different paths. This produces interference. Two-beam and multiple-beam instruments are the two basic types of interferometers used. The measurements are based on the wavelength of the light used. Two-beam interferometers can measure height differences as small as $\lambda/20$; multiple-beam interferometers, as small as $\lambda/200$.

The Linnik-type interferometer is a two-beam reflecting microscope that uses nonpolarized light. A beam-splitting prism produces two light beams from a monochromatic light source. One beam travels through the testpiece objective to the testpiece surface and is reflected back through the objective to the eyepiece. The other beam travels through the reference objective, strikes an optically flat reference mirror, and returns to the beam splitter, then to the eyepiece. If the path difference between the two beams is not equal or not a multiple of $\lambda/2$, interference occurs and contour lines are formed that indicate locations of equal elevation. The height difference between adjacent fringes is $\lambda/2$.

The Tolansky multiple-beam interferometer produces interference between many light beams by placing a reference mirror that is partially transmitting and partially reflecting very near the specimen surface but slightly out of parallel. The reference mirror has a known reflectivity selected to approximate that of the surface. Light passes through the reference mirror and strikes the specimen surface, is reflected by the specimen surface, and interferes with the rays reflected between the reference mirror and the specimen. The fringes produced by the multiple-beam interferometer are sharper than those from the two-beam interferometer, which accounts for the greater accuracy. The distance between the fringes is also $\lambda/2$. Elevations produce displacements of the fringes from parallel alignment. The displacement is compared to the distance between the fringes to obtain height measurements.

**Light-Section Microscopy.** The light-section microscope (Fig. 40), also used to measure surface topography, complements interferometry techniques. Roughness differences from 1 to 400 $\mu$m can be measured, which is useful in examining machined surfaces and for measurement of surface layers or films. In operation, a slit is placed near the field iris in the illumination system and is imaged

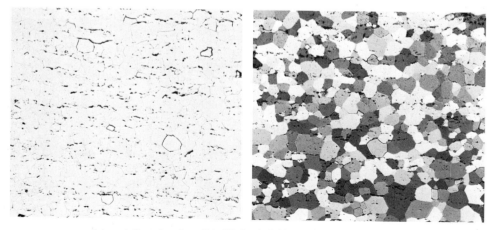

**Fig. 27, 28** Polycrystalline zirconium. Fig. 27: bright-field illumination. Fig. 28: crossed polarized light illumination. Chemically polished in 45 mL HNO$_3$, 45 mL H$_2$O$_2$, and 10 mL HF. 100$\times$

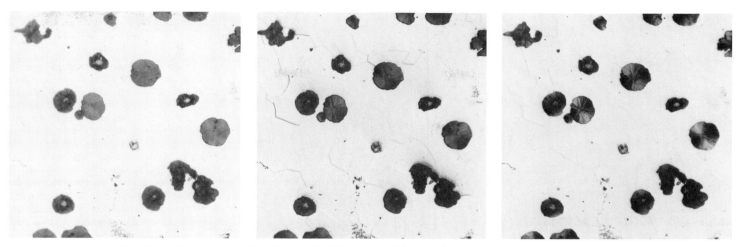

**Fig. 29, 30, 31** Graphite nodules in cast iron. Fig. 29: bright-field illumination. Fig. 30: differential interference-contrast illumination. Fig. 31: crossed polarized light illumination. 2% nital. 400×

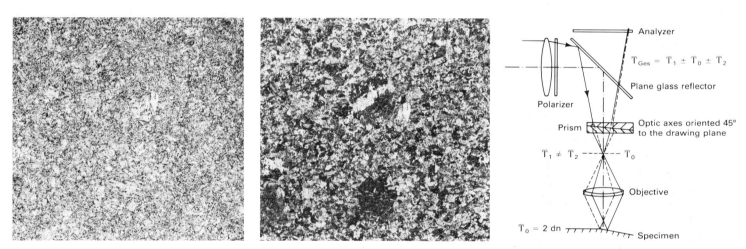

**Fig. 32, 33** AF 1410 alloy steel. Fig. 32: Highly tempered lath martensite is difficult to study under bright-field illumination. Fig. 33: Crossed polarized light reveals the packet size by contrast differences. Tint etched in 10% $Na_2S_2O_5$. 100×

**Fig. 34** Light path in an incident-light DIC microscope. (C. Zeiss, Inc.)

Analyzer

$\overline{T}_{Ges} = \overline{T}_1 \pm \overline{T}_0 \pm \overline{T}_2$

Plane glass reflector

Polarizer

Prism — Optic axes oriented 45° to the drawing plane

$\overline{T}_1 \neq \overline{T}_2$ — $\overline{T}_0$

Objective

$\overline{T}_0 = 2\ dn$ — Specimen

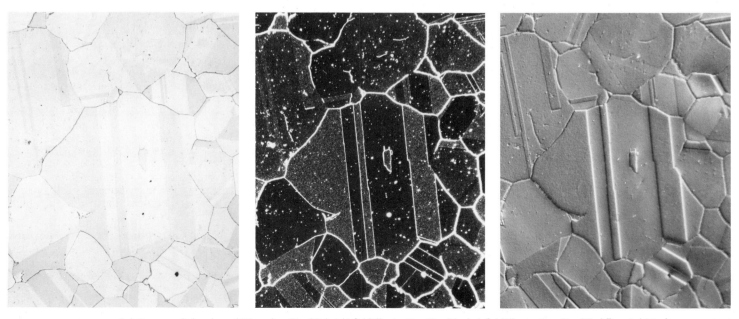

**Fig. 35, 36, 37** Solution-annealed and aged Waspaloy. Fig. 35: bright-field illumination. Fig. 36: dark-field illumination. Fig. 37: differential interference-contrast illumination. Glyceregia. 200×

 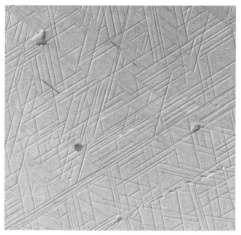

**Fig. 38, 39** Inconel 718 heat treated 100 h at 870 °C (1600 °F) to produce needlelike orthorhombic $Ni_3Nb$. Fig. 38: bright-field illumination. Fig. 39: differential interference-contrast illumination. Particles in relief in Fig. 39 are niobium carbides; particles flush with the surface are niobium nitride. As-polished. 400×

by an objective as a light line on the surface to be measured. Oblique illumination is used with a dark background. The light band is observed using a second objective that is identical to the first. The objectives are 45° to the specimen surface and 90° to each other. A reticle in the eyepiece is used for measurements, or they are made on photographs. Vertical resolution is not as good as with interferometers, but lateral resolution is better.

## Auxiliary Techniques

Several special devices may be used with the optical microscope to obtain additional information. These procedures or techniques are described below.

**Microhardness Testing.** Microindentation hardness data may be obtained by adding indenter attachments to the microscope. Single-purpose units also are made by most manufacturers of hardness test equipment. Loads are generally made from 1 to 1000 g, although some manufacturers have units for low loads (0.05 to 200 g). Knoop or Vickers indenters can be used.

**Hot-Stage Microscopy.** Hot-stage microscope cells are available from several manufacturers. Single-purpose units can also be used. Cold-cell attachments have also been produced, but have rather limited use in metallography. The hot-stage microscope has been used to study phase transformations on heating or cooling or at constant temperature (Ref 22, 23).

Examination of reactions in the hot-stage microscope cell requires use of long-working-distance objectives, because the specimen is held within the cell. Moreover, because the cell window is quartz, the objectives must be quartz-corrected, especially those with magnifications of 20× or more.

Techniques other than chemical etching must be used to view phase changes. Grain boundaries will be thermally etched if the specimen is held at a constant temperature in the vacuum. Grain-boundary grooving is easily observed using bright-field illumination, as shown in Fig. 41. Phase transformations are visible by the relief produced at the surface. Therefore, shear reactions, such as those produced by martensite or bainite formation, are most easily observed (Fig. 42 and 43). Other phase transformations are more difficult or impossible to observe. Transformations may be photographed *in situ*, for which motion picture cameras are commonly used.

**Special stages** are available in a variety of configurations. Autoleveling stages for mounted specimens are a typical example. Universal tilting stages have also been constructed for rapid manipulation of rough, irregular specimens. Special stages have also been designed for handling small objects.

A number of stages have been constructed for performing *in situ* experiments. Basic studies of solidification have been performed by *in situ* observation of the freezing of low-melting-point organic materials, such as camphene, that solidify like metals (Ref 24). Observation of the recrystallization of low-melting-point metals and alloys has been similarly observed (Ref 25).

Special stages have been used to observe the progress of electrolytic polishing and etching (Ref 26). Cells have also been used for *in situ* examination of corrosion processes (Ref 27). Stages have been designed to observe a variety of processes involving static or dynamic stress (Ref 28-32), and devices have also been designed to permit physical extraction of inclusions (Ref 33).

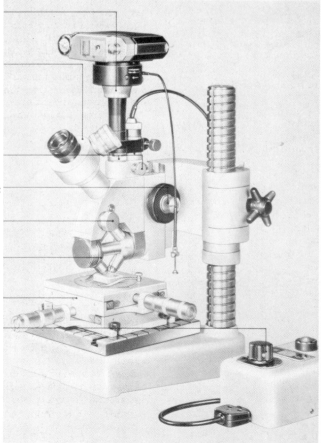

Camera attachment

Eyepiece micrometer

Screw for focusing light on specimen and knob for centering the light band on the reticle

Combined coarse and fine focusing adjustment

Switch for ocular viewing or photographing

Revolving nosepiece for pairs of objective lenses

Mechanical stage

On/off switch with brightness adjuster

**Fig. 40** Light-section microscope. (C. Zeiss, Inc.)

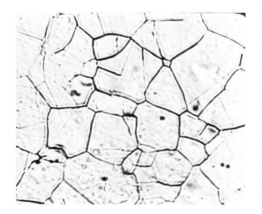

**Fig. 41** Low-carbon Cr-Mo-V steel. Thermally etched austenite grain boundaries are shown *in situ* at 1000 °C (1830 °F) on a hot-stage microscope. 440×. (A.O. Benscoter)

**Hot-Cell Microscopy.** Metallographic preparation of radioactive materials requires remote-control preparation using specially designed hot cells (Ref 34, 35). Special metallographs (Fig. 44) have been designed for use with the hot cell.

**Field Microscopy.** When the microstructure of a component or large object that cannot be cut and moved to the laboratory must be examined, portable laboratory equipment, made by several manufacturers, can be used to polish a section *in situ*. A portable microscope (Fig. 45) may sometimes be used to examine and photograph the microstructure. If this cannot be done, replicas can be made and examined using an optical microscope (Ref 36, 37) or an electron microscope.

**Comparison Microscopes.** The need occasionally arises to compare two microstructures. Generally, this is carried out by placing micrographs from each specimen side-by-side, but it can also be performed using special microscopes. A bridge comparator (Fig. 46) is used to combine images from two bench microscopes for simultaneous viewing.

**Television Monitors.** Projection microscopes can be used for group viewing, but it is more common to display the microstructure on a black-and-white or color monitor. A number of high-resolution closed-circuit systems are available. An example is shown in Fig. 47.

**Clean-Room Microscopy.** The study of small particles is influenced by dust contamination during viewing. Therefore, such work must be performed in a clean box, clean bench, or clean room that is specially constructed to provide a dust-free environment.

**Image Analyzers.** The increased use of quantitative metallography, particularly for characterization of inclusions, has promoted development of automated image analysis systems (Fig. 48) based on television principles. Phases or constituents of interest are detected primarily by differences in light reflectivity that produce gray-level differences on the monitor. Most stereological measurements can be made using these systems. (For

more information on stereological measurements, see the article "Quantitative Metallography" in this Volume.) Considerable automation has been achieved using automated stages and powerful minicomputers.

Features are detected on as-polished or etched specimens, depending on the nature of the feature of interest. If etching is required, selective techniques are generally used (Ref 9). Field and feature-specific measurements are utilized. Field measurements measure all the detected features simultaneously, as in volume fraction measurements. In feature-specific measurements, each separate particle is measured sequentially. This procedure is generally used for shape and size measurements.

Some structures do not lend themselves to accurate measurements using such systems. For example, quantification of fracture surface detail cannot be performed using an automatic image analyzer, because the device cannot separate fracture features by gray level. Many transmission electron micrograph structures also cannot be analyzed using these devices. For such structures, semi-automatic tracing devices (Fig. 49) can be used; the operator performs detection with a light pen or stylus. These lower-cost systems can be used for nearly any stereological measurement. Because of the greater time required for detection, they are less suitable for measurement problems that require sampling of many fields.

 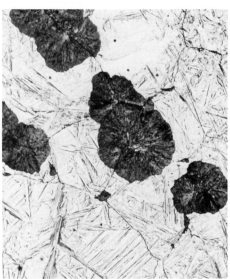

**Fig. 42, 43** High-carbon steel, quenched in the hot stage at a rate that allowed some pearlite (smooth areas) to form before the martensite (rough areas). In hot-stage microscopy, phase transformations are observed by the relief produced at the surface of the specimen. Fig. 43 shows the same area as Fig. 42 after light polishing and etching. 320×. (J.R. Kilpatrick)

**Fig. 44** Metallograph designed for use in hot cells. (E. Leitz, Inc.)

## Photomicroscopy

Prior to the development of photographic attachments, microstructures had to be sketched. Although the need for such documentation has long since past, sketching remains useful as a teaching method. Photomicroscopy is important in metallography, because the photomicrograph can faithfully reproduce the detail observed for others to view. With the equipment currently available, high-quality micrographs are easily produced. However, doing so requires careful attention to specimen preparation, etching, and use of the microscope. Reproduction of false microstructures is all too common and has caused inaccurate interpretations, rejection of good materials, and faulty conclusions in failure analyses.

Historically, darkroom photographic procedures have been most prevalent; since the introduction of instant photographic processes such as Polaroid, however, many photomicrographs have been made using these materials, taking advantage of their speed and efficiency. However, image reproduction is sacrificed, and the process must be repeated for each extra copy. Use of an automatic exposure device is necessary with instant process film to minimize waste. Traditional darkroom photographic procedures require more effort, but yield better micrographs. Considerable automation in wet darkroom processes is possible, but frequent use of photomicroscopy is required to justify the cost of such equipment.

Obtaining good micrographs requires adequate image contrast and resolution, uniform focus over the entire field, uniform lighting, and adequate depth of field. The light source must be properly aligned, and the system should be free of vibration. The yellow-green filter should be employed to correct lens defects. The optics must be clean, and the field and aperture diaphragms must be adjusted correctly. The microscope is focused in a variety of ways, depending on the model. Several film formats may be used, such as plates, sheet film of different size, or 35-mm roll film. The magnification at the film plane must be known. This is a simple procedure if the only variables are the objective and eyepiece magnification, but is more difficult when using a zoom system or bellows. A stage micrometer can be utilized to determine the true magnification.

A range of black-and-white and color films is available for darkroom or instant tech-

**Fig. 45** Microscope designed for use away from the laboratory. Batteries for the light source are contained in the cylindrical stand of the instrument. (Unitron Instruments, Inc.)

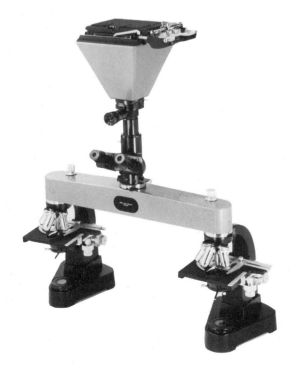

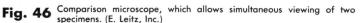

**Fig. 46** Comparison microscope, which allows simultaneous viewing of two specimens. (E. Leitz, Inc.)

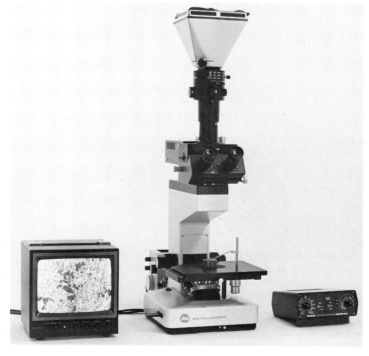

**Fig. 47** Television monitor for group viewing attached to an inverted-type microscope. (E. Leitz, Inc.)

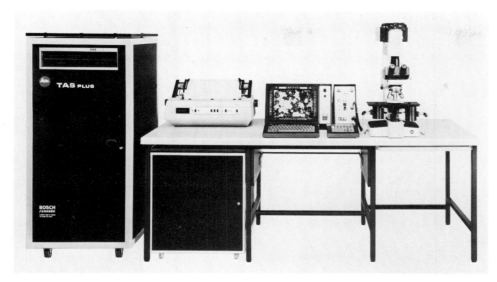

**Fig. 48** Fully automatic image analyzer. Although these devices can be quite expensive, they have stimulated interest in stereology and its application to structure-property correlations. (E. Leitz, Inc.)

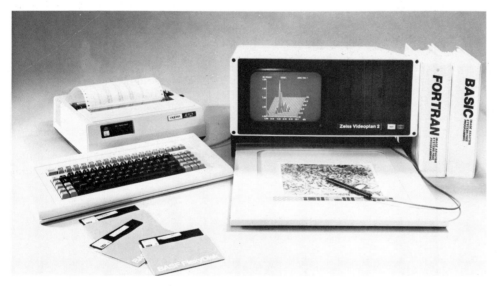

**Fig. 49** Semiautomatic image analyzer. With this system, the operator controls detection of features by tracing with a light pen. (C. Zeiss, Inc.)

niques. The manufacturers of these films document film characteristics. Black-and-white films are most commonly used due to their lower cost. They exhibit better contrast control, are easier to process, and are generally quicker to use than color films. Color film has some important uses for which its cost is justified.

In traditional black-and-white photography, a negative image is produced first and is used to produce a positive image of the microstructure on suitable paper. The micrograph will last for many years without any apparent change. Selection of the negative film is based on the format available, color sensitivity, contrast, resolving power, speed, graininess, and exposure and development latitudes. Some black-and-white films are not sensitive to the entire visible spectrum.

Orthochromatic films are sensitive to all colors except orange and red; panchromatic films are sensitive to all colors, although they emphasize blue and deemphasize yellow. A yellow filter can be used to reduce this color bias. Orthochromatic films can be developed under dark red light, but panchromatic films require total darkness. Orthochromatic films are excellent for photomicroscopy, particularly when a yellow-green filter is inserted to correct lens defects.

Film speed is a critical variable only when illumination is low, as in polarized light, interference-contrast, or dark-field illumination. Orthochromatic film has a medium contrast that is adequate for most structures. Contrast may be enhanced with a high-contrast film. The resolving power of a film defines its ability to record fine details in the

image. Therefore, a high-resolving-power film is desirable. Graininess depends on the size of the silver grains in the emulsion, the developer used, and the development time and temperature. High-speed films are more grainy than low-speed films, making them less suitable for enlarging. Contact printing is preferred. It requires a large film size, but saves enlargement time. It produces better images and eliminates redetermining the magnification of the print. A fine-grain film provides the best resolution.

When a negative is exposed, there is an allowable range of exposures that will produce a useful, printable negative. A wide exposure latitude is quite valuable. Each film includes information on its characteristic relationship between exposure time and density. The exposure selected should be on the linear portion of the density-time curve. A good, dense negative allows suppression of some of the fine image defects during printing. An underexposed negative greatly restricts printing and generally results in a poor print. Development of negatives is rather simple and involves use of a developing solution, a stop bath, a fixing solution, as well as washing and drying.

The correct exposure is most easily determined using a built-in exposure meter. If this is not available, a test exposure series can be made. This is accomplished by pulling out the film slide completely and exposing the entire film for a time judged to be considerably shorter than that required. The slide is then inserted so that it covers about 10 to 20 mm (0.4 to 0.8 in.) of the film, and the exposure is repeated. This is repeated incrementally until the slide is fully inserted, covering the film. After development, the correct time can be assessed based on the density of the negative in each band. Alternatively, the step exposure can be performed using an instant film of the same speed, saving the darkroom time.

Most black-and-white films are contact printed. The negative is placed emulsion side up on the contact printer, and a suitable paper is placed emulsion side down over the negative. The printer is closed, and light is passed through the film onto the paper. The print is developed, stopped, fixed, washed, and dried. Print contrast is controlled by the type of paper and development time. Print contrast types vary from extra-soft (flat) to extra-contrasty (grades 1 to 5). Number 3 paper is used most often. Number 4 paper is used to increase contrast, and No. 2 paper to reduce contrast.

To illustrate the influence of film contrast and paper contrast on image quality, Fig. 50 to 65 show one contrasty and one flat microstructure taken with medium-contrast film (Tri-X Orthochromatic) and high-contrast film (Contrast Process Orthochromatic) and printed on four paper grades, F1 to F4. Figures 50 to 57 show a ferrite-pearlite microstructure etched with picral at 500×. This is a contrasty image, and Tri-X Orthochromatic film produces excellent results using paper

**Fig. 50, 51, 52, 53** High-contrast microstructure (ferrite and pearlite) photographed using a medium-contrast film, Tri-X Ortho, and printed with paper grades F1 (low contrast, left) through F4 (high contrast, right). 500×

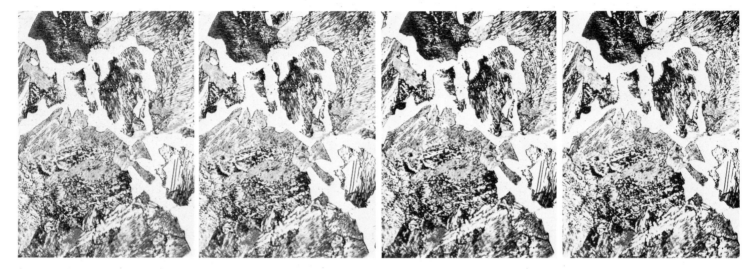

**Fig. 54, 55, 56, 57** Same microstructures as Fig. 50 to 53, photographed with a high-contrast film, Contrast Process Ortho. Again, the negative was printed with paper grades F1 (left) through F4 (right). 500×

grades F2 to F4. The image taken with Contrast-Process Orthochromatic film is a bit harsh; the best images are on papers F1 and F2. Figures 58 to 65 show tempered martensite and sulfide inclusions in a medium-carbon alloy steel etched with 2% nital at 500×. This is a rather flat, low-contrast image that is greatly improved with high-contrast film and paper grades F2 to F4.

Instant process films eliminate the darkroom work, thus hastening the process. Polaroid prints use the diffusion-transfer-reversal process. Development begins when the film is removed from the camera after the exposure. The action of pulling the film out of the camera crushes a pod containing the viscous, caustic developer and spreads it over the film. Black-and-white films develop rapidly; color prints require slightly more time. Some of the Polaroid films have very high speeds, an advantage in dim lighting. Some prints must be coated with a neutralizing stabilizer/protec-

tive varnish to prevent staining and fading. Also available are instant films (55P/N, for example) that produce a negative and a positive print; this negative must be cleared, but a darkroom is not required. Polaroid films used in microscopy are all panchromatic. They are available as roll film, film packs, or sheets. Exposure times must be more accurately controlled to obtain good prints than with traditional wet-process films. Additional information on color photomicroscopy is available in Ref 2 and 38 to 43 and in the article "Color Metallography" in this Volume.

## Macrophotography

Examination and photography are often required for such objects as macroetched disks and broken parts. Examination can be performed visually or with the aid of a simple

hand lens or stereomicroscope. Macrophotography can be performed using most cameras, perhaps aided by the use of closeup lens attachments, a bellows, or a macrolens. Many stereomicroscopes can be equipped with cameras (Fig. 66) for photography; some will take stereopairs. A few manufacturers offer camera stands for macrophotography. Some metallographs also have low-magnification objectives that can perform certain types of macrophotography.

Macrophotography utilizes magnifications from less than 1× to 50×. Most laboratories, especially those engaged in failure analyses, have various cameras, light sources, and stereoviewers to cover the wide range of objects photographed. Correct lighting is necessary to emphasize details and provide even illumination without glare or reflection. Adjustment of lighting requires some experimentation and experience. Available lighting includes flood lamps, rings, coaxial, or fiber

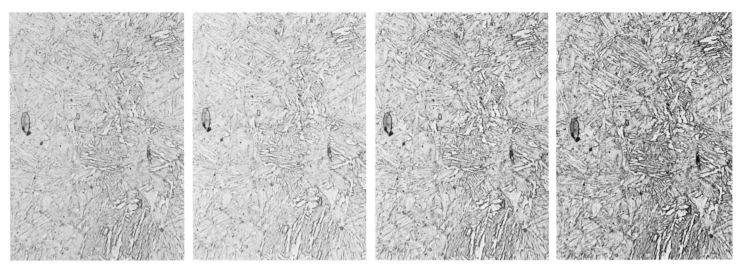

**Fig. 58, 59, 60, 61** Low-contrast microstructure (tempered martensite in a medium-carbon alloy steel) photographed with a medium-contrast film (Tri-X Ortho) and printed with paper grades F1 (low contrast, left) through F4 (high contrast, right). 500×

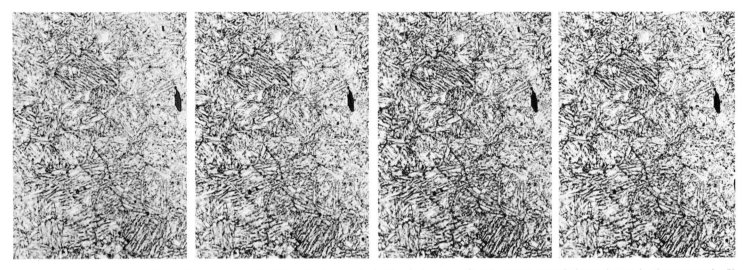

**Fig. 62, 63, 64, 65** Same microstructure as Fig. 58 to 61, photographed with a high-contrast film (Contrast Process Ortho) and printed with paper grades F1 (left) through F4 (right). 500×

optics. A light box is useful for eliminating shadows, but considerable creativity is required to obtain good results.

Depth of field and resolution are important variables. Many of the objects to be photographed are three-dimensional, which requires a certain depth of field and proper lighting to reveal shape and texture. Depth of field varies with the aperture diaphragm lens setting, the magnification, and the focal length of the lens. Stopping down the aperture improves depth of field, but decreases image brightness and clarity. Depth of field also increases as magnification decreases and focal length increases. Depth of field can be estimated by:

Depth of field =

$$2(f\text{-number})(C)\left[1 + \frac{1}{M}\right] \qquad \text{(Eq 5)}$$

where depth of field is in mm, $C$ is the circle of confusion of the subject ($0.33/M$), and $M$ is the magnification. Long-focal-length lenses are preferred for macrophotography to avoid distortion and astigmatism. For magnifications below 5×, focal lengths of 100 mm or more are preferred. Shorter-focal-length lenses are used for higher magnifications. Additional details concerning macrophotography can be found in Ref 44 to 47.

## REFERENCES

1. R.C. Gifkins, *Optical Microscopy of Metals*, American Elsevier, 1970
2. R.P. Loveland, *Photomicrography: A Comprehensive Treatise*, Vol 1 and 2, John Wiley & Sons, 1970
3. V.A. Phillips, *Modern Metallographic Techniques and Their Applications*, Interscience, 1971
4. J.H. Richardson, *Optical Microscopy for the Materials Sciences*, Marcel Dekker, 1971
5. H.W. Zieler, *The Optical Performance of the Light Microscope*, Microscope Publications Ltd., Part 1, 1972, Part 2, 1974
6. R.B. McLaughlin, *Accessories for the Light Microscope*, Microscope Publications, Ltd., 1975
7. R.B. McLaughlin, *Special Methods in Light Microscopy*, Microscope Publications, Ltd., 1977
8. H. Modin and S. Modin, *Metallurgical Microscopy*, Halsted Press, John Wiley & Sons, 1973
9. G.F. Vander Voort, *Metallography: Principles and Practice*, McGraw-Hill, 1984
10. H.W. Zieler, What Resolving Power Formula Do You Use? *Microscope*, Vol 17, 1969, p 249-270
11. C. Van Duijn, Visibility and Resolution of Microscopic Detail, *Microscope*, Vol 11, 1957, p 196-208

12. G.K. Conn and F.J. Bradshaw, Ed., *Polarized Light in Metallography*, Butterworths, 1952
13. W.C. McCrone *et al.*, *Polarized Light Microscopy*, Ann Arbor Science Publishers, 1978
14. A.F. Hallimond, *The Polarizing Microscope*, 3rd ed., Vickers Instruments, 1970
15. E.C.W. Perryman and J.M. Lack, Examination of Metals by Polarized Light, *Nature*, Vol 167 (No. 4247), 1951, p 479
16. A.H. Bennett *et al.*, *Phase Microscopy*, John Wiley & Sons, 1951
17. J. Padawer, The Nomarski Interference-Contrast Microscope: An Experimental Basis for Image Interpretation, *J. Royal Microsc. Soc.*, Vol 88 (Part 3), 1968, p 305-349
18. R. Hoffman and L. Gross, Reflected-Light Differential-Interference Microscopy: Principles, Use and Image Interpretation, *J. Microsc.*, Vol 91 (Part 3), 1970, p 149-172
19. A.S. Holik, Surface Characterization by Interference Microscopy, *Microstruct. Sci.*, Vol 3B, 1975, p 991-1010
20. S. Tolansky, *Multiple-Beam Interferometry of Surface and Films*, Clarendon Press, 1948
21. S. Tolansky, *Surface Microtopography*, Interscience, 1960
22. M.G. Lozinskii, *High Temperature Metallography*, Pergamon Press, 1961
23. B.L. Bramfitt *et al.*, The Use of Hot-Stage Microscopy in the Study of Phase Transformations, in *STP 557*, ASTM, Philadelphia, 1974, p 43-70
24. K.A. Jackson and J.D. Hunt, Transparent Compounds That Freeze Like Metals, *Acta Metall.*, Vol 3, 1965, p 1212-1215
25. P. Tardy, New Methods for Direct Observation of the Recrystallization of Low Melting Metals, *Pract. Metallog.*, Vol 9, 1968, p 485-493
26. M. Markworth, Preparation of Metallographic Specimens of Ferrous Materials by Electrolytic Polish Attack Under Direct Microscope Observation, *Neue Hütte*, Vol 13 (No. 11), 1968, p 684-689
27. R. Wall and D.I. Roberts, A Cell Technique for Microscopic Observation of Selective Corrosion, *Metallurgia*, Vol 68 (No. 410), 1963, p 291-294

28. R.A. Flinn and P.K. Trojan, Examination of Microstructures Under Varying Stress, *Met. Prog.*, Vol 68, July 1955, p 88-89
29. E. Brobery and R. Attermo, A Miniature Tensile-Testing Machine for Deformation During Microscopic Observation, *Jernkontorets Ann.*, Vol 152 (No. 10), 1968, p 525-526
30. D. Godfrey, "Investigation of Fretting by Microscopic Observation," Report 1009, National Advisory Committee for Aeronautics, 1951
31. J.L. Walter and H.E. Cline, Grain Boundary Sliding, Migration, and Deformation in High-Purity Aluminum, *Trans. AIME*, Vol 242, 1968, p 1823-1830

32. S. Takeuchi and T. Homma, Direct Observation for High Temperature Fatigue in Pure Metals by Means of Microscopic Cine-Camera, in *Proceedings of the First International Conference on Fracture*, Sendai, Japan, Vol 2, 1966, p 1071-1086
33. G.L. Kehl *et al.*, The Removal of Inclusions for Analysis by an Ultrasonic "Jack Hammer," *Metallurgia*, Vol 55, March 1957, p 151-154
34. J.H. Evans, Remote Metallography, in *Interpretive Techniques for Microstructural Analysis*, Plenum Press, 1977, p 145-168
35. R.J. Gray *et al.*, Metallography of Radioactive Materials at Oak Ridge National Laboratory, in *STP 480*, ASTM, Philadelphia, 1970, p 67-96
36. L. Kosec and F. Vodopivec, Examples of the Replica Technique in Optical Metallography, *Pract. Metallog.*, Vol 6, 1969, p 118-121
37. J. Neri, Optical Replicas—A Nondestructive Metallographic Evaluation Technique, in *Failure Analysis*, American Society for Metals, 1969, p 241-268
38. *Photomicrography of Metals*, Kodak Scientific Publication P-39, 1971
39. *Photography Through the Microscope*, Kodak Scientific Publication P-2, 1980
40. L.E. Samuels, Photographic Methods, in *Interpretative Techniques for Microstructural Analysis*, Plenum Press, 1977, p 17-42
41. B.H. Carroll *et al.*, *Introduction to Photographic Theory*, John Wiley & Sons, 1980
42. R.S. Crouse *et al.*, Applications of Color in Metallography and Photography, in *Interpretative Techniques for Microstructural Analysis*, Plenum Press, 1977 p 43-64
43. H.E. Exner *et al.*, Some Experiences in the Documentation of Colour Micrographs, *Pract. Metallog.*, Vol 17, 1980, p 344-351
44. *Simplified Photomacrography*, Kodak Scientific Publication P-53, 1970
45. *Photomacrography*, Kodak Technical Publication N-12B, 1972
46. J.R. Dvorak, Photomacrography in Metallography, *Microstruc. Sci.*, Vol 3B, 1975, p 1011-1025
47. *Photomacrography and Photomicrography*, Wild Heerbrugg, Ltd., Switzerland, 1979

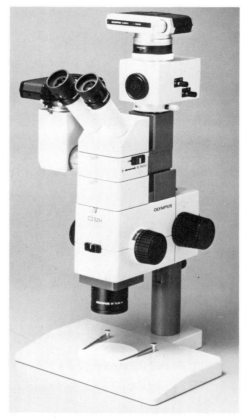

**Fig. 66** Typical stereomicroscope. This type of instrument is useful for macroexamination and can be used in preliminary examinations to point out specific features for more detailed study. (Olympus Corporation of America)

# Scanning Electron Microscopy*

By H.E. Exner
Research Scientist
Max-Planck-Institut für Metallforschung
Institut für Werkstoffwissenschaften

THE SCANNING ELECTRON MICROSCOPE is one of the most versatile instruments for investigating the microstructure of metallic materials. Compared to the optical (light) microscope, it expands the resolution range by more than one order of magnitude to approximately 10 nm (100 Å) in routine instruments, with ultimate values below 3 nm (30 Å). Useful magnification thus extends beyond $10\,000\times$ up to $150\,000\times$, closing the gap between the optical and the transmission electron microscope. Compared to optical microscopy, the depth of focus, ranging from 1 $\mu$m at $10\,000\times$ to 2 mm (0.08 in.) at $10\times$, is larger by more than two orders of magnitude, due to the very small beam aperture.

Scanning electron microscopy (SEM) offers possibilities for image formation that are usually easy to interpret and will reveal clear pictures of as-polished and etched cross sections as well as rough surfaces. Energy-dispersive x-ray analysis using equipment routinely attached to the scanning electron microscope features semiquantitative and, in favorable cases, quantitative analysis of composition from a small volume with good lateral resolution. Since its relatively recent origin, SEM has found a wide range of applications in materials research, materials development, failure analysis, and quality control.

Excellent monographs on physical fundamentals, instrumental details, and applications of the scanning electron microscope are available (Ref 1-6). A short outline of the basic features, a description of various techniques for metals investigations, and a brief review of metallurgical applications follow.

## Basic Design of the Scanning Electron Microscope

The principal features of the scanning electron microscope are shown in Fig. 1. The electron beam is emitted from a heated tungsten cathode and focused by a system of magnetic lenses (usually two condenser lenses and one objective lens) to a small diameter (approximately 10 nm, or 100 Å, in standard instruments to 1 nm, or 10 Å, in high-resolution instruments). Acceleration voltages are 1000 to 50 000 V. The current of primary electrons through the surface is approximately $10^{-8}$ to $10^{-7}$ A. This current can be increased by using more effective electron sources, such as lathanum hexoboride (LaB$_6$) cathodes, which are available with most commercial instruments, or field-emission cathodes, which are not yet used as routine components. To generate the required vacuum, a diffusion pump or a turbomolecular pump is used. The use of turbomolecular pumps is helpful in eliminating hydrocarbon contamination from the pump oil.

The electron beam scans the specimen in much the same way as in a cathode ray tube (CRT) used for image formation on a television screen. A scan generator controlling the current of the scanning coils deflects the beam along closely spaced lines. The magnification is changed by adjusting the current in the deflection coils; the normal range is 10 to $150\,000\times$. The electrons excited by the electron beam and emitted from the specimen surface are collected in an electron detector. The current of electrons hitting the detector is still smaller than the primary beam current (approximately $10^{-12}$ A) and must be amplified by direct electron multiplication and conventional electron amplifiers. The amplified signal controls the brightness of the beam in a CRT, which is synchronized to the

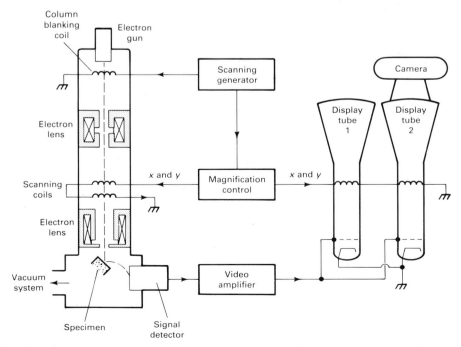

**Fig. 1** Typical design (schematic) of the scanning electron microscope for secondary electron imaging. (Ref 2)

*Based on H.E. Exner, Qualitative and Quantitative Surface Microscopy, in *Physical Metallurgy*, R.W. Cahn and P. Haasen, Ed., 3rd ed., North-Holland, 1983, Chap. 10A, p 598-608. With permission.

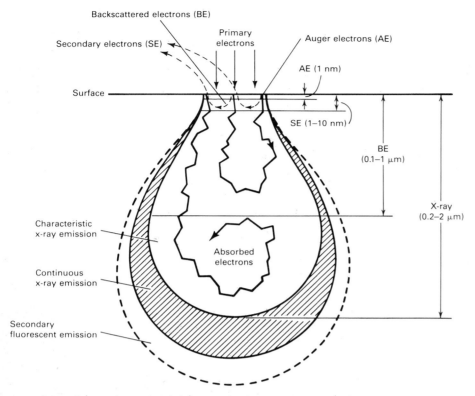

**Fig. 2** Types of electron-beam-excited electrons and radiation used in SEM and the depth of the region below the specimen surface from which information is obtained.

electron beam in the microscope column. In addition to image display on a high-quality television screen, a high-performance CRT is used to "write" the image with typically 1000 (and as many as 4000) lines on a photographic film or plate.

Background noise is the major cause of unclear images. Image quality has improved dramatically during the last two decades due to noise reduction in electronic components and development of more sensitive detectors as well as more powerful electron emitters, more precise scanning devices, and additional image-processing units. An example of the devices required for utilizing the multitude of signals is the coil for periodic blanking of the beam, as shown in Fig. 1. Not shown are accessories for manipulating the specimen and for x-ray analysis.

## Modes of Operation

When the primary electron beam interacts with the specimen, electrons and other radiations are produced that can be used to form images and to analyze chemically the microstructural elements. Figure 2 shows some types of signals and supplies information on the region close to the surface from which information is obtained. Auger electron microscopy and spectroscopy require special instrumentation working at a much higher vacuum than SEM, due to the extremely thin layer of emission that is easily disturbed by surface contamination. All other signals are available using commercial scanning electron microscopes or routine accessories. Data for these modes of operation are listed in Table 1.

Cathodoluminescence and absorbed or transmitted specimen current detection find only limited use in metals investigations. Cathodoluminescence is a long-wave radiation

**Table 1** Physical effects producing radiation, detector types, and detected signals used for imaging and analyzing metal surfaces in the scanning electron microscope

| Detected signal | Type of detector | Information | Basis effects | Resolution | Depth of information | Remarks |
|---|---|---|---|---|---|---|
| Secondary electrons .......... | Scintillator/ photomultiplier with Faraday cage | Surface topography, material contrast, crystal orientation contrast | SE yield depends strongly on surface tilt and weakly on atomic number and crystal orientation | 5–20 nm | 1–10 nm | Background due to secondary electrons excited by backscattered electrons reduces resolution and enlarges depth of information; material contrast can be suppressed by superimposing the inverted BE signal. |
| Backscattered electrons .......... | Solid-state or scintillator/ photomultiplier | Material composition, topography, crystal orientation | BE yield depends on atomic number, increasing for heavier elements | 0.1–1 μm | 0.1–1 μm, depending on primary electron energy (acceleration voltage) | Topological contrast can be suppressed by a ring-shaped detector; higher resolution can be obtained using an energy filter |
| Specimen current (absorbed or target current) ............ | No external detector necessary | Complementary contrast to backscattered electrons | BE yield results in corresponding electrical current | 0.1–1 μm | Same as backscattered electrons | Conventional amplification difficult and noisy |
| X-rays .............. | Semiconductor detector | Element distribution | Emission of characteristic radiation by electron bombardment | Approx. 1 μm | 1–10 μm | Element analysis by spectrometers; x-ray intensity images with point density corresponding to element concentration |
| Cathodoluminescence . | Photomultiplier with mirror | Detection of nonmetallic and semiconduction phases | Emission of photons by electron bombardment | 0.5–10 μm | | Applicable to metallic materials in rare cases only |
| Thermal wave ........ | Acoustic (gas microphone), optical beam detectors, and infrared detectors | Cracks and flaws, phase and grain boundaries | Thermal waves produced by periodic beam blanking | 10 μm for metals, 1 μm for insulators | >100 μm | Three-dimensional information by varying frequency |

**Fig. 3** 60×

**Fig. 4** 335×

**Fig. 5** 3000×

**Fig. 6** 3000×

**Fig. 7** 3000×

**Fig. 8** 3000×

**Fig. 3 to 8** Typical scanning electron micrographs of a sintered WC-12Co cemented carbide (hard metal used in metal cutting operations). Fig. 3: SE image of the surface of a worn drill; strong topographic contrast. Fig. 4: SE image of the fracture surface in a fracture toughness test specimen; strong topographic contrast. Fig. 5: BE image (acceleration voltage 25 kV) of a plane section showing strong material contrast between the tungsten carbide (light) and the cobalt binder phase (black). Fig. 6: BE image at a lower acceleration voltage (15 kV). The material contrast between the cobalt binder phase (dark) and the tungsten carbide is pronounced. In addition, some orientation contrast exists for the different tungsten carbide crystals. Fig. 7: SE image of a plane section showing orientation contrast between the hexagonal carbide crystals and material contrast between the carbide and the binder, which again is darker due to the lower atomic number. The crack edges appear bright due to the pronounced edge contrast. Fig. 8: dot map produced by writing the image with the signal produced by x-ray emission of cobalt. A high frequency of dots indicates the cobalt phase. The dots in the carbide regions are due to noise.

resulting from the recombination of electron-hole pairs created by the primary electron beam. It may be used to detect surface plasmon effects. Specimen current imaging, an early SEM technique, is used to study electronic materials, such as integrated circuits, but has given way to other modes because of its relatively high noise.

Another new development is thermal-wave imaging, which uses periodic blanking of the electron beam in the scanning electron microscope to produce thermal waves that interact with the microstructure (Ref 7). The signals are received by acoustic or infrared detectors. Resolution depends on the frequency of the periodic surface heating (thermal wavelength) and thermal conductivity, which for metals ranges from a few microns at high frequency (1 MHz) to a few millimeters at low frequency (100 Hz). Due to the frequency-dependent depth of information, three-dimensional information on grain- and phase-boundary structures can be obtained without special contrasting. Its main application is the *in situ* study of crack formation.

In contrast to these three modes of operation, which are not or have not yet become popular in the investigation of metals, the other three listed in Table 1—the secondary electron (SE) mode, the backscattered electron (BE) mode, and x-ray spectroscopy—are used routinely with a high level of sophistication. Examples of images obtainable using these techniques are shown in Fig. 3 to 8, which illustrate a sintered cemented carbide, and Fig. 9, which compares the backscattering coefficient and secondary electron yield as a function of the atomic number of the specimen and the angle between the specimen surface and the incident beam.

**Backscattered electrons** are produced by single large-angle or multiple small-angle

**Table 2  Depth of information obtained with secondary and backscattered electrons for some elements as a function of acceleration voltage of the primary electron beam**

| Element | Atomic number | Density, g/cm³ | Secondary electrons | Depth of information, nm — Backscattered electrons | | | | |
|---|---|---|---|---|---|---|---|---|
| | | | | 5 keV | 10 keV | 20 keV | 30 keV | 50 keV |
| C | 6 | 1.0 | 10.0 | 330 | 970 | 2800 | 5300 | 11 600 |
| Al | 13 | 2.7 | 1.2 | 120 | 360 | 1050 | 1950 | 4 290 |
| Cu | 29 | 8.9 | 0.5 | 40 | 110 | 320 | 590 | 1 300 |
| Ag | 47 | 10.5 | 1.0 | 30 | 90 | 270 | 500 | 1 100 |
| Au | 70 | 19.3 | 1.8 | 20 | 50 | 150 | 270 | 600 |

Source: Ref 5

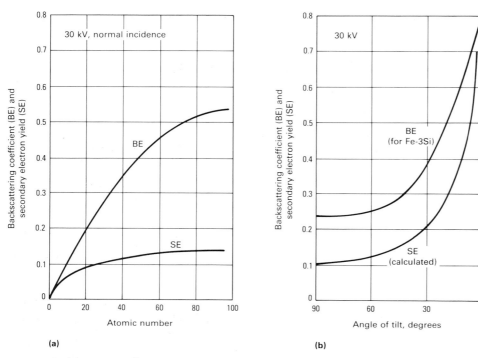

(a)                                            (b)

**Fig. 9** Backscattering coefficient and secondary electron yield as a function of atomic number of the material interacting with the primary electron beam at (a) normal incidence and (b) as a function of surface inclination (angle between surface and incident beam). (Ref 6)

**Fig. 10, 11** Wedge-shaped specimen. Fig. 10: strong shadowing effect exhibited by secondary electrons. Fig. 11: absence of shadowing in the BE image. 32×

bound atomic electrons. The energy spectrum of secondary electrons is independent of the energy of incident electrons and of the specimen material; it shows a pronounced maximum at approximately 3 eV. Seventy percent of the secondary electrons have energies below 15 eV, and at approximately 50 eV, the frequency of secondary electrons approaches zero.

Conventionally, all electrons below 50 eV are considered to be secondary electrons and those having higher energy are considered to be backscattered electrons. The probability that the low-energy secondary electrons will escape from the surface decreases exponentially with the depth of their generation. Over half the total yield of the secondary electrons excited by the primary beam is emitted within a depth of approximately 0.5 nm (5 Å). The depth of information is therefore approximately 1 $\mu$m for most metals, increasing to 10 $\mu$m for carbon (Table 2). The yield is not strongly dependent on atomic number; the yield for gold is higher than that for carbon by only a factor of 2.

The primary factor for secondary electron yield is the angle between incident beam and specimen surface. Because the envelope of the excited volume (Fig. 2) moves closer to the surface when the beam hits the surface with a small angle, the secondary electron yield increases. As shown in Fig. 9, variations in surface inclination cause pronounced changes in secondary electron yield; the atomic weight of the material investigated has a lesser effect on secondary electron yield than it has on backscattered electron yield.

**X-rays** excited by the electron beam form two types of spectra: (1) the *bremsstrahlung* (electromagnetic radiation emitted by electrons when they pass through matter) with a continuous spectrum and (2) the characteristic radiation with a distinct line spectrum. The line spectrum can be analyzed by wavelength-dispersive spectrometry (WDS), which is used nearly exclusively with devoted electron probe microanalyzers, and by energy-dispersive spectrometry (EDS), which is easily implemented in most commercial scanning electron microscopes. A lithium-drifted silicon solid-state detector transfers the x-ray impulses to a multichannel analyzer. The integrated information, after processing in a microcomputer, is displayed on the screen, yielding rapid qualitative and semiquantitative analysis of the composition.

Most elements with higher atomic numbers are easily separated by their significant lines, but detection of elements having small atomic numbers often suffers from background and superposition, especially if their concentrations are small. Due to the interference of the beryllium or plastic window in front of the detector, elements below atomic number 11 (sodium) cannot be analyzed. This range can be extended by using windowless detectors, which are not routinely included in SEM energy-dispersive systems. For point

elastic-scattering events. In the 10 000- to 20 000-V range of acceleration voltage of the primary electron beam, approximately 50% of each type leave the surface with a wide spectrum of energies. The energy distribution of backscattered electrons depends on the primary energy of incident electrons, the number of outer-shell electrons, the atomic number of the material, and the surface inclination of the specimen. As the atomic number of the material hit by the incident beam

decreases, fewer electrons are backscattered, and more energy is lost. In materials with high atomic numbers, many electrons are backscattered by atoms close to the surface, with little change in energy. Therefore, yield, energy spectrum, and depth of escape of backscattered electrons are directly related to the atomic number of the materials, as shown in Fig. 9 and Table 2.

**Secondary electrons** are formed by interaction of the primary electrons with loosely

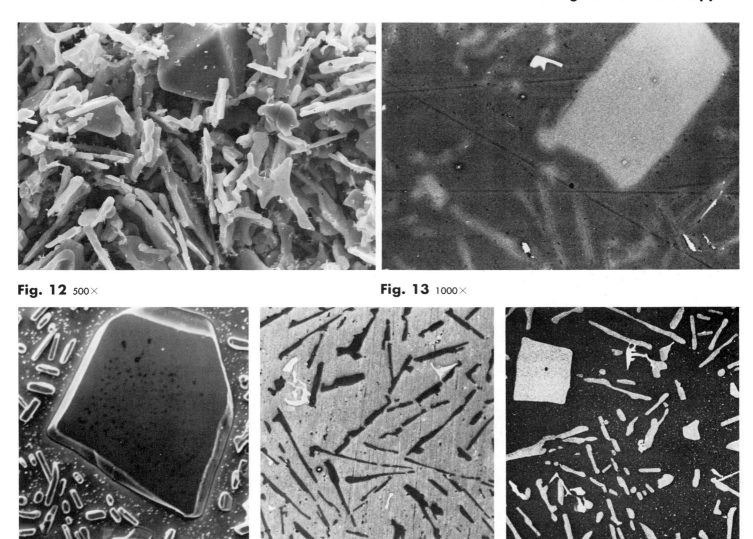

**Fig. 12** 500×

**Fig. 13** 1000×

**Fig. 14** 1000×  **Fig. 15** 1000×  **Fig. 16** 1000×

**Fig. 12 to 16** Contrast formation in a cast Al-11.7Si-0.3Fe alloy by SE and BE imaging. Fig. 12: topographic contrast in an SE image. The aluminum matrix was deep etched using sodium hydroxide. The octahedral shape of a primary silicon crystal and the complex shapes of the eutectic silicon lamellae are clearly revealed. Fig. 13: material contrast in the BE image of an unetched cross section. Despite the low atomic number difference of only 1, the silicon particles appear brighter than the aluminum matrix. The edges are blurred, however, and some particles not intersecting the surface are visible due to the large penetration depth and region of escape of backscattered electrons. Fig. 14: SE image of an electropolished cross section. The positive edges of the large primary silicon crystal and those of the eutectic silicon particles appear bright; the negative edges at the base of the primary crystal are darker, and no clear material contrast is obtained between the silicon particles and the aluminum matrix due to the small difference in atomic number. The small precipitate particles also appear bright due to the edge contrast. Fig. 15: roughness contrast in a freshly polished cross section. The aluminum matrix appears brighter despite the lower atomic number due to the enhanced electron yield at the polishing scratches. The smooth silicon lamellae are dark. Fig. 16: same image conditions as in Fig. 13, but contrasted by a molybdenum oxide layer formed selectively on the silicon particle by dipping the specimen into Mallete's reagent for 15 s (400 mL $CH_5OH$, 10 mL $H_2O_2$, 10 mL $HNO_3$, and 4 g $(NH_4)_2MoO_3$). The silicon appears much brighter due to the high atomic weight of the deposits. The intermetallic phases containing heavy elements (Fe, Ni) are white. Artifacts from below the surface and blurred edges are avoided.

analysis, the beam is stopped on the spot to be analyzed. The depth of information is 1 to 10 $\mu$m, with approximately the same lateral resolution, increasing with increasing energy of the electron beam and decreasing with specific density (atomic weight) of the specimen elements. Quantitative analysis is usually quite accurate using computer correction of absorption and fluorescence as well as suitable standards; relative errors are approximately 10%.

## Typical Forms of Contrast

**Topographic Contrast.** The most pronounced contrast effects result from the dependence of secondary electron yield and backscattering coefficient on the angle between the surface element and the primary electron beam. The resulting contrast is analogous to an optical image in which the light comes from the detector and the obser- vation direction is that of the incident electron beam. The stereoscopic impression is enhanced by shadows in regions hidden from the detector. Figures 10 and 11 demonstrate this shadowing, which can be a disadvantage when deep cracks or holes are to be investigated. Typical SE images with pronounced topographic contrast are shown in Fig. 3, 4, and 12.

**Material (Atomic Number) Contrast.** As shown in Fig. 9, the yield of backscattered

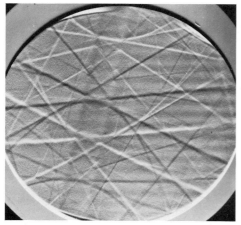

**Fig. 17** Magnification not given

**Fig. 18** 15 000×

**Fig. 19** 1900×

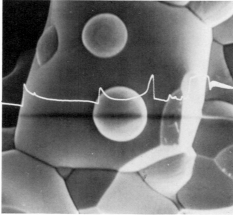

**Fig. 20** 4400×

**Fig. 17 to 20** Various types of special contrast produced in the scanning electron microscope. Fig. 17: selected-area electron-channeling pattern from a W-10Ni heavy-metal alloy. The orientation of the grain onto which the electron beam was focused can be determined from the pattern arising from the penetration and absorption of electrons at those locations where lattice planes in Bragg orientation cut the specimen surface. Fig. 18: high-resolution BE image of partially stabilized zirconia with 3% MgO. The lens-shaped tetragonal platelets formed by a martensitic transformation are normal to the surface and appear very sharp and with high contrast to the monoclinic matrix, owing to an electron-channeling effect. Fig. 19: magnetic contrast in an Fe-3.5Si sheet (mechanically lapped and electrolytically polished in 10% perchloric acid and 90% acetic acid). The magnetic domains are clearly revealed by the varying intensity of backscattered electrons due to the deflection of the primary beam by the Lorentz force. Superimposed are the material contrast (inclusions, bright), the topographic contrast (grain boundaries), and the orientation contrast (grain faces). (Ref 9). Fig. 20: y-modulation profile (white line) superimposed on an SE image of a thermally etched surface of an $Al_2O_3$-$10ZrO_2$ ceramic. The location of the profile is indicated by the black contamination line.

and secondary electrons is a function of atomic number. Material contrast is useful for qualitative identification of phases and is especially suitable for quantitative evaluation of microstructural geometry by image analysis. However, the atomic number contrast is usually obscured by topology contrast and, for secondary electrons, is sufficiently strong only in favorable cases, such as ideally flat surfaces.

The topographic contrast for backscattered electrons is much less pronounced than for secondary electrons (Fig. 10 and 11) and can be greatly reduced using ring-shaped detectors, even if the surface is rough. Edge effects may remain a problem, and ideally flat polishing is necessary for difficult specimens with phases having similar composition or consisting of elements that are closely grouped in the periodic table. A difference in average atomic number smaller than 1, that is, uniform mixtures of closely grouped elements in the periodic table, is sufficient for slight material contrast, at least in the lower range of atomic numbers where the contrast is more pronounced (Fig. 9).

Figure 5 shows an example of strong BE material contrast. The major limitation of

BE material-contrast imaging is the lack of resolution due to the large depth of information, resulting in fuzzy edges and blurred features shining through the specimen surface (Fig. 13).

**Edge Contrast.** At edges, the region of electron escape is deformed, and more secondary electrons and backscattered electrons can exit the specimen at the positive edges through the higher area of the truncated surface; at negative (entrant) edges, the electron yield is reduced by the additional absorption. This effect blurs the exact shape of the edges—for example, their radius of curvature—and can be lessened by reducing the energy of the primary electrons. However, edge contrast is sometimes advantageous. Edges can be detected between facets and phases of identical brightness and small particles (with a large proportion of edges), as shown in Fig. 14. Grain boundaries appear as dark lines after etching. Contrast between phases of different hardnesses can be achieved by producing various degrees of microroughness by polishing, as shown in Fig. 15 and 16. This effect is significantly reduced and usually disappears during extended storage of the polished specimen or extended observation in the scanning microscope due to reduction of microroughness by contamination (Ref 8).

**Electron-Channeling Patterns.** The primary electrons penetrate the crystal to a depth that depends on the atomic packing density along different crystallographic directions. If the electrons follow the channels between rows of atoms, the probability of their re-escaping is lessened. Many Bragg conditions are met with small angular variations. Rocking the primary electron beam around a point on the specimen creates diffraction lines from a small area ($<10$ μm). These selected-area electron-channeling patterns are similar to Kikuchi patterns obtained using transmission electron microscopy (TEM) and are therefore often termed pseudo-Kikuchi patterns. Information on the crystal orientation and crystal perfection, grain boundaries, twins, and other crystallographic features is obtained from minute regions of a surface layer less than 50 nm (500 Å) thick. An example is shown in Fig. 17. Contrast formation due to electron channeling is an important means of showing the different orientation of crystals and grains in the SE and BE modes or the different modifications of a phase with unusually good resolution in the BE mode (Fig. 18).

**Magnetic Contrast.** Magnetic fields of ferromagnetic crystals can affect the interaction of the primary beam or the resulting emission. Type I magnetic contrast uses the deflection of the highly directional electrons by the leakage field and may amount to 20% for materials having strong fields, such as cobalt. The resolution with which the boundaries of magnetic domains can be picked up is only approximately several microns, owing to the diffuse nature of leakage fields. Type II magnetic contrast arises from the deflection of primary electrons by the Lorentz force inside the crystal. Magnetic domains appear in light-dark contrast due to differences in backscattering coefficient, with a strong tilt dependence, and can be enhanced by filtering using only high-energy backscattered electrons with a resolution of approximately 100 nm (1000 Å). An example of magnetic contrast is shown in Fig. 19. Information on details and applications of magnetic contrast is available in Ref 5 and 6.

**Voltage Contrast and Electron-Beam-Induced Current.** Secondary electrons are sensitive to surface potentials. A negative bias of a few volts activates emission; a positive field impedes emission. Electron-beam-induced current depends on creation of excess electron-hole pairs by the electron beam and provides useful information on diffusion length and lifetime of minority carriers in semiconductor devices.

## Resolution and Contrast Enhancement

Each component of a scanning electron microscope has its own characteristics of resolution and noise, which determine image quality. Most instrument parameters are fixed by the designer to achieve maximum performance for the network of components. The operator must know the details only insofar as the instrument allows adjustment of component parameters to optimize image quality for a specific specimen and purpose of investigation. For example, the signal-to-noise ratio of the secondary electrons increases with increasing intensity of the primary beam, with increasing electron yield, and with increasing scanning time. The current of the condenser lenses controlling the spot size, the acceleration voltage, and the scanning time can be set by the operator. Electron yield is determined by the specimen and most other factors by optimum working conditions prescribed by the instrument.

**Secondary Electron Imaging.** The high lateral and depth resolution of images produced in the SE mode is due to the small volume from which secondary electrons are excited (Fig. 2). As shown in Table 2, the depth of information ranges from 1 to 10 nm (10 to 100 Å), depending on the atomic number of the material investigated. In addition to signal-to-noise ratio, the resolution of an SE image produced by a particular scanning microscope depends on the width of the energy distribution of primary electrons controlling chromatic aberrations, the other electron optical-lens aberrations, the precision of the scanning system, the detection efficiency of the detector, and the quality of the amplifiers, among other less significant, instrumental factors. Magnetic stray fields from apparatus and power supplies and vibrations from the floor or the pumping system are external factors that degrade image quality. Avoiding or lessening these disturbances is often difficult.

Factors to be optimized by the operator include the intensity and acceleration voltage of the primary beam, the size of the final aperture and its distance to the specimen surface (working distance), the scan parameters, and the tilt of the specimen surface. For a large depth of focus, which is usually required for rough surfaces at low magnification, a small aperture and a large working distance are selected. For high magnifications, a short working distance and high lens currents must be used to minimize the spot size.

A small spot size results in the emission of a small current of electrons from the specimen surface, which reduces the signal-to-noise ratio. This ratio is determined by the statistical noise of the secondary electrons; the noise of modern detecting and amplifying systems is negligible. To attain an acceptable signal-to-noise ratio, the current hitting the detector should be as high as possible and must exceed $10^{-12}$ to $10^{-11}$ A even for the best scintillator/photomultiplier detector systems. Tilting of the specimen surface may be useful; larger apertures and long exposures are mandatory for high currents.

The optimum choice of the acceleration voltage of the primary beam is dictated by the specimen, considering contrast and depth of escape rather than maximum resolution. At low acceleration voltages, the beam becomes sensitive to contamination and stray field aberrations. However, high beam energy is less suitable for producing topographic contrast at high resolution, due to excessive edge effects discussed above and the contribution of secondary electrons by backscattered electrons. This contribution, which can be as high as two thirds of the total yield, increases considerably the size of the volume of information. Therefore, clear topographic images are obscured, and the resolution is markedly reduced unless special measures are taken. The obvious reduction of the acceleration voltage is a compromise, as are other procedures used in commercial instruments (Ref 5). Superposition of the SE signal by the inverted BE signal virtually eliminates interference from deeper specimen layers (Ref 10).

**Backscattered Electron Imaging.** The resolution in the BE mode is much less than that in the SE mode because of considerably larger width and depth of escape. As shown in Table 2, the information depth depends strongly on the acceleration voltage and decreases with atomic number or density. The lateral width of the information volume is larger than the depth by a factor of 2 to 3 (Ref 5). Therefore, if the beam is focused to 20 nm (200 Å) on the surface and is scanned across a boundary separating two regions of different composition, it begins to interact with the atoms of the second region if it is several hundred nanometers away from it. As a result, the position of the boundary is poorly defined. In addition, if the boundary is inclined relative to the surface or parallel to it, interaction begins when the information depth exceeds the distance between the boundary and the surface. Resolution of the BE image is also influenced by the angle of incidence of the primary beam on the specimen surface and the takeoff angle, which is determined by the position of the detector, as well as some of the factors discussed above for the SE mode, such as stray fields and vibrations.

High-resolution BE images can be obtained by reducing the acceleration voltage (Table 2). However, the depth of information from metal surfaces using BE is at least one order of magnitude larger than that for secondary electrons at 5000 V, and the acceleration energy must be reduced further. This requires high-efficiency detectors; for example, the semiconductor detector can be replaced with a scintillator/photomultiplier (Ref 11). Special contrast enhancement procedures must be developed to compensate for the reduced material contrast at lower acceleration voltages.

If thin foils are used, the depth of information is reduced to the thickness of the foil. Another effective method to improve resolution is energy filtering of the backscattered electrons. Imaging requires high-energy (low-loss) backscattered electrons that have left the specimen without diffusion over a significant distance, that is, originating in a region close to the surface. With high-brightness cathodes, a resolution exceeding 5 nm (50 Å) may be achieved in this way.

**Image Modification and Processing.** The signals from the detector system (output of a scintillator/photomultiplier, a semiconductor, or a specimen current preamplifier) can be modified before final amplification to control the intensity of the CRT (Ref 5, 6). Techniques for producing better or additional information include black-level suppression (differential amplification that distributes contrast over the full range of the CRT or the photographic film) and nonlinear amplification (contrast enhancement by preferential contrast expansion at either end of the gray scale, which improves the visibility of features in otherwise dark holes). In $y$-modulation, the CRT beam is deflected proportionally to the detector signal, allowing detection of low contrast that is often not apparent to the eye in the intensity (brightness) modulated image (Fig. 20).

The number of possibilities of image processing has dramatically increased with the development of gray-level image storages (typically $256 \times 256$ up to $1024 \times 1024$ picture points with 256 gray levels). These storages allow software-controlled filtering, such as background noise reduction, edge sharpness improvement, and contrast enhancement, and software-controlled display, such as producing colored images by pseudo-colors, as described in the article "Color Met-

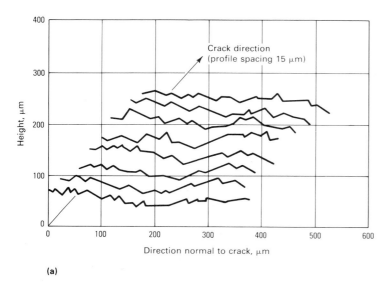

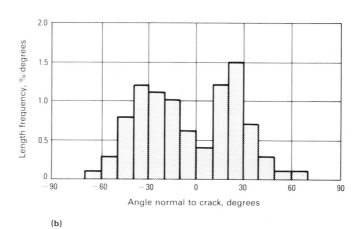

**Fig. 21** Quantitative fracture surface analysis of an $Al_2O_3$-$ZrO_2$ ceramic by instrumented stereometry. (a) A height profile map is shown in perspective. The *x-y-z* coordinate points where the fracture surface changes direction are measured along straight lines in a direction normal to that crack propagation; the spacing of lines in crack direction was selected in the order of the size of fracture facets (15 μm). (b) The frequency (relative length of the crack path) is shown as a function of the angle of inclination between the fracture profile and the normal to the macroscopic crack plane. A typical bimodal distribution with maxima at approximately 30° and a minimum at 0° (flat portions) is obtained. Very steep fracture facets (above 70°) are absent in this brittle material. (Ref 13)

allography" in this Volume. Only a few of these possibilities are currently being fully explored. In interpreting images produced by signal transformation, limitations and deficiencies must be considered to avoid erroneous information and artifacts. In general, however, these techniques are very useful for metals investigations.

## Accessory Equipment

Accessories are useful for obtaining three-dimensional and quantitative information on microstructural geometry or fracture surfaces and on the dynamic changes of microstruc-

tures during heat treatment, mechanical deformation, or changing of magnetic fields.

**Quantitative SEM Image Analysis.** The techniques of image analysis and stereological evaluations for quantitative assessment of microstructural geometry described in the articles "Quantitative Metallography" and "Color Metallography" in this Volume can be applied to images taken using SEM, utilizing the good resolution and the various capabilities of phase discrimination. On-line processing by interfacing a commercial automatic image analyzer to a scanning electron microscope has become feasible only recently with the development of digital gray-level image storages. Processing time per field

is reduced to little more than the scanning time of the image. Several signals can be used simultaneously, and noise reduction and highly sensitive discrimination of two or more phases are carried out routinely.

When contrast formation is not possible or when the resolution limit is reached using the optical microscope, quantitative SEM will frequently be the best solution. A special feature is geometric and chemical analysis of small particles—for example, carbides in high-speed steels or nonmetallic inclusion analysis—by means of computer-controlled positioning of the electron beam. The particles are localized and geometrically characterized in the image analyzer, then the elec-

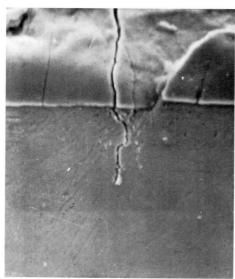

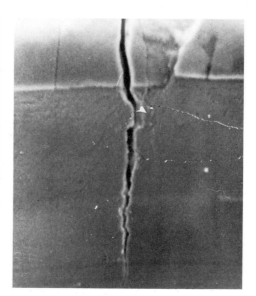

**Fig. 22, 23, 24** Propagation of a fatigue crack from a hard surface coating into a steel specimen. The TiC coating (top) was produced by chemical vapor deposition at 970 °C (1780 °F) on the C100W1 steel. The micrographs were taken after 80 000 cycles (Fig. 22), 190 000 (Fig. 23), and 320 000 (Fig. 24) cycles in the bending stage built into the specimen stage without interrupting the fatigue test. 3000×. (Ref 14)

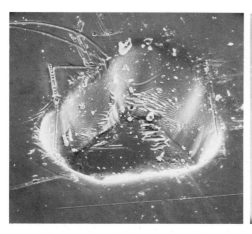 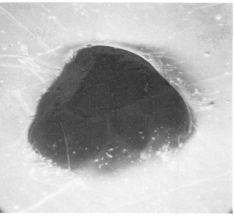

**Fig. 25, 26** Improvement of image quality by coating. Fig. 25: SE image of a depression in a gold-coated semiconductor layer (AsSe) showing the cavity wall and protuberances. 15×. Fig. 26: same specimen and imaging conditions as Fig. 25, but uncoated. 15×

tron beam locates their center and the chemical composition is determined using x-ray analysis (Ref 12).

**Stereomicroscopy.** Simple tilting or goniometer stages allow stereopair micrographs to be taken. When viewed in a stereoscope, they provide an excellent three-dimensional impression of rough surfaces. An alternative is the "anaglyphe" method, which is a stereogram made using a red and a green filter or polarized light for three-dimensional viewing of the two images printed or projected over each other. The tilt angle and the viewing distance determine the subjective impression of depth. Quantitative evaluation of the parallax, which is the change in the apparent relative orientations of objects when viewed from different positions, yields accurate data on the $x$-$y$-$z$ coordinates. These data can then be combined to construct height profiles or height maps and used to obtain characteristic parameters, such as roughness indices and distribution of tilt angles for surface elements for fracture surfaces and other rough surfaces (Ref 13). Figure 21 shows the profile map of a brittle fracture surface, along with the tilt-angle distribution of the fracture facets.

**Dynamic and Non-Ambient-Temperature SEM.** Large depth of focus and the possibility of rapidly changing the magnification in combination with mechanical or low- and high-temperature stages are prerequisites for continuous observation of specimens subject to applied stress, magnetic or electric fields, chemical reaction, and the various effects of cooling or heating. Special stages to be inserted in the usually large specimen chambers of commercial microscopes have been constructed for heating, varying magnetic fields, and mechanical loading (Ref 11, 14-16). Videorecording is ideal for registering events of interest, especially for such dynamic processes as cracking during cyclic loading or martensitic transformation. These events can be registered with markedly higher resolution than with optical micrographs using higher acceleration voltage, fast electron detectors,

and wide band amplifiers; however, the maximum useful magnification is reduced. A number of preliminary results have been documented (Ref 6, 14-16); an example is shown in Fig. 22 to 24.

## Specimen Preparation

Scanning electron microscopy requires little effort in specimen preparation. Good imaging necessitates contamination-free surfaces, resistance of the specimen to the high vacuum and the electron beam, absence of electrical charging, and sufficiently high electron yield. Samples of electrically conductive material free of outgassing substances, which is often the case with solid metallic samples, need only be sectioned to a suitable size and secured to the specimen holder of the microscope. However, careful preparation and proper use of the microscope will usually yield high-quality images and reliable spectrometric information.

**Mounting.** The upper limit of specimen size is defined by the size of the loading door of the specimen chamber. Specimens under 20 mm (0.8 in.) in height, width, or length are usually cut from larger pieces. To prevent charging, conductive adhesives, such as silver, aluminum-containing glues, or carbon adhesives (to avoid unwanted radiation), are used to secure the specimen. Difficulties are encountered in the investigation of small powder particles. Separation of a representative specimen from a large quantity of a powder material, deagglomeration, and uniform distribution are important when quantitative information on particle size and shape distribution is required. Affixing the specimen to the specimen holder using adhesive tapes or direct adhesion yields favorable results. For embedding of powders or small specimens, special resins with a slight tendency toward outgassing should be used. Mechanical securing is often used for larger specimens to avoid contaminating the microscope.

**Surface Treatment.** Cross sections are prepared in the same manner as for optical microscopy, but care must be taken in cleaning, because residual polishing liquids or etchants trapped in pores or cracks contaminate the surface when placing the specimen into the vacuum chamber. Weak contrast mechanisms, such as magnetic or electron channeling contrast, are impossible to detect in the presence of a deformed layer or topographic variations. Therefore, deformation-free and plane cross sections must be prepared by careful polishing when studying microstructures using these contrast mechanisms.

Scratches, height differences of hard and soft phases, and deformed layers, which are unavoidable in mechanical polishing, can usually be removed by electrolytic polishing. Fracture surfaces, if not freshly produced, must be washed clean of oil or grease. Reaction products formed during extended exposure to the atmosphere or by high-temperature reaction can be removed electrolytically (Ref 17), by hydrogen reduction (Ref 18), or chemically (Ref 19). Cleaning corroded surfaces usually changes the character of the fracture surface (Ref 19).

**Conductive Coating.** Insulating materials, even nonconducting particles dispersed in a metallic matrix, build up a space charge region by accumulation of absorbed electrons. This charging deflects the incident beam, leading to image distortion, and significantly changes the emission of secondary electrons. Charging effects can be avoided by operating at a low acceleration voltage of the primary beam, using single-frame exposure, or applying conductive coatings, which is the widely used technique.

The coating layer must be thick enough to provide a conductive path, but should be as thin as possible to avoid obscuring fine details. The minimum thickness depends on surface roughness and may range from 0.5 nm (5 Å) for microscopically flat to 10 nm (100 Å) for slightly profiled and up to 100 nm (1000 Å) for extremely rough surfaces. Because the thickness of the layer can be irregular in the latter cases, only the average thickness can be monitored by adjusting the weight of the material chip used for evaporation (Ref 20) or, more conventionally, by using a piezoelectric crystal monitor. Carbon, gold, platinum, palladium, silver, copper, or aluminum are applied by high-vacuum evaporation or cathode sputtering. The latter method is preferred, because sputtered layers exhibit better adhesion and more diffuse condensation. Therefore, pores and undercuttings are accessible; for evaporation, access is possible only with carbon.

The selection of the coating material is a matter of personal preference. Based on physical considerations, a gold coating approximately 10 nm (100 Å) thick is predicted to produce a maximum SE emission (Ref 6), and gold is used most often. Carbon, which is applied preferentially as a ground material

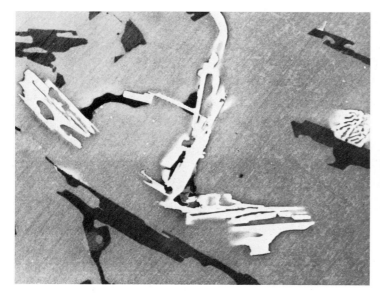

**Fig. 27** 1500×

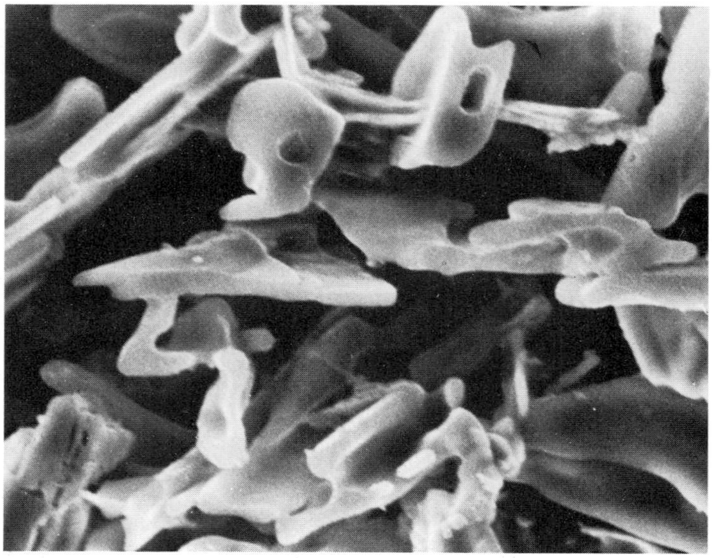

**Fig. 28** 1500×

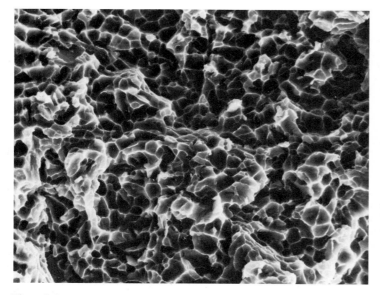

**Fig. 29** 900×

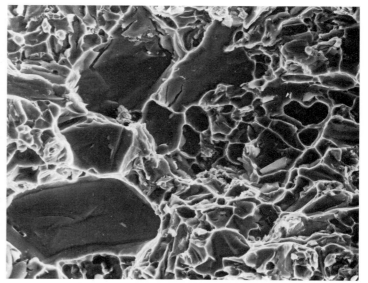

**Fig. 30** 500×

**Fig. 27 to 30** Scanning electron micrographs of a cast Al-11.7Si-1Co-1Mg-1Ni-0.3Fe alloy. Fig. 27: unetched cross section, BE image. The intermetallic phases are clearly revealed by the material contrast. AlFeSiNi appears bright due to the high content of heavy elements; Mg₂Si and Si appear dark. Fig. 28: deep etched using sodium hydroxide, SE image. The three-dimensional shape can be correlated to the two-dimensional cross sections shown in this micrograph. Fig. 29: ductile appearance of a fracture surface, BE image. The alloy was rapidly cooled during casting and has a fine microstructure, giving rise to high elongation to fracture. Fig. 30: brittle appearance of a fracture surface, BE image. The alloy was slowly cooled during casting and has a coarse microstructure. The large silicon plates (large, dark areas) and the intermetallic phases (small, light particles) cause a low elongation to fracture.

for coating porous and rough surfaces, is often used with a low vacuum ($>10^{-3}$ mbar, or 0.1 Pa) to provoke scattering of the carbon and a shield to avoid shadowing and heating of the object by direct radiation from the carbon source. When performing x-ray analysis, the primary electrons and the backscattered electrons from the specimen can excite x-ray radiation in the coating that can interfere with the x-ray lines of interest—for example, gold with zirconium, phosphorus, or platinum. Compared to carbon, aluminum, and

gold-palladium, gold is optimum with respect to electric conductivity, with aluminum approximately 30% of gold and carbon quite poor. No information is available as to which composition is actually the best and why, and even empirical information is rare.

**Contrast Enhancement by Coating.** Coating is sometimes applied to enhance the plastic impression by using the shadowing effect. Using a coating substance with high SE emission, such as gold, a positive image is obtained with bright, outstanding details and

dark shadows in the direction of oblique evaporation (Ref 5). Coatings can also enhance the contrast of materials forming a layer on only one of the phases. As an example, Fig. 16 shows the dramatic improvement in contrast between aluminum and silicon compared to the normal BE image (Fig. 13) as the result of an MoO₂ layer formed on the silicon by reaction with a suitable solution (Ref 8).

Chemical vapor deposition of hard coatings on and carbide particles in high-speed

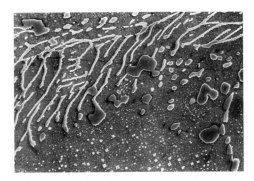

**Fig. 31, 32, 33** SE images of rough surfaces. Fig. 31: corroded surface of an aluminum-bronze alloy (Cu-10Al-5Ni-4Fe-2Mn) in 3% NaCl. 295×. Fig. 32: wear mark on the surface of a metal-cutting insert (WC-TiC-Co). 60×. Fig. 33: titanium nitride layer on a surface of a metal-cutting insert. The high-speed steel insert (lower irregular structure) was coated using physical vapor deposition at approximately 500 °C (930 °F). The hard TiN coating formed in fine elongated crystals. The specimen was broken to show the thickness and structure of the layer. 2000×

steel can be contrasted by evaporated, sputtered, and chemically deposited layers (Ref 21). Coated and uncoated arsenic selenide (AsSe) layers are illustrated in Fig. 25 and 26, demonstrating the improvement in image quality for this semiconducting material (Ref 22). Other developments of this type are numerous and are specific to certain alloys and based on varying chemical or physical principles not yet fully understood in some cases.

**Etching** is not necessary when material (atomic number) contrast is used for image formation; differences in atomic number appear as variations in brightness, the phase containing the lighter elements appearing darker. Etching, harmful in these cases, obscures the weaker effects of magnetic or orientation contrast. If topographic contrast is used for image formation, then chemical, electrolytic, or ion etching is applicable. Ion etching produces a uniform surface layer and leaves none of the residuals of liquid reagents.

Etching is used to produce special effects, such as developing etch pits at dislocations. Deep etching is frequently used to study complexly shaped microstructural constituents. Figures 27 and 28 compare the appearance of intermetallic phases in a cross section

imaged using backscattered electrons (material contrast) and in a deeply etched surface using secondary electrons (topographic contrast). Further examples are shown in Fig. 12 and in Fig. 40 discussed below. Earlier research is reviewed in Ref 23.

## Metallurgical Applications

In all fields in which geometry and composition of microstructures are of interest, the scanning electron microscope and most of its accessories have become routine instrumentation. The wide range of applications in earth and life sciences can best be appreciated by consulting the proceedings of special conferences on SEM. Scanning electron micrographs demonstrating the results of materials investigations are widespread in technical publications, and even SEM studies on metals are too diverse to be reviewed in detail. The examples discussed below illustrate some typical areas in which the scanning electron microscope provides useful information.

**Fractography** is probably the most popular field of SEM. The large depth of focus, the possibility of changing magnification over a wide range, very simple nondestructive specimen preparation with direct inspection, and the three-dimensional appearance of SEM

fractographs make the scanning electron microscope an indispensable tool in failure studies and fracture research. Fracture types are classified by appearance in the scanning electron microscope for steels and other materials. Figures 29 and 30 compare a ductile and a brittle fracture in the same alloy cast at different cooling rates.

Stereoviewing, quantitative analysis of the geometrical details (Fig. 21), *in situ* fracture studies (Fig. 22 to 24), and the possibility of identifying the phases through which the crack has passed by energy dispersive x-ray analysis and mapping are special techniques generally practicable using only the scanning electron microscope. In a recent study, a combination of these techniques was used to quantify the fracture areas in the ductile and brittle phases, the depth of the dimples (Fig. 4), the size of the process zone in front of the crack, and the mode of crack propagation to establish a quantitative model for the fracture toughness of WC-Co cemented carbides (Ref 24).

**Corrosion and wear surfaces** are studied with the scanning electron microscope, utilizing the same advantages as in fractography to characterize the types of corrosion and wear and the kinetics of processes. Figures 31 and 32 show typical examples of rough surfaces formed under heavy corrosive and wear conditions. The structures of protective layers produced by chemical or physical vapor deposition (Fig. 33) and the damage during wear in service are assessed by SE imaging, and ultramicrohardness tests of these layers are performed using the scanning electron microscope (Ref 25).

**Powders and porous materials** are another major application area for SEM. Metal powders are produced by such methods as atomization, reduction of oxides, and electrolysis; each yields a specific type of powder. Figures 12 to 26 and 32 to 38 in the article "Powder Metallurgy Materials" in this Volume illustrate a variety of metal powders examined using SEM.

Particle size distribution and the details of particle shape are controlled by adjusting the process parameters; the scanning electron mi-

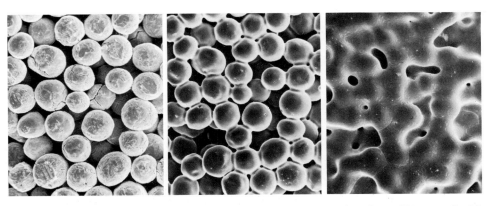

**Fig. 34, 35, 36** Progress of sintering in a loose stack of copper powder spheres, SE images. Fig. 34: light bonding at 600 °C (1110 °F) during heating to sintering temperature. Fig. 35: 1-h sintering at 1050 °C (1920 °F). Clearly visible are neck formations. Fig. 36: 64-h sintering at 1050 °C (1920 °F). The shape of the individual spheres is hardly recognizable; grain growth has occurred across prior particle boundaries and a substantial increase in particle contact has taken place. All at 150×

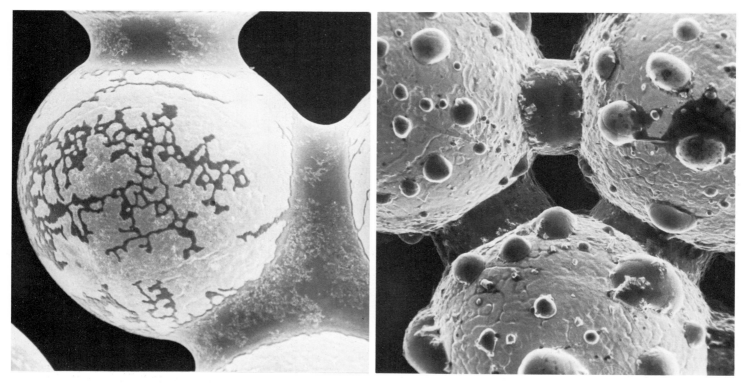

**Fig. 37, 38** Wetting of large spherical tungsten particles by liquid copper during liquid phase sintering. Fig. 37: in vacuum, wetting is very good. Most of liquid copper fills the contact regions, and some of it spreads over the surface of the tungsten spheres. Fig. 38: in an oxygen-containing argon atmosphere, wetting is reduced. The contacts are connected by liquid bridges, and some of the copper is present in droplets, forming a wetting angle of approximately 90° to the surface of the tungsten particles. Both at 500×

**Fig. 39, 40, 41** Typical applications of SEM in physical metallurgy. Fig. 39: deformation marks on the surface of a fatigued copper specimen with protuberances at glide bands. The hill and valley profile and the glide systems are quantitatively characterized by stereoscopic measurement of height and spacing using latex balls for exact scaling. 1520×. Fig. 40: etch pit at the surface of a sheet produced for electrical applications from a Fe-3Si alloy. After mechanical polishing and chemical removal of the deformed layer, preferential attack at a dislocation by three-step etching forms a pit with crystallographically fixed planes. The intersection of {100} and {110} planes form edges. From the angles between these edges, the surface orientation is calculated to approximate {810}. 2280×. (Ref 27). Fig. 41: decay of nickel fibers in a silver matrix of an electrical-conduction material produced by drawing of bundled coated rods. During annealing at 900 °C (1650 °F) for 5 h, the continuous fibers break into shorter ones or into rows of spherical particles.

croscope is used to study these correlations and to ensure uniform powder quality (see the articles "Particle Size and Size Distribution" and "Particle Shape Analysis" in Volume 7 of the 9th Edition of *Metals Handbook*). This is important because the characteristics of the powder determine its behavior during pressing and sintering. The deformation of the powder particles and the change of the pore space morphology during uniaxial, isostatic, and hot pressing have been

confirmed by qualitative and quantitative evaluation of scanning electron micrographs. Fracture surfaces of porous materials or plastic replicas of the pore space are useful for evaluating the internal structures. The same techniques are used to study sintering.

As examples of fundamental studies, Fig. 34 to 36 show the development of particle contacts and pore morphology during sintering of a spherical copper powder; Fig. 37 and 38 show a study of wetting phenomena dur-

ing liquid-phase sintering of spherical tungsten particles with copper. Important information on particle rearrangement during solid- and liquid-phase sintering has been obtained from *in situ* studies using a high-temperature stage. The microstructure and fracture surfaces of a cemented carbide cutting tool material produced by powder metallurgy are shown in Fig. 3 to 8.

**Deformation studies** by SEM have revealed various phenomena and processes.

  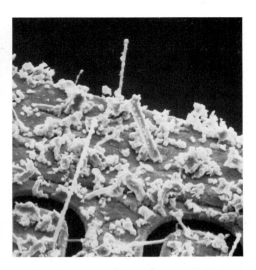

**Fig. 42, 43, 44** Degradation of an electronic circuit due to silver diffusion and whisker formation during storage for 3000 h at 270 °C (520 °F). Fig. 42: SE image showing a general view of the transistor with gold-coated silver pads and gold wires. 20×. Fig. 43: x-ray dot map (silver distribution) showing that silver has diffused from the pads over the wires to the transistor. 20×. Fig. 44: whiskers formed on the base and the emitter, SE image. 1520×

Figure 39 shows a surface of a fatigued copper specimen with typical deformation marks. The appearance of the protuberances and hill and valley profiles has been qualitatively characterized and correlated to experimental conditions and to crack nucleation in fatigue testing (Ref 26).

**The orientation of crystals** relative to each other are revealed qualitatively by the orientation contrast (Fig. 6 and 7) and quantitatively by selected-area electron-channeling patterns (Fig 17). The study of local textures and orientation relationships of twins are prominent examples of applications in physical metallurgy. A useful technique to determine the orientation of grains at the surface of rolled sheets (Ref 27) or other crystals truncated at a surface involves use of etch pits formed at locations where dislocations penetrate the surface (Fig. 40).

**Microstructural morphology** is another major area of application. Nucleation and growth instabilities during solidification produce a variety of shapes and arrangements of microstructural features in cast alloys. The shapes of silicon and intermetallics in cast aluminum alloys are shown in Fig. 12 to 16, 27, and 28. In the 1960s, the shape of graphite in gray cast iron was of great concern. Using stereoviewing of graphite particles etched out from the iron matrix, the complicated shapes can be analyzed, and a systematic characterization of the multitude of graphite morphologies has become available.

Degradation of microstructures during use due to morphological changes (but also by grain growth, particle coarsening, recrystallization, and so forth) is also investigated using SEM. Image analysis is used to obtain quantitative data to assess the kinetics of microstructural transformations and their effect on materials properties. Figure 41 shows the effect of heating on the microstructural geometry of a conduction material. It is obvious

that the decay of the strong fibers during extended heating deleteriously affects the strength of this material. As a final example of the large variety of SEM applications in materials science, Fig. 42 to 44 show the degradation of an electronic component investigated using SEM imaging of an x-ray dot map.

## REFERENCES

1. J.C. Russ, Uses of the Electron Microscope in the Materials Sciences, in *STP 480*, ASTM, Philadelphia, 1970, p 214-248
2. P.R. Thornton, *Scanning Electron Microscopy*, Chapman and Hall, 1968
3. J.W.S. Hearle, J.T. Sparrow, and P.M. Cross, *The Use of the Scanning Electron Microscope*, Pergamon Press, 1972
4. O.C. Wells, *Scanning Electron Microscopy*, McGraw-Hill, 1974
5. L. Reimer and G. Pfefferkorn, *Rasterelektronenmikroskopie*, 2nd ed., Springer-Verlag, 1977
6. J.I. Goldstein and H. Yakowitz, *Practical Scanning Electron Microscopy*, 3rd ed., Plenum Press, 1977
7. A. Rosencwaig, Thermal Wave Imaging, *Science*, Vol 218, 1982, p 223-228
8. J. Paul and B. Bauer, Contrast Techniques for Phase Separation in the Scanning Electron Microscope, *Pract. Metallogr.*, Vol 20, 1983, p 213-221
9. G. Zwilling, Observation of Magnetic Domains in the Scanning Electron Microscope, *Pract. Metallogr.*, Vol 11, 1974, p 716-728
10. G. Pfefferkorn and R. Blaschke, *Beitr. Elektronmikr. Direktabb. Oberfl. (BEDO)*, Vol 15, 1982, p 1
11. B. Bauer and B. Egg, An Optimized Back Scattered Electron Detector for the Scanning Electron Microscope, *Pract. Metal-*

*logr.*, Vol 21, 1984, p 460-471
12. R.J. Lee, W.A. Spitzig, J.F. Kelly, and R.M. Fisher, Quantitative Metallography by Computer-Controlled Scanning Electron Microscopy, *Pract. Metallogr.*, Vol 21, 1984, p 27-41
13. H.E. Exner and M. Fripan, Quantitative Assessment of Three-Dimensional Roughness, Anisotropy and Angular Distribution of Fracture Surfaces by Stereometry, *J. Microsc.*, 1985, to be published
14. K. Wetzig, A. Maslov, and J. Edelmann, Development and Application of a Cyclic Bending Device for in-situ Fatigue Investigations in the Scanning Electron Microscope, *Pract. Metallogr.*, Vol 21, 1984, p 161-172
15. D.L. Davidson and A. Nagy, A Low Frequency Cyclic-Loading Stage for the SEM, *J. Phys. E (Sci. Instrum.)*, Vol 11, 1978, p 207-210
16. W. Krompp, P. Bajons, and B. Weiss, A Scanning Electron Microscope Accessory for the Observation of Deformation Processes, *Pract. Metallogr.*, Vol 13, 1976, p 53-62
17. P.M. Yu Zawich and C.W. Hughes, An Improved Technique for Removal of Oxide Scale from Fractured Surfaces of Ferrous Metals, *Pract. Metallogr.*, Vol 15, 1978, p 184
18. A. Madeski, Hydrogen Reduction of Oxide on Metal Fracture prior to Fractography, *Pract. Metallogr.*, Vol 17, 1980, p 598-607
19. U. Gramberg, T. Günther, and H. Palla, Decontamination of Fracture Surfaces on Steel Specimens for Scanning Electron Microscopy, *Pract. Metallogr.*, Vol 13, 1976, p 31-38
20. A.F. Mornheim, Evaluating Coating Thickness for Scanning Electron Microscopy, *Pract. Metallogr.*, Vol 9, 1972, p 535-537

21. I. Stapf, S. Kühnemann, and U. Kopac, Revealing the Structure of Hard-Coated High-Speed Steel Specimens Using Contrasting by Reactively Sputtered Interference Layers, *Pract. Metallogr.*, Vol 22, 1985, p 111-123

22. T. Hillmer, Practical Experience in Materials Microanalysis with the Scanning Electron Microscope; Part 1: Methods of Preparation, *Pract. Metallogr.*, Vol 16, 1979, p 465-479

23. H.E. Exner, Qualitative and Quantitative Surface Microscopy, in *Physical Metal-lurgy*, 3rd ed., Vol 1, R.W. Cahn and P. Haasen, Ed., Elsevier, 1983, p 581-647

24. L. Sigl, H.E. Exner, and H.F. Fischmeister, Characterization of Fracture Processes and Fracture Relevant Parameters in WC-Co Hardmetals, in *Proceedings of the Second International Conference on the Science of Hard Materials*, Institute of Physics, London

25. H. Jehn and U. Kopacz, Einfluss der Substrattemperatur auf einige Eigenschaften reaktiv aufgestaubter TiN-Schichten, *Z. Metallkd.*, Vol 75, 1984, p 862-867

26. R. Wang, B. Bauer, and H. Mughrabi, The Study of Surface Roughness Profiles on Fatigued Metals by Scanning Electron Microscopy, *Z. Metallkd.*, Vol 73, 1982, p 30-34

27. E. Horn and U. Lotter, Assessment of Grain Orientations at the Surface of Electrical Sheets by Means of Etch Pits, in *Metallography: Modern Methods for Microstructural Preparation for Studies of Materials Properties*, Riederer-Verlag, 1984

# Transmission Electron Microscopy*

By M. Rühle
Research Scientist
Max-Planck-Institut für Metallforschung
Institut für Werkstoffwissenschaften

TRANSMISSION ELECTRON MICRO-SCOPES became commercially available in the 1950s, and it was soon realized that these instruments could be used in applied and fundamental research in materials science and physical metallurgy. Within a few years, the resolution limit for the direct imaging of structural details of solids—up to that time limited by the light wavelength in optical microscopy to some fraction of a micron at best—was reduced to approximately 1 nm (10 Å). During this rapid development, new aspects of research requiring a spatial resolution down to nearly an atomic level were initiated.

However, it became apparent that transmission electron microscopy (TEM) differs significantly from classical optical microscopy in that TEM, especially when applied to crystalline specimens, requires a more profound understanding of the interaction of the imaging (electron) waves with matter. This is particularly applicable to imaging of crystal inhomogeneities, such as lattice defects, and precipitates by TEM using elastic interaction of the imaging electrons with the specimen atoms, as well as to local material analysis with various processes involving inelastic interactions. This article will introduce several methods for imaging various lattice defects and precipitates by diffraction contrast, constituted mainly by elastic interaction. Additional information can be found in the References.

## The Instrument

The technology of modern electron microscopes has developed to the point that commercially available instruments and the sophisticated attachments fulfill practically all requirements necessary for studying crystalline and noncrystalline thin films. Some essential properties of the instrument will be outlined.

The resolution of an electron microscope is governed by errors of the magnetic lenses, specifically by the spherical aberration of the objective lens. The ultimate resolution $r_{min}$ can be reached for an optimum objective aperture angle $\alpha_{opt}$, with:

$$\alpha_{opt} = A\lambda^{1/4}C_s^{-1/4}, \quad r_{min} = B\lambda^{3/4}C_s^{1/4} \quad (Eq\ 1)$$

where $\lambda$ is the wavelength of the incident electrons, and $C_s$ is the spherical aberration coefficient; A and B are constants whose actual values depend on the combination of different contributions to lens error.

Ultimate resolution is usually not necessary for electron microscopy studies in materials science, for which shifting and tilting of the specimen over large ranges and detection of signals of scattered electrons and x-rays in analytical microscopy studies are more important. The objective lenses of the standard instruments have pole pieces with larger borings to facilitate specimen manipulations and mounting of detectors for analytical purposes. Therefore, the resolution of the instrument is reduced to ~0.4 nm (4 Å), which is sufficient for most applications of TEM in materials science.

The components of an electron microscope can be classified according to function. The illumination system, composed of the electron gun and the condenser lenses, produces a fine electron beam to illuminate the specimen. The objective lens produces the diffraction pattern and an initial magnified image of the specimen, and the magnification system yields the final image. In addition to optical components, the microscope also contains a specimen chamber (specimen handling system) and a recording system.

The illumination system projects a beam of adjustable size, intensity, and convergence angle onto the specimen, resulting in a limited coherency. Coherence refers to the range of phase differences in the illuminating beam as it approaches the specimen. If the electrons originate from a single point source, all the waves in the incident beam are in phase with each other, and the illumination is coherent. However, if the source of electrons is so large that there is no phase relation between the incident waves, the illumination is incoherent. In reality, the filament in an electron microscope is between these two extremes, and the incident illumination is defined as partially coherent.

Charged electrons interact strongly with the transmitted specimen; the scattering cross section for electrons is large compared to the cross section of neutrons or x-rays. Specimen thicknesses of 10 nm (100 Å) to 1 μm are required, depending on the imaging mode and the voltage of the transmission electron microscope. Specimen preparation will be discussed below.

**Modes of Operation.** The microscope can be operated in different modes (Fig. 1). In the standard, or conventional, TEM mode, the unit is operated to form images by bright-field, dark-field, or lattice-image (phase) contrast. A bright-field (dark-field) image is formed when only the direct (diffracted) beam is used for image formation. The objective aperture prevents the passage of all other beams to the recording system. The specimen is usually oriented so that the Bragg condition is nearly fulfilled for a set of lattice planes. One reflected beam is then strongly excited in addition to the incident beam. A weak-beam dark-field image is produced if a weakly excited dark-field beam is used for imaging.

A lattice image is formed by the interference of at least two beams in the image plane of the objective lens. Lattice fringes can be observed if a row of systematic beams, re-

*Based on M. Rühle and M. Wilkens, Transmission Electron Microscopy, in *Physical Metallurgy*, R.W. Cahn and P. Haasen, Ed., 3rd ed., North-Holland, 1983, Chap. 11, p 714-762. With permission.

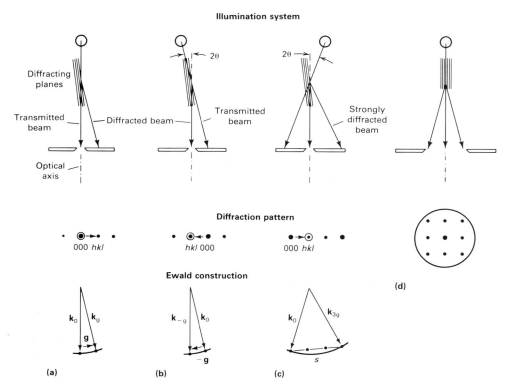

**Fig. 1** Beam diagrams, including Ewald sphere construction, for (a) a conventional two-beam bright-field image, (b) a dark-field image, (c) a weak-beam dark-field image, and (d) a lattice image. The gun of the electron microscope is tilted by the appropriate angle proceeding from (a) to (b) or (a) to (c). $k_0$ is the wave vector of the transmitted beam, $k_g$ the wave vector of the diffracted beam, $g$ the two-beam diffraction vector, and $s$ the excitation error.

flected at the lattice plane in question, is used for imaging; a structure image is formed by using many beams in a low-indexed Laue zone. Special adjustments to the microscope are required to form high-resolution electron microscope images.

The objective lens produces a diffraction pattern of the specimen in its backfocal plane (Fig. 2). The first image of the object is rotated 180° against the diffraction pattern. The diffraction pattern and the first image are magnified by the subsequent intermediate and projector lenses. The information obtainable from the diffraction pattern is summarized below.

In the scanning transmission electron microscopy (STEM) mode, the electron beam is focused as a fine probe on the specimen by the prefield of the objective lens. The beam probe is scanned over the specimen by scanning coils, and the transmitted intensity recorded.

The STEM mode is usually applied in materials science for analytical microscopy, for which the probe is fixed on a selected small area to study the energy losses of the transmitted electrons (electron energy loss spectroscopy) or to investigate the x-rays emitted from the specimens (usually by electron diffraction spectroscopy) to determine the chemical composition of the specimen. The use of small probe (<10 nm, or 100 Å) is often limited by a strongly enhanced contamination rate. In the STEM mode, back-

scattered electrons and secondary electrons can be collected. These scanning micrographs are similar to those obtained using scanning electron microscopy (SEM). Information on the topography of the specimen surface can be obtained.

## Specimen Preparation

Specimens suitable for TEM must have a thickness of several hundred nanometers, depending on the operating high voltage of the instrument. An ideal specimen is thin, representative of the bulk sample, stable, clean, flat with parallel sides, easily handled, conductive, free of surface segregation, and self-supporting. All these requirements cannot always be fulfilled. Specimen preparation techniques often produce a wedge-shaped specimen having a small wedge angle. Characteristic contrast features, such as thickness contours, reveal these details. Preparation can be divided into the initial preparation steps and final thinning. Initial preparation consists of several steps, although some may be omitted.

### Initial Preparation

The first step is to cut a rough specimen from a bulk sample, bearing in mind when choosing the section that the final viewing direction will be perpendicular to the specimen. At this stage, the specimen will probably

have two rough surfaces, and its thickness must be determined by the likely depth of damage caused by the cutting technique selected. A hacksaw, even with fine teeth, will probably most severely damage the structure, which may be affected as far as 1 mm (0.04 in.) from the cut in a soft metal. Less damaging techniques are spark machining, incorporating a low-energy spark, and use of a diamond slitting wheel or a rotating wire saw that carries an abrasive slurry through the specimen. The choice of technique depends on the material. Spark machining, or electric discharge, can be applied only to conductors and tends to be slow. These three techniques are described in the article "Sectioning" in this Volume.

**Preparing Flat Faces.** After the 3- to 0.5-mm (0.1- to 0.02-in.) thick specimen has been cut, its faces must be prepared as flat and parallel-sided as possible. Parallel faces are best achieved by machine milling or lapping; the latter is preferable, because the depth of damage can be minimal using a fine abrasive. Parallel-side sheets 100 μm thick or less can be produced from most materials by lapping with a 600-grit abrasive powder. If only a small specimen, such as a 3-mm (0.1-in.) disk is to be thinned, a commercially available jig can be used to control the thinning (Fig. 3). With such a device it is possible to thin a disk to less than 50 μm while maintaining highly parallel faces. The desired final thickness can be set using the lock rings, and the thinning can then be performed using conventional metallographic papers and wheels.

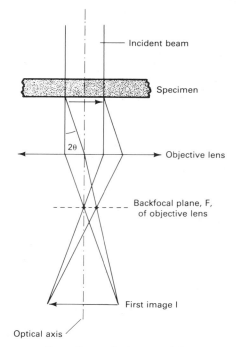

**Fig. 2** Beam diagram in the area of the objective lens of an electron microscope. A diffraction pattern is formed in the backfocal plane, F, of the objective lens, but the (first) image I of the object lies in plane I. The first image of the object is rotated 180° relative to the diffraction pattern.

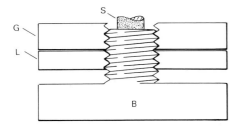

**Fig. 3** A simple jig for hand polishing. The specimen (S) is glued to the central post (B) while a guard ring (G) is set to protrude by an amount equal to the desired final thickness. This is held in place by a lock ring (L).

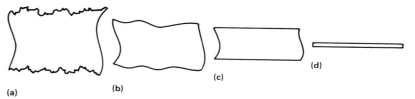

**Fig. 4** The stages of electropolishing. (a) The rough specimen must be (b) polished, (c) smoothed, and (d) uniformly thinned.

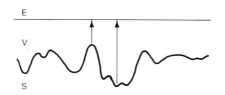

**Fig. 5** Fine electropolishing action. A viscous film (V) forms between the specimen (S) and the electrolyte (E); high spots have a shorter diffusion path through the layer and polish faster.

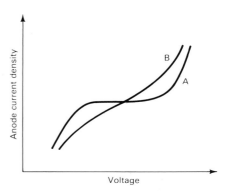

**Fig. 6** Current-voltage curves for electropolishing. Ideally, curve A is followed, and the best polishing condition is on the central plateau. More commonly, a curve such as B is formed.

**Chemical Thinning.** The least damaging method of thinning a specimen is chemical polishing. Although damage introduced by any previous mechanical stage can be removed using this technique, it is difficult to maintain parallelism between the faces of the specimen. Chemical thinning machines are available, but both faces of a specimen can be polished simultaneously in a beaker of thinning solution. If specimen material is abundant, a specimen may be immersed in the solution without attempting to prevent preferential attack at its edges. That the resultant slice is smaller is not normally of consequence if the faces are acceptably polished. Successful chemical thinning requires the appropriate thinning solution. Table 1 details methods and solutions for the thinning of specimens. Additional information on various solutions used is provided in Ref 1 to 11.

**Making a Disk.** Many automated final-thinning techniques require a 3-mm (0.1-in.) diam disk specimen. Such a disk is easily handled, fits directly into most microscopes without a grid, and provides good structural support for the thinnest areas of the specimen. The material may occasionally be prepared initially as a 3-mm (0.1-in.) diam rod, from which disks can be cut using a small diamond slitting wheel or a dedicated mini-cutoff machine. Such disks will usually be approximately 1 mm (0.04 in.) thick and can be thinned further using a technique described above before final thinning.

However, the disk is usually dimpled (dished) in the middle to maintain thicknesses of 1 mm (0.04 in.) at the outer rim, facilitating handling with tweezers, and less than 100 $\mu$m at the center. Dimpling, which requires less time than final thinning, can be performed mechanically by electropolishing or ion bombardment. The dimple need not have a flawlessly polished surface; therefore, dimpling does not have to be as carefully controlled as final thinning.

The quickest preparation of a 3-mm (0.1-in.) disk is to punch out the disk using a hollow punch having an inner diameter of 3 mm (0.1 in.). This method is suitable for ductile metals but not brittle materials. Unexpected damage may occur; for example, it has been reported that steel disks may contain stress-induced martensite in the dimpled area after punching. Gentler techniques for cutting

disks from sheet require more time. The most prevalent methods involve use of hollow drills or ultrasonic hollow cutters.

## Final Thinning

**Electropolishing** is frequently used to thin a specimen to its final thickness. In electropolishing, an electrolytic cell is established; the specimen is the anode, and an appropriate potential is applied to dissolve the specimen in a controlled manner. Electropolishing usually proceeds until a hole (perforation) forms in the specimen. The electron transparent region is the narrow band of material surrounding the perforation.

The electropolishing cell must polish the specimen, that is, remove very fine-scale irregularities. It should also smooth the specimen, that is, remove larger scale irregularities, and it must thin the specimen uniformly and fairly rapidly. The sequence is illustrated in Fig. 4. To produce this electropolishing action, the electrolyte must generally contain an oxidizing agent and reagents that will form a thin but stable viscous film. The fine polishing is achieved by dissolution that is controlled by the length of the diffusion path through the viscous film to the electrolyte, as shown in Fig. 5. High spots, being nearer to the free electrolyte, dissolve faster than the surrounding areas. This results in a fine-scale smoothing that generally is recognizable as a brightening of the surface.

Because the viscous film must be maintained thin, the electrolyte must contain a solvent for the oxide-containing viscous film as well as an oxidizing agent and a film former. One reagent will sometimes act in all three ways, and the electrolyte can be simple. An example is a dilute solution of perchloric acid ($HClO_4$) in ethanol, which is a virtually universal electropolishing agent. However, some electrolytes are complex mixtures of three or four reagents. In these cases, an oxidizing

agent, such as $HClO_4$ or nitric acid ($HNO_3$); a film former, such as phosphoric acid ($H_3PO_4$); another acid, such as sulfuric acid ($H_2SO_4$) to dissolve oxides; and a diluent—perhaps also viscous, such as glycerol—to control the rate of reaction can be identified.

Once the composition of the electrolyte is determined, the primary variable is the applied potential. Too low a potential will generally lead to etching; too high a potential will result in pitting and uneven polishing. Both conditions are to be avoided, and in principle the correct conditions can be determined using an experimental current-voltage curve. In a stable electrochemical cell, a current-voltage curve should appear as curve A in Fig. 6. Optimum polishing then occurs in the plateau region. However, a potentiostat is necessary to measure a reliable current-voltage curve. Less sophisticated attempts to plot an experimental curve are usually complicated by the difficulties of achieving stable steady-state conditions. An actual experiment is more likely to lead to curve B in Fig. 6, which is not very helpful. Therefore, the normal heuristic approach is to begin with a recommended potential, which is then increased if etching occurs or decreased if pitting appears.

**The Window Technique.** The most straightforward and least expensive polishing cell is a beaker of electrolyte into which the cathode and the specimen are dipped. The cathode is a sheet of the same material as the specimen or an inert material, such as platinum or stainless steel. The specimen acts as the anode and a 10- to 20-mm (0.4 to 0.8 in.) square sheet is generally held in metal tweezers so that the potential can be applied using

**Table 1  Preparation of TEM specimens from bulk samples**

| Material | Method | Chemical solution or electrolyte | Final specimen thickness | Comments |
|---|---|---|---|---|
| Alumina | Ion bombardment | ... | Can be thinned to electron transparency | Technique requires several hours for starting thicknesses of ~1 mm (~0.04 in.) |
| Aluminum and aluminum alloys | Chemical dissolution | 20 g NaOH and 100 mL $H_2O$ | <1 $\mu$m | Use solution temperature of ~70 °C (~160 °F) |
| | Liquid jet | 85% $H_3PO_4$ and 15% $H_2O$ | Can be thinned to electron transparency | Requires bath temperature of ~500 °C (~930 °F); specimens can be dipped |
| Beryllium | Chemical dissolution | 60% $H_3PO_4$ and 40% HF | <1 $\mu$m | Agitate vigorously |
| Bismuth selenide | Cleavage | ... | Can be cleared along basal plane to electron transparency | ... |
| Bismuth telluride | Chemical dissolution | Dilute aqua regia | <1 $\mu$m | ... |
| Calcium fluoride | Chemical dissolution | Conc $H_2SO_4$ | Can be thinned to electron transparency | Begin dissolution at 130 °C (265 °F) and lower to 20 °C (68 °F) for final thinning |
| Copper and copper alloys | Chemical dissolution | 80% $HNO_3$ and 20% $H_2O$ | ~1 $\mu$m | Agitate vigorously; electrolytic jet using 20 V can also be used |
| Copper-aluminum | Chemical dissolution | 40% $HNO_3$, 50% $H_3PO_4$, and 10% HCl | ~1 $\mu$m | ... |
| | Electrolytic jet | 75% $H_3PO_4$ and 25% $H_2O$ | <1 $\mu$m | Use approx 100 V dc |
| Diamond | Oxidation | Aqua regia | Can be thinned to electron transparency | Oxidize at 1350 °C (2460 °F) in carbon dioxide, then boil in solution to remove carbon |
| Gallium arsenide | Chemical dissolution and electrolytic jet | Chemical polish with 15% bromine in acetic acid; electrolytically in 25% $HClO_4$ and 75% acetic acid | Can be thinned to electron transparency | Use 42 V electrolytically and wash in conc HF to remove oxide; rinse in distilled $H_2O$ |
| Germanium | Chemical dissolution | 25 mL $HNO_3$, 15 mL HF, 15 mL acetic acid, and 0.3 mL bromine | Can be thinned to electron transparency | Agitate solution; thin specimen will float in solution |
| Inconel (all alloys) | Electrolytic jet | 42% $H_3PO_4$, 34% $H_2SO_4$, and 24% $H_2O$ | Can be thinned to electron transparency | Use total current of roughly 1 A or more |
| Iron, carbon, and alloy steels | Chemical dissolution | 30% $HNO_3$, 15% HCl, 10% HF, and 45% $H_2O$ | ~1 $\mu$m | Keep solution temperature hot (~70 °C, or 160 °F) |
| Iron-manganese | Chemical dissolution | 75% HCl and 25% $H_2O$ | ~1 $\mu$m | Vigorous agitation |
| Magnesium | Chemical dissolution | 5% HCl and 95% $H_2O$ | <1 $\mu$m | Thinning is controlled by agitation |
| Magnesium alloys | Chemical dissolution | 2% HCl and 98% ethanol | <1 $\mu$m | Specimens should be initially thinned in 2% $HNO_3$ in ethanol |
| Magnesium-aluminum and magnesium-zinc alloys | Chemical dissolution | 15% $HNO_3$ and 85% $H_2O$ | <1 $\mu$m | Agitate continuously |
| Magnesium oxide | Chemical dissolution | 95% $H_3PO_4$ and 5% $H_2SO_4$ | Can be thinned to electron transparency | Agitate continuously and maintain solution at ~100 °C (~212 °F) |
| Nickel and nickel alloys | Electrolytic jet | ... | ... | ... |
| Nickel oxide | Liquid jet | Conc $H_3PO_4$ | Can be thinned to electron transparency | Agitate in hot solution |
| Niobium | Chemical dissolution | 70% $HNO_3$ and 30% HF | Can be thinned to electron transparency | When specimen becomes thin, add HCl to increase concentration to approx 40%, then lower temperature to 0 °C (32 °F) |
| Silicon | Chemical dissolution | 75% $HNO_3$ and 25% HF | Can be thinned to electron transparency | Use black-wax protective coatings to outline the desired area |
| Silicon | Chemical dissolution | 95% $HNO_3$ and 5% HF | Can be thinned to electron transparency | Allow specimen to float on solution; stop action by flooding with deionized $H_2O$; use as a sequence to previous technique for final thinning of small pieces |
| Silicon dioxide | Chemical dissolution | 50% $HNO_3$ and 50% HF | Can be thinned to electron transparency | Agitate vigorously |
| Silver | Electrolytic jet | 20% $HNO_3$ and 80% $H_2O$ | <1 $\mu$m | Use approx 20 V at <1 A for mechanically sawed sections |
| Silver alloys | Chemical dissolution | 50% $HNO_3$ in $H_2O$ | Can be thinned to electron transparency | Sections can be mechanically sawed from stock |
| Tantalum | Chemical dissolution | 50% $HNO_3$ and 50% HF | Can be thinned to electron transparency | Agitate vigorously |
| Titanium and titanium alloys | Electrolytic jet | 50% $H_2SO_4$ and 50% $H_3PO_4$ | <1 $\mu$m | Use approximately 30 V dc |
| Tungsten | Electrolytic jet | 80% solution of NaOH | Can be thinned to electron transparency | Agitate jet and use approx 10 to 20 V dc; final polish may require addition of $H_2O$ to electrolyte |
| Uranium and uranium alloys | Chemical dissolution | 50% HCl and 50% $H_2O$ | ~1 $\mu$m | Agitate solution |
| Uranium carbide | Electrolytic jet | 50% methanol and 50% $H_3PO_4$ | ~1 $\mu$m | Use 220 V dc at start and reduce to approx 80 V for final thinning |
| Uranium dioxide | Liquid jet | Conc $H_3PO_4$ | Can be thinned to electron transparency | Solution temperature should be approx 100 °C (212 °F) |
| Vanadium | Electrolytic jet | 70% methanol and 30% $H_2SO_4$ | <1 $\mu$m | Use 30 to 50 V dc and maintain solution under 30 °C (85 °F) |
| Zinc | Chemical dissolution | 10% HCl, 5% $HNO_3$, 10% methanol, and 75% $H_2O$ | <1 $\mu$m | Agitate specimen and maintain temperature under 30 °C (85 °F) |

Source: Ref 11

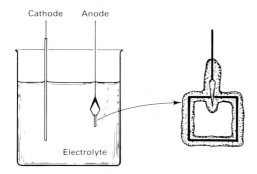

**Fig. 7** The window technique. The sheet specimen is held in tweezers and lacquered; it then forms the anode in the electrolytic cell.

alligator clips (Fig. 7). The edges of the specimen and the tweezers must be coated with an acid-resistant lacquer for protection against attack. A "window" of metal remains exposed, from which the technique derives its name (Fig. 7). The tweezers are held by hand so that the specimen is submerged and the potential is applied. Using this technique, the specimen can be viewed during polishing, because most electrolytes are transparent. Further, polishing can be quickly halted by switching off the power supply after a hole forms. Upon removal from the electrolyte, the specimen should be immersed in a beaker containing solvent, then washed thoroughly.

**The Automatic Jet Polisher.** Most automated electropolishers operate on the principle that a jet of electrolyte is directed at the center of a 3-mm (0.1-in.) disk specimen to accelerate the attack, ensuring perforation at the center before the edge thins appreciably. This produces an ideal specimen for mounting in the microscope; the specimen edges can be handled easily and support the thin areas in the center.

One widely used commercial polisher, a double-jet device, thins both sides of the

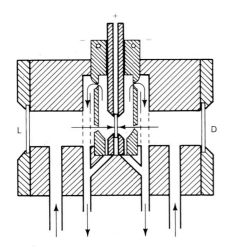

**Fig. 8** Automatic jet polisher. The electrolyte is pumped from the tank below the cell and directed at the disk specimen by two jets. Perforation can be detected by a photodiode at D, which registers light from the lamp L as soon as a hole forms.

specimen simultaneously. Figure 8 illustrates the polishing cell. A pump in the electrolyte reservoir below the cell circulates electrolyte through the dual jets, which are directed at the center of the 3-mm (0.1-in.) disk specimen. This is mounted in a removable holder, and the anode potential is applied using a metal strip that extends through the center of the holder. Polishing must be stopped as soon as a hole forms in the disk specimen. If it is continued beyond this point, the thinnest areas can be rounded by further electrolytic attack, and/or the mechanical action of the liquid jets can deform the thin regions. Because neither effect is desirable, the moment of perforation is usually detected using a light source on one side of the cell and a sensitive photodiode on the other (Fig. 8). Under favorable conditions, perforation can be achieved consistently within 1 to 2 min.

Several electrolyte compositions are usually provided for each material due to slightly different alloy or heat treatments. Table 1 lists several electrolytes for automatic jet polishing. Electrolytes may function best when freshly prepared or sometimes may improve during storage of a week or two. Some improve after use.

In electropolishing, thorough washing of the specimens is imperative. This will generally involve at least four or five clean dishes of solvent and should finish with use of a rapid-drying nonstaining solvent, such as alcohol.

Many electrolytes function better when cooled. Cooling is most easily accomplished by standing the electropolishing cell in a trough of cooled liquid, such as water with ice, alcohol with dry ice (solid carbon dioxide), or alcohol with liquid nitrogen poured on top. Small refrigerators are available that pump cooled liquid through a coil immersed in the electrolyte—an expensive alternative compared to pouring liquid nitrogen on the electrolyte.

**Ion-beam thinning** is also frequently used to thin a sheet to its final thickness. In ion-beam thinning, a beam of inert gas ions or atoms is directed at the specimen, and atoms or molecules are ejected from the specimen at the point of ion impingement. If this can be achieved without creating artifacts, ion-beam thinning is ideal for preparing foils for conducting and nonconducting materials.

However, it is necessary to anticipate and regulate several potentially undesirable effects, such as the implantation of the sputtering ion, the development of rough surface topography, and heating of the specimen. These reasons necessitate controlling the nature of the ions, their energy and direction of incidence, and their frequency of arrival.

Sputtering, the removal of surface atoms, will occur when any ion carrying more than approximately 100 eV of energy strikes a surface. The number of atoms ejected by each incident ion or atom is known as the sputtering yield, $S$. In general, $S$ and therefore the thinning rate increase with ion energy and the

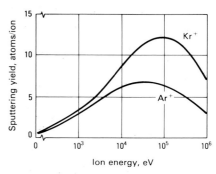

**Fig. 9** Principles of ion-beam thinning. The sputtering yield rises with the energy of the ions until a peak is reached (heavier ions sputter more efficiently).

mass of the bombarding ion, but $S$ decreases as the atomic mass of the specimen increases. Attaining a high sputtering yield with no chemical change in the specimen dictates use of argon; lighter inert gases, such as helium and neon, thin more slowly, and heavier inert gases, for example, krypton and xenon, are too expensive.

The ion energy is also easy to select. At first, $S$ increases with ion energy (Fig. 9), but eventually at high energies the incident ion is deposited far below the surface, and fewer surface atoms are ejected. Therefore, the optimum energy is 1 to 10 keV; a value between 3 and 6 keV is generally used. The sputtering yield also depends on the angle at which the ions strike the surface (Fig. 10). For this reason and others described below, a glancing angle of incidence from 5 to 30° is generally used.

Each of the various ion guns in use wear rapidly, because the ions erode the gun and the specimen. Therefore, regular replacement of gun components, particularly the cathode, is inevitable in ion-beam thinning. Commercial ion-beam thinning machines using different ion guns are available. In addition to components for setting the ion energy and beam current for at least two guns, these machines generally incorporate a specimen holder that accepts 3-mm (0.1-in.) disks and rotates them around their perpendicular axis while they are thinned simultaneously from both sides. Figure 11 shows a typical layout.

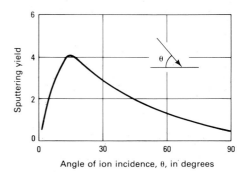

**Fig. 10** The variation of sputtering yield with the angle of ion incidence

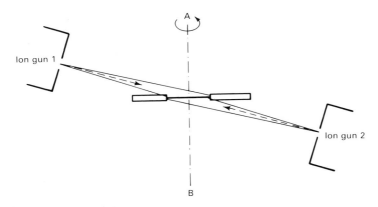

**Fig. 11** Setup for ion-beam thinning. The specimen in an ion-beam thinner is usually held at a glancing angle to the beams from two ion guns. The specimen is rotated around the axis A-B. Perforation can be detected by a light or third ion gun.

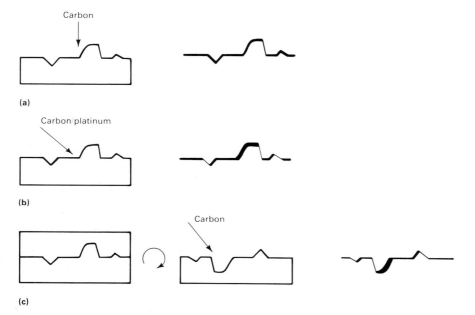

**Fig. 12** Three replication techniques. (a) Direct carbon replica. (b) Shadowed carbon-platinum replica. (c) Two-stage plastic-carbon replica

Automatic termination of thinning is useful, because erosion is generally slow—between one and a few tens of microns per hour. Therefore, thinning of a single 50-μm-thick disk may require several hours. For the same reason, it is beneficial to prepare the disk as thinly as possible before starting ion-beam thinning without inducing damage or making it difficult to handle.

Ion-beam thinning, now widely used, is most applicable to ceramics, glasses, and other nonconductors and to two-phase materials in which one phase always tends to electropolish faster than the other. Not all materials sputter at the same rate under a given set of ion-beam conditions, but when the ion beam is incident at a glancing angle to a rotating specimen, differential thinning is minimized. The technique is least useful for light, ductile, conducting crystals in which microstructural damage introduced and the gas atoms implanted close to the surface may lead to confusing artifacts in the micrographs.

## Replicas

The role of the replica has changed dramatically since its origin in the 1940s. Until the 1970s, a replica was primarily a method of reproducing surface topographic detail for viewing in a transmission electron microscope. Many precise and sophisticated single- and two-stage techniques were developed for this purpose, the majority of which led to a thin carbon film in which topographic detail was revealed by shadowing with a heavy metal (Fig. 12). The use of scanning electron microscopes having resolutions exceeding 5 nm (50 Å) has considerably diminished the need for replication of this type. Direct replication is still used in materials science for a few special problems, such as examining the surface of a large component without cut-

ting it or studying radioactive material that cannot be placed in an ordinary, unshielded microscope.

However, a second type of replica using extraction techniques remains in use, and interest is increasing with the spread of analytical TEM. Many problems involving the determination of the composition, crystal structure, or orientation of small second-phase particles are simplified if the particles are extracted from their matrix, then supported in the microscope using a replica. Extraction replicas can preserve the relative positions and orientation of second-phase particles if they are small enough to be supported by a carbon film less than 1 μm thick.

**The Extraction Replica.** The general principles of the technique are depicted in Fig. 13. The specimen is etched to highlight the particles of interest in relief on the surface. A carbon coating is applied, and the replica is then stripped off, perhaps using a second etch, carrying with it many of the second-phase particles. The use of a suitable etchant will preserve the number, shape, and distribution of particles in the replica.

A metallurgical specimen is generally first polished flat to facilitate lifting the replica, then etched. The chemical or electrolytic etchant selected should remove the matrix but not attack any particles of interest. The etched layer should be shallow so that particles are exposed but not removed. Metallurgical considerations dictate etchant choice; a standard textbook should be consulted. After etching, the specimens are washed and dried. Replication should begin as soon as possible to avoid the deposition of airborne dust, which would contaminate the replica. A thin layer of carbon must be coated onto the etched surface. This is generally achieved by using a carbon arc source in a vacuum coating unit. Many commercial designs are available.

The next stage is to remove the specimen from the vacuum system and strip off the replica. Unless the specimen is small or the replica lifts extremely easily, it is best to score the carbon film with a sharp object into 2- to 3-mm (0.08- to 0.12-in.) squares. The specimen can then be lightly etched again using the same etchant until the replica begins to

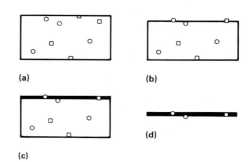

**Fig. 13** Principles of the extraction replica. (a) The two-phase specimen is (b) etched and (c) carbon coated. (d) An additional etch then lifts off the replica containing some second-phase particles.

lift. Etching should not be too vigorous, because the formation of bubbles will probably fracture the replica. Before the replica squares float off, the specimen should be removed from the etchant and slid into a dish of water. The replicas should now float off onto the water surface as the specimen is immersed.

The replica should be allowed to float for a time to wash away the electrolyte; they should then be raised using a 3-mm (0.12-in.) grid by gripping the edge of the grid with tweezers, plunging it under the water, and bringing the grid up underneath the floating replica square. With practice, the replica can be raised so that it remains in the center of the grid. The drop of water that will remain on the grid and the tweezers is best removed by sliding a piece of filter paper between the prongs of the tweezers. When dry, the grid and its replica can be stored or inserted into the microscope. It is generally not advisable to put a wet grid and replica face down on a piece of filter paper, because the fibers of the filter paper will damage a thin replica.

## Information From the Diffraction Pattern

The diffraction spot pattern is formed in the backfocal plane of the objective lens (see Fig. 2). The diffraction pattern provides crystallographic information on qualitative phase identification and on the orientation relations between crystals and the direction of the incoming electron beam. Kikuchi lines* can be used to determine orientation; the conver-

*Kikuchi lines consist of pairs of white and dark parallel lines obtained when an electron beam is scattered (diffracted) by a crystalline solid; the pattern provides information on the structure of the crystal.

gent-beam technique provides information on crystal symmetry and determination of the foil thickness. Kikuchi lines, or patterns, and convergent-beam diffraction are discussed below.

The possibilities and the accuracy of analysis of diffraction patterns are discussed in textbooks on electron microscopy (Ref 1-13). Factors influencing accuracy include (1) crystal shape, which determines the intensity distribution in the reciprocal space, (2) instrumental alignment and beam divergence, (3) specimen perfection, (4) curvature of the Ewald sphere and its orientation to the foil, and (5) double diffraction.

**Double Diffraction.** From the crystal shape, or structure factor, it follows that certain reciprocal lattice points are not present (zero intensity) for certain crystal symmetries. However, each diffracted beam with the crystal can act as an incident beam and can diffract electrons to a reciprocal lattice point forbidden by the structure-factor rules, especially in orientations in which several reflections are excited simultaneously. For example, in the diamond cubic structure, the (002) reflection is not allowed, but this reflection can be excited in a [110] foil using double diffraction. If a $(1\bar{1}1)$ reflection is excited, this reflected beam can act as a primary beam for $(\bar{1}11)$ planes, which yields a total reflection $g_1 + g_2 = (1\bar{1}1) + (\bar{1}11) = (002)$.

**Patterns From Ordered Crystals.** The symmetries of ordered crystals are often different from those of disordered crystals. This results in the appearance of superlattice reflections at positions forbidden for the disordered structure. The intensities of the superlattice reflections correspond to the difference between the atomic scattering factors of the different atoms, as opposed to the intensities

of the fundamental reflections, which are related to the sum of the scattering factors. As an example, the B2 superlattice is selected. It is based on the body-centered cubic (bcc) structure of the cesium chloride (CsCl) lattice with one kind (A) of atoms at 000 and another (B) at ½ ½ ½. The structure factors for complete ordering are:

$$F = f_A + f_B \text{ for } h + k + l$$
$$= \text{even: fundamental reflections}$$

$$F = f_A - f_B \text{ for } h + k + l$$
$$= \text{odd: superlattice reflections}$$

The corresponding diffraction patterns are shown in Fig. 14 and 15. In general, superlattices can be distinguished from their diffraction pattern by comparison with structure-factor calculations. In this method, the ordered lattice is represented by a superposition of concentration waves. Theoretically, it allows the unequivocal determination of superlattice diffraction vectors.

**Kikuchi Lines.** Electrons can be scattered inelastically by interaction with the atoms of the specimen. These electrons lose energies in the range of approximately 100 eV. The inelastically scattered electrons can be subsequently diffracted coherently when Bragg's law is fulfilled at a suitable set of reflection planes. Because inelastic scattering occurs in diverse directions, the loci of the different subsequent coherent scattered electrons are cones with semivertex angles of $(90° -$ the Bragg angle, $\theta_B$) to each side. The two cones are bisected by the reflection plane. Therefore, the lines are produced in pairs that contrast with the background. A deficiency line of less intensity than the background occurs nearer the origin of reciprocal space than its

 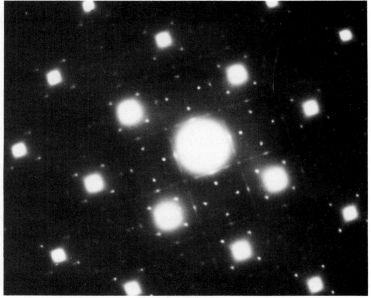

**Fig. 14, 15** Diffraction patterns from ordered crystals. Fig. 14: diffraction pattern of an ordered β-aluminum-nickel alloy (B2 superlattice), [100] zone axis. Superlattice reflections are visible. Fig. 15: diffraction pattern of an ordered tantalum (containing oxygen) structure, [100] zone axis. Variants of different orientations contribute to the pattern.

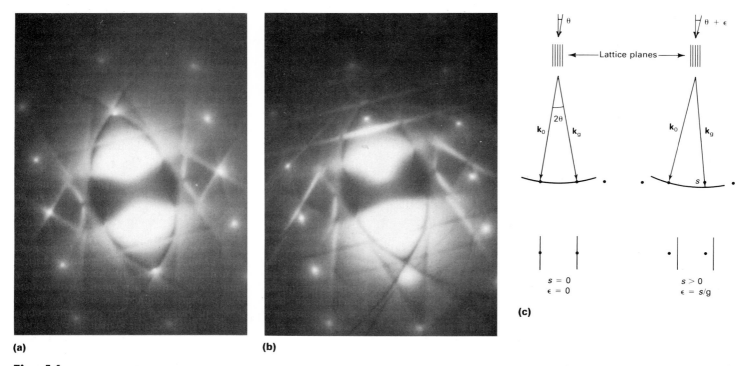

**Fig. 16** Kikuchi lines on a diffraction pattern. (a) Excitation error s ≈ 0. (b) s > 0. (c) Shift in Kikuchi lines produced by a tilt, ε, for s ≈ 0 and s > 0, respectively.

associated excess line with intensity above the background.

Two conditions must be fulfilled to observe these Kikuchi lines: First, the crystal must be thick enough to allow sufficient inelastic scattering to occur and, second, the crystal must be nearly perfect, especially not bent. The width of the lines indicates the curvature range of the crystal planes over the traversed thickness. If this becomes excessive, the lines disappear into the background as their intensity is spread over a larger angle.

The Kikuchi line pattern can be used to determine the orientation of the crystal relative to the incoming electron beam. This can be accomplished by indexing three pairs of Kikuchi lines, then calculating the orientation or by comparing the observed Kikuchi pattern to Kikuchi maps. The orientation of the specimen with respect to the electron beam can be determined with an accuracy exceeding 0.3°. The excitation error, $s$, discussed below can also be determined from the relative position of Kikuchi lines compared to the diffraction spots, as demonstrated in Fig. 16.

**Convergent-Beam Diffraction.** The size of the area producing the diffraction pattern can be substantially reduced if the electron beam is focused onto the specimen. Under this condition, it is practically impossible to maintain the nearly parallel illumination condition. Some convergence of the beam is introduced. As a result, the diffraction spots become disks. A convergence angle $\alpha < 2\theta_B$ is not affected, because the disks do not overlay. Information on orientation, crystal symmetry, crystal thickness, and exact lattice parameters can be obtained from the intensity distribution of these diffraction disks.

**Moiré patterns** result from overlapping crystals, as in composite films in two-phase (or more) systems. Two general cases must be considered. In the first case, parallel moiré fringes are formed if two parallel planes of different spacings are reflecting. The lattice spacings ($d_1 = 1/g_1$ and $d_2 = 1/g_2$) differ only in magnitude. Fringes can be observed with distances $d = (1/\Delta g = 1)/|g_1 - g_2|$. In the second case, a rotational moiré pattern is formed when planes with equal spacing $d$, but rotated through an angle $\alpha$, diffract together. For this situation, the moiré spacing $d_r$ is given by $d_r = 1/g \sin \alpha$.

Moiré patterns sometimes must be distinguished from other periodic defects in crystals, for example, a set of parallel dislocations. This is best carried out by imaging the same area using different diffraction vectors. The moiré lines are usually perpendicular to the diffraction vector.

## Theory of Diffraction Contrast

Diffraction contrast of defects in crystalline specimens is mainly a problem of high-energy electron diffraction in nonperfect crystals. For the imaging of lattice defects—dislocations, stacking faults, and so on—an electron-optical resolution of approximately 1 nm (10 Å) is generally sufficient. In the following section, diffraction in a perfect crystal specimen will be discussed. A second section will outline how the diffraction theory must be extended for specimens containing lattice defects. Electron refraction effects,

which are due to the mean inner potential of the crystal, are omitted.

### Diffraction in Perfect Crystals

**Specimen, Reciprocal Lattice, and Excitation Error.** A specimen of constant thickness $t$ of approximately 0.1 μm will be considered. A Cartesian coordinate system is introduced with its origin in the upper specimen surface and the z-axis (unit vector $\mathbf{e}_z$) perpendicular to the specimen plane and pointing downward. The lateral dimensions $L_x$, $L_y$ of the specimen are orders of magnitude larger than $t$. This means that the intensity distributions $|F(\kappa)|^2$ at the reciprocal lattice points, $\mathbf{g}$, are rod shaped or spike shaped, with the spike axis parallel to $\mathbf{e}_z$ and a spike length of approximately $1/t$. This is indicated in Fig. 17, where the wave vector $\mathbf{k}_0$ of the

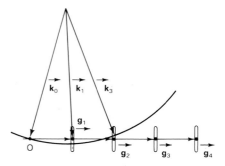

**Fig. 17** The Ewald sphere and the reciprocal space. The intensity distributions $|F(\kappa)|^2$ around the reciprocal lattice points are spike shaped, with spike lengths inversely proportional to the specimen thickness. The excitation error $s$ is positive for $\mathbf{g} = \mathbf{g}_1$ and negative for the other values of $\mathbf{g}$.

incident wave and the Ewald sphere also are inserted. This figure is not to scale. Assuming a modulus of $(0.2 \text{ nm})^{-1}$ for the low-order diffraction vector $\mathbf{g}_1$ and $\mathbf{k}_0 = 1/\lambda = (3.7 \text{ nm})^{-1}$(100 keV electrons), the result is $\mathbf{k}_0/\mathbf{g}_1 = 54$.

Therefore, near the low-order reflections, the Ewald sphere is so flat that if the sphere cuts through the spike of one of the reciprocal lattice points it will also cut through the spikes of other adjacent reciprocal lattice points. Accordingly, in high-energy electron diffraction, several Bragg reflections are generally excited simultaneously; in addition to the primary wave, several diffracted-plane waves leave the crystal. However, the specimen generally can be oriented so that only one diffracted wave is strong. Consequently, a two-beam case refers to the primary plus the diffracted beam. Images taken with either of these two beams are termed strong-beam images. On the other hand, dark-field images taken with an extremely weakly excited beam are called weak-beam images.

The direction of incidence of the primary beam regarding the specimen can be characterized by the excitation error $s_g$, or simply $s$, which is given by the distance between the reciprocal lattice point $\mathbf{g}$ considered and that point on the intensity spike at which the Ewald sphere cuts through it. The value of $s$ is positive (negative) if the point $\mathbf{g}$ lies inside (outside) the Ewald sphere. If $\theta$ is the glancing angle between the direction of $\mathbf{k}_0$ and the lattice planes belonging to $\mathbf{g}$ and if $\theta_g$ is the corresponding Bragg angle, then $s = \mathbf{g}\Delta\theta$, with $\Delta\theta = \theta - \theta_g$.

**Dynamical Diffraction Theory.** The essential points of the dynamical diffraction theory, in contrast to the kinematical theory, are that diffractions among all plane waves involved must be treated as equivalent and that in the absence of absorption effects conservation of intensity must be fulfilled. The dynamical theory for a perfect crystal can be formulated in several ways. One method will be considered here (Ref 14). Another will be outlined when crystals with lattice defects are considered.

The time-independent Schrödinger equation with a periodic potential is solved in terms of independent eigen solutions or Bloch waves $\psi_B$. Generally, Bloch waves can be written as:

$$\psi_B(\mathbf{r}) = b(\mathbf{r}) \exp(2\pi i \mathbf{K} \cdot \mathbf{r}) \qquad \text{(Eq 2)}$$

where the wave vector $\mathbf{K}$ must be determined for a given electron energy and a given direction of $\mathbf{K}$. The function $b(\mathbf{r})$ is periodic with the crystal periodicity. In the two-beam case, two independent Bloch waves belong to a given tangential component of $\mathbf{K}$ parallel to the electron entrance surface of the crystal. It is assumed that the two-beam diffraction vector $\mathbf{g}$ is perpendicular to $\mathbf{e}_z$ and that the origin of the coordinate system lies on a reflecting lattice plane. An important diffraction parameter is the extinction length $\xi_g$:

$$\xi_g = \frac{\kappa_0 V_e \pi}{F_s(\mathbf{g})} \qquad \text{(Eq 3)}$$

where $V_e$ is the volume of the elementary cell, and $F_s$ is the structure factor; $\xi_g$ is approximately 10 nm (100 Å) for low-order reflections. The solution of the problem can be expressed as a function of the normalized excitation error $w = s\xi_g$, the reciprocal of the extinction length $\sigma_0 = 1/\xi_g$, and the effective extinction length:

$$\xi_{g,\text{eff}} = \frac{1}{\sigma(w)} = \frac{1}{\sigma_0(1 + w^2)^{1/2}} \qquad \text{(Eq 4)}$$

**Normal and Anomalous Absorption.** High-energy electrons, when passing through a crystal, are subject to elastic scattering at the atom potential and inelastic scattering, for example, by interaction with the thermal vibration of the crystal atoms (phonons) or with the crystal electrons (plasmons, inner-shell excitation). By these events, energy is transferred between high-energy electrons and the crystal, which leads to a loss of coherency of the wave fields of the elastically and inelastically scattered electrons. This effect can be described formally as an absorption, although the inelastically scattered electrons are not absorbed. This absorption varies for different Bloch waves, depending on the high-energy electron density distribution $|\psi_B|^2$ relative to the atom positions. It has been found that $|\psi_B^{(1)}|^2$ reveals a maximum electron density at the lattice planes characterized by $\mathbf{g}$ and a minimum in between; for $|\psi_B^{(2)}|^2$ the reverse is true (Ref 15).

Accordingly, the first Bloch wave $\psi_B^{(1)}$ interacts more strongly with the crystal atoms and is therefore more strongly absorbed than $\psi_B^{(2)}$. Absorption is subdivided into normal absorption, which a high-energy electron would experience when traveling through the crystal far away from any Bragg reflection, and anomalous absorption, which considers the structure $|\psi_B^{(1)}|^2$. Normal absorption is accounted for by adding a common factor $\exp(-\mu_0 z/2)$, where $\mu_0$ is usually expressed by the normal absorption length $\xi_0'$, with $\mu_0 = 2\pi/\xi_0'$. The anomalous absorption is introduced by adding a positive imaginary part to $1/\xi_g$:

$$\frac{1}{\xi_g} \rightarrow \frac{1}{\xi_g} + i\frac{1}{\xi_g'} \qquad \text{(Eq 5)}$$

where typically $\xi_g' \approx (10 \text{ to } 20)\xi_g$. Accurate values of $\xi_0'$ are not well known, because they depend, for example, on the size of the objective aperture. Normal absorption acts independently of the actual diffraction conditions as only a scaling factor. Therefore, accurate values of $\xi_0'$ are not required, and often $\xi_0' = \xi_g'$ is used for intensity calculations.

Using the dynamical theory, the intensities in bright field and dark field can be calculated as a function of $s$ and of the thickness $t$. In Fig. 18(a) and (b) the bright-field intensity, $I_0$, and the dark-field intensity, $I_g$, are plotted as a function of $t$ for $w = 0$ and $w = 1$ (with $\xi_0' = \xi_g'$ and $\xi_g' = 10\xi_g$). The total intensity oscillates between $I_0$ and $I_g$; a maximum in $I_0$ corresponds to a minimum $I_g$ and vice versa (Pendellösung). These oscillations are due to the z-components of the wave vectors of the Bloch waves $\psi_B^{(1)}$ and $\psi_B^{(2)}$ differing by $\sigma$, which leads to a beating of the partial waves constituting $\psi_0$ and $\psi_g$, respectively. The full oscillation period $\Delta t = \xi_{g,\text{eff}} = \sigma^{-1}$ and the oscillation amplitude decrease with increasing $|w|$. Further, the oscillations are damped with increasing $t$, which is a consequence of the anomalous strong absorption of $\psi_B^{(1)}$; if $\psi_B^{(1)}$ has decayed, a beating between partial waves is no longer possible. On wedge-shaped specimens, the Pendellösung oscillations produce thickness fringes, or thickness contours, along lines of constant specimen thickness. An example is illustrated in Fig. 18(c) and (d).

In Fig. 19(a) and (b), $I_0$ and $I_g$ are shown as a function of $w$ for some values of $t$. Both terms exhibit oscillations with varying $w$ (bend contours), which decrease in amplitude with increasing $t$. Although $I_g$ is symmetric in $w$, this is not true for $I_0$; the maximum in $I_0$, that is, the best transmittivity, occurs at $w > 0$. A complicated system of bend contours is visible in Fig. 20.

## Diffraction in Imperfect Crystals

**The Displacement Field.** Lattice defects cause displacements $\mathbf{R}(\mathbf{r}_n) \equiv \mathbf{R}_n$ of the atoms from their positions $\mathbf{r}_n$ in the defect-free reference lattice. In general, $|\mathbf{R}_n|$ is on the order of or smaller than the interatomic distances. It is assumed that the displacements do not vary appreciably over the atom positions within the elementary cell so that the structure amplitude $F_s$ is unaffected by the lattice defects. Further, this discussion considers only cases in which $\mathbf{R}$ is a continuous function in space, therefore causing strain contrast. Contrast due to stacking faults and other planar defects will be discussed briefly.

**The Kinematical Approach.** A first insight into the intensities $I_0(x,y)$ and $I_g(x,y)$ for perfect and imperfect crystals may be obtained by the kinematical diffraction theory. The kinematical diffraction amplitude $F(\mathbf{s})$ can be written:

$$F(\mathbf{s}) = \frac{F_s(\mathbf{g})}{V_e} \int_{V_c} \exp\{-2\pi i[\mathbf{g} \cdot \mathbf{R}(\mathbf{r})$$
$$+ \mathbf{s} \cdot \mathbf{r}]\}d^3\mathbf{r} \qquad \text{(Eq 6)}$$

where the integration runs over the specimen volume $V_c = L_x L_y t$ with $t \ll L_x, L_y$. The diffracted intensity can also be calculated. It is assumed that $\mathbf{g}$ is perpendicular to the z-axis. The approximate parallelism of the Ewald sphere near $\mathbf{g}$ to the x-y plane, due to the smallness of the Bragg angle, is useful. Therefore, with Eq 3, the amplitude $\phi_g$ follows as:

$$\phi_g(x,y;t) = \frac{i\pi}{\xi_g}\phi_0 \int_0^t \exp\{-2\pi i[\mathbf{g}\cdot\mathbf{R}(x,y;z) + sz]\}dz \qquad \text{(Eq 7)}$$

where the amplitude $\phi_0$ of the primary wave, which is constant ($|\phi| = 1$) within the kinematical approach, has been added. Equation 7 is the kinematical contrast integral; it has been shown that the imaginary unit i should be added (Ref 16). The amplitude of the diffracted beam near a lattice defect with displacement $\mathbf{R}(x,y,z)$ can be calculated by solving the integral of Eq 7.

**Dynamical Diffraction Theory in Terms of Plane Waves.** In the derivation of the dynamical theory, a prerequisite is that all plane waves involved must be treated equivalently; that is, diffraction between all plane waves must be considered. Equation 7 includes one approach: Both sides of Eq 7 are differentiated relative to $t$, then $t$ is set equal to $z$, conceding that $\phi_0$ may be $z$-dependent. An equivalent equation is then constructed, describing the transition from the diffracted into the primary wave, that is, $\mathbf{k}_g$ and $\mathbf{k}_0$ change their roles, which requires changing the signs of $\mathbf{g}$ and $s$. The result is a set of coupled differential equations:

$$d\phi_g/dz = i(\pi/\xi_g)\phi_0(z)\exp\{-2\pi i[\mathbf{g}\cdot\mathbf{R}(z) + sz]\},$$
$$d\phi_0/dz = i(\pi/\xi_g)\phi_0(z)\exp\{+2\pi i[\mathbf{g}\cdot\mathbf{R}(z) + sz]\} \qquad \text{(Eq 8)}$$

These equations are indeed one form of previously established differential equations (Ref 15). They are used here in a more detailed way for describing strain contrast by dynamical diffraction in imperfect crystals. These equations must be integrated down to $z = t$ with the boundary condition $\phi_0 = 1$, $\phi_g = 0$ at $z = 0$. For $\mathbf{R} = 0$ (perfect crystal) they can be integrated analytically; the result is identical to that obtained for thickness and bend contours. Equivalent formulation of Eq 2 can be given for the scattering between Bloch waves or modified Bloch waves. All formulations are identical and, for a specific defect, yield the same result.

**Strain Contrast in Strong-Beam Images.** Figures 21 to 24 show strong-beam images in bright and dark field of dislocations traversing the specimen from the top to the bottom surface. Near the surface, the dislocation contrast reveals characteristic bright-dark oscillations, which are in phase in bright and dark field near the top surface and are in antiphase near the bottom surface. Further, the bright-dark oscillations are reversed if the sign of $\mathbf{g}$ is changed. In the middle of the specimen, the contrast is primarily dark in bright and dark field. These phenomena, observable for all types of lattice defects, can be understood by the different theoretical models. The Bloch wave formalism is especially suitable for un-

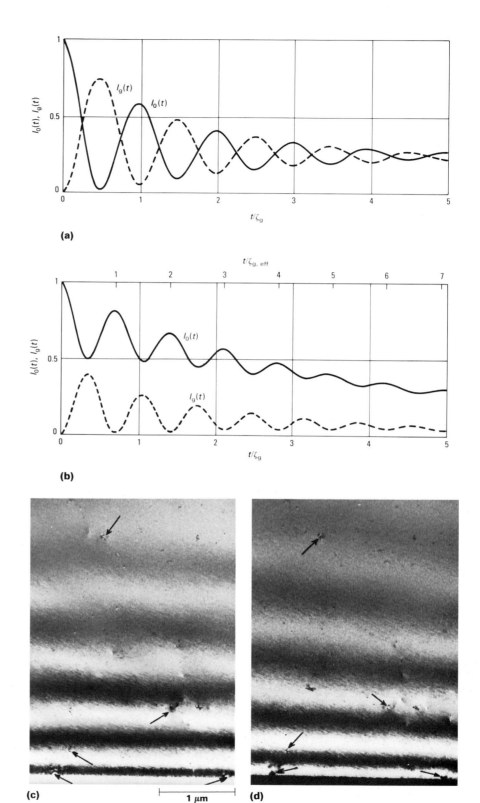

**Fig. 18** Two-beam thickness contours calculated for $\xi_g = \xi_0 = 10\xi_g$ as a function of specimen thickness $t$. Solid line indicates bright-field intensity $I_0$; dashed line, dark-field intensity $I_g$, with (a) excitation error $w = 0$ and (b) $w = 1$. Thickness contours in copper, $\mathbf{g} = (111)$, $w \approx 0$, in (c) bright field and (d) dark field. Arrows indicate equivalent points on the images. The lower arrows show the specimen edge. 20 000×

derstanding this phenomenon. The contrast oscillations do not affect bending or oscillation of the position of the dislocations. Contrast effects cause the shift of the image.

**Structure-Factor Contrast.** Coherent precipitates may reveal a mismatch between the lattice parameters in the precipitate and the surrounding matrix. This produces a space-

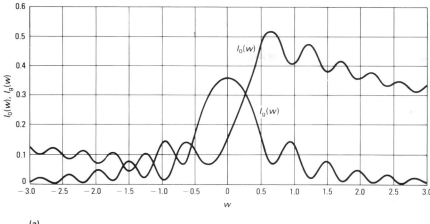

**(a)**

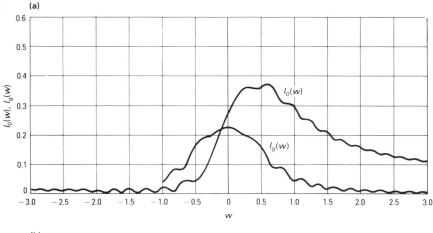

**(b)**

**Fig. 19** Two-beam bend contours calculated for $\xi_g = \xi_0 = 10\xi_g'$ as a function of $w$, with (a) $t = 2.5\xi_g$ and (b) $t = 5\xi_g$. See also Fig. 20.

the numerical integration of the various differential equations by electronic computers. The user need consider only subroutines for computing the displacement field $\mathbf{R}(x,y;z)$ or its derivative $d\mathbf{R}(x,y;z)/dz$. If the diffraction contrast of a particular defect is to be calculated as a function of the specimen thickness $t$ and the depth position $z_0$ of the defect center, considerable computer time can be saved by using specially developed methods. Computer time often can also be saved by applying symmetry relations inherent in the particular diffraction contrast problem or in the displacement field of the defect.

## Dislocations

Dislocations and dislocation distributions, for example, in deformed crystals, are generally best investigated in the two-beam bright-field mode operated at a sufficiently positive excitation error, which ensures optimum transmissivity. This means a maximum specimen volume accessible by TEM and avoidance of pronounced black-white depth oscillations for dislocations close to the specimen surfaces, which may disturb the image. However, if details of the dislocation structure, for example, splitting into partials and so on, are of interest, the weak-beam technique $|w| \gg 1$ is superior at the expense of transmissivity.

**The Displacement Field.** Elastic isotropy is assumed, and the displacement field $\mathbf{R}$ of a straight dislocation in its own (right-handed) coordinate system $x',y',z'$ is introduced. The dislocation line extends along the $y'$-axis, with its line unit vector $\mathbf{u}$ pointing from $y' < 0$ to $y' > 0$. The Burgers vector $\mathbf{b}$ lying in the $x'$-$y'$ plane can be split according to $\mathbf{b} = \mathbf{b}_s + \mathbf{b}_e$, where the screw component $\mathbf{b}_s$ is parallel to and the edge component $\mathbf{b}_e$ is perpendicular to $\mathbf{u}$. Then $R$ is given by:

$$\mathbf{R} = \mathbf{R}_a + \mathbf{R}_s \qquad \text{(Eq 9)}$$

$$\mathbf{R}_a = \frac{1}{2\pi}\left[\mathbf{b}\arctan\frac{z'}{x'} + \mathbf{b}_e\frac{1}{2(1-\nu)}\frac{x'z'}{\hat{r}^2}\right]$$

$$\text{(Eq 10)}$$

dependent displacement field and, accordingly, strain contrast. In addition, if the structure amplitude $F_s$ inside the precipitate differs from that of the matrix, for example, by a change of the chemical composition, an additional contrast, termed structure-factor contrast, may result. The reason is that the extinction length $\xi_g$ (proportional to $1/F_s$) becomes space dependent, $\xi_g = \xi_g(\mathbf{r})$. This can be incorporated into the equations of the dynamical theory.

**Applications of the Differential Equations.** Standard programs are available for

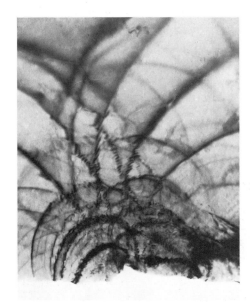

├─── 0.25 µm

**Fig. 20** Bright-field bend contours in copper. The dark lines correspond to specimen orientations where a certain set of lattice planes is in Bragg orientation. The moiré patterns in the center of the figure are due to a thin oxide layer on the specimen surface. $60\,000\times$

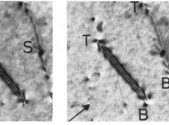
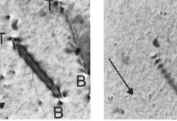
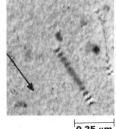

├─── 0.25 µm

**Fig. 21, 22, 23, 24** Diffraction contrast of a single dislocation (S) and a narrow dislocation dipole (D) in copper traversing the specimen from the top (T) to the bottom (B) surface $\mathbf{g} = \{220\}$. The black-white dots in the background are due to ion damage inside the microscope caused by insufficient vacuum in the microscope column. Fig. 21: bright field $(\mathbf{g} \cdot \mathbf{b}) = 2$. Fig. 22: dark field $(\mathbf{g} \cdot \mathbf{b}) = 2$. Fig. 23: bright field $(\mathbf{g} \cdot \mathbf{b}) = 0$. Fig. 24: dark field $(\mathbf{g} \cdot \mathbf{b}) = 0$. $40\,000\times$

$$R_s = -\frac{1}{2\pi}(\mathbf{b} \times \mathbf{u})\left[\frac{1-2}{2(1-\nu)}\ln \hat{r}/r_0\right.$$
$$\left. +\frac{1}{4(1-\nu)} \cdot \frac{x'^2 - z'^2}{\hat{r}^2}\right] \quad \text{(Eq 11)}$$

where $\nu$ = Poisson's ratio, $\hat{r}^2 = x'^2 + z'^2$, and $r_0$ = inner cutoff radius. The value $\mathbf{R}_a$ is anti-symmetric, and $\mathbf{R}_s$ is symmetric in $x'$, $z'$. Further, $\mathbf{R}$ changes its sign if the sign of $\mathbf{b}$ or $\mathbf{u}$ is changed. This is obvious for $\mathbf{R}_s$, but must be noted for $\mathbf{R}_a$.

**Contrast Profiles of Single Perfect Dislocations.** It is assumed that $\mathbf{b}$ is a translation vector of the crystal structure—$\mathbf{b}$ is a "perfect" Burgers vector—so that $\mathbf{g} \cdot \mathbf{b}$ is an integer. Regarding the contrast profiles of such dislocations, the cases $\mathbf{g} \cdot \mathbf{b} \neq 0$ and $\mathbf{g} \cdot \mathbf{b} = 0$ must be differentiated.

*The $\mathbf{g} \cdot \mathbf{b} \neq 0$ Contrast.* In case of $\mathbf{g} \cdot \mathbf{b} \neq 0$, the contrast is governed mainly by the component $\mathbf{R}_a$ of Eq 10. This component causes

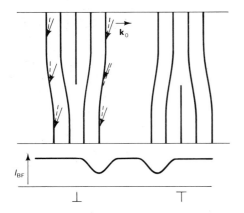

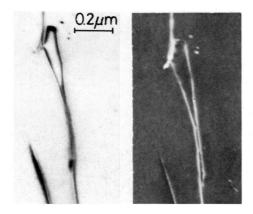

**Fig. 25** Diffraction contrast of an edge dislocation for $(\mathbf{g} \cdot \mathbf{b})s \neq 0$, $s > 0$. Solid arrows represent the direction of incidence of the primary beam. Dashed lines represent local directions of incidence that would fulfill the Bragg condition. The angle between the two types of arrows is a measure of $s_l(z)$. Bright-field intensity is denoted by $I_{BF}$.

**Fig. 26, 27** Dislocations in silicon. Fig. 26: strong-beam bright-field image, $w > 0$. Fig. 27: the same area imaged under weak-beam dark-field conditions, $w \gg 1$. 50 000×

an S-shaped bending of the reflecting lattice planes, as presented in Fig. 25. It is assumed that $s \neq 0$; diffraction contrast is especially strong (weak) where the local excitation error $s_l(z)$ is decreased (increased) as compared to the background value $s$, that is, where the reflecting lattice planes are bent by the dislocation displacement field toward (away from) the exact Bragg orientation. Consequently, for $s \neq 0$, the center of gravity of a dislocation-contrast profile does not coincide with but is shifted with respect to the image position of the dislocation line. Assuming a given direction of the line unit vector $\mathbf{u}$, the direction of this lateral contrast shift depends on the sign of $(\mathbf{g} \cdot \mathbf{b})s$, as will be demonstrated below in conjunction with the images of dislocation dipoles.

The kinematical contrast integral $\phi_g''$ (Eq 7) was evaluated for different dislocations (Ref 16, 17). It was concluded that the width of the kinematical dislocations contrast is approximately $(1/3–1/2)\xi_K$, where $\xi_K = s^{-1}$ indicates the kinematical extinction length. If dynamical diffraction must be considered ($|w| \lesssim 1$), this result remains essentially valid, with $\xi_K$ substituted by $\xi_{g,\text{eff}} = \sigma^{-1}$. In addition, the contrast of a dislocation line is always single lined for $|\mathbf{g} \cdot \mathbf{b}| = 1$, but may be (asymmetrically) double-lined for $|\mathbf{g} \cdot \mathbf{b}| = 2$ and $0 < |w| < 1$.

Under normal strong-beam (bright-field) conditions, $\xi_{g,\text{eff}}$ can be as large as ~30 nm (300 Å); under weak-beam conditions, $\xi_K = s^{-1}$ can be maintained as small as 5 nm (50 Å). Consequently, dislocation images are much sharper in the latter case, as shown in Fig. 26 and 27, which compare the same specimen area imaged under strong-beam and weak-beam imaging conditions, respectively.

*The $\mathbf{g} \cdot \mathbf{b} = 0$ Contrast.* In case of $\mathbf{g} \cdot \mathbf{b} = 0$, dislocation contrast is completely extinguished ($\mathbf{g} \cdot \mathbf{R} = 0$) for screw dislocations and also for edge dislocations if in the latter $\mathbf{g}$ is parallel to the dislocation line. For $\mathbf{g} \cdot \mathbf{b} = 0$, with $|\mathbf{g} \cdot \mathbf{b} \times \mathbf{u}| \neq 0$, a residual contrast due to the displacement component $\mathbf{R}_s$ in Eq 11 is produced that is symmetric with respect to the image position of the dislocation. This re-

sidual contrast is controlled in strength by the modulus $|\mathbf{g} \cdot \mathbf{b} \times \mathbf{u}|$ and is in general significantly weaker than the $\mathbf{g} \cdot \mathbf{b} \neq 0$ contrast; it can therefore be distinguished from the latter. Depending on the strength of $|\mathbf{g} \cdot \mathbf{b} \times \mathbf{u}|$, the contrast may consist of a single, a double, or a triple contrast line (Ref 18). Typical dislocation images for $\mathbf{g} \cdot \mathbf{b} = 0$ are depicted in Fig. 23 and 24.

For dislocations of mixed type, complete contrast extinction is impossible, because the terms $\mathbf{g} \cdot \mathbf{b}$, $\mathbf{g} \cdot \mathbf{b} \times \mathbf{u}$, and $\mathbf{g} \cdot \mathbf{b}_e$ cannot be zero simultaneously. If the first two terms are zero but $\mathbf{g} \cdot \mathbf{b}_e \neq 0$ (see Eq 10), an asymmetrical residual contrast is produced. This is demonstrated in Fig. 28 and 29, in which a curved dislocation segment, which changes in type from screw to edge, is imaged under $\mathbf{g} \cdot \mathbf{b} = 2$ (Fig. 28, strong symmetrical double-line contrast) and $\mathbf{g} \cdot \mathbf{b} = 0$ conditions (Fig. 29). In the latter case, the dislocation is out of contrast in the pure screw and pure edge orientations, but reveals an easily detectable asymmetric contrast around the 45° orientation, where $\mathbf{g} \cdot \mathbf{b}$ and $(\mathbf{g} \cdot \mathbf{b} \times \mathbf{u}) = 0$, but $\mathbf{g} \cdot \mathbf{b}_e \neq 0$. Here $\mathbf{b}_e$ refers to the component of $\mathbf{b}$ perpendicular to the local line direction $\mathbf{u}$.

**Contrast of Dislocation Pairs.** Two parallel dislocations with opposite Burgers vectors $\mathbf{b}$ constitute a dislocation dipole. Another description is that $\mathbf{b}$ is the same for both dislocations, but their line vectors $\mathbf{u}$ are opposite. The most common representation is a dipole comprising two pure edge dislocations. If such a dipole is imaged with $s \neq 0$ and $\mathbf{g} \cdot \mathbf{b} \neq 0$, then $(\mathbf{g} \cdot \mathbf{b})s > 0$ for one, and $(\mathbf{g} \cdot \mathbf{b})s < 0$ for the other dislocation. Consequently, the contrasts of the two dislocations are displaced in opposite directions; the distance between the two contrast lines is smaller or larger than the true projected distance between the dislocations. If $\mathbf{g}$ is changed to $-\mathbf{g}$, leaving the sign of $s$ unchanged, the two cases are interchanged. This phenomenon, termed inside-outside contrast, is exemplified in Fig. 30(a) and 30(b).

In other cases, the two parallel dislocations may exhibit the same sign of $\mathbf{g} \cdot \mathbf{b}$. This may occur in an ordered alloy in which two dislocations with the same perfect Burgers vector

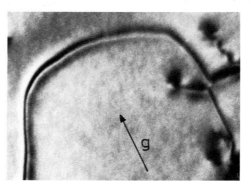

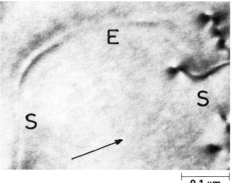

**Fig. 28, 29** Strong-beam images of a curved dislocation segment of Burgers vector $\mathbf{b} = 1/2[110]$. Fig. 28: $\mathbf{g} = (220)$, $(\mathbf{g} \cdot \mathbf{b}) = 2$; dislocation is in strong contrast. Fig. 29: $\mathbf{g} = (220)$, $(\mathbf{g} \cdot \mathbf{b}) = 0$; the dislocation contrast is extinguished only at the edge (E) and the screw (S) orientations. 140 000×. (Ref 19)

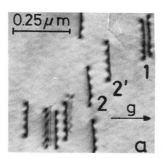 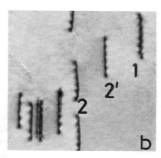 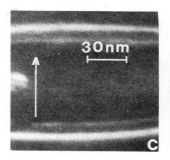 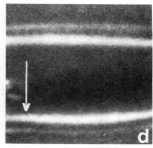

**Fig. 30** Diffraction contrast of dislocation pairs taken with **g** = ±(20$\bar{2}$). (a, b) Strong-beam bright-field images of dislocation dipoles in copper taken with $w > 0$. Dipole 1 is clearly resolved in (a) but unresolved in (b). The distance between the dipole dislocations 2 and 2′ is narrow in (a) and wide in (b). 40 000×. (c, d) Weak-beam images of dislocations in silver that are split into partials. The dislocation at the top (bottom) is referred to as D$_1$ (D$_2$) in the text. ~330 000×

**b** of the disordered lattice constitute a split superdislocation (2**b** = perfect Burgers vector of the ordered alloy) with an antiphase boundary between them. Another example refers to a perfect dislocation split into partial dislocations (Burgers vectors **b**$_p$), where the signs of **g** · **b**$_p$ are the same for both partials. If in such a case the distance between the two dislocations becomes on the order of or smaller than $\xi_{g,eff}$, which may be $\xi_K = 1/s$ in the weak-beam case, the contrast of one of the two dislocations increases in strength, and the contrast of the other decreases, depending on the signs of the (**g** · **b**$_p$). This is demonstrated in Fig 30(c) and 30(d), which illustrate the weak-beam images of an edge-dislocation dipole in silver, where the individual dislocations D$_1$ and D$_2$ are split into partials. For both dislocations, the two partials produce the same sign of **g** · **b**$_p$, which, however, is opposite for D$_1$ and D$_2$. Accordingly, the sequence strong-weak is opposite for D$_1$ and D$_2$. Further, the sequence is changed when changing the sign of **g**, as indicated by the arrows in Fig. 30(c) and 30(d).

Below a critical distance, the contrast of the weakly imaged dislocation disappears in the contrast tail of the strongly imaged one. This effect limits the resolution of dislocation pairs having the same sign of (**g** · **b**) even on weak-beam images to approximately 2 nm

(20 Å). This lower limit is important for evaluating stacking fault energies from the measurement of equilibrium distances of split dislocations (Ref 20).

**Determination of the Dislocation Burgers Vectors and the Dislocation Densities.** Determination of the Burgers vector **b** of individual dislocations requires a number of images of the corresponding specimen area taken under different two-beam conditions. If a given dislocation displays contrast extinction or only residual (**g** · **b** = 0) contrast for two (nonparallel) diffraction vectors, for example, **g**$_1$ and **g**$_2$, then its Burgers vector **b** is perpendicular to **g**$_1$ and **g**$_2$ (regarding the sign of **b**, see below). Anticipation of the general crystallographic direction of **b** facilitates analysis of the Burgers vector; for instance, **b** = ½⟨110⟩ in a face-centered cubic (fcc) lattice.

In this case, three images taken with three diffraction vectors **g** = {111} are sufficient for indexing all dislocations with **b** = ½⟨110⟩, because the six significantly different vectors **b** of this kind yield a different contrast-extinction behavior for the three **g** = {111}. Figures 31 to 33 depict a deformed and subsequently annealed nickel crystal that was taken from a specimen parallel to the primary slip plane (111) with **g** = (11$\bar{1}$), **g** = ($\bar{1}$11), and **g** = (1$\bar{1}$1). In the central part of

Fig. 32 and 33, a network consisting of three types of dislocation segments is visible, as indicated in the figures. The segments indicated by open circles produce a **g** · **b** ≠ 0 contrast in Fig. 33 and a residual (**g** · **b** = 0) contrast in Fig. 31 and 32.

Accordingly, **b**$_1$ = ±½[101]. The segments indicated by crosses show **g** · **b** ≠ 0 contrast in Fig. 32 and 33 but not in Fig. 31. This leads to **b**$_2$ = ±½[1$\bar{1}$0]. The segments indicated by dots are in **g** · **b** ≠ 0 contrast only in Fig. 32; therefore, **b**$_3$ = ±½[001]. Taking always the upper sign, **b**$_2$ + **b**$_3$ = **b**$_1$ is obtained as required for dislocation networks. Other dislocation segments in Fig. 31 to 33 can be so indexed.

Full indexing of a dislocation requires distinguishing between +**b** and −**b** for a given choice of the line direction **u**. This can be achieved using the lateral shift of (**g** · **b**)$s$ ≠ 0 contrast lines as indicative of the sign of the S-shaped bending of the reflecting lattice planes, from which the signs of **u** and **b** can be determined by physical arguments. In this context, certain contrast peculiarities of surface-stress relaxation effects may also be helpful.

Dislocation density $\rho$ is defined as the average dislocation length per unit volume or, in a somewhat misleading way, as the number of dislocations per unit area. A full and reli-

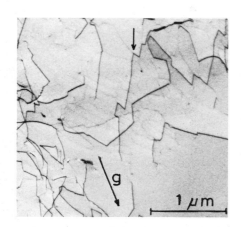 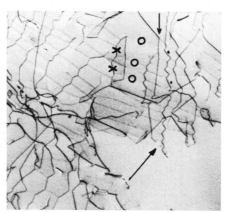 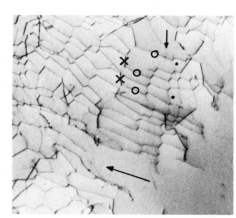

**Fig. 31, 32, 33** Dislocation network in nickel. Two-beam bright-field images of the same specimen area, specimen normal (111). Three types of segment directions (see text) of the network are indicated by open circles, crosses, and dots. Fig. 31: **g** = (11$\bar{1}$). Fig. 32: **g** = ($\bar{1}$11). Fig. 33: **g** = (1$\bar{1}$1). The small arrows indicate the same position on the three images. 20 000×

able evaluation of $\rho$ requires extensive experimentation. Here one aspect only is emphasized. On a given set of micrographs taken with a given two-beam diffraction vector **g**, dislocations of some slip systems may be fully in contrast (**g** · **b** $\neq$ 0). Dislocations of other slip systems may be visible in residual contrast (**g** · **b** = 0) only, or may be completely invisible. This suggests that any reliable determination of $\rho$ requires a careful evaluation of different sets of micrographs of the same specimen area taken with varying **g** vectors.

## Point-Defect Agglomerates, Radiation Damage

Irradiation of crystals with energetic particles, such as electrons, neutrons, or ions, leads to the formation of interstitials and vacancies. Point defects may also be created by plastic deformation or quenching in of thermal vacancies. These point defects, if mobile, may cluster and form point-defect agglomerates, such as dislocation loops. In fcc metal, they may also form stacking-fault tetrahedra. This is especially true for vacancies but in principle also for interstitials. Vacancies may also agglomerate into cavities, such as bubbles and voids. One of the problems to be solved by TEM is determining the crystallographic nature of such agglomerates and their type, vacancy (V) or interstitial (I), that is, whether they are produced by an agglomeration of vacancies or interstitials.

**Dislocation loops** are formed by agglomeration of point defects into plates on densely packed lattice planes. For example, a monolayer (diameter $D$) of agglomerated vacancies on a {111} plane in a fcc metal produces an intrinsic stacking fault surrounded by a dislocation loop (diameter $D$) with a partial Burgers vector $\mathbf{b}_F = \frac{1}{3}\langle 111 \rangle$ of Frank type perpendicular to the loop plane. Agglomeration of interstitials on {111} yields an extrinsic stacking fault over the loop area. If the loop size exceeds a critical value, it becomes energetically more favorable to eliminate the stacking fault area by sweeping a Shockley partial $\mathbf{b}_S = \frac{1}{6}\langle 112 \rangle$ over the loop area to convert the Frank partial into a perfect Burgers vector **b**, for example:

$$\mathbf{b}_F + \mathbf{b}_S = \mathbf{b} \tag{Eq 12}$$

and

$$\frac{1}{3}[111] + \frac{1}{6}[11\bar{2}] = \frac{1}{2}[110] \tag{Eq 13}$$

There is evidence that similar two-step mechanisms for the formation of loops with perfect Burgers vectors also exist for bcc (Ref 21, 22) and for hexagonal close-packed (hcp) metals (Ref 23).

**Analysis of Large Dislocation Loops.** If the loop diameter $D$ is sufficiently large compared to $\xi_{g,eff}$, the loop nature is clearly visible on the micrograph, and the Burgers vector **b** of the loop can be determined by the contrast-extinction rules outlined above. Ap-

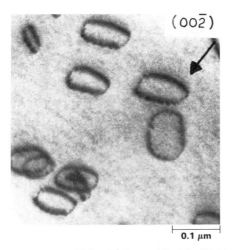 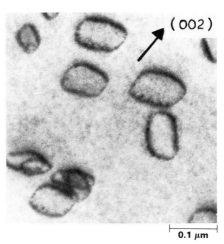

($00\bar{2}$)  (002)

0.1 $\mu$m    0.1 $\mu$m

**Fig. 34, 35** Dislocation loops of the interstitial type in electron-irradiated molybdenum. Two-beam bright-field images taken with $w > 0$. Note the apparent change in the loop size when changing the sign of **g**. Fig. 34: **g**. Fig. 35: $-$**g**. For details, see text. 120 000 $\times$

proximate information on the habit plane of the loop can be obtained by following the change of the projected shape and width of the loop when tilting the specimen around an axis parallel to the operating **g** vector.

Segments of a dislocation loop opposite each other have the same direction of **b** but opposite line direction **u**. Therefore, their contrast behavior is similar to that of a dislocation dipole. Accordingly, if the loop is imaged with $(\mathbf{g} \cdot \mathbf{b})s \neq 0$, it is imaged, depending on the sign of $(\mathbf{g} \cdot \mathbf{b})s$, as inside contrast, that is, loop contrast inside the true projected loop position, or as outside contrast.

This question, inside or outside contrast, can best be clarified by comparing images taken with **g** and $-$**g**, leaving the sign of $s$ unchanged (see Fig. 34 and 35, which show dislocation loops of interstitial type in electron-irradiated molybdenum). The apparent sizes of the loop contrast change remarkably when proceeding from **g** to $-$**g**. The loop type, V or I, can then be determined if the inclination of the loop plane relative to the primary beam (direction of $\mathbf{k}_0$) and the operating **g** vector is known. In application to practical cases, the inside-outside method suffers from several pitfalls that may lead to the incorrect answer regarding loop type. Calculations have been prepared to avoid these pitfalls (Ref 23, 24).

**Small Dislocation Loops.** If the loop diameter $D$ becomes smaller than $\xi_{g,eff}$, dislocation loops are no longer imaged as loops. On kinematical strong-beam images, the loop contrast degenerates into a black-dot contrast containing very little information on details of the loop. Even under weak-beam conditions, the inside-outside contrast method deteriorates for $D \leq 7$ nm (70 Å). For dislocation loops below this limit, the black-white contrast method becomes applicable when the specimen is imaged under two-beam dynamical conditions in bright or dark field with $w = 0$. If located under such imaging conditions within the near-surface regions of depth oscillation, a small dislocation loop

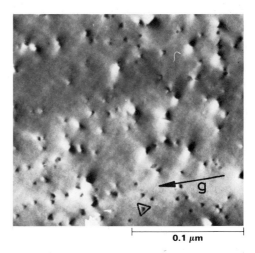

0.1 $\mu$m

**Fig. 36** Black-white contrast of small dislocation loops (Frank loops) in a copper specimen irradiated with 30 keV copper ions. Dynamical dark-field image taken with $w = 0$, specimen normal (110), **g** = (002). The inserted triangle indicates a small stacking-fault tetrahedra. 300 000 $\times$

yields a characteristic black-white contrast figure, as illustrated in Fig. 36, which presents a copper specimen containing primarily small Frank dislocation loops of V-type produced by irradiation with 30-keV copper ions in a surface layer near the bottom surface of the specimen.

Such black-white contrast figures may be characterized by a black-white vector **l**, pointing from the center of the black to the center of the white lobe. Because of the nature of the depth-oscillation contrast, the black-white contrast of a loop is inverted; that is, bright is changed into dark and conversely if the loop type, V or I, is changed or if the loop depth-position $z_0$ is shifted toward $z_0 \pm \frac{1}{2}\xi_{g,eff}$. Accordingly, differentiating loops of V or I type requires information on the sign of $(\mathbf{g} \cdot \mathbf{l})$ and the depth position $z_0$ of the loop. The latter information can be obtained by careful stereo measurements.

Additional information on the direction of the Burgers vector and the loop-plane normal, **n**, can be obtained from the fine structure in the center of a black-white contrast figure and from the outer shape of the black-white contrast figure by comparison of experimentally obtained and calculated contrast figures. For elastically isotropic or nearly isotropic materials, the shape of the contrast figure and in particular the angle between **l** and **g** depend characteristically on the direction of **b** and **n** regarding $k_0$ and **g**, respectively.

The evaluation of the shape of the inner part of the black-white contrast has been successfully applied to the analysis of small dislocation loops in ion-irradiated tungsten and cobalt (Ref 22, 23, 25). More recent analytical calculations have demonstrated that the shapes of the black-white contrast of small loops are sensitive to elastic anisotropy (Ref 26).

**Stacking-Fault Tetrahedra.** Frank dislocation loops in fcc metals can dissociate into stacking-fault tetrahedra consisting of stacking faults on the four {111}-type tetrahedra faces interconnected by stair-rod dislocations having $b = \frac{1}{6}\langle 110 \rangle$ at the edges of the tetrahedra. This transformation is particularly favored in metals of low stacking-fault energy, such as gold, silver, or copper.

One consequence of the small strength of the stair-rod dislocations bounding the stacking-fault tetrahedra is that their strain contrast is weak. Therefore, the contrast of a stacking-fault tetrahedron is predominantly determined by the stacking-fault areas, which may produce a fringe pattern if the stacking-fault tetrahedron is larger than the extinction length, that is, if the contrast shape of a stacking-fault tetrahedron is in general close to the shape of the stacking-fault tetrahedron projected onto the image plane. A stacking-fault tetrahedron, as produced by ion damage in copper, is indicated in Fig. 36 by a symbol reflecting its outer shape, as expected for a specimen orientation near (110).

Despite the weakness of the strain field, stacking-fault tetrahedra may reveal black-white contrast. For large stacking-fault tetrahedra having edge lengths on the order of or larger than $\xi_{g,\mathrm{eff}}$, the black-white contrast degenerates to the so-called Ashby-Brown contrast (Ref 27), in which the depth oscillations are suppressed due to surface-stress relaxation. Under suitable conditions, even small stacking-fault tetrahedra may reveal black-white contrast similar to that of small dislocation loops. However, in contrast to small loops black-white vector **l** always points parallel or antiparallel to **g**, because the strain field does not reveal a pronounced preferential direction. The latter property sometimes helps distinguish between small loops and small stacking-fault tetrahedra.

**Cavities,** such as voids and bubbles, are best imaged under two-beam conditions with $s = 0$. Cavities then act like a local reduction of the specimen thickness $t$. Therefore, in a specimen with foil thickness $t$ in that range where thickness fringes are observable, the contrast of a cavity is dark on the front flank of a bright thickness contour and bright on the rear side. If $t$ is beyond the region of thickness fringes, the contrast is bright, but decreases rapidly with decreasing diameter $d$ of the cavity. Finally, if $d$ is below a critical value (subnanometer size), cavities are no longer visible in focused images. Contrast is then considerably improved by an appropriate defocusing of the objective lens.

## Precipitates

The precipitation of a second phase can be studied by TEM. Depending on the structure of the interface, there may be coherent, partially coherent, or incoherent precipitates. A partially coherent particle may possess one coherent interface and one in which coherency is lost, that is, semicoherent or incoherent. This can be caused by different structures in the precipitate and the matrix or by a large displacement along the interface. An incoherent particle has a crystal structure different from the matrix. Often no orientation relationships exist between the two phases. A precipitate can produce TEM contrast due to the alteration of the electron waves passing through the particle (precipitate contrast) and the electron waves passing through columns near the particle where the crystal has been distorted due to the presence of the precipitate (matrix contrast or strain contrast).

The interpretation of the matrix contrast is straightforward and can be carried out in much the same way as for radiation-induced defects or dislocations. The strain contrast must be observed for different foil orientations and different diffraction vectors under well-defined dynamical two-beam or well-defined kinematical conditions. If a strain contrast can be observed, contrast calculations must be performed, because results of the calculations with the observations provide a qualitative and sometimes even quantitative model of the precipitate.

Black-white contrast can be observed if certain conditions for the size and the magnitude of the strain are fulfilled (Ref 28, 29). Therefore, the strain is expressed as a dimensionless quantity:

$$Q = \varepsilon r_0^3 \cdot g \cdot \frac{1}{\xi_g^2} \qquad \text{(Eq 14)}$$

where $r_0$ is the radius of the particle, $g$ the modulus of the diffraction vector, $\xi_g$ the extinction length, and $\varepsilon$ a parameter describing the constrained strain of the particle. Black-white contrast is expected for certain combinations of $r_0$ and $Q$. Small values of $r_0$ result in black-white contrast with depth oscillations similar to those of radiation-induced defects (see above); for large values of $r_0$ and $Q$, the depth oscillations of the black-white contrast are suppressed by the stress relaxations at the foil surfaces (Ashby-Brown contrast). In this case, the sign of the displacement field can be determined accurately from dark-field images. Very large defects produce no black-white contrast. Calculations of TEM contrast performed by inclusions of different shapes have also taken into account elastic anisotropy (Ref 30). The main problem with such computer simulations is determining the displacement field of the precipitate placed in a thin foil.

Spherical precipitates form in copper-cobalt alloys (Fig. 37); their sizes depend on the annealing treatment. The typical coffee-bean contrast can be observed. A line of no contrast is perpendicular to the diffraction vector **g**. The width of the lobes measured perpendicular to **g** is a measure of the size of the precipitate.

Small plate-like precipitates in aluminum-copper also produce strain contrast. The visibility depends on the operating diffraction vector, because the displacement field is strongly anisotropic. Coherent silver precipitates in aluminum-silver alloys (Fig. 38) do not give rise to strain contrast, because virtually no constrained strain exists around the particle. If the symmetry of the precipitate differs from that of the matrix, additional reflections in the diffraction pattern can be observed (Fig. 42). The shape of the precipitate is revealed by dark-field images taken with this type of reflection belonging to the precipitate (Fig. 40 and 41).

The precipitates themselves can be revealed (1) if differences exist in the structure factor of the two phases (structure-factor contrast), examples of which are shown in Fig. 38, 39, and 40, (2) if the orientation of the foil is such that certain planes in the precipitate are near the exact Bragg condition (strong reflection) while no planes in the matrix are in this position (orientation contrast), (3) if the matrix displacements induced by the precipitate cause an abrupt phase change at the precipitate (stacking-fault contrast), or (4) if a moiré pattern is formed due to different lattice parameters in the matrix and precipitate. The contrast caused for the different cases has been documented (Ref 1-11).

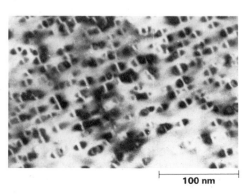

**Fig. 37** Contrast from spherically symmetrical strain fields due to precipitations in a copper-cobalt alloy. The coffee-bean contrast is visible. 200 000×

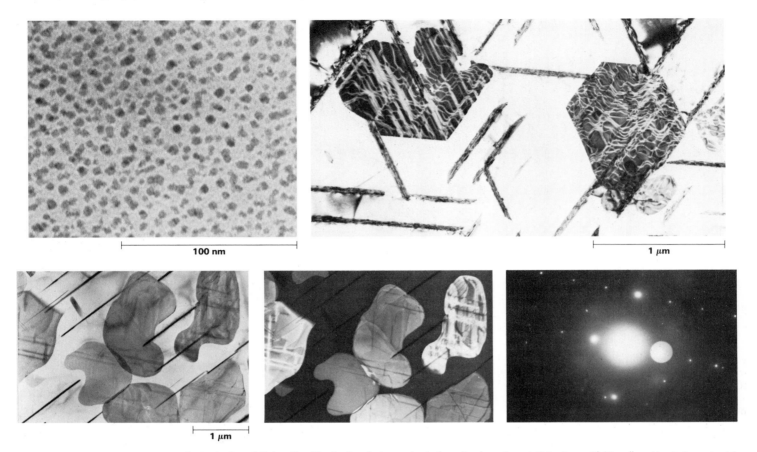

**Fig. 38, 39, 40, 41, 42** Contrast of precipitates. Fig. 38: structure-factor contrast of small coherent precipitates in an Al-6Ag alloy. No strain contrast is visible. 450 000×. Fig. 39: structure-factor contrast of large incoherent precipitates in an Al-6Ag alloy that was annealed for 1000 min at 400 °C (750 °F); foil orientation ~(110). Interface dislocations are visible between the aluminum matrix and the silver precipitates. 35 000×. Fig. 40: structure-factor contrast of incoherent precipitates in an Al-4Cu alloy; foil orientation (106), bright-field image. 17 000×. Fig. 41: same alloy as Fig. 40, but dark-field image with a reflection of the copper precipitate. Only copper precipitates of one variant are in contrast. 17 000×. Fig. 42: diffraction patterns of Fig. 40 and 41

Particles of a second phase alter the diffraction pattern of the pure matrix because (1) there are extra reflections due to the diffraction pattern from the precipitate, (2) the second-phase particles influence the matrix diffraction spots, (3) double diffraction may result if the particle is embedded in the matrix, and (4) the shape of the diffraction spots is reciprocal to the shape of the particles, due to the small size of the precipitates.

## Structure of Grain Boundaries and Interfaces

Internal surfaces determine many properties of materials. Understanding the properties necessitates knowing the structure of the defects, which are actually the regions in space at which two crystals meet. Interfaces between dissimilar materials are termed heterophase boundaries, or interfaces. Interfaces between crystals differing only in relative orientation and/or translation are known as homophase boundaries. Homophase boundaries include grain boundaries, stacking faults, twins, and antiphase boundaries in ordered alloys. In the first part of this section, the possibilities for revealing the structure of homophase boundaries will be discussed. The

second part will present some observations on heterophase boundaries.

Ten parameters (Ref 31) are required for the geometrical description of an interface (Fig. 43). Using this concept includes assuming two interpenetrating crystals that are then misoriented (four parameters) and shifted against each other (three parameters). Three additional parameters are required to specify the location of a plane interface in the interpenetrating crystals. Finally, atoms of one crystal are removed from one side of the surface and those of the second crystal from the other. In this way, the symmetry of the interface can be elegantly described by group theory. Stacking faults and antiphase boundaries are pure translation interfaces; grain boundaries represent general homophase boundaries. The geometric parameters are potentially capable of undergoing relaxation.

**At pure translation interfaces,** such as stacking faults and antiphase boundaries, two perfect crystal parts are shifted against each other. Usually, the plane of the interfaces coincides with a close-packed plane. For example, the translation vector is $\tau = \frac{1}{6}\langle 112 \rangle$ for a stacking fault in fcc materials, although $\tau$ is a lattice vector of the disordered crystal structure for antiphase boundaries in an ordered structure. Contrast by TEM is expected

in the projected area of the usually inclined translation interface. The depth position of the interface may be $t_1$. The crystal part lying below the interface is then shifted against the upper reference crystal by the translation vector $\tau$, which also defines the sign of $\tau$.

The diffraction contrast can easily be calculated using the so-called matrix method (Ref 32), with which contrast can be calculated for a general $n$-beam situation. This discussion is restricted to the two-beam case, which considers only one scattered beam $\phi_g$ in addition to the transmitted beam $\phi_0$. The amplitudes of the scattered beam $\phi_g$ and of the transmitted beam $\phi_0$ are represented by a column vector:

$$\Psi = \begin{pmatrix} \phi_0 \\ \phi_g \end{pmatrix} \qquad \text{(Eq 15)}$$

The changes of the amplitudes after passing through a perfect crystal of thickness $t$ (normalized excitation error $w$) are (Ref 32):

$$\begin{pmatrix} \phi_0(t,w) \\ \phi_g(t,w) \end{pmatrix}_{\text{out}} = \mathbf{M}(t,w) \begin{pmatrix} \phi_0 \\ \phi_g \end{pmatrix}_{\text{in}} \qquad \text{(Eq 16)}$$

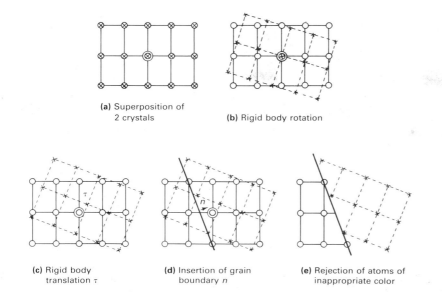

(a) Superposition of 2 crystals

(b) Rigid body rotation

(c) Rigid body translation τ

(d) Insertion of grain boundary n

(e) Rejection of atoms of inappropriate color

**Fig. 43** Idealized construction of a crystalline interface. (a) Superposition of the two crystals. (b) Imposition of rigid body rotation (four parameters). (c) Imposition of rigid body translation (three parameters). (d) Insertion of grain boundary n (three parameters). (e) Rejection of inappropriate atoms at the interface

where the subscripts in and out refer to the incoming and outgoing waves, respectively, for a perfect crystal. The initial values are $\phi_0 = 1$ and $\phi_g = 0$. $\mathbf{M}(t,w)$ represents a response matrix given by:

$$\mathbf{M}(t,w) = \begin{pmatrix} \phi_0^0 & \phi_g^{0-} \\ \phi_g^0 & \phi_0^{0-} \end{pmatrix} \quad (Eq\ 17)$$

with

$$\phi_0^0(t,w) = \cos \pi\sigma t - i \frac{w \sin \pi\sigma t}{(1 + w^2)^{1/2}} \quad (Eq\ 18)$$

and

$$\phi_g^0(t,w) = \frac{i \sin \pi\sigma t}{(1 + w^2)^{1/2}}$$

Anomalous absorption is included, which means σ is complex, but normal absorption is neglected. The normalized excitation error $w$ must be replaced by $-w$ in Eq 18 to form $\phi_0^{0-}$ and $\phi_g^{0-}$ of Eq 17.

The influence of a planar defect included in a transmitted specimen on the amplitude distribution of the different waves can be described by a response matrix of the defect $\mathbf{M}^d$. This matrix is referred to as $\mathbf{M}^\alpha$ for a pure translation interface with:

$$\mathbf{M}^\alpha = \begin{pmatrix} 1 & 0 \\ 0 & e^{i\alpha} \end{pmatrix} \quad (Eq\ 19)$$

and $\alpha = 2\pi\mathbf{g} \cdot \boldsymbol{\tau}$, where $\mathbf{g}$ is the diffraction vector and $\boldsymbol{\tau}$ the translation of the perfect crystal below the defect with respect to the perfect crystal at which the electrons enter.

The amplitudes of the waves transmitted through a specimen (total foil thickness $t$) containing this translation interface [depth position $t_1(x)$] are determined by three contributions: (1) the perfect crystal [foil thickness $t_1(x)$] lying above the planar defect, described in Eq 17 by a response matrix $\mathbf{M}(t_1,w)$, (2) the planar defect itself (response matrix $\mathbf{M}^\alpha$, Eq 19), and (3) the perfect crystal (thickness $t_2 =$ $t - t_1$) lying below the defect [response matrix $\mathbf{M}(t_2,w)$].

The amplitudes of the waves at the lower foil surface are expressed by:

$$\begin{pmatrix} \phi_0 & (t) \\ \phi_g & (t) \end{pmatrix}$$

$$= \mathbf{M}(t_2,w) \cdot \mathbf{M}^\alpha \cdot \mathbf{M}(t_1,w) \begin{pmatrix} \phi_0 & (0) \\ \phi_g & (0) \end{pmatrix} \quad (Eq\ 20)$$

The contrast caused by an inclined defect can be calculated by an evaluation of Eq 20 for different depth positions $t_1$.

The following results can be obtained for an inclined stacking fault (Ref 32):

- Bright and dark fringes are expected in the projected area of the stacking fault.
- With increasing thickness, new fringes are created in the center of the foil.
- The fringes are parallel to the closest surface.
- The bright-field fringe pattern is symmetrical relative to the foil center; the dark-field image is similar to the bright-field image near the top surface but complementary near the bottom surface.

Figures 44 to 47 illustrate the contrast of a stacking fault in a Cu-10Al (at.%) alloy. The image of a stacking fault is characterized by the value of $\alpha = 2\pi\mathbf{g} \cdot \boldsymbol{\tau}$. In fcc materials, stacking faults are predominantly produced on {111} planes by a shear of $\boldsymbol{\tau} = \frac{1}{6}\langle 112\rangle$ or by removal or insertion of a plane of atoms. This may occur when vacancies or interstitial atoms condense on close-packed planes. In fcc materials, the stacking faults are classified as intrinsic or extrinsic.

The type of stacking fault and the sign of $\alpha$ are determined in the same manner. The symmetry rules stipulate that the sign of the contrast fringe in bright field and dark field at the top of the transmitted foil is positive (bright fringe) for $\alpha > 0$ (thick foil). From the bright-field and dark-field images of a stacking fault (see Fig. 44 to 47), the top and bottom surfaces can be determined. Because the sign of $\alpha$ from the edge fringe of the bright-field image is known, there is enough information to determine the sense of $\boldsymbol{\tau}$ (Ref 34). Fault type can be determined solely from a dark-field image; the sense of inclination need not be known (Ref 33).

It has been shown that $\boldsymbol{\tau}$ can be determined by the following method. The diffraction vector $\mathbf{g}$ is drawn as an arrow having its origin at the center of contrast fringes on the dark-field image. The stacking fault is intrinsic (extrinsic) if the limiting fringe on the side of the arrow of $\mathbf{g}$ is dark (bright). This rule is valid in fcc materials for {111}, {220}, and {400} reflections, but is reversed for {200}, {222}, and {440} reflections. The contrast of the stacking fault vanishes for $\mathbf{g} \cdot \boldsymbol{\tau} =$ integer. The direction of $\boldsymbol{\tau}$ can be determined from two images taken with different diffraction vectors on which the stacking fault is out of contrast. The contrast of domain boundaries, twins, and antiphase boundaries can be similarly calculated and analyzed.

**Grain boundaries** have been the object of intensive TEM studies for many years, and many papers and review lectures have appeared (Ref 35 to 38). The structure of grain boundaries is important for understanding the problems of segregation, recrystallization texture, and intergranular embrittlement. In addition, the bonding across the boundary governs these properties. The papers cited above demonstrate that much information can be obtained by TEM diffraction contrast studies, diffraction studies, and recently also by direct-lattice imaging.

Transmission electron microscopy diffraction contrast studies uncover information on the intrinsic structure of grain boundaries; primarily, dislocations can be analyzed. For special situations, the geometrical parameters can be determined using TEM. Diffraction studies allow the determination of the width and symmetry of grain boundaries, but imaging by high-resolution TEM affords an insight into the atomic structure of the boundary.

Grain boundaries can be described using the dislocation model, the plane-matching model, and the coincidence-site model. Each describes the relaxation phenomena that occurs at the grain boundaries in different configuration of defects. The models assume the existence of certain misorientations possessing a low grain-boundary energy that are characterized by a low $\Sigma$ value of the coincidence-site lattice. The coincidence-site lattice can be obtained by allowing two misoriented crystal lattices adjoining the boundary to interpenetrate and translate so that lattice points of each crystal coincide. The space lattice consisting of the coincident lattice points is called the coincidence-site lattice. The fraction of lattice points (in one crystal) in good

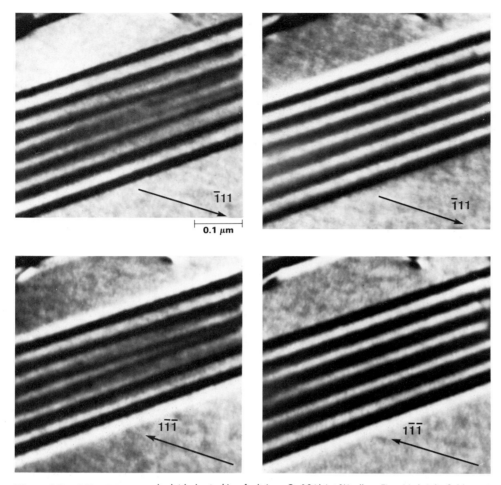

**Fig. 44, 45, 46, 47** An intrinsic stacking fault in a Cu-10Al (at.%) alloy. Fig. 44: bright field, **g** = ($\bar{1}$11). Fig. 45: dark field, **g** = ($\bar{1}$11). Fig. 46: bright field, **g** = (1$\bar{1}\bar{1}$). Fig. 47: dark field, **g** = (1$\bar{1}\bar{1}$). The rule of Gevers *et al.* (Ref 33) is fulfilled. 140 000×. (A. Korner and H.P. Karnthaler)

coincidence is defined as $1/\Sigma$. Coincidence models of grain boundaries are discussed in Ref 39.

If the symmetry of a boundary and the included dislocations are determined, the grain boundary is completely specified. The parameters included in the description can be determined by TEM in principle by comparing experimental micrographs taken under well-defined diffraction conditions, with results of computer simulation carried out using the dynamical theory of electron diffraction. For the computer simulations, the displacement of the atoms (lattice planes) due to relaxation as well as many experimental parameters, such as the thickness, orientation of the interface, and extinction and absorption lengths, must be known. In addition, experimental diffraction parameters, such as the number of beams excited and their *s* values, must be established.

The contrast calculations can be complicated. Each beam excited in the upper crystal is incident on the lower crystal and can produce additional beams in the crystal. Therefore, the total number of beams propagating in the lower crystal can be substantial, and the coupling of the beams is strongly influenced by the crystallographic relationship of the two crystals. Three experimental conditions afford a more straightforward interpretation.

The first condition involves two-beam diffraction in one crystal and negligible diffraction in the other. The upper or lower crystal can be oriented for two-beam diffraction, and the nondiffracting crystal is regarded as a block in which normal but not anomalous absorption occurs. The contrast behavior is similar to thickness fringes. This diffraction condition can only be approximated, because weak beams are inevitably excited in the nondiffracting crystal, and these may be coupled to some extent with the beam selected for image formation.

The second condition consists of simultaneous two-beam diffraction in the two crystals. In this mode, the specimen is exactly oriented so that only one diffracted beam is strongly excited in the upper crystal—and in such a way that this excited beam does not further excite strong beams in the lower crystal. At the same time, only one beam is strongly excited in the lower crystal by the incoming beam. Only bright-field images are usually taken.

In the third condition, when the crystallography permits, two-beam or systematic diffraction by sets of planes with identical spacing and orientation in the adjacent crystals may occur. Such sets of planes are referred to as common, and this case is a special instance of the second condition. This orientation has been used to measure the relative shift of the two adjacent crystals.

Experimentally, the orientation relation between the two adjacent grains of an interface and the normal on the interface can be obtained by three micrographs and accompanying diffraction patterns taken under different, well-established orientations. The lateral shift $\tau$ can be measured for special configurations.

The TEM contrast of grain-boundary dislocations is similar to that of lattice dislocations. However, for the grain-boundary dislocations, additional parameters must be considered, including the geometry of the interface and the diffraction conditions of both crystals. The direction of the Burgers vector **b** of the grain-boundary dislocation can be determined using the $\mathbf{g} \cdot \mathbf{b} = 0$ criterion. However, this semiquantitative method lacks accuracy, because the magnitude of the Burgers vector of secondary grain-boundary dislocations is usually small.

Boundaries between two crystals are assumed to have a low-energy structure for certain misorientations. This low-energy structure can be thought to consist of finely spaced arrays of dislocations, the so-called primary dislocations. Any deviation from such low-energy orientation relationships is accommodated by a network of dislocations, the secondary dislocations. These dislocations were experimentally observed primarily on artificial (001) twist boundaries in gold (Ref 40). The TEM studies revealed the presence of a grid of undissociated secondary dislocations (Fig. 48). The distance of dislocations with the same Burgers vectors depends on the deviation $\Delta\theta$ from the exact coincidence position. The observations agree with the predictions of the theory. Secondary dislocations can split into partial secondary dislocations and stacking faultlike structures. This is observed for metals and semiconductors.

Lattice dislocations can interact with grain boundaries during yielding, creep, and recrystallization. Many TEM observations of reactions of lattice dislocations with grain-boundary dislocations can be explained on the basis of the dislocation model for grain-boundary structures. For the reactions of the lattice dislocations with grain boundaries, it is necessary to observe that Burgers vectors are conserved, and dislocation lines can end at other dislocations or at a free surface.

**Diffraction Studies of Grain Boundaries.** Sass and Bristowe demonstrated that diffraction techniques used in conjunction with TEM can answer questions about the atomic structure of grain boundaries. Each grain boundary represents a periodic arrangement of strains (misfit) and good coincidences.

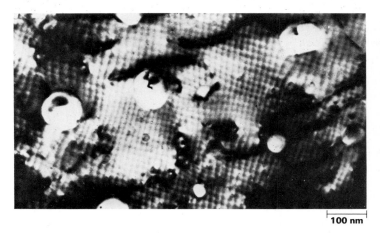

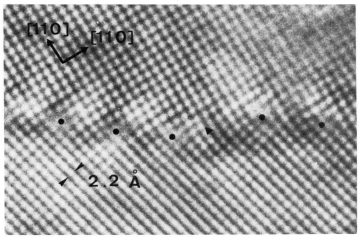

**Fig. 48** Artificial twist boundary in a gold bicrystal, twist angle near $\Sigma = 5$ (36.9°). Square grids of secondary screw grain-boundary dislocations can be observed. Burgers vector **b** = $(a/10)\langle 310\rangle$. The dislocations accommodate the deviations from the exact $\Sigma = 5$ misorientation. 110 000×. (Ref 40)

**Fig. 49** High-resolution image of a $\Sigma = 41$ pure tilt boundary in molybdenum. Foil orientation [001] for both grains. (A. Bourret and J.M. Penisson)

Electrons and x-rays are scattered by this periodic grid, which possesses a unit cell corresponding to the coincidence-site lattice. If the periodic displacements at the grain boundaries are known, the scattering factor of such boundaries (mostly twist boundaries) can be calculated for the different reflections caused by the grain boundaries. For example, the reciprocal lattice of a twist boundary consists of thin rods; the integral intensity in the rod depends on the scattering factor. The length of the rod is proportional to the inverse of the thickness of the disturbed region near the grain boundary. This grain-boundary thickness approximates the distance of the dislocations present in the grain boundary.

**Direct Imaging of Grain Boundaries.** High-resolution electron microscopy (HREM) allows the direct imaging of certain grain boundaries. In HREM, the structure of the specimen must be periodic in the direction of the transmitted electron beam. Therefore, only tilt boundaries in which the tilt axis is parallel to the beam direction can be studied. Because the strong periodicity is disturbed in the core region of the boundaries, the point-to-point resolution of the instrument must be high enough to transfer information on the relaxation of atoms through the objective lenses, despite the high spherical aberration of the best lenses available.

Tilt boundaries in silicon (Ref 41), germanium (Ref 42), and molybdenum (Ref 43) have been studied using HREM. For these studies, the specimen thickness must be below 15 nm (150 Å). Figure 49 depicts a HREM micrograph of a tilt boundary in molybdenum. Contrast simulations must be performed to determine the positions of the atoms near the grain boundary. In the simulation work, a certain atomic configuration near the tilt boundary is assumed. The simulated micrographs must be compared with the experimentally observed pictures for different defocusing values. The atomic arrangements must be modified to achieve a complete fit between the observed and calculated images.

**TEM Contrast of Heterophase Boundaries.** Heterophase boundaries are formed when two materials of differing structure and/or chemical composition meet. For example, upon occurrence of any phase transformation, a heterophase boundary is present where the different phases meet. This is true for the interface of a martensitic phase transformation where two materials with the same chemical composition but different structures converge, as well as for an interface of a thermally grown precipitate.

The importance of the structure of these heterophase boundaries for the nucleation and growth of the precipitate is recognized. However, few systematic TEM studies have investigated this structure. Such studies would require experimental imaging of the inclined interface under different diffraction conditions in which reflections from both crystal structures are excited simultaneously or sequentially. The observations must be compared to contrast simulations. General expressions have been derived even in the framework of anisotropic elasticity theory for the elastic displacement and stress fields (Ref 44). However, the results have yet to be applied to contrast simulations of an interface.

The geometry of the heterophase interfaces can be described by a generalization of the geometry of grain boundaries (Ref 45). These models are essentially fit-misfit models in which the regions of a good fit are patched where partial lattice matching across the boundary is achieved, and the regions of misfit are boundary-line defects that possess the character of a dislocation or a boundary step (facet).

The model has been applied to interfaces between two cubic crystals—copper and silver (Ref 46)—and to hexagonal materials (Ref 47). A metal/metal carbide interface has been studied (Ref 48, 49), and the interface between molybdenum and molybdenum car-

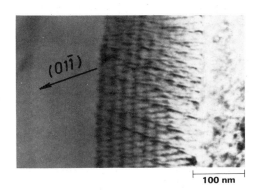

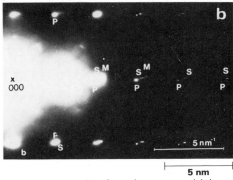

**Fig. 50, 51** Interface between molybdenum and molybdenum carbide. Fig. 50: Dislocation contrasts are visible; the Burgers vector cannot be analyzed unambiguously. 133 200×. Fig. 51: Diffraction pattern of the same interface in an edge-on configuration; additional streaks are observable due to the interface crystal.

bide has been examined. The latter interface forms after cooling from a supersaturated solution of carbon in molybdenum. In TEM micrographs (Fig. 50), a dislocation-type contrast can be observed. The determination of the Burgers vector using the simple $\mathbf{g} \cdot \mathbf{b} = 0$ rule is not possible without ambiguity. The contrast behavior suggests that the Burgers vector is of type $1/2\langle 111\rangle$.

Diffraction patterns yield the orientation

relation between molybdenum and molybdenum carbide. Dense-packed planes of the molybdenum lattices are nearly parallel to dense-packed planes of molybdenum carbide (Burgers relation). Careful diffraction studies performed for an edge-on configuration of the interface (Fig. 51) have revealed the presence of streaks between the reflections of molybdenum and molybdenum carbide. The formation of additional streaks can be explained by the assumption that an interface crystal is present between the pure molybdenum and molybdenum carbide. From the maximum streak length, the minimum thickness of the interface crystal can be determined to within nine lattice parameters of the molybdenum lattice.

## REFERENCES

1. S. Amelinckx, R. Gevers, and J. Van Landuyt, Ed., *Diffraction and Imaging Techniques in Materials Science*, Vol I and II, North-Holland, 1978

2. H. Bethge and J. Heydenreich, Ed., *Elektronenmikroskopie in der Festkörperphysik*, Springer, 1982

3. J.M. Cowley, *Diffraction Physics*, North-Holland, 1975

4. A.K. Head, P. Humble, L.M. Clarebrough, A.J. Morton, and C.R. Forwood, *Computer Electron Micrographs and Defect Identification*, North-Holland, 1973

5. P.B. Hirsch, A. Howie, R.B. Nicholson, D.W. Pashley, and M.J. Whelan, *Electron Microscopy of Thin Crystals*, Krieger, 1977

6. E. Hornbogen, *Durchstrahlungs-Elektronenmikroskopie fester Stoffe*, Verlag Chemie, 1971

7. L. Reimer, *Elektronenmikroskopische Untersuchungs- und Präparations- methoden*, Springer, 1967

8. L. Reimer, *Transmission Electron Microscopy*, Springer, 1984

9. G. Thomas, *Transmission Electron Microscopy of Metals*, John Wiley & Sons, 1962

10. G. Thomas and M.J. Goringe, *Transmission Electron Microscopy of Materials*, John Wiley & Sons, 1979

11. L.E. Murr, *Electron Optical Applications in Materials Science*, McGraw-Hill, 1970

12. S. Amelinckx, *The Direct Observation of Dislocations*, Academic Press, 1964

13. S. Amelinckx, in *Dislocations in Solids*, Vol II, North-Holland, 1979

14. H.A. Bethe, Zur Theorie des Durchgangs schneller Korpuskularstrahlen durch Materie, *Ann. Phys.*, Vol 87, 1928, p 325

15. A. Howie and M.J. Whelan, Diffraction Contrast of Electron Microscope Images of Crystal Lattice Defects, II, *Proc. Roy. Soc. London*, Vol A263, 1961, p 217

16. P.B. Hirsch, A. Howie, and M.J. Whelan, A Kinematical Theory of Diffraction Contrast of Electron Transmission Microscope Images of Dislocations and Other Defects, *Philos. Trans. Roy. Soc. London*, Vol A252, 1960, p 499

17. R. Gevers, On the Kinematical Theory of Diffraction Contrast of Electron Transmission Microscope Images of Edge Dislocations; On the Kinematical Theory of Diffraction Contrast of Electron Transmission Microscope Images of Perfect Dislocations of Mixed Type, *Philos. Mag.*, Vol 7, 1962, p 59, 651

18. A. Howie and M.J. Whelan, Diffraction Contrast of Electron Microscope Images of Crystal Lattice Defects, III, *Proc. Roy. Soc. London*, Vol A267, 1962, p 206

19. A. Korner and H.P. Karnthaler, The Study of Glide Dislocation Loops on {001} Planes in a f.c.c. Alloy, *Philos. Mag.*, Vol A42, 1980, p 753

20. W.M. Stobbs and C.H. Sworne, The Weak Beam Technique as Applied to the Determination of the Stacking-Fault Energy of Copper, *Philos. Mag.*, Vol 24, 1971, p 1365

21. B.L. Eyre and R. Bullough, On the Formation of Interstitial Loops in bcc Metals, *Philos. Mag.*, Vol 11, 1965, p 31

22. W. Jäger and M. Wilkens, Formation of Vacancy-type Dislocation Loops in Tungsten Bombarded by 60 keV Au Ions, *Phys. Status Solidi*, Vol 32, 1975, p 89

23. H. Föll and M. Wilkens, A Simple Method for the Analysis of Dislocation Loops by Means of the Inside-Outside Contrast on Transmission Electron Micrographs, *Phys. Status Solidi*, Vol 31, 1975, p 519

24. D.M. Maher and B.L. Eyre, Neutron Irradiation Damage in Molybdenum, I, *Philos. Mag.*, Vol 23, 1971, p 409

25. F. Häussermann, M. Rühle, and M. Wilkens, Black-White Contrast Figures from Small Dislocation Loops, II, *Phys. Status Solidi*, Vol 50, 1972, p 445

26. M. Wilkens and H.O.K. Kirchner, Black-White Contrast of Transmission Electron Microscope Images of Small Dislocation Loops in Elastically Anisotropic Crystals, *Philos. Mag.*, Vol A43, 1981, p 139

27. M.F. Ashby and L.M. Brown, Diffraction Contrast from Spherically Symmetrical Coherency Strains, *Philos. Mag.*, Vol 8, 1963, p 1083, 1649

28. K.G. McIntyre and L.M. Brown, Anomalous Images in Electron Microscopy, *J. de Phys.*, Vol 27, 1966, p C3-178

29. K.P. Chik, M. Wilkens, and M. Rühle, Die Interpretation des elektronenmikroskopischen Beugungskontrastes von Einschlüssen nahe einer kräftefreien Folienoberfläche, *Phys. Status Solidi*, Vol 23, 1967, p 113

30. D. Lepski, Electron Diffraction Contrast of Small Coherent Particles: I. Ellipsoidal Inclusion in an Isotropic Matrix; II. Spherical Inclusion in a Cubic Crystal, *Phys. Status Solidi*, Vol 23, 1974, p 543; Vol 24, 1974, p 99

31. G. Kalonji and J.W. Cahn, Symmetry Constraints on the Orientation Dependence of Interfacial Properties: The Group of the Wulff Plot, *J. de Phys.*, Vol C6, 1982, p 25

32. S. Amelinckx and J. Van Landuyt, in *Diffraction and Imaging Techniques in Materials Science*, Vol I and II, North-Holland, 1978

33. R. Gevers, A. Art, and S. Amelinckx, Intensity Profiles for Fringe Patterns due to Planar Interfaces as Observed by Electron Microscopy, *Phys. Status Solidi*, Vol 11, 1965, p 689

34. H. Hashimoto, A. Howie, and M.J. Whelan, Anomalous Electron Absorption Effects in Metal Foils, *Proc. Roy. Soc. London*, Vol A289, 1962, p 80

35. R.W. Balluffi, *Grain Boundary Structure and Kinetics*, ASM 1980

36. G.A Chadwick and D.A. Smith, Ed., *Grain Boundary Structure and Properties*, Academic Press, 1976

37. S. Hagege and G. Nouet, Ed., Structure and Properties of Intergranular Boundaries, *J. de Phys.*, Vol 43, Conf. C6, 1982

38. M. Rühle, R.W. Balluffi, H. Fischmeister, and S.L. Sass, Ed., Structure and Properties of Internal Interfaces, *J. de Phys.*, Vol 46, Conf. C4, 1985

39. H. Gleiter, in *Physical Metallurgy*, 3rd ed., North-Holland, 1983, p 649

40. T. Schober and R.W. Balluffi, Dislocation Sub-boundary Arrays in Oriented Thin-Film Bicrystals of Gold, *Philos. Mag.*, Vol 20, 1969, p 511

41. A. Bourret and J. Desseaux, The Low-angle [011] Tilt Boundary in Germanium, I. High-Resolution Structure Determination, *Philos. Mag.*, Vol A39, 1979, p 405

42. O.L. Krivanek, S. Isoda, and K. Kobayashi, Lattice Imaging of a Grain Boundary in Crystalline Germanium, *Philos. Mag.*, Vol 36, 1977, p 931

43. J.M. Penisson, R. Gronsky, and J.B. Brosse, High Resolution Study of a Σ-41 Grain Boundary in Molybdenum, *Scripta Metall.*, Vol 16, 1982, p 1239

44. R. Bonnet, Periodic Displacement and Stress Fields Near a Phase Boundary in the Isotropic Elasticity Theory, *Philos. Mag.*, Vol A43, 1981, p 1165

45. R.W. Balluffi, A. Brokman, and A.H. King, CSL/DSC Lattice Model for General Crystal-Crystal Boundaries and their Line Defects, *Acta Metall.*, Vol 30, 1982, p 1453

46. A. Laffont and R. Bonnet, Diffusion Bonding of Silver Balls to a Copper Substrate and Vice Versa, *Acta Metall.*, Vol 30, 1982, p 763

47. R. Bonnet, E. Cousineau, and D.H. Warrington, Determination of Near-Coincident Cells for Hexagonal Crystals, *Acta Crystallogr.*, Vol A37, 1981, p 184

48. U. Dahmen, K.H. Westmacott, and G. Thomas, A Study of Precipitation in Interstitial Alloys, I, *Acta Metall.*, Vol 29, 1981, p 627

49. M. Florjancic, M. Rühle, and S.L. Sass, in *Proc. 10th Int. Congr. Electron Microscopy*, Vol 2, 1982, p 359

# Quantitative Metallography

By Ervin E. Underwood
Professor of Metallurgy
Fracture and Fatigue Research Laboratory
School of Materials Engineering
Georgia Institute of Technology

QUANTITATIVE METALLOGRAPHY (or, more generally, stereology) deals with the quantitative relationships between measurements made on the two-dimensional plane of polish and the magnitudes of the microstructural features in the three-dimensional metal or alloy. As material specifications become stricter and performance limits are narrowed, it becomes necessary to specify and control microstructure quantitatively. This article will review the important equations, the basic measurements, and the applications of these methods to pure metals alloys. Additional information on quantitative metallography, including the use of automatic image analyzers for determining microstructural characteristics, can be found in the article "Color Metallography" in this Volume.

Table 1 shows the principal symbols used and gives examples of the combined notation in common usage (Ref 1). The term $S_V$, for example, refers to surface area per unit volume and represents the fraction $S/V_T$, in which the numerator is the microstructural feature and the denominator (total test volume) is a test quantity. Each symbol represents a geometrical element and a specific dimension. Therefore, the dimensionality of the combined terms and equations is readily apparent and consistent.

## Basic Measurements

Of greatest interest are the simple counting measurements, $P_P$, $P_L$, $N_L$, $P_A$, and $N_A$, because of the ease and speed with which these data can be gathered. Several theoretical analyses have elucidated efficient sampling techniques. With one technique, it is possible to predict the number of measurements required to achieve the desired accuracy (Ref 2). This has been applied to the point-count method, which refers to the number of test points that fall in some selected areal feature of the microstructure (such as $\alpha$ phase) on the plane of polish.

The number of points, $P_\alpha$, that fall in the $\alpha$ phase divided by $P_T$, the total number of test points, gives the ratio $P_\alpha/P_T$, or $P_P$. Those grid points that appear to fall on a boundary can be counted as one half. This gives the operator a guide to the magnitude of the experimental error.

Figure 1 shows one type of point-count grid (Ref 3) with the test points at the intersections. Figures 2 and 3 show examples of point grids selected for optimum results, depending on the type of microstructure to which they are applied. Note that on average not more than one grid point falls in any second-phase area and that the grid spacing selected is close to the diameter of the second-phase particles. A grid can be inserted in the eyepiece of the microscope, or a grid marked on clear plastic can be used with a photomicrograph or a projection screen. For best operator efficiency in counting, it is useful to

## Table 1  Principal symbols and combined notations for quantitative metallography

| Symbol | Units | Description | Common name |
|---|---|---|---|
| $P$ | ... | Number of point elements or test points | ... |
| $P_P$ | ... | Point fraction (number of point elements per total number of test points) | Point count |
| $L$ | mm | Length of linear elements or test line length | ... |
| $P_L$ | mm$^{-1}$ | Number of point intersections per unit length of test line | ... |
| $L_L$ | mm/mm | Sum of linear intercept lengths divided by total test line length | Lineal fraction |
| $A$ | mm$^2$ | Planar area of intercepted features or test area | ... |
| $S$ | mm$^2$ | Surface area or interface area, generally reserved for curved surfaces | ... |
| $V$ | mm$^3$ | Volume of three-dimensional structural elements or test volume | ... |
| $A_A$ | mm$^2$/mm$^2$ | Sum of areas of intercepted features divided by total test area | Areal fraction |
| $S_V$ | mm$^2$/mm$^3$ | Surface or interface area divided by total test volume (surface-to-volume ratio) | ... |
| $V_V$ | mm$^3$/mm$^3$ | Sum of volumes of structural features divided by total test volume | Volume fraction |
| $N$ | ... | Number of features | ... |
| $N_L$ | mm$^{-1}$ | Number of interceptions of features divided by total test line length | Lineal density |
| $P_A$ | mm$^{-2}$ | Number of point features divided by total test area | ... |
| $L_A$ | mm/mm$^2$ | Sum of lengths of linear features divided by total test area | Perimeter (total) |
| $N_A$ | mm$^{-2}$ | Number of interceptions of features divided by total test area | Areal density |
| $L_V$ | mm/mm$^3$ | Length of features per test volume | ... |
| $N_V$ | mm$^{-3}$ | Number of features per test volume | Volumetric density |
| $\overline{L}$ | mm | Mean linear intercept distance, $L_L/N_L$ | ... |
| $\overline{A}$ | mm$^2$ | Mean areal intercept, $A_A/N_A$ | ... |
| $\overline{S}$ | mm$^2$ | Mean particle surface area, $S_V/N_V$ | ... |
| $\overline{V}$ | mm$^3$ | Mean particle volume, $V_V/N_V$ | ... |

Note: Fractional parameters are expressed per unit length, area, or volume
Source: Ref 1

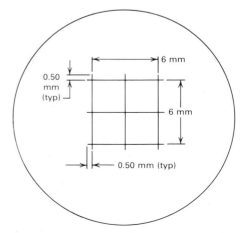

**Fig. 1** Typical point-count grid. Figures 2 and 3 show applications. (Ref 3)

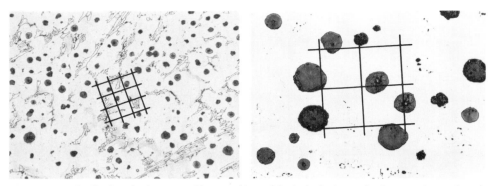

**Fig. 2, 3** Application of point-count grids to graphite nodules in the ferrite matrix of two specimens of grade 60-45-12 ductile iron. Fig. 2: 2% nital. 100×. Fig. 3: 2% nital, lightly etched. 140×

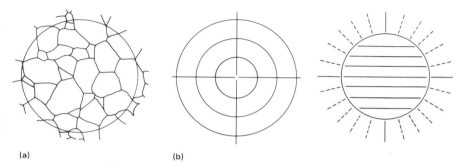

**Fig. 4** (a) Grain-boundary traces in a typical single-phase alloy (Ref 4). (b) Circular (left) and parallel (right) linear test grids for $P_L$ counts. Both types of grids may be used for measuring random structures like that shown in (a); the grid at right is applicable to oriented structures such as the one shown in Fig. 5. (Ref 1)

**Fig. 5** Elongated grain-boundary traces in extruded molybdenum; typical of oriented structures measured with the grid at the right in Fig. 4(b). Etchant and magnification not reported

limit the number of hits on any one application of the grid to five or six. Therefore, a 3 by 3, 4 by 4, or 5 by 5 point grid suffices for most applications, because the magnification can be adjusted for a particular microstructure.

Another important measurement frequently required in quantitative microstructural analysis is the number of points of intersection per unit length of test lines, $P_L$. A test line or linear array is applied randomly to a microstructure containing linear features, such as the structure drawn in Fig. 4(a). The points of intersection along the test lines are counted as they are placed at several positions and angles over the entire microstructure until enough intersections have been counted. Figure 4(b) shows examples of circular and parallel linear test grids for $P_L$ counts (Ref 1). Both grids in Fig. 4(b) may be used for random microstructures (such as the

one in Fig. 4a); the grid with radii spaced at 15° angular intervals finds application for directional measurements on oriented structures, such as the one shown in Fig. 5. The total lengths of the circular and parallel linear test grids are determined in advance to facilitate subsequent calculations.

Other basic measurements that involve counting are $N_L$, $P_A$, and $N_A$. $N_L$ corresponds closely to $P_L$, except that $N_L$ is reserved for objects (such as particles) instead of points (for example, the intersections of grain-boundary traces by test lines). $N_L$ is defined as the number of interceptions of particles per unit length of test line. This definition allows for the possibility that a particle with an irregular outline may be intercepted more than once by the same test line. Therefore, the relationships $P_L = N_L$, for space-filling grains, and $P_L = 2N_L$, for isolated particles, regardless of their shape, are maintained.

$P_A$ and $N_A$ are also related. $P_A$ refers to points per unit area, and $N_A$ to objects per unit area (see the nodules in Fig. 2). If the grain junctions (triple points) in Fig. 4(a) are counted as points, $P = 59$, and for a test area $A_T$ within the circle equal to 0.5 mm², $P_A = 59/0.5 = 118$ mm⁻². A count of the grains in Fig. 4(a) gives a value of $N = 30.5$ (counting border grains intercepted by the circular perimeter as one half a grain each). Therefore, $N_A = 30.5/0.5 = 61$ mm⁻².

When counting objects or points within an area, care must be taken that none is overlooked or counted twice. An open square grid superimposed over the photomicrograph or

microstructure is used frequently to ensure accurate counting. Figure 6 gives an example of using a simple grain count to plot elongation and tensile strength as functions of the number of grains, $N$, in the cross sections of the specimens (Ref 5).

Two procedures using combined measurements are described below. The older method (Ref 6) was proposed to obtain the surface-to-volume ratio of discrete particles. The particles are embedded in a suitable material, then sectioned. In principle, short test lines of length $l$ are "thrown" randomly on the microstructure, as shown in Fig. 7(a). Two types of points are counted: points of intersection with the boundaries, $P$, and the end points that hit within the second-phase areas, $h$. For particles of $\alpha$ phase, the equation is:

$$\frac{S_\alpha}{V_\alpha} = \frac{4P}{hl} \qquad \text{(Eq 1)}$$

where the mean particle surface area, $S_\alpha$, refers to the mean particle volume, $V_\alpha$, not an arbitrary test volume. Figure 7(a) illustrates various counting possibilities, which, for a test line $l = 0.02$ mm, gives $S_\alpha/V_\alpha = (4 \times 7)/(5 \times 0.02) = 280$ mm⁻¹. Figure 7(b) reproduces an excellent grid for these combined measurements (Ref 7).

A combined method for obtaining the $S/V$ ratio of discrete particles has also been proposed (Ref 8). Both a point count, $P_P$, and an intersection count, $P_L$, are made simultaneously using a superimposed square grid, as depicted in Fig. 8. The equation for individual, isolated particles is:

$$\frac{S_\alpha}{V_\alpha} = \frac{2P_L}{P_P} \qquad \text{(Eq 2)}$$

For a system of particles in a matrix, the equation is:

$$\frac{(S_V)_\alpha}{(V_V)_\alpha} = \frac{2P_L}{P_P} \qquad \text{(Eq 3)}$$

Assuming the numbers shown for the individual particles in Fig. 8 represent average values obtained after several random placements of the grid and that the total unmagni-

**Table 2  Relationship of measured (○) and calculated (□) quantities**

Dimensions arbitrarily expressed in millimeters

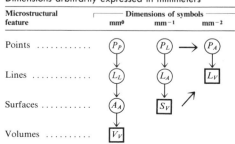

| Microstructural feature | Dimensions of symbols | | |
|---|---|---|---|
| | mm⁰ | mm⁻¹ | mm⁻² |
| Points ........... | $P_P$ | $P_L \rightarrow$ | $P_A$ |
| Lines ............ | $L_L$ | $L_A$ | $L_V$ |
| Surfaces .......... | $A_A$ | $S_V$ | |
| Volumes .......... | $V_V$ | | |

**Basic equations**

$$V_V = A_A = L_L = P_P \text{ (mm}^0\text{)} \qquad \text{(Eq 4)}$$
$$S_V = (4/\pi) L_A = 2P_L \text{ (mm}^{-1}\text{)} \qquad \text{(Eq 5)}$$
$$L_V = 2P_A \text{ (mm}^{-2}\text{)} \qquad \text{(Eq 6)}$$

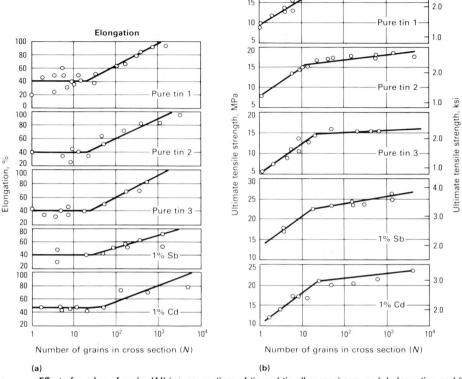

**Fig. 6** Effect of number of grains (*N*) in cross sections of tin and tin alloy specimens on (a) elongation and (b) ultimate tensile strength. (Ref 5)

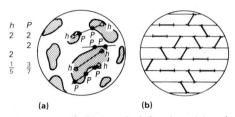

**Fig. 7** (a) Chalkley method for determining the surface-to-volume ratio of discrete particles. (b) A grid for combined point and intersection count. (Ref 7)

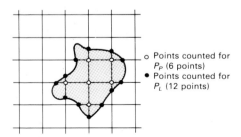

**Fig. 8** Superimposed square grid used in the Saltykov method for determining the surface-to-volume ratio of discrete particles. $P_P$ represents a point count and $P_L$ represents an intersection count. (Ref 1)

fied grid length is 1 mm, then $S/V = (2 \times 12)/(6/36) = 144$ mm$^{-1}$.

## Basic Equations

The basic equations for points, lines, surfaces, and volumes in a microstructure are

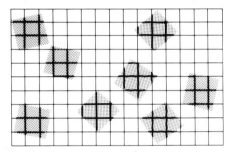

**Fig. 9** Equivalence of areal, linear, and point ratios, $A_A = L_L = P_P$. (Ref 1)

well known and well documented (Ref 1, 3, 8-11). Consequently, derivations will not be given here. Instead, practical applications to actual microstructures will be stressed.

Table 2 shows the interrelationships between microstructural features that can and cannot be measured (Ref 1). Arrows indicate those quantities that yield the normally inaccessible three-dimensional quantities $V_V$, $S_V$, and $L_V$. Below the triangular matrix are written the corresponding basic equations.

Equation 4 in Table 2 states the equality of volume fraction to the areal ratio, linear ratio, and point ratio of the selected phase as seen on random sections through the microstructure. The measurement of volume fraction is usually most efficiently performed with the point count, as illustrated in Fig. 1 to 3. Under unusual circumstances, areal ratios can be obtained with a planimeter; linear

ratios are commonly measured by means of a Hurlbut counter. Quantitative TV-scanning equipment is being used increasingly for routine applications in which large numbers of specimens make automation economically feasible.

Figure 9 shows the interrelationship of areal, length, and point measurements through the equations $A_A = L_L = P_P$ (Ref 1). The volume fraction is used frequently in studies of metallurgical systems and phenomena. Figure 10 depicts the relationship between ductility and the volume fraction of various dispersions in copper (Ref 12), and Fig. 11 illustrates the application of volume-fraction measurements to establish the phase boundaries of a two-phase field (Ref 13).

Equation 5 in Table 2 combines two important equations, both of which require a $P_L$ measurement:

$$S_V = 2P_L \qquad \text{(Eq 5a)}$$

$$L_A = \frac{\pi}{2} P_L \qquad \text{(Eq 5b)}$$

When surface area per unit volume is required, Eq 5(a) is used. For example, total

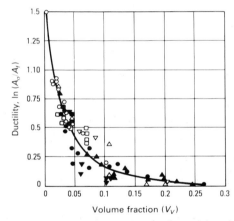

**Fig. 10** Relationship between ductility and the volume fraction of various dispersions in copper. (Ref 12)

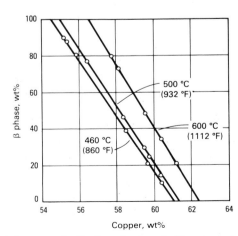

**Fig. 11** Application of volume-fraction measurements to establish the phase boundaries of a two-phase field. (Ref 13)

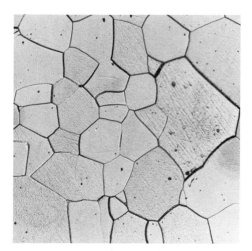

**Fig. 12** Grain-boundary traces outlining the recrystallized grains of a single-phase palladium solid solution. 10% KCN + 10% $(NH_4)_2S_2O_8$. 75×

grain-boundary surface area in a single-phase alloy (Fig. 12) may be desired. Also, $S_V$ could be used for analyzing grain-boundary precipitates (Fig. 13 to 15), for transformation products growing out of grain boundaries (Fig. 16), or for obtaining the interphase boundary area in a eutectic alloy (Fig. 17).

When linear traces in the plane of polish are of interest, $L_A$ is the parameter of choice, and Eq 5(b) would be used. In corrosion studies, for example, the pertinent feature is the length of grain-boundary traces exposed to the corroding medium. In other studies, the microstructural feature may be considered essentially linear, such as the thin twins in Fig. 18. Here, in a $P_L$ traverse, each twin intersected would be counted only once. Using the circular grid around the hardness impression, curves of $L_A$ versus strain can be calculated, as shown in Fig. 19. For other twins, however, the total twin-matrix interface length may be required. The interfaces on each side of the twinned regions would be counted separately, as in Fig. 20, and each

time the twin was intersected by the test line, it would count as two.

In Eq 6, for line length per unit volume ($L_V = 2P_A$), the points counted are those in the test area caused by the intersections of the test plane with the linear elements of the microstructure. Equation 6 usually requires only one test plane for linear elements that are randomly oriented in space. However, randomness in the microstructure is not essential to Eq 6, because random sampling can be ensured by selecting a random orientation of the plane of polish.

Typical examples of linear elements in microstructures are dislocation lines, grain edges where three adjacent grains contact, needlelike precipitate particles, and slag or oxide stringers. Figure 21 shows dislocation etch pits, which are counted ($P_A$) to get the dislocation density ($L_V$). Figures 4(a) and 12 represent single-phase materials with the grain edges revealed at the junctions of grain-boundary traces. These triple points are counted ($P_A$) to find the length of grain-boundary edges ($L_V$). Figure 22 shows elongated, essentially linear, nonmetallic inclusions that can also be analyzed according to Eq 6.

## Oriented Structures

Although the basic equations (Eq 4 to 6) apply to any microstructure, special equations are available for special types of microstructures (Ref 1). For example, oriented systems of lines or surfaces may be encountered, and the directional characteristics, in addition to the mean values, may be desired. In such cases, transverse or longitudinal sections or both are used instead of random sections.

Next, systems of oriented lines in a two-dimensional plane, systems of oriented lines in three-dimensional space, and systems of oriented surfaces in three-dimensional space are discussed. The oriented systems can also be described as completely oriented systems, in which all elements are parallel, or as par-

tially oriented systems, in which random and oriented elements occur. In both cases, however, orientation directions are clearly defined and recognizable; in fact, several orientation systems can exist in the same microstructure, each with its own orientation direction or plane.

Examples of systems of oriented lines in a plane are provided by twin traces in the plane of polish (Fig. 20), dislocation lines in the surface of a silicon crystal (Fig. 23), and grain-boundary traces in extruded molybdenum (Fig. 5).

The three equations applicable to these partially oriented systems of lines in a plane refer to the random (ran) and oriented (or) portions of the system of lines as well as to the total (tot) length per unit area. They are:

$$(L_A)_{ran} = 1.571(P_L)_{\parallel} \qquad (Eq\ 7a)$$

$$(L_A)_{or} = (P_L)_{\perp} - (P_L)_{\parallel} \qquad (Eq\ 7b)$$

$$(L_A)_{tot} = (P_L)_{\perp} + 0.571(P_L)_{\parallel} \qquad (Eq\ 7c)$$

where the $(P_L)_{\perp}$ and $(P_L)_{\parallel}$ measurements are made with test lines perpendicular and parallel to the orientation direction, respectively. Note that $(L_A)_{tot} = (L_A)_{ran} + (L_A)_{or}$. Of course, if the system of lines is completely oriented, $(P_L)_{\parallel}$ will be zero and $(L_A)_{or} = (L_A)_{tot} = (P_L)_{\perp}$.

The twin traces in Fig. 24 represent a system of lines in a plane with essentially four orientation directions. A grid of parallel test lines (such as the one at right in Fig. 4b) is applied perpendicular to each orientation direction, in turn, and the intersections with the twins perpendicular to the test lines are counted. If the twin traces are assumed to be completely oriented, then $(L_A)_{or} = (P_L)_{\perp}$, and the line length is obtained directly for each orientation direction as a function of angle from a reference line. Figure 25 summarizes the results obtained in this way.

Many common microstructures have features that can be described as a system of oriented lines in space (that is, throughout the alloy). Examples are elongated nonmetal-

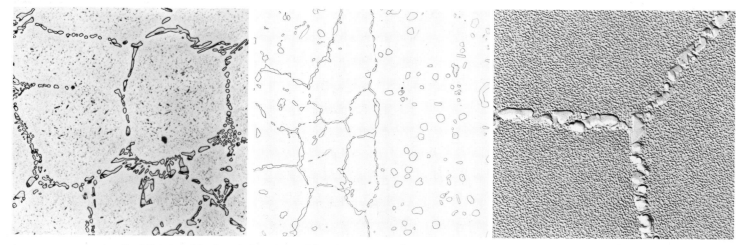

**Fig. 13, 14, 15** Precipitated particles in grain boundaries of three heat-resistant alloys. Fig. 13: Fe-35Ni-16Cr casting alloy. Hot alkaline potassium ferricyanide. 250×. Fig. 14: RA 333, a wrought nickel-base alloy. 25 mL HCl, 10 mL methanol, 7 mL HNO₃. 250×. Fig. 15: Waspaloy, also a wrought nickel-base alloy. Electrolytic etch, $H_2SO_4$, $H_3PO_4$, HNO₃. 10 000×

lic inclusions (Fig. 22), parallel rods in unidirectionally solidified eutectics (Fig. 26), and oriented dislocation arrays (Fig. 27 to 29), all of which show pronounced linear directional characteristics.

For a partially oriented system of lines in the alloy:

$$(L_V)_{ran} = 2(P_A)_\parallel \qquad \text{(Eq 8a)}$$

$$(L_V)_{or} = (P_A)_\perp - (P_A)_\parallel \qquad \text{(Eq 8b)}$$

$$(L_V)_{tot} = (P_A)_\perp + (P_A)_\parallel \qquad \text{(Eq 8c)}$$

where $(P_A)_\perp$ and $(P_A)_\parallel$ refer to measurements of point density on planes perpendicular and

parallel to the orientation direc tively. If the system of lines is co ented, $(P_A)_\parallel$ is zero, and $(L_V)_{or}$ though some microstructural features are not truly linear, they can be considered so for practical purposes if they have sufficient linearity. Of course, if the cross-sectional thickness is too great, the $(P_A)_\parallel$ measurements will be difficult to make.

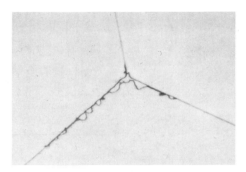

**Fig. 16** Particles of Fe₃C nucleating at grain boundaries of secondary-recrystallized 3.25% silicon steel strip. Nital. 1000×

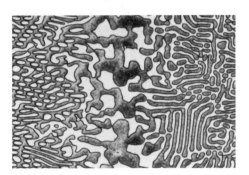

**Fig. 17** Interfaces between phases in a reversible-matrix, aluminum-copper eutectic alloy. Etchant and magnification not reported

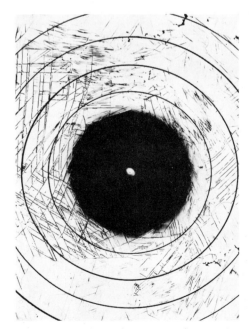

**Fig. 18** Circular grid superimposed on a micrograph, showing twinning around a hardness impression in as-cast Mo-12.5Os alloy. See also Fig. 19. Etchant and magnification not reported. (Ref 14)

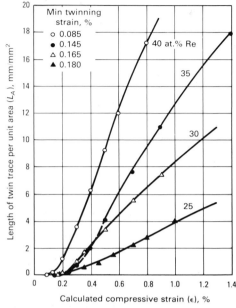

**Fig. 19** Application of data obtained with the aid of circular grids around hardness impressions to calculation of compressive strain in cast chromium-base alloys containing various amounts of rhenium. (Ref 14)

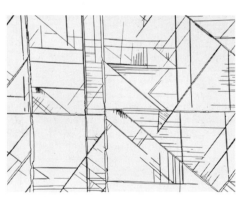

**Fig. 20** Twinned structure in a lightly etched Mo-35Re single crystal. Etchant and magnification not reported

**Fig. 21** Etch pits due to dislocation lines in copper. Etchant and magnification not reported. (Ref 15)

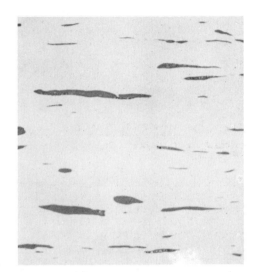

**Fig. 22** Elongated sulfide inclusions in free-cutting type 303 stainless steel bar (0.25% S). Longitudinal section. As-polished. 250×

**Fig. 23** Dislocation lines in (111) surface of silicon crystal. Etchant and magnification not reported. (Ref 16)

**Fig. 24** Twinned structure in a heavily etched Mo-35Re single crystal. Etchant and magnification not reported

Another major type of oriented structure consists of surfaces in the alloy. Examples of oriented planar features in the microstructure are pearlites in steel (Fig. 30), lamellae in unidirectionally solidified eutectics (Fig. 31), and lamellar precipitates observed by thin-foil electron transmission microscopy (Fig. 32).

These oriented surfaces are subclassified as planar orientation, because the planar surfaces are essentially parallel to an orientation plane (or planes). The three equations applicable to a partially oriented system of surfaces with planar orientation are:

$$(S_V)_{ran} = 2(P_L)_\parallel \qquad \text{(Eq 9a)}$$

$$(S_V)_{or} = (P_L)_\perp - (P_L)_\parallel \qquad \text{(Eq 9b)}$$

$$(S_V)_{tot} = (P_L)_\perp + (P_L)_\parallel \qquad \text{(Eq 9c)}$$

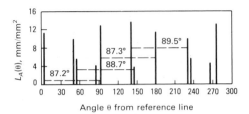

**Fig. 25** Twin-trace length as a function of angle for the structure shown in Fig. 24. (Ref 14)

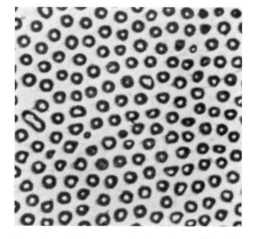

**Fig. 26** Transverse section through parallel rods in a unidirectionally solidified Mg-32Al eutectic alloy. Growth rate was $1.5 \times 10^{-2}$ mm/s ($6 \times 10^{-4}$ in./s). Temperature gradient was 3.7 °C/mm (1.7 °F/$10^{-2}$in.). Etchant and magnification not reported. (Ref 17)

where $(P_L)_\perp$ and $(P_L)_\parallel$ are measurements made perpendicular and parallel to the orientation plane, respectively. If the system of surfaces is completely oriented, as in portions of Fig. 32, $(P_L)_\parallel$ is zero, and $(S_V)_{or} = (P_L)_\perp$.

A sequence of extruded beryllium specimens with different initial powder sizes exemplifies the analysis of a system of partially oriented surfaces (Ref 1). The essential data are as follows:

| Specimen | Initial powder size, mm | $(P_L)_\perp$, mm$^{-1}$ | $(P_L)_\parallel$ mm$^{-1}$ |
|---|---|---|---|
| 1 | 0.004 | 164.8 | 115.0 |
| 2 | 0.100 | 104.2 | 69.5 |
| 3 | 0.250 | 69.0 | 56.8 |

Assuming planar orientation, substitution in Eq 9(b) and 9(c) shows that for specimens 1, 2, and 3, respectively:

$$\begin{aligned}(S_V)_{or} &= (P_L)_\perp - (P_L)_\parallel \\ &= 164.8 - 115.0 = 49.8 \text{ mm}^{-1} \\ &= 104.2 - 69.5 = 34.7 \text{ mm}^{-1} \\ &= 69.0 - 56.8 = 12.2 \text{ mm}^{-1}\end{aligned}$$

and

$$\begin{aligned}(S_V)_{tot} &= (P_L)_\perp + (P_L)_\parallel \\ &= 164.8 + 115.0 = 279.8 \text{ mm}^{-1} \\ &= 104.2 + 69.5 = 173.7 \text{ mm}^{-1} \\ &= 69.0 + 56.8 = 125.8 \text{ mm}^{-1}\end{aligned}$$

The fractional, or percentage, amount of planar orientation, represented by $\Omega_{pl}$ is $(S_V)_{or}/(S_V)_{tot}$, or:

$$\begin{aligned}\Omega_{pl} &= \frac{49.8}{279.8} = 17.8\% \\ &= \frac{34.7}{173.7} = 20.0\% \\ &= \frac{12.2}{125.8} = 9.7\%\end{aligned}$$

for specimens 1, 2, and 3, respectively. The results suggest that some mechanical properties may fall out of sequence even though the mean grain intercept length (equal to the reciprocal of $P_L$) varies directly with the initial powder size.

Where the grains (or particles, inclusions, or precipitates) are markedly elongated, a shape index may prove useful. One of the

simplest indices to express elongation is the ratio of mean length to mean width:

$$Q = \frac{D_\parallel}{D_\perp} = \frac{(P_L)_\perp}{(P_L)_\parallel} \qquad \text{(Eq 10)}$$

Using the data given above for extruded beryllium specimens, Eq 10 becomes:

$$\begin{aligned}Q &= \frac{(P_L)_\perp}{(P_L)_\parallel} \\ &= \frac{164.8}{115.0} = 1.43 \\ &= \frac{104.2}{69.5} = 1.50 \\ &= \frac{69.0}{56.8} = 1.21\end{aligned}$$

for specimens 1, 2, and 3, respectively. For equiaxed grains, of course, $Q$-ratios closer to unity would be expected.

Lamellar structures perhaps most typically exemplify oriented surfaces. A measure of the fineness of lamellae (as in pearlite, for example) is the so-called interlamellar or true spacing, $S_o$, defined as the perpendicular distance across a single pair of contiguous lamellae. Because the true spacing is difficult to determine directly, the mean random spacing, $\sigma$, defined as:

$$\sigma = \frac{1}{N_L} \qquad \text{(Eq 11)}$$

where $N_L$ is the number of alternate lamellae intersected per unit length of random test lines, is measured instead. The true spacing can then be found according to Eq 12, which has been confirmed experimentally:

$$S_o = \frac{\sigma}{2} \qquad \text{(Eq 12)}$$

Figure 33 illustrates three types of spacings and three types of distances. Spacings are essentially center-to-center lengths; distances, edge-to-edge lengths. The interlamellar distances are related to the spacings through the linear intercept ratio $(L_L)$ as in:

$$\lambda = (L_L)\sigma \qquad \text{(Eq 13)}$$

or by the mean intercept length $(L_3)$ as in:

$$L_3 = \sigma - \lambda \qquad \text{(Eq 14)}$$

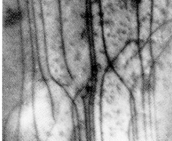
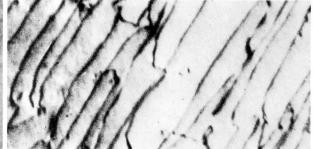

**Fig. 27, 28, 29** Oriented dislocation arrays in thin foils. Fig. 27: copper. (Ref 15). Fig. 28: iron. (Ref 15). Fig. 29: Armco iron. (Ref 18). Etchants and magnifications not reported

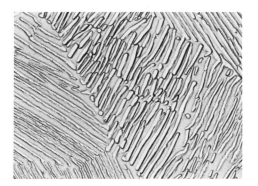

**Fig. 30** Replica electron micrograph showing lamellar pearlite in a 1090 hot-rolled steel bar. Picral. 2000×

**Fig. 31** Lamellae in a unidirectionally solidified aluminum-copper eutectic alloy. Etchant and magnification not reported. (Ref 1)

**Fig. 32** Thin-foil transmission electron micrograph showing lamellar precipitate in Fe-30Ni-6Ti alloy. Magnification not reported. (R.C. Glenn)

The subscript 3 refers to the three-dimensionality of the parameter. Finally, it is noted that:

$$S_V = \frac{4}{\sigma} \qquad \text{(Eq 15)}$$

where $S_V$ is the lamellar interface area per unit volume.

## Grain Size

Grain sizes, or diameters, have been determined by several methods. Because the grains normally found in alloys have irregular shapes, the definition of a diameter is usually arbitrary.

Fortunately, a general, quantitative length parameter provides a unique, assumption-free value for any granular, space-filling structure, regardless of grain shape, size, or position. This length parameter is the mean intercept length $L_3$ obtained from simple $L_2$ intercept measurements on the plane of polish. For many random planes, of course, the averaged $L_2$ values become the true, three-dimensional $L_3$ parameter.

For space-filling grains, the mean intercept length is defined as:

$$L_3 = \frac{1}{N_L} = \frac{L_T}{PM} \qquad \text{(Eq 16)}$$

where $N_L$ has been described above. In essence, $L_3$ equals the total test-line length, $L_T$, divided by the magnification, $M$, and the number of grain-boundary intersections, $P$ ($P$ equals $N$ for space-filling grains).

When $L_3$ is expressed in millimeters, it gives the same value as the intercept procedure described in ASTM specification E 112 (Ref 4). This specification also is the basis for the ASTM grain-size number $N$, defined as:

$$N = \frac{\log n}{\log 2} + 1.0000 \qquad \text{(Eq 17)}$$

where $n$ is the number of grains per square inch at 100× ($n$ is equal to $N_A$ in the notation of this article). Normally, to obtain the ASTM grain-size number, at least 50 grains in each of three areas must be counted, the number per square inch must be determined,

and this value must be converted to its equivalent at 100×. Then, substitution in Eq 17 or recourse to tables gives ASTM $N$.

A particularly quick and useful method for determining an equivalent ASTM $N$ uses the $P_L$ count (Ref 20). Provided are two circular test figures of known lengths, as depicted in Fig. 34 (not shown to size). The test circles can be reproduced on plastic sheet (for analyzing photomicrographs) or placed on the ground glass screen of a metallograph. The best method is to use the test circle as a reticle in the focusing eyepiece of a bench microscope.

The operator selects one of the circles and a magnification for the specimen that will result in more than six intersections per application of the circle, on the average. For equiaxed grains that do not vary much in size, the circle is applied to the microstructure until about 35 intersections are obtained, ensuring that a standard deviation of 0.3 units in $G$, the equivalent grain-size number, is obtained.

To calculate $G$, the equation is:

$$G = -10.00 - 6.64 \log L_3 \quad \text{(cm)} \qquad \text{(Eq 18)}$$

with:

$$L_3 = \frac{L_T}{PM} \qquad \text{(Eq 19)}$$

where $P$ is the total number of grain-boundary intersections made by a test circle laid down several times to give a total length, $L_T$ (in centimeters), on a field viewed at any magnification, $M$. To demonstrate the operation of Eq 18, suppose that a 10-cm (4-in.) circle is applied four times to a microstructure at 250×, totaling 36 intersections. $G$ then equals $-10 - 6.64 \log [40/(36 \times 250)]$ or 5.6. Thus, the equivalent grain-size number is obtained directly and efficiently, because no more intersections are counted than required to ensure the desired accuracy. A nomograph for the graphical solution of Eq 18 is reproduced in Fig. 35.

## Particle Relationships

Many of the relationships pertaining to particulate structures apply with equal valid-

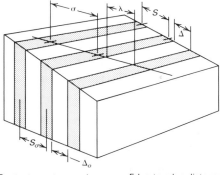

Center-to-center spacings
$S_o$ True spacing
$S$ Apparent spacing
$\sigma$ Intercept spacing

Edge-to-edge distances
$\Delta_o$ True free distance
$\Delta$ Apparent free distance
$\lambda$ Intercept free distance

**Fig. 33** Schematic presentation of three types of spacings and three types of distances in a lamellar structure. (Ref 19)

ity to second-phase regions, voids, and boundary precipitates. One important general relationship involves the mean free distance, $\lambda$, which is the mean edge-to-edge distance, along random straight lines, between all possible pairs of particles (Ref 1). For $\alpha$-phase particles, the mean free distance is:

$$\lambda = \frac{1 - (V_V)_\alpha}{N_L} \qquad \text{(Eq 20)}$$

where $(V_V)_\alpha$ is the volume fraction of the $\alpha$ particles and $N_L$ is the number of particle interceptions per unit length of test line. Equation 20 is valid regardless of size, shape, or distribution of the particles and represents a truly three-dimensional interparticle distance. This parameter is important for studies of strength and other mechanical properties and has been used in several different ways as indicated in Fig. 36 and 37.

There are other types of interparticle distance and spacing parameters, such as the mean particle spacing, $\sigma$, which is essentially the mean particle center-to-center length. The defining equation for mean particle spacing is:

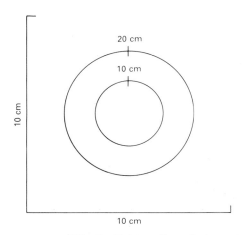

**Fig. 34** Hilliard's circular test figures for measurement of grain size. The size of the circles indicated here is suitable for the ground-glass screen of a metallograph.

$$\sigma = \frac{1}{N_L} \qquad \text{(Eq 11a)}$$

where $N_L$ is the number of particle interceptions per unit length of random test lines. The parameter $\sigma$ is characterized by how easily it can be measured, because only a simple particle interception count is needed. It is also related to $\lambda$ through the mean intercept length, $L_3$, by the equation:

$$\lambda = \sigma - (L_3)_\alpha \qquad \text{(Eq 21)}$$

where $(L_3)_\alpha$ for particles of $\alpha$ phase is defined by $(L_3)_\alpha = (L_L)_\alpha / N_L$. This is a general and assumption-free expression, valid for particles of any size or configuration.

The mean particle intercept length, $(L_3)_\alpha$, is a companion term to $\lambda$, in that $\lambda$ is the mean matrix intercept distance and $(L_3)_\alpha$ is the mean particle intercept distance. They are related through the expression for a two-phase or particulate structure of $\alpha$ phase by:

$$\lambda = (L_3)_\alpha \left[ \frac{1 - (V_V)_\alpha}{(V_V)_\alpha} \right] \qquad \text{(Eq 22)}$$

where $\lambda$ is the mean free distance between particles that have a volume fraction $(V_V)_\alpha$ and mean intercept length $(L_3)_\alpha$. Equation 22 has been used to verify the value of volume fraction in a two-phase alloy, such as in Fig. 38. Size and configuration of the dark second phase can be varied readily by heat treatment, but the volume fraction remains relatively constant. Therefore, the (constant) volume fraction obtained from the slope of the curve for $\lambda$ versus $(L_3)_\alpha$ (73.2 vol%) corresponds well with the volume fractions determined by point counting (73.5 vol%) and from chemical analysis (71.4 vol%).

Note that the mean intercept lengths for space-filling grains and for particles are related through the general expression:

$$L_3 = \frac{L_L}{N_L} \qquad \text{(Eq 23)}$$

In single-phase alloys, $L_L$ (or $V_V$) = 1, and Eq 16 is obtained. For two-phase or particulate alloys, $L_L$ (or $V_V$) has a value less than 1, and Eq 23 is used. Also, $2N_L = P_L$ applies to particulate systems, whereas $N_L = P_L$ applies to the single-phase alloys.

An example of the application of the mean intercept lengths is seen in the well-known relationship:

$$R = \frac{4r}{3V_V} \qquad \text{(Eq 24)}$$

where $R$ is the grain radius and $r$ the particle radius. Experimentally, $L_3$ and $(L_3)_\alpha$ were obtained and used for the grain diameter and particle diameter, respectively; results are shown in Fig. 39. The agreement between calculated and measured grain sizes is considered good.

From the above discussion of grain and particle characteristics, it is evident that there are many points of similarity in their geometrical properties. On the plane of polish, the grain boundaries and particle interphase traces are measured by $L_A$ or $L_p$ (the perimeter length); the intercept distances for both grains and particles are expressed by $L_2$ or $L_3$; and the surface area per particle or grain, $S/V$, and the surface area per unit volume of specimen, $S_V$, apply equally to both volume elements.

However, because the grains are space filling, all grain boundaries are shared by two contiguous grain faces; particles, on the other hand, do not usually occupy 100% of the alloy. Therefore, sharing of particle boundaries does not occur as often. To emphasize these differences, Table 3 summarizes the pertinent equations for planar figures, area-filling and separated; the same information for grains and particles is in Table 4. In general, the quantities in the second and third columns of each table are double those in the first column, except for the $P_L$ measurements.

The parameters defined in Tables 3 and 4 apply equally to interpenetrating two-phase structures and to simple particulate systems. In one study a series of beryllium-aluminum alloys (similar to the alloy shown in Fig. 38) was investigated for possible correlations between microstructure and mechanical properties. Mechanical properties correlated well with such microstructural quantities as $\lambda$, $L_3$, $L_A$, and $V_V$. However, to assess the effects of heat treatment, a new parameter was devised to consider the gradual smoothing of interphase boundaries at higher temperatures. This new parameter, called the "complexity index" (CI), is defined by:

$$CI = \frac{L_p}{(A)_{Al}} \qquad \text{(Eq 25)}$$

where $L_p$, the mean perimeter length of aluminum islands, is equal to $L_A/(N_A)_{Al}$, and $(A)_{Al}$, the mean area of aluminum islands is equal to $(A_A)_{Al}/(N_A)_{Al}$. Therefore, for the complex, jagged interphase traces, $L_p$ (and CI) is large; however, for smooth, rounded phase areas, $L_p$ (and CI) is small. Dividing by $(A)_{Al}$ normalizes $L_p$ in terms of the island size. Note that this is not a dimensionless parameter, but has dimensions of reciprocal length.

Plotting the complexity index against elastic modulus, yield strength, hardness, or elongation yields satisfactory correlations of the experimental data. The most striking results are found with the elastic modulus and yield strength of extruded alloys, with and without annealing; typical curves are shown in Fig. 40 for alloys of three compositions. As a result of this type of curve, patent claims were made for alloys with complexity indices between 1 and 5 per micron. Out of 18 claims in Ref 24, seven were based on complexity index and other quantitative microstructural parameters.

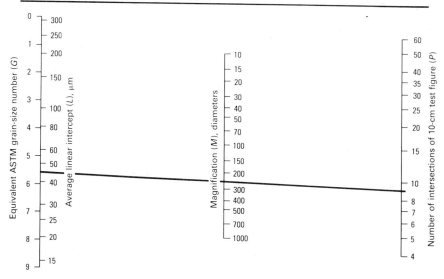

**Fig. 35** Nomograph for obtaining ASTM grain-size numbers. (Ref 20)

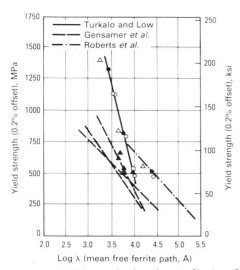

**Fig. 36** Yield strength of steels as a function of the mean free distance between cementite particles. (Ref 21)

## Particle-Size Distributions

Several methods are available for obtaining the spatial size distribution of spheres from the size distribution of their planar sections. Procedures are also available for convex particles of arbitrary shape (Ref 8), ellipsoids (Ref 25), pentagonal dodecahedrons (Ref 26), a statistical grain shape (Ref 27), and the spacings in lamellar structures (Ref 28). Although the equations for the simpler particles provide statistically exact solutions, this is not the case for size distribution of real particles with irregular shapes. Consequently, assumptions are required, with a corresponding loss in the accuracy of the results.

The three main types of measurements made on planar sections are the section diameters, section areas, or section chords. These are depicted in Fig. 41. From the resulting two-dimensional size distribution, the true spatial size distribution of particles or of grains can be calculated.

Frequently, however, the size-distribution curve is not necessary to characterize a microstructure. In fact, numerical parameters, not a curve, are required to relate the size distribution to some material property. Generally, representing a size-distribution curve requires only the mean diameter, $\overline{D}$, the standard deviation, $\sigma(D)$, and the number of particles per unit volume, $N_V$. These parameters can be obtained from the analysis of the particle-size distribution or, in some cases, directly from the appropriate experimental data.

A comparison is made in Table 5 of selected methods for obtaining the spatial size distribution of systems of particles with specific shapes. Methods that deal with nonspherical particles are noted, as are those that employ nonanalytical solutions. The unusually simple methods are given in Ref 8 and 29. The procedures involved in the calculations of size distributions will be briefly discussed.

### Table 3 Equations for two-dimensional planar figures

| Area-filling grains of one phase | Planar sections of α phase in a matrix | Isolated single figure |
|---|---|---|
| $A_A = 1$ | $(A_A)_\alpha < 1$ | Area $= A$ |

$N_L = \frac{1}{2} + 4 + \frac{1}{2} = 5$     $N_L = 4$     $N_L = 1, 2, \ldots$

$P_L = 5$     $P_L = 8$     $P_L = 2, 4, \ldots$

$P_L = N_L = 1/L_2$     $P_L = 2N_L = 2(A_A)_\alpha/L_2$     $P_L = 2N_L$

**Saltykov equations**

$$L_A = \frac{\pi}{2} P_L = \frac{\pi}{2} N_L \qquad (L_A)_\alpha = \frac{\pi}{2} P_L = \pi N_L \qquad \frac{L_p}{A} = \frac{\pi P_L}{2 P_P}$$

**Tomkeieff equations**

$$L_2 = \frac{\pi A}{L_p} = \frac{\pi}{2 L_A} \qquad L_2 = \frac{\pi A_\alpha}{(L_p)_\alpha} = \frac{\pi (A_A)_\alpha}{(L_A)_\alpha} \qquad L_2 = \frac{\pi A}{L_p}$$

**Chalkley equations**

$$L_2 = \frac{lh}{2P} \qquad L_2 = \frac{lh}{P} = \frac{\pi A_\alpha}{(L_p)_\alpha} \qquad L_2 = \frac{lh}{P} = \frac{\pi A}{L_p}$$

$L_p$ = mean perimeter length per planar figure = $L_A/N_A$
$L_2$ = mean intercept length of planar figures = $L_L/N_L = A_A/N_A$
$l$ = constant length of short test lines, thrown randomly on microstructure
$h$ = number of (end) points of $l$ lines that hit in area of interest
$P$ = number of intersections with perimeters made by $l$ lines
$L_T$ = length of test line

Source: Ref 1

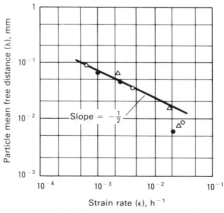

**Fig. 37** Strain rate of copper-aluminum dispersion alloys as a function of mean free distance between particles. (Ref 22)

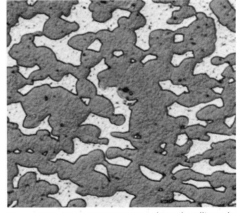

**Fig. 38** Interpenetrating two-phase beryllium-aluminum alloy. Etchant and magnification not reported

The first method is based on relative section areas, $A/A_{max}$, from the planar distribution curve of sections through a sphere. It also applies to any system of convex particles of one shape. A logarithmic scale of diameters is used with the factor $10^{-0.1} = 0.7943$.

Therefore, for sectional areas, the factor is $(10^{-0.1})^2 = 0.6310$. Table 6 gives group numbers, the corresponding diameters, and the relative section-area limits required for the class intervals.

Because the section area is specified in

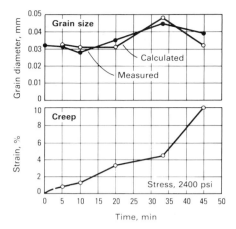

**Fig. 39** Comparison of measured and calculated grain size in creep specimens of particulate aluminum-copper alloys. (Ref 23)

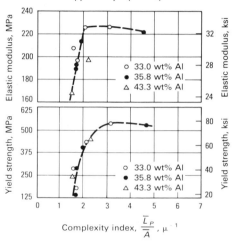

**Fig. 40** Elastic modulus and yield strength of three beryllium-aluminum alloys, as functions of complexity index. (Ref 24)

terms of the largest section area, many sections must be examined to obtain the correct volume of $A_{max}$. Next, the sections per unit area $(N_A)_i$ are counted, then grouped according to the area limits specified in Table 6. A series of graded circles serves this purpose quite well. These values are then substituted in the working equation, which has precalculated coefficients and provisions for 12 class intervals. The equation is:

$$(N_V)_j = \frac{1}{D_j}\Big[1.6461(N_A)_i - 0.4561(N_A)_{i-1}$$

$$-0.1162(N_A)_{i-2} - 0.0415(N_A)_{i-3} - 0.0173(N_A)_{i-4}$$

$$-0.0079(N_A)_{i-5} - 0.0038(N_A)_{i-6} - 0.0018(N_A)_{i-7}$$

$$-0.0010(N_A)_{i-8} - 0.0003(N_A)_{i-9} - 0.0002(N_A)_{i-10}$$

$$-0.0002(N_A)_{i-11}\Big] \qquad \text{(Eq 26)}$$

where $(N_V)_j$ represents the number of particles per unit volume in the $j$th class interval, and $j$ is an integer with any value from 1 to 12. The largest particle size corresponds to a value of $j = 1$. The $i$ values for the sections

**Table 4  Equations for three-dimensional grains and particles**

| Space-filling grains of one phase | Dispersed particles of α phase in a matrix | Isolated single particle |
|---|---|---|
| $V_V = 1$ | $(V_V)_\alpha < 1$ | Volume $= V$ |

| | | |
|---|---|---|
| $N_L = 1/2 + 4 + 1/2 = 5$ | $N_L = 4$ | $N_L = 1, 2, \ldots$ |
| $P_L = 5$ | $P_L = 8$ | $P_L = 2, 4, \ldots$ |
| $P_L = N_L = 1/L_3$ | $P_L = 2N_L = 2(V_V)_\alpha/L_3$ | $P_L = 2N_L$ |

**Saltykov equations**

| | | |
|---|---|---|
| $S_V = 2P_L = 2N_L$ | $(S_V)_\alpha = 2P_L = 4N_L$ | $\dfrac{S}{V} = \dfrac{2P_L}{P_P}$ |

**Tomkeieff equations**

| | | |
|---|---|---|
| $L_3 = 2\dfrac{V}{S} = \dfrac{2}{S_V}$ | $L_3 = \dfrac{4V_\alpha}{S_\alpha} = \dfrac{4(V_V)_\alpha}{(S_V)_\alpha}$ | $L_3 = 4\dfrac{V}{S}$ |

**Chalkley equations**

| | | |
|---|---|---|
| $L_3 = \dfrac{lh}{2P}$ | $L_3 = \dfrac{lh}{P} = \dfrac{4V_\alpha}{S_\alpha}$ | $L_3 = \dfrac{lh}{P} = \dfrac{4V}{S}$ |

$S_\alpha$ = mean surface area of α particles = $(S_V)_\alpha/N_V$
$L_3$ = mean intercept length of three-dimensional bodies = $L_L/N_L$ = $A_A/N_L$ = $V_V/N_L$
$l$ = constant length of short test lines, thrown randomly on microstructure
$h$ = number of (end) points of $l$ lines that hit in phase of interest
$P$ = number of intersections with surfaces made by $l$ lines
$L_T$ = length of test line

Source: Ref 1

**Table 5  Comparison of methods for obtaining size distribution of particles with specific shapes**

| Method | Particle shape | Characteristics of method(a) | Remarks |
|---|---|---|---|
| **Diameters** | | | |
| DeHoff | Ellipsoids | T, I | Uses axial ratios; shape factors obtained from curves |
| Scheil and Wurst | Statistical grain shape | T, S | Based on ingot iron grains |
| Schwartz-Saltykov | Sphere | T, I | ... |
| Paulus | Pentagonal dodecahedron | T, C, L, S | Method based on $d/d_{max}$ distribution curve |
| **Areas** | | | |
| Saltykov | Spheres, convex particles | WE, I, L | Method based on $A/A_{max}$ distribution curve |
| **Chords** | | | |
| Lord and Willis | Sphere | G, I | ... |
| Cahn and Fullman | Lamellar structures | G, I | Slopes taken from experimental distribution curve |
| Bockstiegel | Sphere | WE, I, L | No coefficients required in simplified version |

(a) T = table of coefficients required; G = graphical method of solution; WE = only working equation needed; C = curve comparison method available; I = independent calculation of each class interval; S = sequential calculations required; L = logarithmic scale

depend on the particular sphere size, or $j$ value, chosen for calculation. Therefore, as each value of $j$ is selected, $i$ is set equal to $j$; this determines the number of terms used inside the brackets. For example, to calculate the value of $(N_V)_5$, the first five terms in the brackets would be used: for $i = 5$, $i - 1 = 4$, $i - 2 = 3$, $i - 3 = 2$, and $i - 4 = 1$.

To show how the calculations are made, $(N_V)_4$ will be determined from the data given in Table 7. The equation obtained in this case for $j = 4 (= i)$ is:

$$(N_V)_4 = \frac{1}{D_4}\left[1.6461(N_A)_4 - 0.4561(N_A)_3\right.$$
$$\left. - 0.1162(N_A)_2 - 0.0415(N_A)_1\right] \quad \text{(Eq 27)}$$

Substituting the experimental data,

$$(N_V)_4 = \frac{1}{0.0316}\left[1.65(230) - 0.456(253)\right.$$
$$\left. - 0.116(161) - 0.0415(104)\right]$$
$$= 7630 \text{ mm}^{-3} \quad \text{(Eq 28)}$$

is obtained. This type of calculation would be performed for all particle sizes, and the total would give $N_V$, the total number of particles per unit volume. The results from the calcula-

**Table 6   Limits for grouped planar sections from spheres**

| Group | Relative section diameter, $d/d_{max}$ | Relative section area, $A/A_{max}$ |
|---|---|---|
| 1 | 1.0000 | 1.0000-0.6310 |
| 2 | 0.7943 | 0.6310-0.3981 |
| 3 | 0.6310 | 0.3981-0.2512 |
| 4 | 0.5012 | 0.2512-0.1585 |
| 5 | 0.3981 | 0.1585-0.1000 |
| 6 | 0.3162 | 0.1000-0.0631 |
| 7 | 0.2512 | 0.0631-0.0398 |
| 8 | 0.1995 | 0.0398-0.0251 |
| 9 | 0.1581 | 0.0251-0.0158 |
| 10 | 0.1259 | 0.0158-0.0100 |
| 11 | 0.1000 | 0.0100-0.0063 |
| 12 | 0.0794 | 0.0063-0.0040 |

**Table 7   Measured distribution of ferrite grain section sizes**

| Class interval | Range of section diameters, $d_i$ mm | Relative section area $A/A_{max}$ | Sections per mm², $(N_A)_i$ |
|---|---|---|---|
| 1 | 0.0631-0.0501 | 1.0000-0.6310 | 104 |
| 2 | 0.0501-0.0398 | 0.6310-0.3981 | 161 |
| 3 | 0.0398-0.0316 | 0.3981-0.2512 | 253 |
| 4 | 0.0316-0.0251 | 0.2512-0.1585 | 230 |
| 5 | 0.0251-0.0199 | 0.1585-0.1000 | 138 |
| 6 | 0.0199-0.0158 | 0.1000-0.0631 | 69 |
| $N_A$, per mm² | | | 955 |

**Table 8   Calculated distribution of ferrite grain sizes**

| Class interval | Diameter of particles, $D_j$, mm | No. of grains per mm³, $(N_V)_j$ |
|---|---|---|
| 1 | 0.0631 | 2 713 |
| 2 | 0.0501 | 4 341 |
| 3 | 0.0398 | 8 313 |
| 4 | 0.0316 | 7 630 |
| 5 | 0.0251 | 3 359 |
| 6 | 0.0199 | 491 |
| $N_V$, per mm³ | | 26 847 |

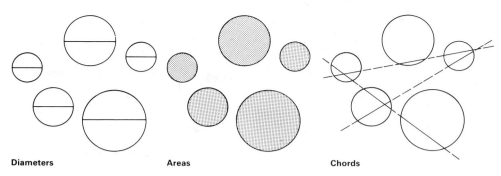

**Fig. 41**  Schematic presentation of three main types of measurements (diameters, areas, and chords) made on planar sections. (Ref 1)

Diameters        Areas        Chords

tions are summarized in Table 8. This method is simple and useful. Of further interest is the possibility of analyzing systems of convex particles of more complex shape.

It may be useful to express the size distribution in terms of the three numerical parameters $\overline{D}$, $\sigma(D)$, and $N_V$, instead of the size-distribution curve itself. The mean diameter is expressed by:

$$\overline{D} = \frac{1}{N_V}\sum (N_V)_j D_j \quad \text{(Eq 29)}$$

the standard deviation by:

$$\sigma(D) = \left[\overline{D_j^2} - \overline{D}^2\right]^{1/2} \quad \text{(Eq 30)}$$

and the total number of particles per unit volume by:

$$N_V = \sum_{i}^{j} (N_V)_j \quad \text{(Eq 31)}$$

Therefore, from the data in Table 8, $\overline{D} = 0.0393$ mm, $\sigma(D) = 0.012$ mm, and $N_V = 27\,000$ mm⁻³. An alternative is to plot the cumulative percentages of $(N_V)_j$ versus particle diameter on log probability graph paper. If the size distribution conforms to the log normal distribution, as most particle and grain-size distributions do, a straight line will result. Then the values of $\overline{D}$ and $\sigma(D)$ can be read from the curve—$\overline{D}$ at a cumulative frequency of 50, and $\sigma(D)$ between 84.13 and 50 or between 50 and 15.87.

Another method for obtaining a particle-size distribution involves measuring the intercept chord-length distribution (Ref 1). Considering ease of data gathering, the chord

methods are quite promising, especially since the advent of electronic scanning devices. An improved derivation of the chord-intercept relationship for spheres is given in Ref 29. The number of chords per unit length, $(n_L)_i$, $(n_L)_{i+1}$, and so on, are obtained experimentally and grouped into suitable class intervals, $l_{i-1}$ to $l_i$, $l_i$ to $l_{i+1}$, and so on, respectively. To obtain $(N_V)_{i+1/2}$, which represents the number of particles per unit volume with diameters between $l_{i-1/2}$ and $l_{i+1/2}$, the general equation is:

$$(N_V)_{i+1/2} = \frac{4}{\pi}\left[\frac{(n_L)_i}{l_i^2 - l_{i-1}^2} - \frac{(n_L)_{i+1}}{l_{i+1}^2 - l_i^2}\right] \quad \text{(Eq 32)}$$

which is valid for any class-interval division. Note that $N_V$ can be obtained independently for any size group and that tables of coefficients are not required.

A further simplification of Eq 32 is possible by defining logarithmic class intervals such that $l_{i+1} = z l_i$. Putting $z = \sqrt{2}$ gives $l_{i+1}^2 = 2l_i^2$, $l_i^2 = 2l_{i-1}^2$, and so on, which, when inserted into Eq 32 gives:

$$(N_V)_{i+1/2} = C\frac{2(n_L)_i - (n_L)_{i+1}}{(2)^i} \quad \text{(Eq 33)}$$

where $C = 4/\pi\, l_0^2$ and is a constant independent of $i$, and $l_0$ is the upper limit of the lowest class interval. If relative values, $(N_V)_{i+1}/\Sigma(N_V)_{i+1/2}$, are desired rather than absolute numbers, $(N_V)_{i+1/2}$, constant $C$ cancels out. Therefore, the relative size distribution is obtained from the experimental data.

As an example of the application of Eq 32,

**Table 9   Properties of a sphere, truncated octahedron, and convex particles**

| Property | Sphere, $D = 2r$ | Truncated octahedron, edge length = $a$ | General equations for convex particles |
|---|---|---|---|
| $V$ | $4\pi r^3/3$ | $11.314a^3$ | $V = A'L_3 = AH'$ |
| $S$ | $4\pi r^2$ | $26.785a^2$ | $S = 4A' = 4V/L_3$ |
| $A'$ | $\pi r^2$ | $6.696a^2$ | $A' = S/4 = V/L_3$ |
| $H'$ | $2r$ | $3.0a$ | $H' = V/A = A'L_3/A$ |
| $A$ | $2\pi r^2/3$ | $3.77a^2$ | $A = V/H' = A'L_3/H'$ |
| $L_3$ | $4r/3$ | $1.69a$ | $L_3 = 4V/S = AN_A/N_L$ |
| $r, a, \rho(a)$ | $r = 2N_L/\pi N_A$ | $a = 0.45N_L/N_A$ | $\rho = H'/2 = N_A A'/2N_L = A'/2L_2'$ |
| $N_V$ | $\pi N_A^2/4N_L$ | $0.744N_A^2/N_L$ | $N_V = N_A/H' = N_L/A'$ |

General equation: $V_V = N_V V = N_A A = N_L L_3$

(a) $\rho$ = half of mean tangent diameter
Source: Ref 1

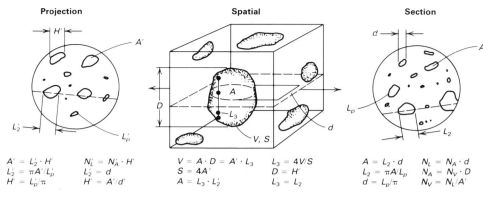

| Projection | Spatial | Section |
|---|---|---|
| $A' = L_2' \cdot H'$    $N_L' = N_A' \cdot H'$ | $V = A \cdot D = A' \cdot L_3$    $L_3 = 4V/S$ | $A = L_2 \cdot d$    $N_L = N_A \cdot d$ |
| $L_2' = \pi A'/L_p'$    $L_2' = d$ | $S = 4A'$    $D = H'$ | $L_2 = \pi A/L_p$    $N_A = N_V \cdot D$ |
| $H' = L_p'/\pi$    $H' = A'/d'$ | $A = L_3 \cdot L_2'$    $L_3 = L_2$ | $d = L_p/\pi$    $N_V = N_L/A'$ |

**Fig. 42** Relationships among convex particles in space, their sections, and their projections (projected quantities are indicated by primes)

consider the case for $i = 4$ given the following data:

| Group | Range of chord lengths, mm | Chords per mm $(N_L)_i$ | Diameters of particles, mm |
|---|---|---|---|
| 4 | 0.0075-0.0100 | 19 | 0.0100 |
| 5 | 0.0100-0.0125 | 13 | 0.0125 |

Substitution in Eq 32 gives:

$$(N_V)_{i+1/2} = \frac{4}{\pi}\left[\frac{19}{(10^2 - 7.5^2)10^{-6}}\right.$$

$$\left. - \frac{13}{(12.5^2 - 10^2)10^{-6}}\right]$$

$$= \frac{4}{\pi}\left[\left(\frac{19}{43.75} - \frac{13}{56.25}\right)10^6\right]$$

$$= 259\,000 \text{ mm}^{-3}$$

Calculation at $i = 4$ according to Eq 33 results in:

$$(N_V)_{i+1/2} = C\left[\frac{(2 \times 19) - 13}{(2)^4}\right] = C\left(\frac{25}{16}\right)$$

$$= C(1.56)$$

This result would be divided by $\Sigma(N_V)_{i+1/2}$ to obtain the relative particle frequency at $i = 4$. Occasionally, negative values are obtained for the smallest particles. Reasons for this are discussed in Ref 1. A practical solution is to equate the negative values to zero.

## Projected Images

In general, microscopists encounter two types of projected images. In the first, the image results from a transmitted beam through the specimen, representing the features located within the three-dimensional space (such as by thin-foil transmission electron microscopy). In the second, the projected image is generated by a reflected beam from the external surface of the specimen (such as by scanning electron microscopy).

Only the most rudimentary quantitative calculations can be made on images projected by the reflection techniques (Ref 30). In rough surfaces, the intensity levels depend on topography, and some features may be masked by others. Three-dimensional characterization is based on the photogrammetric analysis of stereopairs, for which automatic image-analyzing techniques are not yet available (Ref 31).

Quantitative statistical treatment of transmitted-beam images, however, has matured to a much greater extent. These analyses (Ref 32, 33) are too lengthy and complex to be treated here, but are described in the literature (see Ref 1).

One final topic will be included, because of its importance to the analysis of particulate systems. Figure 42 provides interrelated general equations of convex particles that express the important spatial parameters in terms of measurements made on the plane of polish and the projection plane. Application of the equations to specific particles is summarized in Table 9 for the sphere, for the truncated octahedron (or tetrakaidecahedron), and for convex particles in general. Tabulations of the type presented in Table 9 permit the microscopist to approximate microstructures with particles of known shape when other techniques are not feasible.

## REFERENCES

1. E.E. Underwood, *Quantitative Stereology*, Addison-Wesley, 1970
2. J.E. Hilliard and J.W. Cahn, *Trans. Met. Soc. AIME*, Vol 221, 1961, p 344
3. J.E. Hilliard, in *Quantitative Microscopy*, R.T. DeHoff and F.N. Rhines, Ed., McGraw-Hill, 1968, p 72
4. "Standard Methods for Estimating the Average Grain Size of Metals," E 112, *Annual Book of ASTM Standards*, Vol 03.03, ASTM, Philadelphia, 1984, p 120
5. W.T. Pell-Walpole, *J. Inst. Metals*, Vol 69, 1943, p 131
6. H.W. Chalkley, J. Cornfield, and H. Park, *Science*, Vol 110, Sept. 23, 1949, p 295
7. E.R. Weibel, *Lab. Invest.*, Vol 12 (No. 2), 1963, p 131
8. S.A. Saltykov, in *Stereology*, H. Elias, Ed., Springer-Verlag, 1967
9. S.A. Saltykov, *Stereometric Metallography*, 3rd ed., Metallurgizdat, Moscow, 1970 (in Russian)
10. M.G. Kendall and P.A.P. Moran, *Geometrical Probability*, No. 10, Griffin's Statistical Monographs and Courses, C. Griffin and Co., Ltd., London, 1963
11. E.R. Weibel, *Morphometry of the Human Lung*, Springer-Verlag, 1963
12. B.I. Edelson and W.M. Baldwin, Jr., *Trans. ASM*, Vol 55, 1962, p 238
13. L.H. Beck and C.S. Smith, *Trans. AIME, Inst. Metals Div.*, Vol 194, 1952, p 1079
14. *Deformation Twinning*, R.E. Reed-Hill et al., Ed., Gordon and Breach, 1964
15. J.B. Newkirk and J.H. Wernick, Ed., *Direct Observations of Imperfections in Crystals*, Interscience, 1962
16. S. O'Hara, *J. Appl. Phys.*, Vol 35, 1964, p 409
17. A.S. Yue, *Trans. Met. Soc. AIME*, Vol 224, 1962, p 1010
18. J. Nutting and R.G. Baker, *The Microstructure of Metals*, Monograph and Report Series No. 30, Institute of Metals, London, 1965, p 53
19. R.M. Fulrath and J.A. Pask, Ed., *Ceramic Microstructures*, John Wiley & Sons, 1968, p 48
20. J.E. Hilliard, *Met. Prog.*, Vol 85, May 1964, p 99
21. A.M. Turkalo and J.R. Low, Jr., *Trans. Met. Soc. AIME*, Vol 212, 1958, p 757
22. R.W. Guard in *Strengthening Mechanisms in Solids*, American Society for Metals, 1962, p 274
23. E.E. Underwood and G.K. Manning, *Mem. Sci. Rev. Met.*, Vol 60 (No. 9), 1963, p 648
24. U.S. Patent No. 3,337,334, Aug 22, 1967
25. R.T. DeHoff, *Trans. Met. Soc. AIME*, Vol 224, 1962, p 474
26. M. Paulus, *Metaux (Corrosion-Ind.)*, Vol 37 (No. 448), Dec 1962, p 447; Vol 38 (No. 449), Jan 1963, p 14; Parts I and II
27. E. Scheil and H. Wurst, *Z. Metallk.*, Vol 28 (No. 11), 1936, p 340
28. J.W. Cahn and R.L. Fullman, *Trans. AIME, Inst. Metals Div.*, Vol 206, 1956, p 610
29. G. Bockstiegel, *Z. Metallk.*, Vol 57, 1966, p 647
30. J.E. Hilliard, *J. Microsc.*, Vol 95 (Part 1), Feb 1972, p 45-58
31. T.O. Johari, *Res. Develop.*, Vol 22 (No. 7), 1971, p 12
32. E.E. Underwood, The Stereology of Projected Images, *J. Microsc.*, Vol 95 (Part 1), Feb 1972, p 25-44
33. E.E. Underwood, The Mathematical Foundations of Quantitative Stereology, in *Stereology and Quantitative Metallography*, STP 504, ASTM, Philadelphia, 1972, p 3-38

# Color Metallography

By Robert J. Gray
Senior Program Manager of Metallography
American Society for Metals
Metallographic Consultant
Unitron, Inc.

## Introduction

COLOR METALLOGRAPHY as practiced 40 to 50 years ago was used primarily to communicate information on inclusions, although some chemical etching was performed to introduce color to the microstructure (Ref 1). The response of the inclusion to brightfield and polarized light illumination provided information useful in making identifications. Some of the early work of Henry Clifton Sorby in the 1800s incorporated the petrographic approach commonly in use in his day, which involved preparing the specimen to a thin section for transmitted-light examination. This well-recognized method for petrographic studies is not applicable to metals due to their opacity, but is used today for the study of polymers and minerals (Ref 2) using color.

During the past 50 years, color metallography has progressed slowly, primarily because of inferior methods of illuminating the specimen, photographic films that required commercial processing, reluctance of sponsoring companies to provide financial support, lack of interest among some metallographers to pioneer, and the high cost of publishing reports with color photos. Removal of most of these obstacles during the past 10 to 15 years has resulted in significant advances in recording an image in color instead of conventional black-and-white imaging. The human eye can distinguish an incredible number of colors, but nuances of gray are scarcely detectable. The microstructure and the information it contains are more easily recognized, explained, and understood through the use of color. The size and shape of grains presented in various shades of gray or merely outlined at grain boundaries are not nearly so meaningful or remembered so well as when color variations of the whole grains can be viewed. The ease in pointing out specific inclusions or phases in the microstructure that carry distinctive indentifying colors cannot be compared with the same presentation that is limited to varying shades of gray in a black-and-white photomicrograph.

## Methods for Color Metallography

Color metallography can be divided into three categories (Fig. 1): methods for depositing interference films, optical methods, and the arbitrary assignment of color to various gray scales by electronic imaging. Each of the techniques listed under these methodologies in Fig. 1 will be discussed. Following these discussions, an atlas of color micrographs is provided that will illustrate the advantages, applications, and potential of color metallographic techniques. More detailed information is available in the references.

### Interference Film Deposition

In interference film deposition, color formation is caused by interference phenomena (Ref 3). Rays of light striking a metal surface

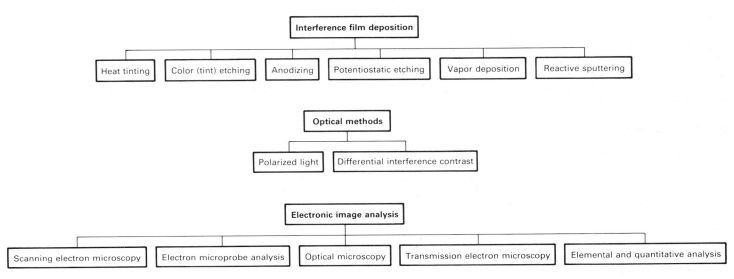

**Fig. 1** Methods for color metallography

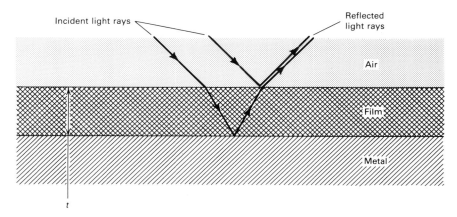

**Fig. 2** Schematic representation of the air-film-metal type of interference effect. See text for discussion.

coated with a film will be reflected from the surface of the film and the metal surface (Fig. 2). As a result, an interference effect is obtained that depends on the wavelength of the light source in air ($\lambda$), thickness of the film ($t$), and refractive index of the film ($n$). Interference may be expected whenever the effective paths traveled by light reflected at the film and metal surfaces differ by an odd number of $\lambda/2$ (half wavelength). The difference in the effective paths of the reflective light is proportional to twice the film thickness. Therefore, if the phase changes due to the slower speed of light in the film are disregarded, interference would occur at film thicknesses that differ by an odd number of $\lambda/4$ (quarter wavelength). When the effect of the slower speed of light in the film is included, interference will occur at odd values of $\lambda/(4n)$.

If incident white light is considered on an air-film-metal system having a film of such thickness that the green portion of the light reflected from the metal surface is exactly out of phase with the light reflected from the surface, interference of the green light will occur, and the light will be magenta, which is the complement to green. The magenta will appear several times: at thicknesses of $\lambda_G/(4n)$, $3\lambda_G/(4n)$, $5\lambda_G/(4n)$, . . . , where $\lambda_G$ is the wavelength of green light in air.

The color of the interference film is related to its thickness. For example, as long as a film, viewed under white light, thickening progressively on a metallic surface is very thin, interference will occur in the ultraviolet region ($\simeq$ 350 nm, or 3500 Å), and no color will be observed. When the film is thickened progressively so that the interference will reach the blue-violet region ($\simeq$ 450 nm, or 4500 Å), a film thickness will be reached where the blue light reflected from the surface will be out of phase, and the complementary yellow will be visible. Upon further thickening of the film, the green waves ($\simeq$ 500 nm, or 5000 Å) will suffer interference, and the complementary magenta will be apparent. Interference in the yellow region ($\simeq$ 600 nm, or 6000 Å) will provide the complementary blue.

Finally, the end of the first band of colors (Band I) is reached, and the interference passes out of the visible spectrum into the infrared region. This occurs before the film thicknesses comprising Band II, and after it Band III, of interference are reached. The colors in Band I are called first-order colors. The repetition of the color sequence as second-order yellow, magenta, blue, and so on, in Band II will be the same, but the interval between them will differ (see Table 1). Not all colors will appear in every band. Additional information on the use and interpretation of interference films can be found in the section "Potentiostatic Etching" in this article.

As shown in Fig. 1, several methods exist for depositing an interference film on a metallographic specimen, including heat tinting (thermal oxidation), color (tint) etching, anodizing, potentiostatic etching, vapor deposition, and reactive sputtering.

**Heat tinting** is performed by exposing a specimen to elevated temperatures in an oxidizing environment to form an epitaxially deposited film (oxide) on the polished surface. The thickness of the film reflects differences in chemical composition and crystallographic orientation. The observed interference colors allow the distinction of different phases and grains. Different metals require different oxidation durations and temperatures. High temperatures may induce phase transformations on the surface, an effect that sometimes limits application of this technique.

Some specimens may oxidize after exposure to ambient atmospheres. This was demonstrated during research on uranium-zirco-

nium-alloys (Ref 4). A U-14Zr (at.%) alloy was oxidized 40 min at 900 °C (1650 °F). Several conventional etching techniques were used without success to reveal the characteristics of the oxide/metallic interface. However, after exposing the specimen to ambient atmosphere for 48 h, a thin zirconium-rich layer with slender fingerlike penetrations into the bulk oxide was visible at 2000X.

Heat tinting can also be performed using a more sophisticated procedure in which temperature and oxidation are closely monitored in an enclosed system. This procedure has been used in studies of surface reactions of single crystals (Ref 5). An example is shown in Fig. 3. These micrographs depict approximately 10-mm (0.4-in.) diam single-crystal spheres of four materials with different crystallographic formations that vividly exemplify the reactions of various crystal planes during oxidation.

Heat tinting can also be preceded by chemical etching to reveal grain and phase boundaries. This has proved successful with uranium alloys, uranium carbides (Ref 6, 7), zirconium and its alloys, high-speed tool steels, and austenitic stainless steel weldments. Examples of etched and heat-tinted specimens are shown in Fig. 31, 32, 36, 37, and 69. Examples of attack-polished and heat-tinted specimens as viewed under polarized light and differential interference contrast are shown in Fig. 33 to 35 and 70.

**Color Etching.** During the last 15 to 20 years, immersion color etchants that produce color contrast have progressed considerably. These developments are associated with Klemm and Beraha, whose work is described in Ref 8 and 9. The colors produced by color (tint) etchants are visible under bright-field illumination, and in many cases further enhancement is attained using polarized light.

One of the advantages of color etching is revealing microstructural and chemical changes after exposure to elevated temperatures. For example, many ferritic and austenitic stainless steels can form $\sigma$ phase after prolonged exposure to temperatures from 480 to 900 °C (900 to 1650 °F). Sigma phase was first detected in iron-chromium-nickel alloys and reported in 1927 (Ref 10). A hard, brittle, nonmagnetic, intermediate phase, $\sigma$ has a tetragonal crystal structure with 30 atoms per unit cell (space group $P4_2/mnm$) and occurs in many binary and ternary alloys of transition elements (Ref 11). The presence of $\delta$-ferrite in the microstructure of austenitic stain-

**Table 1  Colors obtained at various thicknesses of interference films of silver iodide on silver**

| | Interference band No. | | | | | |
| | I | | II | | III | |
| Film color | nm | Å | nm | Å | nm | Å |
| --- | --- | --- | --- | --- | --- | --- |
| Yellow | 20 | 200 | 115 | 1150 | 245 | 2450 |
| Reddish | 43 | 430 | 165 | 1650 | 290 | 2900 |
| Blue | 55 | 550 | 195 | 1950 | . . . | . . . |
| Green | . . . | . . . | 225 | 2250 | 340 | 3400 |

Source: Ref 3

less steel accelerates the formation of σ phase (Ref 12-14).

After creep rupture testing of an E308 stainless steel weld metal at 593 °C (1099 °F) for 7562.6 h and a stress of 165 MPa (24 ksi) with a total elongation of 3.4%, a color etchant was selected to show the microstructural characteristics of the transformation of δ-ferrite to σ phase. The metallographic specimen was selected from the rupture area to correlate the fracture with the microstructure and was prepared using vibratory polishing with diamond abrasive and a nylon cloth (Ref 15). This procedure supplied sharp edge retention of the rupture profile. The specimen was etched by immersion using 10 g potassium ferricyanide ($K_3Fe(CN)_6$), 10 g potassium hydroxide (KOH), and 100 mL $H_2O$ at 95 °C (200 °F).

The microstructure is shown in Fig. 4 at 2000×. Some untransformed δ-ferrite outlined with carbides and some transformed σ phase are visible. The rupture profile shows some σ phase in the outline. The micrograph reveals that the weakest part of the microstructure is the interface between the austenitic matrix and the σ phase, as evidenced by a separation or crack that is apparent. Detailed information on the principles and application of color etching, including the various reagents used, can be found in the section "Color Etching" in this article.

**Anodizing** can produce interference films of oxides. The thickness of the film, which determines the color, depends on the anodizing voltage, the anodizing solution, and the chemical composition or structure of the constituents. Anodizing can be carried out by using a standard electropolishing device. Additional information on the procedures and applications of anodizing can be found in the section "Anodizing" in this article.

**Potentiostatic Etching.** Attempts to make etching reliable and reproducible have resulted in the development of the constant potential potentiostatic etching technique. In this process, the specimen is placed in an electrolytic cell and used as an anode. Its potential is measured against the electrolyte by a reference electrode. During etching, a defined solution pressure (potential of solution) is maintained. This method is based on the different rate of material removal from different phases and on interference film deposition. A comparison of the current density vs. potential curves for the different phases identifies the range of potential corresponding to a specific phase. Detailed information on the electrochemical principles, the conditions for color response, specific etchants, and procedures for potentiostatic etching can be found in the section "Potentiostatic Etching" in this article.

**Vapor Deposition.** In 1960, Pepperhoff demonstrated that interference films that do not chemically or morphologically alter the specimen surface can be produced by vapor deposition (Ref 16). These layers are highly

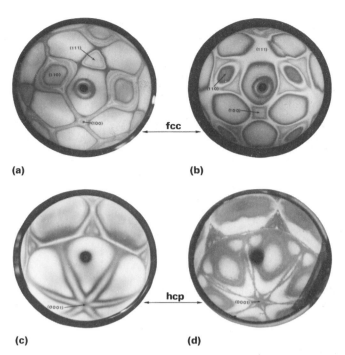

**Fig. 3** Oxidized single-crystal spheres. (a) Copper oxidized at 250 °C (480 °F) for 30 min in $O_2$. (b) Cu-0.1Al oxidized at 250 °C (480 °F) for 30 min in $O_2$. (c) Zirconium oxidized at 360 °C (680 °F) for 15 min in air. (d) Hafnium oxidized at 500 °C (930 °F) for 20 h in steam

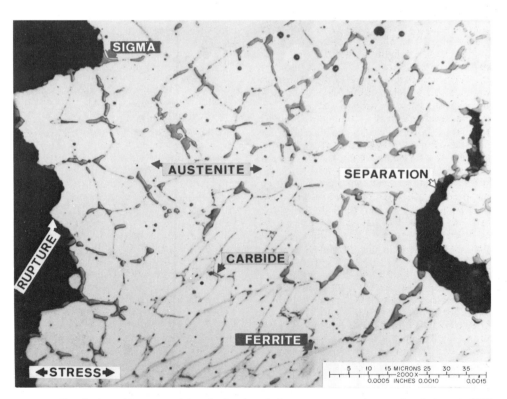

**Fig. 4** Use of color etching to reveal the role of σ phase in the creep rupture and separation of phases in E308 stainless steel weld metal. The brittle σ phase that transformed from the ferrite phase served as a fracture and separation route. Carbide precipitation seen at the interface of ferrite islands, which did not transform, and the austenite matrix. 10 g $K_3Fe(CN)_6$, 10 g KOH, and 100 mL $H_2O$ at 95 °C (200 °F)

refractive and enhance contrast by multiple reflections and interference at the film/metal and film/air interfaces. The deposited film increases differences in reflectivity between the phases and enhances differences in their color. Detailed information on the materials deposited and the principles and applications of this technique can be found in the section

"Interference Films by Vacuum Deposition" in this article.

**Reactive sputtering** is similar to the vapor-deposition technique developed by Pepperhoff. In a contrasting chamber, which is attached directly to the microscope, interference layers are produced on the specimen surface by reactive sputtering. The partly evacuated chamber is filled with oxygen or a mixture of various gases. The anode is the specimen; the cathode is of different metals—iron, for example. The polished, but unetched surface is brought in contrasting position in front of a gas-discharge electron gun.

During the gas discharge, a film forms on the specimen, which acts similarly to the deposited film of the vapor-deposition method. The film deposited has been found to be iron oxide when an iron cathode is used in an oxygen-filled chamber; a lead cathode in oxygen yields lead oxide. Therefore, interference films are formed using this method when the reactive sputtering mechanism is used when reactive cathode materials are used in a reactive-gas atmosphere. Detailed information on the principles, advantages, and applications of this method can be found in the section "Interference Films by Reactive Sputtering" in this article.

## Optical Methods for Color Metallography

Optical color metallographic techniques include polarized light and differential interference contrast.

**Polarized light** as used in metallography is based on the different colors produced by optical anisotropy and surface topography. Anisotropic metals have a noncubic crystal structure and react to polarized light. Some anisotropic metals are beryllium, magnesium, tin, titanium, uranium, zinc, and zirconium. Examination of these metals under polarized light requires well-polished, scratch-free surfaces. Polishing procedures for these materials can be found in the Section "Metallographic Techniques and Microstructures: Specific Metals and Alloys" in this Volume.

Anisotropic metals have different optical characteristics in different crystallographic directions. Therefore, the intensity of light reflected from a certain grain will depend on grain orientation, and a contrast will be obtained. Polarized light can be used to reveal grain structure, to detect preferred orientation in polycrystalline materials, to identify phases in multiphase structures, and to detect internal strains and plastic deformation.

Generally, cubic metals, which are optically isotropic, do not respond in the as-polished condition to cross-polarized light. However, several chemical etchants activate the surfaces of many isotropic metals to polarized light (Ref 17). As illustrated in the atlas of color micrographs at the end of this article, polarized light often enhances the color contrast of surface layers produced by heat tinting (Fig. 35 and 37) or color etching (Fig. 38, 43, and 47), and is also used in conjunction with attack-polishing procedures (Fig. 65).

Sensitive tint, another important application of polarized light, is used to study materials that are weakly birefringent, that is, slightly responsive to polarized light. This is achieved by placing a special retardation plate (crystal quartz) into the optical path with the polarizer and analyzer (Fig. 5). Studies of this kind are accomplished by observing any change in the magenta tint as the specimen is rotated. Sensitive tint has been used to study anodized aluminum specimens, to detect pores in commercial graphite, and to determine grain orientation. Small structural differences not apparent in polarized light may be enhanced using sensitive tint. Additional information on polarized light and phase contrast is provided in the section "Potentiostatic Etching" in this article and the article "Optical Microscopy" in this Volume.

**Differential interference contrast** is another method for optically revealing microstructures in color. With this method, topographical differences in the specimen result in differences in the light reflected from the microtopographical features on the surface. For producing interference contrast, a Wollaston prism splits the reflected rays into partial images, which are left to interfere in a polarizer.

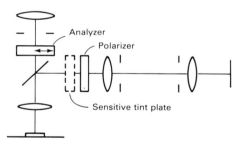

**Fig. 5** Placement of the crystal quartz sensitive tint plate

Differences in surface height are transformed into differences in color. Detailed information on the principles, advantages, and applications of this method can be found in the section "Differential Interference Contrast" in this article.

## Electronic Image Analysis

An electronic image-analysis system can digitize an imaging signal or spatially map an analytical signal into 256 discrete gray levels and present these data as a digital image (typically 512 × 400 pixels, or picture elements). Discrete colors are used to represent the various ranges of gray levels, or signal intensity, within the image.

The ability to "paint" any one of the 256 gray levels of a particular color enhances contrast. Two adjacent gray levels that differ 1/256th of the total range can be displayed as black and white or red and blue. In applications where contrast differences are critical, such as voltage contrast, or when true gray level contrast is minimal, the contrast enhancement provided by the pseudocolor is a useful processing technique.

The image signal that is digitized has many possible sources. From a scanning electron microscope, a signal viewed on the cathode ray tube (CRT) can be routed to the system and digitized. This allows collection of the secondary electron image, backscattered electron image, voltage-contrast images, and electron-beam-induced current images. For light microscopes with a video camera, external video input enables access to the digital imaging capabilities of the image-analysis system. With this interface to a video camera, previously recorded micrographs may be digitized and macroimaging with the appropriate lens on the camera may be performed. Figure 6 illustrates external video input integration in an image-analysis system.

Once specific colors have been assigned to the different gray levels, the CRT can be photographed in color. If an optional multiple-

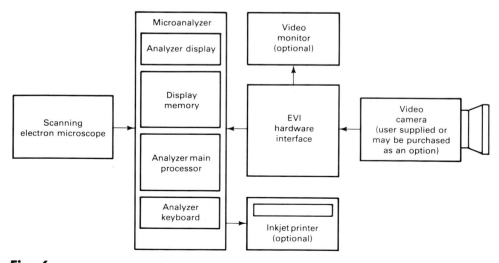

**Fig. 6** Image-analysis system connected to a scanning electron microscope

pen (inkjet) printer is available, a printout of the black-and-white or multicolor display on the CRT can also be made (Fig. 7). More detailed information on the applications and advantages of electronic imaging is available later in the section "Electronic Image Analysis" in this article.

## Color Photography (Ref 17)

Negative color film (print film) and positive transparency (reversal) color film are the two types available. Color negative films produce a negative with complementary colors. Printing is required to obtain the true colors, which are sometimes not achieved, because the film laboratory technician may not be familiar with the subject matter. Processing and

printing one's own work yields optimum results. With slide films, or reversal color films, the colors are substantially the same as the image, lessening the chances of defective printing.

Selecting color film requires attention to the type of light source used, because films are balanced for artificial light or daylight (light sources are described in the article "Optical Microscopy" in this Volume). The xenon light source, particularly valuable in color photomicroscopy, provides a useful daylight spectrum. Other light sources necessitate using color-balancing filters to match the color temperature of the light to that of the film. Figure 8 is a copy of a National Bureau of Standards filter nomograph that aids in the selection of the best filter for a given

light source and color photographic emulsion. The filters suggested may not be exact for accurate color reproduction, but will always be close enough to enable intelligent changes for achieving accuracy. A comparison of several color films has shown that differences in contrast and color rendition occur (Ref 18). Additional recommendations for color film selection can be found in the section "Color Etching" in this article.

# Color Etching*

By George F. Vander Voort
Supervisor
Applied Physics Research & Development
Carpenter Technology Corporation

COLOR ETCHING, also commonly referred to as tint etching, has been used to color many metals and alloys, such as cast irons, steels, stainless steels, nickel-base alloys, copper-base alloys, molydenum, tungsten, lead, tin, and zinc. Success in color etching aluminum and titanium alloys has been limited. A selected list of color etchants is given in Table 2; additional information can be obtained in Ref 3 and 17.

## Principles of Color Etching

Satisfactory color, or tint, etchants are balanced chemically to produce a stable film on the specimen surface. This is contrary to ordinary chemical etchants, in which the corrosion products produced during etching are redissolved into the etchant. Color etchants have been classified as anodic, cathodic, or complex systems, depending on the nature of the film precipitation (Ref 3).

Chemical etching is a controlled corrosion process based on electrolytic action between surface areas of different potentials (see the article "Etching" in this Volume). For pure metals and single-phase alloys, a potential difference exists between grain boundaries and grain interiors, grains with different orientations, between impurity phases and the matrix, or at concentration gradients in single-phase alloys. For multiphase alloys, a potential also exists between phases. These potential differences alter the rate of attack, revealing the microstructure when chemical etchants are used.

For a two-phase alloy, the potential of one phase is greater than that of the other. During etching, the more electropositive (anodic) phase is attacked; the more electronegative (cathodic) phase is not attacked appreciably. The magnitude of the potential difference between two phases is greater than the potential

**Fig. 7** Photograph of an inkjet printout showing digital imaging of the secondary electron signal from a scanning electron microscope during examination of a cerium-bearing iron-magnesium-silicon alloy. Actual printout size is 215 by 280 mm (8½ by 11 in.). Full-color printouts can also be made using inkjet printers. See Fig. 80 to 83 for color micrographs of the same specimen.

*Adapted from G.F. Vander Voort, Tint Etching, *Metal Progress*, Vol 127 (No. 4), March 1985, p 31-41

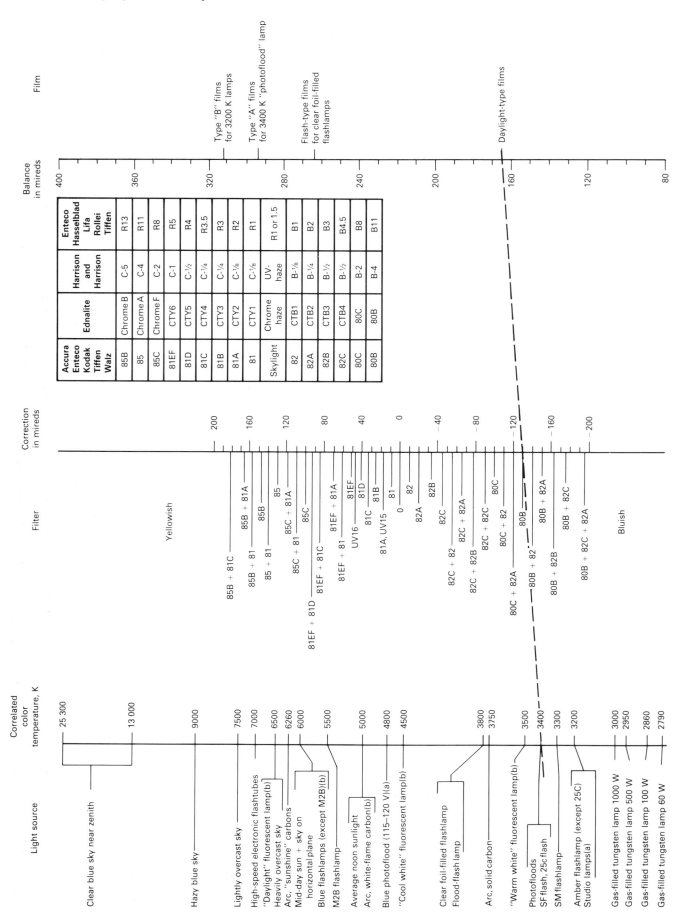

**Fig. 8** Color filter nomograph to aid photographers in determining which color-correcting filters are required to match the film with the light source. The dashed line presents an example. If daylight film is used in the camera with photoflood lamps (3400 K), the line between the film and light source shows that an 80B color-correction filter is required. (a) The correlated color temperature of these lamps increases approximately 11 K for each voltage increase in applied potential of approximately 115 V. As lamps are used, the correlated color temperature (at a given voltage) decreases, often from 50 K above to 50 K below the rated value during the life of the lamp. (b) Color temperature is only an approximate specification of these light sources. (National Bureau of Standards)

## Table 2  Selected color etchants(a)

| Composition(b) | Comments |
|---|---|
| 200 g CrO$_3$, 20 g Na$_2$SO$_4$ (sodium sulfate), 7 mL HCl, 1000 mL H$_2$O | Beraha's tint etch for aluminum alloys; pre-etch with 10% aqueous NaOH followed by 50% aqueous HNO$_3$; rinse in water, dip immediately into tint etch for 1-5 s; rinse and dry; colors matrix grains, outlines second phase particles. |
| 1 g (NH$_4$)$_6$Mo$_7$O$_{24}$ (ammonium molybdate), 6 g NH$_4$Cl (ammonium chloride), 200 mL H$_2$O | Tint etch of Lienard and Pacque for aluminum alloys; colors CuAl$_2$ violet; immerse approximately 2 min. |
| (1) Stock solution: 1:2, 1:1, or 1:0.5 HCl-H$_2$O (2) 100 mL stock solution plus 0.6-1.0 g K$_2$S$_2$O$_5$ (3) Optional additions: 1-3 g FeCl$_3$, 1 g CuCl$_2$ (cupric chloride), or 2-10 g NH$_4$HF$_2$ | Beraha's tint etch for iron-, nickel-, or cobalt-base heat-resistant alloys; colors the matrix—carbides and nitrides are unaffected; immerse specimen in solution at room temperature for 60-150 s; move specimen during etching; start with lowest HCl concentration; if coloration does not result, increase HCl or etch longer. |
| 50 mL saturated Na$_2$S$_2$O$_3$(c), 1 g K$_2$S$_2$O$_5$ | Klemm's I tint etch; good for many alloys; immerse 3 min or more for β-brass, α-β brass, and bronzes; use 10-60 min for α-brass; use 40-100 s for coloring ferrite in steels; reveals phosphorus segregation and overheating; longer time produces line etching of ferrite; etch 30 s for zinc alloys. |
| 50 mL Na$_2$S$_2$O$_3$, 5 g K$_2$S$_2$O$_5$ | Klemm's II tint etch; immerse 6 min or more for α-brass; immerse 30-90 s for steels; reveals phosphorus segregation; good for austenitic manganese alloys; immerse 60-90 s for tin and its alloys. |
| 5 mL Na$_2$S$_2$O$_3$, 45 mL H$_2$O, 20 g K$_2$S$_2$O$_5$ | Klemm's III tint etch; immerse 3-5 min for bronze; immerse 6-8 min for Monels. |
| 240 g Na$_2$S$_2$O$_3$, 30 g citric acid, 24 g Pb(C$_2$H$_3$O$_2$)$_2$, 1000 mL H$_2$O | Beraha's lead sulfide tint etch; dissolve in order given; allow each to dissolve before adding next (cannot get complete dissolution); age in dark bottle at least 24 h before using; do not remove precipitate; when stock solution turns gray after prolonged storage, discard; immerse in solution until surface is violet or blue; excellent for copper and its alloys; to color MnS in steels, add 200 mg NaNO$_3$ sodium nitrate (optional) to 100 mL solution—good for 30 min; colors MnS white; pre-etch with nital or picral. |
| 21-28% aqueous NaHSO$_3$ | Beaujard and Tordeux's tint etch for steels; immerse 10-25 s; reveals grain boundaries and ferrite orientations; darkens as-quenched martensite. |
| 1 g Na$_2$S$_2$O$_5$, 100 mL H$_2$O | Tint etch for lath or plate martensite; immerse 2 min. |
| 8-15 g Na$_2$S$_2$O$_5$, 100 mL H$_2$O | Darkens as-quenched martensite; immerse approximately 20 s. |
| 3-10 g K$_2$S$_2$O$_5$, 100 mL H$_2$O | Darkens as-quenched martensite; immerse 1-15 s. |
| 1 g Na$_2$MoO$_4$, 100 mL H$_2$O | Beraha's tint etch for cast iron and steels; add HNO$_3$ to pH 2.5-4.0 (approximately 0.4 mL); immerse 20-30 s for cast iron, Fe$_3$P and Fe$_3$C, yellow-orange and ferrite, white; for low-carbon steel add 0.1 g NH$_4$HF$_2$, immerse 45-60 s; for medium-carbon steel add 0.2 g NH$_4$HF$_2$; for high-carbon steel add 0.3-0.4 g NH$_4$HF$_2$; carbides, yellow-orange to violet and ferrite, white or yellow. |
| 3 g K$_2$S$_2$O$_5$, 10 g Na$_2$S$_2$O$_3$, 100 mL H$_2$O | Beraha's tint etch for iron and steel; immerse 1-15 min; colors ferrite, martensite, pearlite, and bainite; sulfides are brightened. |
| 0.5-1.0 mL HCl, 100 mL H$_2$O, 1 g K$_2$S$_2$O$_5$ | Beraha's tint etch for irons, steels, tool steels; agitate strongly during etching, then hold motionless until surface is colored; 10-60 s total time; colors ferrite, martensite, pearlite, bainite; reveals grain boundaries. |
| 20 mL HCl, 100 mL H$_2$O, 0.5-1 g K$_2$S$_2$O$_5$ | Beraha's tint etch for stainless steels; immerse 30-120 s with agitation; colors austenite. |
| Stock solution: 20 mL HCl, 100 mL H$_2$O, 2.4 g NH$_4$HF$_2$ | Beraha's tint etch for stainless steels; before use, add 0.6-0.8 g K$_2$S$_2$O$_5$ (0.1-0.2 g for martensitic grades); after mixing, reagent is good for 2 h; use plastic tongs and beaker; immerse 20-90 s, shake gently during etching; colors matrix phases. |
| 40-60 mL FeCl$_3$ solution (1300 g/L H$_2$O), 25 mL HCl, 75 mL ethanol | Hasson's tint etch for molybdenum; immerse without agitation for 40-50 s (do not exceed 70 s); FeCl$_3$ can be dissolved in ethanol but etch is slower, 2-3 min; colors vary with grain orientation. |
| 70 mL H$_2$O, 20 mL 30% H$_2$O$_2$, 10 mL H$_2$SO$_4$ | Tint etch for molybdenum alloys (Oak Ridge National Laboratory); immerse 2 min, wash, and dry; swab removes colors, produces grain-boundary attack. |
| 5 g NH$_4$HF$_2$, 100 mL H$_2$O | Weck's tint etch for α-titanium; for pure titanium, immerse a few seconds, longer times for titanium alloys; colors vary with grain orientation. |
| 3 g NH$_4$HF$_2$, 4 mL HCl, 100 mL H$_2$O | Weck's tint etch for α-titanium alloys; immerse for a few seconds; colors vary with grain orientation. |
| 94 mL 10% aqueous HCl, 20 g CrO$_3$ | Tint etch for tungsten; immerse at 55 °C (130 °F); use 2 or 3 stages (view between etches) of 15, 10, and 10 min; pre-etch with grain-boundary etch. |

(a) Additional tint etchants are listed in Ref 3 and 17. (b) Whenever water is specified, use distilled water. (c) Maximum solubility of anhydrous Na$_2$S$_2$O$_3$ is 50 g/100 mL H$_2$O at 20 °C (70 °F); that of the crystal form (Na$_2$S$_2$O$_3$ · 5H$_2$O) is 79.4 g/100 mL H$_2$O at 0 °C (32 °F) or 291.1 g/100 mL H$_2$O at 45 °C (115 °F).

differences existing in single-phase alloys. Therefore, alloys with two or more phases etch more rapidly than single-phase metals or alloys.

With most chemical etchants, the same phase will usually be anodic or cathodic. It is difficult with standard etchants to reverse the attack, that is, to make the anodic phase cathodic. Only using the potentiostatic method can phases be etched selectively in the same electrolyte by changing the applied voltage (for more information on this method, see the section "Potentiostatic Etching" in this article).

Tint etchants generally color one anodic phase. Some success has been attained in developing color etchants for steels that are selective to the phases that are normally cathodic. However, most tint etchants color the anodic phases. Color etchants are usually acidic solutions, using water or alcohol as the solvent. They have been developed to deposit a 0.04- to 0.5-μm-thick film of an oxide, sulfide, complex molybdate, elemental selenium, or chromate on the specimen surface.

Colors are developed by interference in the same manner as with heat tinting or vacuum deposition (more information on these subjects is available in the appropriate sections of this article). Color etchants work by immersion, never by swabbing, which would prevent film formation. Externally applied potentials are not used.

The thickness of the film controls the colors produced. As film thickness increases, interference creates colors—viewed using white light—usually in the sequence of yellow, red, violet, blue, and green. With anodic systems, the film forms only over the anodic phase, but its thickness can vary with the crystallographic orientation of the phase. For cathodic systems, because the film thickness over the cathodic phase is generally consistent, only one color is produced, which will vary as the film grows during etching. Therefore, to obtain the same color each time, the etching duration must be constant. This can be accomplished by timing the etch and observing the macroscopic color of the specimen during staining.

Color etchants have been developed that deposit a thin sulfide film over a wide range of metals, such as cast irons, steels, stainless steels, nickel-base alloys, copper, and copper alloys (Ref 9, 19). These films are produced in two ways. For reagents containing potassium metabisulfite (K$_2$S$_2$O$_5$) or sodium metabisulfite (Na$_2$S$_2$O$_5$), the iron, nickel, or cobalt cation in the sulfide film originates from the specimen, and the sulfide anion derives from the reagent after decomposition.

The second type of film is produced by a metal-thiosulfate complex in the reagent that consists of an aqueous solution of sodium thiosulfate (Na$_2$S$_2$O$_3$ · 5H$_2$O), citric acid (organic acid), and lead acetate (Pb(C$_2$H$_3$O$_2$)$_2$) or cadmium chloride (CdCl$_2$) (metal salt). In such etchants, the specimen acts as the catalyst, and the film formed is lead sulfide (PbS) or cadium sulfide (CdS). These reagents color only the anodic constituents; the film is not formed over the cathodic features. Color etchants that use reduction of the molybdate ion have also been developed (Ref 20). Sodium molybdate ($Na_2MoO_4 \cdot 2H_2O$) is used. Molydenum in the molybdate ion, $MoO_4^{-2}$, has a valence of $+6$. In the presence of suitable reducing compounds, it can be partially reduced to $+4$. A dilute (1%) aqueous solution of $Na_2MoO_4 \cdot 2H_2O$ is made acidic by the addition of a small amount of nitric acid ($HNO_3$). This produces molybdic acid ($H_2MoO_4$). Addition of a strong reducing agent, such as iron sulfate ($FeSO_4$), colors the solution brown.

When the 1% aqueous $Na_2MoO_4$ solution (made acidic with $HNO_3$) is used to color etch steels, the molybdate is reduced at the cathodic cementite phase. This produces a yellow-orange to brown color, depending on etching duration. If a small amount of ammonium bifluoride ($NH_4HF_2$) is added, the carbides are colored red-violet, and ferrite is colored yellow. Perhaps the most widely applicable color etchant is that developed by Klemm (Ref 8), which colors ferrite in steels, reveals overheating or burning in steels, and develops the grain structure of copper and many copper alloys, as well as those of lead, tin, and zinc.

## Color Etchants

Common constituents in color etchants include $Na_2S_2O_5$, $K_2S_2O_5$, and $Na_2S_2O_3 \cdot 5H_2O$. These are used with water as the solvent and generally color anodic phases. To tint more acid-resistant metals, hydrochloric acid (HCl) is added. Color etchants containing these compounds produce sulfide films; during use, the odor from sulfur dioxide and hydrogen sulfide can be detected. Although this is a minor nuisance, etching should be conducted under a hood.

Color etchants based on selenic acid ($H_2SeO_4$) or $Na_2MoO_4 \cdot 2H_2O$ generally color cathodic constituents, such as cementite in cast irons and steels. Because $H_2SeO_4$ is dangerous to handle, its use should be restricted to those well aware of the necessary safety precautions. Fortunately, the reagents based on $Na_2MoO_4 \cdot 2H_2O$ are relatively safe to use. Reagents containing additions of $NH_4HF_2$ should also be handled carefully.

**Mixing of Reagents.** With most chemical etchants, precise adherence to the stated formula is not necessary. However, formulas for color etchants must be followed closely. For some color etchants, the order of mixing of the various components is also critical. Generally, the recommendations of the developer of the reagent should be followed closely.

Many color etchants can be prepared as 500- to 1000-mL stock solutions. In some cases, one ingredient is omitted until the quantity needed for etching is poured into a beaker. The activating agent is then added. Klemm's I reagent can be used in this man-ner. However, after mixing, this reagent can be stored for many days by covering the beaker tightly with aluminum foil to prevent evaporation. If evaporation does occur, crystals will form that are very difficult to dissolve. When a color etchant contains $NH_4HF_2$, a polyethylene beaker should be used.

## Specimen Preparation for Color Etching

Specimens for color etching must be carefully prepared. Control of scratches is the most challenging difficulty, particularly for alloys such as brass. Scratches are often observed after color etching, even if the specimen appeared to be free of scratches before polishing. This is a common problem with techniques that use interference effects to produce an image. However, preparation is carried out in virtually the same way as for specimens that would be chemically etched, but greater attention must be given to fine scratch removal (for more information on these procedures, see the Section "Metallographic Techniques" in this Volume).

**Etching Technique.** The desired etchant is mixed according to the formula (see Table 2), or the stock solution is poured into a beaker and activated in the specified manner. The specimen must be cleaned carefully before etching; any residue on the surface will interfere with film deposition. Because many color etchants require a 60- to 90-s immersion, the specimen is placed face up on the bottom of the beaker. The solution is then gently swirled. Care should be taken not to splash the solution onto hands or other exposed areas.

After approximately 20 to 40 s, depending on the specimen and the solution, the surface begins to color. The beaker is then held motionless until the surface is red to violet. The specimen is removed, washed in warm water, sprayed with ethanol, and dried. The specimen surface should not be touched. For color etchants that work relatively fast, the specimen is held in the solution with tongs and gently agitated until the surface is darkened. For these etchants, the macroscopic surface color is generally gray-black.

**Specimen Examination.** Specimens are now ready for viewing with an upright or inverted microscope and photographing. Upright and inverted microscopes are discussed and illustrated in the article "Optical Microscopy" in this Volume. Care should be taken during flattening of the specimen, because the surface should not be touched. If an inverted microscope is used, care should be taken in placing the specimen to avoid scratching the interference film.

Specimens are examined first using bright-field illumination, incorporating only neutral-density filters to control brightness. Color filters may enhance contrast between phases in some cases, and crossed or nearly crossed polarized light sometimes intensifies coloration.

Photomicrographs of any type may be obtained. If black-and-white film is used, panchromatic films are preferred; orthochromatic films are not sensitive to reds. If orthochromatic film is used, reds will appear quite dark on the print. For color photography, numerous films may be used to produce transparencies or prints.

## Applications of Color Etching

Color etching is particularly well suited to copper and copper alloys. Klemm's I reagent is efficacious with most of these compositions. It will also color ferrite grains in iron or steel varying shades of blue-brown, depending on crystallographic orientation. Phosphorus segregations are colored yellow or white, depending on concentration. Cementite can be detected using this reagent because it does not become colored; instead, it remains white to contrast with the colored matrix (Ref 8).

Beraha's reagent is also useful for etching carbon and low-alloy steels (Ref 9). After approximately 5 s, martensite is colored an intense bluish brown, and austenite remains white. Used to etch alloy steels, Beraha's reagent will color martensite blue to brown; ferrite and sulfide inclusions remain unetched and retain their inherent colors. Additional applications of color etchants can be found in Table 2. Examples of color-etched specimens are shown in Fig. 38 to 49.

# Anodizing

By Paul E. Danielson
Chief Metallographer
Teledyne Wah Chang Albany

ANODIZING is an electrolytic process for depositing a thin oxide film on the surface of the specimen in a standard electropolishing unit. The resulting interference colors are a function of the anodic film thickness, which depends on the anodizing voltage, the anodizing solution, and the composition and/or structures of the phases present in the specimens.

Anodization procedures have been established for zirconium-, titanium-, niobium-, tantalum-, and uranium-base alloys (Ref 21, 22). Anodization procedures have been reported for identification of oxides, carbides, and nitrides in niobium and niobium alloys (Ref 23). Anodizing has also been used to study grain structure in aluminum (Ref 24-26). Anodic etching is used for phase identification, improvement of optical contrast in bright-field and polarized light examination, and for preservation of the etched surface of the specimen. Zirconium alloy specimens examined three years after anodizing exhibited the same color contrast and delineation of structure as when originally prepared (Ref 21).

## Anodization Procedure

The specimen to be anodized is mounted in a standard Bakelite mount or using epoxy resin that hardens at room temperature (see the article "Mounting of Specimens" in this Volume). After grinding, polishing, and etching (see example below), the specimen is placed in a standard electropolishing unit, as described in the article "Electrolytic Polishing" in this Volume. The specimen, acting as the anode, is placed face up in the anodizing solution inside a stainless steel container, which acts as the cathode. Approximately 6 mm (1/4 in.) of solution should cover the top of the mounted specimens. The electrolyte composition used for zirconium-base alloys is 60 mL ethyl alcohol, 35 mL $H_2O$, 5 mL 85% phosphoric acid ($H_3PO_4$), 10 mL 85% lactic acid, 20 mL glycerine, and 2 g citric acid. This solution is also applicable to titanium, niobium, and tantalum specimens.

Voltages are 15 to 180 V dc, depending on the purpose (constituents or phases observed) and the color desired. The anodizing voltage, which is applied for 5 to 10 s, is usually selected by trial and error, using successively higher voltages on the basis of the greatest color contrast between the phases. Once selected, the voltage is used for other specimens of the same alloy. Additional information on anodization techniques can be found in the article "Zirconium and Hafnium and Their Alloys" in this Volume. A typical specimen preparation sequence is presented in the following example.

**Example 1.** A zirconium-titanium explosively bonded specimen, which consisted of a 3-mm (1/8-in.) thick zirconium cladding material bonded to a 6-mm (1/4-in.) thick titanium plate, was prepared for metallographic examination. The mounted specimen was rough ground wet using 120-grit silicon carbide paper. Fine grinding was carried out by hand using 2, 1, 0, 00, and 000 emery paper. Rough polishing was performed using a nylon cloth charged with a slurry of 10 g 1-$\mu$m $Al_2O_3$ in 150 mL $H_2O$. A solution of 250 mL $H_2O$, 22 mL $HNO_3$, and 3 mL hydrofluoric acid (HF) was added to the slurry on the polishing wheel. Final polishing was executed using a Microcloth charged with 2 to 3 g 0.05-$\mu$m $Al_2O_3$ in 150 mL $H_2O$; 3 to 5 mL of the $H_2O$, $HNO_3$, and HF solution was added to the slurry. The specimen, which was lightly etched due to the attack-polishing solution, was then anodized at 85 V in the anodizing solution described above.

Titanium and zirconium exhibit excellent color separation when anodized, as shown in Fig. 50. The yellow-gold is the zirconium, and the blue-purple is the titanium. Other examples of anodized specimens are depicted in Fig. 51 to 54. Important differences exist between the attack-polished and anodized tantalum/niobium weldments (Fig. 52) and the same weld specimen that was etched and heat tinted (Fig. 31). Anodization is also used to reveal defects (inclusions) in various materials. Figures 53 and 54 illustrate the use of anodizing to reveal metallic and nonmetallic inclusions in zirconium.

# Potentiostatic Etching

By E.E. Stansbury
Professor Emeritus
Materials Science and Engineering
Department
University of Tennessee

POTENTIOSTATIC ETCHING is the selective corrosion of one or more morphological features of a microstructure that results from holding the metal to be etched in a suitable etching electrolyte at a controlled potential relative to a reference electrode. The basis of the method is that the products of electrochemical dissolution reactions and the rates of formation of these products for a given electrolyte are a function of the potential at which a metal or alloy is held relative to a suitable reference electrode. Because specific surface topology, with or without films, is necessary for color contrast metallography, potentiostatic etching can enhance control in producing the requisite surface characteristics. Representative early applications of the potentiostat to etching have been documented (Ref 27, 28), and use of the method for color metallography has been recognized (Ref 29, 30).

## Experimental Procedure

An experimental arrangement for accomplishing potentiostatic etching is shown in Fig. 9. A conventionally mounted and polished metal specimen is modified to provide electrical contact with the specimen without access of the electrolyte to the connecting wire. An auxiliary electrode, usually fabricated of platinum or specially prepared graphite, permits current to pass from or to the specimen through the electrolyte. The potential of the specimen is measured with respect to the potential of a reference electrode placed a few millimeters from the surface. The common reference electrodes are the calomel half-cell [mercury in contact with mercurous dichloride ($Hg_2Cl_2$)] and the silver-silver chloride half-cell. The potential depends on the chloride ion concentration contacting the metal and insoluble metal chloride. The potentials of these half-cells are established with respect to the hydrogen gas (1 atm)/hydrogen ion (unit activity) half-cell assigned the value of zero potential. In the following, all potentials except Fig. 12 are given relative to the standard hydrogen electrode (SHE), although essentially all measurements are made regarding one of the secondary reference half-cells.

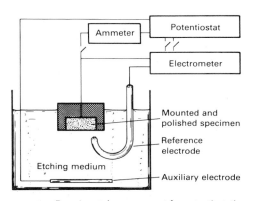

**Fig. 9** Experimental arrangement for potentiostatic etching

## Use of Interference Films

Differences in color relate to interference effects associated with differences in film thickness, to the structure of a film, particularly whether it is single crystalline, polycrystalline, or amorphous, and to other optical characteristics, such as sensitivity to polarized light. When electromagnetic radiation (for present purposes with wavelengths in the visible range) impinges on a thin transparent adherent film, reflection occurs at the film/air and film/metal interfaces (see Fig. 2). Phase shifts also occur at either or both of these interfaces. Consequently, selected wavelengths are cancelled between the incident and reflected light, resulting in the reflected light having colors characteristic of uncancelled wavelengths. The effect is a function of the wavelengths in the incident light and will be sensitive to the light source and any filtering in the source or reflected light paths. Within a good approximation, cancellation of a specific wavelength, $\lambda$, occurs for the thickness, $t \simeq N(\lambda/4n)$, where $n$ is the refractive index of the film and $N$ the integer order of the interference.

As film thickness is increased, and with incident unfiltered light of all wavelengths, interference occurs first for the shorter wavelengths of the blue limit of the visible wavelength range. The longer wavelengths are reflected, giving the first color of red-yellow. With progressive thickening of the film, the color passes through the spectral range to blue, then repeats for successive values of the order, $N$. For $N$ greater than 3 or 4, excessive film thickness leads to absorption and poor color development. Considering that light passes into and from the film at an angle, interference for violet light having a wavelength of 400 nm (4000 Å) begins for films approximately 40 nm (400 Å) thick; these films produce yellow. The first blue will occur for films somewhat thinner than 70 nm (700 Å). Successive sequences occur for progressively thicker films, but clarity of color based on interference decreases for films thicker than 500 nm (5000 Å). The color of interference films is frequently enhanced using polarized light, sensitive-tint plates (Fig. 5), and phase-contrast devices. These rely on the ability of some films to alter the plane of polarization, or they provide a phase shift that is sensitive to wavelength.

## Use of Polarized Light and Phase Contrast

Irregularities in the surface, such as grain boundaries, etch pits, and faceting, and, to a lesser extent, films with rough surfaces allow the repeated reflection of incident polarized light within an irregularity. If the emerging ray enters the microscope objective with a fractional shift in path length relative to light reflected from an adjacent region of different elevation, the resulting light is elliptically polarized and, upon passing through a sensitive tint plate or phase contrast device, results in differences in color. Because upon etching different grains or phases can develop surface topology sensitive to the crystal lattice orientation, such as facets, microstructural detail becomes distinguishable by color without the formation of surface films. The optical principles dictating development of color to enhance microstructural detail are discussed in Ref 3, 17, and 31 to 34.

## Electrochemical Principles

Surfaces containing irregularities or interference films may be produced by several methods, ranging from direct aqueous chemical attack to thermal oxidation (heat tinting) and color, or tint, etching. Aqueous chemical attack involves electrochemical processes in which anodic dissolution—for example, electrons lost, oxidation, or corrosion—occurs spontaneously, supported by cathodic reactions (electrons gained or reduced) of etchant species. The electrochemical potential at which oxidation occurs is established largely by the oxidizing characteristics of the etchant; this potential and etchant species determine the rate of oxidation and the mode of attack. Metal atoms are released from the surface as ions that pass into solution, leaving unfilmed surfaces, or react to form films.

Anodic dissolution is also controlled by removing electrons through an external circuit, which is completed by an auxiliary electrode placed in the etchant solution. If the external circuit is designed to control the current, the process is termed galvanostatic etching. The current causes a shift in electrochemical potential of the metal specimens. For small currents, the effect is superimposed on the potential and currents resulting from the etchant described above; with higher external currents, removal of electrons to the external current dominates the change in potential and current density and therefore etching response. However, the modes of attack remain sensitive to etchant composition. More importantly, though, the type of interface reaction depends largely on electrochemical po-

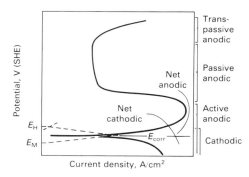

**Fig. 10** Schematic polarization curves representative of an alloy in a deaerated-acid environment showing active/passive behavior. $E_H$ is the equilibrium potential for the hydrogen reaction. $E_M$ is the indefinite potential near which metal dissolution is very small. $E_{corr}$ is the corrosion potential. SHE: standard hydrogen electrode

tential, and often the establishment and control of the potential can be accomplished only by a potentiostat using the arrangement shown in Fig. 9.

The dependence of the dissolution rate of a metal or alloy on the electrochemical potential is represented by the polarization or potential/current-density curve. A representative, experimentally determined curve for a metal forming a corrosion-product film in a deaerated acid environment is shown in Fig. 10. Sections of the curve are identified as potential ranges of net cathodic, net active anodic, passive anodic, and transpassive anodic behavior. Dashed extensions of the curves indicate the potential and current-density ranges over which cathodic and anodic reactions occur when the net current density is anodic and cathodic, respectively. In the net cathodic potential range, the rate of metal dissolution may be slow with little etching.

Upon increasing the potential, the current reverses at $E_{corr}$, the natural corrosion potential of the specimen in the absence of a potentiostat. Further increase in potential causes a net removal of electrons. The entire anodic curve is the potential range of anodic dissolution (oxidation) of the metal to soluble or insoluble corrosion products. In the cathodic potential range, there is a net flow of electrons to the specimen; the predominant effect is a reduction of hydrogen ions to hydrogen gas. In the active anodic region, the dissolution rate increases as potential increases; etching may occur, but corrosion product films do not form. A maximum in current density results from the initiation and growth of films that reduce current density until an adherent oxide film characteristic of the passive state forms. Increasing the potential in the passive range results in progressive thickening of the film such that the current density remains relatively constant. In the transpassive range, the passive film becomes unstable regarding soluble species in solution, such as $CrO_4^=$. The film disappears, and current density increases.

The polarization curve is sensitive to the composition of the environment or, for pres-

ent purposes, etchant composition. Representative examples for type 304 stainless steel are shown in Fig. 11. The reference curve is for 1 $N$ sulfuric acid ($H_2SO_4$), the environment most commonly used to compare corrosion behaviors of various materials. The pH is a major variable, and because much of the reported work on potentiostatic etching relates to 1 to 10 $N$ sodium hydroxide (NaOH), the curve shown in the figure is for a strongly alkaline environment. The curves for 1 $N$ $H_2SO_4$ with additions of 10 ppm S$^=$ and potassium thiocyanate (KCNS$^-$) ions are examples of additives to the 1 $N$ $H_2SO_4$ to increase the dissolution rate in the active range, an important consideration in increasing current density to accomplish etching within a reasonable time. Chloride ions significantly influence the polarization of most active/passive alloys; these and other halide ions increase current density and may break down the passive film at potentials below the transpassive range. This occurs as localized attack on the passive film in the form of pitting. For some alloys, high halide ion concentrations can prevent formation of the passive film, complicating enhancement of potentiostatic etching by chloride ions.

The polarization curve is usually determined by a continuous scan of potentials from the cathodic range or from $E_{corr}$ at 6 V/h. The experimental curve is sensitive to scan rate and surface topology, and films at any potential may be very sensitive to the potential/time history, that is, whether a specimen is scanned to or is initially set at the given potential. Because of this sensitivity, reference to polarization curves in the literature as guides for conditions for potentiostatic etching may be limited to qualitative value, because etching will usually be carried out by directly setting the potential and holding for a specified time to produce the desired etching response. However, polarization curves indicate potential ranges of dissolution with and without film formation and readily reflect changes in etchant composition.

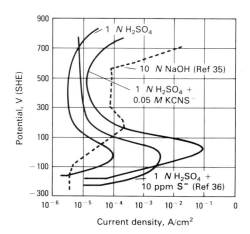

**Fig. 11** Polarization curves for 18-8 austenitic stainless steel showing effects of the indicated environments. SHE: standard hydrogen electrode

In potentiostatic etching, the desired information is the current density as a function of time at various potentials along the polarization curve. Grain-boundary attack, faceting, etch pitting, and preferential dissolution of grains and phases occur predominantly in the active and high-transpassive potential ranges where films do not form. Under these circumstances, the current density is a relatively constant function of time. The major variables, in addition to selection of potential, are time and the environment. The environment influences the mode of attack—for example, faceting. Time determines the extent to which the mode of attack must progress to develop a surface that adequately reveals the microstructure, including development of color under available optical conditions. The major etchant variables to consider are pH and additives, such as $KCNS^-$, which increase current density and therefore decrease etching time if acceptable surface topology develops.

Selective etching of multiphase alloys depends on differential rates of dissolution and on formation of film-free or filmed surfaces on the phases providing color contrast. The principle is illustrated in Fig. 12, which depicts differences in dissolution rates for austenite, ferrite, and σ phases in an austenitic stainless steel. Such curves are constructed by adding curves for the individual phases displaced along the current density axis proportional to the relative areas exposed at the surface. The latter are directly related to the volume fractions of the phases in the alloy. Where current density maxima are indicated for a specific phase, preferential etching of the phase is expected. However, the mode of attack and the optical methods applied will determine if differentiation of phases by color contrast results.

## Conditions for Color Response

As discussed earlier, color contrast resulting from film formation depends on films producing interference effects, rotation of the plane of polarization, and optical effects associated with surface topology. For color to develop due to interference, films 40 to 500 nm (400 to 5000 Å) thick must be produced. Film thickness is directly proportional to charge density, which is the integration of the time/current-density product to a given time expressed in coulombs per square centimeter ($C/cm^2$), if all metal ions oxidized by the anodic current density remain in the film and do not go into solution. Otherwise, a correction must be made for this loss. The relationship (Ref 37) is:

$$\text{Film thickness} = D$$
$$= \frac{M'}{m'\, z'\, d'\, F}\, Q\alpha \qquad \text{(Eq 1)}$$

where the primes refer to average values, and $M'$ is molecular weight of the oxide, $m'$ is metal atoms per molecule of oxygen, $d'$ is density of the oxide, and $z'$ is metal ion valence. F is the Faraday constant, $Q$ is the charge density, and $\alpha$ is the fraction of the metal retained in the film, which allows preferential loss of selected metal atoms to the environment, such as iron and nickel, relative to chromium in an austenitic stainless steel, resulting in an oxide approaching chromic oxide ($Cr_2O_3$). For an austenitic stainless steel, Eq 1 reduces to:

$$D = 0.5\, Q\alpha \text{ nm} \qquad \text{(Eq 2)}$$

where $Q$ is expressed in $mA \cdot s/cm^2$, or $mC/cm^2$.

Theoretical and empirical investigations indicate that the time dependence of current density during film formation is frequently:

$$\log i = A + \log (1/t^n) \qquad \text{(Eq 3)}$$

where A is a constant and values of $n$ have been evaluated from 0.6 to 1 (Ref 35, 37). Further analysis leads to thickening of the films as cubic, parabolic, or logarithmic functions of time. The parameters of the functions depend on the alloy, environment, and potential range in which dissolution occurs. Therefore, the rate of thickening decreases with time and may lead to excessive etching durations to form films capable of yielding interference effects. A limiting thickness may also be reached if the growth rate slows sufficiently that additional growth is balanced by dissolution of the film into the etchant. Growth rate characteristics complicate estimates from a conventional polarization curve of the time required to form a 40- to 500-nm (400- to 5000-Å) thick film, which is necessary for interference contrast.

In the passive potential range of most stainless steels and nickel-base alloys, the passive film in acid environments usually attains a steady thickness under 10 nm (100 Å), which is too thin to produce interference colors. In general, as will be shown, good color contrast has been developed by etching in strong NaOH (5 to 40%) in potential ranges just above the current density peak or in the early stages of the transpassive potential range. Because the rate of dissolution of the film quickens with increases in potential in the transpassive range, careful control of potential and time is required to obtain desired film properties. A significant factor that correlates with the formation of thicker films on stainless steel in strongly alkaline solutions is the preferential loss of chromium and formation of iron- and nickel-rich films, which contrasts with the chromium-rich films observed in acid solution.

For example, potentiostatic etching of a Fe-27.7Cr alloy (Ref 35, 38) at 540 mV (SHE) resulted in a yellow color with an estimated thickness of 35 nm (350 Å) after 20 s; brown at 38 nm (380 Å) after 60 s; orange at 40 nm (400 Å) after 2 min; purple at 44 nm (440 Å) after 6 min; and blue at 48 nm (480 Å) after 20 to 60 min. References 35 and 38 discuss the interrelationship among compositions of several stainless steels, potential, charge density, current density as a function of time, and the development of color for 10 $N$ NaOH etching solution. Observations are correlated with potentiostatic polarization curves obtained by holding the alloys at successive potential intervals for 5 min. For example, a 27.7% Cr ferritic stainless steel developed a golden yellow at 440 mV (SHE) in 5 min, corresponding to a charge density of 106 mA $\cdot$ s/cm². As an example of the decay of the current density with time, during the time re-

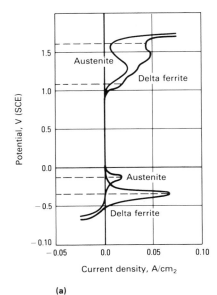

(a)

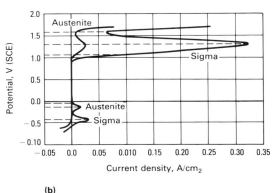

(b)

**Fig. 12** Polarization curves for 18-8 stainless steel showing potential ranges for selective etching of (a) austenite and δ-ferrite and (b) austenite and σ phase. SCE: saturated calomel electrode. (Ref 28)

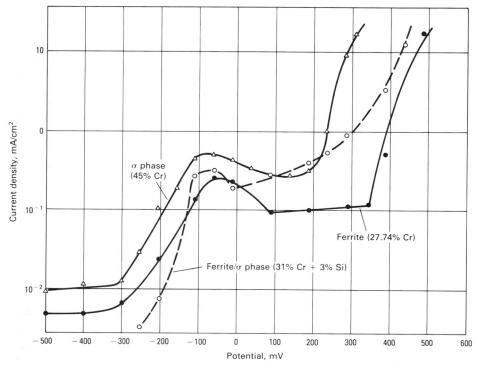

**Fig. 13** Polarization curves for iron-chromium alloys. (Ref 35)

quired to produce this charge density, the current density decreased from 10 mA/cm² at 10 s to 0.1 mA/cm² at 5 min.

The difference in charge density of the ferrite and austenite phases in a two-phase alloy required to give color contrast between the phases has been discussed (Ref 35). After 5 min at +240 mV (SHE), the charge density of a 44.77% Cr σ-phase alloy is 208 mA · s/cm² greater than that of the 27.7% Cr ferritic alloy. In a two-phase alloy of 60% ferrite and 40% σ, the ferrite was blue and the σ phase was brown. A carbide phase was light yellow. These observations are consistent with the polarization curve shown in Fig. 13, in which

current density for the σ phase exceeds that for the α phase and therefore would produce a thicker film. The curve for the two-phase α/σ-phase alloy generally lies between the curves for the individual phases. The effect of the higher chromium content of the σ phase in lowering the potential for onset of transpassivity is evident when curves for the high- and low-content alloys are compared in the potential range of 450 to 650 mV. Therefore, at 500 mV the difference in current density is large and corresponds to excessive attack of the σ phase in the 5-min holding time used in generating these data. The curves suggest that useful etching might result for shorter times,

but that the selection and control of the potential becomes critical.

Interference contrast films providing color differentiation of microconstituents are also produced by the controlled potential oxidation or reduction of species in solution in contrast to dependence on films produced by corrosion products. The method depends on depositing films having thicknesses and/or properties that are sensitive to the substrate phase and its crystal lattice orientation. Again, for interference color development, these films must attain thicknesses of 40 to 500 nm (400 to 5000 Å), although optically active films may be thinner. Examples are the anodic (oxidation) deposition of lead dioxide ($PbO_2$) and manganese dioxide ($MnO_2$), according to the reactions:

$$Pb^{2+} 2H_2O \rightarrow PbO_2 + 4H^+ + 2e \qquad (Eq\ 4)$$

and

$$Mn^{2+} + 2H_2O \rightarrow MnO_2 + 4H^+ + 2e \,(Eq\ 5)$$

For example, a yellow film was obtained in 1 min at 660 mV (SHE) in a $Pb(C_2H_3O_2)_2$ solution; blue was developed in 3 min, and the next order of yellow at 4 min (Ref 38). Potentiostatic deposition of $MnO_2$ from a 10% manganese sulfate ($MnSO_4$) solution has been reported (Ref 39). Higher valent soluble species can be reduced (cathodic deposition) to insoluble film-forming species, such as molybdenum dioxide ($MoO_2$), according to the reaction:

$$MoO_4^= + 4H^+ + 4e \rightarrow MoO_2 + 2H_2O$$
$$(Eq\ 6)$$

Although formation of deposit films by immersion using similar reagents, including formation of sulfide films, has been described (Ref 40), investigation of deposition by control of potential appears limited. Because the film-forming species are in solution, an advantage of the technique is that growth occurs at the film/solution interface without ne-

**Table 3    Potentiostatic etching**

| Solution | Material | Morphology developed | Ref |
|---|---|---|---|
| 10 N NaOH | Fe: 0-62% Cr, 0.78-8% C | Pure $Fe_3C$, $M_{23}C_6$, M-C₃, and as-distributed phases | 41 |
| | Fe: 18-41% Cr, 2.5-39% Ni | Martensite, austenite, α-ferrite, δ phase | 42 |
| | Fe: 25-45% Cr, 2% Mo, 6.4% Ni | $Cr_{23}C_6$, α-ferrite, δ phase | 43 |
| | Fe: 13% Cr, 1.5% Ti, 4% V | TiC, $M_7C_3$ | 29 |
| | Fe: 17-45% Cr, 0-10% Ni, 0-2% Mo | Austenite, α-ferrite, δ phase | 35 |
| 10% NaOH | Co: 20% Cr, 20% Ni, 4% (Nb, W, Mo) | Differentiation of $M_6C$, NbC | 44 |
| | Co: 31% Cr, 13% W, 2.2% C (cast) | $M_2C$ | 44 |
| | Fe: Cr, Ni, Mo, Nb | NbC(a) | 44 |
| 20% NaOH | Cast iron: C, Si, P | Segregation; nodular and flake graphite (effect of etchant temperature) | 45 |
| 40% NaOH | Low-alloy steels | Differentiation of bainite and martensite | 44 |
| | Fe: 27% Cr | Ferrite, δ phase | 44 |
| | Co: 26% Cr, 10% Ni(Mo, W, Nb, Fe) | $M_6C$(a) | 44 |
| $NH_4C_2H_3O_2$ (ammonium acetate) | Tool steels | Mo, W, and V segregation in metal carbides | 44 |
| 10% $Na_2CO_3$ (sodium carbonate) | Fe: Cr, Ni, Mo | $M_{23}C_6$ | 44 |
| | Co: 26% Cr, 20% Ni, 4% (Nb, W, Mo) | $M_{23}C_6$(a) | 44 |
| | Co: 31% Cr, 13% W, 2.2% C (cast) | $M_7C_3$(a) | 44 |
| 85% $H_3PO_4$ | Cu: Be, Zr, Ni | Grain boundaries, dendritic segregation, dispersed phases | 46, 47 |
| $Pb(C_2H_3O_2)$ | Fe: 13% Cr, 1.5% Ti, 4% V | VC, $M_7C_3$ | 29 |
| 10% NH₄Ac (ammonium acetate) | Fe: 10% W, 4% Mo, 4% Cr, 1.3% C | (V, W)C | |
| 10% $MnSO_4$ (manganese sulfate) | Fe: 25% Cr, 20% Ni | $M_7C_3$, $M_{23}C_6$, $MnO_2$ | 39 |

(a) Multiple potential and/or etchant

cessity of diffusion of cations or anions through the film. As a consequence, current density and therefore film growth rate are constant and do not decrease with time, as occurs during thickening of corrosion-product films. Problems may be encountered if the potential required for the formation of deposit films is in the range of rapid dissolution of the substrate. The problem is alleviated by the possibility of solutions used for depositing films being relatively neutral and thus not as aggressive in the required potential range, as would result if film formation required extreme values of pH.

Color differentiation of microconstituents by etching in the active and high-transpassive potential ranges depends on development of surface topology containing irregularities, such as facets, etch pits, and differences in elevation. If the dissolution is uniform, within a factor of approximately 2, a current density of 1 mA/cm² will remove 50 nm (500 Å) per min. Because films are not forming, this dissolution rate is relatively constant with time. Optical features of the microscope, such as sensitive tint and quarter-wave plates as well as phase contrast devices, can develop color for surface irregularities with widths and depths of approximately one quarter of a wavelength or less. For wavelengths at the lower end of the visible range—for example, violet at 40 nm (400 Å)—the dimension of the irregularities can approximate 10 nm (100 Å). Considering that the exposed surface area per unit area of specimen increases rapidly as the surface topology becomes progressively irregular, these approximations lead to current densities of approximately 1 mA/cm² for 1 min to produce surfaces with irregularities capable of yielding color. Whether or not the desired surface topology develops depends on

**Fig. 14** Typical arrangement for vacuum deposition of interference films. The arrow indicates the tungsten wire basket filled with material for evaporation.

the etchant; unfortunately, systematic investigations of the interrelationship of these factors in producing useful microstructural contrast, particularly in color, have not been reported.

## Potentiostatic Etchants

Table 3 surveys potentiostatic etchants that have been reported to develop color useful for microconstituent identification for the indicated materials. The wide range of potentials, times, and temperatures precludes reasonable inclusion of these variables in tabular form. The discussion above provides a guide to the variables that should be investigated to establish useful techniques.

# Interference Films by Vacuum Deposition

By Robert S. Crouse
Group Leader, Metallography
Metals and Ceramics Division
Oak Ridge National Laboratory

INTERFERENCE FILMS, with possible contrast and color enhancement, may be applied by vacuum deposition to metallic systems unsuited to oxidation or anodization. The phase shift in light reflected at the interference film/substrate interface contributes to the colors produced by a transparent film on a metallographic specimen. This phase shift depends on the optical properties of the film and substrate, and if a microstructure contains multiple phases, it should be possible to produce interference colors with a layer of uniform thickness. This was demonstrated in 1960 (Ref 16) and adapted and extended in 1966 (Ref 48).

## Technique

Special specimen preparation is not required for film deposition; typical polishing procedures are used. Etching may be required if phase/grain-boundary relationships are desired. Materials that have been found to produce phase contrast and color when vacuum deposited include titanium dioxide ($TiO_2$), silicon dioxide ($SiO_2$), zirconium dioxide ($ZrO_2$), zinc sulfide ($ZnS$), tin oxide ($SnO_2$), and carbon. Of these, $TiO_2$ is the most commonly used. However, developing contrast for subsequent x-ray microanalysis necessitates using a film that does not contain elements to be analyzed. All these (except carbon) are supplied in powder or chips and must be contained in a tungsten wire basket, such as that shown in Fig. 14, which depicts a typical arrangement for vacuum deposition. The basket is approximately 100 mm (4 in.) from the specimens, but this distance can vary considerably.

The vacuum chamber should be evacuated to $1.3 \times 10^{-2}$ Pa ($10^{-4}$ torr) or lower. The temperature of the filament basket should be raised slowly to prevent the material being evaporated from "jumping out" of the basket. When the material melts and coats the wire, the wire is then raised to white heat for a few seconds, which evaporates the material. Figure 15 shows an evaporation in progress. Heating may continue until all the material is evaporated or may be stopped at any time. It cannot be predicted when the maximum contrast or desired color will be obtained; trial and error must be used. Additional material may be deposited by simply repeating the above procedure. Frequent usage of this technique necessitates experimenting with controlled amounts of material, different compounds, and variable angles of deposition. Because the final mechanical polishing easily removes the film from the specimen, recoating can be carried out quickly.

## Advantages and Applications

Interference films produced by vacuum deposition apply to practically any polished metallographic specimen. The materials required are relatively inexpensive and readily available, and the technique is simple and easy. Five examples of how vacuum-deposited films have been used to define microstructure will be presented. They represent typical situations where such interference films have produced contrast and characteristic colors that aid microstructural analysis.

The first application of this coating technique was the examination of type 316 stainless steel exposed to air for 3000 h at 870 °C (1600 °F). Considerable oxidation occurred, and the specimen was vacuum coated with $TiO_2$ to attempt to contrast more adequately the various phases visible in the microstructure. Figure 56 shows the results. At least two different oxides and subsurface oxidation were evident. Coating enhanced the color differences between the oxides and unexpectedly revealed that the subsurface material was not oxide but epoxy infiltrated from the mounting medium. This was determined by noting that the material in the voids was the

**Fig. 15** An evaporation process in progress. See Fig. 56 to 60 for examples of vacuum-deposited structures.

**Fig. 16** Microstructure of a siliconized silicon carbide heat exchanger tube. Dark gray is silicon carbide; lighter gray is silicon. A third phase (an iron-nickel-silicon intermetallic) is difficult to see in black and white, but is highly visible in color (see Fig. 57). As-polished. 500×

same color as the mounting material. It is sometimes difficult to determine the nature of such a microstructure.

Siliconized silicon carbide is used as a stable, corrosion-resistant material for high-temperature heat exchangers. In this example, it was exposed in testing to residual fuel oil at 1200 °C (2190 °F) for 500 h. Figure 16 shows the as-polished microstructure in black and white. Compare this with the vapor-deposited (TiO₂) structure in Fig. 57 in the atlas of color micrographs. Although three phases are detectable in black and white, color greatly improves contrast in the coated microstructure. Silicon carbide appears gray; silicon, yellow; and an iron-nickel-silicon intermetallic, violet.

Vacuum deposition can also be used to examine cutting tool materials. Figures 58 and 59 show examples of ZnSe deposited on a cemented carbide and a cermet, respectively. Tungsten carbide grinding debris resulting from ball milling the alumina-titanium carbide raw materials is highly visible using vapor deposition (Fig. 59).

Some microstructures have such variable composition as to be virtually impossible to chemically etch properly. Brazed joints frequently pose this problem. Deposition coating may provide enhancement that will completely reveal all details of the microstructure.

Titanium is difficult to polish and etch, especially in combination with a brazing alloy of aluminum and silicon. Several phases are formed in the braze that are chemically etched at different rates, resulting in a microstructure that does not fully reveal all phases. Figure 60 shows such a microstructure that was coated with ZrO₂. All phases are well contrasted and quite colorful. The phases were identified using electron probe x-ray microanalysis. Zirconium dioxide, rather than TiO₂, was used for the coating because titanium was one of the elements to be analyzed.

# Interference Films by Reactive Sputtering*

INTERFERENCE FILM DEPOSITION is necessary for developing the material structure of a specimen, that is, intensifying or revealing phase contrasts using interference film metallography (Ref 49). One method involves contrasting in a gas ion reaction chamber (Ref 50). In this process, the film material is applied by cathode sputtering, transported through a gas chamber, and deposited on an anodically connected specimen. If the contrasting chamber contains a reactive gas with a suitable partial pressure, the sputtered cathode materials may react with the gas before deposition. Therefore, the process is customarily termed reactive sputtering. Oxygen is frequently used as reaction gas and leads to deposition of oxidic interference films. Additional information on reactive sputtering, which was introduced by G. Bartz, can be found in Ref 51.

## Principles of Reactive Sputtering

During gas ion etching, the specimen subject to film deposition is positioned in a vacuum chamber. The specimen is placed under zero potential, that is, connected anodically. The cathode is mounted opposite the specimen at a variable distance. The specimens and the growing interference film may be observed through a window in the vacuum chamber by use of a microscope.

*By Helmut Hoven, Karl Koizlik, Jochen Linke, and Hubertus Nickel, Kernforschungsanlage Jülich, Institut für Reaktorwerkstoffe. Translated from the German by Claus G. Goetzel, Department of Materials Science and Engineering, Stanford University

The protective atmosphere is not filled statically into the chamber, but flows through it, even during deposition. After the voltage is adjusted to the respective distance of the specimen from the cathode (up to a 2500-V maximum is applied), a glow discharge is ignited in the gas chamber.

During the gas discharge, positively charged ions are formed by the accelerated electrons. The ions are preferentially accelerated near the cathode. They impact on the cathode with energies of approximately 100 eV to more than 1 keV and atomize its surface. The atoms or ions, respectively, liberated in this process move in the direction of the specimen surface. They react, at least in part, with the atoms of the reactive carrier gas during passage through the gas chamber before their deposition as interference films on the specimen surface.

If oxygen is selected as the reactive carrier gas, an oxidic interference film is formed, but it does not necessarily consist of a stoichiometric oxide of the cathode materials (Ref 52). Depending on process parameters, different fractions of the reaction gas and the nonoxidized atoms of the cathode material may be incorporated into the interference film.

## Experimental Setup and Deposition Process

Film deposition can be best demonstrated by the following example. A commercially available gas ion contrasting chamber, which is described in Ref 53, is used (Fig. 17). The specimen—in this case the high-temperature alloy Hastelloy X—is typically mounted 10 mm (0.4 in.) from the cathode. The chamber is evacuated to $10^{-3}$ Pa ($7.5 \times 10^{-6}$ torr) or less. The partial pressure of the oxygen flow is adjusted in the chamber to 20 Pa (0.15 torr). At a discharge current of approximately

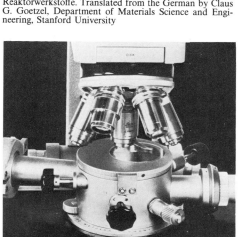
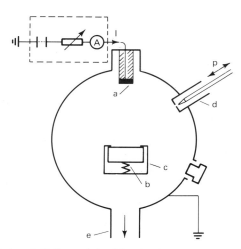

**Fig. 17** Gas ion reaction chamber for reactive sputtering. (Left) Photograph of the chamber mounted on a microscope stage. (Right) Schematic illustrating the various components. (a) Cathode (sputter) material. (b) Specimen. (c) Specimen holder. (d) Gas inlet with needle valve for the reactive carrier gas. (e) Gas outlet to vacuum pump. (p) Power supply

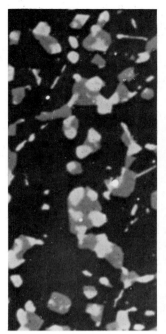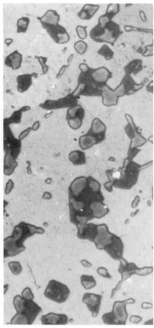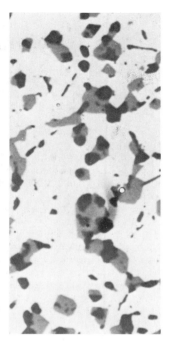

**Fig. 18, 19, 20** Gray value contrast by applying monochromatic incident light at different wavelengths. Fig. 18: 480 nm (4800 Å). Fig. 19: 515 nm (5150 Å). Fig. 20: 565 nm (5650 Å)

2 mA, the desired color ring system is reached in 5 to 10 min. This visually controlled method enables interruption of deposition when the necessary color ring reaches the spot on the specimen to be characterized.

If a ferrous cathode is used, a 30- to 120-nm (300- to 1200-Å) transparent iron oxide layer is formed on the specimen surface that represents the desired interference film. The layer thickness is greatest in the central region and decreases symmetrically toward the outer edge. This explains the concentric interference rings, as shown in Fig. 61.

In white incident light, the various phases of the specimen are discriminated by varying contrast, depending on film thickness, that is, the color ring located on the surface of the specimen area to be analyzed (Fig. 62). If the film thickness is correctly adjusted, that is, correct selection of the color ring, the contrast between any desired microstructural constituents can be adjusted to a maximum in monochromatic light by varying its wavelength, as shown in Fig. 18 to 20.

Selection of film thickness for optimum separation of the constituents depends on the material to be contrasted. Figure 63 shows optimum contrasting obtained on a reactive sputtered superalloy specimen. To obtain reproducible interference layers, the established optimum conditions for deposition should be maintained if possible.

## Process Parameters and Errors (Ref 54)

**Cathode material** selection depends on the specimen material on which the film is to be deposited and the optical contrast conditions to be controlled. Optical constants of various cathode materials are given in Table 4.

**Cathode distance** may be varied over a wide range. Values from 5 to 15 mm (0.2 to 0.6 in.) are favorable for metals. Smaller cathode distances cause higher specimen temperatures. Specimen temperature influences the optical constants of the deposited film.

**Cathode size** may be selected at random and is principally a function of the technical limitations of the gas ion chamber. Larger cathodes necessitate a flatter thickness profile of the deposited interference film.

**Discharge current** may vary from 0.5 to 2.5 kV in the installation at hand. This value substantially influences specimen temperature and therefore the optical constants of the interference film being formed. This value must be kept low for temperature-sensitive specimen materials.

**Partial pressure of the reactive carrier gas** may be selected freely from a few pascals to ~60 Pa (0.45 torr). The gas pressure largely determines the focusing of the discharge column. Together with the discharge current, it determines the necessary deposition time until the predetermined film thickness is reached, that is, until the suitable color ring zone appears. The correlation among discharge current, deposition time, and partial pressure of the reactive gas is depicted in Fig. 21.

**Reaction Gas.** A reactive process gas is essential to reactive sputtering. In principle, distinctly different chamber atmospheres can be applied within this limitation. Only oxygen and oxygen-argon mixtures that produce oxidic interference films have as yet been used as reaction gases.

**Processing period** is determined by the selected data for film thickness and deposition rate. The latter is a function of cathode distance, discharge current, or discharge voltage, respectively, and partial pressure of the gas. Except for very high or very low deposition rates, which could affect the crystalline structure of the interference films, selection of deposition rate, and thus processing time, is not critical.

**Specimen Temperature.** Thermal conductivity of the specimen material and the values for discharge voltage and discharge current affect specimen temperature. High

**Table 4  Optical constants of some cathode materials used in interference film metallography(a)**

| Cathode material | | Wavelength, nm (Å) | | | | |
|---|---|---|---|---|---|---|
| | | 500 (5000) | 525 (5250) | 550 (5500) | 575 (5750) | 600 (6000) |
| Platinum | $n_z$ | 2.78 | 2.55 | 2.66 | 2.61 | 2.57 |
| | $k_z$ | 0.4 | 0.3 | 0.3 | 0.25 | 0.25 |
| Palladium | $n_z$ | 2.45 | 2.58 | 2.65 | 2.65 | ... |
| | $k_z$ | 0.2 | 0.25 | 0.3 | 0.35 | ... |
| Lead | $n_z$ | 2.6 | 2.5 | 2.45 | 2.48 | 2.5 |
| | $k_z$ | 0.1 | 0.05 | 0.04 | 0.04 | 0.1 |
| Gold | $n_z$ | 2.28 | 2.35 | 2.3 | 2.3 | 2.3 |
| | $k_z$ | 0.3 | 0.215 | 0.25 | 0.25 | 0.25 |
| Iron | $n_z$ | 2.61 | 2.65 | 2.65 | 2.65 | 2.6 |
| | $k_z$ | 0.35 | 0.3 | 0.25 | 0.175 | 0.1 |

(a) Data measured with glass substrates. $n_z$ is the refractive index; $k_z$ is the absorption coefficient.

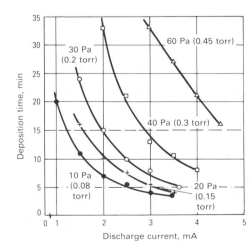

**Fig. 21** Correlation among discharge current, deposition time, and partial pressure of the reactive carrier gas in the reactive sputtering process

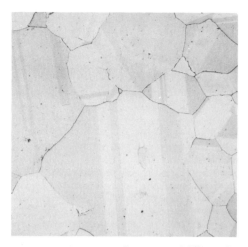 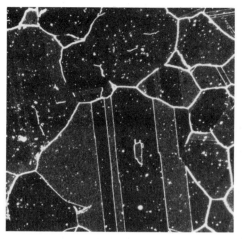 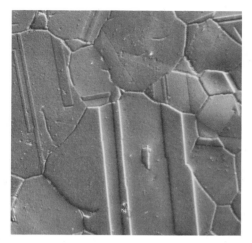

**Fig. 22, 23, 24** Comparison of different illumination modes for studying grain structure in solution-annealed and aged Waspaloy. Fig. 22: bright-field illumination. Fig. 23: dark-field illumination. Fig. 24: differential interference contrast. 145×. (G.F. Vander Voort)

values for specimen temperature can influence the optical constants of the emerging interference films and thus the specimen itself in the case of heat-sensitive material.

**Specimen Preparation.** Grinding and polishing scratches, deformation zones, and surface impurities on the specimen surface lead to an uncontrollable influence on the effective optical constants of the microstructural constituents to be analyzed. Some mounting materials under the effect of the glow discharge release volatile substances onto the specimen or into the gas chamber. This affects deposition.

Films produced by reactive sputtering in interference film metallography are characterized essentially by layer thickness, refractive index of the film, and the absorption coefficient of the film (Ref 54). The refractive index and absorption coefficient are primarily a function of the deposition material (cathode) used. Furthermore, wavelength of the transmitted light affects the optical film constants.

# Differential Interference Contrast

By C.E. Price
Professor
School of Mechanical and Aerospace
Engineering
Oklahoma State University

THE DIFFERENTIAL INTERFERENCE CONTRAST microscope distinguishes small variations in height on an apparently flat surface by changes in brightness or color of the image. There is a sense of three-dimensionality as compared to the bright-field microscope (Fig. 22 to 24), and finer details are revealed. Various color backgrounds may be selected, the colors being

**Table 5   Newton's rings: an abbreviated scale**

| Path difference | | Color |
|---|---|---|
| nm | Å | |
| 0 | 0 | Black |
| 40 | 400 | Iron gray |
| 158 | 1580 | Bluish gray |
| 234 | 2340 | Greenish white |
| 259 | 2590 | White |
| 332 | 3320 | Bright yellow |
| 430 | 4300 | Brownish yellow |
| 505 | 5050 | Reddish orange |
| 536 | 5360 | Red |
| 565 | 5650 | Purple |
| 575 | 5750 | Violet |
| 589 | 5890 | Indigo |
| 664 | 6640 | Sky blue |
| 747 | 7470 | Green |

those of Newton's rings* (Table 5). In the microscope, a polarized light beam is split into two beams that are superimposed after reflection from the specimen surface. Differences in height on the specimen surface result in differences in path length between the two beams, which affects the degree of interference when superimposed.

The instruments are usually based on systems proposed by Francon and Yamamoto (Ref 55) or Nomarski (Ref 56, 57). The systems are described in detail in Ref 58 to 61. The key feature is the device for splitting and recombining the beam. A Savart polaroscope and a modified Wollaston prism are used in the Francon-Yamamoto and Nomarski microscopes, respectively. The device, shown in Fig. 25, is simply inserted behind the objective lens of the microscope. It is matched to the objective lens and is available with most metallurgical microscopes. The same technique works for transmission electron microscopes, except separate units are needed for splitting and superimposing the beam.

If a complementary device, the polarization interferometer, is inserted instead, height

*Newton's rings are a series of circular bright and dark bands that appear about the point of contact between a glass plate and a convex lens that is pressed against it and illuminated with monochromatic light.

differences can be qualitatively measured routinely down to $\lambda/20$, where $\lambda$ is the wavelength of the light. Sodium illumination, for example, has a wavelength of 589 nm (5890 Å). Smaller height differences down to $\lambda/200$ are detectable and are reportedly measurable using special photographic procedures (Ref 61). In the differential interference contrast microscope, it is sometimes possible to detect height differences as small as 1 nm, or 10 Å (Ref 62). The more common Nomarski unit will be described here. A description of the principles and use of the Francon-Yamamoto microscope can be found in Ref 59. The two microscopes yield equivalent results.

## The Nomarski System

A schematic of the light path in a Nomarski system is shown in Fig. 26. The polarizer and the analyzer are set in the crossed position. The Nomarski unit incorporates a Wollaston prism to split the incident polarized light beam into two coherent components of equal intensity that are linearly polarized perpendicular to each other. The Wollaston prism consists of two similar wedges of a birefringent crystal cemented together to produce a plane-parallel plate (Fig. 27a). The di-

**Fig. 25** The Nomarski interference contrast attachment for a Reichert microscope connected to an objecive lens. The 25-mm (1-in.) long pin serves as a scale indicator.

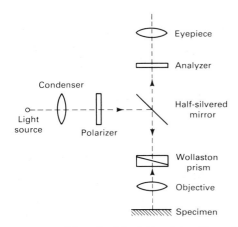

**Fig. 26** Schematic of the light path in a Nomarski differential interference microscope

vergence, $\varepsilon$, of the two beams is related to the wedge angle, $\alpha$, by the equation:

$$\varepsilon = 2(n_e - n_o) \tan \alpha \qquad \text{(Eq 7)}$$

where $n_o$ and $n_e$ are the refractive indices of the two rays, termed the ordinary ray and extraordinary ray, respectively. In the Nomarski unit, the wedges are quartz, and $(n_e - n_o)$ equals +0.009. The divergence of the two beams is such that they appear to originate inside the Wollaston prism and give rise to a series of interference fringes. In the polarization interferometer, these fringes are observed together with a double image, one from each beam. Any step on the specimen surface causes a displacement of the fringes at the interface between the two images, from which the height difference can be calculated.

The width of the interference fringes and their spacing can be varied somewhat by moving the Wollaston prism along the optical axis of the microscope. If the point of convergence of the two beams coincides with the rear focal plane of the objective, one interference fringe encompasses the field of view, and the appearance is uniform. To achieve this condition, the point of convergence must be brought outside the Wollaston prism, which could be achieved by modifying the Wollaston prism so that the optical axis of one prism is inclined at an angle $\eta$ to the surface (Fig. 27b). This is the condition in the differential interference contrast microscope. Furthermore, the angle $\alpha$ of the wedge is reduced such that the separation of the two beams does not exceed the resolving power of the objective lens. Therefore, only one image is seen.

The ordinary and extraordinary rays travel at different velocities: $v_o = c/n_o$ and $v_e = c/n_e$, where $c$ is the velocity (speed) of light in a vacuum. Because the optical axes of the two component prisms are at right angles, the ordinary ray in the first prism becomes the extraordinary ray for the second prism. Therefore, when the Wollaston prism is located along the optical axis of the microscope and the specimen is flat, the two split beams travel equal paths, and the crossed analyzer does not pass the resultant beam. A local difference in height of the specimen surface leads to a path difference, and this region appears bright. If the prism is moved sideways with respect to the optical axis, the two split beams do not travel equivalent paths (Fig. 28). Therefore, the analyzer will pass the spectrum, except for the wavelength corresponding to the path difference.

For example, if the path difference corresponds to a wavelength in the yellow region, the specimen appears blue or purple (white light minus the yellow). Any height difference on the specimen surface alters the path difference and therefore appears as a variation in color or brightness. The microscope is most sensitive in the gray region (Fig. 66 and 67). The height differences are relative. A feature that appears as a depression upon moving the prism to the left will appear elevated upon moving the prism to the right (Fig. 75 and 76). A polishing scratch or a microhardness indentation can be used for reference to identify depressions correctly. When height changes, one slope is made brighter, and the reverse slope less bright (Fig. 29). This may also be visible in the photomicrographs.

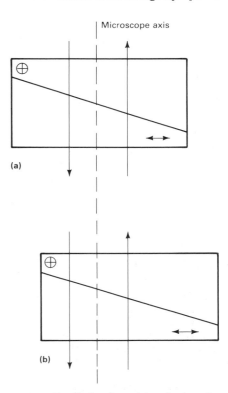

**Fig. 28** Travel of ordinary (o) and extraordinary (e) rays. The o ray in the first prism becomes the e ray in the second prism. The rays travel at different velocites. (a) If the Wollaston prism is located symmetrically relative to the microscope axis there is no resultant phase difference. (b) If the Wollaston prism is displaced sideways, there will be a resultant phase difference of approximately $\varepsilon x$, where $x$ is the displacement. The relatively small divergence, $\varepsilon$, of the o and e rays is not shown here.

## Applications

An advantage of the differential interference contrast microscope is that without changing the specimen preparation technique, the image can be made to appear blue, orange, gray, and so on, by moving a lever. Bright-field view can be obtained for comparison without removing the device by rotating the analyzer 45°, which extinguishes one beam. There are specific advantages in any situation in which small height differences may arise on a prepared specimen surface. For example, the microstructure of chemically polished or electropolished specimens can usually be revealed without etching. This is also true for mechanically polished specimens having different phases of sufficiently different hardness levels that relief develops during preparation. Upon etching, such features as subgrain networks and dislocation etch pits may be revealed more clearly.

A different category of usage involves the development of height differences on a specimen in service or during experiments, for example, because of wear, corrosion, phase tranformations, or mechanical deformation. The device is particularly useful for studying the progression of surface changes during a test. Therefore, the development of persistent

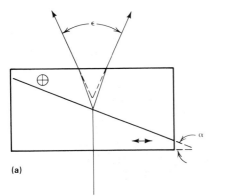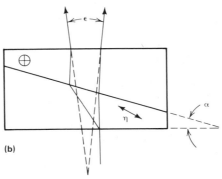

**Fig. 27** (a) Wollaston prism. The divergent rays appear to originate inside the unit. (b) By inclining the optical axis of one of the component wedges, the apparent point of origin can be brought outside the unit. By opposite inclinations, the image plane can be made real or virtual.

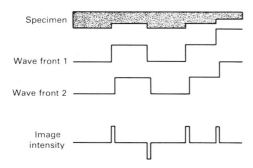

**Fig. 29** When changes in height occur, one slope appears brighter, the other less bright. See text for details.

slip bands and slip-band cracks during fatigue, the initiation of slip and/or stress-corrosion cracking during slow strain rate tensile tests, or the development of plastic zones around a stationary or propagating crack are clearly revealed under differential interference contrast, although during the early stages the surface may display little or nothing. Mechanical twins are similarly revealed. Interference contrast is useful for studying surface films or coatings and cleaved surfaces or for detecting incipient melting. Figures 33 and 34, 66 to 70, and 73 to 77 illustrate various applications of differential interference microscopy.

# Electronic Image Analysis

By Tommy Henson
Oak Ridge National Laboratory
and
Helen Henson
Oak Ridge Gaseous Diffusion Plant

ELECTRONIC IMAGING is a versatile materials-characterization tool that is assuming a greater role in the metallographic laboratory. Using this technique, a group of people can participate in the examination of a specimen surface while its image is displayed on a television monitor. Video recorders can document the microstructure as the specimen is being studied. Color cameras and recording equipment are often used.

However, electronic imaging is not always performed in color. A monochromatic electronic image consists of a spatial matrix of $x$-$y$ coordinate points, each of which is associated with a $z$ coordinate, or signal value, typically displayed as image brightness. The range of signal values comprises the gray scale of the image. The $x$-$y$ coordinates and the signal may be inherently digital or may consist of digitized analog signals, depending on the equipment used. The use of a single signal input for gray scale determination vastly simplifies quantitative image-analysis procedures; therefore, processing and feature

recognition for optical microscopy is commonly carried out in black and white.

The resolution of an electronic image is limited by the number of $x$-$y$ points, or pixels, present in the spatial matrix. An image obtained using special equipment can have as many as $10^8$ pixels; color cameras and monitors normally have less spatial resolving power than black and white and are limited to approximately $500 \times 500$ pixels. Electron micrographs are inherently monochromatic; the highest resolution black-and-white imaging equipment is used for scanning electron microscopy (SEM) or transmission electron miscroscopy (TEM).

It is often advantageous to add color to these monochromatic electronic images by arbitrarily assigning colors to signal levels (shades of gray). The human eye can differentiate only 24 gray levels, but can discern several thousand shades of color. Therefore, assigning individual shades of color to over 250 gray levels will significantly increase the amount of information recognizable in an image. In addition, color recognition occurs rapidly; the identification of a specific gray level within a monochromatic image is often tedious. The dramatic effect of highlighting a gray-scale level in red is invaluable in the rapid searching of large specimen areas for a specific feature of interest.

Pseudocolor may be used to enhance monochromatic electronic images and is therefore useful in many metallographic and microanalytical applications. The pixel points forming the spatial matrix can be produced in several ways; the signal associated with each pixel may be simple or complex, depending on the type of imaging used, the information the image is intended to convey, and the image-processing or feature-recognition techniques involved.

## Scanning Electron Microscopy and Electron Microprobe Images

The spatial matrix may be formed through direct computer control of the electron beam scanning system or through the use of a programmable video interface. Any of the output signals from the microscope may be supplied as the $z$ coordinate, including secondary and backscattered electron intensity, transmitted electrons, cathodoluminescence, target current, and outputs from the multichannel analyzer x-ray analysis system (see also the information on elemental analysis and quantitative analysis later in this section).

Figure 30 shows the black-and-white image produced by digital scanning of the beam of an electron microprobe during examination of a composite superconducting wire. This image consists of three major gray levels. After obtaining the black-and-white image, a histogram of the backscattered electron intensities (gray levels) was obtained, and the three peaks in the histogram were arbitrarily

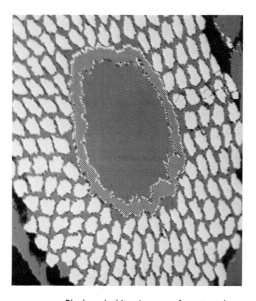

**Fig. 30** Black-and-white image of a tantalum-copper-niobium composite superconducting wire that was produced by digitally scanning the beam of an electron microprobe. Compare with the pseudocolor image shown in Fig. 78.

assigned colors. The resulting pseudocolor image is shown in Fig. 78.

Figure 84 shows the result of contrast enhancement through use of pseudocolor during examination of a metal-matrix composite specimen. Small differences in secondary electron signal become obvious matrix-phase differences when the color spectrum is compressed into a small region of the secondary electron gray scale. This enhancement of small intensity differences can also provide valuable feedback for microscope operation. Nonuniform intensity over a uniform field of view may indicate misalignment of the electron optical system; however, reproducible color imaging of a standard field indicates—with a sensitivity unavailable using meters or waveform monitors—that brightness and contrast conditions remain constant.

## Optical Microscopy

Digital imaging is commonly associated with image processing and feature-enhancement systems (see also the information on elemental analysis and quantitative analysis later in this section). A video tube is mounted in a camera port, and the optical signal directed to the camera. The intensity of transmitted or reflected bright field, polarized light, differential interference contrast, or any imaging technique that produces enough illumination for the video tube used can produce the gray-scale signal for pseudocolor imaging. The contrast enhancement for imaging and operational feedback information described above is also useful in optical imaging. In addition, the real-time imaging available through use of the video camera tube allows the rapid search through many fields of view for features that are pseudocolor imaged in vivid contrast.

## Transmission Electron Microscopy

Bright- or dark-field images can be digitized through the use of a video camera focused on a fluorescent screen and mounted beneath the film chamber of the microscope or on a side port of the viewing chamber. Color enhancement of these images and electron-diffraction patterns is then possible.

## Elemental Analysis

The simplest form of imaging signal is a binary response at each pixel point. This is the signal commonly used in elemental mapping with scanning electron microscopes and electron microprobes. The signal displayed is the response to the question, "Are there x-ray pulses at this point?" Displaying the one-level gray response in assigning color to the one-level positive response allows the combination of several elemental images, in different colors, to produce a single composite display containing all the information of the individual maps. Such a display is shown in Fig. 79.

A more complex signal for elemental analysis is intensity value at each pixel point. A histogram of these values may be produced, and pseudocolor used to provide a map of elemental concentration. X-ray signal images of this type are combined in Fig. 83 to yield information on distribution and elemental concentration.

Image processing and storage capability allows the generation of a new signal based on one or several digital images. For example, the histogram of the aluminum-to-magnesium x-ray intensity ratio might be coded in pseudocolor; the resultant image could clearly delineate phases in a mixed-metal matrix. Logically combining several images—aluminum and/or magnesium x-rays detected—is also possible. The specific function displayed is selected to emphasize features of interest.

Figure 85 shows an x-ray ratio image of an iron-base corrosion test coupon. The x-ray signal produced at each point when an electron beam digitally scans the surface of the specimen is used to define a gray scale; regions of this intensity gray scale are then color coded. The resultant image reflects elemental concentration. Similar maps can be obtained using other microanalytical techniques, such as Auger electron spectroscopy or secondary ion mass spectrometry.

## Quantitative Image Analysis

The use of pseudocolor in digital image-processing and feature-recognition systems has become widespread. Pseudocolor can be used to define several bins, or groups of gray-scale levels; each bin is then identified as an individual feature and analyzed separately. If a scanning electron beam instrument is used to perform the intensity separation, further characterization of features may be based on x-ray analysis. Multiple features can be characterized simultaneously; recognition of each individual feature is possible only through the use of color. Figures 80 to 82 depict the use of color to display several phases, along with quantitative measurements of the relative amounts of each phase.

The use of pseudocolor during the actual image analysis to indicate features meeting specified selection criteria provides operator feedback during analysis. In this case, the color might indicate the binary response to the question, "Is this part of a round feature less than 5 $\mu$m in diameter emitting between 4 and 8 secondary electrons per pixel and containing both phosphorus and iron, but no calcium?" The complexity of the feature-selection criteria depends on the image-processing equipment used and the signal inputs available. The random selection of color to indicate analysis of individual features may be used to monitor the process.

## REFERENCES

1. *Symposium on Metallography in Color,* STP 86, ASTM, Philadelphia, 1949
2. D.E. Brownlee, B. Bates, and R.J. Beauchamp, "Meteor Ablation Spherules and Chondrule Analoys, Chondruls and Their Origins," NASA Contract No. NASW3389, Lunar and Planetary Institute, Houston, 1983
3. E. Beraha and B. Shpigler, *Color Metallography*, American Society for Metals, 1977
4. R.J. Gray, R.S. Crouse, and B.C. Leslie, Decorative Etching, in *Metallographic Specimen Preparation: Optical and Electron Microscopy*, J.L. McCall and W.M. Muller, Ed., Plenum Press, 1974
5. J.V. Cathcart, G.F. Peterson, and C.J. Sparks, Oxidation Rate and Oxide Structural Defects, in *Surfaces and Interior Chemical and Physical Characteristics*, Burke, Reed, Weiss, Ed., Syracuse University Press, 1967
6. R.J. Gray, W.C. Thurber, and C.K.H. Dubose, Preparation of Arc-Melted Uranium Carbides, *Met. Prog.*, Vol 74 (No. 1), July 1958, p 65-70
7. R.J. Gray, E.S. Bomar, and R.W. McClung, Evaluating Coated Particles of Nuclear Fuel, *Met. Prog.*, Vol 86 (No. 1), July 1964, p 90-93
8. E. Weck and E. Leistner, *Metallographic Instructions for Colour Etching by Immersion—Part I: Klemm Colour Etching*, Deutscher Verlag für Schweisstechnik, 1982
9. E. Weck and E. Leistner, *Metallographic Instructions for Colour Etching by Immersion—Part II: Beraha Colour Etchants and Their Different Variants*, Deutscher Verlag für Schweisstechnik, 1983
10. E.C. Bain and W.E. Griffiths, *Trans. AIME*, Vol 75 (No. 166), 1927
11. *Metals Handbook*, Vol 1, 8th ed., American Society for Metals, 1961, p 34
12. *Symposium on the Nature, Occurrence and Effects of Sigma Phase*, STP 110, ASTM, Philadelphia, 1951
13. F.R. Beckitt, The Formation of Sigma Phase from Delta Ferrite in a Stainless Steel, *J. Iron Steel Inst.*, Vol 207, 1969, p 632-638
14. R.J. Gray, V.K. Sikka, and R.T. King, Detecting Transformation of Delta Ferrite to Sigma-Phase in Stainless Steels by Advanced Metallographic Techniques, *J. Met.*, Nov 1978, p 18-26
15. E.L. Long, Jr. and R.J. Gray, Better Metallographic Techniques, Polishing by Vibration, *Met. Prog.*, Vol 74 (No. 4), Oct 1958, p 145-148
16. W. Pepperhoff, Sechtbarmachung von Gefügestrukturen durch Interferenz—Aufdampfschichten, *Die Naturwissenschaften*, Vol 16, 1960, p 375
17. G.F. Vander Voort, *Metallography—Principles and Practice*, McGraw-Hill, 1984, p 180-181, 316-317
18. R.S. Crouse, R.J. Gray, and B.C. Leslie, Applications of Color in Metallography and Photography, in *Interpretive Techniques for Microstructural Analysis*, J.L. McCall and P.M. French, Ed., Plenum Press, 1977, p 43-64
19. E. Beraha, Metallographic Reagents Based on Sulfide Films, *Prakt. Metallogr.*, Vol 7, 1970, p 242-248
20. E. Beraha, Metallographic Reagents Based on Molybdate Solutions, *Prakt. Metallogr.*, Vol 11, 1974, p 271-275
21. M.L. Picklesimer, "Anodizing as a Metallographic Technique for Zirconium Base Alloys," Report ORNL-2296, Oak Ridge National Laboratory, Oak Ridge, TN, 1957
22. M.L. Picklesimer, Anodizing for Controlled Microstructural Contrast by Colors, *Microscope*, Vol 15, Oct 1967
23. R.S. Crouse, "Identification of Carbides, Nitrides, and Oxides in Niobium and Niobium Alloys by Anodic Staining," Report ORNL-3821, Oak Ridge National Laboratory, Oak Ridge, TN, July 1965
24. A. Hone and E.C. Pearson, Grain Orientation in Aluminum Revealed by Anodic Film, *Met. Prog.*, Vol 53, March 1948, p 363-365
25. E.C.W. Perryman, The Examination of Metal Surfaces, in *Polarized Light in Metallography*, G.K. Conn and F.J. Bradshaw, Ed., Butterworths, 1952, p 70-89
26. P.A. Jacquet, Improvements and New Applications of Non-Destructive Metallography, *Rev. Met.*, Vol 55, 1958, p 531-554
27. M.A. Edeleanu, *J. Iron Steel Inst.*, Vol 185, 1957, p 482-487
28. V. Cihal and M. Prazak, *J. Iron Steel Inst.*, Vol 193, 1959, p 360-367
29. P. Lichtenegger, A. Kulmburg, and R. Bloch, *Pract. Metallogr.*, Vol 6, 1969, p 535-539

30. F. Jeglitsch, *Aluminium*, Vol 45, 1969, p 45-49
31. H. Gahm and F. Jeglitsch, *Microstruc. Sci.*, Vol 9, 1981, p 65-80
32. J.H. Richardson, *Optical Microscopy for the Materials Sciences*, Marcel Dekker, 1971
33. H. Modin and S. Modin, *Metallurgical Microscopy*, Butterworths, 1973
34. V.A. Phillips, *Modern Metallographic Techniques and Their Applications*, Wiley-Interscience, 1971
35. G. Grutzner and J.H. Schuller, *Werkst. Korros.*, Vol 20, 1969, p 3203-3251
36. N.D. Greene and B.E. Wilde, *Corrosion*, Vol 26, 1970, p 533-538
37. W.A. Mueller, *Corrosion*, Vol 18, 1962, p 73t-79t
38. G. Grutzner and H.J. Schuller, *Pract. Metallogr.*, Vol 6, 1969, p 246-258
39. P. Helbach and E. Bullock, "Potentiostatic Etching of Carburized Steels," Petten, Establ., Netherlands: Committee of European Communities, EUR 8138, 1982
40. G.F. Vander Voort, Tint Etching, *Met. Prog.*, Vol 127, 1985, p 31
41. F.K. Naumann and G. Langenscheid, *Arch. Eisenhüttenwes.*, Vol 38, 1967, p 463-468
42. W. Schaarwachter, H. Ludering, and F.K. Naumann, *Arch. Eisenhüttenwes.*, Vol 31, 1960, p 385-391
43. F.K. Naumann, *Arch. Eisenhüttenwes.*, Vol 34, 1963, p 187-194
44. R. Bloch and P. Lichtenegger, *Pract. Metallogr.*, Vol 12, 1975, p 186-193
45. H. Ludering, *Arc. Eisenhüttenwes.*, Vol 2, 1964, p 153-159
46. A. Mance, *Metallography*, Vol 4, 1971, p 287-296
47. A. Mance, V. Perovic, and A. Mihajlovic, *Metallography*, Vol 6, 1973, p 123-130
48. J.O. Stiegler and R.J. Gray, Microstructural Discrimination by Deposition of Surface Films, in *Advances in Metallography, Technical Papers of the 20th Metallographic Conference*, R.J. Jackson and A.E. Calabra, Ed., RFP-658, The Dow Chemical Co., Midland, MI, Oct 1966, p 11-17
49. H.E. Bühler and H.P Hougardy, *Atlas der Interferenzschichten-Metallographie*, Deutsche Ges. für Metallkunde, Oberursel, 1979
50. H.J.Blumenkamp, H. Hoven, K. Koizlik, and H. Nckel, Optimierung der Phasenkennung mittels Konstrastierkammer für hochwarmfeste metallische Legierungen, *Ber. der Kernforschungsanlage Jülich*, Jül-1654, 1980
51. G. Bartz, Contrasting of Microscopic Objects in a Gas-Ion-Reaction Chamber, *Prakt. Metallogr.*, Vol 10 (No. 311), 1973
52. S. Hofmann and H.E. Exner, Auger-elektronenspektroskopische Untersuchungen von Kontrastierschichten auf Metallen, *Z. Metallkd.*, Vol 65 (No. 778), 1974
53. H.J. Blumenkamp, E. Wallura, H. Hoven, K. Koizlik, and H. Nickel, Quantitative Gefügenalyse farbkontrastierter hochwarmfester metallischer Legierungen, *Ber. der Kernforschungsanlage Jülich*, Jül-1673, 1980
54. K. Schmidt, H. Hoven, K. Koizlik, J. Linke, and H. Nickel, *Gefügeanalyse metallischer Werkstoffe*, Carl Hanser Verlag, Munich, 1985
55. M. Francon and T. Yamamoto, A New and Very Simple Interference System Applicable to the Microscope, *Optica Acta*, Vol 9, 1962, p 395-408
56. M.G. Nomarski, Microinterférométrie Differentiel à Ondes Polarisées, *J. Phys. Radium*, Vol 16, 1955, p 9
57. M.G. Nomarski and A.R. Weill, Application à la Métallographie des Méthodes Interférentielles á Deux Ondes Polarisées, *Revue de Metall.*, Vol 52, 1955, p 121-134
58. F. Herzog, Polarization Interferometric Methods in Incident-light Microscopy, With Special Reference to Material Testing, *Ind. Anz.*, Vol 60, July 1962, p 27-31
59. R. Hoffman and L. Gross, Reflected-Light Differential-Interference Microscopy: Principles, Use and Image Interpretation, *J. Microsc.*, Vol 91, 1970, p 149-172
60. M. Francon and S. Mallick, *Polarization Interferometers*, Wiley-Interscience, 1975
61. A.S. Holik, Surface Characterization by Interference Microscopy, *Microstruc. Sci.*, Vol 3, Part B, 1975, p 991-1010
62. W. Lang, "Nomarski Differential Interference Contrast Microscopy, Part IV: Applications," Zeiss Information, No. 77/78, 1971, p 22-26

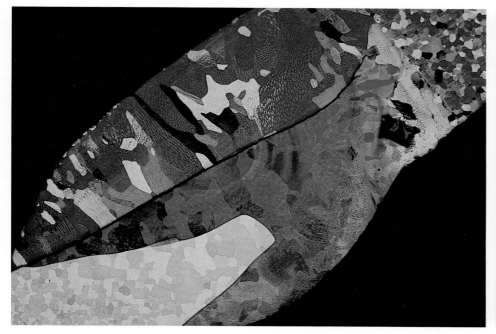

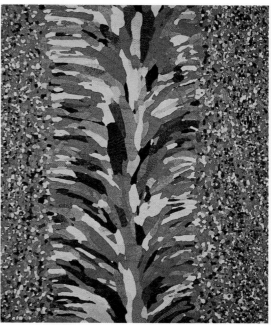

**Fig. 31** Ta-10W to Nb-10Hf-1Ti (C103) gas tungsten arc weldment. The Ta-10W is light brown and yellow, the C103 is red, and the alloyed area is blue. Attack polished, swab etched in 5 mL lactic acid, 5 mL H₂O₂, 5 mL HNO₃, and 5 mL HF, and heat tinted at 425 °C (800 °F). 15×. (P.E. Danielson)

**Fig. 32** Electron beam welded 32-mm (1¼-in.) thick C103 plate. The vivid grain color separation is due to heat tinting. See Fig. 31 for specimen preparation. 10×. (P.E. Danielson)

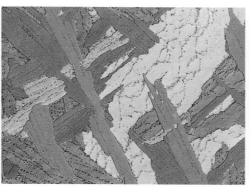

**Fig. 33** Hafnium crystal bar showing twins caused by cold working. Attack polished, heat tinted at 480 °C (900 °F), and viewed under differential interference contrast. 65×. (P.E. Danielson)

**Fig. 34** Zircaloy 4 as-cast ingot. Use of attack polishing, heat tinting (425 °C, or 800 °F), and differential interference contrast reveals the basic crystal structure and the iron-chromium second phase. 200×. (P.E. Danielson)

**Fig. 35** Mechanically twinned hafnium weld. Specimen was attack polished and heat tinted (~400 °C, or 750 °F). Polarized light. 60×. (P.E. Danielson)

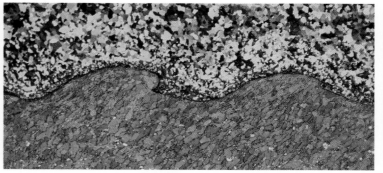

**Fig. 36, 37** Explosive-bonded 3.2-mm (⅛-in.) thick zirconium clad to 32-mm (1¼-in.) thick carbon steel plate. Attack polished, swab etched with 97% methanol and 3% HNO₃, and heat tinted at 370 °C (700 °F). Fig. 36: Under bright-field illumination, the zirconium is brown-blue and shows some grain orientation. The steel is yellow-green. 15×. Fig. 37: Note the difference between the anisotropic zirconium (top) and the isotropic steel (bottom) under polarized light illumination. 85×. (P.E. Danielson)

**Fig. 38** Color etching (10% aqueous $Na_2S_2O_5$) revealed the lath martensite packet size of AF 1410 ultrahigh-strength steel that was heat treated (austenitized at 900 °C, or 1650 °F, water quenched, and tempered at 675 °C, or 1250 °F). Polarized light. 100×. (G.F. Vander Voort)

**Fig. 39** Fe-1C alloy etched with acidified 1 g $Na_2MoO_4$ in 100 mL $H_2O$ to color the cathodic cementite. The cementite in the pearlite is blue; grain-boundary cementite is violet. 500×. (G.F. Vander Voort)

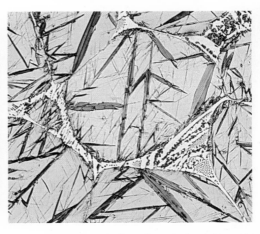

**Fig. 40** Fe-1.86C alloy color etched with 2% nital to reveal plate martensite within austenite grains and ledeburite in the grain boundaries. 500×. (A.O. Benscoter)

**Fig. 41** Aluminum bronze (ASTM B 148, Grade 9C) heat treated to form $Al_4Cu_9$. Preetched with aqueous 10% $(NH_4)_2S_2O_8$, color etched with Beraha's lead sulfide reagent. 500×. (G.F. Vander Voort)

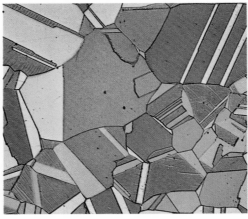

**Fig. 42** Alpha-brass (Cu-30Zn), cold worked and annealed. Color etching with Klemm's I reagent, which required approximately 1 h, revealed all the grains and annealing twins. 100×. (G.F. Vander Voort)

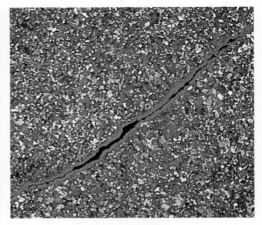

**Fig. 43** Recrystallized Ti-6Al-4V alloy with a crack resulting from creep rupture testing. Attack polished, color etched in 100 mL distilled $H_2O$, 4 mL HCl, and 3 g $NH_4HF_2$. Polarized light. 100×. (G. Müller)

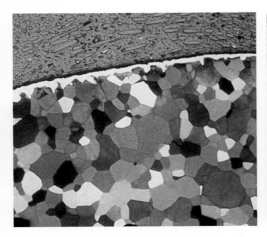

**Fig. 44** Equiaxed $\alpha$ structure of pure titanium. The white surface layer is oxygen-stabilized $\alpha$. The green at the top is mounting resin. Color etched with 100 mL distilled $H_2O$ and 5 g $NH_4HF_2$. 50×. (G. Müller)

**Fig. 45** Armco iron friction welded to carbon steel. Structure is ferrite (smaller grains) and pearlite plus ferrite (large grains). Color etched with Klemm's I reagent. 200×. (G. Müller)

**Fig. 46** Chromized sheet steel (Fe-0.06C-0.35Mn-0.04Si-0.40Ti) color etched to delineate ferrite structure. 3 g $K_2S_2O_5$, 10 g $Na_2S_2O_3$, and 100 mL $H_2O$. 100×. (A.O. Benscoter)

**Fig. 47** Ti-6Al-4V alloy containing martensite needles formed at elevated temperature (>840 °C, or 1540 °F). Color etched in 100 mL $H_2O$, 4 mL HCl, 3 g $NH_4HF_2$. Polarized light. 100×. (G. Müller)

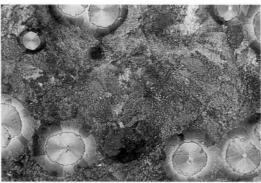

**Fig. 48** Ductile iron (3.63 to 3.69% C, 2.74% Si, 0.26% Mn, 0.084% S, 0.13% Cu, 0.060% Mg), as-cast alloy. Structure consists of graphite nodules in envelopes of free ferrite in a pearlite matrix. Color etched with Klemm's I reagent. 200×. (G. Müller)

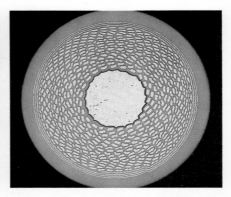

**Fig. 49** Multifilamentary superconducting alloy. Cu matrix: orange, Nb filaments: white. Sn core: white area at the center. The three rings encircling the filaments are Ta diffusion barriers. Color etched: 10 mL $H_2O_2$ and 2 to 3 drops HF. 5×. (P.E. Danielson)

**Fig. 50** Explosive-bonded 3.2-mm (1/8-in.) thick zirconium clad to 6.4-mm (1/4-in.) thick titanium. The zirconium is yellow; the titanium, blue-purple. Attack polished and anodized in 60 mL ethanol, 35 mL $H_2O$, 20 mL glycerine, 10 mL 85% lactic acid, 5 mL 85% $H_3PO_4$, and 2 g lactic acid at 85 V. 15×. (P.E. Danielson)

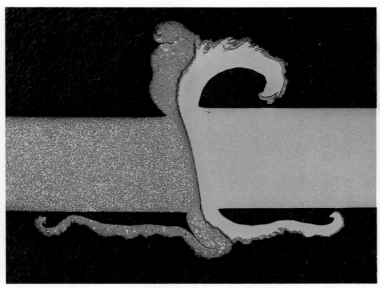

**Fig. 51** Friction-welded tubing (zirconium to titanium). Note the small heat-affected zone produced by this weld process. The zirconium is yellow; the titanium, blue-purple. See Fig. 50 for specimen preparation. 10×. (P.E. Danielson)

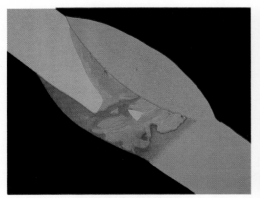

**Fig. 52** Same weld as shown in Fig. 31, but specimen swab etched in 5 mL lactic acid, 5 mL $H_2O_2$, 5 mL $HNO_3$, and 5 mL HF, then anodized (see Fig. 50 for solution) at 115 V. The Ta-10W is yellow, the C103 blue-green, and the alloyed area pink-red. 10×. (P.E. Danielson)

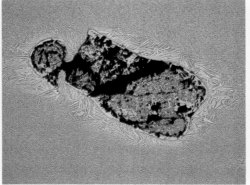

**Fig. 53** Light element contamination (mostly nitrogen) in hot-rolled 6.4-mm (1/4-in.) thick Zr-2.5Nb plate. Defect core is highest in contamination, as evidenced by the turquoise, yellow, and red. Black areas are voids. Attack polished and anodized (as in Fig. 50) at 110 V. 10×. (P.E. Danielson)

**Fig. 54** As-cast zirconium containing niobium-base (green) and tantalum-base (yellow) inclusions. The defects resulted from scrap zirconium added to the melt. Attack polished and anodized (as in Fig. 50) at 115 V. 10×. (P.E. Danielson)

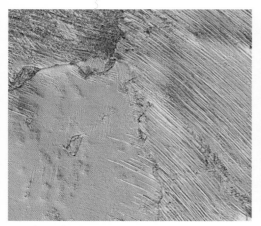

**Fig. 55** Cast austenitic manganese steel (ASTM A128, Grade D) tensile test specimen. Large grains show localized changes in orientation due to twinning. Electrolytic etch: 80 g $Na_2CrO_4$ in 420 mL glacial acetic acid. 100×. (G. Grube and D. Subramanyam)

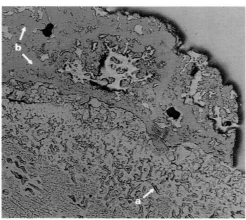

**Fig. 56** Type 316 stainless steel exposed to air for 3000 h at 870 °C (1600 °F). Vapor depositing a $TiO_2$ coating onto the as-polished surface reveals two oxide compositions (arrow b) and subsurface void formation. Epoxy-filled voids are shown by arrow a. 100×. (R. Crouse)

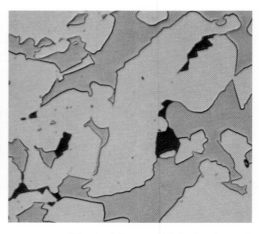

**Fig. 57** Siliconized silicon carbide heat exchanger tube, vapor deposited with $TiO_2$. Silicon carbide is gray-tan, silicon is yellow, and an iron-nickel-silicon intermetallic is violet. 500×. (R. Crouse)

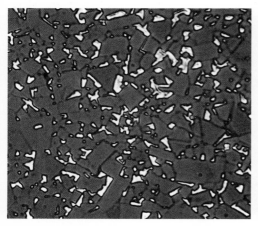

**Fig. 58** WC-Co cemented carbide, etched with Murakami's reagent, then vapor deposited with ZnSe to color the tungsten carbide grains violet and the cobalt binder white-blue. 1125×. (G.F. Vander Voort)

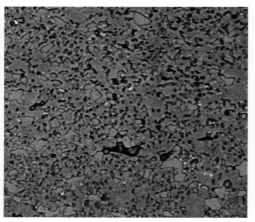

**Fig. 59** Use of vapor deposition to reveal entrapped tungsten carbide inclusions in an $Al_2O_3$-TiC cermet cutting tool. The as-polished surface was vapor deposited with ZnSe. The tungsten carbide is dark red, the titanium carbide is pink, and the $Al_2O_3$ is blue. 1125×. (G.F. Vander Voort)

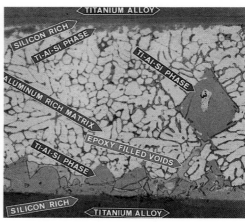

**Fig. 60** Titanium alloy brazed with an aluminum-silicon brazing alloy. As-polished and vapor deposited with zirconium dioxide. 500×. (R. Crouse)

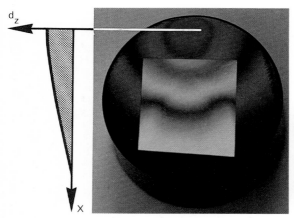

**Fig. 61** Interference film, visible as a nearly concentric color ring system in white incident light. The thickness of the sputtered film from the center in the radial direction is shown schematically. See Fig. 62 for the influence of film thickness on the chromatic contrast between phases. (K. Koizlik)

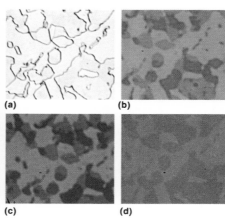

**Fig. 62** Reactive sputtered Hastelloy X specimen. (a) As-etched. (b) Yellow ring. (c) Purple ring. (d) Blue center, zero-order ring. Cathode material: iron. See also Fig. 61. (K. Koizlik)

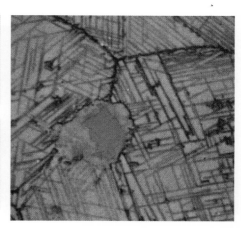

**Fig. 63** Optimum conditions of chromatic contrast by an interference film (iron oxide) deposited by reactive sputtering and aged (750 °C, or 1380 °F, for 3400 h) Inconel 625 specimen. (K. Koizlik)

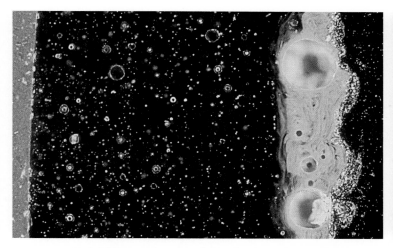

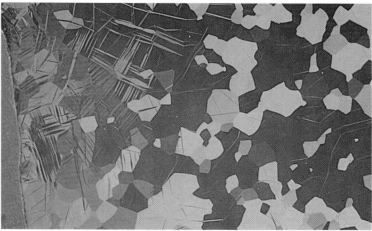

**Fig. 64** Dark-field image of an enameled steel. Left to right: mounting material (light blue), cover coat enamel (dark blue), glass enamel (gold), and the steel base metal (black). A nickel layer between the glass and steel is not visible using dark-field illumination. As-polished. 100×. (G. Müller)

**Fig. 65** Titanium alloy with a zone of mechanical deformation caused during shearing the specimen from an 8-mm (0.3-in.) diam bar. The light blue area on the side is mounting resin. Attack polished. Polarized light. 200×. (G. Müller)

**Fig. 66, 67** As-cleaved antimony specimen viewed under differential interference contrast illumination. Views under different contrast conditions show the greater sensitivity in the gray regime (Fig. 66) than in the non-gray regime (Fig. 67). Twins, river patterns, and cracks are present. As-polished. 200×. (C.E. Price)

**Fig. 68** Nickel 200 specimen, fatigued in reverse bending for 10⁴ cycles. Use of differential interference contrast shows persistent slip bands with associated cracks outlined against a blue background. Chemically polished. 800×. (C.E. Price)

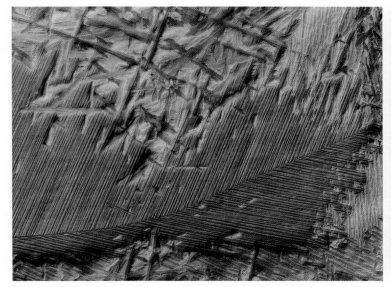

**Fig. 69** Zircaloy forging as viewed under differential interference contrast. The parallel platelet structure is an area lower in carbon content. Etched in 45 mL $H_2O$, 45 mL $HNO_3$, and 10 mL HF and heat tinted at 425 °C (800 °F). 100×. (P.E. Danielson)

**Fig. 70** As-cast Zircaloy structure as viewed under differential interference contrast. The high mechanical deformation evident was induced deliberately during specimen preparation. Attack polished and heat tinted at 420 °C (800 °F). 100×. (P.E. Danielson)

**Fig. 71** Bright-field illumination

**Fig. 72** Cross-polarized light illumination

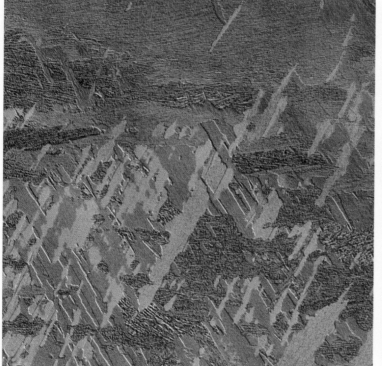

**Fig. 73** Differential interference contrast illumination

**Fig. 74** Differential interference (reverse topography) illumination

**Fig. 71 to 74** Comparison of bright-field, cross-polarized light, and differential interference contrast used to examine the basket-weave pattern of an $\alpha$-$\beta$ Ti-6Al-4V alloy. Figures 73 and 74 illustrate the influence of adjusting the Wollaston prism on the observed topography. The same effect can be seen in Fig. 75 and 76. Kroll's reagent. 200×. (G.F. Vander Voort)

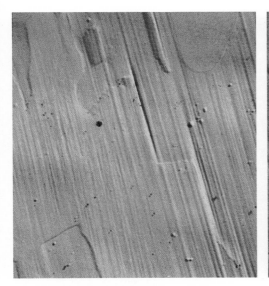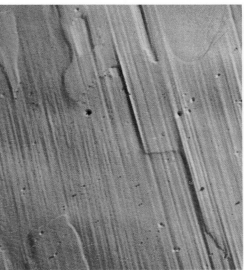

**Fig. 75, 76** Plastically deformed Nickel 200 specimen viewed under orange differential interference contrast to either side of the Wollaston prism symmetry position so that the height differences appear reversed. Chemically polished. 800×. (C.E. Price)

**Fig. 77** Heat-tinted niobium alloy (C103) plate as viewed under differential interference contrast illumination. Some of the grains exhibit a second phase (note small particlelike features) due to alloying additions. 65×. (P.E. Danielson)

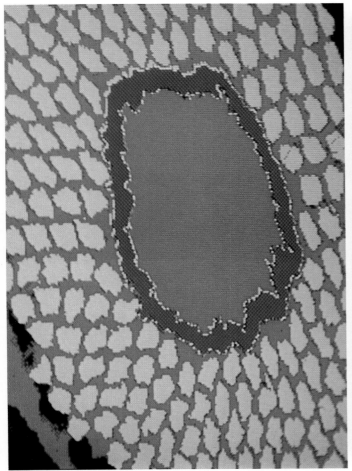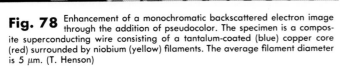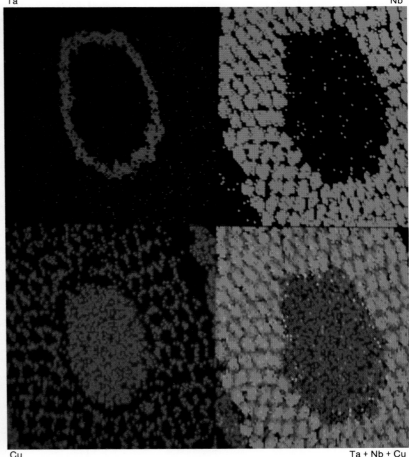

**Fig. 78** Enhancement of a monochromatic backscattered electron image through the addition of pseudocolor. The specimen is a composite superconducting wire consisting of a tantalum-coated (blue) copper core (red) surrounded by niobium (yellow) filaments. The average filament diameter is 5 μm. (T. Henson)

**Fig. 79** X-ray elemental images of the same specimen shown in Fig. 78, but color coded differently. Three individual x-ray maps are combined to yield the composite image shown at the bottom right. (T. Henson)

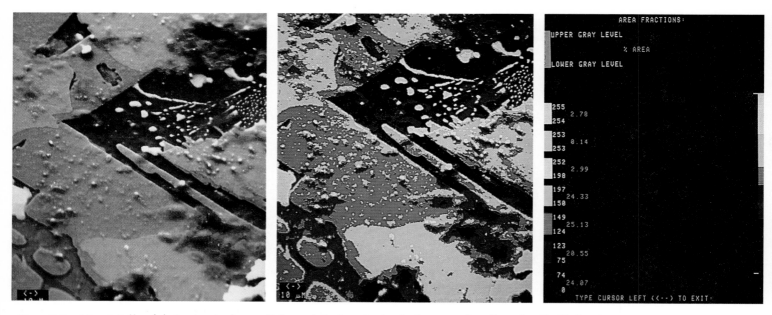

**Fig. 80, 81, 82** Use of electron imaging for quantitative analysis of a cerium-bearing iron-magnesium-silicon alloy. Fig. 80: digital image of a secondary electron signal from a scanning electron microscope. The image is digitized into 256 discrete gray levels. Fig. 81: pseudocolor digital image of Fig. 80. Each major gray range has been "painted" with a different color, corresponding to the various phases in the materials. Fig 82: quantitative area fraction information obtained from the color-coded digital image. The system determines the number of pixels within a specific gray level range (indicated by color) relative to the total number of pixels that form the image. (D. Skinner)

**Fig. 83** Digital x-ray maps for Mg, Si, Ca, Fe, and Ce collected simultaneously with the SE image show the spatial distribution of the elements in this Fe-base specimen. (D. Skinner)

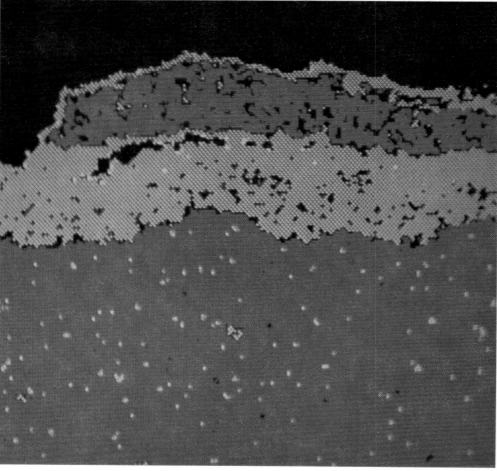

**Fig. 84** SE image of a composite cross section. Al-Mg matrix surrounds carbon fibers (blue-purple). The sky-blue material is a heavy-metal contaminant. Fibers, ~10 μm diam. (T. Henson)

**Fig. 85** X-ray concentration mapping of a steel corrosion test coupon. The surface corrosion film consists of an iron sulfide (red). A mixed oxide forms a brown iron-depleted zone below the surface; the matrix is iron-rich. 340×. (T. Henson)

# Metallographic Techniques and Microstructures: Specific Metals and Alloys

# Carbon and Alloy Steels

By Arlan O. Benscoter
Metallographer
Bethlehem Steel Corporation

CARBON AND ALLOY STEELS can be manufactured with a wide range of properties, which are made possible by the various microstructures that can be produced in these alloys. To describe these microstructures, it is necessary to identify the constituents present, then determine their proportions and distributions. Correct assessments of microstructure depend on proper preparation of metallographic specimens.

This article will describe preparation techniques for carbon and alloy steels. The micrographs presented following this article include examples of the effects of alloying, thermal and thermomechanical treatments, and cooling rates on certain alloys.

## Specimen Preparation

**Sectioning.** A sample to be metallographically examined generally must be sectioned to a convenient size before other steps to reveal its microstructure can be performed. The microstructure is more vulnerable to alteration during sectioning than in any other metallographic preparation step. An altering of the microstructure, commonly called an artifact, can occur by excessive heat, mechanical deformation, or both. Artifact microstructures often prevent correct interpretation of the true microstructure. Abrasive wheel cutting, sawing, and shearing are common methods of sectioning steel samples.

Shearing is a fast method of sectioning, but results in extreme mechanical deformation. Care must be taken to remove the deformation zone by rough grinding. If the specimen is mounted in a clamp after shearing, material should be left protruding from the clamp and removed later by grinding. If the specimen is mounted in epoxy or a thermosetting material, the thickness of the mount should be measured to ensure that enough material is removed during grinding.

An artifact microstructure caused by mechanical deformation as the result of shearing a dual-phase steel is shown in Fig. 1. The microstructure consists of small islands of pearlite and martensite in a ferrite matrix. The true microstructure (Fig. 2) consists of small

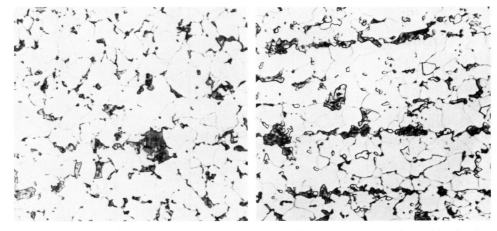

**Fig. 1, 2** Dual-phase steel (0.11C-1.40Mn-0.58Si-0.12Cr-0.08Mo). Specimen was obtained by shearing. Fig. 1: an artifact microstructure resulting from mechanical deformation during shearing. Fig. 2: a polished plane 2 mm (0.08 in.) below the structure shown in Fig. 1. The true structure consists of islands of martensite (dark), small patches of pearlite (black), and retained austenite (white, outlined) in a ferrite matrix. 12% aqueous Na$_2$S$_2$O$_5$. 1000×

islands of pearlite, martensite, and retained austenite (white phase) in a ferrite matrix. The retained austenite of this particular grade of steel is stable and can withstand temperatures as low as −200 °C (−330 °F) without transforming to martensite, yet it can be readily transformed by mechanical deformation. The same specimen is illustrated in Fig. 1 and 2, except the polished plane in Fig. 2 is 2 mm (0.08 in.) below that in Fig. 1.

Sectioning using a low-speed band saw or power hacksaw can be slow and tedious. The specimen should be softer than 350 HB for the saw to be effective. The resulting surface is rough and generally uneven if manually fed. The frictional heat generated can be minimized by using oil or water-soluble oil as the cutting fluid. The cutting fluid also prolongs the life of the saw blade by preventing tempering of the teeth.

Abrasive-wheel cutting, if properly executed, is by far the best technique for obtaining a steel specimen surface that is smooth, has minimal deformation, and has no microstructural changes caused by overheating. The many abrasive-wheel cutting machines available range from small, gravity-fed models using 100-mm (4-in.) diam wheels to large floor models with 305-mm (12-in.) diam, 1.5-mm (1/16-in.) thick wheels.

Steel samples should be sectioned using alumina (Al$_2$O$_3$) wheels of the proper rubber-bonded hardness. The specimen is kept cool during cutting by an ample flow of water-soluble oil; cutting can also be performed with the specimen submerged in the coolant. The appropriate wheel hardness should be selected, and the proper force applied during cutting. Manufacturers code wheels differently, ranging from a soft bond that readily deteriorates and exposes fresh Al$_2$O$_3$ particles needed for cutting hard specimens to hard-bonded wheels that break down slowly. The latter are preferred for softer materials.

Care must be taken when cutting with an abrasive wheel. If the specimen is not properly secured with a clamp, the wheel is likely to break. A steady, firm pressure must be maintained against the specimen. Careless use of an abrasive cutoff machine with coolant capability can result in artifacts, as depicted in Fig. 3 to 5. In this example, too

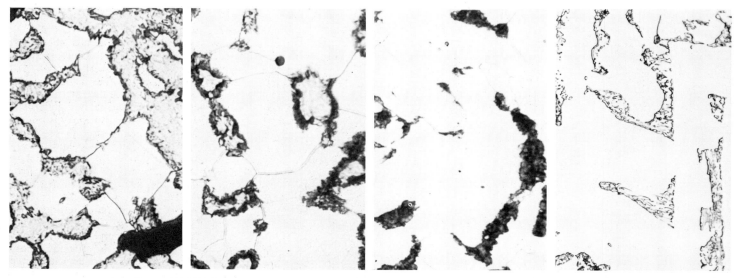

**Fig. 3, 4, 5, 6** Low-alloy steel (0.15% C). Fig. 3, 4, and 5: artifact structures caused by overheating of the specimen during sectioning on an abrasive cutoff wheel. Fig. 6: Specimen was reground and polished to reveal the true structure consisting of coarse pearlite and carbides in a ferrite matrix. 4% picral. 1000×

much force and insufficient coolant caused the steel specimen to heat above 720 °C (1330 °F) at the surface. The metallographically prepared surface exhibits structures of martensite in a ferrite matrix (Fig. 3), islands of martensite surrounded by fine pearlite (Fig. 4), and islands of very fine pearlite in a ferrite matrix (Fig. 5). The photomicrographs display scratch-free, well-defined microstructures, but all are artifacts. The true microstructure (Fig. 6), a coarse pearlite and carbide structure in a ferrite matrix, was revealed after regrinding and polishing. The artifact structures of martensite and fine pearlite were caused by heating the patches of coarse pearlite and carbides into the austenitizing temperature range for their composition, followed by rapid cooling.

Examples of surface deformation in an AISI 1010 steel specimen are shown using dark-field illumination in Fig. 7 to 9. Figure 7 is a cross section illustrating the depth of de-

formation caused by sectioning with an abrasive cutoff wheel. The specimen shown in Fig. 8 was sectioned using a band saw, and that in Fig. 9 was obtained by shearing. These micrographs demonstrate the degree of increasing deformation. Figure 10 depicts a planar polish perpendicular to that in Fig. 9, and Fig. 11 shows the same specimen after removal of 2 mm (0.08 in.) of material.

**Mounting.** Not all metallographic specimens must be mounted before examination. A bulk specimen that is convenient to handle can be successfully prepared and examined at 1000×. This requires beveling the edges to prevent tearing or catching of the polishing cloths, which can cause an uneven surface.

Various considerations must precede the mounting of a specimen, such as use of an etchant to reveal the microstructure that may also attack the mounting medium. For example, alkaline sodium picrate used to darken

cementite attacks Bakelite mounts. In addition, examination of a specimen edge for decarburization, carburization, internal oxidation, degree of oxide scale, and so on, will require a mounting material with minimal shrinkage properties, such as epoxy or thermosetting epoxy. Further, if an oxide scale is to be examined, a material requiring the use of pressure may get in between and separate the scale from the base material.

Figures 12 and 13 depict the same nickel plated steel. The nickel illustrated in Fig. 12 has been lifted from the steel during mounting in a thermosetting material; in the castable epoxy mount (Fig. 13), the nickel has not been disturbed. Another consideration is the effect of heat on the microstructure. Figures 14 and 15 depict the same material that has been sectioned, ground, polished, and etched identically. The specimen shown in Fig. 15 was mounted in castable epoxy and is the true microstructure; Fig. 14 illustrates tem-

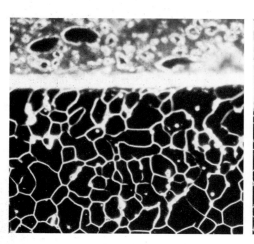
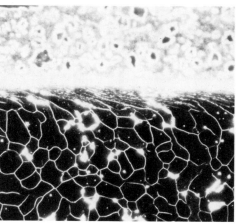
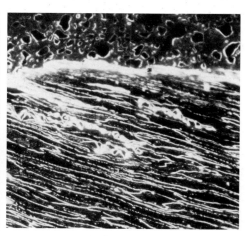

**Fig. 7, 8, 9** The effects of sectioning techniques on AISI 1010 hot-rolled steel. Fig. 7: specimen obtained by using an abrasive cutoff wheel. Minimal deformation at the cut surface. Fig. 8: specimen obtained by band sawing. Some deformation at the cut surface. Fig. 9: specimen sectioned by shearing, causing severe deformation at the cut surface. Dark-field illumination. Marshall's reagent. 400×

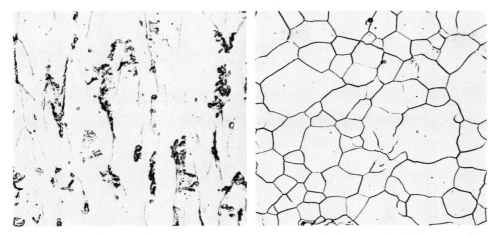

**Fig. 10, 11** AISI 1010 steel, as hot rolled, showing the effects of insufficient grinding following sectioning. Fig. 10: broken carbides, voids around carbides, and heavily cold-worked ferrite grains (the result of shearing). Fig. 11: a polished plane approximately 2 mm (0.08 in.) below that shown in Fig. 10. The true microstructure consists of ferrite grains. Marshall's reagent. 500×

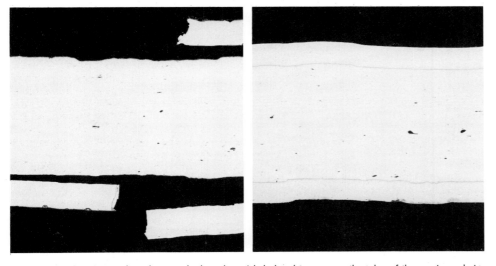

**Fig. 12, 13** Low-carbon sheet steel, electroless nickel plated to preserve the edge of the specimen during preparation. Fig. 12: specimen mounted in Bakelite. The pressure required to cure the mount material caused the nickel plating to pull away from the steel. Fig. 13: A castable epoxy mounting material was used. The nickel plate is intact. As-polished. 100×

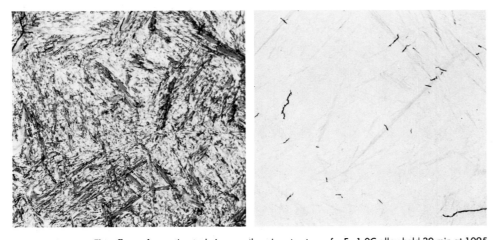

**Fig. 14, 15** The effects of mounting technique on the microstructure of a Fe-1.0C alloy held 30 min at 1095 °C (2000 °F) and water quenched. Fig. 14: specimen mounted in Bakelite. The heat needed to cure the mount tempered the martensite. Fig. 15: A castable epoxy mount was used. The structure is as-quenched martensite. Both etched using 10% aqueous $Na_2S_2O_5$. 500×

pering in a specimen mounted with a thermosetting material heated to 150 °C (300 °F).

Castable mounting materials should be used when heat may affect the microstructure or when pressure may disturb a fragile surface condition. A common technique used for castable mounts is to glue Bakelite ring forms to aluminum foil supported by a glass plate or thin sheet steel. After the epoxy is poured into the mold, a vacuum is used to remove air bubbles trapped in small cracks and crevices in the specimen; it will also remove bubbles introduced during mixing. An air-cure mixture will often become tacky after exposure to different solvents. This condition can be minimized if the mount, after setting up, is placed in an oven at 65 °C (150 °F) for 4 h. Mounts larger than 38 mm (1.5 in.) in diameter should be placed in a refrigerator until they have set up to prevent an exothermic reaction; otherwise, stresses resulting from such a reaction may cause the large mass of epoxy to crack.

Another possible application of epoxy is examination of a surface condition obscured by the mounting medium. An example is shown in Fig. 16. The material is Zincrometal covered with black paint. The top of the mount was polished to permit light from a fiber optic lamp to pass through the epoxy, clearly delineating the paint from the mount. If the light is not used, viewing the mount/paint interface is difficult (Fig. 17).

Epoxy can also be used to salvage compression mounts having voids between the specimen and mount, which causes the etchant to bleed onto the specimen. Masking tape is wrapped around the mount, leaving the mount recessed approximately 6 mm (0.25 in.). Epoxy is then poured into the recess to a depth of approximately 1.5 mm (0.0625 in.), and a vacuum is used to remove air from the voids, allowing the epoxy to flow between the compression medium and the specimen.

Ferrous specimens for routine examination are often mounted in Bakelite. The powder should be free of moisture; sharp corners on bulk specimens should be rounded when possible; and the mount should be cooled slightly before ejection from the mold.

Bakelite or thermosetting epoxies can be used to mount any gage wire by first preparing a blank mount, then drilling holes slightly larger than the wire. The wire is placed into the holes, and masking tape is wrapped around the mount, extending approximately 6 mm (0.25 in.) above it. Epoxy is poured into the recess created by the tape; the mount is placed in a vacuum for several minutes, purged several times, then allowed to cure.

Mounting specimens using steel clamps is very rapid and versatile. Multiple sheet, small bulk, and wire specimens can be secured with clamps. The main disadvantage of this technique is that a clamp mount must be ultrasonically cleaned to remove debris after the final grinding and after each polishing step.

Clamp mounts are shown in Fig. 18. The clamps are usually fabricated of 3- to 6-mm

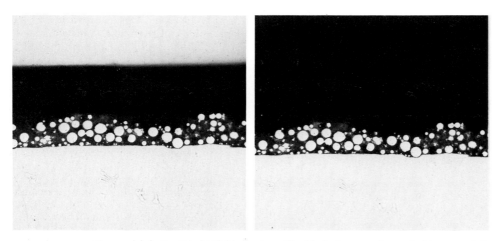

**Fig. 16, 17** Zincrometal sheet painted with black primer. Fig. 16: A clear mounting material was used. A light passed through the mount from the back highlights the primer/mounting material interface. Fig. 17: Using an opaque mounting material, it is difficult to see the primer/mounting material interface. As-polished. 200×

(0.125- to 0.25-in.) thick 1020 steel plate. Each clamp is approximately 13 mm (0.5 in.) wide and 25 to 51 mm (1 to 2 in.) long, with holes at each end. One half is threaded to receive a bolt, and the other half has a mating hole through which the bolt can pass.

Mounting using clamps involves placing the specimen or specimens so that enough material protrudes to ensure removal of any deformation zone caused by sectioning. The two bolts are then tightened, and the clamp with specimen is secured in a vise, after which the bolts are tightened further. This will minimize seepage.

**Grinding.** As previously mentioned, regardless of the type of equipment used to section a sample, surface damage will be present to some degree. A series of grinding steps using successively finer grits must be used to remove the damaged layer and produce a flat surface having minimal deformation.

Silicon carbide papers should be used to prepare ferrous materials. The first grit size depends on the sectioning of the specimen. For example, a saw-cut or sheared surface may require an 80-grit paper, followed by 120, 240, 320, 400, and 600 grit; a specimen sectioned using an abrasive wheel may require starting with a 240-grit abrasive. During grinding, water must be used to flush the disk and keep the specimen cool, except when water-soluble particles (for example, aluminum nitrates), are present in the specimen. If water-soluble particles are suspected and require examination, mineral spirits, kerosene, or a commercial lapping oil that does not contain water must be used during grinding.

To obtain a flat surface with minimal deformation, the specimen should be held with the fingertips as close as possible to the grinding paper, using a moderately heavy pressure, and slowly moved back and forth from center to edge of the grinding disk. The specimen surface should be examined periodically to determine when scratches from the previous grinding have been removed. Grinding

should continue two to three times longer than the time required to remove the scratches from previous operations. This will ensure elimination of the deformed zone. If a facet occurs during grinding, the pressure point should be changed. For example, more pressure can be applied with the thumb and less with the fingers or conversely. Grinding should proceed using the abrasive on which the facet occurred or the previous grit; a finer grit should not be used until the surface is flat. The specimen should be rotated 45 to 90° between steps.

If the specimen—whether mounted or unmounted—is not square, the grinding sequence should be planned so that the longest

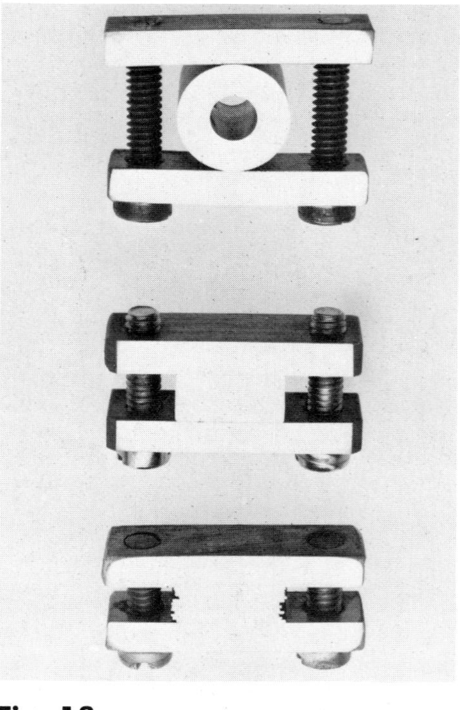

length is parallel to the final grinding; otherwise the specimen can rock, causing an uneven or rounded surface. When changing papers, the wheel should be moistened with water to prevent slippage of the paper while grinding.

Flushing of the specimen before proceeding to the next step will prevent contamination of the next grinding papers. After final grinding, all specimen surfaces should be cleaned with cotton and water, flushed with alcohol, then dried. Clamp-mounted specimens should be cleaned with cotton and water, ultrasonically cleaned with alcohol, and dried.

Examples of artifacts caused by improper grinding are shown in Fig. 19 and 20. Figure 19 depicts the result of proceeding to the next grinding step as soon as the scratches from the previous step have disappeared; random lines, mottled surface, and obscured grain boundaries are visible. When this occurs, the specimen must be reground to remove the artifacts. Figure 20 illustrates the same specimen after correct grinding. Deformation caused by grinding can also alter the microstructure.

Figure 21 shows the effects of grinding on retained austenite in a dual-phase steel. The 25- by 51-mm (1- by 2-in.) specimen was planar polished for x-ray diffraction using a new paper for each grinding; it was then polished using 6-μm, then 1-μm diamond. X-ray diffraction revealed the presence of 7.8% retained austenite. The specimen was reground using worn papers, followed by the diamond polishing, resulting in 5.7% retained austenite. Repetition of the experiment using worn papers resulted in an even lower austenite count. The two chemically polished planes were used as a standard. Both planes that were polished using worn papers resulted in the austenite transforming to martensite due to mechanical deformation.

**Polishing** techniques for steel specimens depend on their microstructure. For a specimen with a pearlite or carbide microstructure, polishing times should be short and steps few to minimize relief. A specimen in which the ferrite grain boundaries are to be etched would require longer polishing times and an etch after each polishing.

Pearlite or carbide microstructures can be polished using 6-μm diamond on a canvas cloth for 1 min, followed by 1-μm diamond on a medium-nap cloth. Both diamond steps should be executed using moderately heavy pressure on a low-speed polishing wheel while rotating the specimen clockwise.

If a water-soluble diamond compound is used, the specimen should be cleaned after polishing with a good grade of natural cotton and water, flushed with alcohol, then dried. The specimen should then be polished on a stationary wheel using a medium-nap cloth and a colloidal suspension of 0.04-μm silicon dioxide ($SiO_2$). If an adhesive-backed cloth is used, a thick glass or plastic plate can be substituted for the wheel. If the specimen contains 1.0% Si or more, the $SiO_2$ polishing

**Fig. 18** Clamps used for metallographic mounting

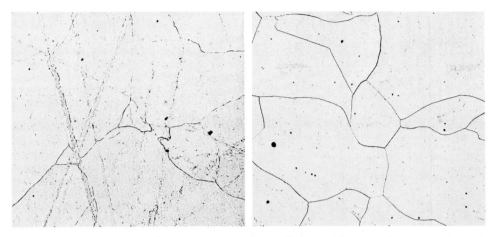

**Fig. 19, 20** Low-carbon (0.01% C) sheet steel, showing effects of insufficient grinding. Fig. 19: Specimen was ground only until scratches from the previous operation disappeared. The structure is an artifact. Fig. 20: Specimen was ground 2 to 3 times longer than that in Fig. 19 to reveal the true microstructure. 2% nital. 200×

compound should be cleaned off with denatured alcohol and cotton to prevent staining; otherwise the specimen should be cleaned with water, flushed with alcohol, and dried. Figure 191 shows a specimen that was polished using this procedure.

A specimen in which the ferrite grains are to be revealed can be polished 1 min using a low-speed wheel and 6-μm diamond on a low-nap cloth. The specimen is then etched 15 s in 2% nital, repolished 2 min using 0.3-μm $Al_2O_3$ on a medium-nap cloth and a low-speed polishing wheel, re-etched 15 s in 2% nital, and repolished 1 min using 0.3-μm $Al_2O_3$. The final polishing should be carried out with $SiO_2$ for 30 s on a stationary medium-nap cloth. After each step, the abrasive should be removed with cotton and water and the specimen flushed with denatured alcohol, then dried immediately. Figure 224 illustrates a specimen that was polished using this procedure.

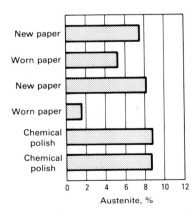

**Fig. 21** The effect of using worn grinding papers on retained austenite in a dual-phase steel. The specimen was first ground using new papers. X-ray diffraction revealed 7.8% retained austenite. The specimen was repolished using worn papers, resulting in 5.7% retained austenite. The experiment was repeated, resulting in an even greater difference in austenite count. Austenite transformed to martensite due to mechanical deformation. The two chemically polished planes were used as the standard.

Nonmetallic inclusions can be retained by polishing with 6-μm diamond on a stationary napless cloth for 2 min, 1-μm diamond on a stationary napless cloth, then 1-μm diamond on a low-nap cloth for 1 min. After each polishing, the specimen should be cleaned with denatured alcohol and cotton, flushed with alcohol, and dried.

The following procedures will keep specimens flat and free of polishing artifacts during polishing. The edges of a clamp, mount, or bulk specimen should always be beveled to prevent catching on the polishing cloth, which can result in a rounded surface. Beveling also prevents tearing of the cloth. The specimen should always be rotated counter to wheel direction to avoid a comet tail effect, as shown in Fig. 22. Figure 23 illustrates the same specimen polished correctly. Polishing abrasives should be removed from the specimen as quickly as possible to prevent their drying and causing an artifact. For example, $SiO_2$ drying on the specimen can sometimes appear as coarse pearlite. A commercially available free-standing blow dryer works well

on metallographic specimens because of the large volume of warm air it produces.

## Microetching

The specimen should be etched immediately after the final polishing. Etching solutions used to reveal the microstructures of carbon and alloy steels are listed in Table 1, along with their primary characteristics. Nital and picral are the most widely used etchants for carbon and alloy steels. Nital is generally used in concentrations of 1 to 3% $HNO_3$ in ethanol or methanol. In solutions containing more than 4 to 5% $HNO_3$, only methanol should be used, because ethanol becomes unstable as the concentration of $HNO_3$ increases.

Picral generally consists of a 4% solution of picric acid in ethanol. Four or five drops of 17% zephiran chloride per 100 mL 4% picral solution will hasten the etchant reaction and prevent preferential attack. Picral works best when it turns dark with use. Etching times generally range from 15 to 30 s, with the polished face held upward. The specimen should be held with tongs and agitated gently. After etching, the specimen should be held under water to remove excess etchant, flushed with denatured alcohol, and dried. If the water causes stains—for example, in steels having more than 1% Si—the etching solution should be removed by placing the specimen in a sequence of alcohol baths, flushing with alcohol, and drying.

A 1:1 solution of 4% picral and 2% nital is sometimes used, or the specimen can be etched using picral, then nital. The latter technique is useful for etching ferrite grain boundaries in a pearlite-ferrite microstructure without overetching the pearlite (Fig. 106). Etching times are 10 to 15 s in 4% picral and 5 to 10 s in 2% nital.

**Ferrite grain boundaries** can be etched using nital in most carbon steels, although Marshall's reagent (etchant 8, Table 1) appears to be the better etchant for low-carbon

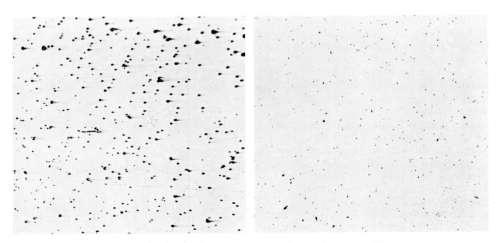

**Fig. 22, 23** Decarburized AISI 1010 steel, showing the effects of improper polishing. Fig. 22: comet tails from polishing. Fig. 23: the same material polished correctly showing very small manganese sulfide inclusions. As-polished. 100×

**Table 1 Metallographic reagents for iron and steel**

| Etchant | Composition | Remarks | Uses |
|---|---|---|---|
| 1. Nital | 2 mL HNO$_3$ and 98 mL ethanol or methanol (95% or absolute; also amyl alcohol) | Not as good as picral for high-resolution work with heat-treated structures; excellent for outlining ferrite grain boundaries; etching time: a few s-1 min | For carbon steels; gives maximum contrast between pearlite and a ferrite or cementite network; reveals ferrite boundaries; differentiates ferrite from martensite |
| 2. Picral | 4 g picric acid, 100 mL ethanol or methanol (95% or absolute; use absolute alcohol only when acid contains 10% or more moisture), and 4 or 5 drops 17% zephiran chloride (wetting agent) | Not as good as nital for revealing ferrite grain boundaries; gives superior resolution with fine pearlite, martensite, tempered martensite, and bainitic structures; detects carbides; etching time: a few s-1 min or more | For all grades of carbon steels; annealed, normalized, quenched, quenched and tempered, spheroidized, austempered |
| 3. Sodium metabisulfite | (A) 8 g Na$_2$S$_2$O$_5$ and 100 mL distilled H$_2$O | General reagent for steel; results similar to picral; etching time: few s-1 min | Darkens as-quenched martensite |
| | (B) 10 g Na$_2$S$_2$O$_5$ and 100 mL distilled H$_2$O | Pre-etch 2 s in 2% nital rinse followed by 20 s in Na$_2$S$_2$O$_5$ solution | General uses for dual phase steels; reveals pearlite, darkens martensite, and outlines austenite; a pre-etch of 10-15 s in 2% nital followed by 20 s in Na$_2$S$_2$O$_5$ will outline the ferrite grain boundaries and identify pearlite, martensite, and austenite |
| 4. Vilella's reagent | 5 mL HCl, 1 g picric acid, and 100 mL ethanol or methanol (95% or absolute) | Best results obtained when martensite is tempered | For revealing austenitic grain size in quenched and quenched and tempered steels |
| 5. Heat tinting | Heat only | Heat by placing specimen face up on a hot plate that has been preheated to 205-370 °C (400-700 °F); time and temperature have decided effects; bath of sand or molten metal may be used | Pearlite first to pass through a given color, followed by ferrite; cementite less affected, iron phosphide still less |
| 6. Picric acid with sodium tridecylbenzene sulfonate | 1 g sodium tridecylbenzene in 100 mL saturated aqueous picric acid | Etching time varies with grade, heat treatment, and concentration of the wetting agents; etching time can be reduced and results improved by placing solution with specimen in an ultrasonic cleaner; for steels containing high silicon, add varying amounts of CuCl$_2$ to reveal grain boundaries more sharply | Reveals prior austenite grain boundaries in martensitic steels |
| 7. Klemm's reagent | 50 mL saturated (in H$_2$O) Na$_2$S$_2$O$_3$ solution and 1 g K$_2$S$_2$O$_5$ (potassium metabisulfite) | Etching time: 40-120 s; ferrite appears black-brown, but carbides, nitrides, and phosphides remain white; phosphorus distribution can be detected more sensitively than with usual phosphorus reagents based on copper salts | Tint etches pearlite, hardened structures of unalloyed steel, and cast iron |
| 8. Marshall's reagent | (A) 100 mL H$_2$O, 8 g oxalic acid, and 5 mL H$_2$SO$_4$<br>(B) 30% H$_2$O$_2$ | Mix equal volumes of solutions (A) and (B) just before using; etch 2-3 s; 3 s pre-etch in 2% nital may be needed | Uniform ferrite grain boundary etch for low-carbon or electrical steels |
| 9. Alkaline sodium picrate | 2 g picric acid, 25 g NaOH, and 100 mL distilled H$_2$O | Use boiling, 5-10 min; do not boil dry; solution will attack mounts made from Bakelite | Colors cementite, but not carbides high in chromium; attacks sulfides; delineates grain boundaries in hypereutectoid steels in slowly cooled condition |
| 10. Beraha's reagent | 3 g K$_2$S$_2$O$_5$, 10 g Na$_2$S$_2$O$_3$, and 100 mL H$_2$O | Pre-etch 3-5 s with 2% nital | Colors ferrite grains |

and decarburized steels (Fig. 224). Ferrite grain boundaries in low-carbon, 1% Si, titanium-bearing steels are difficult to delineate. In this case, Beraha's tint etchant (etchant 10, Table 1) will differentiate the grains by color (Fig. 59). Tint etchants such as Beraha's or sodium metabisulfite (Na$_2$S$_2$O$_5$) should not be agitated; the specimen should be pre-etched 2 to 3 s in picral or nital. A specimen etched in a tint etchant cannot be reimmersed if the structure is too light, but repolishing for 15 s using 0.3-$\mu$m Al$_2$O$_3$ will remove the tint etchant.

**Pearlite, cementite, and Fe$_3$C carbides** in all carbon steels can be etched using 4% picral with zephiran chloride. Alloyed steels to be etched using 4% picral may require a few drops HCl to each 100 mL of solution to enhance contrast among the phases. Pearlite will not always appear lamellar (Fig. 157), because the spacing between the cementite and ferrite constituting the phase cannot always be resolved using an optical (light) microscope (Fig. 158). Figure 159 is a replica electron micrograph of the pearlite patch circled in Fig. 158. The lamellar structure is visible. Special cases require other etchants to reveal pearlite, cementite, and other carbides.

Figure 200 shows a pearlite structure etched using Beraha's tint etchant to darken the ferrite and highlight the cementite. Figure 105 illustrates a carburized structure etched using alkaline sodium picrate (etchant 9, Table 1). The etchant attacks the cementite in the prior austenite grain boundaries. Figure 49 demonstrates that Marshall's reagent colors carbides light brown and lightly etches the ferrite grain boundaries. If picral had been used, the grain boundaries would not have been revealed; if nital had been used, the small carbides would not have appeared in the boundaries.

**Bainite** can be etched using picral or a picral-nital procedure in much the same way as pearlite. Figure 109 was etched using 4% picral, and Fig. 122 was etched using 4% picral, then 2% nital.

**Martensite,** low-carbon lath-type, can be etched using 2% nital or an 8% aqueous solution of Na$_2$S$_2$O$_5$, as shown in Fig. 107. High-carbon plate-type martensite can also be etched in nital or Na$_2$S$_2$O$_5$, although nital is preferred (Fig. 201).

**Multiphase microstructures** with martensite combined with bainite, pearlite, or ferrite can be etched using a 10% aqueous solution of Na$_2$S$_2$O$_5$ (etchant 3, Table 1) without overetching any single phase (Fig. 108).

**Internal oxidation** is etched using 4% picral (Fig. 226).

**Nonmetallic inclusions,** if etched 2 to 4 s in aged 4% picral, will be more sharply contrasted.

## Macroetching

Macroetching is an inspection procedure for revealing certain aspects of the quality and structure of a steel by subjecting it to the corrosive action of an etchant and examining it visually or at low magnification.

Macroetching is widely used to inspect bars, billets, forgings, castings, and other steel products. Specimens are usually selected to represent a given batch or lot of metal and destructively tested by etching in acid until the structural characteristics or conditions are revealed. Some bars or forgings to be further worked or machined are inspected nondestructively using this method. Macroetching may be used to reveal bursts, pipe, segregation, overheating, flakes, cracks, porosity, nonmetallic inclusions, seams, grain flow, macrograin size, decarburization, local or surface hardening, grinding burns, and weld penetration.

**Specimen Selection.** A specimen usually consists of a full section of material and should be thick enough to permit easy handling and subsequent surface preparation. Transverse specimens are the most common. When taken to investigate the effect of structural elongation by rolling or forging, longitudinal specimens should be cut parallel to the direction of metal flow and preferably through the centerline of the piece.

When surface condition is the principal consideration, the part itself may serve as a suitable specimen. In surface inspection for the presence of seams and laps, the specimens are randomly selected.

Consideration should be given to the stage of mechanical working at which the specimen is selected. Because macroetching exaggerates inhomogeneities, conditions that may be detrimental in a completely formed steel are not necessarily objectionable in a steel that is to be mechanically worked.

**Specimen Preparation.** If the mass of steel from which a specimen is to be taken is relatively soft, for example, less than approximately 300 HB, the specimen usually can be most easily extracted by sawing or by some other machining operation. Difficulty in extraction by sawing increases with hardness; specimens are extracted from hard steel by abrasive-wheel cutting. Gas cutting is sometimes used to obtain specimens from very large sections.

However, if gas cutting is used, areas affected by heat must be removed by machining or abrasive-wheel cutting before the specimen is etched. When abrasive-wheel cutting is used, a copious flow of water or other coolant must be supplied to prevent overheating of any portion of the specimen during cutting. If portions of the specimen overheat, results of macroetching are likely to be misleading. Regardless of how the specimen is prepared, oil, grease, and dirt should be removed using a suitable solvent before etching.

**Surface Finish.** Required surface finishes for specimens for macroetching vary from saw-cut or machined surfaces to polished surfaces. The permissible degree of surface roughness depends largely on the severity of the etchant to be used. In general, the more severe the etchant, the rougher the permissible surface finish.

The allowable surface roughness also depends on the type of examination. For instance, surfaces to be inspected for such imperfections as seams, laps, or checks require no surface preparation. For this type of examination, a severe etchant is used to remove rust or scale. When machined surfaces are to be inspected for defects, the normal ma-

chined or ground finishes provide acceptable surfaces for macroetching.

When the purpose of etching is to reveal structural details such as those developed in induction hardening or welding, a far less severe etchant is used, and a smoother surface finish is required. The surfaces of specimens are often ground and polished to achieve the same degree of smoothness as that used for microscopic examination.

## Equipment for Macroetching

The primary equipment for macroetching consists of a container for the etchant, provision for heating the etchant (if necessary), a ventilating system to contain and remove corrosive fumes, and some means for washing and drying the specimen.

For occasional work with small specimens, equipment available in most metallographic laboratories is adequate. However, for production macroetching, equipment is needed that will give satisfactory service over a long period, and hoists or conveyor systems are commonly used to minimize handling difficulties. The installation should have a covered hood equipped with a forced exhaust system to remove the corrosive fumes. For safety, a spray nozzle or shower head should be located near the etch tank.

**Etch tanks** can be dishes or trays made of porcelain, heat-resistant glass, or a corrosion-resistant alloy. For large production installations, three types of tanks are in general use: (1) tanks molded from a mixture of special acid-digested asbestos or graphite filler and synthetic resin, (2) steel tanks coated with rubber or synthetic resin and lined with properly bonded acid-resistant brick or carbon brick, and (3) tanks made of corrosion-resistant metal. Tanks of nonmetallic construction are more widely used than metal tanks. When metal is used, lead is the most common for resisting sulfuric acid ($H_2SO_4$) solutions, and high-nickel alloy or high-silicon iron for hydrochloric acid (HCl). Nickel-molybdenum alloy tanks are also used.

**Rinse tanks** can be made of the same material as etch tanks or can be made of stoneware or other ceramic material. A neutralizing solution, such as dilute ammonium hydroxide ($NH_4OH$), can be held safely in a container of low-carbon sheet steel.

**Hoods and exhaust systems** can be made of treated wood, molded asbestos, plastic, or steel coated with acid-resistant synthetic resin. The exhaust system preferably consists of a blower to raise the room pressure and, adjacent to the stack, another blower that delivers air into the stack to exhaust the fumes collected under the hood.

**Heating Equipment.** Tanks may be heated by a gas or electric hotplate or by a steam jacket. Large tanks can be heated by a low-pressure steam heat exchanger or by a steam jet discharging directly into the etching solution. The method of heating that is most adaptable or that can be controlled most ef-

fectively with the particular equipment should be selected.

Temperature usually is measured using a mercury thermometer, and the heat source is controlled manually. However, use of a thermostat provides greater uniformity of etching.

**Plumbing.** The necessary piping and fittings can be made from ceramics, plastics, or alloys, as indicated for the other acid-resistant equipment.

**Acid Disposal.** Where large volumes of acid are being disposed of, the same precautions apply as for the disposal of spent pickling solutions (see the article "Pickling of Iron and Steel" in Volume 5 of the 9th Edition of *Metals Handbook*).

## Etchants

Table 2 lists the etchants most commonly used for macroetching carbon and alloy steels. A solution of equal parts HCl and water (etchant 1, Table 2) is the most widely used.

Concentrated HCl (etchant 2, Table 2) is sometimes used instead of the 50% solution. The concentrated etchant is often preferred for etching lower-carbon, more highly alloyed steels.

Various mixtures of $H_2SO_4$ and HCl with water are also alternatives to the 50% HCl solution (note etchants 3, 4, 6, and 7, Table 2). Mixtures of nitric acid ($HNO_3$) and hydrofluoric acid (HF) with water (etchant 5, Table 2) are sometimes preferred for macroetching carbon and alloy steels, especially those with higher alloy contents. However, etchants containing HF cannot be used in glass containers, and hazards attend its use. Burns are extremely painful and slow to heal.

All the above etchants are intended for use at elevated temperature, as shown in Table 2. When the use of a hot etchant is infeasible, a mixture of 10 to 25% $H_2SO_4$ in water at room temperature will reveal the general characteristics listed for etchant 1 in Table 2. However, the 8 to 24 h required for etching with $H_2SO_4$ at room temperature is much longer than for etching in heated acid.

Etchants 8 to 13 in Table 2 are intended for use at room temperature. They are also useful for general macroetching. However, more often, they are used for revealing details of specific conditions, such as those listed in Table 2.

**Etchant Life.** For most routine etching, it is not necessary to discard the etchant after etching of each specimen or group of specimens, although this is recommended for best results. Life of an etching solution depends largely on etching time and temperature. For instance, the acid deteriorates faster at 80 °C (175 °F) than at 70 °C (160 °F). Further, the recommended time may vary widely, permitting a significant variation in the amount of metal dissolved in the acid. As the amount of dissolved metal increases, the action of the etchant decreases, and longer etching time is

# 172/Metallographic Techniques and Microstructures

**Table 2  Etchants and recommendations for macroetching of carbon and alloy steels**

| No. | Etchant Composition (parts listed are by volume(a) | Etching time(b) | Surface required(c) | Purpose, or characteristic revealed |
|---|---|---|---|---|
| **Etchants for use at 70 to 80 °C (160 to 175 °F)(b)** | | | | |
| 1 | 1 part HCl and 1 part $H_2O$ | 15-60 min | A or B | Segregation, porosity, hardness penetration, cracks, inclusions, dendrites, flow lines, soft spots, structure, weld examination |
| 2 | Conc HCl | 15-60 min | A or B | Same as for etchant 1 |
| 3 | 2 parts $H_2SO_4$, 1 part HCl and 3 parts $H_2O$ | 30-60 min | A | Same as for etchant 1 |
| 4 | 50 parts HCl, 7 parts $H_2SO_4$, and 18 parts $H_2O$ | 30-60 min | A | Same as for etchant 1 |
| 5 | 10-40 parts $HNO_3$, 4-10 parts 48% HF, and 50-87 parts $H_2O$ | Until desired etch is obtained | B or C | Same as for etchant 1; ratio of $HNO_3$ to HF can vary, as shown at left |
| 6 | 38 parts HCl, 12 parts $H_2SO_4$, and 50 parts $H_2O$ | 30-60 min | B or C | Same as for etchant 1 |
| 7 | 10 parts $H_2SO_4$ and 90 parts $H_2O$ | 15-60 min | A | Sulfide and oxide inclusions |
| **Etchants for use at room temperature** | | | | |
| 8 | 2-25% $HNO_3$ in $H_2O$ or ethanol | 5-30 min | B or C | Carburization and decarburization, hardness penetration, cracks, segregation, weld examination |
| 9 | 2.5 g $CuCl_2$, 20 g $MgCl_2$ (magnesium chloride), 10 mL HCl, and 500 mL ethanol | Until coppery sheen appears | B or C | Phosphorus-rich areas, banding |
| 10 | 50 g $(NH_4)_2S_2O_8$ (ammonium bisulfite) and 500 mL $H_2O$ | Swab until desired etch is obtained | C | Grain size, weld examination |
| 11 | 40 g $FeCl_3$, 3 g $CuCl_2$, 40 mL HCl, and 500 mL $H_2O$ | 15-30 s | B or C | Dendritic structure of cast steel; precede use of this etchant with etch in 10% nital for 1-20 s |
| 12 | 30 g $FeCl_3$, 1 g $CuCl_2$, 0.5 g $SnCl_2$, 50 mL HCl, 500 mL ethanol, and 500 mL $H_2O$ | 30 s-2 min | C | Dendritic structure of cast steel; overetching deposits excessive copper, which may obscure details of structure |
| 13 | 4 g picric acid in 100 mL methanol | 3-5 h | C | Carbon segregation |

(a) All acids listed are of concentrated strength; commercial grades ordinarily can be used instead of laboratory or reagent grades. Water or alcohol should never be poured into an acid; rather, the acid should always be poured and gradually stirred into the other liquid. (b) See text for discussion of variations in time and temperature. (c) A = saw-cut or machined surface; B = average ground surface; C = polished surface

required. With experience, it is possible to estimate the increase in etching time needed to allow for solution deterioration and to judge when the solution should be discarded.

## Etching Procedure

The usual procedure in macroetching is to immerse the prepared specimens in the etching solution, with the surfaces to be examined face up or vertical to permit the gas generated to escape freely. Nonuniform etching will result if the specimens overlap or are racked too close together.

**Heated Solutions.** When using heated etchants, the etching solution should be at the pre-established temperature before the specimens are immersed. It is difficult to reproduce desired results when the specimens are placed in the etching solution before the temperature is reached. For maximum uniformity, especially when the total volume of the specimens is high compared to the volume of solution, the specimens should be preheated in a water bath to the same temperature as the etching solution. This permits more accu-

rate control of etching time and simplifies control of the solution temperature.

For the seven etchants in Table 2 used above room temperature, an etching temperature of 70 to 80 °C (160 to 175 °F) is recommended. At temperatures on the lower side of this range, etching reaction is sufficiently vigorous to provide effective etching without excessive evaporation of solution. However, in production-control etching, temperatures on the higher side of the range are preferred, because they decrease etching time.

**Etching time** depends on the type of steel, surface condition, and physical condition of the specimen. For best reproducibility of results with many specimens, the time should be measured and should not vary from batch to batch. If etching time is too brief, not all the desired information will be revealed; if too long, some of the finer details of structure will be masked or obliterated by the general destruction of the surface resulting from overheating.

The etching times recommended in Table 2 are for average results on annealed speci-

mens. The time actually required to develop the desired results in a particular test can be determined by frequent examination of the specimen as etching proceeds. Marked variations in the susceptibility to attack by the acid solution will be found among different heats of steel and with different methods of heat treatment. Susceptibility to attack also varies with the position of the specimen in the ingot, which determines the amount of segregation, and with the degree of smoothness of the specimen surface. Resulfurized carbon and alloy steels usually etch very rapidly. Higher carbon steels (0.50% C and greater) normally etch more rapidly than low-carbon steels. Cold-worked steels, such as fasteners produced by upsetting, also etch readily, and care must be taken to avoid over-etching.

**Specimen Preservation.** After a specimen has been properly etched, it should be removed from the etchant, rinsed thoroughly under running water, scrubbed with a stiff fiber brush to remove any "smut" from the surface, rinsed again, and dried by a warm-air blast or by blotting with paper or cloth towels. A cold-water rinse usually will result in a better appearing etched surface than that obtained using a hot-water rinse. Immersion in the etchant for a few minutes after scrubbing improves definition, especially of flow lines.

As a temporary means of avoiding rust, the etched specimen may be rinsed in water, dipped in a dilute alkaline solution such as ammonium hydroxide ($NH_4OH$) to neutralize the remaining traces of acid, and washed in hot water. The residual acid can also be neutralized by dipping the specimen in a dilute solution of potassium carbonate ($K_2CO_3$) or sodium carbonate ($Na_2CO_3$); in addition to neutralizing the acid, these solutions leave a film that prevents rust after drying. For longer preservation, the dried specimen should be covered with a thin film of transparent plastic, clear lacquer, or oil. Spray-type packaged plastics provide the most convenient method of applying this protective film. Protective films should be removed before the macroetched specimen is studied further.

Rusting can be delayed temporarily, and some rust can be removed from dried specimens by applying a 1:1 solution of phosphoric acid ($H_3PO_4$) and water. Excess solution can be blotted with cloth or paper towels. Caution is recommended in using this technique, because the strong acid solution will attack the skin and disintegrate cloth upon prolonged contact.

## Recording of Results

In recording the results of macroetching, the observed conditions may be grouped by type and location. Records should include full information on type and composition of the steel, cross-sectional dimensions of the specimen, and conditions or defects observed.

**Table 3 Checklist of principal macroetch observations to be recorded for semifinished steel products**

| Surface or subsurface | Center or central area | General |
|---|---|---|
| (A) Cracks | (a) Pipe | ($\alpha$) Flakes or cooling cracks |
| (B) Seams or laps | (b) Porosity | ($\beta$) Dendritic pattern |
| (C) Decarburization | (c) Bursts | ($\gamma$) Ingot pattern |
| (D) Pinholes | (d) Segregations | ($\delta$) Grain size |
| (E) Segregations | | |

Table 3 provides a suggested checklist for use in recording results of macroetching. The coded defects or conditions may be further coded to indicate degrees of severity and applicability to particular parts or uses.

## Interpretation of Results

The results obtained on properly etched specimens are of maximum value when interpreted correctly. Surface seams, internal cracks, and pipe are easily recognized. Incorrect interpretation of the evidences of segregation and dendritic structure as revealed by macroetching may cause expensive errors and needless rejection of metal. For example, not every pit indicates an inclusion or evidence of an undesirable condition, because pitting may result from the use of partly spent acid or from attack around normal carbide particles.

Irregular etching effects, such as blotchiness or pitting, can be obtained if the etching solution is dirty or contaminated, or if the surface being etched has retained oil or grease, was smeared or cold worked in machining, or was protected from the etchant by contact with other specimens in the bath. Specimens cut with an abrasive wheel may, unless cut slowly or under a flood of coolant, show broad, dark streaks resulting from surface burning and having no relationship to the actual structure.

Results of macroetching can be interpreted only in terms of the type and grade of steel being inspected. Rimmed, semikilled, and killed steels will exhibit characteristics of the methods of their manufacture. Poor control of etchant temperature or etching time will greatly affect the appearance of the characteristics of etched surfaces. When questionable results are obtained, the surface should be machined again and etched in a fresh solution under carefully controlled conditions.

**Cracks From Etching.** If hardened or highly stressed steels are not tempered sufficiently before etching, sound steel may crack by stress corrosion in the etching solution and lead to false conclusions.

## Conditions Revealed by Macroetching

Macroetching can be used to reveal a variety of conditions, many of which are described below and illustrated in accompanying macrographs.

**Dendritic Structure.** Etching often reveals a dendritic structure that results from the solidification of the ingot. Dendritic structure is detected even in steel that has been subjected to repeated mechanical reduction. This is not detrimental if the steel has been worked enough and the segregation accompanying the dendritic structure is not in the form of excessively large nonmetallic inclusions.

Dendritic structure present in cast steel and persisting in wrought steels can be revealed by an etchant composed of ferric chloride ($FeCl_3$), cupric chloride ($CuCl_2$), stannous chloride ($SnCl_2$), HCl, ethanol, and water (etchant 12, Table 2). A polished specimen is etched by immersion for 30 s to 2 min. Etching for too long a period deposits excessive copper, which may obliterate the details of the dendritic structure.

Dendritic structure can also be revealed by the use of an etchant that contains $FeCl_3$, $CuCl_2$, HCl, and water (etchant 11, Table 2). The specimen surface, which may be smoothly ground through 00 emery paper or metallographically polished, is etched 10 to 20 s using 10% nital, washed and dried, then immersed 15 to 30 s in the above etchant. The dendritic pattern developed is revealed by visual examination in incident light.

**Ingot Pattern.** The conditions leading to the formation of ingot pattern develop during solidification of the ingot. The pattern appears as a zone of demarcation between the columnar and heterogeneous regions of ingot solidification, which may persist during reduction of the ingot to billets and bars. Because inclusions, particularly sulfides, may segregate to a minor degree in this region, macroetching may reveal the presence of ingot pattern through preferential-etching effects. In the absence of large amounts of sulfide and silicate inclusions, ingot pattern is of no serious consequence. One such pattern is presented in Fig. 24. Ingot patterns often persist after forging.

**Center porosity,** if the result of a discontinuity within the metal, may be evident before etching. However, the porosity usually is not evident until the metal has been etched. Center porosity varies widely in degree, and interpretation of its relationship to quality should include consideration of the grade of steel and cross-sectional dimensions of the product represented. For example, the conditions observed in a 305- by 305-mm (12- by 12-in.) bloom may be more pronounced than in small sections.

**Nonmetallic inclusions,** although they usually appear as pits or pinholes, must not be confused with pits that result from etching out metallic segregations or from variations in etching procedure. When nonmetallic inclusions are suspected in highly alloyed steels that may contain metallic segregations, an annealed specimen should be compared with a hardened and tempered specimen etched in the same way. If the etching pits are the result of nonmetallic inclusions, they will appear similar in the annealed and the hardened specimens. If they are the result of metallic segregation, they will differ in appearance, being more prominent in the hardened specimen.

Although macroetching may furnish a good indication of the cleanliness of the steel, it is preferable to conduct research studies by metallography if information is desired regarding the character of nonmetallic inclusions that may be present.

**Segregations** are revealed by differences in the severity of the acid attack on the affected areas. Segregations at the center may be attacked so deeply that they appear as a pipe, or may be grouped in some fairly regular form about the center, depending on the shape of the ingot and the mechanical work done on it.

The American Society for Testing and Materials has established a graded series (ASTM E 381) for center segregation. Figures 25 to 29 show the various degrees of center segregation represented in that series. The intended use of the product usually determines the acceptability of center segregation.

Segregation as revealed by macroetching does not always indicate defective metal. A polished specimen should be examined under the microscope to determine whether the revealed segregation is metallic or is a concentration of nonmetallic impurities. The microscopic identification of segregation may be supplemented by chemical or other means of testing.

**Carbon spots** are a type of segregation that is most likely to occur in carbon or alloy steels that contain more than 0.40% C. A degree of segregation no greater than that illustrated in Fig. 30 is usually considered acceptable.

**Splash** is a condition sometimes found in steel billets taken from the bottom of an ingot. Such a condition may take place when the mold is too cold or if it has not been coated. When the molten steel first strikes the bottom of the ingot mold, some may splash and freeze immediately, which causes the type of segregation depicted in Fig. 31. Splash is not acceptable and is easily detected by macroetching.

**Flakes** are internal cracks, which are sometimes called cooling cracks or thermal cracks. They can be detected by macroetching, and their identity can be verified by a fracture test of a hardened specimen in which the cracks are revealed as bright crystalline spots. Figure 32 shows an alloy steel billet with a typical flake considered unacceptable.

**Bleeding** results from a gassy condition that is most likely to occur in billets from near the top of an ingot (Fig. 33). This condition is unacceptable in any degree.

**Butt tears and flute marks** are cracks that are revealed by macroetching and are unacceptable in any degree. Butt tears (Fig. 34) are internal cracks that resemble bursts. Flute marks appear at the surface, as shown in Fig. 35.

**Pipe** is an internal shrinkage cavity formed during solidification of ingots of fully deoxidized steel. It may be carried through the various manufacturing processes to the finished product. Pipe invariably is associated with segregated impurities, which are deeply attacked by the etchant. Cavities in the center that are not associated with deeply etched impurities often are mistaken for pipe, but such cavities usually can be traced to bursts caused by incorrect processing of the steel during forging or rolling. Pipe should be visible after deep etching; it usually can be distinguished from bursts by the degree of sponginess surrounding the defect. Piped metal usually exhibits considerably more sponginess than burst metal.

**Bursts** usually display a distinct pattern of cracks and do not show spongy areas, thus distinguishing them from pipes. Bursts are readily detected by macroetching; a typical burst is illustrated in Fig. 36.

**Flow lines,** which indicate the direction in which the steel was mechanically worked, have become part of the engineering specifications for certain designs of forgings and other parts, especially aircraft-engine components.

The longitudinal face on which flow lines are to be developed by macroetching should have a smooth ground surface. Best results are obtained by using a fresh solution of 1 part HCl to 1 part $H_2O$ at 70 to 80 °C (160 to 175 °F) (Fig. 37). Temperature must be closely controlled, because too violent an attack will pit and roughen the ground surface so severely that flow lines may be obliterated. The specimen should be frequently removed from the etchant to observe the progress of etching. The etched surface is usually scrubbed with a brush or cloth under running water to remove the smut produced by etching. However, the flow lines sometimes show more clearly if the smut is left on.

A 10 to 12% solution of ammonium persulfate $[(NH_4)_2S_2O_8]$ at room temperature is also used to reveal flow lines. This etchant works rapidly and typically produces good contrast.

**Grain Size.** Macroetching can be used to reveal areas of excessive grain size in some highly alloyed steels. It is not used for routine determination of grain size in the standard carbon and alloy steels. Figure 38 illustrates how localized coarse grain can be revealed in high-alloy steels by macroetching.

**Decarburization and Carburization.** Areas that have been decarburized or carburized ordinarily etch differently from the remainder of the specimen. The chief difference is in color; decarburized parts appear lighter, and carburized parts darker.

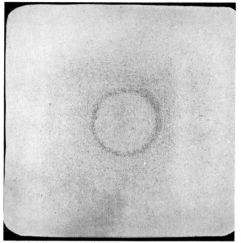

**Fig. 24** Ingot pattern in a low-carbon steel billet; acceptable in any degree (see ASTM E 381). 50% aqueous HCl. 0.5×

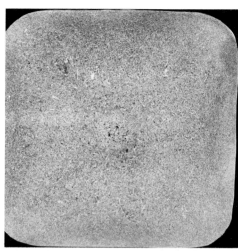

**Fig. 25** Center segregation in an alloy steel billet; C-1 in the graded series (ASTM E 381). See also Fig. 26 to 29. 50% aqueous HCl. 0.625×

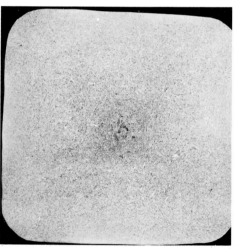

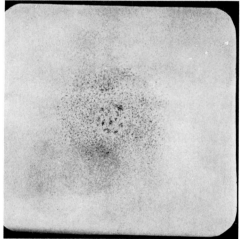

**Fig. 26, 27** Same as Fig. 25, except specimen shown in Fig. 26 is graded C-2 in the series and that in Fig. 27 is graded C-3. 50% aqueous HCl. Fig. 26: 0.625×. Fig. 27: 0.33×

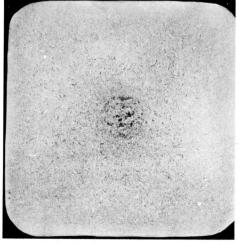

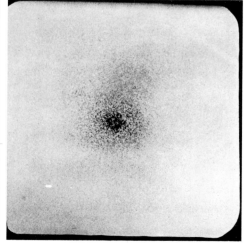

**Fig. 28, 29** Same as Fig. 25, except specimen illustrated in Fig. 28 is graded C-4 in the series and that in Fig. 29 is graded C-5. 50% aqueous HCl. Both 0.5×

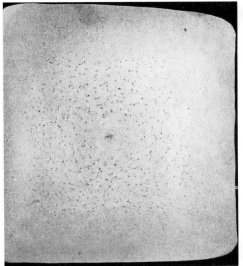

**Fig. 30** Carbon spots (segregation) in the top billet of medium-carbon alloy steel. This degree of segregation is acceptable. 50% aqueous HCl. 0.33×

**Fig. 31** Splash in bottom billet of an alloy steel ingot; unacceptable in any degree (see ASTM E 381). 50% aqueous HCl. 0.33×

**Fig. 32** Flakes in a billet of alloy steel; unacceptable in any degree (see ASTM E 381). 50% aqueous HCl. 0.5×

The section to be examined, if small enough, can be metallographically polished, then etched cold for 5 to 30 s in 7 to 10% nital. This will usually result in excellent contrast, and if the polish is good enough, the same specimen can be examined microscopically and visually.

**Hardened Zones.** Macroetching is used to determine the location and depth of hardened zones controlled by the hardenability of the steel or by localized heating (see Fig. 39 to 41).

The etchant selected for determining depth or other characteristics of hardened zones depends on the surface finish of the specimen and the amount of detail required; hot 50% HCl (etchant 1, Table 2) and 5 to 10% nital

are most commonly used. Nital etchant is most useful for etching the polished surfaces of rolls used for cold rolling mills to reveal surface areas damaged by work hardening.

Figure 39 shows the depth of hardness (black rims) on cross sections of bars of water-hardening tool steel. The etchant was hot 50% HCl, but the surface finishes were relatively rough, such as those obtained on a belt grinder. Only the zone depths are illustrated; there is no detail, and the specimens would not be suitable for microscopic examination.

The specimen presented in Fig. 40 is similar to that in Fig. 39, except that it was polished, which permitted a less severe etch (5% aqueous $HNO_3$), and more detail is shown. The outer, light gray rim is martensite, and

the inner, very dark rim is the transition zone between the martensite and the dark gray core.

Figure 41 depicts the results obtained by macroetching a cross section of a 1060 steel guide bar that had been flame hardened. This specimen was ground but not polished and was etched in 10% nital. The outer, dark gray zone is martensite and is separated from the light gray core by a transition zone that etched black.

**Welds** are commonly examined by macroetching to reveal incomplete fusion, porosity or other defects, heat patterns, and columnar structure of the weld metal (Fig. 42 to 44). Nital (2 to 4%) or a 10% solution of $(NH_4)_2S_2O_8$ is most often used to etch sec-

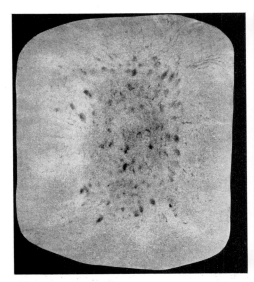

**Fig. 33** Bleeding (gassy) in top billet of alloy steel; unacceptable in any degree (see ASTM E 381). 50% aqueous HCl. 0.33×

**Fig. 34** Butt tears in bottom billet of alloy steel; unacceptable in any degree (see ASTM E 381). See also Fig. 36. 50% aqueous HCl. 0.33×

**Fig. 35** Flute marks in bottom billet of alloy steel; unacceptable in any degree (ASTM E 381). 50% aqueous HCl. 0.33×

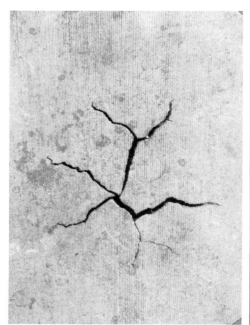

**Fig. 36** Center burst in an alloy steel forging. Bursts are caused by incorrect processing during rolling or forging. 50% aqueous HCl. Actual size

tions of weldments if specimens are not too large to be polished. Large specimens may be suitably etched in hot 50% HCl or in one of the other solutions of the first six etchants listed in Table 2.

**Grinding cracks** can be distinguished easily in a short-time macroetch test and are usually identified by a symmetrical pattern. Hardened pieces should be softened by tempering before hot etching.

**Seams and laps** in rolled steel vary in depth and usually extend in a straight path parallel to the direction of rolling. In forged steel, seams generally follow the contour of the forging and the flow of the metal.

## Special Techniques

In addition to the routine use of macroetching as a guide to quality control of semifinished steel in production, several specialized uses of macroetching methods are common, as indicated below.

**Overheating of Steel.** When etched in 1 part HCl to 1 part $H_2O$ at 70 to 80 °C (160 to 175 °F), overheated steel forgings will display on the as-forged surface a network structure resembling fine chicken wire. For best results, the forgings should not be cleaned by shot, grit, or sandblasting before etching. Results should be verified by examining a fractured section for facets after normalizing, quenching, and tempering.

**Tempering from grinding, or soft spots from inadequate quenching,** can be revealed on a smoothly ground surface by a two-stage etch consisting of 5% $HNO_3$ (conc) in water, followed by 50% HCl (conc) in water. The specimen is washed in hot water, etched in the first solution until black,

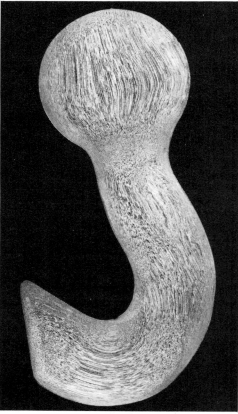

**Fig. 37** Hook forged from 4140 steel, showing flow lines in a longitudinal section. 50% aqueous HCl. 0.5×

washed in hot water, immersed 3 s in the second solution, washed in hot water, and dried in an air blast.

The presence of lighter or darker areas indicates that structure and hardness have been altered during grinding. Soft spots, which often result during hardening of carbon or low-alloy steels, can generally be distinguished by this method.

**Sulfur Segregation.** In an ingot, a forging, or a hot-rolled product, the distribution of sulfur can be revealed by sulfur printing. The section to be printed should have a smoothly ground surface or a metallographic polish. Ordinary sensitized photographic silver bromide paper, preferably with a semimatte finish, is soaked in 2% $H_2SO_4$. The emulsion side of the paper is applied for 1 to 2 min to the prepared surface being investigated. Air bubbles should be rubbed out carefully with a roller or a squeegee, and the paper should not be moved after firm contact with the specimen. After removal from the specimen, the paper should be rinsed with water, fixed in a hypo solution, washed thoroughly, and dried.

The brown pattern of silver sulfide formed on the paper indicates the relative distribution of sulfur as sulfide inclusions in the steel. The best results are obtained only on first or second prints made from a surface.

**Phosphorus segregation** can be revealed by etchants that, when properly used, deposit

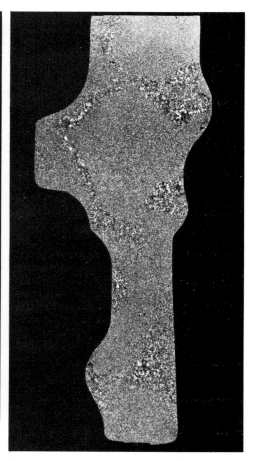

**Fig. 38** Localized coarse grain in a cross section of a high-alloy steel forging. 50% aqueous HCl. 0.25×

copper selectively on areas low in phosphorus. Etchant 9 in Table 2 is suitable. Etching in this solution requires immersion of the polished face of the specimen just long enough for a coppery sheen to appear; polished specimens of wrought iron show a clear delineation of areas of phosphorus segregation with a 5-s etch. Too long an etch permits copper deposition even in phosphorus-segregated areas, obscuring the presence of the segregate.

**Fig. 39** W1 water-hardening tool steel (0.60-1.40C), austenitized at 800 °C (1475 °F), brine quenched, and tempered 2 h at 150 °C (300 °F). Black rings are hardened zones in bars (from left) 76, 51, and 25 mm (3, 2, and 1 in.) in diameter. Case hardness (36.5 to 45 HRC) increases with decreasing bar diameter. Hot 50% aqueous HCl. 0.5×

**Fig. 40** 38-mm (1.5-in.) diam W1 steel bar, austenitized at 800 °C (1475 °F) and brine quenched. Hardened zone appears as a light gray rim. 5% aqueous HNO₃. 2×

**Fig. 41** Cross section through a flame-hardened steel guide bar, showing the hardened case. Dark gray area at outside edge is fully hardened martensitic structure; black area is a transition zone between case and core. 10% nital. Actual size

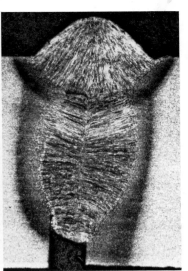

**Fig. 42** Section through a two-pass butt weld in API 5L-X60 pipe, 76 cm (30 in.) outside diameter by 6 mm (¼ in.) wall thickness. Note incomplete fusion at the bottom of the macrograph. 4% nital. 10×

Another method of delineating areas high in phosphorus is to make a phosphorus print on filter or gelatin paper. The paper is saturated with a solution containing 35 mL 32% HNO₃ and 100 mL 5% by weight ammonium molybdate [(NH₄)₆Mo₇O₂₄]. In a procedure similar to that used for sulfur printing, the paper remains in contact with the smoothly ground surface of the specimen for 3 to 5 min. The print is then carefully removed and immersed in a developer of 5 mL saturated SnCl₂ solution, 50 mL HCl, 100 mL H₂O, and 1 g alum (AlK(SO₄)₂). After 3 to 4 min, a blue color develops in high-phosphorus areas.

## Microstructures of Carbon and Alloy Steels*

In this section, the more common microstructures observed in carbon and alloy steels are described and depicted. These microstructures occur as a result of variations in chemical composition and processing. Compositions of AISI and alloy steels are listed in Table 4.

A wide range of constituents is encountered in carbon and alloy steels. Single-phase constituents include austenite, ferrite, δ-ferrite, cementite, various alloy carbides, and martensite, as well as various intermetallic phases, nitrides, and nonmetallic inclusions. Two-phase constituents include tempered martensite, pearlite, and bainite. Nonmetallic inclusions consisting of two or more phases can be present in steels. More information is available in the article "Solidification Structures of Steel" in this Volume.

*This section was adapted from G.F. Vander Voort, Typical Microstructures of Iron Base Alloys, in *Metals Handbook*, Desk Edition, American Society for Metals, 1985

**Ferrite.** Fully ferritic steels are obtained only when the carbon content is low. The most obvious microstructural features are the ferrite grain boundaries, as illustrated in Fig. 225. Ferrite is a soft low-strength phase. If the ferrite grain size is fine, good ductility and formability are obtained. Because ferrite has a body-centered cubic (bcc) crystal structure, ferritic steels exhibit a transition from ductile to brittle behavior as temperature decreases or as strain rate increases.

**Austenite.** Obtaining fully austenitic steels requires careful balancing of chemical composition, that is, large amounts of the austenite-stabilizing elements—carbon, nitrogen, nickel, and manganese—must be present compared with those elements that stabilize ferrite. Examples of fully austenitic ferrous

**Table 4    Compositions of AISI carbon and alloys steels**

| Steel | C | Mn | P, max | S, max | Si | Ni | Cr | Mo |
|---|---|---|---|---|---|---|---|---|
| 1008 | 0.10 max | 0.30-0.50 | 0.040 | 0.050 | ... | ... | ... | ... |
| 1010 | 0.08-0.13 | 0.30-0.60 | 0.040 | 0.050 | ... | ... | ... | ... |
| 1020 | 0.18-0.23 | 0.30-0.60 | 0.040 | 0.050 | ... | ... | ... | ... |
| 1025 | 0.22-0.28 | 0.30-0.60 | 0.040 | 0.050 | ... | ... | ... | ... |
| 1030 | 0.28-0.34 | 0.60-0.90 | 0.040 | 0.050 | ... | ... | ... | ... |
| 1035 | 0.32-0.38 | 0.60-0.90 | 0.040 | 0.050 | ... | ... | ... | ... |
| 10B35 (a) | 0.32-0.38 | 0.60-0.90 | 0.040 | 0.050 | ... | ... | ... | ... |
| 1038 | 0.35-0.42 | 0.60-0.90 | 0.040 | 0.050 | ... | ... | ... | ... |
| 1040 | 0.37-0.44 | 0.60-0.90 | 0.040 | 0.050 | ... | ... | ... | ... |
| 1045 | 0.43-0.50 | 0.60-0.90 | 0.040 | 0.050 | ... | ... | ... | ... |
| 1050 | 0.48-0.55 | 0.60-0.90 | 0.040 | 0.050 | ... | ... | ... | ... |
| 1052 | 0.47-0.55 | 1.20-1.50 | 0.040 | 0.050 | ... | ... | ... | ... |
| 1055 | 0.50-0.60 | 0.60-0.90 | 0.040 | 0.050 | ... | ... | ... | ... |
| 1060 | 0.55-0.65 | 0.60-0.90 | 0.040 | 0.050 | ... | ... | ... | ... |
| 1064 | 0.60-0.70 | 0.50-0.80 | 0.040 | 0.050 | ... | ... | ... | ... |
| 1065 | 0.60-0.70 | 0.60-0.90 | 0.040 | 0.050 | ... | ... | ... | ... |
| 1070 | 0.65-0.75 | 0.60-0.90 | 0.040 | 0.050 | ... | ... | ... | ... |
| 1074 | 0.70-0.80 | 0.50-0.80 | 0.040 | 0.050 | ... | ... | ... | ... |
| 1080 | 0.75-0.88 | 0.60-0.90 | 0.040 | 0.050 | ... | ... | ... | ... |
| 1095 | 0.90-1.03 | 0.30-0.50 | 0.040 | 0.050 | ... | ... | ... | ... |
| 1151 | 0.48-0.55 | 0.70-1.00 | 0.040 | (b) | ... | ... | ... | ... |
| 1541 | 0.36-0.44 | 1.35-1.65 | 0.040 | 0.050 | ... | ... | ... | ... |
| 1340 | 0.38-0.43 | 1.60-1.90 | 0.035 | 0.040 | 0.20-0.35 | ... | ... | ... |
| 4047 | 0.45-0.50 | 0.70-0.90 | 0.035 | 0.040 | 0.20-0.35 | ... | ... | 0.20-0.30 |
| 4130 | 0.28-0.33 | 0.40-0.60 | 0.035 | 0.040 | 0.20-0.35 | ... | 0.80-1.10 | 0.15-0.25 |
| 4140 | 0.38-0.43 | 0.75-1.00 | 0.035 | 0.040 | 0.20-0.35 | ... | 0.80-1.10 | 0.15-0.25 |
| 4340 | 0.38-0.43 | 0.60-0.80 | 0.035 | 0.040 | 0.20-0.35 | 1.65-2.00 | 0.70-0.90 | 0.20-0.30 |
| 4350 | 0.48-0.53 | 0.60-0.80 | 0.035 | 0.040 | 0.20-0.35 | 1.65-2.00 | 0.70-0.90 | 0.20-0.30 |
| 5046 (c) | 0.43-0.48 | 0.75-1.00 | 0.035 | 0.040 | 0.20-0.35 | ... | 0.20-0.35 | ... |
| 5132 | 0.30-0.35 | 0.60-0.80 | 0.035 | 0.040 | 0.20-0.35 | ... | 0.75-1.00 | ... |
| 8645 | 0.43-0.48 | 0.75-1.00 | 0.035 | 0.040 | 0.20-0.35 | 0.40-0.70 | 0.40-0.60 | 0.15-0.25 |
| 8650 (c) | 0.48-0.53 | 0.75-1.00 | 0.035 | 0.040 | 0.20-0.35 | 0.40-0.70 | 0.40-0.60 | 0.15-0.25 |
| 8822 | 0.20-0.25 | 0.75-1.00 | 0.035 | 0.040 | 0.15-0.30 | 0.40-0.70 | 0.40-0.60 | 0.30-0.40 |

(a) Also contains 0.005 min B. (b) Range of sulfur content is 0.08 to 0.13%. (c) SAE only

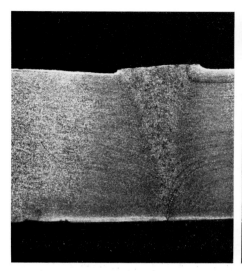

**Fig. 43** Cross section of a resistance weld in API 5L-X60 pipe, 46 cm (18 in.) outside diameter by 10 mm (0.375 in.) wall thickness. Weld is sound. (NH₄)₂S₂O₈. 5×

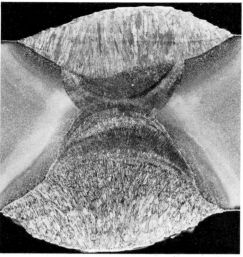

**Fig. 44** Section through an arc butt weld joining two 13-mm (0.5-in.) thick plates of ASTM A517, grade J steel. Note columnar structure of weld metal in outer portion of weld. 2% nital. 4×

alloys are austenitic stainless steels and austenitic manganese steel. Additional information is provided in the articles "Wrought Stainless Steels," "Stainless Steel Casting Alloys," and "Austenitic Manganese Steel Castings" in this Volume. Again, the most visible microstructural features of these single-phase alloys are the austenite grain boundaries. These alloys also contain annealing twins in the wrought, solution-annealed conditions. Austenite is also a soft low-strength phase; however, cold working produces substantial strengthening and, if extensive, can produce strain-induced martensite. Because of their face-centered cubic (fcc) crystal structures, austenitic alloys remain ductile irrespective of temperature or strain rate unless phase changes occur.

**Cementite,** or iron carbide, contains 6.67% C (by weight), corresponding to the formula $Fe_3C$. In carbon alloy steels, some of the carbide-forming elements, for example, manganese and chromium, will replace some of the iron in cementite. Therefore, the formula for cementite is often referred to as $M_3C$, where M represents the carbide-forming elements present. Pure $Fe_3C$ is approximately 800 HV and is brittle. Substitution of other elements for some of the iron in cementite will increase the hardness appreciably. Because of the brittleness of cementite, only limited amounts are present in steels.

**Martensite** is not an equilibrium phase in steels. Formation of martensite depends on chemical composition and cooling rate from the high-temperature austenite region. Unlike other austenite transformation products, martensite usually forms instantaneously once the specimen is cooled below a specific temperature, the martensite start ($M_s$) temperature, which is a function of the carbon and alloy content of the parent austenite phase. The transformation is completed when the specimen reaches a lower temperature,

the martensite finish ($M_f$) temperature. The hardness of martensite is governed primarily by carbon content, but is also influenced by alloy content. The ability to form martensite in a steel as a function of section size and quench rate depends on the hardenability of the steel. Hardenability is increased by increasing carbon and alloy contents and by enlargement of austenite grain size. Grain size is rarely coarsened to improve hardenability in wrought steels, because most mechanical properties are impaired.

Carbon content markedly influences the nature of martensite. Basically, two types of martensite can be formed in steels. At low carbon contents, lath martensite is formed (Fig. 107). The laths are present in a packet arrangement in which the individual laths within the packet have essentially the same orientation. At high carbon contents, plate martensite is formed (Fig. 201). The plates form as individual lenticular crystals in a wide range of sizes. At intermediate carbon contents, mixtures of lath and plate martensite are obtained. Additional information is provided in the article "Martensitic Structures" in this Volume.

Because of the important influence of grain size on the properties of martensitic steels, much effort has been expended on reducing the grain size of such steels. However, unlike ferritic and austenitic alloys, the critical grain size for martensitic steels is that of the parent austenite phase, that is, the prior austenite grain size. Delineation of the prior austenite grain boundaries in martensitic steels using selective etchants is difficult, but can often be achieved. In general, the low-carbon martensitic steels are more difficult to etch in this manner than medium- and high-carbon steels. In the case of lath martensite, the packet size also is an important microstructure measurement.

The hardness and strength of martensite

increase with increasing carbon content. However, it also becomes more brittle. Martensite has a body-centered tetragonal (bct) structure. The degree of tetragonality increases with carbon content. Tempering decreases the strength of martensite, but increases its toughness. However, tempering of alloy steels within certain temperature ranges can reduce toughness because of embrittlement (temper martensite embrittlement or temper embrittlement). However, tempering, along with composition selections, can permit achievement of a wide range of useful strengths and toughness. More information is available in the articles "Tempering of Steel" and "Martempering of Steel" in Volume 4 of the 9th Edition of *Metals Handbook* and in the Section "Heat Treatment of Carbon and Alloy Steels" in Volume 1 of the 9th Edition of *Metals Handbook*.

**Pearlite** is a mixture of ferrite and cementite in which the two phases are formed from austenite in an alternating lamellar pattern. Formation of pearlite requires relatively slow cooling from the austenite region and depends on the steel composition. Pearlite forms at temperatures below the lower critical temperature of the steel in question and may be formed isothermally or by continuous cooling. As the hardenability of the steel decreases, the cooling rate can be increased without the formation of other constituents. As isothermal reaction temperature decreases or the cooling rate increases, the interlamellar spacing decreases. The strength and toughness of pearlitic steels increase as the interlamellar spacing decreases.

Because the maximum solubility of carbon in ferrite is nearly zero at room temperature and a fully pearlitic microstructure is obtained when a steel containing 0.8% C is slowly cooled from the austenite region, the volume fractions of ferrite and pearlite can be estimated.

In low-carbon steels, ferrite forms before the eutectoid reaction, which produces pearlite, and is termed proeutectoid ferrite. Below approximately 0.4% C, the proeutectoid ferrite forms as equiaxed patches and is the continuous phase. Above approximately 0.4% C, the proeutectoid ferrite generally exists as isolated equiaxed patches or as a grain-boundary layer, depending on thermal history.

Carbon steels are referred to as hypoeutectoid, eutectoid, or hypereutectoid when their carbon contents are below 0.8% approximately 0.8%, or above 0.8%, respectively. In the case of hypereutectoid steels, excess cementite above the amount required to form pearlite will precipitate in the austenite grain boundaries before the eutectoid reaction. This excess cementite is referred to as proeutectoid cementite. A grain-boundary cementite network embrittles such steels.

The strength and hardness of ferrite-pearlite steels increase with increasing pearlite content and are further increased by reductions in the interlamellar spacing. Pure ferrite (no carbon) has a hardness of approximately 70 HV; fine pearlite in a eutectoid carbon steel has a hardness of nearly 400 HV. Fine pearlite is the most desirable structure for wire drawing, where extremely high strengths can be obtained.

Carbon steels are widely used in the hot-rolled condition. The austenite grain size of the steel as it enters the final rolling pass establishes the relative sizes of the ferrite and pearlite produced during subsequent air cooling, but the cooling rate influences the fineness of the pearlite, the morphology of the proeutectoid ferrite, and the amounts of the various constituents.

**Bainite,** an austenite transformation product, is a lathlike aggregate of ferrite and cementite that forms under conditions intermediate to those that result in formation of pearlite and martensite. Bainite is commonly classified as upper bainite or lower bainite. Upper bainite forms isothermally or during continuous cooling at temperatures just below those that produce bainite. Lower bainite forms at still lower temperatures, down to the $M_s$ temperature or slightly below in certain cases.

Formation of upper bainite begins by growth of long ferrite laths devoid of carbon. Because the carbon content of the ferrite laths is low, the austenite at the lath boundaries is enriched in carbon. The shape of the cementite formed at the lath boundaries varies with carbon content. In low-carbon steels, the cementite will precipitate as discontinuous stringers and isolated particles, but at higher carbon contents the stringers are more continuous. In some instances, carbide is not precipitated, but is retained as austenite or transforms to plate martensite. More information is provided in the article "Bainitic Structures" in this Volume.

Lower bainite has a more platelike appearance than upper bainite. The ferrite plates are broader than those in upper bainite and are more similar in appearance to plate martensite. As with upper bainite, the appearance of lower bainite varies with carbon content. Lower bainite is characterized by formation of rodlike cementite within the ferrite plates.

**Nonmetallic Inclusions.** Inclusions in steel are indigenous or exogenous in origin. Indigenous inclusions form as a natural result of the decrease in solubility of oxygen or sulfur that occurs as the metal freezes. Exogenous inclusions are introduced from external sources, for example, slag or refractories, that enter the steel and become trapped during solidification. In most instances, these included phases are undesirable. Examples of nonmetallic inclusions in carbon and alloy steels are presented in Fig. 96 to 104.

## SELECTED REFERENCES

- E. Beraha and B. Shpigler, *Color Metallography*, American Society for Metals, 1977
- L.E. Samuels, *Metallographic Polishing by Mechanical Methods*, 3rd ed., American Society for Metals, 1967
- L.E. Samuels, *Optical Microscopy of Carbon Steels*, American Society for Metals, 1980
- "Standard Method of Macroetch Testing, Inspection, and Rating Steel Products, Comprising Bars, Billets, Blooms, and Forgings," E 381, *Annual Book of ASTM Standards*, Vol 03.03, ASTM, Philadelphia, 1984
- G.F. Vander Voort, *Metallography: Principles and Practice*, McGraw-Hill, 1984

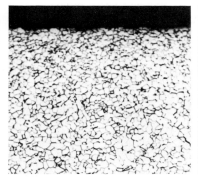

**Fig. 45** Rimmed steel (0.08C), as rolled. The structure is ferrite grains; note the slight difference in grain size from case (top) to core. 3% nital. 100×

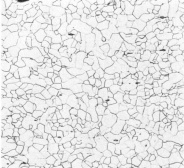

**Fig. 46** Rimmed steel (0.013% C), finish rolled at 940 °C (1720 °F) and coiled at 725 °C (1340 °F). The relatively fine ferrite grain is unusual for a steel rolled at a temperature this high. Nital. 100×

**Fig. 47** Same as Fig. 46, except finish rolled at 845 °C (1550 °F) and coiled at 695 °C (1280 °F). At this rolling temperature, low carbon content contributed to development of a duplex ferrite grain. Nital. 100×

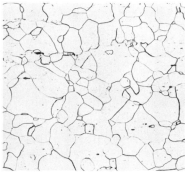

**Fig. 48** Rimmed steel (0.012% C), finish rolled at 820 °C (1510 °F) and coiled at 680 °C (1260 °F). Strain imparted by rolling at low finishing temperature enhances grain growth at coiling temperature. Nital. 100×

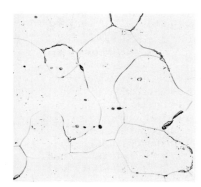

**Fig. 49** Low-carbon (0.05% C) steel, showing Fe₃C carbide at ferrite grain boundaries. 2% nital, 3 s, followed by Marshall's reagent, 3 s. 340×

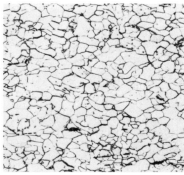

**Fig. 50** Rimmed steel (0.06 %C), finish rolled at 845 °C (1550 °F) and coiled at 620 °C (1150 °F). A fine-grain ferrite developed. Nital. 100×

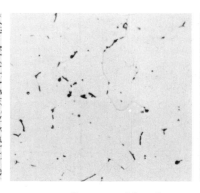

**Fig. 51** Same material and processing as Fig. 50, but at a higher magnification showing particles of cementite at the ferrite grain boundaries. Picral. 500×

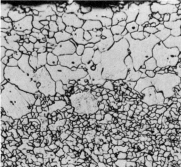

**Fig. 52** Same as Fig. 50, except finish rolled at 790 °C (1450 °F) and coiled at 620 °C (1150 °F). The rolling temperature developed fine grains, but self-annealing caused surface grain enlargement. Nital. 100×

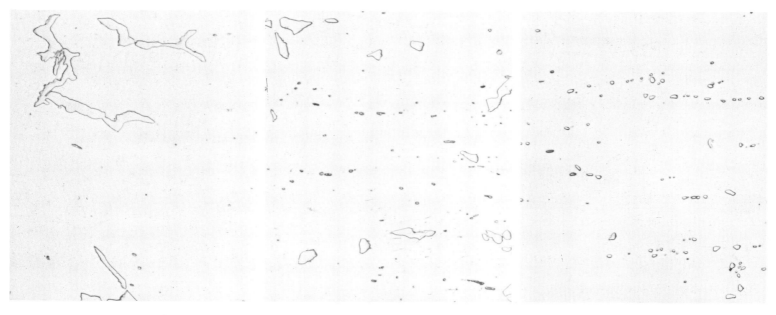

**Fig. 53, 54, 55** Low-carbon (0.06% C) steel, cold rolled and annealed. Fig. 53: massive carbide particles. Fig. 54: medium size carbide particles. Fig. 55: small, dispersed carbides. Picral. All 1000×

**Fig. 56** Rimmed steel (0.06% C), finish rolled at 890 °C (1630 °F) and coiled at 655 °C (1210 °F). Ferrite matrix contains cementite particles (light, outlined) and traces of pearlite. Picral. 1000×

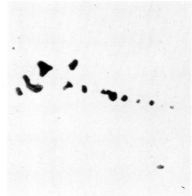

**Fig. 57** Same as Fig. 56, except the steel was subsequently cold rolled to 60% reduction. Cold rolling fragmented the cementite particles. Picral. 500×

**Fig. 58** Same as Fig. 57, but decarburized in wet hydrogen at 705 °C (1300 °F). The cementite particles were depleted of carbon, resulting in the formation of voids in the ferrite matrix. Picral. 500×

**Fig. 59** Sheet steel (0.06C-0.35Mn-0.04Si-0.40Ti), tint etched to color ferrite grains. Color depends on grain orientation. Beraha's tint etchant. 100×

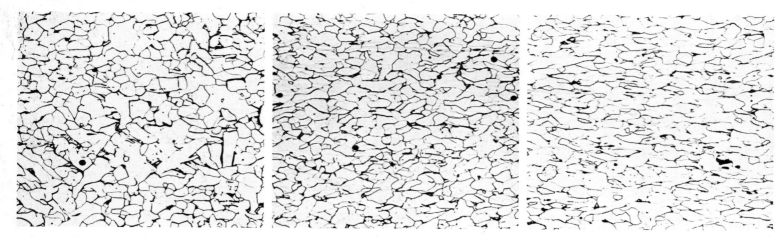

**Fig. 60, 61, 62** Capped 1008 steel, finished hot, coiled cold, then hot rolled from a thickness of 3 mm (0.13 in.). Note increasing grain elongation as reduction increases. Fig. 60: 10% reduction. Fig. 61: 20% reduction. Fig. 62: 30% reduction. 4% nital. 250×

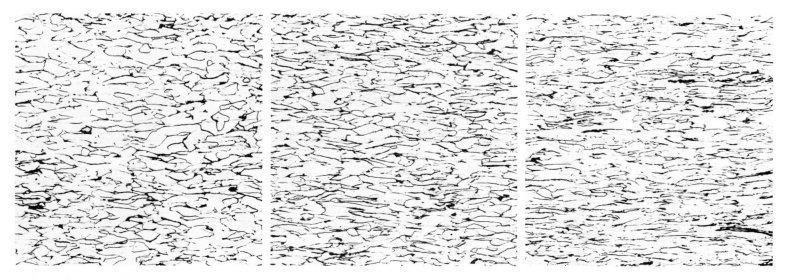

**Fig. 63, 64, 65** Same as Fig. 60 to 62. Fig. 63: 40% reduction. Fig. 64: 50% reduction. Fig. 65: 60% reduction. 4% nital. All 250×

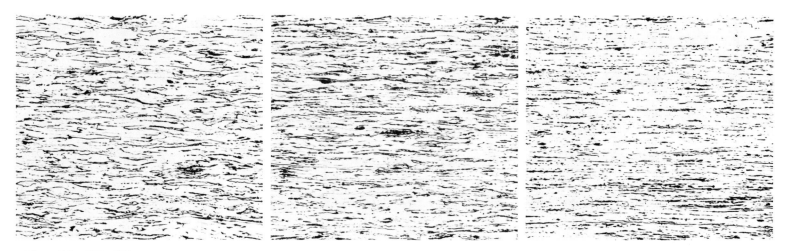

**Fig. 66, 67, 68** Same as Fig. 60 to 65. Fig. 66: 70% reduction. Fig. 67: 80% reduction. Fig. 68: 90% reduction. 4% nital. All 250×

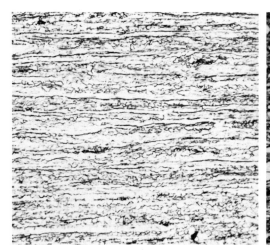

**Fig. 69** Low-carbon steel (0.10% C), cold rolled 90% to a thickness of 0.25 mm (0.01 in.) with HR30-T = 80 and annealed 106 s at 550 °C (1025 °F). Recrystallized 10%; HR30-T reduced to 79. Nital. 1000×

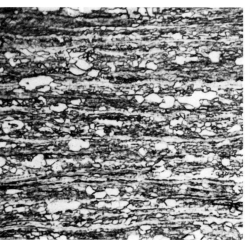

**Fig. 70** Same steel and cold rolling as Fig. 69, but annealed 7 min at 550 °C (1025 °F). Recrystallization increased to 40%; HR30-T reduced to 76. Nital. 1000×

**Fig. 71** Same steel and cold rolling as Fig. 69, but annealed 14.5 min at 550 °C (1025 °F). Recrystallization is 80%; HR30-T reduced to 70. Nital. 1000×

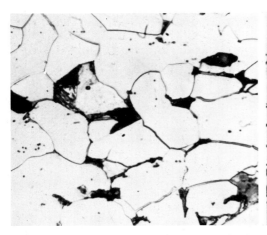

**Fig. 72** Aluminum-killed 1008 steel, normalized after 60% cold reduction to a final thickness of 0.8 mm (0.03 in.). The ferritic structure contains fine pearlite (dark areas) at the grain boundaries. 4% nital. 1000×

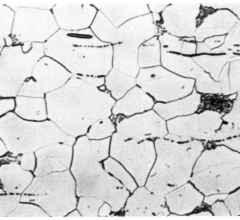

**Fig. 73** Same as Fig. 72, except process annealed at 595 °C (1100 °F) after normalizing. Ferritic structure contains some fine pearlite and some spheroidized cementite at the grain boundaries. 4% nital. 1000×

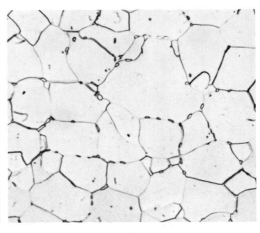

**Fig. 74** Same as Fig. 72, except process annealed at 705 °C (1300 °F) after normalizing. The ferritic structure contains some cementite particles at the grain boundaries. 4% nital. 1000×

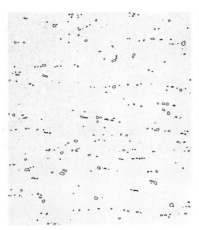

**Fig. 75** Rimmed 1008 steel, coiled at 570 °C (1060 °F), cold rolled, heated rapidly in a vacuum to 690 °C (1270 °F), held 20 h, and cooled slowly. Structure is ferrite and finely spheroidized cementite. Picral. 500×

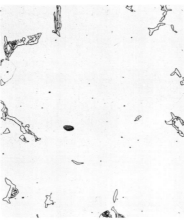

**Fig. 76** Same as Fig. 75, except after cold rolling the sheet was heated rapidly to 740 °C (1360 °F), held 20 h, then cooled slowly. Structure is ferrite, cementite particles, and pearlite. Picral. 500×

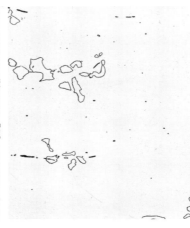

**Fig. 77** Same as Fig. 75, except the steel was coiled at 680 °C (1260 °F), cold rolled, heated rapidly to 690 °C (1270 °F), held for 20 h, and cooled slowly. Structure is ferrite and coarse cementite. Picral. 500×

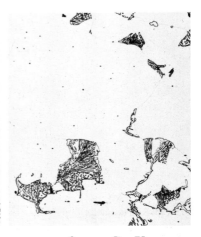

**Fig. 78** Same as Fig. 75, except coiled at 680 °C (1260 °F), cold rolled 70%, heated rapidly to 740 °C (1360 °F), cooled slowly to 690 °C (1270 °F), held 20 h, and cooled slowly. The structure is ferrite and pearlite. Picral. 500×

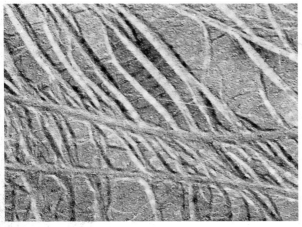

**Fig. 79** Rimmed 1008 steel with stretcher strains (Lüders lines) on the surface resulting from the sheet being stretched beyond the yield point during forming. Not polished, not etched. 0.875×

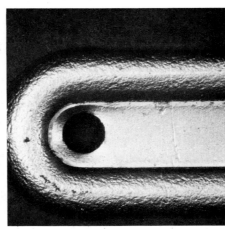

**Fig. 80** Rimmed 1008 steel part, formed from sheet, with surface roughness (orange peel). See also Fig. 81. Not polished, not etched. Actual size

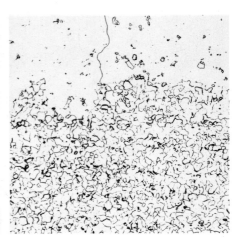

**Fig. 81** Same as Fig. 80. Magnified cross section shows the coarse surface grain that caused the orange peel. Nital. 50×

**Fig. 82** Aluminum-killed, hot-rolled 1008 steel, with an open skin lamination that appeared on the surface after drawing. Not polished, not etched. 2×

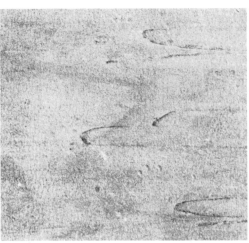

**Fig. 83** Aluminum-killed, hot-rolled 1008 steel sheet, with a pickled surface having a concentration of "arrowhead" defects. See also Fig. 84. Not polished, not etched. Actual size

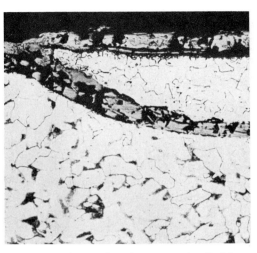

**Fig. 84** Section through an "arrowhead" defect seen in Fig. 83. Oxidized and decarburized slivers, rolled back into the surface, caused these defects. Nital. 200×

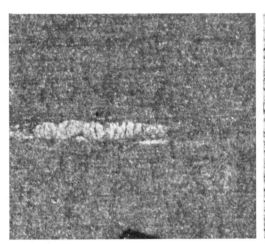

**Fig. 85** Cold-rolled 1008 steel sheet. The surface defect is mill scale that was rolled into the sheet at the hot mill. See also Fig. 86 and 87. Not polished, not etched. 3×

**Fig. 86** Same as Fig. 85, but at higher magnification to show the darker shading and different texture of the mill scale. See also Fig. 87. Not polished, not etched. 15×

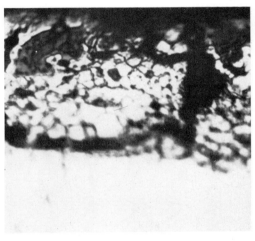

**Fig. 87** Same as Fig. 85. Magnified cross section through the surface defect shows the hot-mill scale pressed into the sheet surface. Nital. 1250×

**Fig. 88** Cold-rolled 1008 steel sheet. Sliver on the surface, the result of an ingot scab, is partially welded to the surface. See also Fig. 89. Not polished, not etched. Actual size

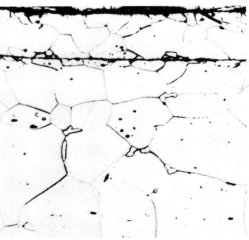

**Fig. 89** Same as Fig. 88. Cross section through the part of the sliver adhering to the surface shows a thin film of oxide separating it from the sheet. Nital. 500×

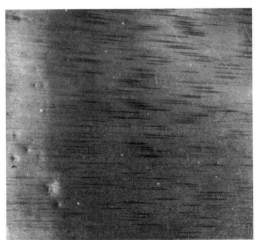

**Fig. 90** Cold-rolled 1008 steel, with longitudinal streaks on the surface that were caused by slippage between rolls in the tandem mill. See also Fig. 91. Not polished, not etched. 0.25×

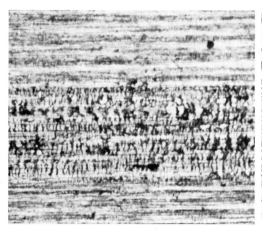

**Fig. 91** Same as Fig. 90, at moderate magnification. A single streak reveals the distinctive texture typical of all streaks on the sheet. See also Fig. 92. Nital. 28×

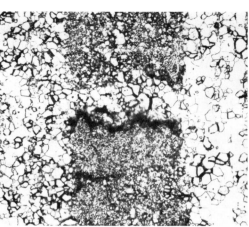

**Fig. 92** Same as Fig. 90. After light polishing, the surface streak shows a dark-etching area of very fine grain. Nital. 500×

**Fig. 93** Cold-rolled 1008 steel sheet, with numerous surface pits caused by rolled-in sand. See also Fig. 94. Not polished, not etched. 2.5×

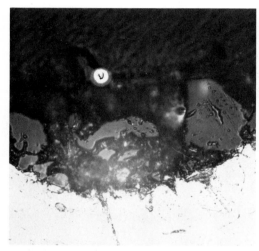

**Fig. 94** Same as Fig. 93. A cross section through one of the pits shows a grain of sand rolled into the sheet during temper rolling. See also Fig. 95. Nital. 1000×

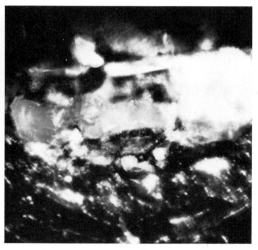

**Fig. 95** Same as Fig. 93. Polarized light illumination confirms the defect. The sand was picked up from the seals at the annealing pit. Nital. 1000×

**Fig. 96** Manganese oxide (dark) with manganese sulfide tails (light) and thin stringers of sulfide. As-polished. 1000×

**Fig. 97** Mixed sulfides of iron and manganese containing a few small oxide spots (dark areas at the edge of the inclusions). As-polished. 1000×

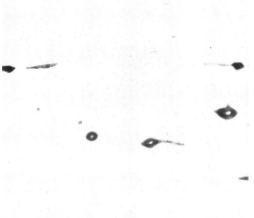

**Fig. 98** The major inclusions are globular, glassy silicates. The tails attached to the silicates are sulfides. As-polished. 1000×

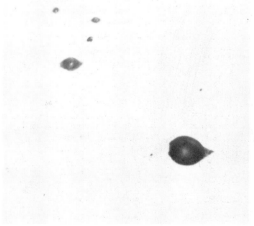

**Fig. 99** Iron oxide with manganese oxide causing internal reflection. Tails are probably manganese sulfide. As-polished. 1000×

**Fig. 100** Glassy globules of SiO₂ showing internal reflections. Under polarized light, these globules produce an optical cross. As-polished. 1000×

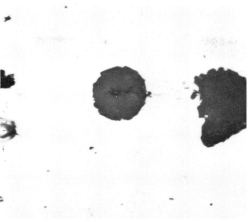

**Fig. 101** The glassy inclusion at the left is SiO₂. The irregular-shaped inclusions above it and to the right are FeO-SiO₂. As-polished. 1000×

**Fig. 102** These mixed inclusions are Al₂O₃, which is colorless under polarized light, and hercynite. As-polished. 1000×

**Fig. 103** A complex mixture consisting of Al₂O₃, hercynite, silica, and mullite. As-polished. 1000×

**Fig. 104** These irregularly shaped masses are typical of refractory brick. Under polarized light illumination, they emit reddish blue-gray tinges. As-polished. 1000×

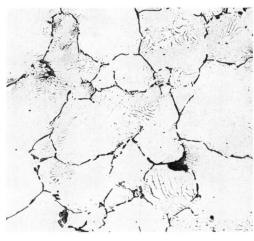

**Fig. 105** AISI 1020 steel, carburized. Prior austenite grain boundaries are revealed by an etchant that darkens Fe₃C in the boundaries. Hot (100 °C, or 212 °F) alkaline sodium picrate. 500×

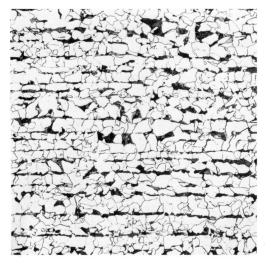

**Fig. 106** High-strength low-alloy steel (0.2% C), hot rolled. The structure is ferrite and pearlite. 4% picral, then 2% nital. 200×

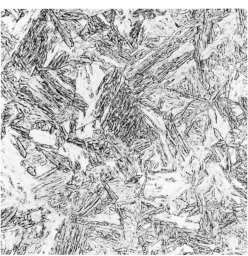

**Fig. 107** 0.20% C steel, water quenched. The structure is lath martensite. 8% Na₂S₂O₅. 500×. (R.L. Perry)

**Fig. 108** 0.20C-1.0Mn steel, as-quenched. The structure is pearlite (dark), martensite (light), and ferrite (white). 10% Na₂S₂O₅. 1000×. (M. Scott)

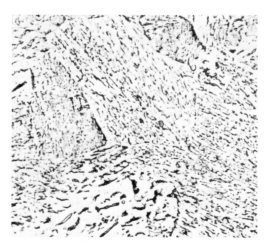

**Fig. 109** Steel specimen (Fe-0.22C-0.88Mn-0.55Ni-0.50Cr-0.35Mo) taken 38 mm (1.5 in.) from the quenched end of a Jominy bar. The structure is bainite. 4% picral. 1000×

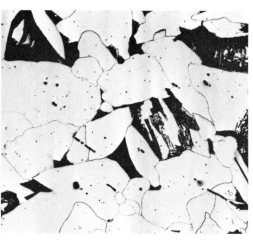

**Fig. 110** 1025 steel, normalized by austenitizing at 1095 °C (2000 °F) and air cooling. Coarse grain structure is pearlite (black) in a ferrite matrix. See also Fig. 111. Picral. 500×

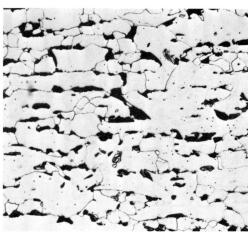

**Fig. 111** Same as Fig. 110, except normalized by austenitizing at 930 °C (1700 °F) and air cooling. The lower austenitizing temperature is responsible for the finer grain size of the steel. Picral. 500×

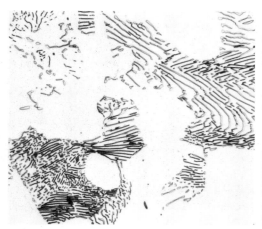

**Fig. 112** 1030 steel, austenitized 1 h at 930 °C (1700 °F) then 2 h 40 min at 775 °C (1430 °F), and held at 705 °C (1300 °F) for isothermal transformation of austenite and brine quenched. Structure is coarse pearlite and ferrite. Picral. 1000×

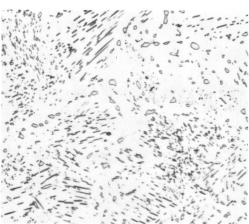

**Fig. 113** 1030 steel, austenitized 40 min at 800 °C (1475 °F), held 15 min at 705 °C (1300 °F) for isothermal transformation, then heated to 705 °C (1305 °F) and held 192 h. Partly spheroidized pearlite in a ferrite matrix. Picral. 1000×

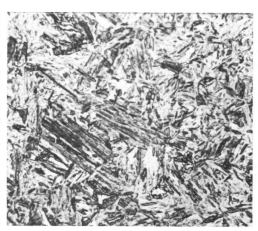

**Fig. 114** 10B35 steel, austenitized 1 h at 850 °C (1560 °F), quenched in still water, and tempered 1 h at 175 °C (350 °F). Structure is ferrite (small white areas) and lower bainite (dark acicular areas) in tempered martensite. 1% nital. 550×

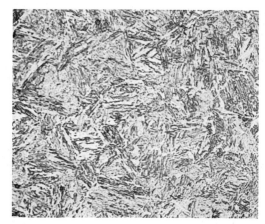

**Fig. 115** Same steel and austenitizing as Fig. 114, but quenched in agitated water and tempered 1 h at 230 °C (450 °F). The more severe quench suppressed formation of ferrite and bainite. The structure is tempered martensite. 1% nital. 500×

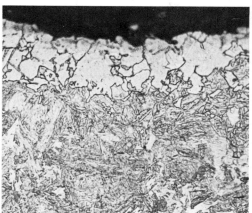

**Fig. 116** Same steel as Fig. 114, austenitized 1 h at 870 °C (1600 °F), water quenched, and tempered 1 h at 230 °C (450 °F). Core is tempered martensite; the surface of the specimen (ferrite) is severely decarburized (white area at top). 1% nital. 500×

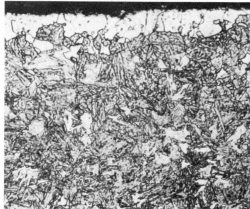

**Fig. 117** Same steel and heat treatment as Fig. 116, but austenitized in an atmosphere with a carbon potential closer to that of the steel. Surface (top) is less severely decarburized. 1% nital. 550×

**Fig. 118** Same steel and heat treatment as Fig. 116 and 117, except tempered 1 h at 175 °C (350 °F). Austenitizing was carried out in an atmosphere of correct carbon potential. No decarburization at the surface (top). 1% nital. 500×

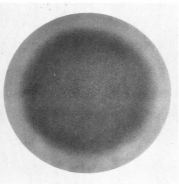

**Fig. 119** 1035 steel bar, austenitized 1 h at 850 °C (1560 °F), water quenched, and tempered 1 h at 175 °C (350 °F). Cross section shows light outer zone of martensite and a dark core of softer transformation products. 10% nital and 1% picral. Actual size

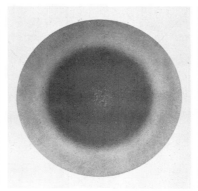

**Fig. 120** 10B35 steel bar (same as 1035, but boron treated) after same heat treatment as bar shown in Fig. 119. Effect of boron on hardenability is evident from the greater depth of the martensite zone. 10% nital and 1% picral. Actual size

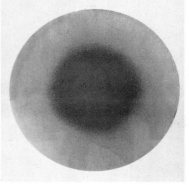

**Fig. 121** Same steel as Fig. 120, modified for even greater hardenability. After same heat treatment as Fig. 119, the martensite zone is still deeper than in Fig. 120. 10% nital and 1% picral. Actual size

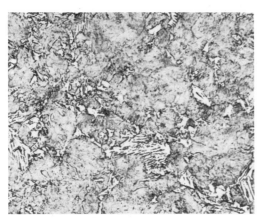

**Fig. 122** 1040 steel bar (25-mm, or 1-in., diam), austenitized 30 min at 915 °C (1675 °F), oil quenched, and tempered 2 h at 205 °C (400 °F). Structure consists of tempered martensite (gray) and ferrite (white). Nital. 500×

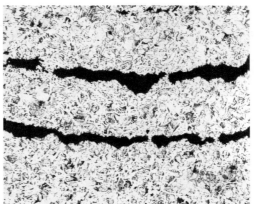

**Fig. 123** 1038 steel bar, as-forged. Longitudinal section displays secondary pipe (black areas) that was carried along from the original bar stock into the forged piece. Gray areas are pearlite; white areas, ferrite. 2% nital. 50×

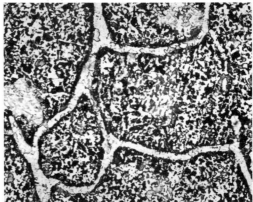

**Fig. 124** 1038 steel, as-forged. Transverse section of severely overheated specimen shows initial stage of "burning." Ferrite (white) outlines prior austenite grains, and the matrix consists of ferrite (white) and pearlite (black). 2% nital. 100×

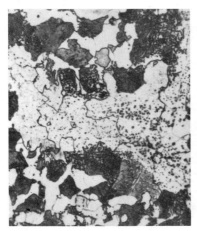

**Fig. 125** Same as Fig. 124, but at a higher magnification. Massive ferrite outlines prior austenite grains and contains particles of oxide (black dots). The matrix consists of ferrite (white) and pearlite (black). 2% nital. 550×

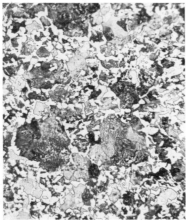

**Fig. 126** 1040 steel bar, 25 mm (1 in.) in diameter, austenitized 30 min at 915 °C (1675 °F) and cooled slowly in the furnace. White areas are ferrite; dark areas, pearlite. See also Fig. 127. Nital. 200×

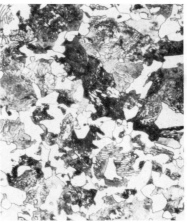

**Fig. 127** Same as Fig. 126, but at higher magnification to resolve more clearly the pearlite and ferrite grains. Wide difference in grain size is evident here and in Fig. 126. Nital. 500×

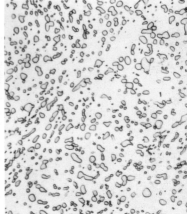

**Fig. 128** 1040 steel, austenitized 40 min at 800 °C (1475 °F) and held 6 h at 705 °C (1305 °F) for isothermal transformation. Structure is spheroidized carbide in a ferrite matrix. Picral. 1000×

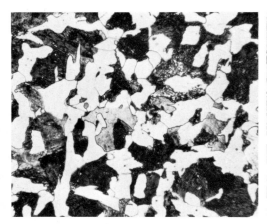

**Fig. 129** 25 mm (1-in.) 1045 steel bar, normalized by austenitizing at 845 °C (1550 °F) and air cooling and tempered 2 h at 480 °C (900 °F). Structure is fine lamellar pearlite (dark) and ferrite (light). 2% nital. 500×

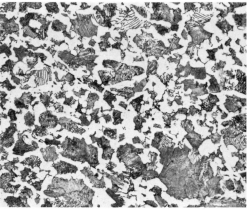

**Fig. 130** 1045 steel sheet. 3 mm (0.13 in.) thick, normalized by austenitizing at 1095 °C (2000 °F) and cooling in air. Structure consists of pearlite (dark gray) and ferrite (light). Picral. 500×

**Fig. 131** 1045 steel bar, normalized same as Fig. 130. Grain size is much larger than that in Fig. 130. Structure is pearlite (gray), with a network or grain-boundary ferrite (white) and a few plates of ferrite. Picral. 500×

**Fig. 132** 1045 steel forging, as air cooled from the forging temperature of 1205 °C (2200 °F). Structure consists of envelopes of proeutectoid ferrite at prior austenite grain boundaries, with emerging spines of ferrite, in a matrix of pearlite. Picral. 330×

**Fig. 133** 1045 steel, 51-mm (2-in.) bar stock, austenitized 2 h at 845 °C (1550 °F), oil quenched 15 s, air cooled 5 min, and oil quenched to room temperature. Ferrite at prior austenite grain boundaries; acicular structure is probably upper bainite. The matrix is pearlite. 4% picral. 500×

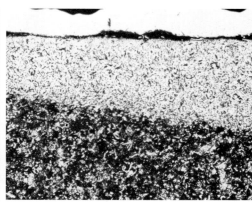

**Fig. 134** 1045 steel forging, austenitized 3 h at 900 °C (1650 °F), air cooled, and tempered 2 h at 205 °C (400 °F). At top is a layer of chromium plate; below it is martensite formed due to overheating during abrasive cutoff. The remainder of the structure is ferrite and pearlite. 2% nital. 100×

**Fig. 135** 1045 steel austenitized 10 min at 1205 °C (2200 °F), held 10 min at 340 °C (640 °F) for partial isothermal transformation, and cooled in air to room temperature. Lower bainite (dark) in a matrix of martensite (white). Picral. 500×

**Fig. 136** 51-mm (2-in.) 1045 steel bar, austenitized 2 h at 845 °C (1550 °F), oil quenched 15 s, air cooled 3 min, and water quenched to room temperature. Specimen taken 3 mm (0.13 in.) below surface. Dark stripes at prior austenite grain boundaries are probably upper bainite; the matrix is martensite. 2% nital. 500×

**Fig. 137** 51-mm (2-in.) 1045 steel bar stock, austenitized 2.5 h at 845 °C (1550 °F), water quenched 4 s, air cooled 3 min, and water quenched to room temperature. Specimen is from 3 mm (0.13 in.) below the surface. The dark acicular structure is probably lower bainite; the matrix is martensite. 4% picral. 500×

**Fig. 138** Same steel, bar size, and heat treatment as Fig. 137, but a different structure developed. The gray aggregates are probably upper bainite; the fine acicular dispersion is probably lower bainite. The matrix is martensite. 4% picral. 500×

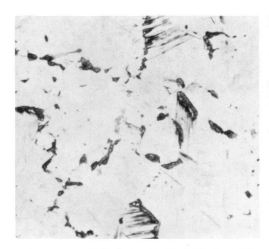

**Fig. 139** 1050 steel, austenitized 30 min at 870 °C (1600 °F) and oil quenched. The quench was slow enough to permit formation of some grain-boundary ferrite and bainite (feathery constituent). The matrix is martensite. Nital. 825×

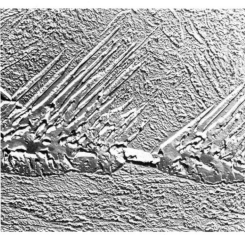

**Fig. 140** Replica electron micrograph of same steel as Fig. 139 after identical processing. Structure is proeutectoid ferrite at a prior austenite grain boundary, and emerging spines of bainite, in a martensite matrix. Nital. 9130×

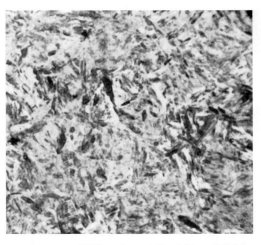

**Fig. 141** 1050 steel, austenitized 1 h at 870 °C (1600 °F), water quenched, and tempered 1 h at 260 °C (500 °F). The structure is fine tempered martensite. No free ferrite is visible, indicating an effective quench. Nital. 825×

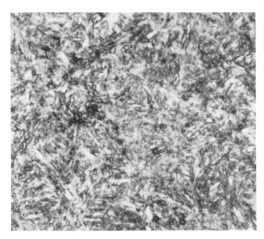

**Fig. 142** Same steel and heat treatment as Fig. 141, except the steel was tempered 1 h at 370 °C (700 °F). The structure is tempered martensite. See also Fig. 145. Nital. 825×

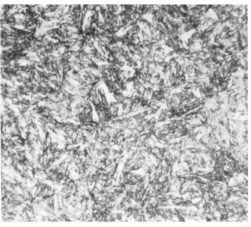

**Fig. 143** Same steel and heat treatment as Fig. 141, but tempered 1 h at 480 °C (900 °F). Structure is tempered martensite, with ferrite and carbide constituents barely resolved. See also Fig. 146. Nital. 825×

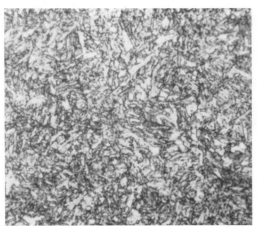

**Fig. 144** Same steel and heat treatment as Fig. 141, but tempered 1 h at 595 °C (1100 °F). Structure is tempered martensite. Ferrite and carbide are better resolved than in Fig. 143. See also Fig. 147. Nital. 825×

**Fig. 145** Replica electron micrograph of specimen in Fig. 142. The tempered martensite is typical of a thoroughly quenched structure. Nital. 9130×

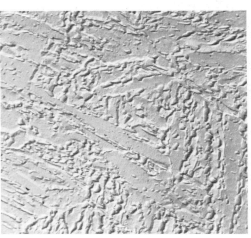

**Fig. 146** Replica electron micrograph of the specimen in Fig. 143. The structure is typical of a thoroughly quenched structure. Nital. 9130×

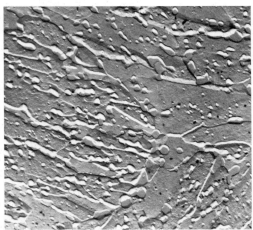

**Fig. 147** Replica electron micrograph of the specimen in Fig. 144. Resolution of ferrite and carbide has increased markedly. Nital. 9130×

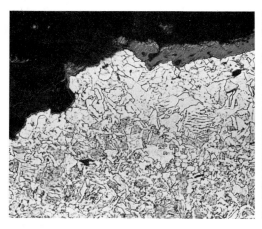

**Fig. 148** 1052 steel forging, austenitized 1 h at 850 °C (1560 °F), water quenched, and tempered 1 h at 570 °C (1060 °F). Top to bottom: a dark layer of iron oxide, a lighter gray area of decarburization, and a core of ferrite and tempered martensite. The dark particles in the core are manganese sulfide. 1% nital. 250×

**Fig. 149** 1052 steel forging, austenitized 2 h at 850 °C (1560 °F), water quenched, and tempered 2 h at 650 °C (1200 °F). Heat of friction in service produced a layer of martensite (white crust) and retained austenite (white) between martensite needles; the core is ferrite (white) in tempered martensite. 1% nital. 275×

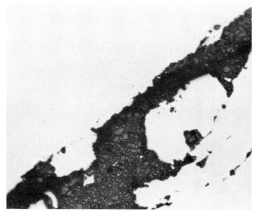

**Fig. 150** 1052 steel forging. Structure is a massive inclusion with a matrix of $Al_2O_3$, $SiO_2$, magnesium oxide, and calcium oxide. Rectangular particles in the matrix are $Al_2O_3$ with iron oxide; others are $Al_2O_3$ with magnesium oxide. See Fig. 151 for a higher magnification view of a similar inclusion. As-polished. 100×

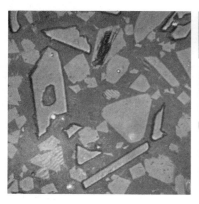

**Fig. 151** Massive, stringer-type inclusion in a 1052 steel forging. Particles in the matrix of the inclusion are clearly resolved. As-polished. 500×

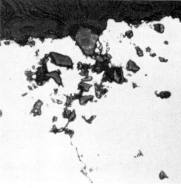

**Fig. 152** 1052 steel forging, with massive iron aluminide inclusions at the surface. Note the crack extending downward from the inclusions. As-polished. 500×

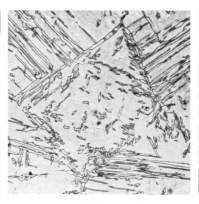

**Fig. 153** 1541 steel forged at 1205 °C (2200 °F) and cooled in an air blast. Structure is Widmanstätten platelets of ferrite nucleated at prior austenite grain boundaries and within grains. The matrix is martensite. Nital. 330×

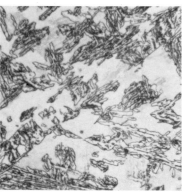

**Fig. 154** Same steel and forging temperature as Fig. 153, but cooled in a milder air blast. The slower cooling rate resulted in the formation of upper bainite (dark). The matrix is martensite. Nital. 550×

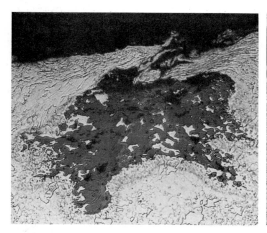

**Fig. 155** Forging lap in 1541 steel, austenitized 2 h at 870 °C (1600 °F), water quenched, and tempered 2 h at 650 °C (1200 °F). The dark area is iron oxide; the adjacent lighter area is ferrite and tempered martensite. Core: ferrite and tempered martensite. 1% nital. 100×

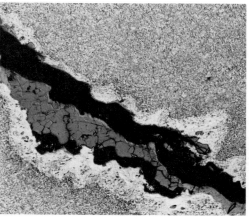

**Fig. 156** Elongated forging lap in 1541 steel that was austenitized, water quenched, and tempered to 25 to 30 HRC. The dark area is iron oxide; the white area surrounding the lap is the result of decarburization. The remainder of the structure is tempered martensite. 1% nital. 100×

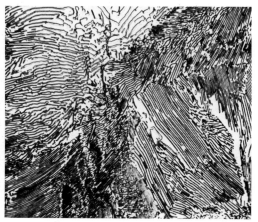

**Fig. 157** High carbon steel (Fe-0.75C) that was held 24 h at 1095 °C (2000 °F) and air cooled. Slow cooling from the austenite region produced this pearlite structure. 4% picral. 500×

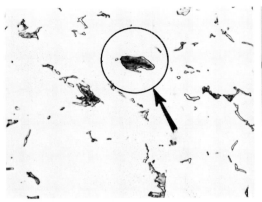

**Fig. 158** Dual-phase steel (0.11C-1.40Mn-0.58Si-0.12Cr-0.08Mo), heat treated at 790 °C (1450 °F) and air cooled. The structure is ferrite and pearlite. See Fig. 159. 4% picral. 1000×

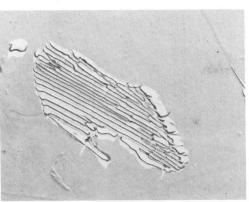

**Fig. 159** Replica electron micrograph of the area circled in Fig. 158. The pearlite is resolved at this higher magnification. 4% picral. 4970×

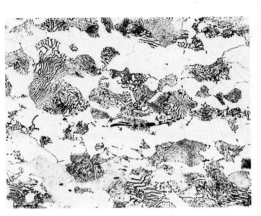

**Fig. 160** 4130 steel normalized by austenitizing at 870 °C (1600 °F) and air cooling to room temperature. Structure consists of ferrite (white) and lamellar pearlite (dark). 2% nital. 500×

**Fig. 161** 4130 hot-rolled steel bar, 25 mm (1 in.) in diameter, annealed by austenitizing at 845 °C (1550 °F) and cooling slowly in the furnace. The structure consists of coarse lamellar pearlite (dark) in a matrix of ferrite (light). 2% nital. 750×

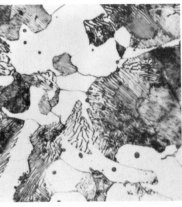

**Fig. 162** Resulfurized 4140 steel forging normalized by austenitizing 30 min at 900 °C (1650 °F) and air cooling, and annealed by heating 1 h at 815 °C (1500 °F), furnace cooling to 540 °C (1000 °F), and air cooling. The structure is blocky ferrite and lamellar pearlite. The black dots are sulfide. 2% nital. 825×

**Fig. 163** 25-mm (1-in.) diam 4140 steel bar, austenitized 1 h at 845 °C (1550 °F), cooled to 650 °C (1200 °F) and held 1 h for isothermal transformation, then cooled to room temperature. White areas are ferrite; gray and black areas, pearlite with fine and coarse lamellar spacing. Nital. 500×

**Fig. 164** 25-mm (1-in.) diam 4140 steel bar, austenitized 1 h at 845 °C (1550 °F) and water quenched. The structure consists entirely of fine, homogeneous untempered martensite. Tempering at 150 °C (300 °F) would result in a darker-etching structure. 2% nital. 500×

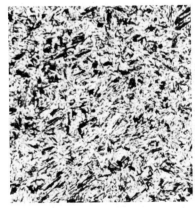

**Fig. 165** Same material and processing as Fig. 164, except quenched in oil instead of water; this resulted in the formation of bainite (black) along with the martensite (light). 2% nital. 500×

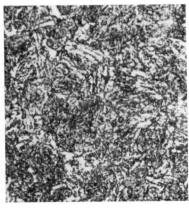

**Fig. 166** 4140 steel bar, austenitized at 845 °C (1550 °F), oil quenched to 65 °C (150 °F), and tempered 2 h at 620 °C (1150 °F). Structure is a martensite-ferrite-carbide aggregate. 2% nital. 750×

**Fig. 167** Oxide inclusions (stringers) in a 25-mm (1-in.) diam 4140 steel bar. The stringers are parallel to the direction of rolling on the as-polished surface of the bar. As-polished. 200×

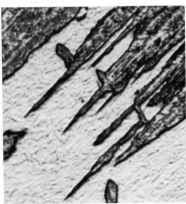

**Fig. 168** 4350 steel bar austenitized at 845 °C (1550 °F), quenched to 455 °C (850 °F) and held 4 min for partial isothermal transformation, and water quenched. Dark areas are upper bainite, with aligned carbide particles. The light areas are martensite. Nital. 1500×

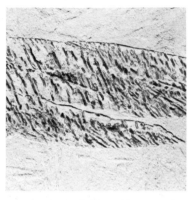

**Fig. 169** 4350 steel bar austenitized at 845 °C (1550 °F), quenched to 345 °C (650 °F) and held 12 min for partial isothermal transformation, and water quenched. Dark areas are lower bainite with carbide particles aligned at 60°; light areas are martensite. Nital. 11 000×

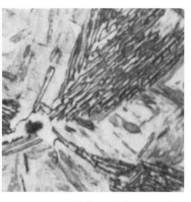

**Fig. 170** 5132 steel forging austenitized at 845 °C (1550 °F) and water quenched. Structure consists of some blocky ferrite (light) and bainite (dark) in a martensite matrix. Nital. 1650×

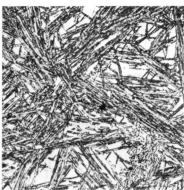

**Fig. 171** AMS 6419 steel center of a 102-mm (4-in.) thick section austenitized 1.5 h at 860 °C (1575 °F), salt quenched 30 min at 290 °C (550 °F), then quenched in oil to room temperature. Structure is self-tempered martensite and some bainite. 2% nital. 500×

**Fig. 172** Same steel and processing as Fig. 171, except air cooled to room temperature after salt bath. Structure is a mixture of bainite, tempered martensite, and untempered martensite. 2% nital. 500×

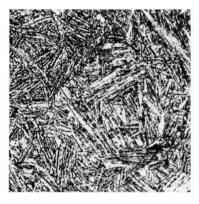

**Fig. 173** Same steel as Fig. 171, but quenched 15 min from the austenitizing temperature in a salt bath at 290 °C (550 °F), placed 1 h in an air furnace at 205 °C (400 °F), and air cooled. Structure is tempered martensite and probably some retained austenite. 2% nital. 500×

**Fig. 174** Same as Fig. 171, but quenched 15 min from the austenitizing temperature in a salt bath at 290 °C (550 °F), then 20 min in oil at 80 °C (175 °F), then air cooled. The structure is tempered martensite and probably some retained austenite. 2% nital. 500×

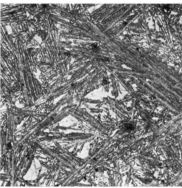

**Fig. 175** Same steel and austenitizing as Fig. 171, but quenched 15 min in a salt bath at 290 °C (550 °F), then air cooled to room temperature. The structure is tempered martensite and probably some retained austenite. 2% nital. 500×

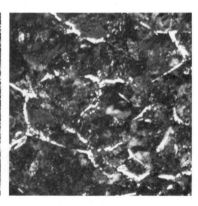

**Fig. 176** 6.5-mm (0.25-in.) diam 1055 steel rod, patented by austenitizing 2 min 20 s in a lead bath at 550 °C (1020 °F) and air cooling. Structure is unresolved pearlite (dark) with ferrite (white) at prior austenite grain boundaries. Picral. 1000×

**Fig. 177** 1055 steel wire, 3 mm (0.13 in.) in diameter, patented by austenitizing 1.5 min at 1030 °C (1890 °F) and air cooling in strand form. Fine lamellar pearlite with discontinuous precipitation of ferrite at prior austenite grain boundaries. Picral. 1000×

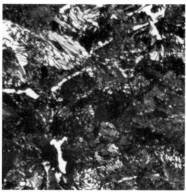

**Fig. 178** 1060 steel rod, 6.7 mm (0.26 in.) diam, air cooled from hot rolling in a 454-kg (1000-lb) coil. Dark areas are unresolved pearlite, with some distinct lamellar pearlite; white areas are ferrite partly outlining prior austenite grain boundaries. Picral. 1000×

**Fig. 179** 6.5-mm (0.25-in.) diam 1060 steel rod, cooled from hot rolling in a single strand by a high-velocity air blast. The structure is mostly unresolved pearlite, with some distinctly lamellar pearlite. The scattered white areas are ferrite partly outlining prior austenite grain boundaries. Picral. 1000×

**Fig. 180** 6.7-mm (0.26-in.) diam 1060 steel rod, patented by austenitizing 2.5 min at 945 °C (1730 °F), quenching 55 s in a lead bath at 530 °C (990 °F), and air cooling. The structure is pearlite (dark) and ferrite (light) at prior austenite grain boundaries. Picral. 1000×

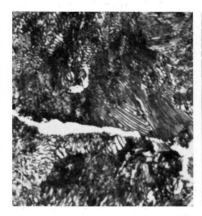

**Fig. 181** 7.1-mm (0.28-in.) diam 1060 steel wire, air patented by austenitizing 3 min at 1055 °C (1930 °F) and air cooling in strand form. The dark areas are partly resolved pearlite; white areas are ferrite at prior austenite grain boundaries. Picral. 1000×

**Fig. 182** 2.5-mm (0.10-in.) diam 1060 steel wire, air patented by austenitizing 1 min at 1015 °C (1860 °F) and air cooling in strand form. Structure is fine pearlite (dark), mostly unresolved, and some ferrite at prior austenite grain boundaries. Picral. 1000×

**Fig. 183** Decarburized 1060 steel, heated 1 h at 1205 °C (2000 °F) before rolling to size. Note the thin layer of scale at the surface (top) and the decarburized layer (white, near top). Below that is unresolved pearlite and ferrite. Picral. 100×

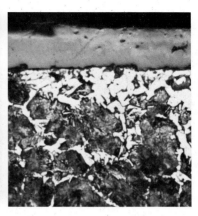

**Fig. 184** Decarburized 1060 steel, heated 12 min at 870 to 930 °C (1600 to 1700 °F) and cooled in air. Top to bottom: Scale, a decarburized layer, pearlite, and some grain-boundary ferrite. Picral. 500×

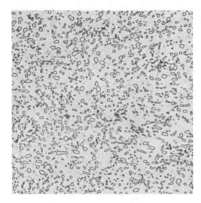

**Fig. 185** 1064 cold-rolled steel strip, heated to 745 °C (1370 °F), furnace cooled to 650 °C (1200 °F), and air cooled to room temperature. Structure is fine spheroidal cementite in a matrix of ferrite. This structure is preferred for subsequent heat treatment. Picral. 500×

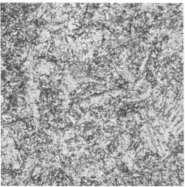

**Fig. 186** 1064 cold-rolled steel strip, austenitized at 815 °C (1500 °F), quenched to 315 °C (600 °F) and held to complete isothermal transformation, air cooled, and tempered at 370 °C (700 °F). The structure is a mixture of bainite and tempered martensite. Picral. 500×

**Fig. 187** 1065 steel wire, 3.4 mm (0.14 in.) in diameter, patented by austenitizing 1.5 min at 930 °C (1710 °F), quenching 30 s in a lead bath at 545 °C (1010 °F), and air cooling. The structure is mostly unresolved pearlite with some grain-boundary ferrite. Picral. 500×

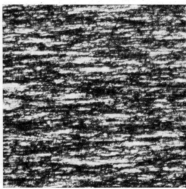

**Fig. 188** 1070 hard drawn steel valve-spring wire, tensile strength of 1690 MPa (245 ksi) obtained by 80% reduction. Longitudinal section has a structure of deformed pearlite. 2% nital. 100×

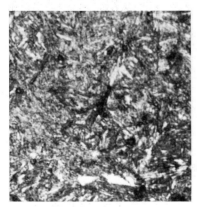

**Fig. 189** 1070 steel valve-spring wire, quenched and tempered. Austenitized at 870 °C (1600 °F), oil quenched, and tempered at 455 °C (850 °F). Structure is mainly tempered martensite, with some free ferrite (white). 2% nital. 1000×

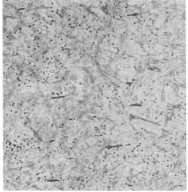

**Fig. 190** 1074 cold-rolled steel sheet, austenitized 5 min at 815 °C (1500 °F) and oil quenched. Structure is predominantly untempered martensite, with scattered, poorly resolved cementite. Picral. 500×

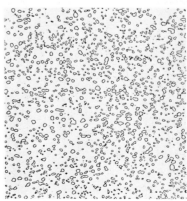

**Fig. 191** AISI 1074 steel, cold rolled, then batch annealed 10 h at 695 °C (1285 °F). The structure is spheroidized carbides in a ferrite matrix. 4% picral. 500×. (J.E. Gatehouse)

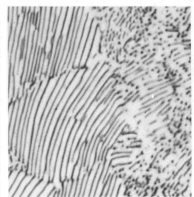

**Fig. 192** 1080 hot-rolled steel bar, austenitized 30 min at 1050 °C (1920 °F) and furnace cooled to room temperature at 28 °C (50 °F) per h. The structure is mostly pearlite, with some spheroidal cementite particles. Picral. 2000×

**Fig. 193** Thin-foil transmission electron micrograph of the same steel and heat treatment as in Fig. 192, but the cooling rate was increased to 55 °C (100 °F) per h. The structure is almost entirely fine lamellar pearlite. 2000×

**Fig. 194** 1095 steel wire, austenitized at 940 °C (1725 °F) and oil quenched. The dark areas are a mixture of fine pearlite and lower bainite; light areas are untempered martensite. This structure resulted from slack quenching. 2% nital. 500×

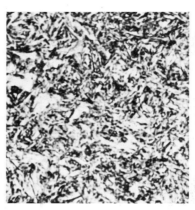

**Fig. 195** 1095 steel, austenitized at 870 °C (1600 °F) and air cooled (normalized) then austenitized at 815 °C (1500 °F) and water quenched. Fine untempered martensite caused by a more severe quench than in Fig. 194 and some spheroidal cementite. Picral. 1000×

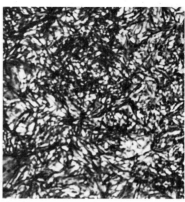

**Fig. 196** Same steel and heat treatment as Fig. 195, but tempered at 150 °C (300 °F) after quenching. The structure is tempered martensite (darker than that in Fig. 195) and some spheroidal cementite particles. Picral. 1000×

**Fig. 197** 1095 steel wire, austenitized 30 min at 885 °C (1625 °F) quenched to 330 °C (625 °F), held 5 min, and oil quenched. The structure is lower bainite (dark) and untempered martensite. 2% nital. 550×

**Fig. 198** Same steel and austenitizing treatment as Fig. 197, but held 20 min in 330 °C (625 °F) quench and air cooled. Dark areas are lower bainite; light areas, untempered martensite. 2% nital. 550×

**Fig. 199** Same steel and austenitizing treatment as Fig. 197, but held 1 h in a 455 °C (850 °F) quench and air cooled (austempered). The structure is mainly upper bainite. 2% nital. 550×

**Fig. 200** Iron-carbon alloy (1.4% C), austenitized at 1010 °C (1850 °F), furnace cooled to 315 °C (600 °F), and air cooled. The structure is ferrite (dark) and cementite (light). Beraha's tint etchant. 320×

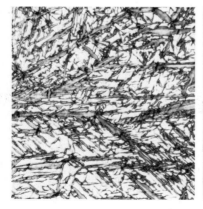

**Fig. 201** Same alloy as Fig. 200, austenitized at 1095 °C (2000 °F) and water quenched. Structure is acicular martensite, with some retained austenite (white). 2% nital. 1000×

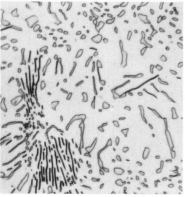

**Fig. 202** 0.55C-2.40Mn steel, held 2 h 40 min at 750 °F (1380 °C), cooled to 680 °C (1255 °F), and held 48 h. Structure is spheroidized carbide particles and lamellar pearlite in a ferrite matrix. Picral. 1000×

**Fig. 203** Hot-rolled alloy steel bar (1.2C-0.5Cr-0.9Mo-0.2V), austenitized 30 min at 925 °C (1700 °F) and oil quenched. Structure is untempered martensite (dark, needle-like) and retained austenite (white). Picral. 550×

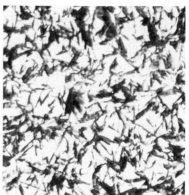

**Fig. 204** Same steel and heat treatment as Fig. 203, but at a higher magnification. The large amount of retained austenite (white) indicates that the austenitizing temperature was too high for this steel. Picral. 1100×

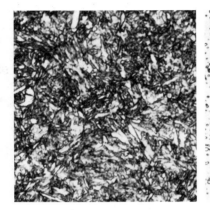

**Fig. 205** 51B60 hot-rolled steel bar 32 mm (1.25 in.) in diameter, austenitized at 870 °C (1600 °F), air cooled (normalized), austenitized at 815 °C (1500 °F), and water quenched. Structure is untempered martensite, some retained austenite, and fine spheroidal carbide. Picral. 1000×

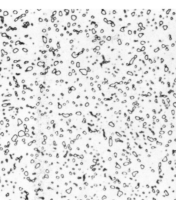

**Fig. 206** 51B60 hot-rolled steel bar, 32 mm (1.25 in.) in diameter, austenitized and quenched to obtain a martensitic structure, then tempered 15 h at 675 °C (1250 °F). Structure consists of spheroidal carbide particles in a ferrite matrix. Nital. 1000×

**Fig. 207** 52100 steel bar, 124 mm (4.8 in.) in diameter, hot rolled at 1175 to 925 °C (2150 to 1700 °F) and air cooled to room temperature. Cross section shows pits (cluster of small dark spots); in center are inclusions. 50% aqueous HCl. Actual size

**Fig. 208** Microstructure of specimen taken from bar section in Fig. 207. The structure is predominantly pearlite (light and dark gray), with thin films of carbide (black lines) outlining the prior austenite grain boundaries. Equal parts 4% picral and 4% nital. 100×

**Fig. 209** Same specimen as Fig. 208, but at a higher magnification. The grain-boundary carbide rejected from solid solution during cooling is resolved and appears as white lines. Equal parts 4% picral and 4% nital. 500×

**Fig. 210** Same specimen as in Fig. 208, but a still higher magnification to show the grain-boundary carbide as areas rather than thin lines. The matrix is pearlite. Equal parts 4% picral and 4% nital. 1000×

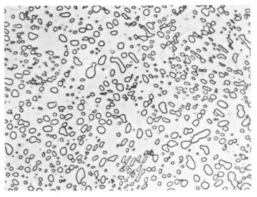

**Fig. 211** 52100 steel bar, 124 mm (4.8 in.) in diameter, heated to 770 °C (1420 °F) in 10 h, held 5 h, cooled at 10 °C (20 °F) per h to 650 °C (1200 °F), furnace cooled to 27 °C (80 °F). Fine dispersion of spheroidal carbide in a matrix of ferrite. See also Fig. 212 to 219. 4% picral + 0.05% HCl. 1000×

**Fig. 212** Same steel as Fig. 211, except austenitized 30 min at 790 °C (1450 °F), oil quenched, and tempered 1 h at 175 °C (350 °F). The black areas are bainite, the gray areas are tempered martensite, and the white dots are carbide particles that did not dissolve during austenitizing. Equal parts 4% picral and 4% nital. 500×

**Fig. 213** Same steel as Fig. 211, except austenitized 30 min at 845 °C (1550 °F), oil quenched, and tempered same as in Fig. 212. Structure is tempered martensite, along with carbide particles (white) that were not dissolved during austenitizing. Equal parts 4% picral and 4% nital. 500×

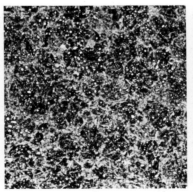

**Fig. 214** Same steel as Fig. 211, except austenitized 30 min at 855 °C (1575 °F), oil quenched, and tempered 1 h at 260 °C (500 °F). The structure is tempered martensite and undissolved carbide particles. Equal parts 4% picral and 4% nital. 500×

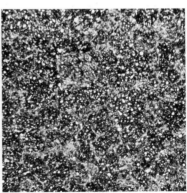

**Fig. 215** Same steel as Fig. 211, except austenitized 30 min at 845 °C (1550 °F), oil quenched, and tempered 1 h at 400 °C (750 °F). Structure is tempered martensite and a dispersion of carbide particles not dissolved during austenitizing. Equal parts 4% picral and 4% nital. 500×

**Fig. 216** Same steel as Fig. 211, except austenitized 30 min at 925 °C (1700 °F), oil quenched, and tempered 1 h at 175 °C (350 °F). The structure is mainly tempered martensite. High austenitizing temperature has resulted in some retained austenite and a few carbide particles. Equal parts 4% picral and 4% nital. 500×

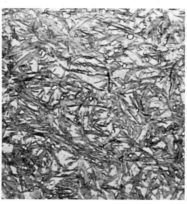

**Fig. 217** Same specimen as Fig. 216, except at a higher magnification. Dark areas are tempered martensite; retained austenite (angular, light gray) is well resolved. A few undissolved carbide particles remain from the original structure. Equal parts 4% picral and 4% nital. 1000×

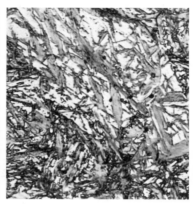

**Fig. 218** Same steel as Fig. 211, except austenitized 30 min at 980 °C (1800 °F), oil quenched, and tempered 1 h at 175 °C (350 °F). Structure is coarse plates (needles) of tempered martensite and retained austenite (white). Carbides are almost completely dissolved. Equal parts 4% picral and 4% nital. 1000×

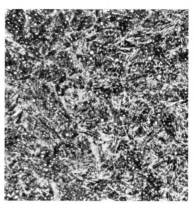

**Fig. 219** Same steel as Fig. 211, except austenitized 30 min at 855 °C (1575 °F), quenched in a salt bath at 260 °C (500 °F), held 30 min, and air cooled to room temperature. Structure consists of spheroidal carbide particles in lower bainite and some retained austenite. Equal parts 4% picral and 4% nital. 500×

**Fig. 220** 52100 steel rod, austenitized 20 min at 900 °C (1650 °F) and slack quenched in oil to room temperature. The dark areas are a mixture of fine pearlite and bainite. Light areas are untempered martensite. 4% nital. 500×

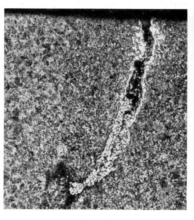

**Fig. 221** Crack in a 52100 steel roller after austenitizing, water quenching, and tempering. The crack, extending down from the surface, was caused by a seam in the bar stock. The structure is martensite. See also Fig. 222. 1% nital. 100×

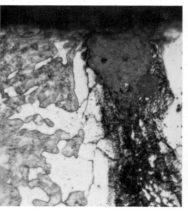

**Fig. 222** Same crack as Fig. 221, but at a higher magnification. Decarburization (white areas) along the crack is evidence that the crack preceded heat treatment (surface is not decarburized). 1% nital. 750×

**Fig. 223** Hardened 52100 steel, damaged by an abrasive cutoff wheel. Dark areas are martensite tempered by overheating; light areas, untempered martensite, which had been reaustenitized by frictional heat. 1% nital. 100×

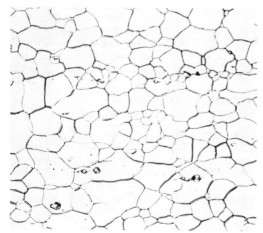

**Fig. 224** Electrical sheet steel, decarburized. The structure consists of ferrite grains. Marshall's reagent. 500×

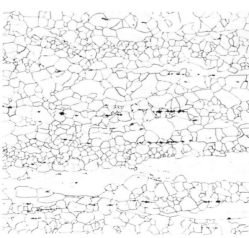

**Fig. 225** Same steel as Fig. 224, but not decarburized. The structure consists of ferrite grains. Marshall's reagent. 200×

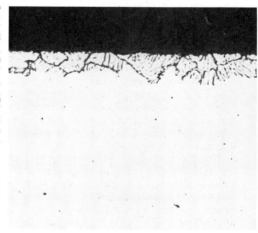

**Fig. 226** Same steel and processing as Fig. 224, showing internal oxidation. 4% picral. 1000×. (S.A. Wright)

# Coated Sheet Steel

COATED SHEET STEEL specimens for metallographic examination are prepared in much the same way as specimens of uncoated sheet steel; however, cutting of coated sheet steel specimens requires special care to prevent delamination of cut edges or chipping of edges of sheet steel coated with a brittle material. Special mounting techniques are sometimes required for coated sheet steel, and etching procedures may differ from those for uncoated steel. Detailed information on the coating techniques discussed in this article can be found in Volume 5 of the 9th Edition of *Metals Handbook*. Additional information on the properties of these coatings can be found in the articles "Precoated Steel Sheet" and "Steel Sheet for Porcelain Enameling" in Volume 1 of the 9th Edition of *Metals Handbook*.

## Zinc-Coated Sheet Steel

Care in cutting zinc-coated sheet steel is necessary to avoid delamination of cut edges at the interface of the coating and the steel substrate. Cutting should be performed using an abrasive wheel or a low-speed diamond saw, rather than by shearing. Satisfactory results can also be obtained by using a micropunch to punch out specimens.

**Grinding and Polishing.** Conventional wet grinding using silicon carbide papers through 600 grit is typical. Rough grinding may be completed with a dry 0000 emery paper or 800-grit silicon carbide paper lubricated with a No. 2 soft graphite pencil or with kerosene.

The use of water must be avoided throughout polishing of galvanized specimens, because it will stain the zinc coating. For rough polishing, a low-nap silk cloth and 3-$\mu$m diamond paste in a vehicle of kerosene is generally preferred. The final polish should be on a soft low-nap cloth with 0.05-$\mu$m alumina ($Al_2O_3$) suspended in an alcohol-glycerol mixture; the specimen should then be cleaned by swabbing with ethanol. Rough and final polishing should be accomplished in 1 min or less. In polishing galvanized steels, the use of a low-nap cloth will minimize rounding of edges.

**Etching of Hot-Dip Galvanized Steels.** Details of the zinc-iron alloy layer in hot-dip galvanized steels can be revealed by these etchants:

- Amyl-nital, consisting of 1 drop nitric acid ($HNO_3$) in 10 mL amyl alcohol. Immersion: 1 to 30 s. Etching in amyl nital is sometimes followed by a brief picral etch. Amyl alcohol is a toxic substance; this etchant should be prepared and used under a hood, and skin contact should be avoided.
- A few drops of $HNO_3$ in 10 mL acetone. Immersion: 10 to 30 s
- 0.5% $HNO_3$ in ethyl or methyl alcohol. Immersion: 1 to 3 s
- 1 g picric acid in 100 mL $H_2O$ to which 1 drop of a solution of 6 g chromic acid ($CrO_3$) in 94 mL $HNO_3$ has been added. Immersion: 3 s. Promotes good contrast between the coating and the zinc-iron alloy layer

**Etching of Hot-Dip Zinc-Aluminum Coatings.** These materials have been successfully etched with a 100 mL solution of 0.5% $HNO_3$ plus 1 to 1.5% hydrofluoric acid (HF) in methanol. The amyl-nital etch mentioned previously has also been used for zinc-aluminum-coated steels. Immersion times range from 1 to 5 s.

**Etching of Electrogalvanized Steel.** The absence of an alloy layer in electrogalvanized steels requires an alternative for revealing detail in the coating. A modification to an etchant used for pure zinc effectively defines cell boundaries on multicell electrogalvanized coatings. The etch consists of 8 to 10 g $CrO_3$ in 100 mL distilled $H_2O$ to which 1 g sodium sulfate ($Na_2SO_4$) has been added. It may be useful to experiment with the quantity of $Na_2SO_4$ added. Sodium sulfate appears to affect the rate of attack to the coating; therefore, the smaller the quantity of $Na_2SO_4$ used, the greater the degree of control exercised.

## Aluminum-Coated Sheet Steel

The preparation of hot-dip aluminum-coated steel for metallographic study is similar to that of galvanized steel; both coatings are relatively soft. Because staining is not a problem with aluminum-coated sheet steels, water can be used as a suspending fluid and lubricant.

A vibratory polisher, if available, is recommended for rough polishing, using 0.3-$\mu$m $Al_2O_3$ and distilled water on a wax-covered disk or a napless cloth. Final polishing may be performed using a vibratory polisher or by hand on a rotating disk covered with a soft-nap cloth. A suspension of 0.05-$\mu$m $Al_2O_3$ in distilled water is the abrasive most commonly used.

To examine the aluminum coating and the aluminum-iron alloy layer, an etchant of 0.5% HF in distilled water is most often used. A nital etch is used to reveal the structure of the steel base. This etch also outlines the interface between the aluminum-iron alloy layer and the base metal.

## Stainless-Clad and Chromized Sheet Steel

Stainless-clad and chromized sheet steels, although manufactured by different processes, consist of a relatively soft low-carbon steel core sandwiched between stainless steel or chromium-rich surface layers. The surface layers are harder than the low-carbon steel base metal (unlike galvanized and aluminum-coated steels).

To avoid delamination of cut edges at the interface between the coating and the base metal, cutting to produce specimens of stain-

Revised by T.E. Dwyer, Chief Metallographer, National Steel Corporation

less-clad or chromized steel should be performed using an abrasive wheel, rather than by shearing. Cuts should be made toward the base metal, not toward the coating. Mounting technique is the same as that for other sheet steels.

**Grinding and polishing** techniques generally are the same as those for other sheet steels and are somewhat less critical than those for galvanized steel, because the edges of stainless-clad or chromized steel specimens are harder and less easily rounded. To ensure a scratch-free surface in the outer zones, final polishing of stainless-clad or chromized steel may require more time than for galvanized steel. This step is critical, because overpolishing creates a relief zone between the base metal and the coating.

**Etching and Examination.** Stainless-clad or chromized steels are first etched in nital or picral (Fig. 14 to 16). Because these etchants attack only the steel and the diffusion zone, further etching is necessary to examine the structures of the outer layer. The nital or picral etch is usually followed by an electrolytic etch in a 10% $CrO_3$ solution at approximately 3 V. These coated steels are examined for coating thickness, porosity in the coating, structure of the interfaces, presence of second phases (such as chromium carbide), and structure of the base metal.

## Tin Mill Products

Almost all tin plate is produced by electroplating approximately 0.4 $\mu$m (16 $\mu$in.) of tin onto low-carbon sheet steel that is often as thin as 0.15 mm (0.006 in.). Preserving the various zones—the sheet steel, the alloy layer, and the unalloyed tin—requires use of the best possible edge-preparation techniques (see the discussion of the preparation of galvanized specimens in this article and the article "Mounting of Specimens" in this Volume). The use of vibratory polishers is preferred. Rough polishing on waxed disks with 3-$\mu$m diamond, followed by final polishing on soft low-nap cloths with 0.05-$\mu$m $Al_2O_3$, usually gives good results.

The thinness of the electroplated tin coating precludes using optical microscopy, except for mounted taper sections (see the discussion of this technique later in this article). Frequently, the purpose of microscopic examination is to study the structure of the $FeSn_2$ layer that forms at the interface between the steel and the tin when the tin plate is flow brightened by melting the tin. Alloy structures are revealed by selectively removing the tin and are examined by transmission electron microscopy (Fig. 17 to 19) or by scanning electron microscopy.

## Porcelain Enameled Sheet Steel

Because of the brittleness of porcelain enamel coatings, cutting a specimen from porcelain enameled sheet steel requires procedures that will minimize or prevent chipping of the friable coating. Two procedures have been used successfully. The first employs a thin $Al_2O_3$ cutoff wheel. The cut should be made approximately 3 mm (1/8 in.) away from the area to be examined. The specimen is then mounted and ground back approximately 3 mm (1/8 in.) to remove areas damaged in cutting. The second procedure uses a jeweler's coping saw, which permits cutting directly into the area to be examined.

**Mounting.** Specimens of porcelain enameled sheet steel may present a problem in mounting, because they cannot be bent into L or Z shapes without damaging the coating. However, several techniques are available.

Clamp mounting can be used for porcelain enameled specimens and is preferred in some laboratories. Mechanical clamping devices are also described in the article "Mounting of Specimens" in this Volume.

Another method for mounting several specimens simultaneously is to clip them together or to glue them together with an epoxy resin. The specimens may be interleaved with strips of soft metal, such as copper. Clipping or gluing will provide a section thickness sufficient to be self-supporting when placed upright in a mold.

A single specimen can be mounted by supporting it between two suitably bent pieces of shim stock. An alternative is to use two molding operations, as illustrated in Fig. 1, although this technique is time consuming. A hard mounting material, such as an epoxy with a filler material, is generally preferred for specimens of porcelain enameled sheet steel, although a cold-mounting epoxy resin is also used.

**Grinding,** with silicon carbide of increasingly finer grit sizes, follows the procedures for other steels. During rough grinding, the mount must be held so the direction of belt or wheel movement is toward the enameled side. If the direction is reversed, the enamel may be pulled away from the steel. This problem does not arise during fine grinding or polishing.

**Polishing.** Rough polishing is performed using 3-$\mu$m diamond paste and kerosene lubricant on a napped cloth. Final polishing is performed using 0.25-$\mu$m diamond paste and kerosene on a napped cloth. An alternate final polishing consists of using a vibratory polisher, cerium oxide ($CeO_2$) abrasive, and distilled water on a napped cloth.

**Etching and Examination.** Many specimens of porcelain enameled sheet steel are not etched for metallographic examination. When etching is indicated, nital is most often used to etch the matrix (Fig. 20 to 22). Several optical microscopy techniques are used for examining porcelain enameled sheet steel specimens—notably, taper sections, brightfield and dark-field illumination, and polarized light.

**Taper sections** are used to obtain additional "magnification" (or, more properly, distortion) in one direction. An apparent magnification ratio of 10:1 is obtained by mounting the specimen at an angle of 5° 44' 21″, instead of at the usual 90° angle. The broadened interface assists the examination of thin layers, such as those observed on porcelain enameled sheet. Taper may, however, introduce problems of interpretation when the layers are discontinuous or nonuniform. Taper sections are often used to examine the steel-enamel interface.

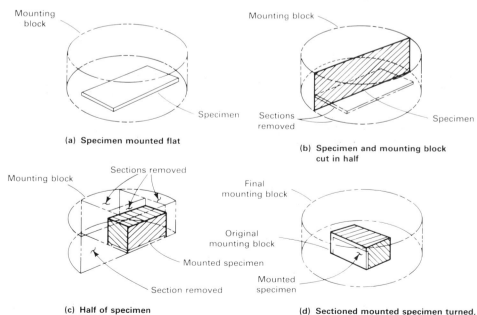

(a) Specimen mounted flat

(b) Specimen and mounting block cut in half

(c) Half of specimen and mounting block sectioned further

(d) Sectioned mounted specimen turned, specimen edge down, and remounted

**Fig. 1** Procedure for mounting a sheet-metal specimen that should not be bent. Sectioning of a mounted specimen must be done with extreme care to avoid overheating and to prevent separation of the specimen from the mount.

**Illumination.** For general examination and the examination of enamel defects, bright-field illumination is commonly used. It reveals the microstructure of the steel, and the general condition and thickness of the enamel. Figure 21 shows a conventional cross section of porcelain enameled steel by bright-field illumination.

Figure 22 shows the same specimen photographed with dark-field illumination, which reveals interface details. In Fig. 22, the iron oxide crystals and oxide-saturated enamel at the interface are apparent, and the ground coat on the steel can be distinguished from the white cover coat. Polarized light provides approximately the same effect as dark-field illumination, but dark-field illumination provides sharper definition.

**Fig. 2** Hot-dip galvanized 1006 steel, "galvannealed." This coating consists of zinc-iron compounds with no free zinc. Coating weight: 275 g/m² (0.9 oz/ft²). Amyl-nital. 550×

**Fig. 3** Hot-dip galvanized 1006 steel showing a "regular galvanized" free-zinc coating. Zinc-iron compounds are present at the coating interface. Coating weight: 320 g/m² (1.05 oz/ft²). Compare with Fig. 4. Amyl-nital. 550×

**Fig. 4** Hot-dip galvanized 1006 steel (culvert stock). Much heavier than "regular galvanized" coatings. Contains more free zinc and has more zinc-iron alloy at the interface. Coating weight: 655 g/m² (2.15 oz/ft²). Amyl-nital. 550×

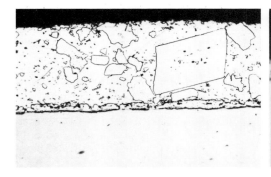

**Fig. 5** Hot-dip galvanized 1008 steel (culvert stock). Imperfections in this heavy galvanized coating consist of crystals of $FeZn_7$, which originate from dross in the galvanizing bath. Nital. 500×

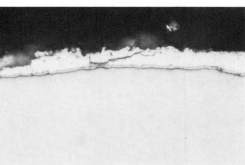

**Fig. 6, 7** Differentially coated hot-dip galvanized 1006 steel. Post-coating anneal produced diffusion zinc-iron alloy on both surfaces. Fig. 6: The lighter coated surface (38 g/m², or 0.12 oz/ft²) consists of $FeZn_7$ and a thin layer of $Fe_5Zn_{21}$ at the steel interface. Fig. 7: The heavier coated surface (130 g/m², or 0.43 oz/ft²) features free zinc at the surface due to incomplete interdiffusion between the zinc coating and the steel substrate. 0.5% nital + 1.5 mL HF. Both at 1000×

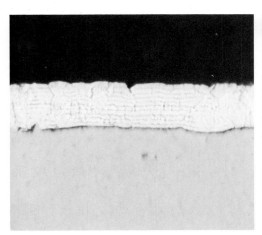

**Fig. 8** Electrogalvanized 1006 steel. Careful etching with $CrO_3$ + $Na_2SO_4$ reveals the interface between layers of zinc deposited in individual cells in a multicell electrogalvanizing line. Note the absence of an alloy layer at the interface between the coating and the steel. Coating weight: 80 g/m² (0.26 oz/ft²). 8 to 10 g $CrO_3$, 100 mL $H_2O$, 1 g $Na_2SO_4$. 1000×

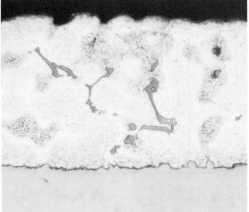
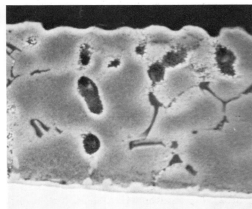

**Fig. 9, 10** Galvalume (Al-43.5Zn-1.5Si) coated 1010 steel. The coating features silicon needles (gray) in an aluminum-zinc matrix. Silicon is added to the coating bath to control the growth of the intermetallic layer. Fig. 9: Using optical microscopy, it is difficult to resolve the aluminum-zinc-iron-silicon alloy layer at the interface. Fig. 10: Using backscattered electron image from a scanning electron microscope, the alloy layer is readily apparent. 0.5% nital + 1.5 mL HF. Both at 1000×

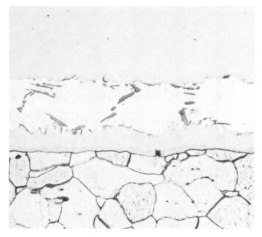

**Fig. 11** 1008 steel with type 1 hot-dip aluminum coating. This is an aluminum-silicon alloy coating that forms aluminum-silicon and aluminum-silicon-iron layers. Top to bottom: a nickel filler, aluminum-silicon alloy, aluminum-silicon-iron alloy, and the sheet steel. Nital. 1000×

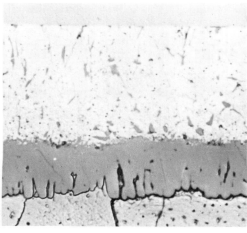

**Fig. 12** 1008 steel with type 2 hot-dip aluminum coating. This coating forms a layer of essentially pure aluminum and a layer of aluminum-iron alloy. Upper layer is pure aluminum with scattered particles of aluminum-iron; lower layer, aluminum-iron. Nital. 1000×

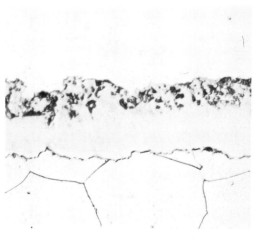

**Fig. 13** 1008 steel with type 1 hot-dip aluminum coating. The coating, essentially the same as that shown in Fig. 11, has been exposed to elevated temperature in air, thus accounting for the surface oxides (dark etching). Nital. 1000×

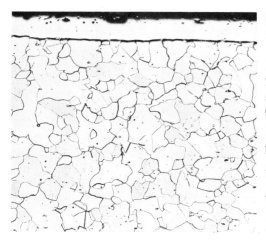

**Fig. 14** Chromized 1006 steel. Stainless (20% Cr, 80% Fe) layer at steel surface was formed by powder compacting, then diffusion annealing. 2% nital. 110×

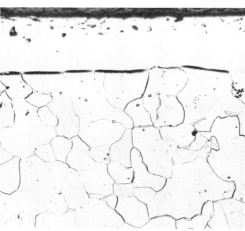

**Fig. 15** Same as Fig. 14, but at higher magnification, which shows interdiffusion that occurs at interface between the coating and the steel. 2% nital. 220×

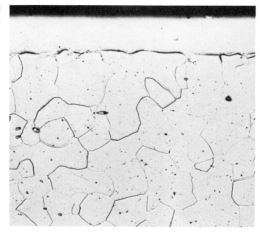

**Fig. 16** Chromized 1006 steel. Chromium was deposited on the steel by gaseous transfer, then diffused to form chromium-iron layer. Picral-nital. 275×

**Fig. 17** Replica electron micrograph of alkaline-bath tin-plated 0.10% C steel showing fine, randomly oriented crystals of $FeSn_2$ over larger, oriented crystals of $FeSn_2$. NaOH-orthonitrophenol + $H_2O$. 8000×

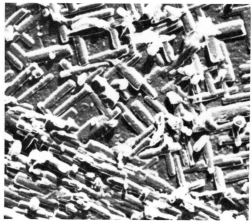

**Fig. 18** Replica electron micrograph of acid-bath tin-plated 0.10% C steel showing three modes of growth of the acicular crystals of $FeSn_2$ on the steel base. NaOH-orthonitrophenol + $H_2O$. 8000×

**Fig. 19** Replica electron micrograph of surface of tin-plated 1008 steel showing modes of growth of crystals of $FeSn_2$ that formed during fusion of halogen-electroplated tin. 2% nital. 6050×

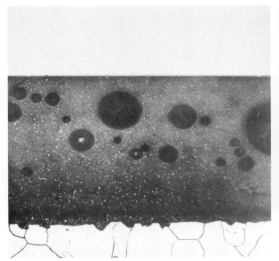

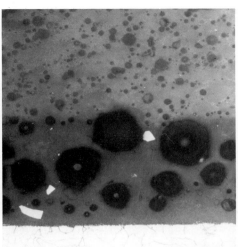

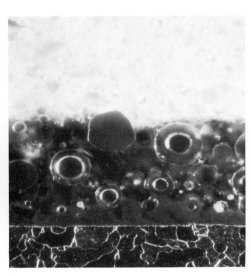

**Fig. 20** Extra-low-carbon steel (0.01% C, approx) with a single coating of white porcelain enamel (dark layer above steel surface). Nital. 100×

**Fig. 21, 22** Ground-coat and cover-coat porcelain enamel on enameling iron sheet (bottom), as shown by bright-field illumination (Fig. 21) and dark-field illumination (Fig. 22). 2% nital. Both at 125×

# Plate Steels

PLATE STEELS cover a wide range of compositions. Most are low-carbon steels (<0.20% C), but some are medium-carbon grades (0.20 to 0.40% C). Plate is usually made of plain carbon or low-alloy steels, although high-alloy plate (>5% alloy content) is occasionally produced. Plate thicknesses range from 6 to 300 mm (0.25 to 12 in.); widths from 200 to 2000 mm (8 to 80 in.).

## Specimen Preparation

Specimen preparation is usually the same as for other carbon and alloy steels. Preparation of specimens made from ferritic and austenitic stainless steels is described in the article "Wrought Stainless Steels" in this Volume.

**Sectioning.** Because thicknesses of plate can range to 300 mm (12 in.) or more, it is often necessary to examine specimens from three or more locations through the thickness to observe all microstructural conditions. Extracting specimens from a thick plate is likely to require considerable cutting. Various machining methods, including sawing and hollow boring, are used to obtain the initial testpieces. During machining, the specimen must not overheat, which may alter the structure.

**Procedures for final sectioning, mounting, grinding, and polishing** of plate steels are the same as those described for other carbon and alloy steels (see the Section "Metallographic Techniques" and the article "Carbon and Alloy Steels" in this Volume). With plate forms, the desired information and the large size of the specimens sometimes make it unnecessary to mount specimens; however, mounting is preferable for best results.

**Etching.** Nital, consisting of 1 or 2% nitric acid ($HNO_3$) in alcohol, is the etchant most widely used for plate steels. It is preferred for delineation of ferrite grain boundaries. Picral, consisting of alcohol saturated with picric acid, is preferred for examining carbide particles in annealed steels and in quenched and tempered steels. A combination of nital plus picral is also used (see Fig. 46 to 52).

## Examination of Welded Joints

Because plate steels are often welded, techniques for metallographic examination of

## Table 1 Compositions of ASTM plate steels

| Steel | Composition, % | | | | | | | | | | | | | |
|---|---|---|---|---|---|---|---|---|---|---|---|---|---|---|
| | C | Mn | Si | S | P | Cu | Cr | Mo | V | Ti | B | Ni | Nb | Al |
| A36 | 0.25–0.29 | ... | ... | 0.05 max | 0.04 max | ... | ... | ... | ... | ... | ... | ... | ... | ... |
| A201 Grade A (superseded by A515) | 0.20–0.35(a) | 0.80 max | ... | ... | ... | ... | ... | ... | ... | ... | ... | ... | ... | ... |
| A201 Grade B (superseded by A515) | 0.24–0.35(a) | 0.80 max | ... | ... | ... | ... | ... | ... | ... | ... | ... | ... | ... | ... |
| A285 Grade C | 0.28 max | 0.90 max | ... | 0.045 max | 0.035 max | 0.20–0.35 | ... | ... | ... | ... | ... | ... | ... | ... |
| A387 Grade D | 0.15 max | 0.30–0.60 | 0.50 max | 0.035 max | 0.035 max | ... | 2.00–2.50 | 0.90–1.10 | ... | ... | ... | ... | ... | ... |
| A515 Grade 70 | 0.31–0.35(a) | 0.90 max | 0.15–0.30 | 0.04 max | 0.035 max | ... | ... | ... | ... | ... | ... | ... | ... | ... |
| A516 Grade 70 | 0.27–0.31(a) | 0.85–1.20 | 0.15–0.30 | 0.04 max | 0.035 max | ... | ... | ... | ... | ... | ... | ... | ... | ... |
| A517 Grade B | 0.15–0.21 | 0.70–1.00 | 0.20–0.35 | 0.040 max | 0.035 max | ... | 0.40–0.65 | 0.15–0.25 | 0.03–0.08 | 0.01–0.03 | 0.0005–0.005 | ... | ... | ... |
| A517 Grade J | 0.12–0.21 | 0.45–0.70 | 0.20–0.35 | 0.040 max | 0.035 max | ... | ... | 0.50–0.65 | ... | ... | 0.001–0.005 | ... | ... | ... |
| A517 Grade M | 0.12–0.21 | 0.45–0.70 | 0.21–0.35 | 0.040 max | 0.035 max | ... | ... | 0.45–0.60 | ... | ... | 0.001–0.005 | 1.20–1.50 | ... | ... |
| A533 Grade B | 0.25 max | 1.15–1.50 | 0.15–0.30 | 0.040 max | 0.035 max | ... | ... | 0.45–0.60 | ... | ... | ... | 0.40–0.70 | ... | ... |
| A537 Grades A and B | 0.24 max | 0.70–1.35(b) | 0.15–0.50 | 0.040 max | 0.035 max | ... | ... | ... | ... | ... | ... | ... | ... | ... |
| A542 Class 2 | 0.15 max | 0.30–0.60 | 0.50 max | 0.035 max | 0.035 max | ... | 2.00–2.50 | 0.90–1.10 | ... | ... | ... | ... | ... | ... |
| A553 Grade A | 0.13 max | 0.90 max | 0.15–0.30 | 0.040 max | 0.035 max | ... | ... | ... | ... | ... | ... | 8.50–9.50 | ... | ... |
| A562 | 0.12 max | 1.20 max | 0.15–0.50 | ... | ... | 0.15 max(c)(d) | ... | ... | ... | ... | ... | ... | ... | ... |
| A572 Grade 55 | 0.25 max | 1.35 max | 0.30 max(c)(e) | ... | ... | ... | ... | ... | ... | ... | ... | ... | ... | ... |
| A572 Grade 65 | 0.26 max | 1.35 max | 0.30 max(c)(e) | ... | ... | ... | ... | ... | ... | ... | ... | ... | ... | ... |
| A633 Grade C | 0.14 | 1.46 | 0.17 | 0.0063 | 0.007 | 0.24 | 0.21 | 0.08 | ... | ... | ... | 0.26 | 0.025 | 0.032 |
| A710 Grade A, Class 3 | 0.06 | 0.50 | 0.28 | 0.004 | 0.013 | 1.16 | 0.75 | 0.21 | ... | ... | ... | 0.88 | 0.030 | 0.030 |
| A737 Grade B | 0.12 | 1.32 | 0.17 | 0.005 | 0.023 | 0.18 | 0.12 | 0.02 | ... | ... | ... | 0.10 | 0.023 | 0.065 |
| A808 | 0.10 | 1.55 | 0.21 | 0.014 | 0.004 | 0.11 | 0.09 | 0.02 | ... | ... | ... | 0.08 | 0.055 | 0.026 |
| API X60 | 0.11 | 1.33 | 0.37 | 0.001 | 0.008 | 0.10 | 0.12 | 0.02 | ... | ... | ... | 0.15 | 0.029 | 0.024 |

(a) Maximums, depending on plate thickness. (b) 1.00–1.60% Mn for plate 40–64 mm (1.5–2.5 in.) thick. (c) Also contains 0.04% max P, 0.05% max S. (d) Also contains 4 × C min Ti. (e) Also contains niobium (columbium) and/or vanadium

Revised by Charles R. Roper, Jr., Senior Research Engineer, Lukens Steel Company

welded joints are needed. Welds are usually examined at a low magnification to view a large area. Detailed information on specimen preparation of welded joints can be found in the article "Weldments" in this Volume.

Etching poses no problem when the metals joined and the filler metal, if used, are similar. A 10% aqueous solution of ammonium persulfate $[(NH_4)_2S_2O_8]$ is often used (see Fig. 4 and 5). Nital is also used and is preferred for etching welds in carbon and alloy steels (see Fig. 22). An etchant composed of 10 mL $HNO_3$, 5 mL acetic acid, and 85 mL $H_2O$ satisfactorily etches welded joints in carbon and low-alloy steels.

When carbon or low-alloy steels are welded to stainless steels, as in oil-refinery equipment, specimens from the weldment can be etched in a solution of 10 g cupric chloride $(CuCl_2)$, 200 mL hydrochloric acid (HCl), and 500 mL ethanol or in a solution of 4 g copper ammonium chloride, 25 mL $H_2O$, 15 g ferric chloride $(FeCl_3)$, and 50 mL HCl. Both are applied by swabbing.

## Macroexamination

Macroexamination of plate steels is similar to that for sections from ingots or continuously cast slabs and requires macroetching to reveal the solidification pattern. The type and size of grains (columnar or equiaxed) can be observed, as can inclusions or macrochemical segregation. A commonly used macroetchant consists of equal parts HCl and water at 95 °C (200 °F). After grinding the desired surface smooth, the specimen is immersed in this solution for 20 to 60 min, depending on the steel chemistry. The specimen is examined visually without a microscope.

## Examination for Nitrides, Carbides, and Inclusions

Nitrides in plate steels are of two sizes. The large nitrides, such as zirconium nitride and titanium nitride, are easily resolved by optical microscopy. Metallographic examinations are made on as-polished specimens using unfiltered white light. Zirconium nitride is pale yellow; titanium nitride, copper-orange.

The submicron nitride particles are not visible using optical microscopy and so cannot be analyzed using the electron micro-probe. Moreover, no etchant can identify them. These particles can be observed on a replica in a transmission electron microscope and identified by electron diffraction, which is also conducted using this microscope. This technique was used for analyzing the particles shown in Fig. 30. Examples of such particles are aluminum nitride, vanadium nitride, niobium nitride, and niobium carbonitride. Niobium nitrides and niobium carbides are soluble in each other—hence, the niobium carbonitride particles. Replica transmission electron microscopy is also used for resolution of alloy carbide particles and examination of second-phase particles that are difficult or impossible to resolve using optical microscopy.

Large inclusions can be identified by shape and color with the use of optical microscopy. However, the electron microprobe is the most useful tool for the analysis of nonmetallic particles.

## Classification and Microstructures of Plate Steels

Plate steels are classified according to ASTM standards. These standards, in addition to establishing chemical compositions and mechanical property requirements, often include provisions, such as heat treatments, that apply to fabrication and to end use.

Compositions of the plate steels illustrated in this article are given in Table 1; mechanical properties are listed in Table 2. Compositions vary from plain, low-carbon steel with minimum restrictions (ASTM A36, for example) to steels that include total alloy content of greater than 5%. Carbon content is usually less than 0.25% and rarely higher than 0.30%. Details of these composition requirements are given in the *Annual Book of ASTM Standards*, Section 1, Volume 01.04. Data on properties and selection of plate steels are given in Volume 1 of the 9th Edition of *Metals Handbook*, particularly in the articles "Classification and Designations of Carbon and Alloy Steels" and "Carbon and Low-Alloy Steel Plate."

The representative micrographs in this article demonstrate that heat treatment and section thickness more significantly affect the microstructure than does composition.

Good weldability is important for plate steels, because most are fabricated into welded structures. They can be welded in the annealed or normalized condition, but some of the high-strength grades, such as ASTM A517 and A542, are welded in the quenched and tempered condition. For information on welding plate steels, see Volume 6 of the 9th Edition of *Metals Handbook*, particularly "Arc Welding of Hardenable Carbon and Alloy Steels."

**Table 2  Mechanical properties of ASTM plate steels(a)**

| Steel | Material grade, class or type | Tensile strength MPa | ksi | Yield strength MPa | ksi | Elongation in 200 mm (8 in.), % | Elongation in 50 mm (2 in.), % |
|---|---|---|---|---|---|---|---|
| A36 | ... | 400–550 | 58–80 | 220–250(b) | 32–36(b) | 20(b) | 23 |
| A201(c) | A, B | 380–620 | 55–90 | 205–260 | 30–38 | 17–23 | 21–27 |
| A285 | C | 380–515 | 55–75 | 205 | 30 | 23 | 27 |
| A387 | D | 415–585 | 60–85 | 205 | 30 | ... | 18 |
| A515 | 70 | 485–620 | 70–90 | 260 | 38 | 17 | 21 |
| A516 | 70 | 485–620 | 70–90 | 260 | 38 | 17 | 21 |
| A517 | B, J, M | 725–930(b) | 105–135(b) | 620(b) | 90(b) | ... | 14–16(b) |
| A533 | B | 550–860 | 80–125 | 345–570 | 50–83 | ... | 16–18 |
| A537 | A, B | 485–690(b) | 70–100(b) | 310–415(b) | 45–60(b) | 18 | 20–22(b) |
| A542 | 2 | 795–930 | 115–135 | 690 | 100 | ... | 13 |
| A553 | A | 690–825 | 100–120 | 585 | 85 | ... | 20 |
| A562 | ... | 380–515 | 55–75 | 205 | 30 | 22 | 26 |
| A572 | 55 | 485 | 70 | 380 | 55 | ... | ... |
| A572 | 65 | 550 | 80 | 450 | 65 | 15 | 17 |
| A633 | C | 450–620(b) | 65–90(b) | 315–345(b) | 46–50(b) | 18 | 23 |
| A710 | Grade A, Class 3 | 515–585(b) | 75–85(b) | 450–515(b) | 65–75(b) | ... | 20 |
| A737 | B | 485–620 | 70–90 | 345 | 50 | 18 | 23 |
| A808 | ... | 415–485(b) | 60–70(b) | 290–345(b) | 42–50(b) | 18 | 22 |

(a) Where a single value is shown, it is a minimum. (b) Minimum and/or maximum values depend on the plate thickness. (c) Superseded by ASTM A515

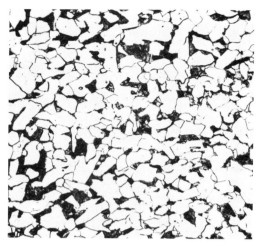

**Fig. 1** ASTM A36 steel plate, 9.5 mm (3/8 in.) thick, as-rolled. Structure consists of equiaxed ferrite (white areas) and pearlite (black areas). 1% nital. 250×

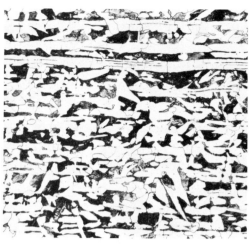

**Fig. 2** ASTM A36 steel plate, 25 mm (1 in.) thick, as-rolled. Pearlite (black) and ferrite (white) with small nonmetallic inclusions. 2% nital. 100×

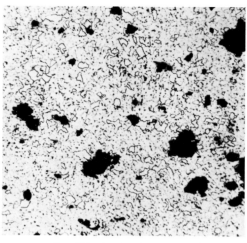

**Fig. 3** Graphitization in ASTM A201, Grade A, steel plate after 5 years of service at 595 to 650 °C (1100 to 1200 °F). Structure consists of graphite nodules in a ferrite matrix. Nital. 110×

**Fig. 4** Crack in a weld in ASTM A201, Grade B, firebox steel plate. The crack was the result of stresses that were induced by poor alignment of the two steel plates. $(NH_4)_2S_2O_8$. 4×

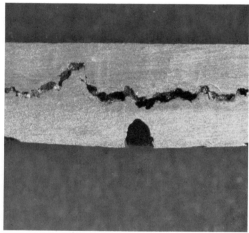

**Fig. 5** Crack in ASTM A285, Grade C, firebox steel plate, 9.5 mm (3/8 in.) thick. Severe blistering, caused by hydrogen, was followed by cracking in high-carbon areas. $(NH_4)_2S_2O_8$. 3×

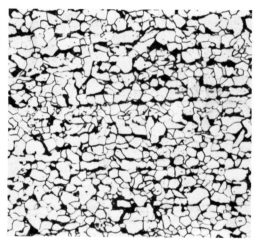

**Fig. 6** ASTM A285, Grade C, firebox steel plate, hot rolled, as-received (essentially annealed). The white areas are ferrite, and the black areas are pearlite. 4% nital. 220×

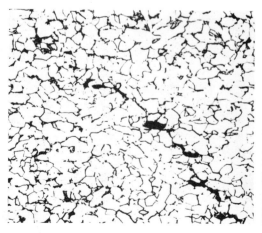

**Fig. 7** Fissures in ASTM A285, Grade C, steel plate, exposed to hydrogen at 540 °C (1000 °F) and 5 MPa (700 psi) for 348 h. Hydrogen combined with carbon to form methane. 2% nital. 220×

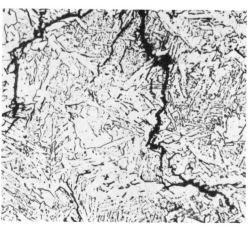

**Fig. 8** Cracks in weld metal in ASTM A285, Grade C, steel plate. The cracks, which resulted from caustic embrittlement, are transgranular and intergranular. Nital. 275×

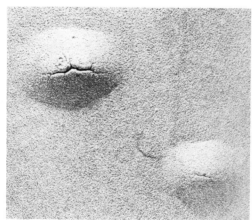

**Fig. 9** Blisters, caused by hydrogen penetration in 9.5-mm (3/8-in.) thick ASTM A285, Grade C, steel plate that had been in service one year at 480 °C (900 °F) in a refinery vessel. See also Fig. 10. Not polished, not etched. 1.5×

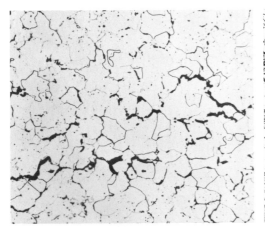

**Fig. 10** Same as Fig. 9. Wide black lines are fissures caused by hydrogen penetration. Ferrite with only a few carbide particles—a result of hydrogen decarburization in service. Nital. 275×

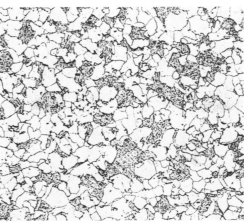

**Fig. 11** ASTM A387, Grade D, steel plate, 200 mm (8 in.) thick, normalized and tempered. Austenitized at 955 °C (1750 °F) for 8 h, air cooled, tempered at 675 °C (1250 °F) for 8 h. Structure is ferrite and probably upper bainite (dark). Saturated picral. 100×

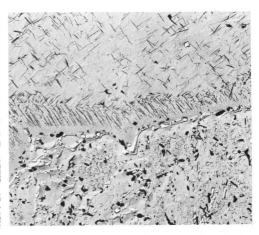

**Fig. 12** Same structures as in Fig. 11, but shown by a replica electron micrograph. Upper portion shows ferrite containing acicular and fibrous carbide particles; lower portion, probably upper bainite with fine acicular carbide. Saturated picral. 3600×

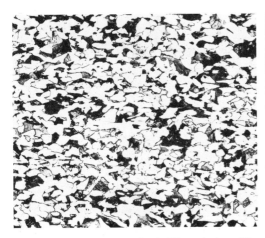

**Fig. 13** ASTM A515, Grade 70, steel plate, 32 mm (1.25 in.) thick, in the as hot rolled condition. The structure consists of ferrite (light constituent) and pearlite (dark constituent); note that grains are somewhat elongated. 1% nital. 100×

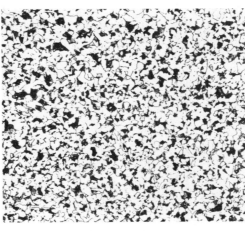

**Fig. 14** Same steel and plate thickness as for Fig. 13. Normalized by austenitizing at 900 °C (1650 °F) for 1 h and cooling in air. Light areas are ferrite, and dark areas are pearlite. Compare with Fig. 15, which shows effect of overheating. 1% nital. 100×

**Fig. 15** Overheated ASTM A515, Grade 70, steel plate, 38 mm (1.5 in.) thick. Normalized by austenitizing at 1125 °C (2060 °F) for 1.5 h and air cooling. Note ferrite at prior austenite grain boundaries and within grains. 1% nital. 100×

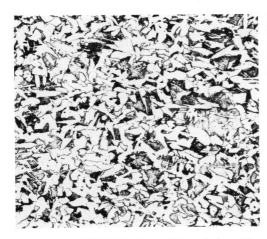

**Fig. 16** ASTM A516, Grade 70, steel plate, 17 mm (¹¹/₁₆ in.) thick, in the as hot rolled condition. The structure consists of ferrite (light constituent) and pearlite (dark constituent); note that grains are somewhat elongated. 1% nital. 100×

**Fig. 17** Same steel and plate thickness as for Fig. 16. Normalized by austenitizing at 900 °C (1650 °F) for 1 h and cooling in air. Structure consists of ferrite and pearlite. Compare with Fig. 18, which shows effect of overheating. 1% nital. 100×

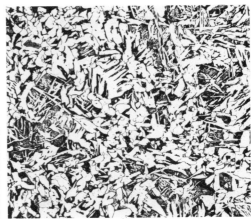

**Fig. 18** Overheated ASTM A516, Grade 70, steel plate, 38 mm (1.5 in.) thick. Normalized by austenitizing at 1125 °C (2060 °F) for 1.5 h and air cooling. Structure consists of ferrite, pearlite (dark), and probably bainite. 1% nital. 100×

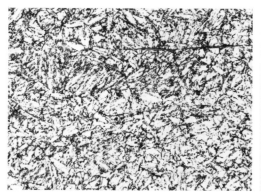

**Fig. 19** ASTM A517, Grade B, steel plate, 6 mm (0.25 in.) thick, austenitized 1 h at 900 °C (1650 °F), water quenched, tempered 1 h at 620 °C (1150 °F). Structure is tempered martensite. Saturated picral. 500×

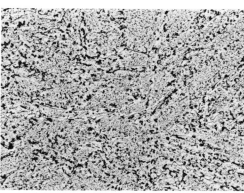

**Fig. 20** Same steel and heat treatment as for Fig. 19, but shown by a replica electron micrograph. Structure is mainly tempered martensite, but a dispersion of fine carbide is now resolved. Saturated picral. 3000×

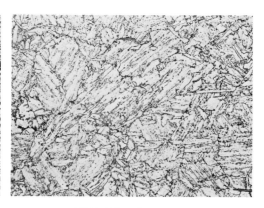

**Fig. 21** ASTM A517, Grade M, steel plate, 50 mm (2 in.) thick, quenched and tempered. Austenitized at 900 °C (1650 °F), water quenched, tempered at 645 °C (1190 °F). Specimen was taken from the surface. 2% nital. 500×

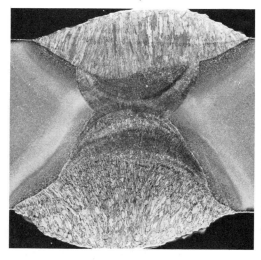

**Fig. 22** Cross-sectional view of a butt welded joint between two 13-mm (1/2-in.) thick plates of ASTM A517, Grade J, steel. Arc welding and a joint of double-V-groove design were used. Note the columnar structure of the weld metal in the outer portion of the weld. The heat-affected zone is also apparent. 2% nital. 4×

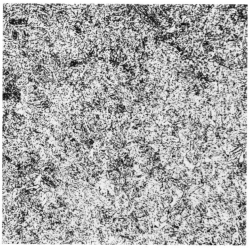

**Fig. 23** ASTM A533, Grade B, steel plate, 300 mm (12 in.) thick. Austenitized at 915 °C (1675 °F) for 12 h, water quenched, re-austenitized at 855 °C (1575 °F) for 12 h, water quenched, tempered at 665 °C (1225 °F) for 12 h, air cooled, and stress relieved twice: 40 h at 605 °C (1125 °F) and 42 h at 550 °C (1025 °F). See also Fig. 24. Saturated picral. 250×

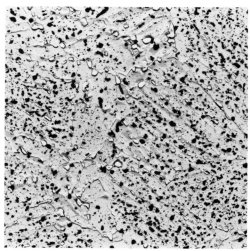

**Fig. 24** Same steel and heat treatment as for Fig. 23, but shown by a replica electron micrograph. Specimen was taken from the surface, as was specimen for Fig. 23. Structure in Fig. 23 is identifiable only as tempered martensite, but is resolved here as tempered martensite that contains a dispersion of carbide particles. Saturated picral. 3000×

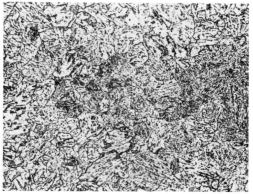

**Fig. 25** Same steel and heat treatment as for Fig. 23, but specimen was taken at one quarter of plate thickness. Structure is mainly tempered bainite; dark constituent is probably tempered martensite. Saturated picral. 250×

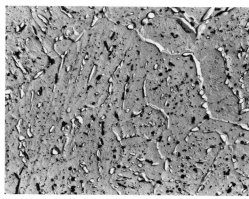

**Fig. 26** Same as Fig. 25, but a replica electron micrograph. Tempered bainite and probably martensite with carbide particles replicated (white) or extracted from specimen surface when plastic replica was stripped (black). Saturated picral. 3000×

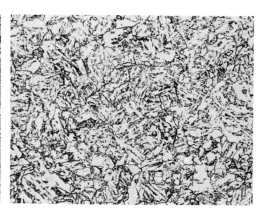

**Fig. 27** Same steel and heat treatment as for Fig. 23, but specimen was taken from center of plate. Structure is largely tempered bainite; some proeutectoid ferrite (more equiaxed light gray constituent) is evident. Saturated picral. 250×

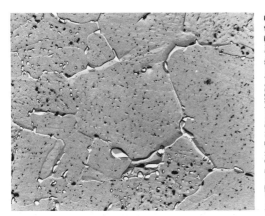

**Fig. 28** Same steel, heat treatment, and location of specimen as for Fig. 27, but shown by a replica electron micrograph. The structure consists of proeutectoid ferrite and bainite containing particles of carbide. Saturated picral. 3000×

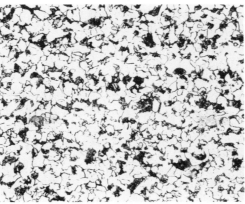

**Fig. 29** ASTM A537, Grade A, steel plate, 13 mm (0.5 in.) thick, that was normalized by austenitizing at 900 °C (1650 °F) for 30 min and cooling in air. The microstructure consists of ferrite and pearlite. Some banding is apparent. 1% nital. 250×

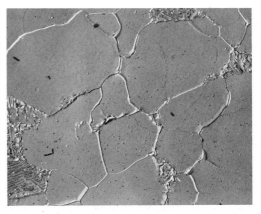

**Fig. 30** Same steel and heat treatment as for Fig. 29, but shown by a replica electron micrograph. Smooth areas in structure are ferrite, lamellar areas are pearlite, and fine black particles are aluminum nitride. 1% nital. 3000×

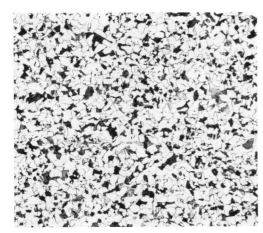

**Fig. 31** ASTM A537, Grade A, steel plate, 50 mm (2 in.) thick. Normalized by austenitizing at 910 °C (1670 °F) and cooling in air. Specimen was taken near the plate surface. Light areas are ferrite; dark areas, pearlite. 2% nital. 100×

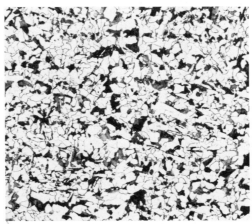

**Fig. 32** Same steel and heat treatment as for Fig. 31, but the specimen was taken from the center of the plate. Note that the grains are larger than those shown in the specimen taken from near the plate surface. 2% nital. 100×

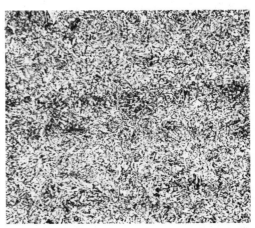

**Fig. 33** ASTM A537, Grade B, steel plate, 13 mm (0.5 in.) thick, quenched and tempered. Austenitized at 900 °C (1650 °F) for 30 min, water quenched, tempered at 595 °C (1100 °F) for 1 h. Structure is carbide particles in tempered martensite. Saturated picral. 250×

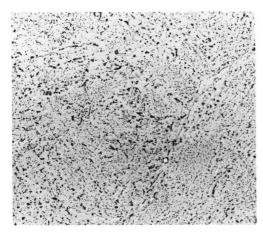

**Fig. 34** Same steel and heat treatment as for Fig. 33, but shown by a replica transmission electron micrograph. The carbide particles now appear as small black dots. The matrix (gray) is tempered martensite. Saturated picral. 3000×

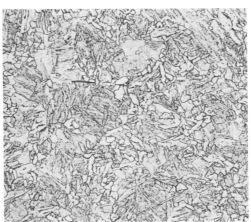

**Fig. 35** ASTM A537, Grade B, steel plate, 19 mm (0.75 in.) thick, quenched and tempered. Austenitized at 925 °C (1700 °F), water quenched, tempered at 640 °C (1180 °F). The structure consists of tempered martensite. 2% nital. 500×

**Fig. 36** ASTM A542, Class 2, steel plate, 25 mm (1 in.) thick, quenched and tempered. Austenitized at 955 °C (1750 °F), water quenched, tempered at 675 °C (1250 °F) for 1 h. Structure is probably tempered bainite. Saturated picral. 100×

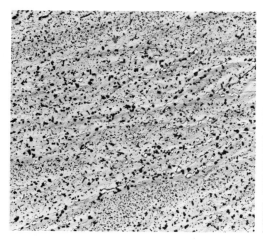

**Fig. 37** Same steel and heat treatment as for Fig. 36, but a replica electron micrograph that resolves a general distribution of fine carbide particles (see Fig. 26 for explanation). Matrix is probably tempered bainite. Saturated picral. 3600×

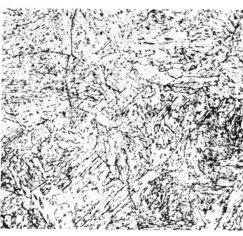

**Fig. 38** ASTM A542, Class 2, steel plate, 116 mm (4.575 in.) thick, austenitized 4 h at 955 °C (1750 °F), quenched in agitated brine, tempered 4 h at 565 °C (1050 °F). Specimen from midthickness. Structure is tempered bainite. Nital. 275×

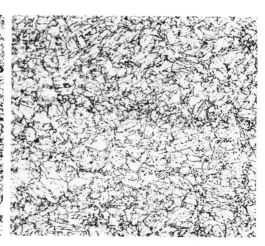

**Fig. 39** ASTM A553, Grade A, steel plate, 13 mm (0.5 in.) thick, quenched and tempered. Austenitized at 800 °C (1475 °F) for 1 h, water quenched, tempered at 605 °C (1125 °F) for 1 h and cooled in air. Tempered martensite. 1% nital. 250×

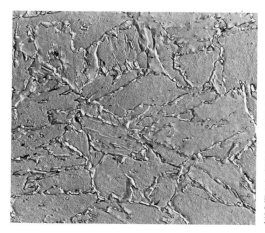

**Fig. 40** Same steel and heat treatment as for Fig. 39, but shown by a replica electron micrograph. Structure is tempered martensite; carbide particles are present, mainly at grain boundaries. 1% nital. 3000×

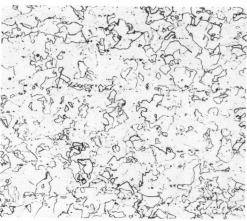

**Fig. 41** ASTM A562 steel plate, 25 mm (1 in.) thick. Normalized by austenitizing at 900 °C (1650 °F) for 1 h and cooling in air. The microstructure consists largely of ferrite, with small particles of titanium carbide. 1% nital. 100×

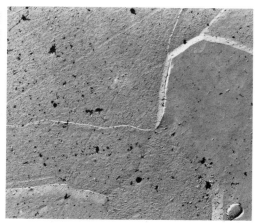

**Fig. 42** Same steel and heat treatment as for Fig. 41, but shown by a replica electron micrograph. The titanium carbide particles (black constituent) are well resolved at the higher magnification. 1% nital. 3000×

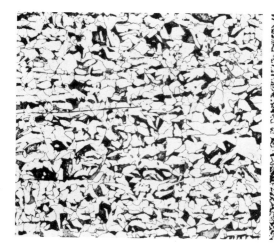

**Fig. 43** ASTM A572, Grade 55, steel plate, 19 mm (0.75 in.) thick, as hot rolled. The structure is ferrite and pearlite. Note presence of a few nonmetallic stringers in the ferrite. 2% nital. 100×

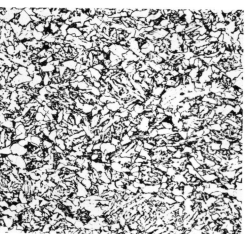

**Fig. 44** ASTM A572, Grade 65, steel plate, 6 mm (0.25 in.) thick, as hot rolled. The microstructure consists of ferrite and pearlite (dark), with possibly some bainite. 1% nital. 250×

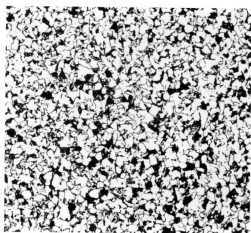

**Fig. 45** ASTM A572, Grade 65, steel plate, 6 mm (0.25 in.) thick. Normalized by austenitizing at 900 °C (1650 °F) for 1 h and cooling in air. Structure is ferrite and pearlite (dark). 1% nital. 250×

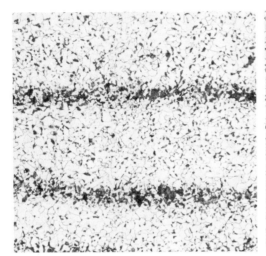

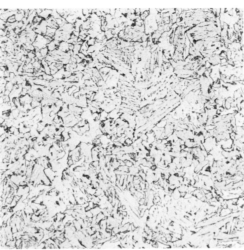

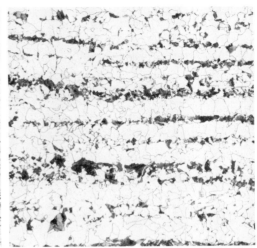

**Fig. 46** ASTM A633, Grade C, 100-mm (4-in.) thick plate. Austenitized at 900 °C (1650 °F) and air cooled (normalized). Fine, polygonal ferrite and fine, partially banded pearlite. Nital plus picral. 200×

**Fig. 47** ASTM A710, Grade A, Class 3, 25-mm (1-in.) thick plate. Austenitized at 900 °C (1650 °F), water-spray quenched, and aged at 650 °C (1200 °F). Predominantly acicular ferrite with fine, tempered carbides. Nital plus picral. 500×

**Fig. 48** ASTM A737, Grade B, 38-mm (1.5-in.) thick plate. Austenitized at 900 °C (1650 °F) and air-cooled normalized. Fine, polygonal ferrite and banded pearlite. Nital plus picral. 200×

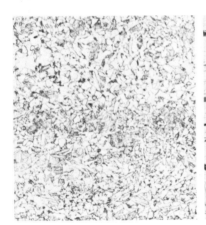

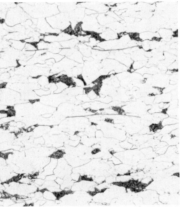

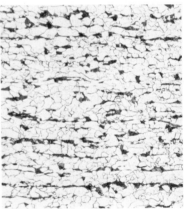

**Fig. 49** Same as Fig. 48, but austenitized at 900 °C (1650 °F), water-spray quenched, and tempered at 595 °C (1100 °F). Mixed fine polygonal and acicular ferrite with tempered carbides. Nital plus picral. 200×

**Fig. 50** ASTM A808, 8-mm (5/16-in.) thick plate, as-rolled condition. Fine-grain, slightly elongated ferrite-pearlite. Several thin, elongated MnS inclusions are evident. Nital plus picral. 500×

**Fig. 51** Same as Fig. 50, but 50-mm (2-in.) thick as-rolled plate. Structure consists of polygonal ferrite-pearlite. Note effect of gage dimension on grain size (compare with Fig. 50). Nital plus picral. 500×

**Fig. 52** API X60, 10-mm (0.4-in.) thick plate (skelp) for line-pipe, control-rolled. Fine-grain, polygonal ferrite; moderately banded pearlite. Nital plus picral. 200×

# Steel Tubular Products

By Donald S. Dabkowski
Product Manager
Tubular Metallurgy
United States Steel Corporation

and

Frederick W. Kern
Metallurgical Engineer
Tubular Metallurgy
United States Steel Corporation

STEEL TUBULAR PRODUCTS are usually classified commercially according to common usage, as shown in Table 1. Further subdivisions and product descriptions may be found in the article "Steel Tubular Products" in Volume 1 of the 9th Edition of *Metals Handbook*.

Property requirements for oil country goods may be found in the following American Petroleum Institute (API) Specifications:

- 5A: "Welded or Seamless Steel Pipe for Oil or Gas Well Casing, Tubing, or Drill Pipe"
- 5AC: "Welded or Seamless Steel Pipe with Restricted Yield-Strength Range for Oil or Gas Well Casing or Tubing"
- 5AX: "High-Strength Seamless Steel Pipe for Oil or Gas Well Casing, Tubing, or Drill Pipe"

Specifications for line pipe are covered by API Specification 5L, "Welded or Seamless Steel Line Pipe for Oil and Gas Transmission." *The Annual Book of ASTM Standards*, Section 1, Volume 01.01, contains materials specifications for standard pipe and mechanical and pressure tubing. Some tubular product compositions are produced in accordance with American Iron and Steel Institute designations.

Typical compositions of steel tubular products depicted in the micrographs in this article are listed in Table 2. Steels used for tubular products cover various low-carbon, medium-carbon, low-alloy, and higher alloy grades. Most common, however, are the carbon and low-alloy steels.

## Specimen Preparation

Tubular products present no special problems in specimen extraction. Once the tubular steel testpieces are obtained, the procedures for final sectioning, mounting, grinding, and polishing are the same as those described in the article "Carbon and Alloy

**Table 1   Classification of steel tubular products**

| Product | Typical use | Production processes | Outside diameter(a), in. | Typical grades | Usual finished status |
|---|---|---|---|---|---|
| Oil country goods | | | | | |
| Casing ........ | To line oil and gas wells to prevent collapse of the hole | Seamless, electric resistance welding | 4.5-20 | H-40, J-55, K-55 C-75, L-80, N-80, C-90, G-95, P-110, Q-125 | As-rolled Normalize or quench and temper |
| Tubing ........ | To convey oil or gas from the producing strata to the earth's surface | Seamless, continuous welding, electric resistance welding | 1.050-4.5 | All others H-40, J-55, N-80, P-105 | Quench and temper As-rolled Normalize or quench and temper |
| Drill pipe ...... | Rotary stem for drill bits | Seamless | 2.375-6.625 | E | Normalize and temper, or quench and temper |
| | | | | X-95, G-105, S-135 | Quench and temper |
| Line pipe ........ | Conveys oil, gas, or water | Seamless, electric resistance welding, continuous welding, double submerged arc welding | 0.125(nom)-80 | All grades B, X42, X46, X52, X60, X65, X70 | As-rolled As-rolled Control rolled |
| Standard pipe .... | Plumbing, electrical conduit, low pressure conveyance of fluids, and nonstringent structural applications | Seamless, electric resistance welding, continuous welding, double submerged arc welding | 0.125(nom)-80 | All grades | As-rolled |
| Mechanical tubing ........ | Variety of round, hollow mechanical parts, such as automotive axles, bearing races, and hydraulic pistons | Seamless, electric resistance welding | 0.375-10.75 | Carbon and alloy | Hot rolled or cold drawn |
| Pressure tubing ........ | Boiler tubes, condenser tubes, heat exchanger tubes, and refrigeration tubes | Seamless, electric resistance welding | 0.5-10.75 | Carbon and alloy | Hot rolled or cold drawn |

Note: Because steel tubular products manufactured in the United States are customarily produced to standard inch and fractional inch sizes, tubular product sizes are given only in inches in this article. 1 in. = 25.4 mm or 2.54 cm.
(a) nom: nominal

Steels" in this Volume. The large size of the specimens and the desired information often make mounting unnecessary.

**Etching.** Nital is a widely used etchant for tubular steels. It is preferred for delineating ferrite grain boundaries. Picral is preferred for examining carbide particles in annealed steels and in quenched and tempered steels.

Vilella's reagent is used for the higher alloy grades of steel, such as those found in ASTM A 200 and A 213. It consists of 5 mL hydrochloric acid (HCl), 1 g picric acid, 100 mL ethanol, and 2 drops zephiran chloride. It is usually applied by immersion.

**Examination of Welded Joints.** Steel tubular products are often welded, which re-

quires techniques for metallographic examination of welded joints. These techniques are discussed in the article "Weldments" in this Volume. Details on etchants used to examine welds between carbon and low-alloy steels or between carbon or low-alloy steels and stainless steels can be found in the article "Plate Steels" in this Volume.

| Steel | C | Mn | Si | P | S | Cr | Mo | Nb | V | Ti | Al | B | Ni |
|---|---|---|---|---|---|---|---|---|---|---|---|---|---|
| **ASTM and API pipe steels** | | | | | | | | | | | | | |
| A106, Grade A | 0.25 max | 0.27–0.93 | 0.10 min(a) | … | … | … | … | … | … | … | … | … | … |
| A106, Grade B | 0.30 max | 0.29–1.06 | 0.10 min(a) | … | … | … | … | … | … | … | … | … | … |
| A335, Grade P2 | 0.10–0.20 | 0.30–0.61 | 0.10–0.30 | 0.045 max | 0.045 max | 0.50–0.81 | 0.44–0.65 | … | … | … | … | … | … |
| A335, Grade P5 | 0.15 max | 0.30–0.60 | 0.50 max | 0.030 max | 0.030 max | 4–6 | 0.45–0.65 | … | … | … | … | … | … |
| A335, Grade P7 | 0.15 max | 0.30–0.60 | 0.50–1 | 0.030 max | 0.030 max | 6–8 | 0.44–0.65 | … | … | … | … | … | … |
| A335, Grade P11 | 0.15 max | 0.30–0.60 | 0.50–1 | 0.030 max | 0.030 max | 1–1.50 | 0.44–0.65 | … | … | … | … | … | … |
| A335, Grade P22 | 0.15 max | 0.30–0.60 | 0.50 max | 0.030 max | 0.030 max | 1.90–2.60 | 0.87–1.13 | … | … | … | … | … | … |
| A381, Class Y52 | 0.26 max | 1.40 max | … | 0.040 max | 0.050 max | … | … | … | … | … | … | … | … |
| API 5L–X46 | 0.30 max | 1.35 max | … | 0.04 max | 0.05 max | … | … | … | … | … | … | … | … |
| API 5L–X60 | 0.26 max | 1.35 max | … | 0.04 max | 0.05 max | … | … | 0.05 min | 0.02 min | 0.03 min(b) | … | … | … |
| API 5L, Grade X52 | 0.21 | 0.90 | 0.26 | 0.015 max | 0.015 max | … | … | … | 0.09 | … | 0.030 | … | … |
| API 5A, Grade K–55 | 0.45 | 1.30 | 0.26 | 0.015 max | 0.015 max | … | … | … | … | … | 0.007 | … | … |
| API 5AX, Grade N–80 | 0.28 | 1.48 | 0.26 | 0.015 max | 0.015 max | 0.20 | 0.10 | … | … | … | 0.007 | … | … |
| API 5AX, Grade P–110 | 0.28 | 1.48 | 0.26 | 0.015 max | 0.015 max | 0.22 | 0.23 | … | … | … | 0.007 | … | … |
| API 5AC, Grade C–90 | 0.29 | 0.50 | 0.26 | 0.015 max | 0.015 max | 1.08 | 0.33 | … | 0.03 | … | … | 0.0015 min | … |
| API 5L, Grade A | 0.17 | 0.50 | … | 0.020 | 0.020 | … | … | … | … | … | … | … | … |
| API 5L, Grade X60 | 0.05 | 1.11 | 0.017 | 0.007 | 0.006 | … | … | 0.045 | … | … | 0.045 | … | … |
| **ASTM and AISI tube steels** | | | | | | | | | | | | | |
| A161 | 0.10–0.20 | 0.30–0.80 | 0.25 max(a) | … | … | … | … | … | … | … | … | … | … |
| A200, Grade T5 | 0.15 max | 0.30–0.60 | 0.50 max | 0.030 max | 0.030 max | 4–6 | 0.45–0.65 | … | … | … | … | … | … |
| A209, Grade T1 | 0.10–0.20 | 0.30–0.80 | 0.10–0.50 | 0.045 max | 0.045 max | … | 0.44–0.65 | … | … | … | … | … | … |
| A213, Grade T5c | 0.12 max | 0.30–0.60 | 0.50 max | 0.03 max | 0.03 max | 4–6 | 0.45–0.65 | … | … | 4 × C min (0.70 max) | … | … | … |
| A254, Class I | 0.05–0.15 | 0.27–0.63 | … | 0.050 max | 0.060 max | … | … | … | … | … | … | … | … |
| 1015 | 0.13–0.18 | 0.30–0.60 | … | 0.040 max | 0.050 max | … | … | … | … | … | … | … | … |
| 1018 | 0.15–0.20 | 0.60–0.90 | … | 0.040 max | 0.050 max | … | … | … | … | … | … | … | … |
| 1025 | 0.22–0.28 | 0.30–0.60 | … | 0.040 max | 0.050 max | … | … | … | … | … | … | … | … |
| 1215 | 0.09 max | 0.75–1.05 | … | 0.04–0.09 | 0.26–0.35 | … | … | … | … | … | … | … | … |
| 4140 | 0.38–0.43 | 0.75–1 | 0.20–0.35 | 0.035 max | 0.040 max | 0.80–1.10 | 0.15–0.25 | … | … | … | … | … | … |
| 4620 | 0.17–0.22 | 0.45–0.65 | 0.20–0.35 | 0.035 max | 0.040 max | … | 0.20–0.30 | … | … | … | … | … | 1.65–2 |
| 5048 | 0.48 | 0.30–0.60 | 0.20–0.35 | 0.035 max | 0.040 max | 0.30–0.50 | … | … | … | … | … | … | … |
| 8620 | 0.18–0.23 | 0.70–0.90 | 0.20–0.35 | 0.035 max | 0.040 max | 0.40–0.60 | 0.15–0.25 | … | … | … | … | … | 0.40–0.70 |

(a) Also contains 0.048% max P and 0.058% max S. (b) Niobium, vanadium, and titanium used at manufacturer's option.

**Fig. 1** API 5L, Grade X52, as-rolled seamless steel pipe. Microstructure consists of small colonies of pearlite in a ferrite matrix. Picral. 500×

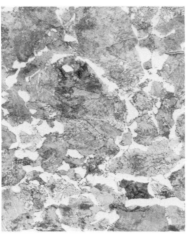

**Fig. 2** API 5A, Grade K55, as-rolled seamless steel pipe produced by press-piercing. Pearlite colonies with ferrite partially outlining the prior-austenite grain boundaries. Picral. 500×

**Fig. 3** API 5AX, Grade N-80, seamless steel pipe, austenitized at 845 °C (1550 °F), water quenched, and tempered at 620 °C (1150 °F). Microstructure is tempered martensite. Picral. 500×

**Fig. 4** API 5AX, Grade P-110, seamless steel pipe, austenitized at 845 °C (1550 °F), water quenched, and tempered at 595 °C (1100 °F). Microstructure is tempered martensite. Picral. 500×

**Fig. 5** API 5AC, Grade C-90, seamless steel pipe, (24 HRC maximum), austenitized at 870 °C (1600 °F), water quenched, and tempered at 705 °C (1300 °F). Tempered martensite. Picral. 500×

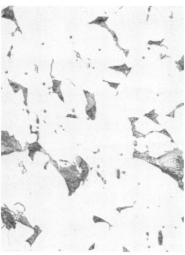

**Fig. 6** API 5L, Grade A, continuous welded pipe, as-rolled. Microstructure consists of large pearlite colonies in a ferrite matrix. Picral. 500×

**Fig. 7** API 5L, Grade X60, electric resistance welded pipe, as-rolled. Small angular carbides in a ferrite matrix. Picral and nital. 500×

**Fig. 8** API 5L, Grade X52, double submerged arc welded pipe showing pearlite colonies in a ferrite matrix. Picral. 500×

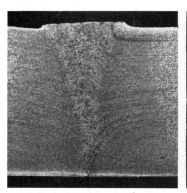

**Fig. 9** Section through a resistance weld in API 5L-X46 steel pipe, 18-in. OD by 0.375-in. wall. Weld is sound. $(NH_4)_2S_2O_8$.

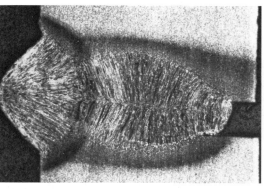

**Fig. 10** Section through a two-pass butt weld (automatic gas metal arc process, $CO_2$ shielding) in API 5L-X60 steel pipe, 30-in. OD by 0.25-in. wall. A defective weld (note incomplete fusion, right). 4% nital. 10×

**Fig. 11** Section through a two-pass butt weld made in the same size of API 5L-X60 steel pipe as in Fig. 10 and by the same process (automatic gas metal arc, $CO_2$ shielding). Fusion is complete. A defective weld (note shrinkage crack in the weld bead, which occurred during solidification). 4% nital. 15×

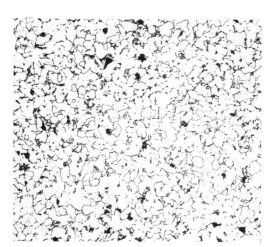

**Fig. 12** ASTM A106, Grade A, seamless steel pipe, 0.84-in. OD, 0.147-in. wall, normalized by austenitizing at 870 °C (1600 °F), air cooling. Longitudinal midwall section. Ferrite (light areas) and pearlite (dark). Nital. 250×

**Fig. 13** ASTM A106, Grade A, seamless steel pipe, 1.315-in. OD by 0.179-in. wall, as hot drawn. Specimen was longitudinal at midwall thickness. Structure is ferrite (light gray) in a matrix of pearlite (gray and black). Nital. 275×

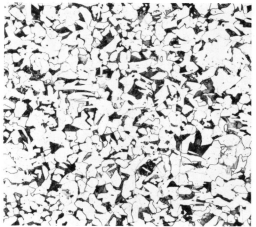

**Fig. 14** ASTM A106 Grade B, seamless steel pipe, 3-in. OD by 0.43-in. wall, as-fabricated. Specimen was taken in longitudinal direction. Structure consists of ferrite (light areas) and pearlite (dark areas). Nital. 100×

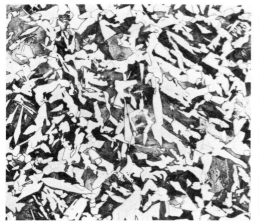

**Fig. 15** ASTM A106, Grade B, seamless steel pipe, 12-in. OD by 1.3-in. wall, as-fabricated. Specimen was taken in longitudinal direction. Light areas are ferrite; dark areas are pearlite. Nital. 100×

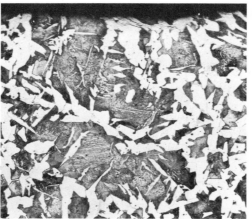

**Fig. 16** ASTM A106, Grade B, steel pipe, 28-in. OD by 1.22-in. wall, as-extruded. Specimen taken near surface. Ferrite at grain boundaries and as plates in grains. Nital. 100×

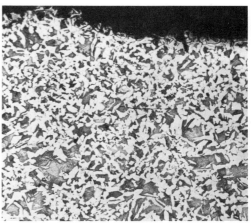

**Fig. 17** Same grade and size of pipe as for Fig. 16, but normalized by austenitizing at 870 °C (1600 °F) and air cooling. Specimen was taken near surface. Note absence of decarburization. Nital. 100×

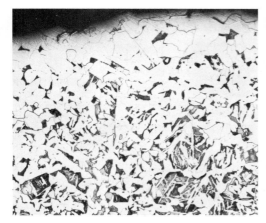

**Fig. 18** Same grade and size of pipe as for Fig. 16, but normalized by austenitizing at 1095 °C (2000 °F) for 1 h and air cooling. Surface shows decarburization (light gray areas near top). The light areas near bottom of micrograph are ferrite; the matrix is pearlite. Nital. 100×

**Fig. 19** Same grade and size of pipe as for Fig. 16, and same heat treatment as for Fig. 18, but specimen was taken from center of pipe wall. Structure consists of ferrite (light) at prior austenite grain boundaries and as plates within grains in a matrix of pearlite. Nital. 100×

**Fig. 20** Same grade and size of pipe as for Fig. 16, but normalized by austenitizing at 1315 °C (2400 °F) for 1 h and air cooling. The light areas in the structure are ferrite along boundaries of very coarse prior austenite grains and as plates within grains; the matrix is pearlite. Nital. 100×

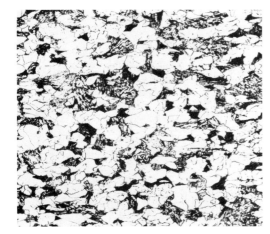

**Fig. 21** ASTM A335, Grade P2, seamless steel pipe, cold drawn and stress relieved at 690 °C (1275 °F). Specimen was taken in longitudinal direction. Light areas are blocky ferrite; dark areas, pearlite containing ferrite plates. Nital. 100×

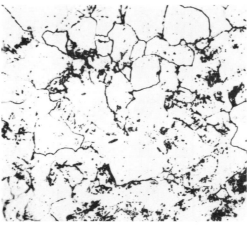

**Fig. 22** ASTM A335, Grade P5, seamless steel pipe, 4.75-in. OD by 5/8-in. wall. Annealed by austenitizing at 900 °C (1650 °F) for 1 h and furnace cooling. Specimen was taken at midwall thickness. Alloy carbide in a ferrite matrix. Nital. 500×

**Fig. 23** ASTM A335, Grade P7, seamless steel pipe, 5.563-in. OD by 0.375-in. wall, fully annealed. Specimen was taken in longitudinal direction. Structure is fine ferrite grains (white) with a dispersion of alloy particles. Vilella's reagent. 100×

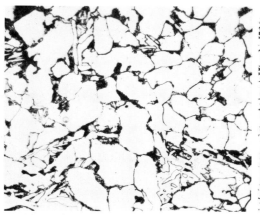

**Fig. 24** ASTM A335, Grade P11, seamless steel pipe, 5.563-in. OD by 0.375-in. wall, fully annealed. Specimen was taken in longitudinal direction. Light areas are ferrite; dark areas are pearlite containing some Widmanstätten plates of ferrite. Nital. 500×

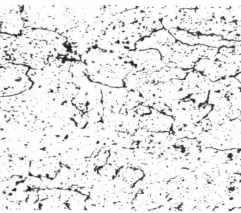

**Fig. 25** ASTM A335, Grade P22, seamless steel pipe, 1.312-in. OD by 0.25-in. wall, hot drawn and annealed by austenitizing at 900 °C (1650 °F) for 1 h and furnace cooling. Structure consists of a fine dispersion of alloy carbide particles in a matrix of ferrite. Nital. 550×

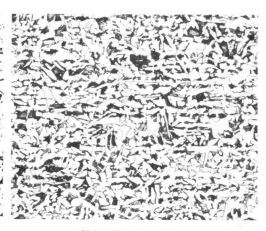

**Fig. 26** ASTM A381, Class Y52, gas metal arc welded steel pipe, 36-in. OD by 0.406-in. wall, fully annealed. Light areas in the structure are ferrite; dark areas are pearlite; some nonmetallic stringers are present in the ferrite (toward the top of the micrograph). 2% Nital. 100×

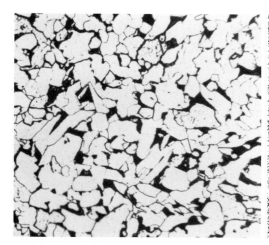

**Fig. 27** ASTM A161 seamless steel tube, 5-in. OD by 7/16-in. wall, as hot drawn. Specimen from midthickness of wall in longitudinal section. Structure is ferrite and pearlite (dark). Nital. 110×

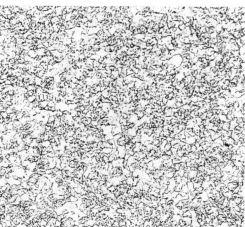

**Fig. 28** ASTM A200, Grade T5, seamless alloy steel tube, annealed. Longitudinal section. Structure is a fine dispersion of alloy carbide in a matrix of ferrite (light background). Vilella's reagent. 100×

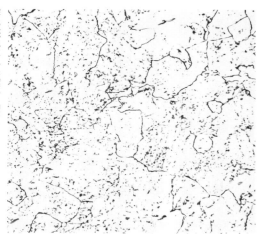

**Fig. 29** Same specimen as shown in Fig. 28, but at a higher magnification. Light areas are ferrite; black particles are alloy carbide, located mostly within the ferrite grains. Vilella's reagent. 500×

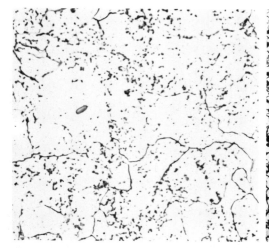

**Fig. 30** Same specimen as shown in Fig. 28 and 29, but at a still higher magnification. Black constituents are alloy carbide; matrix is ferrite. Vilella's reagent. 1000×

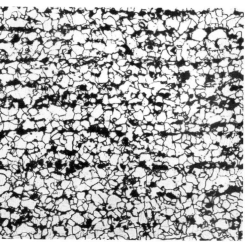

**Fig. 31** ASTM A209, Grade T1, seamless alloy steel tube, hot finished and annealed. Ferrite (light) and pearlite; some banding. Nital. 100×

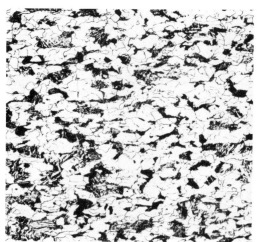

**Fig. 32** Same steel as Fig. 31, but cold drawn and stress relieved. Micrograph from longitudinal section. Ferrite and pearlite (see also Fig. 33). Nital. 100×

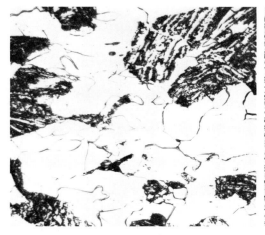

**Fig. 33** Same specimen as shown in Fig. 32, but at a higher magnification. The light areas in the structure are ferrite, and the dark areas are pearlite. Nital. 500×

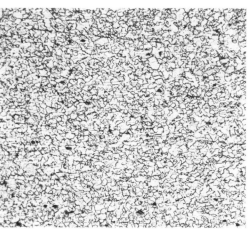

**Fig. 34** ASTM A213, Grade T5c, steel tube, hot finished to a 2-in. OD by 0.22-in. wall, held at 730 °C (1350 °F) and air cooled. Dispersed chromium and titanium carbides in ferrite. Vilella's reagent. 100×

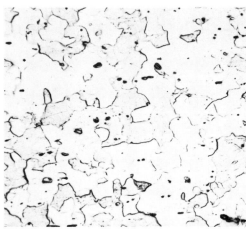

**Fig. 35** Same specimen as shown in Fig. 34, but at a higher magnification. The carbide particles are more completely resolved. The small dark areas are titanium carbide. Vilella's reagent. 500×

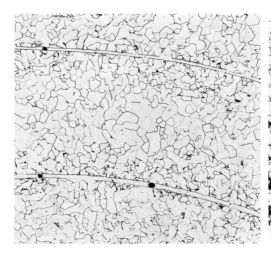

**Fig. 36** Copper brazed joints (outlined white bands) in spiral-wound tubing made from ASTM A254, Class I, steel. Specimen is a cross section. Structure is mostly ferrite. 2% Nital. 100×

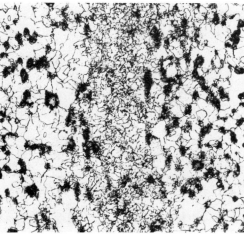

**Fig. 37** 1015 steel tube, resistance welded without filler metal. Vertical band through the center is the fusion zone; heat-affected zones are on each side. Transverse section. Nital. 100×

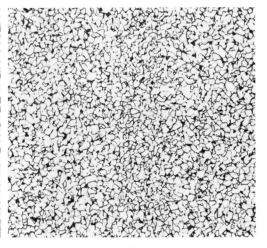

**Fig. 38** Same as Fig. 37, except that the tube has been normalized. Light areas are ferrite; dark areas, pearlite. Weld zone is at center. Note general uniformity of structure. Nital. 100×

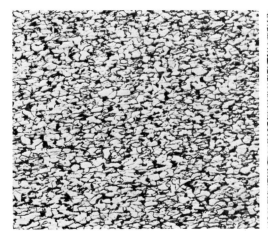

**Fig. 39** Same as Fig. 38, except the tube has been cold drawn (note elongated grains). A longitudinal section that was taken near the weld zone. The structure of the weld is the same as the base steel. Nital. 100×

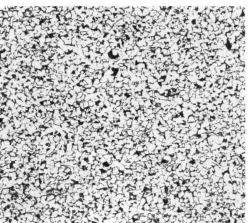

**Fig. 40** Same as Fig. 39, but specimen is transverse to the direction of the weld. The tube has been normalized and cold drawn after welding. Structure is ferrite (light constituent) and pearlite (dark constituent). Nital. 100×

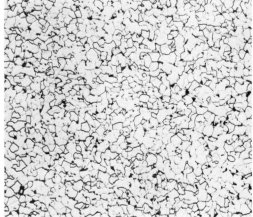

**Fig. 41** Same as Fig. 40, except the tube has now been renormalized after cold drawing. Structure is equiaxed ferrite and pearlite. Renormalizing apparently caused some coarsening of the grains (compare with Fig. 38). Nital. 100×

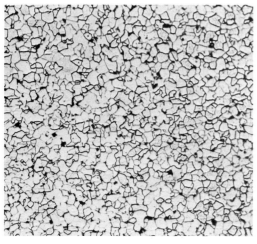

**Fig. 42** Same as Fig. 39, except after normalizing, cold drawing, and renormalizing. Specimen is longitudinal. Note equiaxed ferrite grains. Nital. 100×

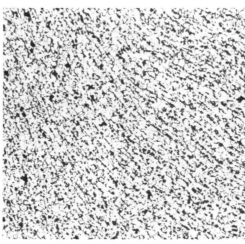

**Fig. 43** 1018 steel tubing, showing a transverse section near the longitudinal seam after welding and normalizing. Note flow pattern. Nital. 100×

**Fig. 44** Aluminate inclusion (longitudinal) in 1025 cold drawn steel tube. As-polished. 500×

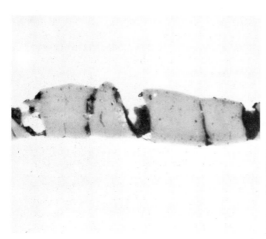

**Fig. 45** Segmented sulfide inclusion (longitudinal) in 1215 cold drawn steel tube. As-polished. 1000×

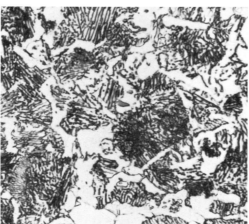

**Fig. 46** 4140 steel tube, annealed by austenitizing at 845 °C (1550 °F), for 3 h, furnace cooling to 620 °C (1150 °F), and air cooling to room temperature. Structure is ferrite and pearlite. Nital. 1000×

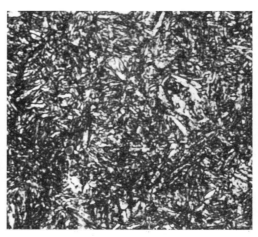

**Fig. 47** 4140 steel tube, austenitized at 830 °C (1525 °F) for 1 h, oil quenched, tempered at 595 °C (1100 °F) for 2 h. The structure consists of some ferrite (white) in tempered martensite. Nital. 1000×

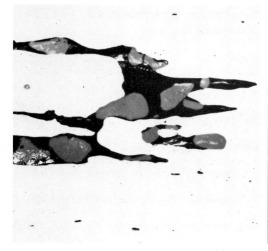

**Fig. 48** Silicate (black) and sulfide (gray) inclusions in 4620 steel tube. As-polished. 500×

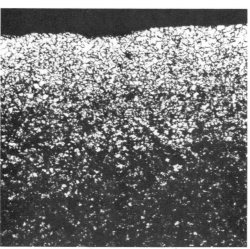

**Fig. 49** Decarburization at the surface of 5048 steel seamless tube (transverse). Nital. 100×

**Fig. 50** Large silicate inclusion (longitudinal) in 8620 steel tube. As-polished. 250×

# Case Hardening Steel

CASE HARDENING STEEL specimen preparation is discussed in this article. Techniques for carburized and carbonitrided steels are addressed specifically. These procedures also apply to specimens of cyanided steels. Specimens of nitrided steels require special procedures that are covered as well.

## Specimen Preparation: Carburized and Carbonitrided Steels

Most steels used for carburizing and carbonitriding have an initial carbon content of 0.10 to 0.30%. Medium-carbon steels (0.30 to 0.50% C) are sometimes carburized to satisfy special requirements. Because the carbon content of a carburized steel may range from 0.10 to 0.30% C in the uncarburized core to as much as 1.20% in the case, specimens are difficult to extract and prepare.

In the metallographic study of carburized steel, the structure of the high-carbon case is usually very important. The techniques and specific precautions described in the article "Carbon and Alloy Steels" in this Volume generally apply to preparation of carburized steel specimens.

**Sectioning.** Small, separate testpieces that minimize the amount of sectioning required are often used. They are treated along with the production parts being carburized and hardened. If the production parts are very small, one or more of them are sectioned for metallographic study. When the specimen must be removed from a large mass of material, the same meticulous care must be used as that described in the article "Carbon and Alloy Steels" in this Volume.

**Mounting.** The mounting techniques and precautions used for specimens of high-carbon steels apply to those of carburized steels. Compression-mounting materials (for example, Bakelite or the thermosetting epoxies) can be used for routine examination, but cold mounting is required to examine for retained austenite.

Edge preservation, very important for carburized cases, is achieved by using hard or filled mounting materials or by nickel plating of the specimen. Thermosetting epoxies have simplified the problem of edge retention. Silica-filled thermosetting epoxies can provide excellent edge retention without nickel plating.

On unmounted specimens, total prevention of edge rounding is virtually impossible. However, it is possible to obtain acceptable flatness by clamping together two specimens with their carburized edges abutting at the center of the two-specimen arrangement. It is preferable to place a thin strip of copper, plastic, or other material between the specimens. For maximum edge retention, the spacer material should have abrasion and polishing rates similar to those of the specimens.

**Grinding and polishing** techniques are the same as those described for specimens of other steels in the article "Carbon and Alloy Steels" in this Volume. Carburized and hardened cases are extremely susceptible to alteration by overheating from grinding. Consequently, grinding must be performed carefully.

It is highly desirable to minimize the amount of polishing. Because of the wide differences in hardness within a single specimen, some constituents will polish in relief, and flatness of the specimen will be destroyed. Specimens that have been overpolished must be completely reworked to regain flatness. Use of napless polishing cloths also helps to minimize polishing in relief.

**Etching.** Nital is the etchant most often used for specimens of carburized steel and carbonitrided steel. Nital can contain 1 to 5% nitric acid ($HNO_3$). At a constant temperature, higher acid concentrations in the solution yield shorter etching times. In addition, etching time or acid concentration should be decreased when the specimen is to be examined at higher magnifications. Nital, a general-purpose etchant for routine metallography, is well suited to revealing case depth, retained austenite, carbide networks, and surface decarburization.

Picral is equivalent to nital for revealing the characteristics noted above. In addition, picral (usually 2 to 4% picric acid) or 4% picral to which 0.01% hydrochloric acid ($HCl$) has been added will produce sharper definition of carbide structures than nital.

**Electron Microscopy.** Transmission electron microscopy (TEM), replica or thin-foil, and scanning electron microscopy (SEM) are used for case hardened parts. Transmission electron microscopy is used to relate fine microstructure (traces of ferrite and bainite) to mechanical properties. In addition, replicas of fracture surfaces are examined by electron microscopy for determination of fracture mechanism, such as brittle, ductile, cleavage, and fatigue.

## Specimen Preparation: Nitrided Steels

Preparation techniques for nitrided steel specimens must be even more exacting than those normally required. The extreme hardness differential between the case and the core causes problems. The case is often 1000 HK or more. In addition, the nitride concentration at the surface (white layer), which often is the primary subject of metallographic examination, is invariably partly or entirely destroyed by ordinary preparation techniques.

**Testpieces.** The principal use of metallography for nitrided steels is quality control of production nitriding. The workpieces being nitrided are often too valuable to permit destructive testing; therefore, separate testpieces of the same steels and heat treatment as the workpieces are prepared.

Two or more of these testpieces are placed in different parts of the nitriding furnace when it is loaded; for example, one near the top, one in the center, and one near the bottom. They can be placed at other locations as well, depending on the size and design of the furnace. The testpieces are identified so that they can be correlated with their location in the furnace. In addition to serving as specimens for metallographic examination, the testpieces serve for immediate visual inspection (by color), for superficial hardness testing (such as the Rockwell 15N), and for later microhardness surveys. Sizes and shapes of testpieces are not standardized, but the simplest design is a button 38 mm (1.5 in.) in diameter and 6 mm (0.25 in.) thick.

Care must be taken to ensure that testpieces are treated exactly the same as the load. Bars of convenient length and 40 mm (1.6 in.) in diameter are quenched and tempered, unless they are already in the heat-treated condition, then turned and ground to a diameter of 38 mm (1.5 in.) to remove any decarburization or carburization that may have occurred in the preliminary heat treatment. The ground surface should be no rougher than 0.127 $\mu$m. Next, the turned and ground bars are cut into slices approximately 6 mm (0.25 in.) thick. This is preferably carried out on a lathe, but an abrasive cutoff machine can be used if abundant coolant is supplied to prevent burning. A hole can be drilled in the completed testpiece so it can be hung in the basket or from the workpiece to prevent its being lost during nitriding.

**Plating** of nitrided testpieces before sectioning is essential for protection of the edges and preservation of the white layer. Plating must be performed without blasting or severe etching. Nickel plating has proved best. The thickness of the deposit is not critical; 0.05 mm (0.002 in.) is usually sufficient, but a greater thickness is not harmful. Chromium plating is unsatisfactory, because the plate does not adhere well to nitrided surfaces without an unacceptable amount of surface preparation. Copper, zinc, and cadmium plates are too soft.

Surface preparation of a testpiece for nickel plating can be accomplished by two methods, neither of which will impair the surface to be examined. One method is to clean the testpiece in a detergent solution, preferably by the ultrasonic method. The other is to etch the testpieces for a few seconds in a metallographic etchant, such as nital.

**Cutting and Mounting Test Specimens.** The plated test specimens are clamped in the vise of a cutoff machine and cut so that one half of the testpiece remains (the width of cut is taken from the discard side). The half testpiece is then halved again by a cut perpendicular to the first cut, and the rounded portion is cut off. The size of the specimen facilitates positioning in the mold.

Various cutoff wheels have proved satisfactory for cutting testpieces, but 54-grit rubber-bonded alumina ($Al_2O_3$) wheels are generally recommended. Use of copious coolant on the specimen is essential; water, synthetic compounds, or soluble-oil emulsions are satisfactory.

The mounting technique is the same as that described in the article "Carbon and Alloy Steels" in this Volume. Bakelite is usually preferred for mounting specimens of nitrided steel. The high mounting temperature of Bakelite, which is critical for some steels, does not affect nitrided steels. Use of hard, filled mounting materials is recommended for preserving flatness of the specimen during grinding and polishing.

**Sectioning Nitrided Parts.** When the workpieces being nitrided are very small, it is simpler and more economical to section actual parts for examination. The parts to be examined are completely nickel plated, then cut and mounted using the procedure described above for specially prepared testpieces.

The procedure for extracting specimens from completed parts (service failures, for example) may vary, depending primarily on surface condition—whether the surface to be examined has been finished by grinding, honing, or lapping or is in the original nitrided condition. Finishing by grinding, honing, or lapping will have removed the white layer, and specimens can be extracted normally. However, unfinished surfaces should be nickel plated before sectioning to preserve the white layer.

**Grinding and polishing** of nitrided steel specimens is the same as grinding and polishing of other steel specimens. These operations are described in the article "Carbon and Alloy Steels" in this Volume. As is true for other case hardened steels, which have large hardness variations in the same specimen, it is highly desirable to minimize grinding and polishing. Excessive grinding and polishing often produce out-of-flat specimens that must be reworked.

**Etching.** The optimum procedure is to etch the polished specimen, immediately repolish very lightly (just enough to remove evidence of etching), then etch again. This procedure may be repeated two or more times to ensure that all disturbed metal is removed and that the true structure is revealed.

For routine examination, nitrided steel specimens are most often etched in nital—2% nital for microscopic examination and up to 5% nital for case-depth measurements at low magnification. Nital reveals the white layer, the depth of case, and the structure of nitrided alloy steels and nitrided carbon steels.

Several other etchants are used for specific nitrided steels and for clearer resolution of certain microconstituents. Picral or a mixture of picral and nital (10 parts 4% picral and 1 part 4% nital) is often used as an alternative

to nital. This mixture serves the same purpose as nital, but often is preferred for revealing the structure of the nitrided case, especially at high magnification. Marble's reagent, consisting of 4 g cupric sulfate ($CuSO_4$), 20 mL HCl, and 20 mL $H_2O$, is used and is often preferred for revealing total depth of nitrided case. A mixture of 1.25 g $CuSO_4$, 2 mL cupric chloride ($CuCl_2$), 10 g magnesium chloride ($MgCl_2$), 2 mL HCl, and 100 mL $H_2O$ diluted to 1000 mL with 95% ethanol is sometimes used for etching high-chromium, vanadium-containing steels that have been nitrided. A solution of 1 to 4 g potassium ferricyanide ($K_3Fe(CN)_6$), 10 g potassium hydroxide (KOH), and 100 mL $H_2O$ (modified Murakami's reagent) has also been used for etching specimens of nitrided steels to increase contrast between nitrides and carbides. Ferric chloride ($FeCl_3$) and modified Fry's reagent are also used to etch some steels, such as maraging steels.

## Microstructures of Case Hardening Steels

Of the case hardening processes that depend for their effectiveness on the introduction of carbon or carbon and nitrogen into the surface of steel, carburizing, carbonitriding, and cyaniding are the most widely used. In general, the steels best suited to these processes are low-carbon steels that rely on a surface layer, or case, of high hardness to provide a level of strength and wear resistance not obtainable from the core metal. Steels for nitriding—whether specially formulated for this purpose or adopted because of satisfactory performance in processing and in service—are usually medium-carbon low-alloy steels of high hardenability; stainless and tool steels can also be nitrided. Compositions of some typical case hardening steels are given in Table 1.

**Processes.** The Section "Case Hardening of Steel" in Volume 4 of the 9th Edition of *Metals Handbook* contains descriptions of some case hardening processes, including gas carburizing, carbonitriding, gas nitriding, pack carburizing, liquid carburizing and cyaniding, liquid (salt bath) nitriding, gaseous ferritic nitrocarburizing, and vacuum carburizing. Other processes currently in use include plasma (ion) nitriding and plasma (ion) carburizing. Micrographs of specimens processed by all of these methods can be found at the end of this article.

**Microstructure and Process Control.** The microstructure of the case and of the underlying core metal serves as a fundamental guide for the control of all heat-treating processes used in case hardening and provides a dependable method for detecting abnormalities and defects that may adversely affect the performance and service life of case hardened parts.

**Table 1    Compositions of case hardening steels**

| Steel | Composition, % | | | | | | | |
|---|---|---|---|---|---|---|---|---|
| | C | Mn | P | S | Si | Ni | Cr | Mo |
| **Carbon steels** | | | | | | | | |
| 1010 .......................... | 0.08-0.13 | 0.30-0.60 | 0.040 max | 0.050 max | ... | ... | ... | ... |
| 1012 mod ..................... | 0.10-0.15 | 0.30-0.60 | 0.040 max | 0.050 max | ... | 0.30 | 0.30 | ... |
| 1018 .......................... | 0.15-0.20 | 0.60-0.90 | 0.040 max | 0.050 max | ... | ... | ... | ... |
| 1020 .......................... | 0.17-0.23 | 0.30-0.60 | 0.040 max | 0.050 max | ... | ... | ... | ... |
| 1039 .......................... | 0.37-0.44 | 0.70-1.00 | 0.040 max | 0.050 max | ... | ... | ... | ... |
| **Resulfurized steels** | | | | | | | | |
| 1113 .......................... | 0.13 max | 0.70-1.00 | 0.07-0.12 | 0.24-0.33 | ... | ... | ... | ... |
| 1117 .......................... | 0.14-0.20 | 1.00-1.30 | 0.040 max | 0.08-0.13 | ... | ... | ... | ... |
| **Alloy steels** | | | | | | | | |
| 3310 .......................... | 0.08-0.13 | 0.45-0.60 | 0.025 max | 0.025 max | 0.20-0.35 | 3.25-3.75 | 1.40-1.75 | ... |
| 3310H ........................ | 0.07-0.13 | 0.30-0.70 | 0.035 max | 0.040 max | 0.20-0.35 | 3.20-3.80 | 1.30-1.80 | ... |
| 4118 .......................... | 0.18-0.23 | 0.70-0.90 | 0.035 max | 0.040 max | 0.20-0.35 | ... | 0.40-0.60 | 0.08-0.15 |
| 4118H ........................ | 0.17-0.23 | 0.60-1.00 | 0.035 max | 0.040 max | 0.20-0.35 | ... | 0.30-0.70 | 0.08-0.15 |
| 4140 .......................... | 0.38-0.43 | 0.75-1.00 | 0.035 max | 0.040 max | 0.20-0.35 | ... | 0.80-1.10 | 0.15-0.25 |
| 4320 .......................... | 0.17-0.22 | 0.45-0.65 | 0.035 max | 0.040 max | 0.20-0.35 | 1.65-2.00 | 0.40-0.60 | 0.20-0.30 |
| 4620 .......................... | 0.17-0.22 | 0.45-0.65 | 0.035 max | 0.040 max | 0.20-0.35 | 1.65-2.00 | ... | 0.20-0.30 |
| 8617 .......................... | 0.15-0.20 | 0.70-0.90 | 0.035 max | 0.040 max | 0.20-0.35 | 0.40-0.70 | 0.40-0.60 | 0.15-0.25 |
| 8617H ........................ | 0.14-0.20 | 0.60-0.95 | 0.035 max | 0.040 max | 0.20-0.35 | 0.35-0.75 | 0.35-0.65 | 0.15-0.25 |
| 8620 .......................... | 0.18-0.23 | 0.70-0.90 | 0.035 max | 0.040 max | 0.20-0.35 | 0.40-0.70 | 0.40-0.60 | 0.15-0.25 |
| 8620H ........................ | 0.17-0.23 | 0.60-0.95 | 0.035 max | 0.040 max | 0.20-0.35 | 0.35-0.75 | 0.35-0.65 | 0.15-0.25 |
| 8720 .......................... | 0.18-0.23 | 0.70-0.90 | 0.035 max | 0.040 max | 0.20-0.35 | 0.40-0.70 | 0.40-0.60 | 0.20-0.30 |
| 8822H ........................ | 0.19-0.25 | 0.70-1.05 | 0.035 max | 0.040 max | 0.20-0.35 | 0.35-0.75 | 0.35-0.65 | 0.30-0.40 |
| 9310 .......................... | 0.08-0.13 | 0.45-0.65 | 0.025 max | 0.025 max | 0.20-0.35 | 3.00-3.50 | 1.00-1.40 | 0.08-0.15 |
| AMS 6470 (a) ................. | 0.38-0.43 | 0.50-0.70 | 0.040 max | 0.040 max | 0.20-0.40 | ... | 1.40-1.80 | 0.30-0.40 |
| **Tool steel** | | | | | | | | |
| H13 (b) ....................... | 0.35 | ... | ... | ... | ... | ... | 5.0 | 1.50 |
| **Maraging steel** | | | | | | | | |
| 18% Ni (300 CVM) (c) ............. | 0.03 max | 0.10 max | 0.010 max | 0.010 max | 0.10 max | 18.5 | ... | 4.8 |

(a) AMS 6470 also contains 0.90 to 1.35% Al. The steel for which structures are shown in Fig. 80-85 was modified by adding 0.15-0.35% Pb. (b) H13 steel also contains 1.0% V. (c) This steel also contains 0.10% Al, 0.60% Ti, 9.0% Co, 0.003% B, 0.02% Zr, and 0.05% Ca.

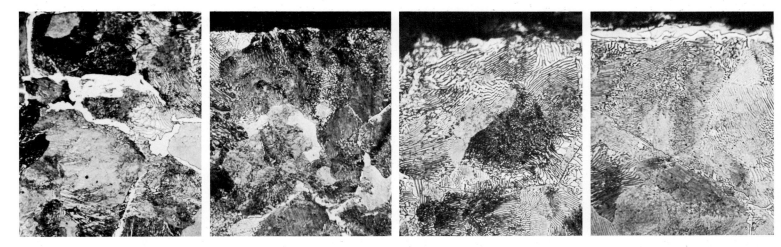

**Fig. 1, 2, 3, 4**  1018 steel, gas carburized at 925 °C (1700 °F) for different lengths of time to different surface carbon contents. Fig. 1: carburized 2 h; surface carbon content is 0.60 to 0.70%. Structure is ferrite (light), outlining prior austenite grain boundaries, and pearlite. Fig. 2: carburized 4 h. Surface (0.70 to 0.80% C) is pearlitic; below surface, same structure as Fig. 1. Fig. 3: carburized 6 h, with a surface carbon content of 0.90 to 1.00%. A thin film of carbide outlines prior austenite grain boundaries; matrix is pearlite. Fig. 4: carburized 16 h. Surface (1.00 to 1.10% C) is carbide; below the surface, structure is identical to Fig. 3. All etched in 1% nital. 500×

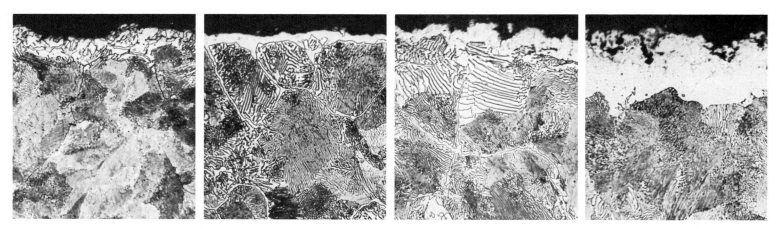

**Fig. 5, 6, 7, 8** Same steel as Fig. 1 to 4. Fig. 5: gas carburized 18 h and cooled in the furnace vestibule. A partially separated layer of carbide (approximately 0.90% C) covers the pearlitic matrix. Fig. 6: gas carburized 12 h. Carbide (approximately 1.10% C) on surface; a film of carbide outlines prior austenite grain boundaries in the pearlite matrix. Fig. 7: gas carburized 5 h in a furnace with an air leak, furnace cooled to 535 °C (1000 °F), then air cooled to room temperature. A thin decarburized layer (ferrite) caused by the air leak covers the surface; below the surface, the structure is pearlite and carbide in prior-austenite grain boundaries. Fig. 8: processed under same conditions as Fig. 7, but the air leak was more severe. The decarburized surface layer is thicker. Carbon has diffused from grain boundaries in the pearlite matrix. All etched in 1% nital. 500×

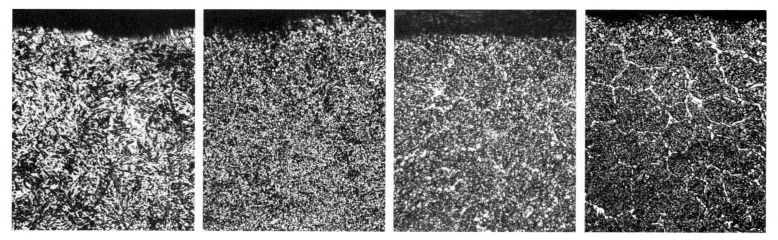

**Fig. 9, 10, 11, 12** 9310 steel, gas carburized 4 h at 925 to 940 °C (1700 to 1725 °F), furnace cooled, austenitized at 815 to 830 °C (1500 to 1525 °F), oil quenched, and tempered 4 h at 150 °C (300 °F). Specimens have different surface carbon contents because of variations in the carbon potential of the furnace atmosphere. Fig. 9: case carbon content is 0.60%. Fig. 10: case is 0.85% C. Fig. 11: case is 0.95% C. Fig. 12: case is 1.05% C. All etched in 2% nital. 500×

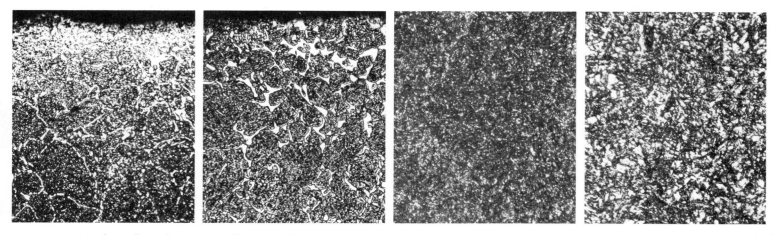

**Fig. 13, 14** Same alloy and processing as Fig. 9 to 12. Fig. 13: case carbon content of 1.10%. Fig. 14: case carbon content of 1.20%. Variations in the carbon potential of the furnace atmosphere produced the different carbon contents. Both etched in 2% nital. 500×

**Fig. 15, 16** 4620 steel, gas carburized. Fig. 15: carburized 8 h at 940 °C (1725 °F), austenitized at 820 °C (1510 °F), oil quenched, tempered 1 h at 180 °C (360 °F), and retempered 2 h at 260 °C (500 °F). Tempered martensite, lower bainite, and carbide. Fig. 16: same as Fig. 15, but retempered 2 h at 230 °C (450 °F). Structure is tempered martensite, lower bainite, dispersed carbide, and 10% retained austenite (by x-ray). Both etched in nital. 1000×

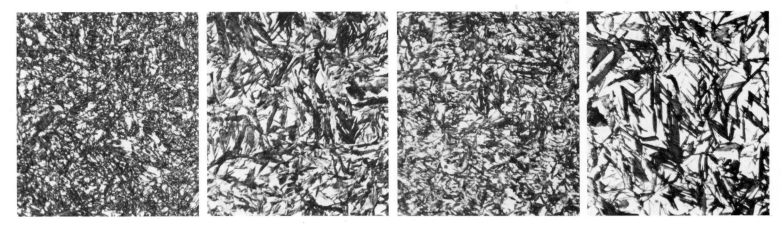

**Fig. 17, 18, 19, 20** 4620 steel, gas carburized at 100% carbon potential. Fig. 17: same as Fig. 15 and 16, but retempered 2 h at 220 °C (425 °F). Structure (0.95% C) is tempered martensite, lower bainite, and carbide, with 20% retained austenite by x-ray. Fig. 18: carburized 4 h at 940 °C (1725 °F), oil quenched, and tempered 1 h at 180 °C (360 °F). Microstructure (0.90% C) is tempered martensite and 35% retained austenite (by x-ray). Fig. 19: carburized 8 h at 940 °C (1725 °F), oil quenched, heated 30 min to 820 °C (1510 °F), oil quenched, and tempered 20 min at 95 °C (200 °F). Structure (0.95% C): tempered martensite and 40% (by x-ray) retained austenite. Fig. 20: same carburization as Fig. 19, oil quenched and tempered 1 h at 180 °C (360 °F). Microstructure consists of tempered martensite and 45% retained austenite (by x-ray). All etched in nital. 1000×

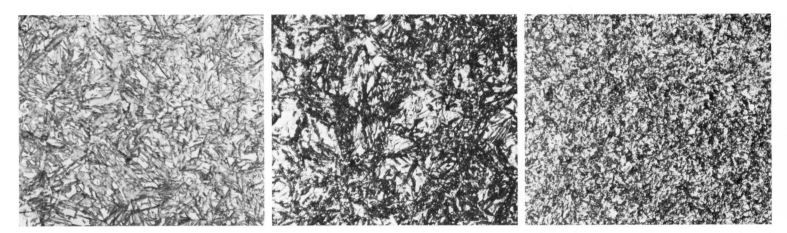

**Fig. 21** 4620 steel, gas carburized 4 h at 955 °C (1750 °F), austenitized 30 min at 820 °C (1510 °F), and oil quenched. Structure is martensite and 25% (by x-ray) retained austenite. Nital. 1000×

**Fig. 22, 23** 3310 steel, gas carburized 16 h at 1.20% carbon potential at 955 °C (1750 °F), oil quenched, heated to 795 °C (1460 °F), oil quenched, and tempered 1 h at 180 °C (360 °F). Fig. 22: structure (1.00% C) is tempered martensite with 30% retained austenite (by x-ray). Fig. 23: same as Fig. 22, but tempered 13 h at 595 °C (1100 °F) before being heated for hardening. Structure (1.00% C): tempered martensite, undissolved carbides, and 20% (by x-ray) retained austenite. Both etched in nital. 1000×

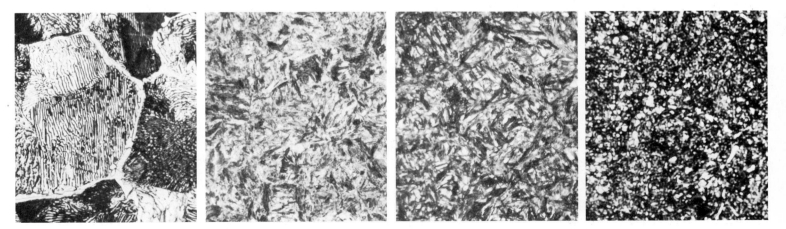

**Fig. 24, 25, 26, 27** 8720 hot-rolled steel, gas carburized at 1.35% carbon potential for 9 h at 925 °C (1700 °F) and diffused 2 h at the same temperature. Fig. 24: specimen was slowly cooled in the furnace. Microstructure is a light carbide network in a matrix of pearlite. Fig. 25: austenitized at 0.90% carbon potential for 1 h at 815 °C (1500 °F), oil quenched, and tempered 1 h at 190 °C (375 °F). Structure is relatively low-carbon tempered martensite. Fig. 26: same austenitizing and tempering as Fig. 25. Structure is globular carbide and retained austenite in a matrix of tempered martensite with a higher carbon content than Fig. 25. Fig. 27: austenitized at 1.35% carbon potential for 1 h at 815 °C (1500 °F), oil quenched, and tempered 1 h at 190 °C (375 °F). Carbide (light network, globular particles) in a tempered martensite matrix; retained austenite is not visible. All etched in 5% nital. 1000×

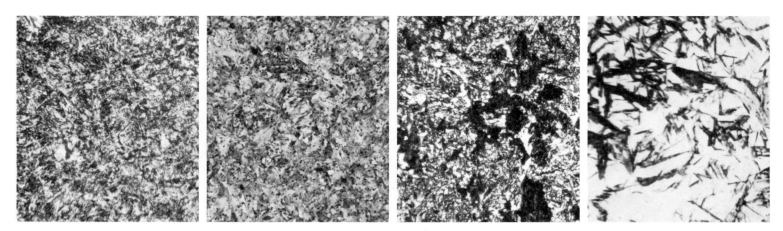

**Fig. 28, 29, 30, 31** 8720 hot-rolled steel, gas carburized at 1.35% carbon potential for 9 h at 925 °C (1700 °F). Fig. 28: specimen was austenitized 1 h at 815 °C (1500 °F), oil quenched, and tempered 1 h at 260 °C (500 °F). A small amount of retained austenite (white areas) is visible in a matrix of overtempered martensite. Fig. 29: specimen was austenitized and quenched same as Fig. 28, then tempered 1 h at 120 °C (250 °F). Tempered martensite structure shows the effects of undertempering. Fig. 30: specimen was austenitized same as Fig. 28 and 29, rapidly air cooled, and tempered 1 h at 190 °C (375 °F). Structure consists of fine pearlite (dark) in a matrix of bainite. Fig. 31: same processing as Fig. 29, but oil quenched. This specimen was overheated during grinding, then rapidly cooled. As a result, the structure consists of retained austenite (white) and untempered martensite. All etched in 5% nital. 1000×

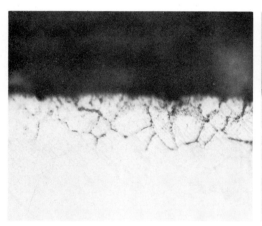 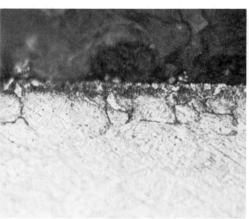 

**Fig. 32** 8620 steel, gas carburized at 955 °C (1750 °F). Specimen shows grain-boundary oxidation to a depth of approximately 0.02 mm (0.0009 in.). 1% nital. 750×

**Fig. 33** 4118 steel, gas carburized at 955 °C (1750 °F). Grain-boundary oxidation to a depth of approximately 0.02 mm (0.0009 in.). As polished. 750×

**Fig. 34** 8620H steel, gas carburized 18 h at 925 °C (1700 °F), reheated to 840 °C (1540 °F) and held 40 min, oil quenched, and tempered 1 h at 175 °C (350 °F). Grain-boundary oxides near the surface and carbide particles and retained austenite in a tempered martensite matrix. 4% picral. 500×

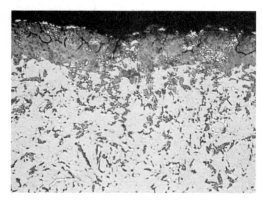 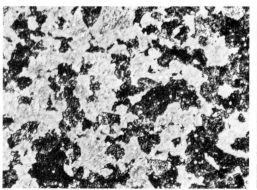 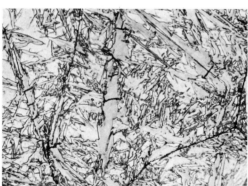

**Fig. 35** 8822H steel, gas carburized 15 h at 925 °C (1700 °F), reheated to 840 °C (1540 °F) and held 40 min, oil quenched, and tempered 2 h at 150 °C (300 °F). Structure is similar to Fig. 34, but a bainite-pearlite mixture near the surface is visible because of the lighter etching. 2% picral. 500×

**Fig. 36** 4320 steel, gas carburized 8 h at 940 °C (1725 °F), reheated to 830 °C (1525 °F) and held 1 h, slack quenched by end quenching the cylinder in oil, and tempered 1 h at 180 °C (360 °F). Structure is 50% pearlite (dark) and undissolved particles of alloy carbide in a matrix of tempered martensite. Nital. 1000×

**Fig. 37** 3310H steel, gas carburized 12 h at 925 °C (1700 °F), furnace cooled to 535 °C (1000 °F), and air cooled. The structure consists of large plates of martensite that show microcracks in a matrix of retained austenite. 4% picral with 0.01% HCl. 500×

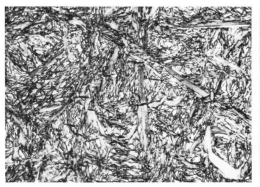

**Fig. 38** Same as Fig. 37, except more heavily etched. Details of the structure are improved, but the microcracks in the martensite plates have been obscured by the darker etch. 4% picral with 0.01% HCl. 500×

**Fig. 39** 8620 steel, gas carburized 11 h at 925 °C (1700 °F), furnace cooled to 845 °C (1550 °F), oil quenched, and tempered 2 h at 195 °C (380 °F). Specimen was subjected to maximum compressive stress of 4135 MPa (600 ksi) for 11.4 million cycles in a contact-fatigue test. ''Butterfly'' structural alterations developed at microcracks. Picral. 1000×

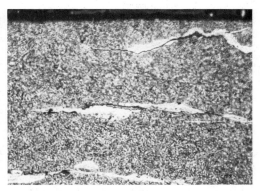

**Fig. 40** 8822H steel roller for a contact-fatigue test, gas carburized 15 h at 925 °C (1700 °F), furnace cooled, heated to 805 °C (1480 °F) and held 1 h, oil quenched, and tempered 1 h at 175 °C (350 °F). Structural alterations developed at subsurface cracks. See also Fig. 43. 1% nital. 275×

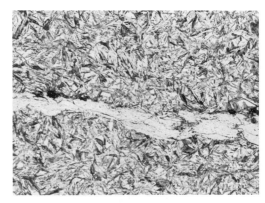

**Fig. 41** 4620 steel, gas carburized and hardened, showing a microstructural alteration (light gray streak) formed at an $Al_2O_3$ stringer inclusion. The stress-induced alteration is approximately 0.25 mm (0.01 in.) from the rolling contact surface. Nital. 500×

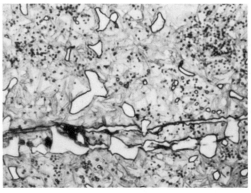

**Fig. 42** Gas-carburized 8822H steel roller for a contact-fatigue test, showing structural alterations associated with carbide phase. The roller was carburized, furnace cooled, reheated, oil quenched, and tempered. The structure consists of retained austenite, martensite, and carbide. 4% picral. 1500×

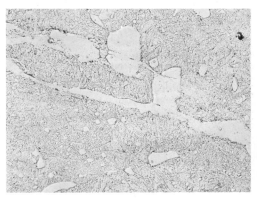

**Fig. 43** Replica electron micrograph of the specimen in Fig. 40. These structural alterations form at microcracks just as ''butterfly'' alterations form at inclusions. 4% picral. 1600×

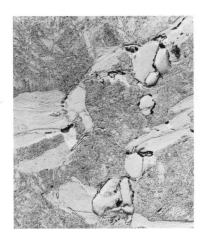

**Fig. 44** Replica electron micrograph of a gas-carburized 1039 steel roller for use in contact-fatigue tests. ''Butterfly'' alterations, which form at inclusions, are approximately 0.12 mm (0.005 in.) from the contact surface and are believed to be oriented in the direction of principal stress. 2% picral. 1950×

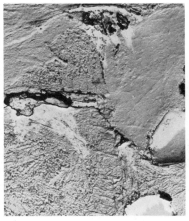

**Fig. 45** Same material and heat treating conditions as Fig. 44, but the area of alteration is at a higher magnification, which shows that microcracks surround the altered metal; slip bands in martensite to the left of the lower inclusion are also visible. 2% picral. 7500×

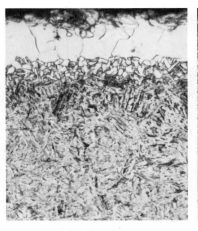

**Fig. 46** 4118H steel bar, gas carburized 8 h at 925 °C (1700 °F), oil quenched, heated to 845 °C (1550 °F) and held 15 min, oil quenched, and tempered 1 h at 170 °C (340 °F). Completely decarburized surface layer (white), a transition zone of ferrite and low-carbon martensite, and a matrix of tempered martensite and retained austenite. 4% nital. 500×

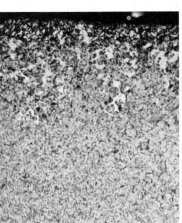

**Fig. 47** Same material and heat treating conditions as Fig. 46. Surface is only partially decarburized, because this low-alloy steel specimen previously contained precipitated, intergranular carbide particles. Matrix is same as described in Fig. 46. 4% nital. 100×

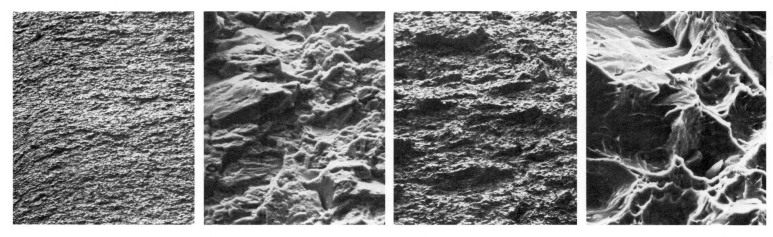

**Fig. 48, 49, 50, 51** 8620H steel tubing, gas carburized 8 h at 925 °C (1700 °F), hardened, and tempered. Fig. 48: scanning electron micrograph of the fractured carburized case. Compare with Fig. 49, which shows the same specimen at a higher magnification. The structure of the case consists of carbide, retained austenite, and tempered martensite. Fig. 50: scanning electron micrograph of the uncarburized core material (low-carbon martensite). Fig. 51: higher magnification shows that the fractured core material has elongated dimples formed during transgranular rupture. All not polished, not etched. Fig. 48 and 50: 23×; Fig. 49 and 51: 1100×

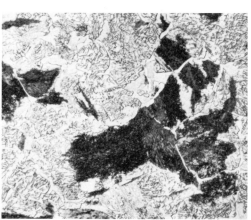

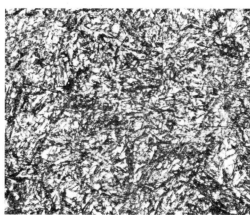

**Fig. 52** 4620 steel, pack carburized 16 h at 940 °C (1725 °F) and cooled in the pot. Structure contains 1% C and consists of ferrite (light), pearlite (dark), and a trace of carbide envelopes at prior austenite grain boundaries. Nital. 1000×

**Fig. 53** 3310 steel, pack carburized 16 h at 940 °C (1725 °F) and cooled in the pot. Structure is fine pearlite (dark) and carbide envelopes at prior austenite grain boundaries in a matrix of ferrite and dispersed alloy carbide. Nital. 1000×

**Fig. 54** Same steel and carburizing as Fig. 53, but tempered 13 h at 595 °C (1100 °F), air cooled, heated to 795 °C (1460 °F), oil quenched, and tempered 1 h at 180 °C (360 °F). Structure is tempered martensite, retained austenite (30% by x-ray), and carbide. Nital. 1000×

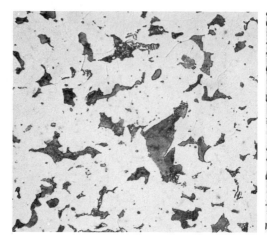

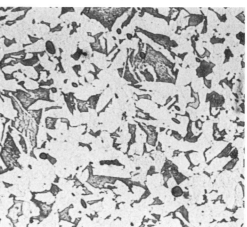

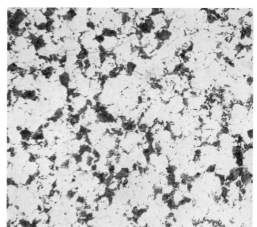

**Fig. 55** 1018 steel bar, austenitized 2 h at 885 °C (1625 °F), then furnace cooled. The structure before carburizing is patches of pearlite (dark) in a matrix of ferrite. Picral. 200×

**Fig. 56** 1117 steel bar, normalized by austenitizing 2 h at 900 °C (1650 °F) and cooled in still air. Ferrite (light) with traces of Widmanstätten ferrite, fine pearlite (dark), and particles of MnS. Picral. 200×

**Fig. 57** 8617 steel bar, annealed by austenitizing 2 h at 870 °C (1600 °F) and furnace cooled. Fine pearlite (dark) in a ferrite matrix. Magnification is too low for good resolution of the structure. Picral. 200×

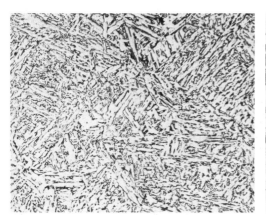

**Fig. 58** 8620 steel bar, normalized by austenitizing 2 h at 900 °C (1650 °F) and cooled in still air. Structure is a mixture of ferrite and carbide. Cooling was too rapid to produce an annealed structure. Picral. 200×

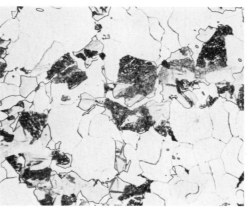

**Fig. 59** 8822H steel bar austenitized 1 h at 925 °C (1700 °F) and furnace cooled 2 h and 10 min to 540 °C (1000 °F), then air cooled. Structure is pearlite (dark) in matrix of ferrite. 1% nital. 500×

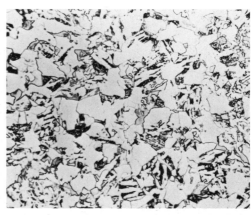

**Fig. 60** Same steel and processing as Fig. 59, but cooled in still air. Blocky ferrite (light) and areas of fine ferrite and bainite in a matrix of pearlite. 1% nital. 500×

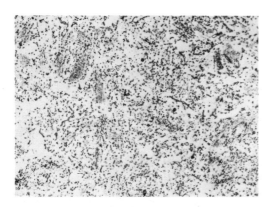

**Fig. 61** 3310 steel bar, austenitized 4 h at 830 °C (1525 °F), cooled to 620 °C (1150 °F) and held 24 h, and tempered 20 h at 640 °C (1180 °F). Structure consists of fine, dispersed carbide particles in a matrix of ferrite. Picral. 1000×

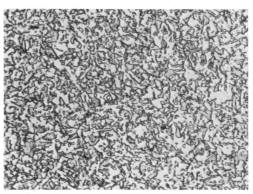

**Fig. 62** 9310 steel bar, normalized by austenitizing 2 h at 885 °C (1625 °F) and cooled in still air. Structure is scattered carbide particles and unresolved pearlite in a matrix of ferrite (light). Picral. 200×

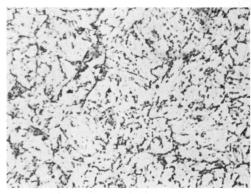

**Fig. 63** Same steel and processing as Fig. 62, except cooled slowly in the furnace. Structure consists of scattered carbide particles (dark) in a ferrite matrix (light). 3% nital. 500×

**Fig. 64** 8620H steel, vacuum carburized 69 min at 980 °C (1800 °F), diffused 78 min, cooled to 845 °C (1550 °F), equalized 30 min, and quenched in oil at 40 °C (100 °F). Microstructure consists of martensite needles and retained austenite. Case depth is 1.8 mm (0.070 in.). Nital. 500×

**Fig. 65** Same steel as Fig. 64, ion carburized 40 min, diffused 100 min at 980 °C (1800 °F), cooled to 845 °C (1550 °F), equalized 30 min, then quenched in oil at 40 °C (100 °F). Structure is martensite, with a small amount of retained austenite. Case depth is 1.8 mm (0.070 in.). Nital. 500×

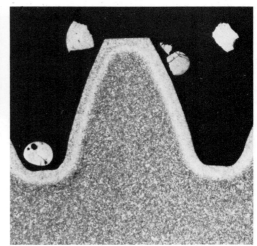

**Fig. 66** 12H2N4A steel gear [0.16% C(max), 0.6% Mn(max), 0.37% Si(max), 0.03% P(max), 0.025% S(max), 1.65% Cr(max), 3.65% Ni(max)], ion carburized and diffused at 920 °C (1690 °F), austenitized at 830 °C (1525 °F), oil quenched, and tempered at 150 °C (300 °F). Uniform case depth on a 40-tooth gear. See also Fig. 67. Nital. 6×

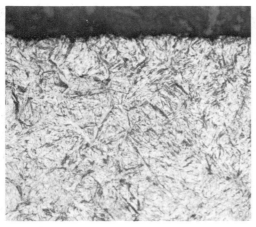

**Fig. 67** Microstructure of ion-carburized gear in Fig. 66. The structure is uniformly distributed tempered martensite, with no evidence of carbide or retained austenite. Nital. 200×

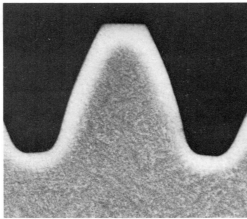

**Fig. 68** Same steel and processing as Fig. 67. Uniform case depth on a 40-tooth gear. Effective case depth is 0.8 to 1.0 mm (0.03 to 0.04 in.). See Fig. 69 for microstructure. Nital. 6×

**Fig. 69** Microstructure of ion-carburized gear in Fig. 68. Tempered martensite. There is no evidence of carbide or retained austenite. Nital. 200×

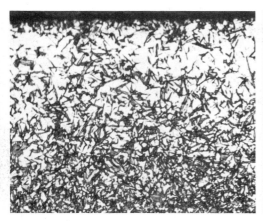

**Fig. 70** 8617 steel, carbonitrided 4 h at 845 °C (1550 °F) in 8% ammonia, 8% propane, and remainder endothermic gas; oil quenched; and tempered 1.5 h at 150 °C (300 °F). Structure is tempered martensite (dark) and retained austenite. 3% nital. 200×

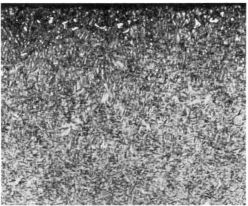

**Fig. 71** 8617 steel bar, carbonitrided and tempered same as Fig. 70, except held 2 h at −75 °C (−100 °F) between quench and tempering. The structure is scattered carbide in a matrix of tempered martensite. Most of the retained austenite was transformed during low-temperature hold. 3% nital. 200×

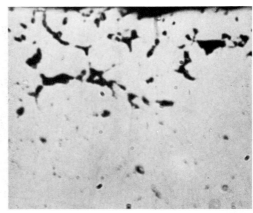

**Fig. 72** 1012 modified (0.03% Ni, 0.30% Cr) steel, cold-rolled strip carbonitrided 1 h at 845 °C (1550 °F) and oil quenched. Specimen shows networks of subsurface grain-boundary voids. See also Fig. 73 and 74. As-polished. 1000×

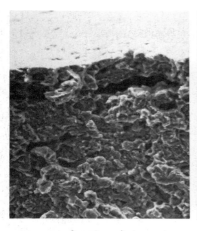

**Fig. 73** Scanning electron micrograph of a fracture surface in the same steel as Fig. 72. Void formation appears to involve the formation of diatomic gas molecules (probably nitrogen) at prior austenite grain boundaries. Not polished, not etched. 750×

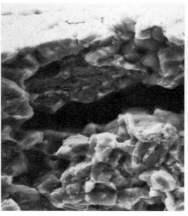

**Fig. 74** Same as Fig. 73, but at higher magnification. The formation of grain-boundary voids is promoted by carbonitriding above 855 °C (1575 °F) and by total carbon and nitrogen potentials above 1%. Not polished, not etched. 2000×

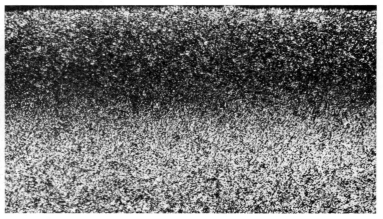

**Fig. 75** 1018 steel bar, carbonitrided 4 h at 845 °C (1550 °F), oil quenched, and stabilized by sub-zero treatment. The structure contains martensite and carbide particles, and a small amount of retained austenite. Additional carbonitrided materials and their representative microstructures can be found in Fig. 70 to 74 and 76 to 79. Nital. 100×

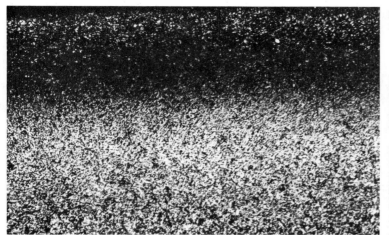

**Fig. 76** 8620 steel bar, processed under the same conditions as Fig. 75. Structure is the same as Fig. 75, but the appearance of the carbonitrided case differs because of the alloy content of 8620 steel. Nital. 100×

**Fig. 77** 1020 steel, carbonitrided and oil quenched. The effects on microstructure of too high a carbon potential: a white layer of cementite in the case (left), retained austenite interlaced with martensite needles, and a martensite matrix (right). Nital. 500×

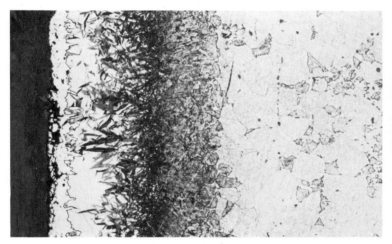

**Fig. 78** 1010 steel, carbonitrided at 790 °C (1450 °F) and oil quenched. The case (left) is high carbon, with a structure similar to that in Fig. 77; the core (right) is predominantly ferrite. Nital. 200×

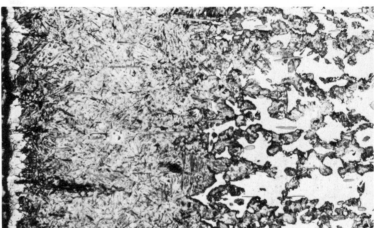

**Fig. 79** 1117 steel, carbonitrided and oil quenched. A surface layer of decarburized ferrite (left) is superimposed on a normal case structure of martensite. The core (right) contains patches of ferrite (white). Nital. 200×

**Fig. 80** 1020 steel, cyanided 1 h in a salt bath at 845 °C (1550 °F) and water quenched. The case (top) is martensite with some carbide. The core is ferrite. Microhardness indents 0.08 mm (0.003 in.) apart illustrate hardness difference between case (61 HRC) and core (25.5 HRC). 2% nital. 100×

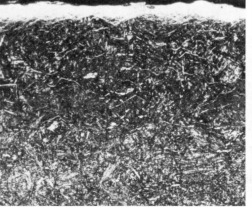

**Fig. 81** AMS 6470 steel with 0.15 to 0.35% Pb added, oil quenched from 900 °C (1650 °F), tempered 2 h at 605 °C (1125 °F), surface activated in manganese phosphate, and gas nitrided 30 h at 525 °C (975 °F). Structure is a white layer of $Fe_2N$ and a matrix of tempered martensite. 2% nital. 400×

**Fig. 82** Same material and heat treating conditions as described in Fig. 81, except nitrided 36 h. The depth of the nitride layer has increased, and platelets of iron nitride can be seen in the case. 2% nital. 400×

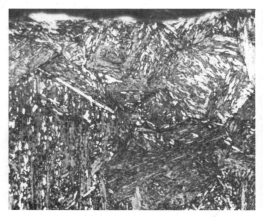

**Fig. 83** Same steel and prenitriding conditions as Fig. 81, but double stage nitrided: 5 h at 525 °C (975 °F), followed by 20 h at 565 °C (1050 °F). The white nitride layer shown in Fig. 81 and 82 has been eliminated by dissociation in the second stage of nitriding. 2% nital. 400×

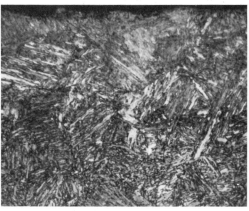

**Fig. 84** Same steel and processing as Fig. 81, but the surface was heavily burnished and not chemically activated before nitriding. The lack of surface activation retarded diffusion into the case. 2% nital. 400×

**Fig. 85** Same steel and processing as Fig. 81, except slack quenched and ground heavily before nitriding. Because the surface was not chemically activated before nitriding, nitrogen diffusion was retarded. 2% nital. 400×

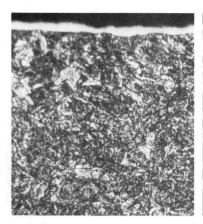

**Fig. 86** 4140 steel, oil quenched from 845 °C (1550 °F), tempered 2 h at 620 °C (1150 °F), surface activated in manganese phosphate, and gas nitrided 24 h at 525 °C (975 °F). Structure is white layer of Fe₂N, Fe₃N, and Fe₄N, and tempered martensite. 2% nital. 400×

**Fig. 87** Same steel and prenitriding conditions as described in Fig. 86, except double-stage gas nitrided: 5 h at 525 °C (975 °F), then 20 h at 565 °C (1050 °F). Structure consists of diffused nitride layer and a matrix of tempered martensite. 2% nital. 400×

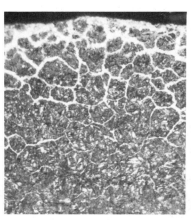

**Fig. 88** H13 steel, heated to 1030 °C (1890 °F) in a vacuum, quenched in nitrogen gas, triple tempered at 510 °C (950 °F), surface activated in manganese phosphate, and gas nitrided 24 h at 525 °C (975 °F). White surface layer is iron nitride. Grain-boundary networks of nitride are present throughout the martensitic case. 2% nital. 300×

**Fig. 89** 18% Ni maraging steel (300 CVM), solution treated 1 h at 815 °C (1500 °F), surface activated, and gas nitrided 24 h at 440 °C (825 °F). Etching has made the nitride surface layer and grain-boundary nitrides appear black. Modified Fry's reagent. 1000×

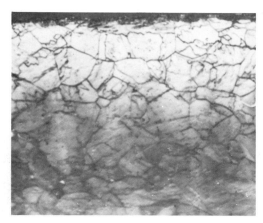

**Fig. 90** Same steel and processing as Fig. 89, but etched with nital. Note that this etchant does not clearly reveal the nitrided microstructure. 1000×

**Fig. 91** Same steel and processing as Fig. 89, but etched with FeCl₃. Iron nitride appears as black layer, similar to the specimen in Fig. 89. 500×

**Fig. 92** 4118 steel, hot rolled and annealed, surface activated, then gas nitrided 24 h at 525 °C (975 °F). White layer of iron nitride over a core of ferrite and pearlite. 2% nital. 600×

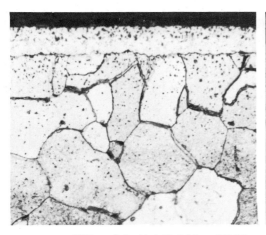

**Fig. 93** 1010 steel, liquid nitrided 1 h at 570 °C (1060 °F) in an aerated salt bath. Layer of nitride over a core of blocky ferrite and grain-boundary carbide. No transition zone is evident. 2% nital. 700×

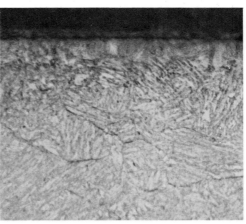

**Fig. 94** Fe-0.31C-2.50Cr-0.2Mo-0.15V steel, ion nitrided 36 h at 525 °C (975 °F). Tempered before nitriding to 35 HRC. Specimen was nitrided to produce a pure diffusion zone with no white layer. The matrix is tempered martensite. 2% nital. 750×

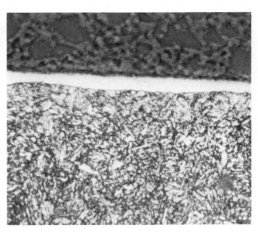

**Fig. 95** 4140 steel, quenched and tempered to 30 HRC, then ion nitrided 24 h at 510 °C (950 °F). Monophase surface layer of $Fe_4N$, plus a diffusion zone of nitride containing tempered martensite. Nital. 750×

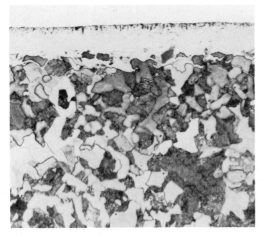

**Fig. 96** SAE 1035 modified (0.20% Al added) steel, salt bath nitrided 90 min at 580 °C (1075 °F) and water quenched. Surface layer of iron nitride over a matrix of ferrite and pearlite. 1% nital. 500×

**Fig. 97** SAE 1045 modified (niobium added) steel, salt bath nitrided 90 min at 580 °C (1075 °F) and water quenched. White nitride layer over a pearlitic matrix. 1% nital. 500×

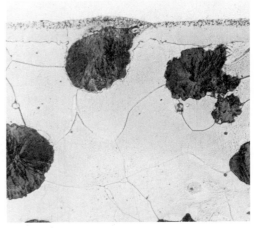

**Fig. 98** Nodular ferritic cast iron, salt bath nitrided 2 h at 580 °C (1075 °F) and water quenched. Structure is a white layer of iron nitride over a core of graphite nodules in ferrite. 1% nital. 500×

# Carbon and Low-Alloy Steel Castings

CARBON AND LOW-ALLOY STEEL CASTING specimens are prepared using the techniques described in the article "Carbon and Alloy Steels" in this Volume.

**Sectioning.** As-cast and heat-treated steel castings are usually soft enough to permit sawing or hollow boring for initial extraction of test pieces. The oversize pieces are then sawed or abrasive-wheel cut to specimen size. If the casting is hard, abrasive-wheel cutting is used. Precautions must be taken against overheating during cutting. Even with the application of copious water, it is possible to overheat the piece being sectioned.

**Section thickness** in a single steel casting can vary from a fraction of an inch to many inches, resulting in different cooling rates and thus in different microstructures within as-cast and heat-treated castings. Therefore, for complete examination of a casting, several specimens may have to be extracted. Some of the micrographs in this article compare the structures observed in sections of different thicknesses (Fig. 4 to 6).

**Mounting.** Bakelite is often used for mounting specimens. The microstructures of most steel castings are not affected by the thermosetting temperature of Bakelite. In some foundry laboratories, cold-mounting materials (described in the article "Mounting of Specimens" in this Volume) are used more often than Bakelite.

**Grinding and polishing** techniques described for specimens of wrought steels apply to specimens from steel castings. Steel castings frequently are examined for the presence and identification of inclusions, and methods of inclusion preservation are essential. Grinding usually includes use of a belt or disk grinder and 180-, 240-, 400-, then 600-grit silicon carbide abrasive paper.

The specimen is then rough polished on a nylon or canvas polishing cloth charged with 3- to 9-$\mu$m diamond paste. Final polishing is performed using a low-napped rayon cloth charged with a slurry of water containing 0.05-$\mu$m alumina ($Al_2O_3$). Excessive polishing must be avoided to prevent extraction of inclusions. Examination for inclusions is performed before etching.

**Etching.** Nital is the etchant most often used for specimens from steel castings. Picral is sometimes used, especially for castings with carbon contents of more than 0.30%. Carbide structures usually are resolved better with picral than with nital. Electrolytic etching is only rarely employed for specimens from carbon or low-alloy steel castings.

## Microstructures of Carbon and Low-Alloy Steel Castings

The microstructures presented in this article are those of carbon and low-alloy steel castings in the as-cast, annealed, normalized, normalized and tempered, and quenched and tempered conditions in 25-mm (1-in.), 75-mm (3-in.), and 150-mm (6-in.) thick sections. Stainless steel castings, austenitic manganese steels, and heat-resistant alloy castings are covered in separate articles in this Volume.

Steel castings are classified in accordance with the standards provided in Volumes 01.01 and 01.02 of the *Annual Book of ASTM Standards*. The composition limits of steels illustrated in this article are listed in Table 1. The structures of castings meeting the same ASTM standard often differ widely because of the permissible limits in composition, differences in section thickness, and variations in foundry and heat treating practice from plant to plant. Properties and selection of steel castings are discussed in the article "Steel Castings" in Volume 1 of the 9th Edition of the *Metals Handbook*.

**Carbon Steel Castings.** The microstructures of carbon steel castings shown in this article are for castings conforming to ASTM Standards A 27 (Ref 1), A 148 (Ref 2), and A 216 (Ref 3). Most of the steels have a carbon content of more than 0.25%, and some contain 0.45% C.

ASTM A 27 covers low to medium-strength carbon steel castings for general applications. The grades are not severely restricted as to composition. Maximum carbon ranges from 0.25 to 0.35% and maximum manganese from 0.60 to 1.20%, depending on the grade. Strength specifications range from no specific requirements to those for grade 70-40, which must exhibit minimum tensile strength of 485 MPa (70 ksi) with minimum yield strength of 275 MPa (40 ksi). Figures 1 to 14 show microstructures of ASTM A27 grade 70-36 steel.

Higher strength carbon steel castings are covered by ASTM A 148, in which maximums on sulfur and phosphorus are the only composition restrictions. Minimum tensile strength requirements vary from 550 to 1795

**Table 1   Compositions of carbon and low-alloy steel castings(a)**

| Steel | Composition, % | | | | | |
| --- | --- | --- | --- | --- | --- | --- |
| | C | Mn | Si | P | S | Other |
| A27, grade 70–36 ............. | 0.35 max | 0.70 max | 0.80 max | 0.05 max | 0.06 max | ... |
| A128, grade B–3 ............. | 1.12–1.28 | 11.5–14.0 | 1.00 max | 0.07 max | ... | ... |
| A148 | Specification sets mechanical-property limits | | | | | |
| A216, grade WCA ........... | 0.25 max | 0.70 max | 0.60 max | 0.04 max | 0.045 max | (b) |
| A216, grade WCB ........... | 0.30 max | 1.00 max | 0.60 max | 0.04 max | 0.045 max | (b) |
| A352, grade LC3 ........... | 0.15 max | 0.50–0.80 | 0.60 max | 0.04 max | 0.045 max | 3–4 Ni |
| A487, class 2 ................. | 0.30 max | 1.00–1.40 | 0.80 max | 0.04 max | 0.045 max | (c) |

(a) Where not specified by ASTM number, composition is given in the micrograph figure caption. (b) Residual elements, 1% max total, including 0.50% max Cu, 0.50% max Ni, 0.40% max Cr, 0.25% max Mo, 0.03% max V. (c) Also contains 0.10 to 0.30% Mo. Residual elements, 1% max total, including 0.50% max Cu, 0.50% max Ni, 0.35% max Cr, 0.10% W

MPa (80 to 260 ksi) and minimum yield strengths from 275 to 1450 MPa (40 to 210 ksi) for the 14 grades in A 148. Figures 15 to 21 illustrate microstructures of steel covered by this standard.

Carbon steel castings suitable for fusion welding for high-temperature service are represented in ASTM A 216. Micrographs in this article are for two grades: WCA (Fig. 22 to 28) and WCB (Fig. 29 to 35). A third grade, WCC, is not shown. All grades are categorized as carbon steels, because alloying or residual elements are not specified; maximum limits on copper, nickel, chromium, molybdenum, and vanadium vary from 0.03% V to 0.50% Ni and Cr. The maximum total of all residual elements is set at 1.00%.

Heat treatment and section thickness influence the microstructure of cast steel. Therefore, the micrographs in this article show each steel in various conditions. Slower cooling rates of thicker sections usually result in different constituents and in coarsening of the structure.

Two micrographs (Fig. 36 and 37) of a medium-carbon steel in the normalized condition show the effect of increasing magnification on the resolution of the microconstituents.

**Low-Alloy Steel Castings.** The microstructures of low-alloy steel castings shown in this article are for castings conforming to ASTM Standards A487 (Ref 4) and A352 (Ref 5). ASTM A487 steel castings are intended for pressure service and must be heat treated by normalizing, normalizing and tempering, or by quenching and tempering. The castings must also be weldable. Figures 38 to 40 are micrographs of normalized ASTM A487 steel castings.

ASTM A352 steel castings are intended for pressure-containing parts suitable for service to −115 °C (−175 °F). Ferritic castings are normalized and tempered or liquid-quenched and tempered (Fig. 41) before being placed in service. The one martensitic grade, CA6NM, in ASTM A352 should be heated to 955 °C (1750 °F) minimum and air cooled to 95 °C (200 °F) maximum prior to any optional intermediate temper. This grade, however, should be cooled to 40 °C (100 °F) maximum before the final temper, which is between 565 and 620 °C (1050 and 1150 °F).

**REFERENCES**

1. "Standard Specification for Steel Castings, Carbon, for General Application," A 27, *Annual Book of ASTM Standards*, Vol 01.02, ASTM, Philadelphia, 1984
2. "Standard Specification for Steel Castings, High Strength, for Structural Purposes," A 148, *Annual Book of ASTM Standards*, Vol 01.02, ASTM, Philadelphia, 1984
3. "Standard Specification for Steel Castings, Carbon, Suitable for Fusion Welding, for High Temperature Service," A 216, *Annual Book of ASTM Standards*, Vol 01.02, ASTM, Philadelphia, 1984
4. "Standard Specification for Steel Castings, Suitable for Pressure Service," A 487, *Annual Book of ASTM Standards*, Vol 01.02, ASTM, Philadelphia, 1984
5. "Standard Specification for Steel Castings, Ferritic and Martensitic, for Pressure Containing Parts, Suitable for Low Temperature Service," A 352, *Annual Book of ASTM Standards*, Vol 01.02, ASTM, Philadelphia, 1984

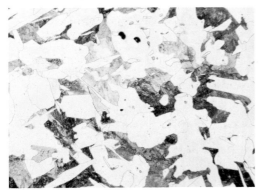

**Fig. 1** ASTM A27 steel (0.25% C), 25 mm (1 in.) thick, in as-cast condition. Structure is proeutectoid ferrite (white) at prior austenite grain boundaries, and a mixture of ferrite and pearlite within grains. Nital. 100×

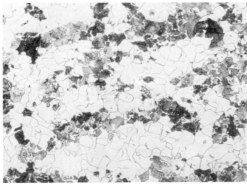

**Fig. 2** Same steel as for Fig. 1, 25 mm (1 in.) thick, annealed by austenitizing at 925 °C (1700 °F) for 1 h at temperature and furnace cooling. Ferrite (white) and pearlite (dark) outline the original dendritic structure. Nital. 100×

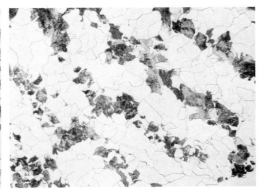

**Fig. 3** Same steel as for Fig. 1, 150 mm (6 in.) thick. Heat treatment was the same as for Fig. 2. Structure is essentially the same as for Fig. 2, but grains are coarser because of the greater thickness of the section. Nital. 100×

**Fig. 4** Same steel as for Fig. 1, 25 mm (1 in.) thick, quenched and tempered. Austenitized at 925 °C (1700 °F) for 1 h at temperature, quenched in mildly agitated water, tempered at 675 °C (1250 °F) for 2 h. Note fine-grained microstructure of ferrite (white) and pearlite. Nital. 200×

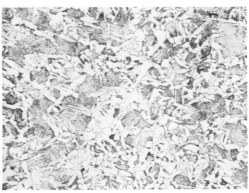

**Fig. 5** Same steel as for Fig. 1, 75 mm (3 in.) thick. Quenching and tempering treatment was the same as for Fig. 4. The microstructure is nearly the same as for Fig. 4, but slightly coarser. See Fig. 6 for the structure of a thicker section after the same heat treatment. Nital. 200×

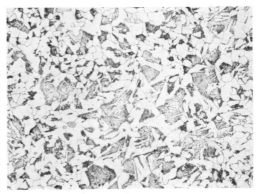

**Fig. 6** Same steel as for Fig. 1, 150 mm (6 in.) thick. Quenching and tempering treatment was the same as for Fig. 4. The microstructure consists of the same constituents as Fig. 4 and 5, but grains are significantly coarser because of the greater thickness of the section. Nital. 200×

**Fig. 7** ASTM A27 steel, grade 70-36 (0.26% C, 0.71% Mn), 25-mm (1-in.) cube, normalized by austenitizing at 1205 °C (2200 °F) for 30 min and air cooling. Widmanstätten pattern of proeutectoid ferrite in a matrix of ferrite and pearlite. 4% Nital. 250×

**Fig. 8** ASTM A27 steel, grade 70-36 (0.30 to 0.40% C), 25 mm (1 in.) thick, as cast. Ferrite (white) and pearlite (dark). Higher carbon content than that of steel in Fig. 1 results in a greater proportion of pearlite. Nital. 250×

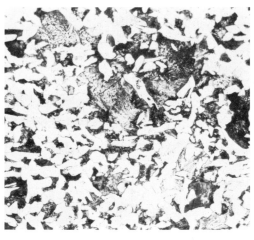

**Fig. 9** Same steel as for Fig. 8, 25 mm (1 in.) thick, but after being normalized by austenitizing at 900 °C (1650 °F) for 1 h and air cooling. Structure consists of ferrite (white constituent) and pearlite (dark constituent). Nital. 250×

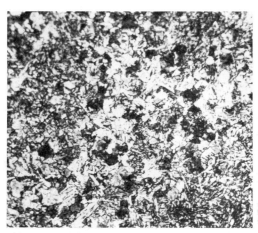

**Fig. 10** Same steel as for Fig. 8, 25 mm (1 in.) thick, quenched and tempered. Austenitized at 900 °C (1650 °F) for 1 h, water quenched, tempered at 620 °C (1150 °F) for 2 h. Structure is tempered martensite and ferrite (white). Nital. 250×

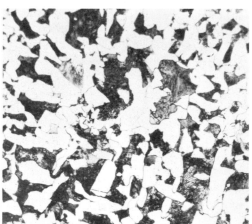

**Fig. 11** Same steel as for Fig. 8, 75 mm (3 in.) thick, but after being normalized by austenitizing at 900 °C (1650 °F) for 3 h and air cooling. The structure consists of pearlite (dark constituent) and ferrite (light constituent). Nital. 250×

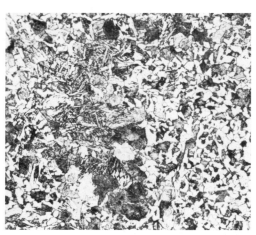

**Fig. 12** Same steel as for Fig. 8, 75 mm (3 in.) thick, quenched and tempered. Austenitized at 900 °C (1650 °F) for 3 h, water quenched, tempered at 620 °C (1150 °F) for 4 h. Structure: tempered martensite, pearlite, and ferrite. Nital. 250×

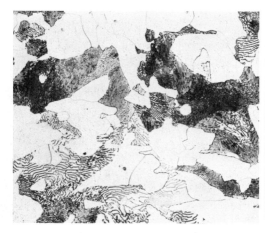

**Fig. 13** Same steel as for Fig. 8, 150 mm (6 in.) thick, normalized by austenitizing at 900 °C (1650 °F) for 6 h and air cooling. The microstructure consists of lamellar pearlite (gray and black) and ferrite (white). Nital. 250×

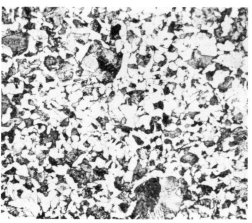

**Fig. 14** Same steel as for Fig. 8, 150 mm (6 in.) thick, quenched and tempered. Austenitized at 900 °C (1650 °F) for 6 h, water quenched, tempered at 620 °C (1150 °F) for 6 h. Structure is fine pearlite and ferrite (white). Nital. 250×

**Fig. 15** ASTM A148 steel, grade 90-60 (0.30% C, 1.65% Mn), 25 by 25 by 13 mm (1 by 1 by 0.5 in.), in the as-cast condition. The microstructure consists of ferrite (white) in a matrix of pearlite (dark). 4% nital. 100×

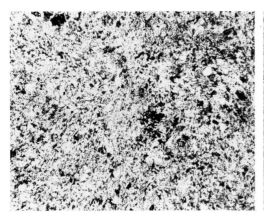

**Fig. 16** Same steel and size as for Fig. 15, normalized by austenitizing at 900 °C (1650 °F) for 20 min and air cooling. Structure: a fine-grained aggregate of ferrite and pearlite. 4% nital. 100×

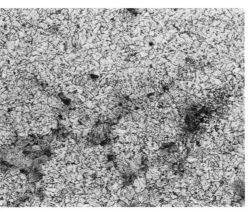

**Fig. 17** ASTM A148 steel, grade 90-60 (0.27% C, 0.80% Mn, 0.51% Si, 0.35% Mo), 25 mm (1 in.) thick, normalized and tempered. Austenitized at 925 °C (1700 °F) for 1 h, air cooled, tempered at 705 °C (1300 °F) for 3 h. Structure is fine-grained ferrite and pearlite. 5% nital. 100×

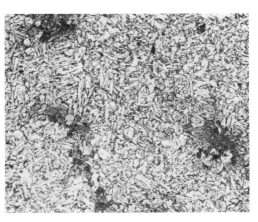

**Fig. 18** Same steel as for Fig. 17, 150 mm (6 in.) thick, normalized and tempered. Austenitized at 925 °C (1700 °F) for 6 h, air cooled, tempered at 705 °C (1300 °F) for 4 h. Structure: fine-grained aggregate of ferrite and pearlite. Note dendritic segregation of carbon and manganese. 5% nital. 100×

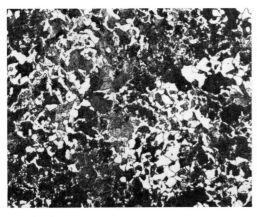

**Fig. 19** ASTM A148 steel (0.45% C), 75 mm (3 in.) thick, annealed by austenitizing at 900 °C (1650 °F) for 5 h and furnace cooling to room temperature in 10 h. Structure consists of blocky ferrite and ferrite at prior austenite grain boundaries in a matrix of pearlite (dark). 5% nital. 100×

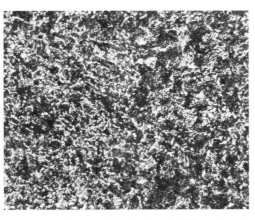

**Fig. 20** Same steel as for Fig. 19, 150 mm (6 in.) thick, quenched and tempered. Austenitized at 900 °C (1650 °F) for 3 h to temperature and held 5 h, water quenched, tempered at 595 °C (1100 °F) for 4 h to temperature and held 6 h, air cooled. Very fine ferrite and spheroidized pearlite. 5% nital. 100×

**Fig. 21** ASTM A148 steel, grade 105-85 (0.27% C, 0.80% Mn, 0.51% Si, 0.35% Mo), 150 mm (6 in.) thick, quenched and tempered. Austenitized at 925 °C (1700 °F) for 4 h, water quenched, tempered at 650 °C (1200 °F) for 4 h. Proeutectoid ferrite (white) in a matrix of tempered martensite. 5% nital. 500×

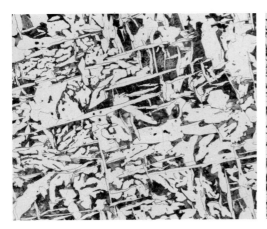

**Fig. 22** ASTM A216 steel, grade WCA (0.21% C, 0.60% Mn, 0.49% Si), 25 mm (1 in.) thick, as-cast. The microstructure consists of pearlite (dark constituent), blocky ferrite, and Widmanstätten platelets of ferrite. 2% nital. 100×

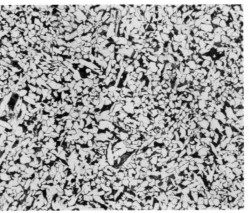

**Fig. 23** Same steel as for Fig. 22, 25 mm (1 in.) thick, normalized and tempered. Austenitized at 925 °C (1700 °F) for 1 h, air cooled, tempered at 705 °C (1300 °F) for 3 h. The structure consists of fine pearlite in a matrix of ferrite (white). 2% nital. 100×

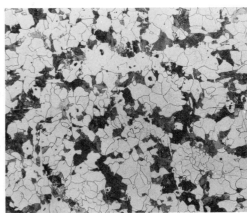

**Fig. 24** Same steel as for Fig. 22, 25 mm (1 in.) thick, annealed by austenitizing at 925 °C (1700 °F) for 1 h, and furnace cooling. Structure consists of ferrite (light) and pearlite (dark). Pattern of pearlite reflects primary dendritic segregation of carbon and manganese. 2% nital. 100×

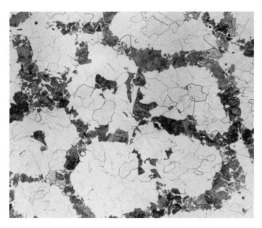

**Fig. 25** ASTM A216 steel, grade WCA (0.21% C, 0.60% Mn, 0.49% Si), 75 mm (3 in.) thick, annealed by austenitizing at 925 °C (1700 °F) for 6 h, and furnace cooling. Same structure as Fig. 24, but "cell" size of carbon and manganese segregation is larger, because the section is thicker. 2% nital. 100×

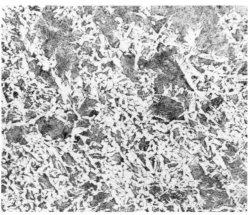

**Fig. 26** Same steel as for Fig. 25, 75 mm (3 in.) thick, quenched and tempered. Austenitized at 925 °C (1700 °F) for 3 h, water quenched, tempered at 650 °C (1200 °F) for 4 h. Structure consists of fine pearlite and probably some upper bainite (dark) in a matrix of ferrite (white). 2% nital. 100×

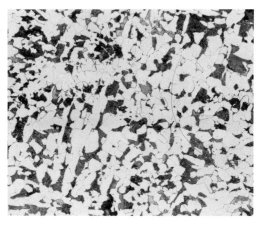

**Fig. 27** Same steel as for Fig. 25, 150 mm (6 in.) thick, normalized and tempered. Austenitized at 925 °C (1700 °F) for 6 h, air cooled, tempered at 705 °C (1300 °F) for 4 h. Structure consists of fine pearlite in a matrix of blocky ferrite (light) with platelets of Widmanstätten ferrite. 2% nital. 100×

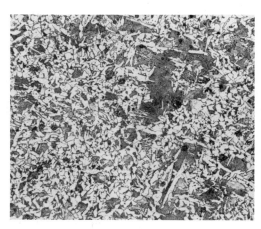

**Fig. 28** Same steel as for Fig. 25, 150 mm (6 in.) thick, quenched and tempered. Austenitized at 925 °C (1700 °F) for 6 h, water quenched, tempered at 650 °C (1200 °F) for 4 h. Structure is fine-grained ferrite with some platelets of Widmanstätten ferrite and fine pearlite (dark). 2% nital. 100×

**Fig. 29** ASTM A216, grade WCB (0.27% C), 25 mm (1 in.) thick, annealed by austenitizing at 870 °C (1600 °F) for 8 h and furnace cooling. Structure consists of blocky pearlite (dark) and blocky ferrite (white). 2% nital. 500×

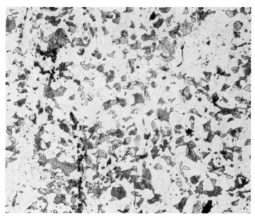

**Fig. 30** Same steel as for Fig. 29, 75 mm (3 in.) thick, normalized by austenitizing at 925 °C (1700 °F) and air cooling. Structure consists of fine pearlite in a matrix of ferrite (light). 3% nital. 75×

**Fig. 31** Same steel and heat treatment as for Fig. 30, but at a higher magnification. White grains (note distinct boundaries) are blocky ferrite; dark areas are fine, lamellar pearlite. 2% nital. 500×

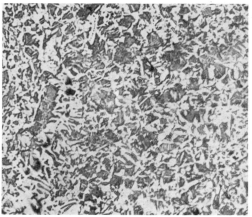

**Fig. 32** Same steel as for Fig. 29, 75 mm (3 in.) thick, as-quenched condition. Austenitized at 925 °C (1700 °F) and quenched in oil. The structure consists of fine pearlite in a matrix of ferrite. 3% nital. 75×

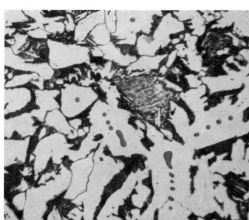

**Fig. 33** ASTM A216, grade WCB (0.27% C) 75 mm (3 in.) thick, heat treated as for Fig. 32, but shown at higher magnification. Fine pearlite in a ferrite matrix. Note MnS inclusions (globular). 2% nital. 500×

**Fig. 34** Same steel as for Fig. 33, 150 mm (6 in.) thick, normalized by austenitizing at 925 °C (1700 °F) and air cooling. Structure: fine and coarse pearlite in a coarse-grained ferrite matrix. 2% nital. 500×

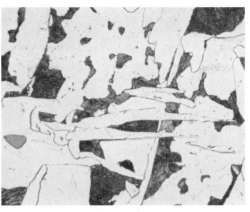

**Fig. 35** Same steel as for Fig. 33, 150 mm (6 in.) thick, in the as-quenched condition. Austenitized at 925 °C (1700 °F) and oil quenched. Pearlite (dark), randomly dispersed in ferrite (white). Note the gray MnS inclusion at the left. 2% nital. 500×

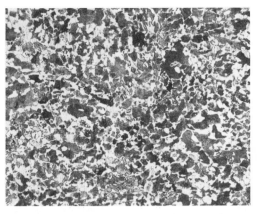

**Fig. 36** Cast steel with 0.45% C, 0.70% Mn, 0.40% Si, normalized by austenitizing at 955 °C (1750 °F) for 30 min and cooling in air. Structure is a mixture of ferrite (white) and pearlite (dark), which is not well resolved. 4% nital. 100×

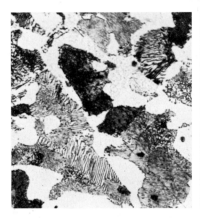

**Fig. 37** Same area as for Fig. 36, but at a still higher magnification. Parallel plate structure of the pearlite is now well resolved. A magnification of 500× (as here) is often best for this structure and grain size. 4% nital.

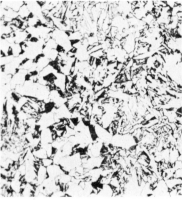

**Fig. 38** ASTM A487 steel, class 2, 25 mm (1 in.) thick, normalized by austenitizing at 900 °C (1650 °F) and air cooling. The structure consists of pearlite and ferrite. See Fig. 39 and 40 for influence of alternate heat treatment and section size. 4% nital. 250×

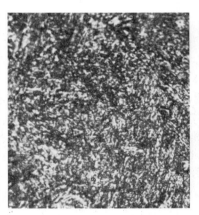

**Fig. 39** ASTM A487 steel, 25 mm (1 in.) thick, normalized by austenitizing at 955 °C (1750 °F) for 3 h, held 5 h, air cooled, tempered at 660 °C (1225 °F) for 4 h to temperature, and held 6 h. The lighter areas are fine ferrite; the darker areas are probably bainite delineating prior austenite grain boundaries. 5% nital. 1000×

**Fig. 40** Same steel as for Fig. 38, but 75 mm (3 in.) thick, normalized by austenitizing at 900 °C (1650 °F) and cooling in air. The structure consists of ferrite (light constituent) and pearlite (dark constituent). Some martensite may be present in dark areas of the structure. 4% nital. 250×

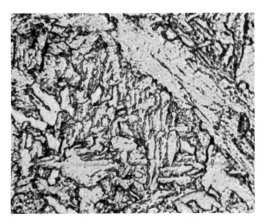

**Fig. 41** ASTM A352 steel, grade LC3, 25 mm (1 in.) thick. Austenitized at 900 °C (1650 °F) for 3 h to temperature, held 5 h, water quenched, tempered at 620 °C (1150 °F) for 4 h to temperature, and held 6 h. The microstructure consists of fine, acicular ferrite (light constituent), some pearlite (dark), and minute particles of cementite. 5% nital. 1000×

**Fig. 42** Aluminum deoxidized low-alloy steel casting, 50 mm (2 in.) thick, normalized at 900 °C (1650 °F) for 30 min, air cooled, then tempered at 565 °C (1050 °F) for 2 h, air cooled. Fine-grained uniform ferrite and pearlite with bainite transformed during moderately rapid cooling rate. 4% nital. 500×. (L.L. Bright)

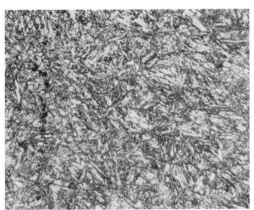

**Fig. 43** Same steel as for Fig. 42, 50 mm (2 in.) thick, quenched and tempered. Austenitized at 900 °C (1650 °F) for 30 min, water quenched, and tempered at 565 °C (1050 °F) for 2 h, air cooled. Structure consists of tempered martensite-bainite. 4% nital. 500×. (L.L. Bright)

**Fig. 44** Low-alloy cast steel (0.28C-0.55Mn-1.3Si-1.00Ni-1.5Cr-0.40Mo), normalized at 925 °C (1700 °F), hardened by water quench from 900 °C (1650 °F), and tempered at 290 °C (550 °F) to ~500 HB. Tempered martensite with some bainite. 2% nital. 1000×. (D. Subramanyam)

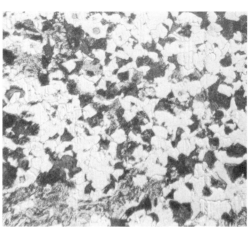

**Fig. 45** Low-alloy cast steel (0.32C-0.85Mn-0.80Ni-0.80Cr-0.32Mo), annealed at 870 °C (1600 °F). Structure consists of ferrite (light areas) and pearlite (dark areas). 5% nital. 100×. (G.J. Wiskow)

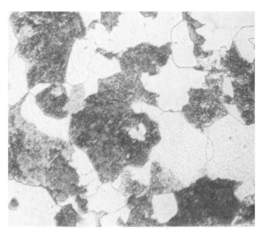

**Fig. 46** Same low-alloy cast steel as for Fig. 45, annealed at 870 °C (1600 °F), except at higher magnification. Structure consists of ferrite (light areas) and pearlite (dark areas). 5% nital. 400×. (G.J. Wiskow)

# Austenitic Manganese Steel Castings

By Dilip K. Subramanyam
Metallurgist
Abex Corporation

Gary W. Grube
Associate Metallurgist
Abex Corporation

and

Henry J. Chapin
Consultant
Abex Corporation

AUSTENITIC MANGANESE STEELS have microstructures that are extremely sensitive to section size. These steels are metastable, austenitic, solid solutions of carbon, manganese, and silicon in iron (in the simplest case); therefore, the development of a single-phase austenitic microstructure depends on the rapidity and effectiveness of water quenching during heat treatment. However, in heavier-section-size castings, which are not uncommon for this grade of steel, the thermal conductivity of the metal, which is relatively poor, determines cooling rate. This results in interdendritic and grain-boundary cementite precipitation, which is compounded by increased solute segregation in heavy sections. Thus, the microstructure of the heaviest section should be included in examination.

The grain size in austenitic manganese steel castings depends on the amount of superheat in the liquid metal during casting and can vary widely. Consequently, to determine representative grain size and distribution, it may be useful to macroetch an entire cross section if one is available. This procedure is discussed in a subsequent section. Additional information on the properties and selection of austenitic manganese steels can be found in the article "Austenitic Manganese Steel" in Volume 3 of the 9th Edition of *Metals Handbook*.

## Specimen Preparation

**Sectioning.** After suitable locations of specimens to be examined are decided upon, the next step is to extract them without excessive thermal or mechanical damage. Depending on the size of the original casting, various sectioning methods can be used. For example, flame or arc cutting can be used to isolate the sections of interest in very large castings. However, sufficient stock should be allowed to minimize thermal damage to the area of interest. Dry abrasive-wheel cutting can also be used with the same precautions.

The next series of cuts to reduce the specimen to metallographic dimensions should be performed using a "soft" silicon carbide abrasive wheel with flood-cooling and a slow feed rate. Immersion electric discharge cutting is also suitable, because the associated heat-affected zones are fairly narrow. However, care should be taken subsequently to grind the specimen below the heat-affected zone before metallographic examination. Laboratory-size diamond-edge cutting wheels are appropriate for thin specimen preparation for electron microscopy. Metal saw cutting is not recommended because of the work-hardening property of this alloy. Additional information is available in the article "Sectioning" in this Volume.

**Mounting.** Specimens can be mounted using conventional metallographic mounting materials. For edge preservation, electrolytic or electroless coatings can be applied before grinding. Another useful method involves simultaneously mounting hardened-steel ball bearings or similar guards around the specimen to facilitate flat, even grinding. The article "Mounting of Specimens" in this Volume provides additional information on edge retention techniques.

**Grinding.** Automatic and manual grinding methods may be used. Manual grinding is carried out wet using 80-, 180-, 320-, then 600- or 1000-grit waterproof silicon carbide abrasive papers. The specimen should be thoroughly cleaned, rinsed, and rotated 90° between grindings. The abrasive paper should be replaced often, because dull abrasive can cause light surface deformation and work hardening. Moderate pressure will minimize work hardening. Automated grinding equipment may also be used, and precautions should be taken to minimize surface deformation and contamination. Additional information is available in the article "Mechanical Grinding, Abrasion, and Polishing" in this Volume.

**Polishing** is usually a two-step process. Rough polishing can be performed using 6-$\mu$m diamond paste on a napless nylon cloth, which enhances edge retention, followed by 1-$\mu$m diamond paste on a medium-nap rayon cloth. Use of diamond extender fluid is recommended in both cases. Fine polishing is carried out using a 0.6-$\mu$m colloidal silica or alumina ($Al_2O_3$) suspension and a medium-nap cloth.

The specimen should always be rotated in a direction opposite that of the lapping wheel. Moderate pressure is recommended. Between polishings, the specimen should be washed with soap and running water, rinsed with alcohol, and dried in a blast of warm air. After fine polishing, however, the specimen should be rinsed in alcohol (commercially available 99.9% isopropyl alcohol, for example) to prevent staining by water. Alternate light etching and additional polishing can be used to minimize the effects of surface deformation resulting from specimen preparation; however, this procedure can result in poor retention of inclusions.

Electrolytic polishing also yields satisfactory results. A solution of 80 g sodium chromate ($Na_2CrO_4$) in 420 mL glacial acetic acid at room temperature is used as the electrolyte. The solution is prepared by slowly adding $Na_2CrO_4$ crystals to acetic acid in slow stages with simultaneous stirring to prevent settling. Current densities should approximate 1 $A/cm^2$ (6.5 $A/in.^2$) at 30 to 50 V for 6 to 8 min. However, depending on the type of polishing apparatus used and on the nature of the specimen and the mount, some experimentation may be necessary for optimum results. Copper-containing conductive specimen mounts are preferable.

Because electrolytic polishing can often magnify any microporosity in a cast specimen into larger "pits," polishing time should be kept to a minimum. For additional information on polishing, see the articles "Mechanical Grinding, Abrasion, and Polishing" and "Electrolytic Polishing" in this Volume.

## Macroexamination

Examination of a fracture surface can provide information on grain size, mode of failure, hot tears, and casting soundness. Tensile fractures can be dimpled or fibrous. The relative coarseness of the "orange peel" appearance on gage surfaces of broken tensile specimen stubs can sometimes indicate grain size, because very little necking occurs during tensile testing. Failures that occur from exposure to temperatures above 315 °C (600 °F) are usually intergranular because of grain-boundary embrittlement by precipitated carbide. Poor heat treatment can also contribute to intergranular fracture.

Hot tears are usually caused by high levels of phosphorus in the steel, and macroshrinkage invariably results from pouring a casting with very low superheat (less than 5 °C, or 40 °F) or poor casting design (improper gating, risering and so on). The presence of this kind of shrinkage can result in low ductility and rapid wear in service. Blow holes or gas porosity are usually due to inadequate deoxidation of the steel or excess dissolved nitrogen or hydrogen.

**Macroetching.** A smooth, unburned surface produced by wet abrasive cutting is most often adequate for macroetching. Special grinding is not required. Two macroetchants are commonly used to reveal grain size and shape and other features, such as the presence of weld (repair), in austenitic manganese steel. The first etchant, to be used at room temperature, consists of 2 parts $H_2O$, 2 parts concentrated hydrochloric acid (HCl), and 1 part hydrogen peroxide ($H_2O_2$) by volume. For safety reasons, care should be taken to add HCl to water, followed by $H_2O_2$. Etching should proceed for 15 to 25 s, during which a black film forms almost immediately, covering the entire surface of the sample. Etching by immersion is preferred, although swabbing is more convenient for large cross sections.

Once etched, the specimen should be placed under running water, and the black film scrubbed off with a soft-bristle brush. This must be done as quickly as possible to avoid staining the etched surface. If the etch is too light, the specimen can be immersed again for 5 to 10 s, then scrubbed under running water. Next, the specimen is well rinsed with alcohol, dried in a blast of warm air, and immediately sprayed with a thin, protective coating of a fast-drying clear lacquer, which also sometimes improves overall contrast.

If the surface becomes overetched, regrinding is necessary before the specimen can be etched again. For larger specimens, the grinding can be performed using a standard wet-grinding machine, taking precautions to ensure minimum surface deformation. Because of the nonmagnetic nature of manganese steel, a special holder or vise is usually required during grinding.

The second etchant frequently used consists of a 50% aqueous solution (by volume) of concentrated HCl at 60 to 70 °C (140 to 160 °F). Etching should be followed by scrubbing in water, rinsing in alcohol, drying, and protective spraying. Macroetching with either etchant can be carried out in the as-cast or heat-treated conditions. No significant grain growth occurs during heat treatment, however, and better grain definition is often obtained after this operation.

**Grain Size Measurements.** Grain size in these steels is primarily a function of the pouring temperature of the casting, and it is not unusual to encounter grain sizes larger than can be measured by the standard ASTM scale (00 to 10). Grain size can then be estimated from a metallographic specimen at a magnification lower than that specified by the standard practice (100×) using the procedures detailed in ASTM Standard E 112, "Standard Methods for Determining Average Grain Size," to find the macro grain size number.

Another method of estimating grain size from a macroetched specimen involves determining by actual measurements the average equivalent grain diameter and using the following relationship to convert this grain diameter $d$ (in inches) to the corresponding ASTM grain size number $n$:

$$n = -6.64(1.8 + \log d)$$

If the equivalent grain diameter is larger than approximately 0.5 mm (0.02 in.), grain size number determined by this relationship will be negative, for example, $-3.8$ for an equivalent grain diameter of 1.5 mm (0.06 in.). Because the ASTM grain size scale uses whole numbers, this would be rounded to $-4$. Thus, a negative scale can be established and used.

## Microexamination

Table 1 summarizes etchants and procedures that are commonly used for austenitic

**Table 1  Selected etching reagents for microscopic examination**

| Etchant | Procedure | Comments |
|---|---|---|
| Nital: 1–6 mL conc $HNO_3$ (nitric acid) and 94 to 99 mL ethanol or methanol | Swab (with cotton) or immerse for a few seconds. Rinse thoroughly in alcohol and dry. If surface is covered with a light yellowish brown film, remove by swabbing or immersing in 10% HCl solution. Rinse again in alcohol and dry. | Shows general structure. Etches grain boundaries where carbide is present. Also reveals pearlite colonies if present |
| Picral: 4–5 g picric acid, 95 mL ethanol or methanol, and 5 mL distilled $H_2O$ | Immerse 20 s or more if necessary. Rinse thoroughly in alcohol and dry. | |
| Cyclic etch: 3% nital, 10% HCl solution, and 2% $NH_4OH$ (ammonium hydroxide) solution | Alternate immersion in nital and 10% HCl for 15 s. Rinse specimen in alcohol and dry between solutions. Repeat 2–3 times, then immerse in $NH_4OH$ 15 s. Rinse in alcohol and dry. Swab with cotton. Rinse in alcohol and dry. | |
| Villela's reagent: 1 g picric acid, 5 mL HCl, and 100 mL ethanol | Swab with cotton. Rinse in alcohol and dry. Use 10% HCl solution to remove surface film if present. | |
| Boiling alkaline sodium picrate: 2 g picric acid, 100 mL $H_2O$, and 25 g NaOH (sodium hydroxide) | Immerse for 5–10 min. Rinse well and dry. | Reveals as-cast austenite grain boundaries in the presence of a pearlitic microstructure |
| Electrolytic etchant: 80 g $Na_2CrO_4$ dissolved in 420 mL of glacial acetic acid | 0.03–0.05 $A/cm^2$ (0.2–0.3 $A/in.^2$) at 5–10 V for 5–10 min. Higher current densities can be used to shorten etching time if surface rippling or waviness is a problem. Note: This same solution can be used to polish specimens electrolytically (see section on specimen preparation). | Reveals grain boundaries and annealing and deformation twins |
| Electrolytic etch: 20% HCl solution in methanol | 0.25–0.5 $A/cm^2$ (1.6–3.2 $A/in.^2$) at 4–6 for 30 s. For polishing, current densities of 0.6–0.8 $A/cm^2$ (3.9–5.2 $A/in.^2$) have given satisfactory results in some cases | Reveals deformation twinned structure |
| Color (tint) etch(a): 2% nital (pre-etch) and 20% aqueous $Na_2S_2O_5$ (sodium metabisulfite) | Light pre-etch in nital for 3 s, followed by 20 s immersion in $Na_2S_2O_5$ | Reveals general grain structure |

(a) Ref 5

manganese steels, including weld metal. The cyclic procedure often yields a clean etched surface. Nital, picral, and Vilella's reagent are also useful for quick results on as-cast and heat-treated grades. However, these solutions sometimes produce a thin, irregular, yellowish brown film on the surface of the specimen that can distort subsequent microscopic interpretation. This film can be removed by immersion in a 10% solution of HCl in water or alcohol. Cementite is usually better defined by using the 4% picral etch.

Insufficient grain-boundary contrast, which is due to the virtual absence of carbide precipitates along the austenite grain boundaries, can often be compensated for by electrolytic etching or tint (color) etching. Techniques that improve contrast in the microscope, such as oblique lighting, darkfield, or differential interference contrast may also be helpful. Electrolytic etching can be used as well to reveal the presence of deformation and annealing twins in the austenite grains. Alcohol rinsing is again recommended to minimize staining of the specimen surface.

Deep immersion etching, that is, longer etching times, can be used to reveal the solute segregation pattern within the austenite grains. In addition, when a large volume fraction of pearlite in the microstructure obscures the as-cast austenite grain size, the grain boundaries can be revealed by an immersion etch in boiling alkaline sodium picrate, which preferentially colors the cementite.

## Microstructure

With the exception of vanadium-containing precipitation-hardenable alloys and some molybdenum-containing dispersion-hardened alloys, the desirable microstructure in austenitic manganese steels is generally a single-phase austenitic solid solution.

In the as-cast state, the microstructure is characterized by an austenite matrix with precipitated carbide and small colonies of pearlite resulting from carbon rejection from the austenite during cooling. These carbides lie along grain boundaries and in interdendritic areas within grains. Interdendritic carbides can be fairly massive, especially at triple points, and are sometimes surrounded by lamellar carbide zones. The alloy is usually given a "toughening" heat treatment, which consists of solutionizing at a temperature high enough to dissolve the carbides, followed by rapid quenching in agitated water at room temperature to retain as much carbon as possible in metastable solid solution. In practice, the presence of some grain-boundary carbide is typical, especially in heavier sections.

These alloys are nonmagnetic. However, because of the loss of carbon and some manganese from the surface during solidification within a mold and during heat treatment, there sometimes exists a thin "skin" of magnetic (martensite) metal on the surface of the casting.

When properly heat treated austenitic manganese steel is reheated (by accident or intent) to 345 to 480 °C (650 to 900 °F), carbide precipitates appear along the austenite grain boundaries and throughout the grains along crystallographic planes. At higher temperatures (480 to 705 °C, or 900 to 1300 °F), conditions are favorable for pearlite formation.

Austenitic manganese steels deform by twinning and by slip mechanisms. Upon deformation, the alloys work harden, making them progressively more difficult to strain. Deformation twins are easily visible in an etched sample under the optical microscope and should not be mistaken for slip bands (Ref 1-4).

When a manganese steel containing a large volume fraction of pearlite is heat treated, the new austenite grains that nucleate from the pearlite colonies frequently contain annealing twins. Annealing twins are also observed in hot-rolled or cold-worked manganese steels that have been reheated above their recrystallization temperatures.

**Alloying Elements.** The regular elements, such as carbon, manganese, and silicon, as well as other alloying elements, enhance specific properties in various applications. Chromium additions dissolve in austenite and carbide phases, making it necessary to raise the solutionizing temperature to promote more effective carbide solution during heat treatment. Small amounts of residual chromium are usually present from melting scrap.

Depending on the level of addition and the nature of heat treatment to which the alloy is subjected, molybdenum additions exist in solid solution in the austenite and as a dispersed carbide phase (for example, in the "dispersion-treated" grade). Nickel additions to austenitic manganese steels remain in solid solution in austenite.

Titanium, vanadium, and zirconium additions appear primarily in the form of carbonitrides. Depending on the nature of charged scrap and melting practice employed, the nitrogen content in the alloy can range from 100 to 400 ppm. In the unetched condition, titanium carbonitrides appear shiny, faceted, and pink when viewed under an optical microscope; zirconium carbonitrides appear golden yellow.

In precipitation-hardening austenitic manganese steels containing vanadium, the small,

relatively rounded, dispersed vanadium carbides present after solidification are first partially redissolved by a very high-temperature solutionizing treatment. The carbon is retained in metastable solid solution by a water quench, and subsequently precipitated again during a lower temperature aging treatment. These precipitated carbides are not resolvable under optical microscopy.

Because of the high manganese content, all the sulfur appears as small, rounded, dispersed bluish gray particles of manganese sulfide (MnS). Hence, sulfur is seldom a cause for concern as a "tramp" element in this alloy.

Phosphorus, however, can be very detrimental to mechanical properties and castability. Phosphorus segregates along with carbon to interdendritic areas during solidification, where it forms a low-melting eutectic with iron, manganese, and carbon. This makes a higher phosphorus alloy—greater than 0.06% P in bulk concentration, for example—more prone to hot tearing in the mold. In addition, during the subsequent solutionizing treatment, the low-melting eutectic can result in incipient melting. This is extremely detrimental to mechanical properties. Molybdenum-containing alloys are particularly susceptible to incipient fusion. The use of lower solutionizing temperatures can, to a certain extent, alleviate this problem.

Aluminum is added primarily to deoxidize the steel, and the products sometimes appear as clusters of small, dark, purplish-gray particles of alumina ($Al_2O_3$) and aluminates. When the aluminum content in regular Hadfield steels exceeds approximately 5%, stabilizing the austenite phase to room temperature becomes increasingly difficult, even after water quenching.

Special grades of austenitic manganese steels exist. Included in this category are (1) alloys containing higher manganese (up to 35%) and very low carbon (less than 0.05%) that are used mostly in cryogenic and magnetic applications and (2) alloys containing lower manganese (7 to 9%) and higher carbon (for example, 1.3%) that are used in the mining industry. The former alloys exhibit single-phase austenitic microstructures; the latter are initially single-phase austenitic but for hardening rely on a strain-induced transformation to martensite during service. Compositions of alloys depicted in micrographs following this article are listed in Table 2.

**Table 2  Chemical compositions of austenitic manganese steels**

| Alloy | Chemical composition, % | | | | | | | |
| --- | --- | --- | --- | --- | --- | --- | --- | --- |
|  | C | Mn | Si | Al | Cr | Mo | Others | Fe |
| ASTM A128 .............. 1.11 | 1.11 | 12.8 | 0.20 | 0.025 | ... | 0.54 | 0.05P 0.006S | rem |
| ASTM A128 grade A ........ 1.25 | 1.25 | 12.9 | 0.66 | 0.06 | 0.05 | ... | ... | rem |
| ASTM A128 grade C ........ 1.35 | 1.35 | 12.98 | 0.28 | 0.025 | 2.06 | ... | ... | rem |
| ASTM A128 grade D ........ 0.88 | 0.88 | 12.86 | 0.83 | 0.026 | 0.82 | ... | 3.77Ni 0.026P | rem |
| ASTM A128 grade E2 ....... 1.09 | 1.09 | 13.9 | 0.67 | 0.055 | ... | 2.00 | 0.032P | rem |
| Experimental alloy .......... 1.76 | 1.76 | 10.5 | 0.55 | 2.5 | 0.70 | ... | 0.016P | rem |

### REFERENCES

1. Y.N. Dastur and W.C. Leslie, Mechanism of Work Hardening in Hadfield Manganese Steel, *Met. Trans. A*, Vol 12, May 1981, p 749
2. S.A. Sastri and R. Ray, Mössbauer Studies on Aging of Highly Deformed Hadfield Manganese Steel, *Met. Trans.*, Vol 5, June 1974, p 1501
3. H.M. Otte, The Formation of Stacking Faults in Austenite and its Relation to Martensite, *Acta Metall.*, Vol 5, 1957, p 614
4. L. Rémy, The Interaction Between Slip and Twinning Systems, and the Influence of Twinning on the Mechanical Behavior of fcc Metals and Alloys, *Met. Trans. A*, Vol 12, March 1981, p 387
5. A.J. Sedriks and T.O. Mulhearn, Austenitic Manganese Steel: Structure and Properties of Decarburized Layer, *Journal of the Iron Steel Institute*, Vol 202, Nov 1964, p 907–911

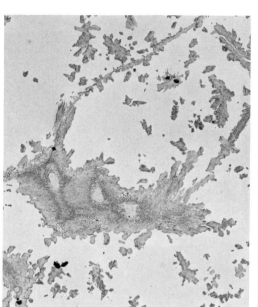

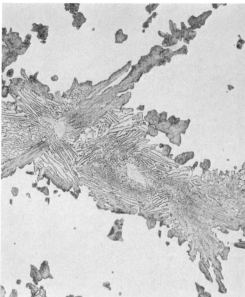

**Fig. 1, 2** ASTM A128 grade A alloy, as-cast. Microstructure consists of austenite grains with darker carbides. In Fig. 2, the carbides consist of a relatively massive core surrounded by lamellar carbides. 4% picral. Fig. 1: 100×. Fig. 2: 200×

**Fig. 3** ASTM A128 alloy, heat treated at 1065 °C (1950 °F), and water quenched. Structure near the casting wear surface shows martensite formed during deformation as a result of decarburization of the austenite (light phase). 4% picral. 500×

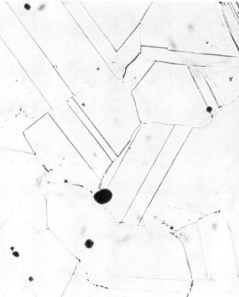

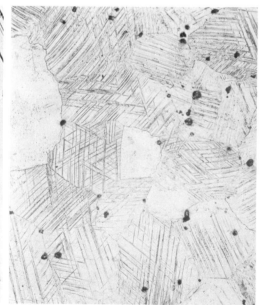

**Fig. 4** Experimental alloy, as-cast. Microstructure shows untransformed austenite and cementite in interdendritic positions, along with the outlines of pearlite colonies (grayish areas). Boiling alkaline sodium picrate (see Table 1 for composition). 100×

**Fig. 5** Experimental alloy, heat treated at 1120 °C (2050 °F) for 3 h and water quenched. Austenite grains show annealing twins formed during transformation from as-cast pearlite. Only traces of grain-boundary carbides are visible. This microstructure is acceptable. Sodium chromate in glacial acetic acid (see Table 1 for composition). 100×

**Fig. 6** ASTM A128 alloy, cast and heat treated at 1065 °C (1950 °F), water quenched, machined into tensile specimen, and tested. Austenite grains show different amounts of twinning, depending on individual grain orientation. Etchant: Same as Fig. 5. 100×

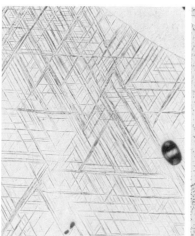

**Fig. 7** ASTM A128 grade D alloy, cast and heat treated at 1035 °C (1900 °F) for 3 h, water quenched, machined into tensile specimen, and tested. Depicted is a single austenite grain with deformation twins. This figure also illustrates the tendency of large "primary" twins to obstruct further twinning. Sodium chromate in glacial acetic acid (see Table 1 for composition). 100×

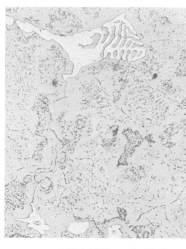

**Fig. 8** ASTM A128 grade E2 alloy, aged at 595 °C (1100 °F) for 12 h, air cooled, then partially solutionized at 980 °C (1800 °F) for 2 h and water quenched. Microstructure consists of austenite grains with dispersions of undissolved carbide. This is the so-called "dispersion-hardened" grade of austenitic manganese steel. 4% picral. 500×

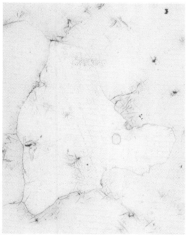

**Fig. 9** ASTM A128 alloy, cast, heat treated at 1065 °C (1950 °F), and water quenched. Microstructure shows an austenite grain with continuous grain-boundary carbide films and carbide precipitates in interdendritic areas due to "slack" quenching. Some undissolved carbide is also visible in each grain. The grains also exhibit some twinning. This is an undesirable microstructure. 4% picral. 72×

**Fig. 10** ASTM A128 alloy, cast, solutionized at 1065 °C (1950 °F), and water quenched. Microstructure consists of austenite with faintly etched grain boundaries containing only traces of carbide precipitates. Some dispersed microporosity is visible within the austenite grains. This is an acceptable microstructure. 4% picral. 100×

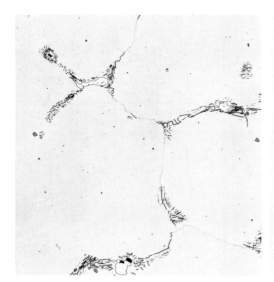

**Fig. 11** ASTM A128 grade C alloy, cast, heat treated at 1095 °C (2000 °F) for 2 h, and water quenched. Microstructure consists of austenite grains, with undissolved carbides in interdendritic areas (including grain boundaries). Carbides surrounded by lamellae and spheroids indicate the successive steps in carbide dissolution. In general, this is an undesirable microstructure. Cyclic etch (see Table 1 for composition and method). 100×

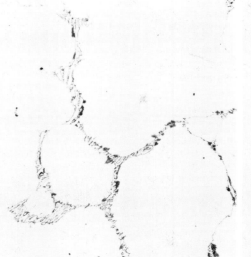

**Fig. 12** ASTM A128 grade A alloy, cast, heat treated at 1150 °C (2100 °F) for 2 h, and water quenched. Photomicrograph shows austenite grains, with incipient fusion associated with grain-boundary carbide due to excessive solutionizing temperature. This is an unacceptable microstructure. Etchant: Same as Fig. 11. 100×

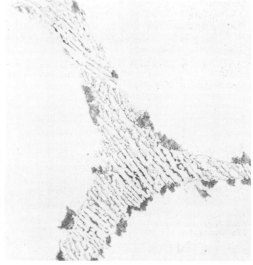

**Fig. 13** ASTM A128 grade A alloy, cast and deliberately overheated to 1205 °C (2200 °F) for 1 h, then water quenched. Photomicrograph illustrates a triple point in the austenite grain structure, with detail of the eutectic pattern of incipient fusion associated with the carbide due to excessive solutionizing temperature. Cyclic etch (see Table 1 for composition and method). 500×

# Cast Irons

By James A. Nelson
Manager
Research & Development Laboratory
Buehler Ltd.

CAST IRONS are a family of ferrous alloys that possess a wide range of microstructures and physical properties that directly affect service performance. Therefore, the ability to monitor the microstructures of ferrous foundry alloys is an extremely useful method of controlling product properties and quality. Metallography is also a valuable failure-analysis tool. Table 1 lists the microconstituents commonly found in cast irons and their general effects on physical properties.

The broad variation in microstructure that makes cast irons so useful also poses some challenging problems to the foundry metallographer or technician responsible for preparing specimens for examination. For example, ferritic gray irons are extremely soft; grinding scratches are difficult to remove, and graphite tends to pull out easily. White iron, by contrast, contains extremely hard iron carbide that resists abrasion and tends to remain in relief above the softer matrix after polishing. Retention of graphite has always been a major problem in the preparation of graphitic irons.

To achieve accurate visual analysis, specimens must reveal the true microstructure with minimum preparation defects. An acceptably prepared metallographic surface should be free of surface deformation and scratches, flat from edge to edge, and exhibit minimum microstructural relief. These prerequisites are met only when specimens are correctly prepared using sound metallographic procedures. Acceptable results may be achieved using various polishing sequences, but certain key elements are common to most successful techniques. This article describes a basic procedure and the modifications required to accommodate extreme conditions imposed by certain alloy properties.

## Specimen Preparation

Complete microstructural analysis requires microscopic examination of a specimen that has been fully polished. However, some useful information may be obtained from specimens prepared to various degrees of finishing. Table 2 lists the steps used in a typical specimen preparation procedure and indicates tests that may be performed at various stages.

**Table 2   A systematic approach to foundry metallography**

| Abrasive step | Tests available |
|---|---|
| Sectioning ........... | ... |
| Rough grinding (60-180 grit) ............... | Brinell hardness (HB); gross defects; geometry Macroetched specimens: porosity; segregation; dendritic structure |
| Mounting ............ | ... |
| Fine grinding (240, 320, 400, 600 grit) ........ | Rockwell hardness (HR); diamond pyramid hardness; rough graphite typing |
| Rough polishing (6 μm) | ... |
| Final polishing (0.05 μm) ............... | Microhardness; defect study; precise graphite typing (ASTM A 247); phase identification; volume fraction; photomicrography |

**Sampling.** Specimens for metallographic examination can be obtained in various ways. Smaller castings, if expendable, can be cut to produce specimens for preparation and analysis. It may be useful to destroy large castings that have been rejected by nondestructive tests. In such cases, a specimen may be obtained from the bulk materials by any suitable method if care is taken to avoid accidentally altering the microstructure.

Standard test bars, such as microlugs, keel blocks, and ears, are more practical sources of metallographic specimens that do not require destruction of the casting. However, interpretation of microstructures from these sources must be tentative, because their geometry, which is different from the actual casting, may produce microstructures that do not represent the bulk material.

**Sectioning** is performed to reduce the specimen to a reasonable size for further preparation. Such devices as band saws or flame cutters may be used to remove rough bulk specimens from larger castings, but the surface they produce may require secondary cutting or substantial grinding to eliminate

**Table 1   Effect of microstructure on properties of ferrous casting alloys**

| Microstructure | Identity | Impact |
|---|---|---|
| Austenite ................. | Soft phase that forms first; usually transforms into other phases; seen only in certain alloys | Soft and ductile; low strength |
| Ferrite .................... | Iron with elements in solid solution; soft matrix phase | Contributes ductility, but little strength |
| Graphite ................. | Free carbon in any size and shape | Improves machinability and damping properties, reduces shrinkage, and may reduce strength severely depending on shape |
| Cementite ................. | Iron carbide hard intermetallic phase | Imparts hardness and wear resistance; severely reduces machinability |
| Pearlite ................. | Lamellar phase consisting of alternate layers of ferrite and cementite | Contributes strength without brittleness and has good machinability |
| Martensite ................ | Hard structure produced by specific thermal treatment | Hardest transformation structure; brittle unless tempered |
| Steadite .................... | Iron-carbon-phosphorus eutectic; hard and brittle | Sometimes confused with ledeburite; aids fluidity in molten state, but is brittle in solid state |
| Ledeburite ................ | Massive eutectic phase composed of cementite and austenite; transforms to cementite and pearlite upon cooling | Produces high hardness and wear resistance; virtually unmachinable |

gross deformation and to produce a flat surface.

Abrasive cutters are preferred, because they can produce flat surfaces with low deformation, obviating subsequent heavy grinding. When correctly performed, abrasive cutting produces suitable specimens in less time than other methods and with greater assurance that the microstructure has not been altered. If possible, the abrasive cutter should be maintained by the laboratory and used only for cutting metallographic specimens.

The abrasive wheels used must be recommended for the alloy being cut. Alumina ($Al_2O_3$) abrasive wheels are generally best for ferrous alloys. Wheels with harder, denser bonds are used for cutting softer alloys, such as gray and ductile irons. Softer bond grades are recommended for cutting harder alloys, such as white iron, or softer alloys that have been hardened by heat treatment.

Successful abrasive cutting also requires adequate cooling to minimize heating the cut surface. Modest pressure and feed rate will prevent sample burn and premature wheel failure. The actual specimen size depends on the nature of the investigation, but in general the larger the specimen, the more difficult the preparation. For manual preparation, the specimen size should not exceed 25 mm (1 in.) square by 10 mm (³/₈ in.) high.

**Mounting.** It is possible to prepare metallographic specimens without mounting if the edges are beveled to prevent snagging of the abrasive papers and polishing cloths. However, this beveling prevents examination of specimen edges. This is a particular problem when heat-treated castings, such as camshafts and gears, must be examined for case depth. Mounting is recommended to keep the specimen edges flat and to provide a safe, convenient means of holding the specimen during preparation (see the article "Mounting of Specimens" in this Volume).

Compression molding is a rapid and economical method of mounting solid metal specimens. The specimen and a suitable resin are placed in the mold cylinder and heated under pressure to produce a solid cured mount in 4 to 8 min, depending on the mold size and the resin selected. The specimen should be thoroughly cleaned before mounting.

Phenolic resins, such as Bakelite, are the best compression-molding mediums for routine mounting of most common ferrous alloys. For white irons and hardened alloys, epoxy thermosetting resins containing hard fillers are recommended, because they are more wear resistant and therefore provide better edge protection. Room-temperature curing (castable) resins, which do not require the application of high temperatures and pressures, may also be used.

**Grinding.** Coarse grinding using 60- to 180-grit abrasives is performed to correct out-of-flat conditions on the surface as well as to remove resin flash, to produce a common plane between the specimen and the mounting resin, and to bevel the edge of the mount to prevent snagging. It is also possible to produce a beveled edge without a separate grinding; the beveled edge is created during mounting by a specially designed mold. Rough grinding may be performed using a belt grinder or a rotating-wheel disk grinder and an appropriate coolant.

Fine grinding involves abrading the specimen using a series of abrasive papers of decreasing grit size, usually 240 to 600 grit. Each successive grinding operation should replace the deformation from the previous step with less abrasive damage. This operation may be variously performed, depending on the skill of the technician and the number of specimens required per day. Fine grinding can be performed using a manual grinder with four stationary positions, each devoted to a different abrasive size in the typical sequence of 240, 320, 400, and 600 grit. Silicon carbide is a commonly used grinding medium. The specimen should be stroked across the abrasive paper, which is usually lubricated with water.

If graphite retention is of primary importance, water is not used in the 400- and 600-grit stages. Figure 1 shows how the use of water lubrication throughout fine grinding removes graphite. This condition continues to decline during cloth polishing. Figure 2 illustrates how graphite remains intact when the 400- and 600-grit steps are performed dry. However, water lubrication is necessary with the 240- and 320-grit grindings to minimize heat and deformation. When the scratches from the previous step have been removed, four or five additional strokes should be applied to ensure complete removal of prior deformation. Before proceeding to the next step, the specimen is rotated 90° to provide a visual reference. This helps to determine completion of the next step.

Fine grinding can also be performed using belt or disk grinders equipped with similar abrasives. This method offers increased specimen output and is particularly helpful in preparing white iron, alloy irons, and heat-treated alloys. Water must be used to lubricate and to control frictional heat, except for graphite-retaining procedures. Power grinders eliminate the need to supply horizontal motion, allowing the operator to concentrate on pressure application and specimen orientation. When using a disk grinder, the specimen is moved side to side, not in a circular motion against wheel rotation. After fine grinding, the specimen surface should appear similar to that shown in Fig. 2. A rough graphite-type identification may be made at this point.

**Polishing.** After thorough cleaning, the specimen is rough polished on a rotating wheel covered with napless cloth and charged with micron-graded diamond abrasive. Formerly, this operation was performed using a napped cloth charged with 5- to 0.3-μm $Al_2O_3$. Although the results were acceptable, there was a tendency toward edge rounding, microstructural relief, and graphite plucking, because of the excessively long polishing times dictated by low material-removal rates. The use of diamond abrasives on napless cloths enables rapid removal of fine grinding scratches, leaving a surface with superior flatness and edge retention.

To achieve optimum graphite retention, silk cloth should be charged with 3-μm diamond paste and a modest amount of extender (lapping oil or fluid). The specimen is moved side to side using medium to heavy pressure. Through-hardened alloys, alloy irons, and white iron require 6- and 1-μm rough polishings to remove deformation and scratches while maintaining surface flatness. For these alloys, the specimen is rotated

**Fig. 1, 2** The effect of wet versus dry fine-grinding procedures on graphite retention. Fig. 1: water lubrication was used throughout grinding, and graphite was pulled out of the structure. Fig. 2: fine grinding was performed dry, and graphite was retained. Not polished, not etched. Both at 255×

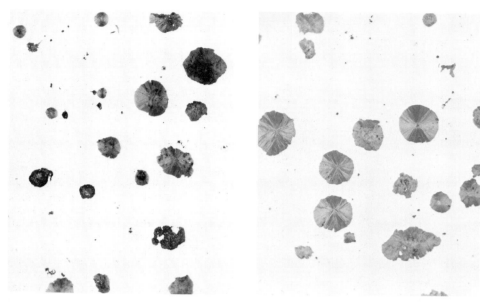

**Fig. 3, 4** Effect of cloth selection on final polishing results. Graphite, even if retained during grinding, can be pulled out during polishing. Fig. 3: the specimen was polished using 0.05-μm Al₂O₃ on a red felt cloth, and graphite was removed. Fig. 4: the specimen was polished using 0.05-μm Al₂O₃ on synthetic rayon cloth, and graphite was retained. As-polished. Both at 130×

counter to wheel rotation using heavy pressure to prevent directional polishing lines. Rough polishing should be performed thoroughly; there is little danger of overpolishing using diamond abrasives on a napless cloth.

Fine polishing must remove all remaining deformation and scratches to produce a smooth, highly reflective surface for microscopic examination. Final polishing is usually performed using a suspension of 0.05-μm Al₂O₃ on a short-nap cloth. The cloth should be wet enough to provide adequate lubrication, but not so wet as to hydroplane the specimen. This latter condition extends polishing times, causing edge rounding, microstructural relief, and pulled-out graphite.

To prevent graphite washout, the specimen should be held against the rotating wheel in a more or less fixed position for approximately 1 min. It is then rotated slowly on its own axis for an additional 30 to 40 s to prevent comet tailing (directional polishing lines).

Final polishing results depend on cloth selection, cloth wetness, and manual technique. Figure 3 shows how the wrong cloth, excessive wetness, and poor technique can remove graphite even after satisfactory fine grinding and rough polishing. Figure 4 illustrates the excellent results possible when the correct cloth is selected, the moisture content is appropriate, and correct manual technique is used. Specimens of harder alloys, such as the white iron shown in Fig. 5, are finished by rotation counter to wheel rotation. With all alloys, hard and soft, the briefest final polishing and the least amount of moisture should be used.

When final polishing is complete, the specimen is washed thoroughly to remove all polishing debris. Because Al₂O₃ abrasive particles cling to the metal surface, it is necessary

to wipe a cotton swab saturated with a detergent solution lightly across the polished surface. It may be helpful to use an ethyl alcohol rinse after the water wash to hasten drying and prevent corrosion; use of a forced-air dryer is also helpful. Blow drying with compressed air is not recommended due to the possible presence of contaminants.

Upon completion of polishing, the specimen is microscopically examined at 50 to 100× to determine the quality of the polish. Table 3 lists various polishing defects, their probable causes, and recommended preventive steps. Minor problems, such as fine scratches or mildly pulled-out graphite, may be corrected using a simple etch-polish sequence described below. More serious problems, such as coarse scratches, gross rounding, relief, and severely pulled-out graphite, are corrected only by returning to an earlier stage of preparation—for example, 600-grit

**Fig. 5** White iron, polished to reveal minimum structural relief. Harder alloys, such as this specimen, should be rotated counter to wheel rotation during final polishing to prevent directional polishing lines. Vilella's reagent. 530×

fine grinding—and repeating the normal polishing sequence from that point. Extended final polishing will only worsen serious problems.

The technique described above is a proven procedure that is used to prepare small to moderate numbers of specimens. Larger foundries that exercise close quality control may require greater numbers of polished specimens for microscopic examination. In such cases, use of automated equipment may be necessary to prepare sufficient numbers of specimens quickly and cost efficiently. Although the basic principles previously described apply, some slight modifications may be necessary due to the larger surface areas involved.

**Etching.** A limited amount of information may be obtained from as-polished specimens (see Fig. 6); graphite may be rated, and such defects as entrapments, shrinkage, and porosity are visible. However, etched specimens yield the most information. Microetching reveals the microstructure by selective dissolution of sensitive areas, such as grain and phase boundaries. Etchants usually consist of mineral acids in a water or alcohol solution. Nital, the most versatile etchant for revealing ferrous microstructures, consists of 2 to 5% nitric acid (HNO₃) in alcohol. Figure 7 shows a ductile iron that has been etched in 2% nital to reveal a bull's-eye microstructure of approximately equal parts of ferrite and pearlite. The etchant may be applied by immersion or by swabbing the polished surface for 3 to 8 s, depending on the alloy. Highly alloyed, corrosion-resistant irons require more aggressive etchants. Some of the more commonly used etchants are listed in Table 4.

Figures 8 and 9 illustrate the effects of different etchants on the same microstructure. Figure 8 depicts the results of using nital to reveal steadite in a gray iron; Fig. 9, the results of using alcoholic ferric chloride (FeCl₃). This etchant darkens the matrix to contrast the steadite microstructure. Etching may also be performed at other stages of specimen preparation. As-cut and ground surfaces may be macroetched to reveal gross imperfections, such as shrinkage, cold shuts, and severe segregation of constituents. One macroetchant is listed in Table 4.

Microetching may also be used to improve the surfaces of as-polished specimens. Even with extreme care, it is sometimes difficult to remove the last traces of fine scratches and slightly pulled-out graphite. The condition of the polished surface may be improved by applying the etchant briefly, then eliminating its effects by polishing in the final steps only long enough to remove etched layers. This etch-polish procedure may be repeated several times to improve the surface, but will eventually cause pitting if performed too many times.

The same cursory, low-magnification examination given as-polished specimens should be performed after etching. During this examination, it is easy to estimate phase

**Table 3   Specimen preparation problems and solutions**

| Preparation defect | Involved alloys | Cause | Suggested solutions |
|---|---|---|---|
| Pulled-out graphite | All graphitic iron | Excessive moisture | No H$_2$O on 400- and 600-grit fine grind; etch-polish sequence after final polish; repeat from 600 grit |
| Scratches | Most nonferrous alloys | Coarse: previous scratches not removed; debris from mount shrinkage<br>Fine: cloth contamination | Thorough preparation steps; use epoxy mounts; change cloths; etch-polish sequence; cleaner lab conditions |
| Rounded edges | Heat-treated castings | Poor edge protection; excessive fine polishing | Epoxy mounts with hard fillers; double rough polishing step with diamond abrasives; minimum final polish |
| Microstructural relief | White iron, alloy irons | Ineffective rough polishing; excessive fine polish; highly napped cloths | Longer or double rough polish with diamond; use napless rough polish; minimum final polish |
| Surface undulations; unclear microstructure | Ferritic and austenitic irons | Excessive surface deformation | Thorough sequence; lighter pressures on final polish; etch-polish sequence |

distribution—for example, percentages of pearlite and ferrite. Magnifications from 100 to 500× are required principally to resolve fine carbide, steadite, and pearlite for more positive identification.

## Microstructures

Graphitic cast irons, including those that contain small amounts of alloying elements, are classified as gray, ductile, and malleable

**Fig. 6** A specimen of gray iron, illustrating the minimum amount of information revealed without etching. Graphite may be rated, and defects may be examined, but microstructural detail is best seen after etching. Compare with Fig. 7. As-polished. 105×

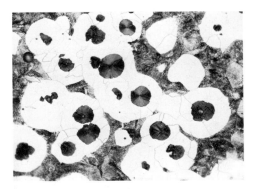

**Fig. 7** Ductile iron, with the bull's-eye structure of graphite nodules surrounded by ferrite revealed by etching. Matrix is pearlite. 2% nital. 105×

according to graphite shape and method of graphite production. More highly alloyed graphitic and white irons are classified by their in-service requirements, such as abrasion-resistant, heat-resistant, and corrosion-resistant.

**Gray iron** contains graphite in the form of flakes. The matrix phase is normally pearlitic; additions of approximately 15% Ni produce an austenite matrix. Figures 10 to 14 illustrate various distributions of graphite flakes in gray iron.

The basic structure of gray iron can be altered by changing the cooling rate of the casting. Cooling too quickly is likely to produce free cementite. Very slow cooling usually produces free ferrite.

Gray iron is classified in ASTM A 48 (Ref 1) according to the minimum tensile strength of separately cast test bars. For example, Class 20A refers to a size A test bar 22 mm (0.88 in.) in nominal diameter with a minimum tensile strength of 138 MPa (20 ksi).

**Ductile iron** contains graphite in the form of nodules, which develop when alloying elements, such as magnesium, are added to the melt. The as-cast microstructure normally consists of graphite nodules surrounded by ferrite (bull's-eye structure) in a matrix of pearlite and may also include some free cementite. Annealing produces secondary graphite, surrounding the primary graphite nodules, in a ferrite matrix.

Ductile iron is classified in ASTM A 536 (Ref 2); for example, Grade 60-40-18 refers to cast test coupons with minimum 414 MPa (60 ksi) tensile strength, 276 MPa (40 ksi) yield strength, and 18% elongation in 51 mm (2 in.). ASTM A 439 (Ref 3) classifies nine austenitic ductile irons according to composition and mechanical properties.

**White iron** is virtually free of graphite through the casting and is obtained by selecting alloy composition to inhibit graphitization.

**Malleable iron** is the result of annealing white iron castings to convert carbon contained in cementite to graphite in the form of temper-carbon nodules. Malleable iron can be ferritic or pearlitic, depending on the annealing process used.

Five-digit designations are assigned in ASTM A 47 (Ref 4), which covers two grades of ferritic malleable iron, and in A 220 (Ref 5), which deals with pearlitic. The first three digits indicate the minimum yield strength (× 100 psi), and the last two indicate the minimum percent elongation in 51 mm (2 in.). Another standard, ASTM A 602 (Ref 6), covers both types of malleable iron; it assigns an "M" and four digits. The first two digits are typical yield strength in ksi, and the last two are typical percent elongation in 51-mm (2-in.) test specimens cut from actual cast parts.

**Abrasion-resistant cast iron** consists of: (1) graphitic iron that has been cast against a chill set at the area of the surface requiring abrasion resistance and (2) white iron, which may or may not be cast against a chill. Microstructures may be pearlitic, austenitic, or martensitic. Three classes of abrasion-resistant martensitic white iron are covered in ASTM A 532 (Ref 7): type I (nickel-chromium), type II (chromium-molybdenum), and type III (high-chromium).

**Corrosion-resistant cast irons** may be high-silicon gray iron, high-chromium white iron, or high-nickel austenitic gray or ductile irons, as specified in ASTM A 518 (Ref 8) and ASTM A 436 (Ref 9).

**Heat-resistant cast irons** include silicon gray and ductile irons, chromium gray and white irons, and high-nickel austenitic gray and ductile irons. Chromium gray irons are covered in ASTM A 319 (Ref 10).

**Table 4   Some common etchants for ferrous cast alloys**

| Etchant | Function | Composition | Application |
|---|---|---|---|
| Al-7 | Macroetch | 50 mL HCl and 50 mL H$_2$O | Dip at 70-80 °C (160-175 °F) |
| Nital | General-purpose etch for iron and steels | 2-10 mL HNO$_3$ and 90-98 mL ethanol or methanol | Swab |
| Villela's | High-carbon cast steels | 5 mL HCl, 100 mL ethanol or methanol, and 1 g picric acid | Swab |
| Persulfate | Darkens matrix to show carbides | 10 g (NH$_4$)$_2$S$_2$O$_8$ (ammonium persulfate) and 100 mL H$_2$O | Dip until matrix is darkened. |
| Ferric chloride | Contrasts steadite; general microetch for higher alloys | 60 mL HCl, 20 g FeCl$_3$, and 300 mL ethanol or methanol | Swab |
| Chromic electrolytic | Microstructure of corrosion-resistant alloys | 10 g CrO$_3$ and 90 mL H$_2$O | 3-5 V dc |

Note: Only reagent grade ethanol or methanol should be used. Use of isopropyl alchohol poses serious safety hazards.

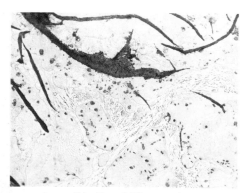 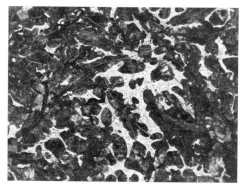

**Fig. 8, 9** The effect of different etchants on the same gray iron microstructure containing steadite. Fig. 8: use of 2% nital to reveal the general microstructure. Fig. 9: the results of using alcoholic FeCl₃. This etchant darkens the matrix to contrast the steadite microstructure. Both at 100×

**Graphite** found in cast irons is classified in ASTM A 247 (Ref 11). Distribution and orientation types are lettered A through E. Size numbers range from 1 (largest) to 8; form types I through VI are nodular, and type VII is in flake form. For more information on compositions, microstructures, and properties of cast irons, see the section "Cast Irons" in Volume 1 of the 9th Edition of *Metals Handbook*.

## REFERENCES

1. "Standard Specification for Gray Iron Castings," A 48, *Annual Book of ASTM Standards*, Vol 01.02, ASTM, Philadelphia, 1984, p 20-26

2. "Standard Specification for Ductile Iron Castings," A 536, *Annual Book of ASTM Standards*, Vol 01.02, ASTM, Philadelphia, 1984, p 343-347

3. "Standard Specification for Austenitic Ductile Iron Castings," A 439, *Annual Book of ASTM Standards*, Vol 01.02, ASTM, Philadelphia, 1984, p 267-273

4. "Standard Specification for Malleable Iron Castings," A 47, *Annual Book of ASTM Standards*, Vol 01.02, ASTM, Philadelphia, 1984, p 11-19

5. "Standard Specification for Pearlitic Malleable Iron Castings," A 220, *Annual Book of ASTM Standards*, Vol 01.02, ASTM, Philadelphia, 1984, p 123-132

6. "Standard Specification for Automotive Malleable Iron Castings," A 602, *Annual Book of ASTM Standards*, Vol 01.02, ASTM, Philadelphia, 1984, p 382-388

7. "Standard Specification for Abrasion-Resistant Cast Irons," A 532, *Annual Book of ASTM Standards*, Vol 01.02, ASTM, Philadelphia, 1984, p 339-342

8. "Standard Specification for Corrosion-Resistant High-Silicon Iron Castings," A 518, *Annual Book of ASTM Standards*, Vol 01.02, ASTM, Philadelphia, 1984, p 332-338

9. "Standard Specification for Austenitic Gray Iron Castings," A 436, *Annual Book of ASTM Standards*, Vol 01.02, ASTM, Philadelphia, 1984, p 256-261

10. "Standard Specification for Gray Iron Castings For Elevated Temperatures for Non-Pressure Containing Parts," A 319, *Annual Book of ASTM Standards*, Vol 01.02, ASTM, Philadelphia, 1984, p 146-148

11. "Standard Method for Evaluating the Microstructure of Graphite in Iron Castings," A 247, *Annual Book of ASTM Standards*, Vol 01.02, ASTM, Philadelphia, 1984, p 133-135

**Fig. 10** Gray iron, showing type A distribution of graphite flakes (uniform distribution and random orientation). As-polished. 100×

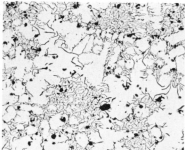

**Fig. 11** Gray iron, showing type B distribution of graphite (rosette grouping and random orientation). As-polished. 100×

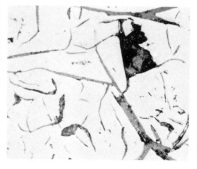

**Fig. 12** Gray iron, showing type C graphite distribution characterized by superimposed flake size and random orientation. As-polished. 100×

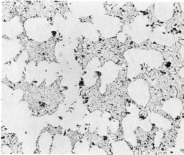

**Fig. 13** Gray iron, showing type D graphite distribution (interdendritic segregation and random orientation). As-polished. 100×

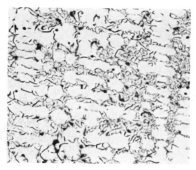

**Fig. 14** Gray iron, showing type E graphite distribution characterized by interdendritic distribution and preferred orientation. As-polished. 100×

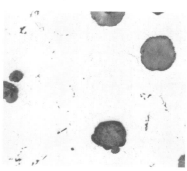

**Fig. 15** Fe-3.29C-2.40Si-0.054Mg ductile iron tube, centrifugally cast. Structure shows graphite nodules of sizes 4 and 5. As-polished. 100×

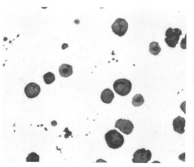

**Fig. 16** Fe-3.40C-2.51Si-0.067Mg ductile iron tube, centrifugally cast, showing graphite nodules of size 6. As-polished. 100×

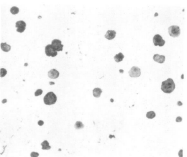

**Fig. 17** Fe-3.30C-2.25Si-0.082Mg ductile iron tube, centrifugally cast. Structure shows graphite nodules of sizes 6 and 7. As-polished. 100×

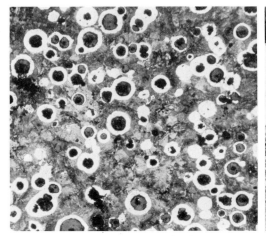

**Fig. 18** Grade 80-55-06 pearlitic ductile iron, as-cast. Typical bull's-eye structure of graphite nodules surrounded by ferrite in a matrix of pearlite. 3% nital. 100×

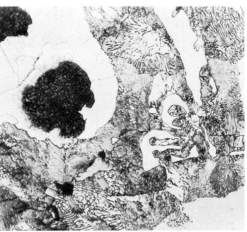

**Fig. 19** Grade 60-45-12 pearlitic ductile iron, as-cast. Same structure as Fig. 18, but higher magnification shows the free carbide (white) in the pearlite matrix. 2% nital. 525×

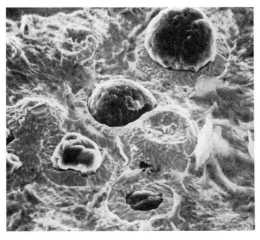

**Fig. 20** Scanning electron micrograph of as-cast pearlitic ductile iron. Matrix has been etched away to reveal secondary graphite and bull's-eye ferrite around primary graphite nodules. 3:1 methyl acetate-liquid bromine. 475×

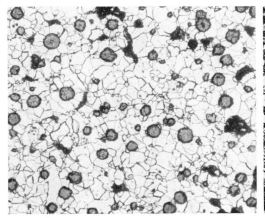

**Fig. 21** Same iron as Fig. 18, annealed 6 h at 790 °C (1450 °F) and furnace cooled to grade 60-40-18. Most of the original pearlite has decomposed into a matrix of free ferrite (light) and 5% (approx.) pearlite (black, irregular). 3% nital. 100×

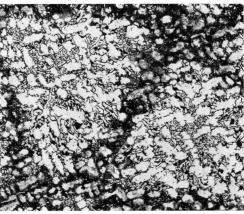

**Fig. 22** Class 20 gray iron, stress relieved 1 h between 605 and 620 °C (1125 and 1150 °F). Structure consists of type D graphite flakes in a matrix of ferrite with dark bands of pearlite at the cell boundaries. 3% picral. 100×

**Fig. 23** Class 30 gray iron, as-cast. Structure is type A graphite flakes in a matrix of pearlite. 3% nital. 500×

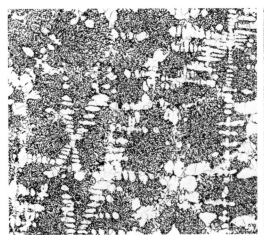

**Fig. 24** Class 30 gray iron, cast in a permanent mold, then annealed 45 min at 885 °C (1625 °F) and furnace cooled. Ferrite dendrites and type D graphite in a ferrite matrix. 3% nital. 100×

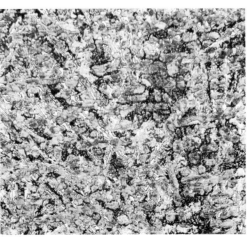

**Fig. 25** Class 40 gray iron, as-cast. Structure is type D, size 7 graphite flakes in matrix of fine pearlite. Numerous carbide particles (light) are the result of rapid solidification. 2% nital. 100×

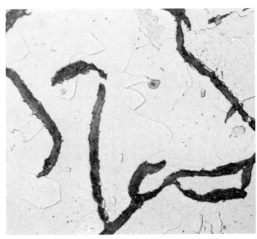

**Fig. 26** Same as Fig. 25, except annealed by holding 3 h at 790 °C (1450 °F), cooling at 20 °C (40 °F) per h to 690 °C (1275 °F), holding 4 h, and furnace cooling. Graphite and remnants of spheroidized pearlite in ferrite matrix. 2% nital. 750×

**Fig. 27** Class 50 gray iron, as-cast. Matrix is fine pearlite with some free carbide (white) that may have resulted from rapid solidification. 2% nital. 750×

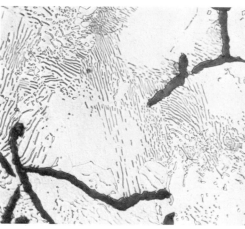

**Fig. 28** Same as Fig. 27, but held 3 h at 900 °C (1650 °F), cooled at 20 °C (40 °F) per hour to 690 °C (1275 °F), held 5 h, and furnace cooled. The free carbide and much of the pearlite have been converted to graphite and free ferrite. 2% nital. 750×

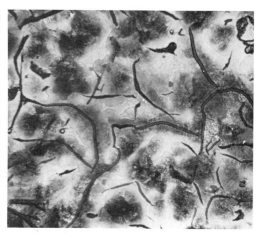

**Fig. 29** Fe-3.85C-2.65Si-0.10S-0.30P-0.65Mn-0.12Cr gray iron, as sand cast. Structure consists of a broken network of steadite (light, irregular areas) in a matrix of fine pearlite. 5% nital. 500×

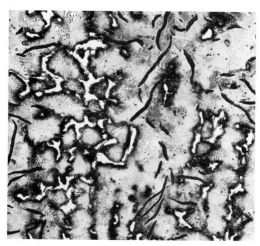

**Fig. 30, 31** Fe-3.26C-1.75Si-0.06P-0.11S-0.63Mn-0.52Cr-0.98Mo-0.064Sn gray iron, as sand cast. Fig. 30 (100×): type A graphite in a pearlite matrix, with some free carbide (white, outlined). Fig. 31: higher magnification (500×) shows that the pearlite matrix contains fine and coarse lamellae. 4% picral

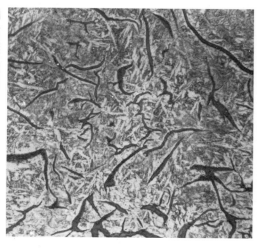

**Fig. 32** Fe-3.80C-2.55Si-0.3P-0.7Mn-0.3Cr-0.65Mo-1.5Cu gray iron, stress relieved at 595 °C (1100 °F). Structure is acicular bainite (light gray) in fine pearlite (dark gray) and graphite (black). 5% nital. 500×

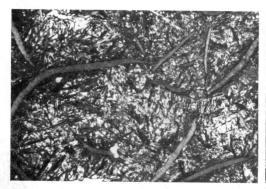

**Fig. 33** Class 30B gray iron (Fe-3.54C-2.17Si), austenitized at 870 °C (1600 °F) and oil quenched. Type A graphite in a matrix of martensite (dark), some carbide particles (light, outlined), and retained austenite (white). 2% nital. 500×

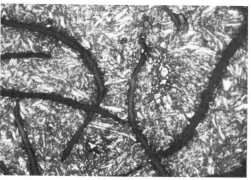

**Fig. 34** Same as Fig. 33, except tempered at 480 °C (900 °F) after quenching. Type A graphite flakes in a matrix of tempered martensite. Compare with Fig. 35. 2% nital. 500×

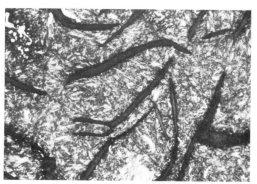

**Fig. 35** Same as Fig. 33, except tempered at 540 °C (1000 °F) after quenching. Type A graphite flakes in a matrix of tempered martensite. 2% nital. 500×

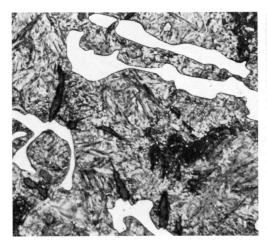

**Fig. 36** Fe-0.8-1.1Cr-0.4-0.6Mo alloy gray iron, austenitized at 870 °C (1600 °F) and oil quenched. Type A graphite, carbide particles (white), and a small amount of retained austenite in a matrix of fine martensite. Compare with Fig. 37. 3% nital. 750×

**Fig. 37** Same as Fig. 36, but austenitized at 980 °C (1800 °F) and oil quenched. Structure shows effects of austenitizing at too high a temperature: matrix is coarser martensite and contains large amounts of retained austenite (light areas). 3% nital. 750×

**Fig. 38** Fe-3.05C-2.11Si-0.83Mn-0.12Cr-0.05Ni-0.17Mo alloy gray iron, flame hardened. Type A graphite in a pearlite matrix in the core (left) and in a matrix of tempered martensite in the case (right). See also Fig. 39 and 40. Vilella's reagent. 50×

**Fig. 39** Same as Fig. 38, showing the unhardened core (241 HB) at a higher magnification. Type A graphite in a matrix consisting essentially of pearlite. 2% nital + 4% picral. 500×

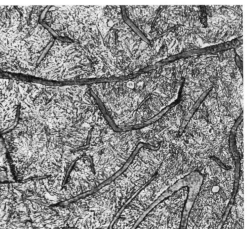

**Fig. 40** Same as Fig. 38, this time showing the flame-hardened case (601 HB) at a higher magnification. Type A graphite flakes in a matrix of tempered martensite. 2% nital. 500×

**Fig. 41** Class 35 gray iron, as-cast against a chill. White iron in the chilled zone shows free ferrite (light), cementite (light, outlined), and patches of

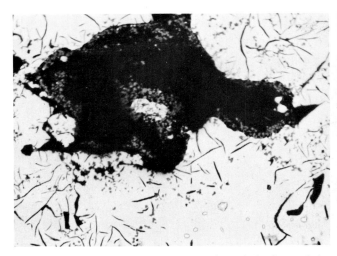

**Fig. 42** Class 30 gray iron, showing a slag inclusion (large, dark area) that was trapped in the stream of molten metal during pouring. As-polished. 200×

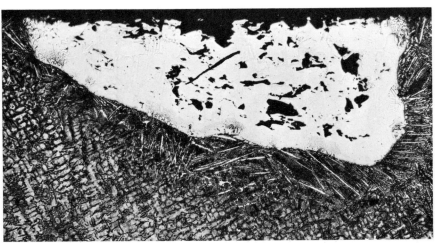

**Fig. 43** Class 30B gray iron with an entrapped particle of ferrosilicon inoculant (large, light area). The particle chilled the adjacent area and caused plates of free cementite (light needles) to form around the inclusion. Saturated picral. 50×

**Fig. 44** Class 20 gray iron, with surface partly removed to reveal porosity (row of small holes) caused by gas entrapment during solidification. Not polished, not etched. 2×

**Fig. 45** Class 30B gray iron, with areas of steadite (eutectic of small, rounded particles in light-colored ferrite) and type A graphite in a pearlite matrix. 3% nital. 1500×

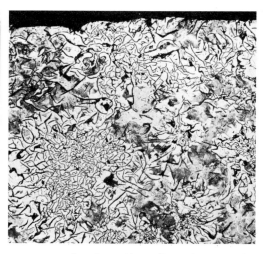

**Fig. 46** Gray iron, with an abnormal structure of type B graphite and excessive ferrite in pearlite matrix. This microstructure resulted in poor strength and wear resistance. 4% nital. 100×

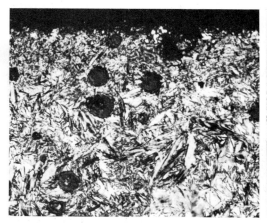

**Fig. 47** Grade 80-55-06 ductile iron, flame hardened. Hardened zone shows graphite nodules in matrix of martensite (dark) and some retained austenite (white). Compare with Fig. 48 and 49. 3% nital. 500×

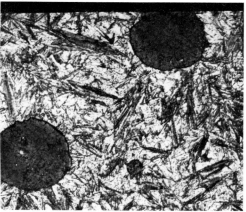

**Fig. 48** Same as Fig. 47, but cast in a thicker section. Slower cooling resulted in larger graphite nodules. Compare with Fig. 49. 2% nital. 500×

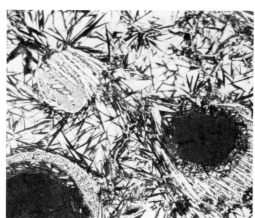

**Fig. 49** Same as Fig. 47, except overheated during flame hardening. Basically same structure as previous two figures, but carbide at rims of graphite nodules is evidence of incipient melting. 2% nital. 500×

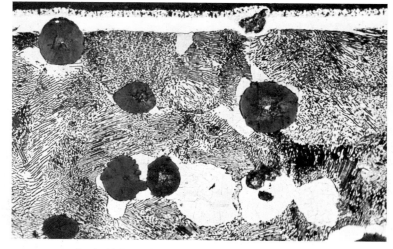

**Fig. 50** Grade 80-55-06 ductile iron, liquid nitrided 3 h in a salt bath at 570 °C (1060 °F) and water quenched. Surface layer of iron nitride (white) has porous skin; substrate consists of graphite nodules in a matrix of pearlite and free ferrite. Compare with Fig. 51. 3% picral. 500×

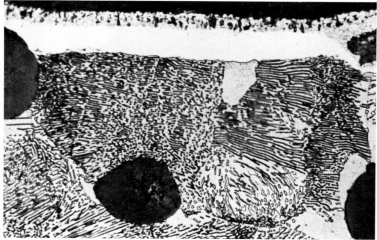

**Fig. 51** Same as Fig. 50, except at higher magnification, which reveals details of the graphite nodules, the pearlite matrix (alternating lamellae of ferrite and darker cementite), and the porous skin of the iron nitride surface layer. 3% picral. 1000×

**Fig. 52** Shielded metal arc surface weld on grade 60-45-12 ductile iron, nickel-iron filler metal. Structures are the weld deposit (light, top), the dark heat-affected zone in the middle, and the base metal at bottom. See also Fig. 53. 4% picral. 12×

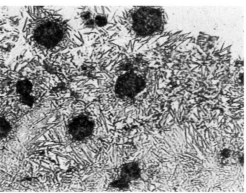

**Fig. 53** Heat-affected zone of the weld in Fig. 52. Graphite nodules in a matrix of martensite and some retained austenite. 4% picral. 250×

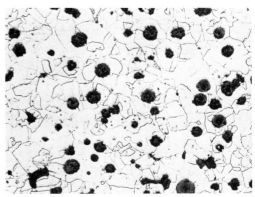

**Fig. 54** Grade 60-45-12 ductile iron, 90-mm (3.5-in.) section thickness, as-cast. Graphite nodules in a ferrite matrix produced by addition of a calcium silicon compound during pouring. 2% nital. 100×

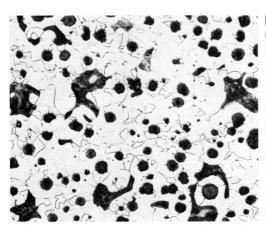

**Fig. 55** Same iron as Fig. 54, as-cast in a 25-mm (1-in.) section. The faster cooling rate of the thinner section produced some fine pearlite (irregular dark areas) in the ferrite matrix. 2% nital. 100×

**Fig. 56** Grade 65-45-12 ductile iron, liquid nitrided 3 h in a salt bath at 570 °C (1060 °F) and quenched in water. Graphite nodules in a matrix of free ferrite (light) with some pearlite (gray, irregular) and the white layer of iron nitride on the surface. 3% picral. 500×

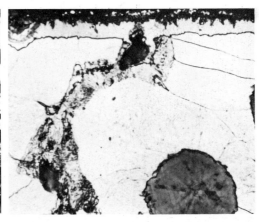

**Fig. 57** Same as Fig. 56, except at higher magnification to reveal details of the iron nitride surface layer and of the graphite nodules and patches of pearlite. Note the porous skin of the surface layer. 3% picral. 1000×

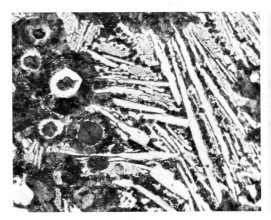

**Fig. 58** Grade 80-55-06 ductile iron, as-cast. Microstructure of the centerline chill shown in Fig. 59. Massive carbide platelets (white) that resist decomposition during annealing in a matrix of pearlite and bull's-eye ferrite. 4% picral. 250×

**Fig. 59** Section through ductile iron casting, showing centerline chill (light area) in an alloy-enriched zone that was the last to solidify. 10% $(NH_4)_2S_2O_8$. Actual size

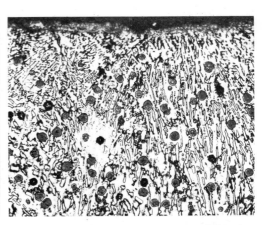

**Fig. 60** Ductile iron, as-cast against a chill (top). Structure of the chilled zone consists of small graphite nodules and columnar cementite (light, outlined) in a matrix of free ferrite. 2% nital. 250×

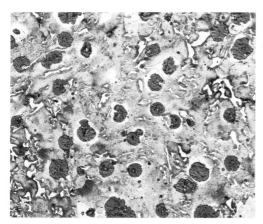

**Fig. 61** Grade 80-55-06 ductile iron, as-cast. Structure shows an excessive amount of free carbide particles (light, outlined) together with graphite nodules enveloped in free ferrite. Matrix is pearlite. 2% nital. 100×

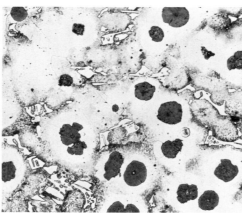

**Fig. 62** Grade 80-55-06 ductile iron, as-cast. Same constituents as in Fig. 61, with a larger amount of free ferrite surrounding the graphite. Compare with Fig. 63. 2% nital. 250×

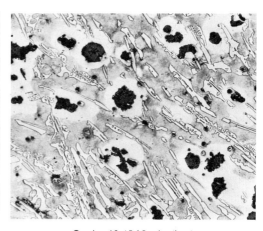

**Fig. 63** Grade 60-45-12 ductile iron, as-cast. Structure is similar to Fig. 61 and 62, but free carbide is more columnar. Excessive amounts of free carbide impair ductility and machinability of the casting. 2% nital. 100×

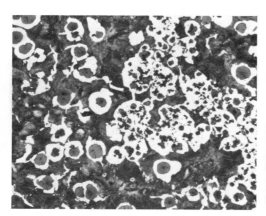

**Fig. 64** Grade 80-55-06 ductile iron, as-cast. Small particles of nonmetallic dross (irregular, gray) and graphite nodules (rounded) dispersed in free ferrite (white areas). The matrix is pearlite. 4% picral. 100×

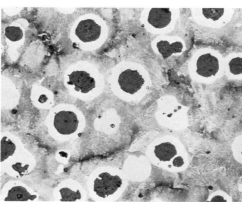

**Fig. 65** Grade 80-55-06 ductile iron, as-cast. The molten metal was held 1 min at 1345 °C (2450 °F) in an induction furnace before pouring. Structure is graphite nodules in envelopes of ferrite in a pearlite matrix. Compare with Fig. 66 and 67. 2% nital. 250×

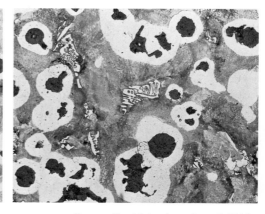

**Fig. 66** Same as Fig. 65, but the melt was held 10 min at 1345 °C (2450 °F) before pouring. The longer holding time caused graphite nodules to deteriorate and some free carbide to form. 2% nital. 250×

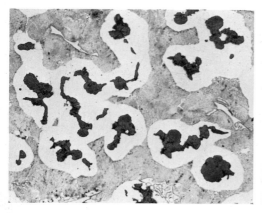

**Fig. 67** Same as Fig. 65, but the molten metal was held 24 min at 1345 °C (2450 °F) before pouring. The increased holding time caused graphite nodules to deteriorate further. 2% nital. 250×

**Fig. 68** Pearlitic malleable iron, first-stage annealed by austenitizing 13.5 h at 970 °C (1780 °F), then air cooled slowly. Temper carbon graphite nodules in envelopes of free ferrite. 2% nital. 500×

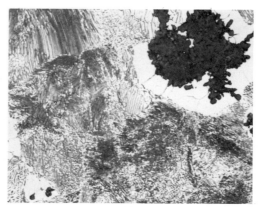

**Fig. 69** Grade 45008 pearlitic malleable iron, first-stage annealed under the same conditions as Fig. 68, then tempered 2 h at 675 °C (1250 °F). Nodules of tempered carbon graphite (black) in bull's-eye ferrite. The pearlite matrix has been slightly spheroidized by tempering. 2% nital. 500×

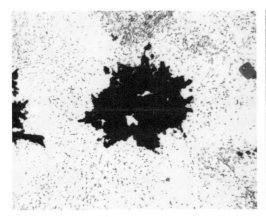

**Fig. 70** Pearlitic malleable iron, first-stage annealed by holding 2 h at 955 °C (1750 °F), then tempered 1 h at 725 °C (1340 °F). Tempered carbon graphite nodules in a pearlite matrix that has been almost completely spheroidized. 2% nital. 500×

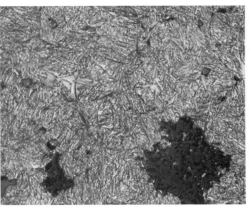

**Fig. 71** Pearlitic malleable iron, first-stage annealed by holding 13.5 h at 945 °C (1730 °F), then oil quenched at 80 °C (180 °F). Nodules of tempered carbon graphite (black) and particles of MnS (gray) in a matrix of tempered martensite. 2% nital. 500×

**Fig. 72** Pearlitic malleable iron, first-stage annealed by holding 2 h at 955 °C (1750 °F), then oil quenched. Specimen was tempered at 260 °C (500 °F) to facilitate polishing. Structure has same constituents as in Fig. 71, except martensite is coarser and some retained austenite (white) is evident. 2% nital. 500×

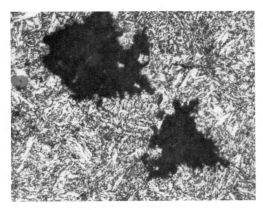

**Fig. 73** Pearlitic malleable iron, first-stage annealed by holding 2 h at 955 °C (1750 °F), oil quenched, then tempered 1 h at 675 °C (1250 °F). Graphite nodules (black) in tempered martensite matrix. Compare with Fig. 74 and 75, which show the effects of increasing tempering temperature. 1% nital. 500×

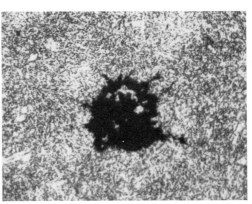

**Fig. 74** Pearlitic malleable iron, first-stage annealed and oil quenched same as Fig. 73, then tempered 1 h at 705 °C (1300 °F). Same constituents as Fig. 73, but higher temperature during tempering has produced many small spheroidal carbide particles. 1% nital. 500×

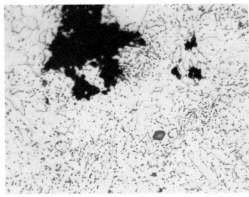

**Fig. 75** Pearlitic malleable iron, first-stage annealed and oil quenched same as Fig. 73, then tempered 1 h at 725 °C (1340 °F). The higher tempering temperature has changed the matrix to granular ferrite. Excess carbon has graphitized. 1% nital. 500×

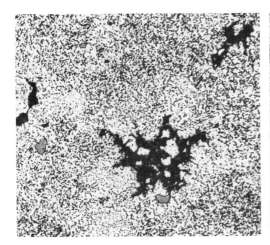

**Fig. 76** Pearlitic malleable iron, held at 860 °C (1580 °F), oil quenched, and tempered at 595 °C (1100 °F). Temper-carbon nodules (black) and MnS particles (gray) in a matrix of tempered martensite. 3% nital. 500×

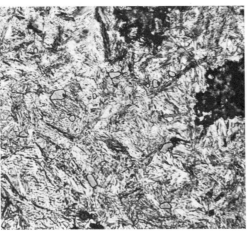

**Fig. 77** Same iron and heat treatment as for Fig. 76, but flame hardened after tempering. Hardened zone at surface has been reconverted to untempered martensite with some retained austenite (white). Compare with Fig. 78. 3% nital. 500×

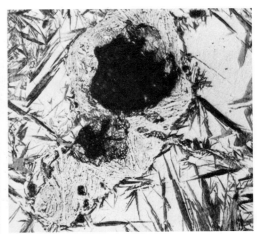

**Fig. 78** Same as Fig. 76, but the specimen was overheated during flame hardening, which caused incipient melting. Diffusion of carbon from the graphite nodules into the matrix to form cementite resulted in voids (black areas). 3% nital. 500×

**Fig. 79** Pearlitic malleable iron, centrifugally cast and first-stage annealed by holding 1 h at 1095 °C (2000 °F) and air cooling. Nodules of temper-carbon graphite (black) in a matrix of fine pearlite. See also Fig. 80. 5% nital. 100×

**Fig. 80** Same pearlitic malleable iron as Fig. 79, but at higher magnification to reveal the presence of less than 5% free ferrite (black) in the matrix of fine pearlite. 5% nital. 500×

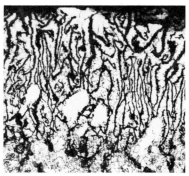

**Fig. 81** Pearlitic malleable iron, with gray iron rim at surface (top) consisting of graphite flakes formed in the white iron, possibly by a reaction of liquid metal with mold gas, in a ferrite matrix. The core is nodules of temper-carbon in a tempered martensite matrix. 1% nital. 100×

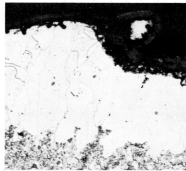

**Fig. 82** Pearlitic malleable iron, with an excessively decarburized surface resulting from a low ratio of CO to $CO_2$ in the furnace atmosphere. Ferrite skin at surface (top) and core of temper-carbon graphite (black) in a matrix of tempered martensite. 1% nital. 100×

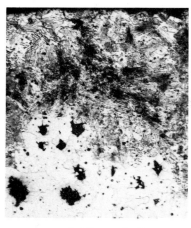

**Fig. 83** Ferritic malleable iron, with insufficiently decarburized surface (top) caused by too high a ratio of CO to $CO_2$ in annealing furnace atmosphere. Structure is a dark rim of pearlite at the surface and a core of temper-carbon graphite in a ferrite matrix. 2% nital. 100×

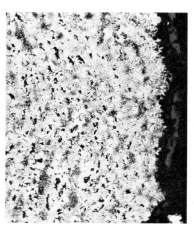

**Fig. 84** Pearlitic malleable iron, containing a crack (right) that formed in the brittle white iron casting before heat treatment. Note increased number and decreased size of graphite nodules and slight decarburization near the crack surface. 2% nital. 50×

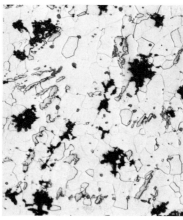

**Fig. 85** Ferritic malleable iron with primary cementite (light, outlined) resulting from incomplete first stage of a two-stage annealing. Other constituents are temper-carbon graphite and a ferrite matrix. 2% nital. 100×

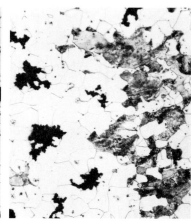

**Fig. 86** Ferritic malleable iron, with an excessive amount of fine pearlite (gray) resulting from incomplete second stage of a two-stage annealing. Also seen are nodules of temper-carbon graphite in a matrix of ferrite. 1% nital. 100×

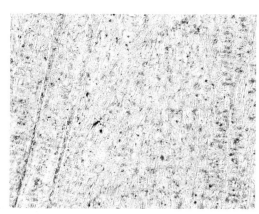
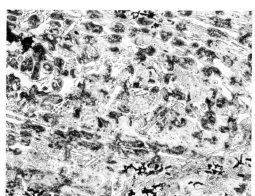

**Fig. 87, 88, 89** Fe-3.25C-0.5Si-2.5Ni-1.5Cr abrasion-resistant cast iron, as-cast against a chill. Fig. 87: white iron near the chill, with a fine dendritic pattern of pearlite (gray) and interdendritic carbide (white). Fig. 88: white iron 51 mm (2 in.) from chill, showing a coarse dendritic pattern of pearlite (gray) and interdendritic carbide (white). Fig. 89: gray iron 102 mm (4 in.) from chill, showing type B graphite flakes in a matrix of fine pearlite with some free ferrite. All etched in 2% nital + 5% picral. 100×

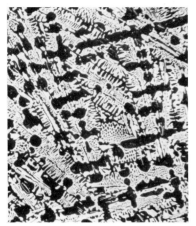

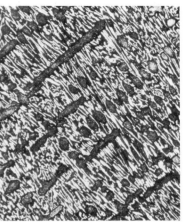

**Fig. 90** Fe-3.3C-0.55Si-2.0Cr-4.2Ni-0.75maxMo, as-cast in a 25-mm (1-in.) diam bar. White iron showing a dendritic pattern of austenite (black) and an interdendritic eutectic of austenite (black dots) and carbide (white). The austenite transforms to martensite during abrasive service. Compare with Fig. 91 and 92. 3% nital. 100×

**Fig. 91** Same iron as Fig. 90, as-cast in a 25-mm (1-in.) thick section. Carbide (white) in a matrix of austenite (gray) containing a few needles of martensite (dark). Size of the microhardness indentations shows the relative hardness of the constituents. 3% nital. 500×

**Fig. 92** Same iron as Fig. 90, except with 4.0% Mo content, as-cast in a 25-mm (1-in.) thick section. Structure is carbide (white) in a matrix of austenite (gray). Sizes of the microhardness indentations indicate the relative hardness of the constituents. 3% nital. 500×

**Fig. 93** High-chromium (Fe-2.7C-26Cr-1.2maxCu-1.0Mn-1.5maxMo-1.5maxNi) abrasion-resistant cast iron, as-cast. White iron shows the interdendritic network of iron-chromium carbide (white) and the dendritic pattern of martensite (gray). 3% nital. 100×

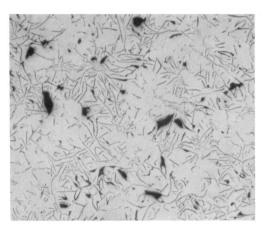

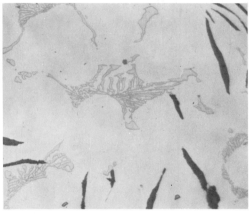

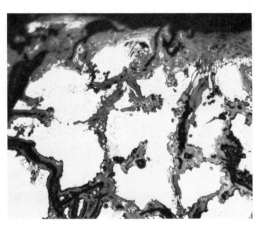

**Fig. 94** High-silicon (14.5% Si) corrosion-resistant iron, as-cast. Gray iron showing type A graphite flakes (dark) in a matrix of iron-silicon ferrite solid solution (light). HNO₃ + HF in glycerol. 100×

**Fig. 95** High-alloy (30Ni-3Cr) corrosion-resistant iron, as-cast. Structure is gray iron showing type A graphite flakes (dark) and some interdendritic iron-chromium carbide (gray, outlined) in a matrix of high-nickel austenite. 2% nital + 5% picral. 250×

**Fig. 96** Same corrosion-resistant iron as in Fig. 95, as-cast but after exposure to air above 705 °C (1300 °F). Austenitic gray iron with oxides (gray constituent) in grain boundaries and around graphite near the casting surface (top). As-polished. 400×

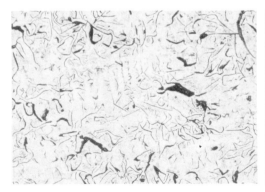

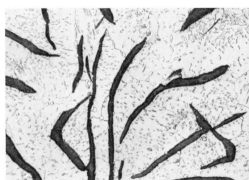

**Fig. 97** Fe-2.9C-4.5Si-0.8Mn-2.0Cr heat-resistant cast iron, as-cast. Gray iron with structure of type A graphite (dark) and interdendritic iron-chromium carbide (gray) in a matrix of iron-chromium-silicon ferrite. 3% nital. 100×

**Fig. 98** Heat-resistant cast iron, as-cast. Gray iron with type A graphite flakes in a matrix of pearlite. Compare with Fig. 99 for effects of service at high temperature. 2% nital + 4% picral. 500×

**Fig. 99** Same heat-resistant iron as Fig. 98, after extended service at high temperature. Nearly all of the cementite in the original pearlite matrix has been spheroidized; the matrix has transformed to ferrite. 2% nital. 500×

# Tool Steels

By George F. Vander Voort
Supervisor
Applied Physics Research & Development
Carpenter Technology Corporation

TOOL STEELS can be prepared for macroscopic and microscopic examination using the same basic procedures used for carbon and alloy steels. However, because many tool steels are highly alloyed and are generally heat treated to much higher hardnesses than most carbon and alloy steels, specific aspects of their preparation differ slightly. The reasons for these differences and the required procedural modifications are discussed in the following sections. Also covered are the effects of hot working, composition, austenitizing, and tempering on microstructure.

## Macroexamination

**Specimen selection** is generally based on the original ingot locations. Sampling is usually performed after primary hot working to billet or bloom shapes. Disks 12- to 25-mm (0.5- to 1.0-in.) thick are most often cut from billet or bloom locations corresponding to the top and bottom of the ingot. They are sometimes cut from the middle location. The hardness of these products can be rather high, unless the billet or bloom was subjected to a full annealing cycle. Thus, sectioning of such specimens may be more difficult than for carbon or alloy steels. For most work, transversely oriented disks (perpendicular to the hot-working axis) are preferred. However, longitudinal disks are better suited to studying deformation fiber or segregation. Transverse disks are preferred for general quality evaluations. If very hard, the disks should be tempered before etching. For routine quality studies, a saw-cut surface is adequate. If better resolution of detail is required or if photography is to be conducted, surface grinding is performed after cutting.

**Macroetching.** The macroetchant most widely used to evaluate macrostructural quality of tool steels is the standard immersion solution of equal parts of hydrochloric acid (HCl) and water at 70 to 80 °C (160 to 180 °F) for 15 to 45 min. Such etching will reveal segregation, cracks, porosity, inclusions (manganese sulfides, for example), flow lines,

surface decarburization or carburization, and hardness variations. Interpretation of results is aided by referring to standard charts (Ref 1-4).

This etching procedure can also be used to evaluate disks cut from sections smaller than billets or disks cut from failed components; however, room-temperature macroetching, which is also quite common, often uses a 10% aqueous nitric acid (HNO$_3$) solution. Smooth-ground specimens are immersed for up to a few minutes in this solution to reveal such surface conditions as decarburization, carburization, nitriding, hardened layers, and grinding damage. Internal quality problems, such as segregation, are also revealed, but usually less effectively than by hot-acid etching. After etching, the surface is washed, scrubbed to remove etching smut, and dried. Etching of small polishable sections in 2 to 5% nital will also bring out surface conditions that cannot be revealed by the cold 10% aqueous HNO$_3$ solution. However, nital is less effective on a smooth, ground surface.

The sulfur print test (Ref 5), another prevalent technique, is used to evaluate the distribution of manganese sulfides. Fracturing of hardened transverse etch disks is also performed to detect oxide inclusion stringers or graphite on the longitudinally oriented fracture. The fracture surface is often heated to produce a blue temper color, because the uncolored oxides exhibit strong contrast against the dark fracture.

## Microexamination

**Sectioning.** Relatively soft specimens (less than 35 HRC) can be cut using band saws or hacksaws. However, such operations produce a substantial zone of deformation beneath the cut and rather rough surfaces. Thus, the initial rough grinding with a coarse abrasive (80- to 120-grit silicon carbide, for example) must remove this damage.

Higher-hardness specimens must be cut using water-cooled abrasive cutoff wheels. The blade should have a soft bonding for ef-

fective cutting and avoidance of burning. Submerged cutting limits heat generation, which is most severe when cutting as-quenched or quenched and lightly tempered tool steels. Heat generated by improper technique can produce a highly tempered appearance in the martensite and, if heating is excessive, can reausterinitize the surface. Such damage cannot be easily removed by subsequent grinding steps.

When working with as-quenched high-alloy tool steels, it may be helpful to fracture the specimen. This will produce a flat, damage-free surface due to the extreme brittleness of such steels. The fractured surface can then be ground and polished for examination.

For high-hardness, high-alloy steels, sectioning with a low-speed diamond or boron nitride wheel saw can provide high-quality surfaces with minimum cutting-induced damage. Although the cutting rate is low, such surfaces are smooth, and grinding can begin with rather fine grits (320- or 400-grit silicon carbide, for example).

**Mounting.** Bulk samples frequently can be polished without mounting. Although many modern automatic polishing devices can handle unmounted specimens, some cannot. If edge retention is important, mounting may be desired. Plating the surface prior to mounting (Ref 5) produces optimum results, but is not always necessary. The newly developed compression-mounting epoxy resins provide excellent edge retention even with unplated specimens. Automatic polishing devices rather than hand polishing yield better edge retention.

For small or oddly shaped specimens, mounting is preferred. If the edge is not of particular interest, most mounting mediums are satisfactory. However, some mounts have poor resistance to solvents such as alcohol, and many are badly degraded if heated etchants are required. The compression-mounting epoxies prevent these problems. If a transparent mount is required to control grinding to a specific feature, transparent Lucite compression-mounting material can be used, and many cold-mounting epoxies are also satisfactory. Cold-mounting epoxies are the only materials that produce true adhesive bonding to the sample. They also produce the lowest heat during curing and are useful when the sample cannot tolerate the higher heat used in compression mounting. When edge retention is not required and heat degradation is not anticipated, low-cost Bakelite compression-molding materials can be used.

**Grinding** is performed in the same manner as for carbon and alloy steels. Various manual or automated devices may be used. Water-cooled silicon carbide paper (200- to 300-mm, or 8- to 12-in. diam) is preferred; the initial grit size selected depends on the technique used to generate the cut surface. The usual grit sequence is 120, 240, 320, 400, and 600 grit. Finer grit sizes may be used for highly alloyed tool steels in which carbide pullout is a problem. Grinding pressure should be moderate to heavy, and grinding times of 1 to 2 min are typical to remove the scratches and deformation from the previous step. Fresh paper should be used; worn or loaded paper will produce deformation.

**Polishing** is most commonly performed using one or more diamond abrasive stages followed by one or more final abrasive stages. For routine work, polishing with 6- and 1-$\mu$m diamond is generally adequate. The diamond abrasive may be applied to the polishing cloth in paste, slurry, or aerosol form. For the coarser diamond abrasives, low-nap or napless cloths are preferred; a medium-nap cloth is generally used with the finer diamond abrasives. A lubricant, or "extender," compatible with the diamond abrasive should be added to moisten the cloth and minimize drag. Wheel speeds of 150 to 300 rpm and moderate pressure should be used. Polishing times of 1 to 2 min are usually adequate.

Final polishing can also be conducted manually or automatically using various devices. Alumina abrasives, generally 0.3-$\mu$m $\alpha$-alumina ($Al_2O_3$) and 0.05-$\mu$m $\gamma$-$Al_2O_3$, are widely employed with medium-nap cloths for final polishing. Colloidal silica ($SiO_2$), with a particle size range of 0.04- to 0.06-$\mu$m, is also very effective (Ref 5). Wheel speeds, pressure, and times are the same as for rough polishing with diamond abrasives. In general, tool steels are relatively easy to polish to scratch-free and artifact-free condition due to their relatively high hardnesses.

**Microetching.** The etchant most widely used for tool steels is 2 to 5% nital. Stock solutions exceeding 3% $HNO_3$ in ethanol should not be stored in pressure-tight bottles. If higher concentrations are desired as a stock reagent, a bottle with a pressure-relief valve should be used, or methanol should be substituted for ethanol.

Nital is generally used for tool steels regardless of the anticipated microstructural constituents. Although nital is superior to picral (4% picric acid in ethanol) for etching martensitic structures, picral produces better results for examining annealed samples.

When examining spheroidize-annealed tool steels (the most common annealed condition), picral reveals only the interfaces between carbide and ferrite. Nital also reveals the ferrite grain boundaries that generally obscure the carbide shape. Also, because nital is orientation sensitive, carbides within some of the ferrite grains will be poorly delineated, making spheroidization ratings more difficult. Figures 9 and 10 illustrate the difference in etching response between nital and picral.

A 2% nital solution is usually preferred. Stronger concentrations increase the speed of etching, making it more difficult to control. Etching of martensitic high-alloy tool steels, such as the high-speed steels, may require a 5% concentration. Etching with nital or picral is usually performed by immersion. If swabbing is used, pressures should be light. Etching times are difficult to generalize, because of the wide range of tool steel compositions and because heat treatment can markedly alter etch response. Trial and error will determine the degree of surface dulling necessary to obtain the correct degree of etching.

Other etchants, although infrequently used, can be of great value. Table 1 lists compositions of a number of specialized reagents for achieving selective etching or enhancing contrast among microconstituents.

**Table 1  Microstructural etchants for tool steels**

| Etchant | Comments |
|---|---|
| 1. 1–10 mL $HNO_3$ and 99–90 mL alcohol | Nital. Most commonly used etchant. Do not store solutions with more than 3% $HNO_3$ in ethanol. Reveals ferrite grain boundaries and ferrite-carbide interfaces in annealed sample. Preferred etchant for martensite. Reveals prior-austenite grain boundaries in as-quenched and lightly tempered high alloy tool steels. 2–3% nital most common, 5–10% nital used for high alloy grades. Use by immersion. |
| 2. 4 g picric acid and 100 mL ethanol | Picral. Recommended for annealed structures or those containing pearlite or bainite. Does not reveal ferrite grain boundaries in annealed specimens. Etching response improved by adding 10–20 drops zephiran chloride. For high alloy grades, add 1–5 mL HCl to improve etching response. Use by immersion. |
| 3. 1 g picric acid, 5 mL HCl, and 100 mL ethanol | Vilella's reagent. Used in the same manner as picral or picral plus HCl |
| 4. 10 g picric acid and 100 mL ethanol | Superpicral. Must be heated to dissolve picric acid. Use by immersion, up to 1 min or more. A few drops of HCl may be added to increase etch rate. |
| 5. 2 g picric acid, 25 g NaOH, and 100 mL $H_2O$ | Alkaline sodium picrate. Immerse sample in boiling solution for 1–15 min or use electrolytically at 6 V dc, 20 °C (68 °F), 30–120 s, stainless steel cathode. Colors cementite and $Fe_4W_2C$ |
| 6. 10 g $K_3Fe(CN)_6$ (potassium ferricyanide), 10 g KOH or 7 g NaOH, and 100 mL $H_2O$ | Murakami's reagent. Use by immersion, fresh solution, hot or cold, up to 10 min. Cold-darkens chromium carbides and tungstides, cementite not attacked. Hot-attacks cementite |
| 7. 1 g $CrO_3$ and 100 mL $H_2O$ | Electrolytic etch, 2–3 V dc, 20 °C (68 °F), 30 s, stainless steel cathode. MC and $M_7C_3$ darkened, $Mo_2C$ outlined |
| 8. 10 mL $H_2O_2$ (30%) and 20 mL 10% aqueous NaOH | Immerse 10 s at 20 °C (68 °F). $Fe_2MoC$, $Mo_2C$, and $M_6C$ outlined (latter also colored) |
| 9. 4 g $KMnO_4$ (potassium permanganate), 4 g NaOH, and 100 mL $H_2O$ | Groesbeck's reagent. Immerse at 20 °C (68 °F). $Fe_2MoC$ and $M_6C$ outlined and colored (blue and brown, respectively), $Mo_2C$ colored brown, $(Fe,Cr)_{23}C_6$ attacked but $(Fe,Mo)_{23}C_6$ not attacked |
| 10. 4 g NaOH and 100 mL saturated aqueous $KMnO_4$ | Immerse at 20 °C (68 °F). $Mo_2C$ and $M_7C_3$ attacked, $M_6C$ outlined and colored brown |
| 11. Saturated aqueous picric acid plus small amount of wetting agent | Prior-austenite grain boundary etch for hardened steels. Many wetting agents can be used, sodium tridecylbenzene sulfonate most commonly used. Use at 20 to 100 °C (68 to 212 °F) by immersion for 2 to 60 min. Addition of about 1% HCl useful for higher alloy grades. Room temperature etching most common. Etching with solution in a beaker in an ultrasonic cleaner works well. Lightly back-polish to remove surface smut. |
| 12. 50 mL cold saturated aqueous $Na_2S_2O_3$ (sodium thiosulfate) and 1 g $K_2S_2O_5$ (potassium metabisulfite) | Klemm's I (tint etch) reagent. Immerse (never swab) at 20 °C (68 °F) for 40–100 s to color ferrite (blue or red) and martensite (brown). Cementite and austenite unaffected |
| 13. 1 g $Na_2MoO_4$ (sodium molybdate) and 100 mL $H_2O$ | Beraha's tint etch for cementite. Add 0.2–0.3 g $NH_4F \cdot HF$ (ammonium bifluoride). Add $HNO_3$ to produce a pH of 2.5–3.0. Preetch sample with picral. Colors $Fe_3C$ yellow-orange. Immerse up to 60 s; never swab. |
| 14. 3 g $K_2S_2O_5$, 10 g anhydrous $Na_2S_2O_3$ and 100 mL $H_2O$ | Beraha's tint etch. Immerse (never swab) until surface is colored red-violet. Colors ferrite, martensite, bainite, and pearlite. Cementite unaffected |

Note: When water is specified, use distilled water.

**Pepperhoff interference film technique** also improves contrast among constituents. A thin layer of a dielectric compound, such as zinc selenide (ZnSe), is vapor deposited onto the surface of the sample in a bell jar (Ref 5). As the thickness of this layer increases above 400 nm, colors are observed. First-order red to violet produces the best results. Examples of this method are shown in Fig. 51 to 54.

**Prior-austenite Grain Size.** Many tool steels can be etched with nital to reveal the prior-austenite grain boundaries. The high-speed steels can be handled in this way as long as the tempering temperature used is not too high. Etching techniques that reveal the prior-austenite grain boundaries are employed, but can be difficult to implement successfully; therefore, a fracture grain size method is widely used. The Shepherd fracture grain size technique is simple, quick, and accurate as long as the sample is martensitic—retained austenite may be present in substantial amounts—and not tempered to such an extent that reasonably flat, brittle (macroscopic) fractures cannot be obtained (Ref 5).

## Microstructures of Tool Steels

A wide range of microstructures is observed in tool steels because of variations in composition and heat treatment. The mill metallurgist is generally most concerned with annealed microstructures and undesired surface decarburization. The failure analyst sees a broad spectrum of microstructures, both normal and abnormal.

**Annealed Microstructures.** Because most tool steels are relatively hard, even when annealed, it is usually necessary to control carbide morphology during annealing to maximize machinability and formability. For most tool steels a spheroidal carbide shape is the desired condition, although for a few of the low-alloy tool steels certain machining operations are improved when the structure is partially pearlitic.

Most tool steels and all high-alloy grades are spheroidize annealed at the mill. Control of annealed microstructures is discussed in the article "Introduction to Heat Treating of Tool Steels" in Volume 4 of the 9th Edition of *Metals Handbook*. For a given grade, the hardness decreases as the degree of spheroidization increases. Once spheroidization has been obtained, growth of the carbides, which produces fewer carbides per unit volume and a greater apparent spacing, further reduces hardness. However, if the carbide structure is too coarse, dissolving the required amount of carbon during austenitization will be more difficult. In addition, many tool steels require a fine, uniform distribution of undissolved carbides to resist grain growth during austenitization.

The amount and type of carbides present depend on the bulk carbon content and the quantity of carbide-forming elements (chromium, molybdenum, vanadium, and tungsten, for example) in the grade. Cementite is present in the carbon and low-alloy grades; more complex carbide types are found in the highly alloyed grades. The hardness of carbides varies with their composition, from approximately 800 HV for cementite to approximately 1400 HV when other elements, such as chromium, are substituted for a portion of the iron. The high wear resistance of heat-treated tool steels is attributable to the hardness of the matrix phase, chiefly martensite, and the amount and type of carbides remaining undissolved in the matrix.

**Hot-Worked Microstructures.** The structure produced after hot working can have a marked influence on the distribution and morphology of carbides after the subsequent spheroidize anneal. The micrographs in this article illustrate the complex microstructures that are often present in the as-hot-worked condition prior to annealing and the influence of this structure on the annealed microstructure. In general, the cooling after hot working must be controlled to produce as uniform a carbon distribution as possible so that the annealed carbide distribution does not vary.

Some tool steels, such as the 5% Cr hot-work grades, tend to form carbide networks at the prior-austenite grain boundaries present at the end of the hot-working operation. Such networks can be difficult to remove during annealing and can degrade tensile ductility and toughness even if they are semicontinuous.

**Effect of Composition on Microstructure.** Because tool steels are somewhat more difficult to machine than carbon and alloy steels, the compositions of some grades are adjusted to retain a certain amount of the carbon present as graphite. When viewed on a transverse plane (Fig. 19), the graphite appears as small, globular particles, but they are not nodular in shape as in ductile cast iron. On the longitudinal plane (Fig. 20), the graphite particles are observed to be elongated, although their aspect ratios are not excessively high. The most commonly used graphitic tool steel is AISI O6, which typically contains approximately 0.3 to 0.5% of the total carbon content as graphite. The amount of carbon as graphite must be controlled carefully to ensure uniform hardening response. The presence of graphite improves machining and wear characteristics.

Undesired graphitization can occur in high-carbon tool steels if those elements that promote graphitization are not controlled. Processing procedures can also affect graphitization; therefore, in carbon tool steels with more than approximately 1.1% C, processing must also be carefully controlled.

Sulfur is added to several tool steel grades, although not as much as is added to free-machining carbon steels. Because manganese sulfide inclusions degrade toughness, certain tool steel grades are made with very low sulfur contents, often less than 0.003%, for critical applications. Although this practice enhances mechanical properties, these tool steels can be more difficult to machine.

Hobbing steels must be quite soft to permit optimum cold workability and maximum life of the master hob. Such steels are very low in carbon, although some medium-carbon alloy grades, such as AISI S5, are hobbed. The low-carbon hobbing steels, such as AISI P2, must be carburized after hobbing and before hardening. These low-carbon grades are rather soft as-annealed and are designed to minimize work hardening during forming. Medium-carbon AISI S5 must be very carefully spheroidize annealed to as low a hardness as possible to enhance hobbability. Achieving a low annealed hardness with this grade is difficult, however, because its high silicon content substantially strengthens the ferrite.

**Heat-Treated Microstructures.** Tool steel compositions range from carbon tool steels with no alloy additions to high-speed steels containing 20% or more alloying elements. Consequently, hardenabilities vary widely, producing quenching requirements that vary from brine to air. Each tool steel grade has been studied to determine the proper quench media, as a function of section size, to permit hardening to martensite. Although the carbon tool steels are usually not through hardened, most of the other grades are. Another exception is the low-carbon hobbing grades that are carburized and surface hardened. A few grades are also nitrided or carbonitrided for special applications.

Most tool steels are hardened and tempered to rather high hardnesses, generally 58 HRC or greater, to obtain good wear resistance. Exceptions are the hot-work tool steels that are quenched and tempered to hardnesses from approximately 42 to 55 HRC and prehardened plastic molding steels, such as AISI P20, that are sold in the heat-treated condition at approximately 30 HRC. The preheated tool steels are machined and used in this condition without subsequent heat treatment except, perhaps, for a stress-relief temper.

The correct austenitizing temperature for each grade has been determined experimentally by using an austenitizing series. Samples are heated to various temperatures and quenched at a rate consistent with the anticipated hardenability. Each as-quenched sample is fractured to rate the prior-austenite grain size by the Shepherd comparison method. Next, the samples are carefully ground on one of the fracture faces and tested for hardness. As the austenitizing temperature increases, hardness will increase, level off, then decrease. The fracture grain size will remain relatively constant, usually up to the austenitizing temperature where the as-quenched hardness levels out, then will decrease due to grain growth. The optimum austenitizing temperature is that temperature or range where the hardness is highest and the grain size is finest. Dilatometry is generally conducted before such tests to establish the optimum temperature range.

Carbon tool steels are hypereutectoid and contain only cementite, which is easily dissolved. The iron-carbon equilibrium diagram is a good starting point for establishing the correct austenitizing temperature. For these steels, maximum hardness results when approximately 0.60 to 0.65% C is put into solution. Therefore, the as-quenched structure will consist of martensite and residual cementite; that is, the carbides not put into solution. A small amount of retained austenite will also be present, but it will not be detectable with an optical microscope if the proper austenitizing temperature is used.

If a sufficiently high austenitizing temperature is used, the carbon content of the austenite will be raised to such an extent that the martensite finish temperature, $M_f$, is well below room temperature. Because retained austenite is relatively soft compared to martensite, the bulk hardness will be lower. The microstructure will exhibit coarse-plate (acicular) martensite and retained austenite. As the austenitizing temperature exceeds the optimum temperature, the amount of residual cementite decreases, the amount of retained austenite increases, the hardness decreases, and the grain size increases.

In general, if the amount of retained austenite is high enough to be observed with an optical microscope, the steel has been over-austenitized. Tempering will not convert high levels of retained austenite to martensite or bainite unless the tempering temperature is rather high. Moreover, the retained austenite will not be stable enough to withstand shock-induced transformation to martensite during service. When such transformation occurs, the high-hardness matrix lacks enough ductility to accommodate the transformation stresses, and cracking results.

Low heat-treated hardnesses may also result if the section size and quench rate are selected incorrectly for a particular grade. When the hardenability is inadequate to permit full hardening, pearlite or bainite will be observed in the microstructure. Ferrite may also be visible in the few tool steels that are hypoeutectoid, although this is less common. Brine- and water-quenching grades are also susceptible to formation of soft spots within the case caused by localized slow cooling from tongs holding the sample or inadequate agitation (failure to break up vapor pockets due to localized boiling of the quench media).

After quenching, tool steels must be immediately tempered to reduce the very high transformation stresses, or quench cracking may occur. Quench cracking is more likely to occur as the quench rate increases and if the geometry of the specimen exhibits stress raisers. Air-hardenable steels are less susceptible to quench cracking, because the slow rate of cooling helps to relieve some of the transformation stresses.

Many tool steels are often tempered at 175 to 230 °C (350 to 450 °F). These low tempering temperatures do little to the structure ex-

cept relieve quenching stresses. Hot-work and high-speed steels are usually tempered at relatively high temperatures. Due to their high alloy content, these grades can resist softening during tempering to rather high levels. These higher alloy steels are often tempered hot enough to cause secondary hardening and to change the nature of the carbides present. These changes, however, can be detected only by methods more sophisticated than optical microscopy. In general, the lowest alloy tool steels receive a single temper, typically 2 h for every 25 mm (1 in.) of thickness. Higher alloy tool steels are usually tempered twice; high-speed steels may be tempered three times. Double and triple tempering is required to condition and stabilize the microstructure.

For many tool steels, tempering to approximately 540 °C (1000 °F) produces only subtle differences in the microstructure viewed optically. The speed at which etching occurs and the darkness of the matrix will change with tempering. Tempering just below the lower critical temperature is required to produce pronounced microstructural changes, but such high tempers have no practical applications for tools and dies, except as an anneal.

Heat-treated tool steel microstructures are similar in appearance when the grades are properly heat treated. The primary differences are the amount and type of the residual, undissolved carbides that will influence the coarseness of the plate martensite. In many tool steels, the martensite phase is so fine that little detail is observed. This is not the case for grades that exhibit very little residual carbides—for example, AISI S1, S5, and S7. These shock-resisting tool steels have lower carbon contents, and nearly all of the carbon is dissolved in the austenite. Consequently, the martensite is coarser, with more detail observable by optical microscopy.

Compositions for the tool steels illustrated in this article are listed in Table 2. Information on properties, tempers, designations, and applications of tool steels can be found in the article "Tool Steels" in Volume 3 of the 9th Edition of *Metals Handbook*.

## REFERENCES

1. "Recommended Practice for Macroetch Testing of Tool Steel Bars," A 561, *Annual Book of ASTM Standards*, Vol 01.05, ASTM, Philadelphia, 1984, p 507-511
2. "Macroetch Testing of Consumable Electrode Remelted Steel Bars and Billets," A 604, *Annual Book of ASTM Standards*, Vol 01.05, ASTM, Philadelphia, 1984, p 577-591
3. "Macroetch Testing, Inspection and Rating Steel Products Comprising Bars, Billets, Blooms and Forgings," E 381, *Annual Book of ASTM Standards*, Vol 01.05, ASTM, Philadelphia, 1984, p 895-899
4. "Macrograph Standards for Steel Bars, Billets and Blooms," MIL-STD 430A, Department of Defense, Washington, DC, June 30, 1966
5. G.F. Vander Voort, *Metallography: Principles and Practice*, McGraw-Hill, 1984

**Table 2  Nominal compositions of illustrated tool steel grades**

| AISI type | C | Mn(a) | Si(b) | Cr | Ni | V | W | Mo | Co | Ti |
|---|---|---|---|---|---|---|---|---|---|---|
| W1 | 0.6–1.4 | ... | ... | ... | ... | 0.25 | ... | ... | ... | ... |
| W2 | 0.6–1.4 | ... | ... | ... | ... | ... | ... | ... | ... | ... |
| S1 | 0.5 | ... | 0.75 | 1.5 | ... | 0.2(c) | 2.5 | ... | ... | ... |
| S2 | 0.5 | 0.4 | 1.0 | ... | ... | ... | ... | 0.5 | ... | ... |
| S4 | 0.55 | 0.8 | 2.0 | ... | ... | ... | ... | ... | ... | ... |
| S5 | 0.55 | 0.8 | 1.9 | 0.25(c) | ... | 0.2(c) | ... | 0.4 | ... | ... |
| S7 | 0.5 | 0.7 | ... | 3.25 | ... | ... | ... | 1.40 | ... | ... |
| O1 | 0.9 | 1.0 | ... | 0.5 | ... | 0.2(c) | 0.5 | ... | ... | ... |
| O2 | 0.9 | 1.6 | ... | ... | ... | ... | ... | ... | ... | ... |
| O6 | 1.45 | 0.8 | 1.1 | ... | ... | ... | ... | 0.25 | ... | ... |
| A2 | 1.0 | 0.7 | ... | 5.25 | ... | 0.2(c) | ... | 1.1 | ... | ... |
| A6 | 0.7 | 2.0 | ... | 1.0 | ... | ... | ... | 1.35 | ... | ... |
| A7 | 2.00–2.85 | 0.8 | 0.5 | 5.0–5.75 | ... | 3.9–5.15 | 0.5–1.5 | 0.90–1.40 | ... | ... |
| A10 | 1.25–1.50 | 1.6–2.1 | 1.0–1.5 | ... | 1.55–2.05 | ... | ... | 1.25–1.75 | ... | ... |
| D2 | 1.5 | 0.5 | ... | 12.0 | ... | 0.2–0.9(c) | ... | 0.8 | ... | ... |
| D3 | 2.1 | ... | ... | 12.0 | 0.5(c) | ... | ... | ... | ... | ... |
| H11 | 0.35 | ... | 0.9 | 5.0 | ... | 0.4 | ... | 1.5 | ... | ... |
| H13 | 0.35 | ... | 1.0 | 5.25 | ... | 1.0 | ... | 1.3 | ... | ... |
| H21 | 0.35 | ... | ... | 3.5 | ... | 0.4(c) | 9.0 | ... | ... | ... |
| H23 | 0.25–0.35 | 0.15–0.40 | 0.15–0.60 | 11.0–12.75 | 0.3 | 0.75–1.25 | 11.0–12.75 | ... | ... | ... |
| H26 | 0.45–0.55 | 0.15–0.40 | 0.15–0.40 | 3.75–4.5 | 0.3 | 0.75–1.25 | 17.25–19.0 | ... | ... | ... |
| T1 | 0.7 | ... | ... | 4.0 | ... | 1.0 | 18.0 | ... | ... | ... |
| T15 | 1.5 | ... | ... | 4.0 | ... | 5.0 | 12.0 | ... | 5.0 | ... |
| M1 | 0.8 | ... | ... | 4.0 | ... | 1.1 | 1.5 | 8.5 | ... | ... |
| M2 | 0.85 | ... | ... | 4.0 | ... | 2.0 | 6.0 | 5.0 | ... | ... |
| M4 | 1.3 | ... | ... | 4.5 | ... | 4.0 | 5.5 | 4.5 | ... | ... |
| M42 | 1.1 | ... | ... | 3.75 | ... | 1.15 | 1.5 | 9.5 | 8.0 | ... |
| L1 | 1.0 | ... | ... | 1.4 | ... | ... | ... | ... | ... | ... |
| L6 | 0.75 | 0.75 | ... | 0.9 | 1.75 | ... | ... | 0.35 | ... | ... |
| F2 | 1.25 | 0.75 | ... | ... | ... | ... | 0.35 | ... | ... | ... |
| P5 | 0.1 | ... | ... | 2.25 | ... | ... | ... | ... | ... | ... |
| P20 | 0.35 | ... | ... | 1.25 | ... | ... | ... | 0.4 | ... | ... |
| AHT | 1.0 | ... | ... | ... | ... | 0.25 | 1.05 | 1.1 | ... | 1.0 |

(a) All tool steels contain some manganese, generally 0.2–0.4% when not listed. (b) Tool steels usually contain 0.2–0.35% Si unless listed otherwise. (c) Optional addition at discretion of manufacturer

**Fig. 1** AISI W1 (1.3% C), as-rolled, containing pearlite and acicular cementite. 4% picral. 500×

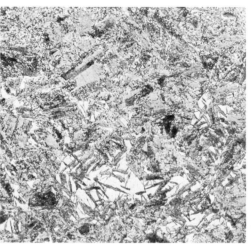

**Fig. 2** AISI L6, as-rolled, containing bainite and martensite (white). 2% nital. 500×

**Fig. 3** AISI S4, as-rolled, containing ferrite (white) and pearlite. 4% picral. 500×

**Fig. 4** AISI S4, as-rolled, containing bainite and martensite (featureless patches). This bar was cooled at a faster rate after rolling than the one in Fig. 3. 4% picral. 500×

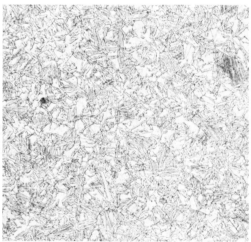

**Fig. 5** AISI S5, as-rolled, containing bainite and martensite (white). 2% nital. 500×

**Fig. 6** AISI O1, as-rolled, containing bainite and martensite (white patches). The dark patches are pearlite. 4% picral. 500×

**Fig. 7** AISI L1, as-rolled, containing pearlite and a grain boundary cementite network. Boiling alkaline sodium picrate. 100×

**Fig. 8** AISI A2, as-rolled, containing plate martensite (black) and retained austenite (white). 2% nital. 500×

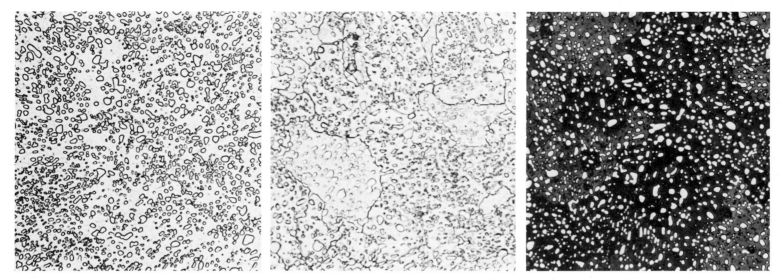

**Fig. 9, 10, 11** AISI W2 (1.05% C) spheroidize annealed. Fig. 9: etched with 4% picral to outline only cementite (uniform dissolution of the ferrite matrix). Fig. 10: etched with 2% nital, which reveals ferrite grain boundaries and outlines cementite. Note that the ferrite in some grains is not attacked, and the carbides within these grains are barely visible. Fig. 11: etched lightly with 4% picral, then tint-etched with Klemm's I reagent to color the ferrite (blue and red). 1000×

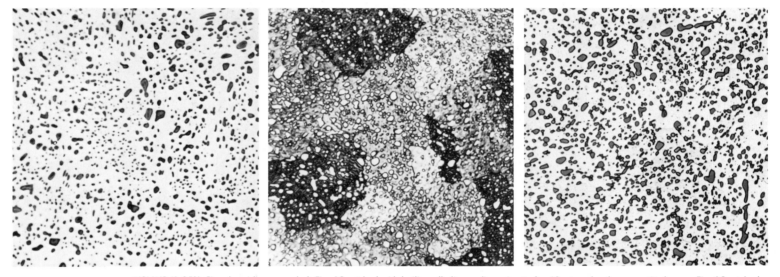

**Fig. 12, 13, 14** AISI W2 (1.05% C), spheroidize annealed. Fig. 12: etched with boiling alkaline sodium picrate for 60 s to color the cementite brown. Fig. 13: etched lightly with 4% picral and tint etched with Beraha's $Na_2S_2O_3/K_2S_2O_5$ reagent to color the ferrite (wide range of colors). Fig. 14: etched lightly with 4% picral and tint etched with Beraha's $Na_2MoO_4$ reagent to color the cementite dark orange. See also Fig. 9, 10, 11. 1000×

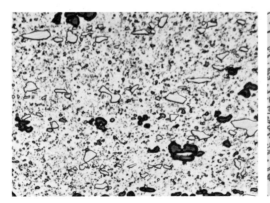

**Fig. 15** A7 tool steel, as-received (mill annealed), longitudinal section. Dark particles are chromium carbide; light particles, vanadium carbide; matrix ferrite. 4 g NaOH, 4 g $KMnO_4$, 100 mL $H_2O$. 500×

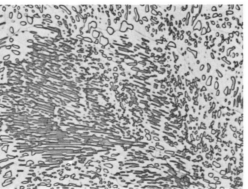

**Fig. 16** W4 water-hardening tool steel (0.98C-0.74Mn-0.14Cr-0.19Ni), as-received (mill annealed). 187 HB. Spheroidal cementite in a matrix of ferrite; a considerable amount of lamellar pearlite is also present. 4% picral. 1000×

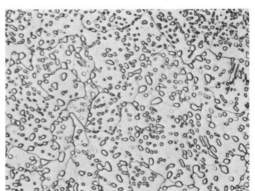

**Fig. 17** W4 water-hardening tool steel (0.96C-0.66Mn-0.23Cr), as-received (full annealed). 170 HB. Structure consists of spheroidal cementite in a ferrite matrix; no lamellar constituent is present. Compare with Fig. 16. 4% picral. 1000×

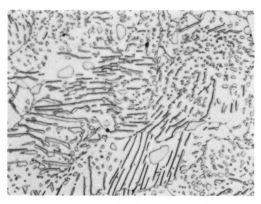

**Fig. 18** W1 water-hardening tool steel (0.94C-0.21Mn), as-received (mill annealed). 170 HB. Structure: mixture of lamellar pearlite and spheroidal cementite in a matrix of ferrite, with a few large, globular carbide particles. 3% nital. 1000×

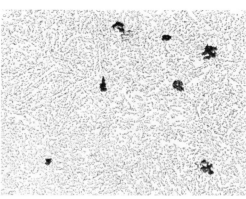

**Fig. 19** AISI O6, spheroidize annealed, transverse section. Note the globular appearance of the graphite (black). 4% picral. 500×

**Fig. 20** AISI O6, spheroidize annealed, longitudinal section. Note that the graphite is elongated in the rolling direction. 4% picral. 500×

**Fig. 21, 22, 23, 24** AISI W1 (1.05% C). Influence of starting structure on spheroidization. Fig. 21: as-rolled, contains coarse and fine pearlite. Fig. 22: after spheroidization (heat to 760 °C, or 1400 °F, cool at a rate of 11 °C/h, or 20 °F/h to 595 °C, or 1100 °F, air cool). Fig. 23: austenitized at 870 °C (1600 °F) and oil quenched to produce fine pearlite. Fig. 24: austenitized as in Fig. 23; annealed as in Fig. 22. Note the more uniform spherical carbide shape compared to Fig. 22. 4% picral. 500×

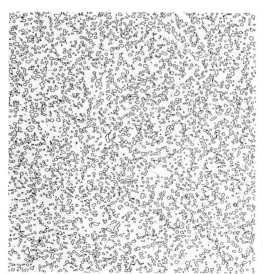

**Fig. 25** AISI L1, spheroidize annealed. Note the very well formed spheroidal carbides. 4% picral. 500×

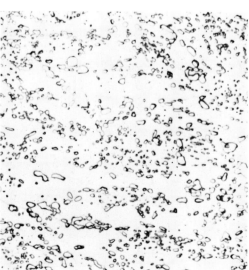

**Fig. 26** AISI S2, spheroidize annealed. 4% picral. 1000×

**Fig. 27** AISI S5, spheroidize annealed. 4% picral. 500×

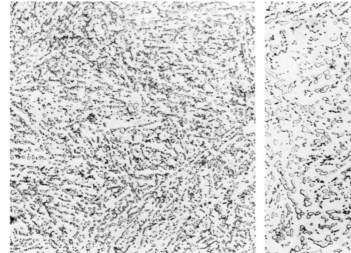

**Fig. 28** AISI S7, spheroidize annealed. 4% picral. 1000×

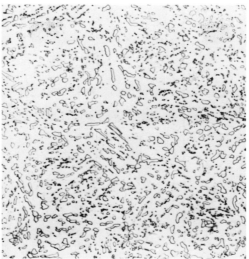

**Fig. 29** AISI A6, spheroidize annealed. 4% picral. 1000×

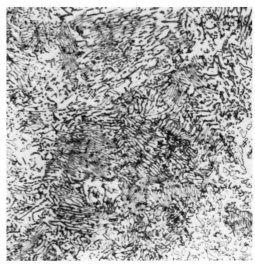

**Fig. 30** AISI A6, partially spheroidized. Note lamellar pearlite. 4% picral. 1000×

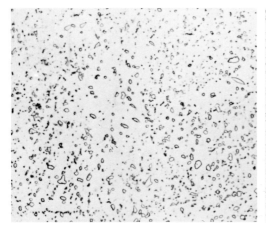

**Fig. 31** AISI H13 chromium hot-worked tool steel, spheroidize annealed. 4% picral. 1000×

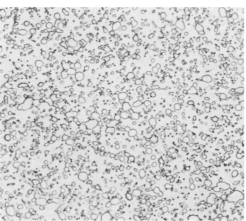

**Fig. 32** AISI M2 molybdenum high-speed tool steel, spheroidize annealed. 4% picral. 1000×

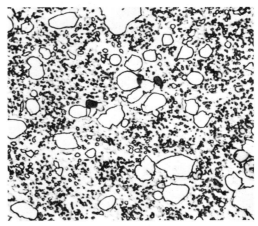

**Fig. 33** A7 tool steel, box annealed at 900 °C (1650 °F) for 1 h per 25 mm (1.0 in.) of container thickness and cooled at no more than 28 °C/h (50 °F/h). Massive alloy carbide and spheroidal carbide in a ferrite matrix. 4% nital. 1000×

**Fig. 34** A10 tool steel as-received (mill annealed). Section transverse to rolling direction. At the magnification used, the structure is poorly resolved. Nital. 100×

**Fig. 35** H23 tool steel, annealed by austenitizing at 870 °C (1600 °F) for 2 h and cooling at 28 °C/h (50 °F/h) to 540 °C (1000 °F), then air cooling. 98 HRB. Structure consists of tiny spheroidal and some larger alloy carbide particles in a matrix of ferrite. Kalling's reagent. 500×

**Fig. 36** H26 tool steel, annealed by austenitizing at 900 °C (1650 °F), cooling at 8.5 °C/h (15 °F/h) to 650 °C (1200 °F), then air cooling. 22 to 23 HRC. Structure consists of a dispersion of fine particles of alloy carbide in a matrix of ferrite. Picral with HCl, 10 s. 500×

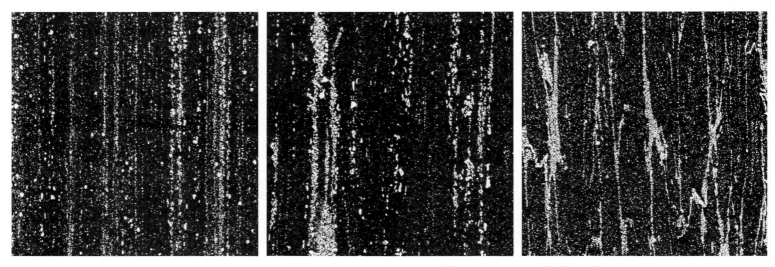

**Fig. 37, 38, 39** AISI M2, round bars. Carbide segregation at the center of round bars of different diameters. Fig. 37: 27-mm (1$^1$/$_{16}$-in.) diam. Fig. 38: 67-mm (2$^5$/$_8$-in.) diam. Fig. 39: 105-mm (4$^1$/$_8$-in.) diam. 10% nital. 100×

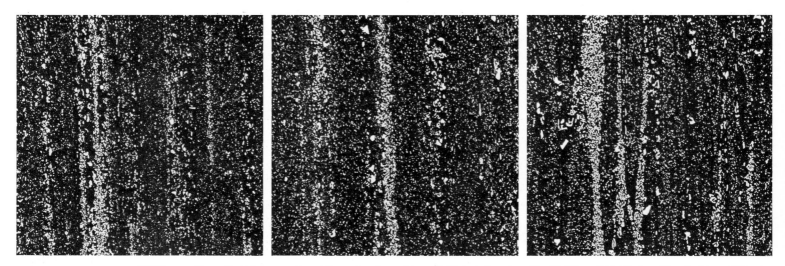

**Fig. 40, 41, 42** AISI T1, round bars. Carbide segregation at the center of round bars of different diameters. Fig. 40: 35-mm (1$^3$/$_8$-in.) diam. Fig. 41: 64-mm (2$^1$/$_2$-in.) diam. Fig. 42: 83-mm (3$^1$/$_4$-in.) diam. 10% nital. 100×

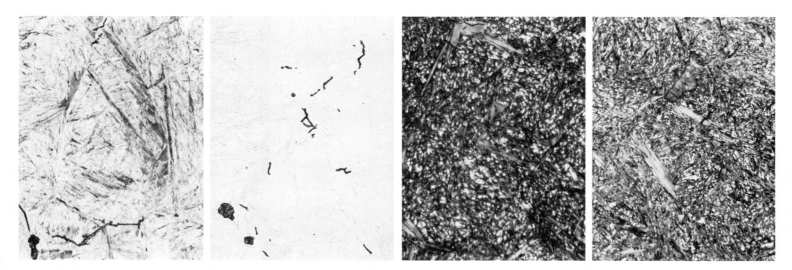

**Fig. 43, 44, 45, 46** AISI W1 (1% C), overaustenitized at 925 °C (1700 °F) and water quenched, producing martensite, retained austenite, and small patches of pearlite. Influence of etchant on revealing as-quenched martensite. Fig. 43: 2% nital etch reveals martensite and pearlite (black). Fig. 44: 4% picral etch reveals pearlite, but only faintly reveals martensite. Fig. 45: 5% aqueous sodium metabisulfite etch produces a strong contrast between the martensite and retained austenite (white). Fig. 46: Beraha's Na$_2$S$_2$O$_3$/K$_2$S$_2$O$_5$ reagent produces similar results to Fig. 45, but pearlite is more visible. 500×

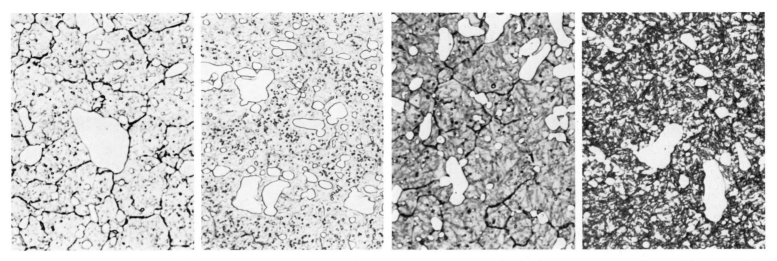

**Fig. 47, 48, 49, 50** AISI D2, austenitized at 1040 °C (1900 °F), air quenched and tempered at 200 °C (400 °F). Influence of etchant on revealed martensite. Fig. 47: 10% nital etch reveals grain boundaries, carbides, and martensite (light). Fig. 48: 4% picral plus HCl etch reveals carbides and martensite (light). Fig. 49: heat tinted at 540 °C (1000 °F) for 5 min after 10% nital etch to produce greater contrast and reveal the retained austenite. Fig. 50: superpicral etch reveals retained austenite as white, but carbide also appears white. 1000×

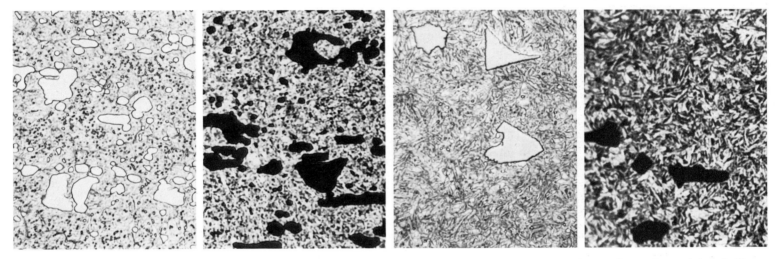

**Fig. 51, 52, 53, 54** Fig. 51, 52: AISI D2, quenched and tempered. Fig. 53, 54: AHT tool steel, quenched and tempered. Use of vapor-deposited zinc selenide to accentuate carbide detection and retained austenite. Samples were etched first with 4% picral plus HCl (Fig. 51, 53) to outline the carbides, then coated with a thin layer of zinc selenide (Fig. 52, 54) to reveal the carbides (dark violet), retained austenite (white), and martensite (dark). 1000×

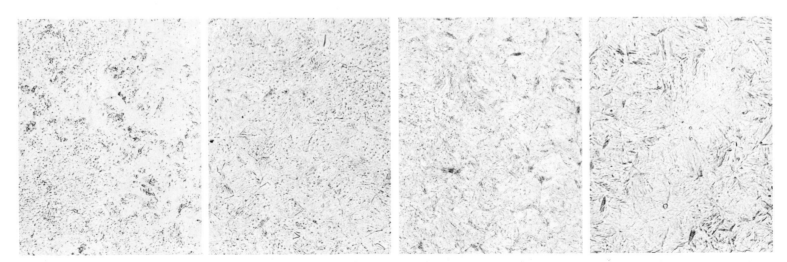

**Fig. 55, 56, 57, 58** AISI S7 (0.5% C). Influence of austenitizing temperature. Fig. 55: austenitized at 915 °C (1675 °F) 1 h for every 25 mm (1.0 in.) of thickness and air quenched. Sample is underaustenitized. Fig. 56: austenitized at 925 °C (1700 °F). Slightly underaustenitized. Fig. 57: austenitized at the preferred temperature of 940 °C (1725 °F). Fig. 58: austenitized at 955 °C (1750 °F). Slightly overaustenitized, note coarsening, no visible carbide. 4% picral. 500×

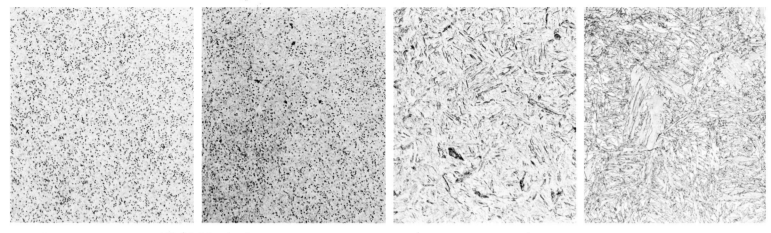

**Fig. 59, 60, 61, 62** AISI O1. Influence of austenitizing temperature on microstructure. Fig. 59: austenitized at 800 °C (1475 °F) 1 h for every 25 mm (1.0 in.) of thickness. 65 HRC, grain size 9.5. Specimen properly austenitized. Fig. 60: austenitized at 870 °C (1600 °F). 65 HRC, grain size 9. Overaustenitized. Fig. 61: austenitized at 980 °C (1800 °F). 64 HRC, grain size 7. Very overaustenitized; all carbide dissolved. Fig. 62: austenitized at 1100 °C (2010 °F). 64 HRC, grain size 3. Severely overaustenitized, note retained austenite (white). 4% picral 500×

**Fig. 63, 64, 65** AISI A2. Influence of austenitizing temperature on microstructure. Fig. 63: underaustenitized at 870 °C (1600 °F), air quenched. 48 HRC. 2% nital. 500×. Fig. 64: austenitized at 950 °C (1750 °F) air quenched and tempered at 200 °C (400 °F). 61 HRC. Correctly austenitized. Vilella's reagent. 1000×. Fig. 65: overaustenitized at 1095 °C (2000 °F), air quenched. Most of the carbides have been dissolved, and the grains are quite large. Retained austenite is faintly visible. 2% nital. 500×

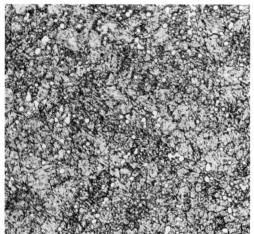 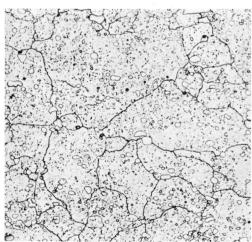 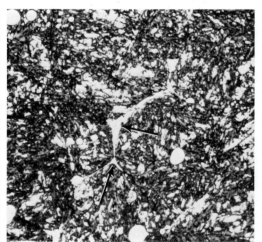

**Fig. 66** AISI M2, normal quenched and tempered condition. 1200 °C (2200 °F) for 5 min in salt, oil quench, double tempered at 595 °C (1100 °F). 64 to 65 HRC. 3% nital. 500×

**Fig. 67** AISI M2. Heat treated at 1220 °C (2225 °F) for 5 min in salt, oil quench, 1175 °C (2150 °F) for 5 min in salt, oil quench. 64 HRC. Grain growth due to rehardening without annealing between heat treatments. 10% nital. 400×

**Fig. 68** AISI M2. Heat treated at 1260 °C (2300 °F) for 5 min in salt, oil quench, double tempered at 540 °C (1000 °F). 66 HRC. Overaustenitization and onset of grain boundary melting (arrow). 3% nital/Vilella's reagent. 1000×

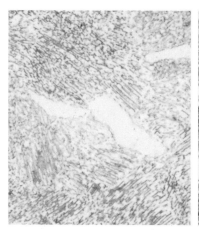

**Fig. 69** AISI S5 austenitized and isothermally transformed at 650 °C (1200 °F) for 4 h (air cooled) to form ferrite and coarse pearlite. 23 to 24 HRC. 4% picral. 1000×

**Fig. 70** AISI S5 austenitized, isothermally transformed at 595 °C (1100 °F) for 8 h and air cooled to form ferrite and fine pearlite. 36 HRC. 4% picral. 1000×

**Fig. 71** AISI S5 austenitized, isothermally transformed (partially) at 540 °C (1000 °F) for 8 h, and water quenched to form upper bainite (dark); balance of austenite formed martensite. 4% picral/2% nital. 1000×

**Fig. 72** AISI S5 austenitized, isothermally transformed at 400 °C (750 °F) for 1 h, and air cooled to form lower bainite. 37 to 38 HRC. 4% picral/2% nital. 1000×

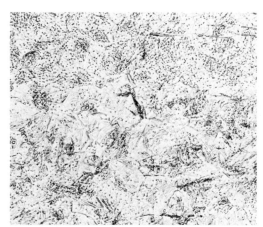

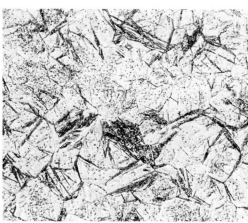

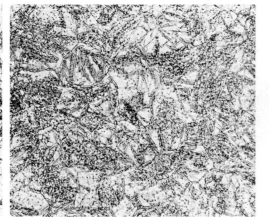

**Fig. 73, 74, 75** AISI S7. Continuous cooling transformations. Some very fine undissolved carbide is present in all specimens in this series. Fig. 73: austenitized at 940 °C (1725 °F) and cooled at 2780 °C/h (5000 °F/h). 62 HRC. Structure is martensite plus a small amount of bainite. Fig. 74: cooled at 1390 °C/h (2500 °F/h) to produce a greater amount of bainite. 61.5 HRC. Fig. 75: cooled at 830 °C/h (1500 °F/h). 56.5 HRC. Structure is mostly bainite plus some martensite (light). 4% picral. 500×

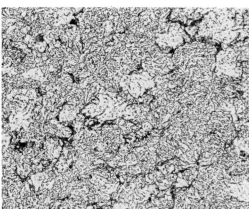

**Fig. 76, 77, 78** AISI S7. Continuous cooling transformations. Some very fine carbide is present in all specimens in this series. Fig. 76: austenitized at 940 °C (1725 °F) and cooled at 445 °C/h (800 °F/h). 51.5 HRC. Structure is nearly all bainite with some small patches of martensite (white). Fig. 77: cooled at 220 °C/h (400 °F/h). 45 HRC. Structure is mostly bainite with fine pearlite at the prior-austenite grain boundaries. Fig. 78: cooled at 28 °C/h (50 °F/h) to 620 °C (1150 °F), then water quenched. Austenite present at 620 °C (1150 °F) was transformed to martensite. Structure is mostly fine pearlite with patches of martensite (white). See also Fig. 73, 74, 75. 4% picral. 500×

**Fig. 79, 80, 81, 82** AISI O1. Influence of tempering temperature. All specimens austenitized at 800 °C (1475 °F), oil quenched, and tempered at different temperatures. Fig. 79: 200 °C (400 °F). 60 HRC. Fig. 80: 315 °C (600 °F). 55 HRC. Fig. 81: 425 °C (800 °F). 49 HRC. Fig. 82: 540 °C (1000 °F). 43 HRC. 4% picral. 500×

**Fig. 83, 84, 85** AISI W1. Austenitized at 800 °C (1475 °F), brine quenched, and tempered 2 h at 150 °C (300 °F). Black rings are hardened zones in 75-, 50-, and 25-mm (3-, 2-, and 1-in.) diam bars. Core hardness decreases with increasing bar diameter. Fig. 83: shallow-hardening grade. Case, 65 HRC; core, 34 to 43 HRC. Fig. 84: medium-hardening grade. Case, 64.5 HRC: core, 36 to 41 HRC. Fig. 85: deep-hardening grade. Case, 65 HRC; core, 36.5 to 45 HRC. Hot 50% HCl. One half actual size.

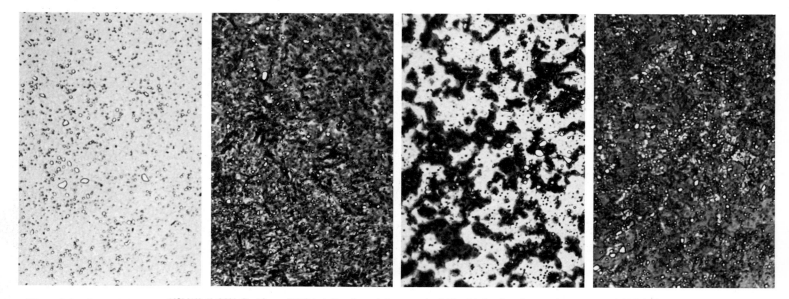

**Fig. 86, 87, 88, 89** AISI W1 (1.05% C), 19-mm (0.75-in.) diam bars; brine quenched. Fig. 86: hardened case microstructure. 64 HRC. Case contains as-quenched martensite and undissolved carbides. 4% picral. Fig. 87: 2% nital etch reveals martensite as dark rather than light. Fig. 88: transition zone. 55 HRC. Martensite is light, undissolved, carbide is outlined, and pearlite is dark. 4% picral. Fig. 89: core microstructure. 42 to 44 HRC. 4% picral etch reveals fine pearlite matrix (black) containing some patches of martensite (white) and undissolved carbides (outlined white particles). 1000×

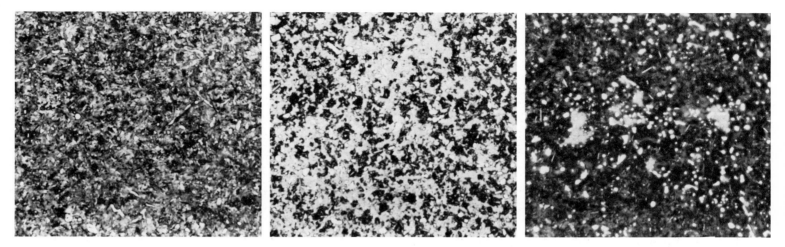

**Fig. 90, 91, 92** AISI F2, heated to 870 °C (1600 °F), water quenched, and tempered at 150 °C (300 °F). Fig. 90: case microstructure. 63 HRC. 2% nital. Fig. 91: transition region. Martensite (light) and pearlite (dark) are present between the surface and center. 4% picral. Fig. 92: core microstructure. 48 HRC. 4% picral etch reveals pearlite, carbides, and some martensite. 1000×

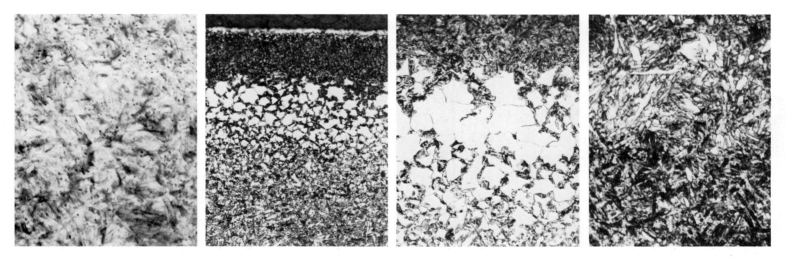

**Fig. 93, 94, 95, 96** AISI S2, heated to 845 °C (1550 °F), water quenched, and tempered at 150 °C (300 °F). Fig. 93: 59.5 HRC. Structure consists of martensite and some very fine undissolved carbide. 2% nital. 1000×. Fig. 94: surface of part that was decarburized, then carburized and heat treated. Note white ferrite grains below the dark surface layer. 3% nital. 200×. Fig. 95: as in Fig. 94, but at 400×. Ferrite at 260 HK, martensite in surface layer at 665 HK, martensite beneath ferrite increased from 400 to 635 HK going away from ferrite. Fig. 96: core structure. 580 HK. Martensite (dark), some undissolved carbides and ferrite (white) formed during quenching. 3% nital. 1000×

 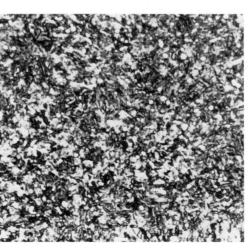 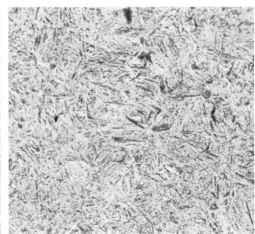

**Fig. 97** AISI L6, heated to 840 °C (1550 °F), oil quenched and tempered at 150 °C (300 °F). 61 HRC. Martensite and undissolved carbides are revealed. 2% nital. 1000×

**Fig. 98** AISI O2, heated to 850 °C (1500 °F), oil quenched and tempered at 175 °C (350 °F). 61 HRC. Martensite and a small amount of undissolved carbide are revealed. 2% nital. 1000×

**Fig. 99** AISI S1, heated to 955 °C (1750 °F), oil quenched and tempered at 150 °C (300 °F). 58 to 59 HRC. Only martensite is visible. 2% nital. 500×

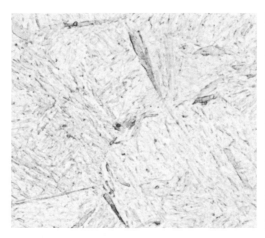

**Fig. 100** AISI S5, heated to 870 °C (1600 °F) and oil quenched. 62 HRC. Only martensite is visible. 4% picral/2% nital. 1000×

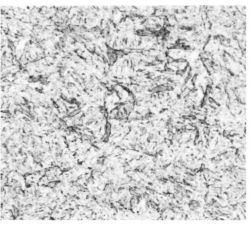

**Fig. 101** AISI S5 heated to 870 °C (1600 °F), oil quenched and tempered at 175 °C (350 °F). 60 HRC. Only martensite is visible. 2% nital. 1000×

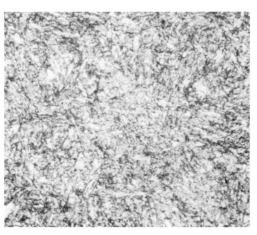

**Fig. 102** AISI S5 heated to 870 °C (1600 °F), oil quenched and tempered at 480 °C (900 °F). 51 to 52 HRC. Only martensite is visible. 2% nital. 1000×

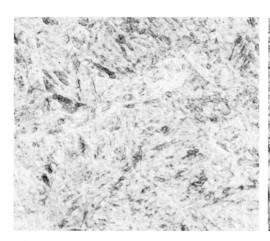

**Fig. 103** AISI S7, heated to 940 °C (1725 °F), air quenched and tempered at 200 °C (400 °F). 58 HRC. Martensite and a small amount of undissolved carbides are observed. Vilella's reagent. 1000×

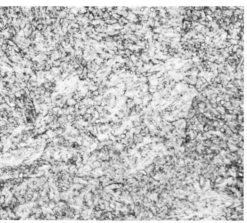

**Fig. 104** AISI S7 heated to 940 °C (1725 °F), air quenched and tempered at 495 °C (925 °F). 52 HRC. Martensite and a small amount of undissolved carbide are observed. Vilella's reagent. 1000×

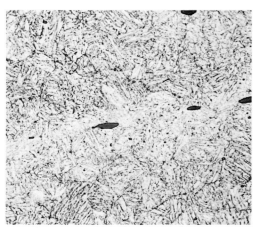

**Fig. 105** AISI P20 heated to 900 °C (1650 °F), water quenched and tempered at 525 °C (975 °F). 32 HRC. Matrix is martensite. Dark particles are manganese sulfides. Contrast process orthochromatic film. 2% nital. 500×

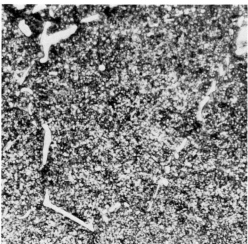

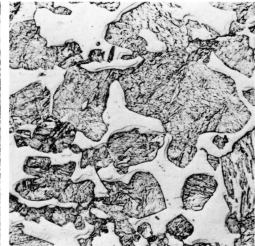

**Fig. 106, 107, 108** AISI P5, heat treated. Case, 59.5 HRC; core, 22 HRC. Fig. 106: carburized case. Note the carbide enrichment and networking in the case region. Matrix is martensite. 100×. Fig. 107: carburized case microstructure. 1000×. Fig. 108: differential interference contrast micrograph, core microstructure. Austenitization temperature used to harden the case is too low for the core; note the ferrite (white) and martensite (dark) in the underaustenitized core. 2% nital. 400×

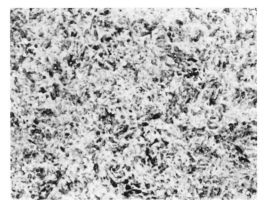

**Fig. 109** AISI A6, heated to 840 °C (1550 °F), air quenched and tempered at 150 °C (300 °F). 61.5 HRC. Martensite plus a small amount of undissolved carbide are observed. 2% nital. 1000×

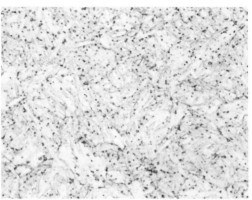

**Fig. 110** AISI H11, heated to 1010 °C (1850 °F), air quenched and double tempered at 510 °C (950 °F). 52 HRC. Martensite plus a small amount of very fine carbide are visible. Vilella's reagent. 1000×

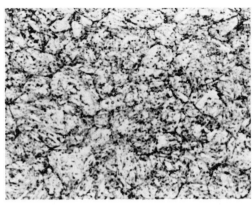

**Fig. 111** AISI H13, heated to 1025 °C (1875 °F), air quenched and double tempered at 595 °C (1100 °F). 42 HRC. All martensite plus a small amount of very fine undissolved carbide. 2% nital. 1000×

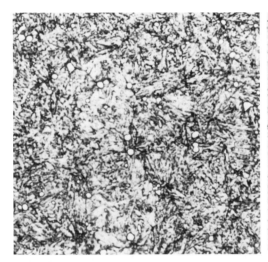

**Fig. 112** AISI H21, heated to 1200 °C (2200 °F), oil quenched and tempered at 595 °C (1100 °F). 53.5 HRC. Martensite and undissolved carbide are observed. 2% nital/Vilella's reagent. 1000×

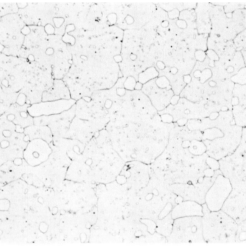

**Fig. 113** AISI D2, heated to 1010 °C (1850 °F), air quenched and tempered at 200 °C (400 °F). 59.5 HRC. Martensite plus substantial undissolved carbide; note the prior-austenite grain boundaries. 2% nital. 1000×

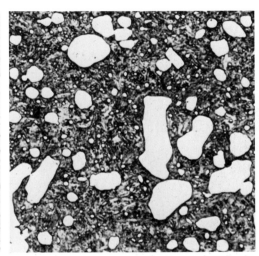

**Fig. 114** AISI D3, heated to 980 °C (1800 °F), oil quenched and tempered at 200 °C (400 °F). 60.5 HRC. Martensite plus substantial undissolved carbide are visible. 2% nital/Vilella's reagent. 1000×

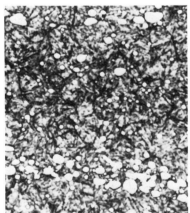

**Fig. 115** AISI M1, heated to 1175 °C (2150 °F), oil quenched and triple tempered at 480 °C (900 °F). 62 HRC. Martensite plus undissolved carbide are revealed. 2% nital. 1000×

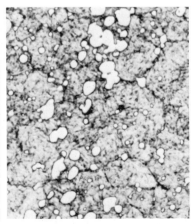

**Fig. 116** AISI M2, heated to 1120 °C (2050 °F), oil quenched and double tempered at 480 °C (900 °F). 62 HRC. Martensite plus undissolved carbide are revealed. Vilella's reagent. 1000×

**Fig. 117** AISI M4, heated to 1220 °C (2225 °F), oil quenched and double tempered at 480 °C (900 °F). 62 HRC. Martensite plus undissolved carbide are revealed. Vilella's reagent. 1000×

**Fig. 118** AISI M42, heated to 1175 °C (2150 °F), oil quenched and triple tempered at 565 °C (1050 °F). 65 HRC. Martensite plus undissolved carbide are observed. Vilella's reagent. 1000×

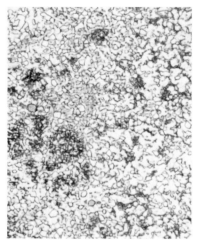

**Fig. 119** AISI T15, powder-made. Sample was slow cooled after hot isostatic pressing. 28 HRC. Structure is partially annealed. 3% nital. 1000×

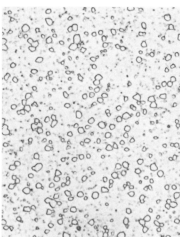

**Fig. 120** AISI T15, powder-made. Sample was hot isostatically pressed, forged, and annealed. 24 HRC. Structure is fully annealed. 3% nital. 1000×

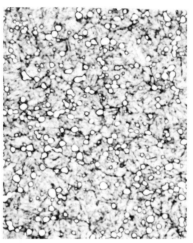

**Fig. 121** AISI T15, powder-made. Processed as in Fig. 120, then hardened: heated to 1230 °C (2250 °F) for 5 min in salt, oil quenched, triple tempered 2 h each at 540 °C (1000 °F). 65 HRC. 3% nital. 1000×

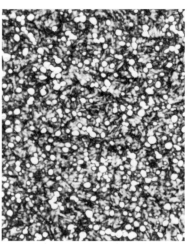

**Fig. 122** AISI T15, powder-made. Same sample as in Fig. 121, but etched in 100 mL $H_2O$, 1 mL HCl, 1 g $K_2S_2O_5$, and 1 g $NH_4F \cdot HF$. 1000×

# Cemented Carbides

By Martin N. Haller
Staff Engineer
Kennametal, Inc.

CEMENTED CARBIDES are liquid phase sintered materials whose hardness, toughness, yield strength, abrasion and wear resistance, and thermal stability make them suitable for cutting tool and wear, metalforming, and rock drilling and mining applications. The physical properties are directly related to those of the constituents, such as carbide particles and the metallic binder phase, as well as to the particle size and distribution of these phases. In general, the carbide particles range in size from 0.1 to approximately 10 $\mu$m, with an average size of less than 2 $\mu$m. Most metal cutting carbide inserts are further coated by chemical vapor deposition (CVD) with 0.2- to 10-$\mu$m thick refractory layers. This necessitates using the highest practical magnifications in the optical metallography of these materials, requiring high optical resolution at magnifications of 1500×.

The very properties that commend cemented carbides as good tool materials significantly restrict the techniques used to grind and polish them. The high hardness and relative toughness of cemented carbides require the use of diamonds in grinding and polishing. Automatic machinery capable of exerting forces up to 200 N (45 lb) normal to the sample is also necessary. Although it is possible to grind and polish manually, the effort and time required as well as requirements for reproducibility generally rule out these techniques (Ref 1). All of the micrographs in this article are from specimens prepared using an automatic machine.

## Specimen Preparation

**Sectioning.** Cemented carbides are best cut into sizes suitable for metallography by the high-speed cutoff machines used for most metals. Cutting wheels should be metal-bonded diamond, and attention must be paid to the cutting forces or pressure, because these materials will fracture readily if too heavily stressed. Wheel speeds exceeding 1000 rpm are recommended. Water is used as a coolant, and the pressure should be regulated to eliminate deflection or binding of the cutting wheel, which causes fracturing near the end of the cut. The final few percent of thickness usually fractures despite all precautions, leaving a small burr, which is easily removed by a short hand-dressing on a 15- to 30-$\mu$m metal-bonded diamond lap at 150 to 300 rpm.

**Mounting** should be performed using thermosetting resins or castable epoxy resins containing a hard filler addition. Typical examples are diallyl phthalate with fiberglass (thermosetting) or epoxy resins to which alumina ($Al_2O_3$) particles have been added (castable). These are required due to the extreme edge rounding that occurs during polishing when hard materials, such as cemented carbides, are mounted in soft embedding media. No embedding medium without hardener has been found to yield adequate edge retention and flatness for machine grinding and polishing.

Mounted specimens suitable in size for standard 25- to 38-mm (1- to 1.5-in.) diam cylinders are most frequently used. Unmounted specimens as large as 150 mm (6 in.) square may also be used on most automatic machines; however, the high density of carbides and their subsequent weight may cause difficulties with optical microscope stages.

Preservation of refractory coatings requires that the specimens be mounted, which is readily performed with available mounting presses. Epoxy casting resins, depending on their chemical formulation, require 15 min to 8 h to harden, but the thermosetting resins will produce a mount ready for polishing in 15 min. For more information on mounting materials and procedures, see the article "Mounting of Specimens" in this Volume.

**Grinding and Polishing.** After mounting, the specimens are flattened, ground, and polished in holders appropriate for the automatic machine being used. The holders typically accept six 25-mm (1-in.) diam or four 38-mm (1.5-in.) diam specimens simultaneously. The initial grinding and flattening takes 1 to 2 min using a 220-grit resin-bonded diamond lap. Scratches and work-hardened regions must be removed with finer abrasives until the desired surface finish is obtained.

For carbides, grinding proceeds for 1 min on a 600-grit diamond lap, followed by fine grinding using 6-$\mu$m diamond on a cast iron lap. Coarse polishing is performed using 6-$\mu$m diamond on hard plane cloth for 2 min. Next, the specimen is polished using 3-$\mu$m diamond on hard plane cloth for 2 min, then final polished using 1-$\mu$m diamond on hard plane cloth for 1 min. All grindings are performed at 200 Pa (29 psi) and 300 rpm, using copious water for coarse grinding and an alcohol-based lubricant for fine grinding. The coarse and fine polishings are performed at 400 Pa (58 psi) and 150 rpm using an alcohol-based lubricant. The surfaces should be cleaned between steps with an alcohol rinse, because the cobalt surface is chemically active during polishing and will be electrolytically attacked by tap water.

Automatic machine manufacturers can supply detailed information for grinding and polishing cemented carbides following the general procedures outlined above. For the preservation of coatings and retention of adequate flatness, fine grinding is necessary. The alternate steps of deposition of a nickel film or sandwiching support pieces nearby to preserve edges and flatness are more time consuming and less reliable than the use of epoxies and hard fillers. Details concerning typical equipment, materials, and methodology for metallographic preparation are available in Ref 2.

## Macroexamination

Cemented carbides are not usually macroscopically examined at 10× or less. However, examination with a low-power microscope at 20× or 30× is useful for detecting pits, pressing flaws, contamination, segregation, free (excess) carbon, and carbon deficiency ($\eta$ phase). Examination of fracture surfaces at 20× reveals defects larger than approximately 0.02 mm (0.001 in.). Free carbon appears on an as-sintered or fracture surface as clustered dark spots (Fig. 1). A specimen with free carbon often has an as-sintered surface that is slippery to the touch.

Carbon deficiency, or $\eta$ phase ($Co_3W_3C$), can be detected by examining the fracture surface and, depending on the degree of deficiency, is often detectable on an as-sintered surface. Carbon deficiency appears as shiny stringers, dots, and clusters that turn black when etched 3 to 5 s in Murakami's reagent (Fig. 2 and 3). Fracture will initiate in and propagate through such defects as pits and pressing flaws, which lessen the strength of the material. For this reason, they are easy to identify on a fracture surface. The shape and appearance of a defect may indicate its origin.

Eta phase and free carbon are also visible on metallographic cross sections. Because the number, size, and distribution of these defects can be quantified, they are usually evaluated by quantitative metallography on polished specimens. For more information on stereological measurements, see the section "Quantitative Metallography" later in this article.

## Microexamination

The heterogeneity of cemented carbides leads to various contrasting methods, because no universal etchant has been found for these materials. Qualitative metallography, which is based on the use of ASTM standards B 276 (Ref 3) for apparent porosity, B 390 (Ref 4) for grain size and B 657 (Ref 5) for microstructure, can be performed using Murakami's reagent and the optical microscope.

The initial examination is performed for porosity evaluation on the as-polished specimen. The ASTM method rates vol% porosity using standard comparison charts as follows:

| | | |
|---|---|---|
| A-porosity .... | Pore diameter: $d_p < 10 \ \mu m$ | Rate at $200\times$ |
| B-porosity ..... | Pore diameter: $10 \mu m \leq d_p \leq 25 \ \mu m$ | Rate at $100\times$ |
| C-porosity .... | Rosette pattern: $d_p > 25 \ \mu m$ | Rate at $100\times$ |

The ratings give pore volume as a percentage of total volume; acceptance criteria vary with application. A- and B-porosity are illustrated in Ref 1; Fig. 4 shows that C-porosity is due to the precipitation of free carbon in the form of graphite at some point during sintering. The rigorous grinding and polishing required for these specimens usually result in almost complete removal of the graphite from the polished surface, leading to the concept of "porosity" for this phase. Its effect on fracture toughness of the carbides allows the graphite to act as though it were porosity.

Grain size is determined by comparing the structure of the prepared specimen at $1500\times$ with micrographs in ASTM B 390. Structures are rated according to cobalt content and grain size (fine, medium, or coarse). For example, a 90WC-10Co alloy would be rated as 10-F, 10-M, or 10-C, depending on grain size and concentration of tungsten carbide.

Microstructural evaluation is based on the different reaction rates of Murakami's re-

**Table 1    Relative reaction rates of cemented carbide phases to Murakami's reagent**

| Component | Reaction rate (WC = 1) | Etching duration, s |
|---|---|---|
| Co, Ni ...................... | 0 | ... |
| WC ......................... | 1 | 120 |
| (Ta,Ti,Nb,W) C ............. | 4 | 30 |
| $\eta$ phase ($Co_3W_3$) C ........... | 20 | 3 |
| $\eta$ phase ($Co_6W_6$) C ........... | 40 | 3 |
| $W_2C$ ....................... | 400 | 0.3 |

agent with the various phases of the cemented carbide microstructure, which include:

- Tungsten carbide ($\alpha$ phase): WC
- Binder ($\beta$ phase): Co, Ni, Fe
- Mixed carbides ($\gamma$ phase): (Ti,Ta,Nb,W)C
- Eta phase ($\eta$ phase); $Co_3W_3C$ ($M_6C$), $Co_6W_6C$ ($M_{12}C$)
- Di-tungsten carbide: $W_2C$
- Coatings: TiC (titanium carbide), TiCN (titanium carbonitride), TiN (titanium nitride), and $Al_2O_3$ (alumina)

The variable reaction rate of these phases is apparent in the backscattered scanning electron micrograph in Fig. 5, which shows that the cobalt binder phase is not attacked and is therefore the highest feature in the micrograph (light areas). These points actually define the polished plane before etching. At mid-height, the structure consists of angular tungsten carbide grains. The mixed carbides (cubic crystals of solid solutions of tantalum, titanium, and niobium with tungsten and carbon) are etched to 2-$\mu m$ deep.

Etching experiments have led to a classification of the reaction rates of the carbide constituents using Murakami's reagent, as listed in Table 1. Therefore, cemented carbides are usually etched in several stages to assess the possible constituents. Compositions of etchants used in the microexamination of cemented carbides, including Murakami's reagent, are listed in Table 2.

The varying reaction rates with Murakami's reagent also lead to arbitrary decisions as to the best method of qualitatively evaluating cemented carbide microstructures. A good general technique can be performed in three steps: (1) porosity assessment, as-pol-

ished, (2) a 3-s etch using Murakami's reagent for $\eta$ phase, and (3) a final 2-min etch for the overall structure. An example of a specimen after the 2-min etch is shown in Fig. 6. This is an ISO P20 grade alloy with a composition of 80WC-13(Ti,Ta,Nb)C-7Co. The example shown would be rated as a medium structure and grain size by ASTM B 390 and B 657. Cobalt is unetched and difficult to see, tungsten carbide particles are partially etched (simple, regular shapes), and mixed carbides are irregular, rounded shapes that are overetched as seen by the dark border surrounding each grain.

The structure shown can be qualitatively characterized as to constituent size, shape, and distribution. All but two of the specimens shown in the accompanying photomicrographs were subjected to this 2-min etch. An alternative that more clearly shows only the cobalt phase in this grade is shown in Fig. 7, in which the cobalt has been completely removed by a 10-s etch with ferric chloride ($FeCl_3$). No other constituent is attacked by this etchant. The vol% and distribution of cobalt are much better shown in Fig. 7 than in Fig. 6. A combination of both etches (2 min Murakami's and 10 s $FeCl_3$) on this grade is shown in Fig. 8. Although Fig. 8 is an excellent representation of the individual carbide components, it overestimates the binder phase (black), because all of the grain boundaries are also black. Therefore, the three-step examination technique mentioned above is recommended.

The only exception to the use of Murakami's reagent is found in the examination of grades designed for high-temperature use. These are high in titanium carbide content and have a complex nickel-molybdenum binder. A typical example might have a composition of 5WC-8Mo-8Ni-79TiC. These materials are rapidly attacked by Murakami's reagent, which leaves an obscuring reaction layer on the etched surface. A good general etchant for these materials is hydrogen peroxide ($H_2O_2$), which is listed in Table 2. Figure 9 shows the typical microstructure revealed by this etch; it consists of irregular gray shapes with distinct cores, which are unreacted TiC surrounded by (Mo,Ti)C. The nickel binder is white, and the complex metal carbides ((W,Ti,Mo)C) are the dark, rounded phase distributed as a matrix.

**Table 2    Chemical etchants for cemented carbides**

| Reagent | Composition | Procedure |
|---|---|---|
| Murakami's ................... | 10 g $K_3Fe(CN)_6$ (potassium ferricyanide), 10 g NaOH (sodium hydroxide), and 100 mL $H_2O$ Make fresh daily | Swab specimen continuously for appropriate time (see Table 1) |
| Ferric chloride ................. | 3 g $FeCl_3$ and 100 mL $H_2O$ Make fresh daily | Swab specimen continuously for 10 s (for nickel or cobalt binder removal) |
| Hydrogen peroxide(a) .......... | 20 vol% in water. Mix as needed | Immerse specimen at 70-90 °C (160-195 °F) for 4 min, swabbing surface occasionally to remove reaction products. Etches nickel-bonded molybdenum, TiC materials |

(a) From Ref 6

**W₂C.** Tungsten carbide grades formulated for extreme corrosion resistance (those containing less than 1.5% binder) may contain di-tungsten carbide as well as tungsten carbide. Di-tungsten carbide is a stable product of the formation of tungsten carbide by all processes and is a precursor of tungsten carbide in most carburizing reactions. As noted in Table 1, di-tungsten carbide reacts so rapidly with Murakami's reagent that detection of this phase is best accomplished by the use of Murakami's reagent at one tenth its normal strength. Figures 10 through 13 depict the same field and show progressive etching of the di-tungsten carbide.

In Fig. 10 (as-polished), the angular, gray patches are typical of tungsten carbide crystals; the black patches are gross porosity. A 10-s etch (Fig. 11) reveals immediately that for certain orientations the di-tungsten carbide has already been deeply etched; for other orientations no perceptible reaction has occurred. After 30 s (Fig. 12), the initially etched material has been dissolved, while other, less favorably oriented di-tungsten carbide has begun to etch. Figure 13 shows that after 30 s with full-strength Murakami's reagent almost all of the di-tungsten carbide has been removed. The di-tungsten carbide/tungsten carbide mixture exists, because there is not enough carbon present to achieve the tungsten carbide stoichiometry. In the presence of larger amounts of the binder phase, the thermodynamics favor the formation of mixed carbides (η phase).

**Eta phase.** Two η phases exist in cobalt-bonded carbides. The first consists of the approximate formula $(Co_3W_3)C$; the second is $(Co_6W_6)C$. Both result from decarburizing reactions (Ref 7) during sintering or during high-temperature chemical vapor deposition (CVD) coating of refractory films on carbide substrates.

The $(Co_3W_3)C$ form $(M_6C)$ is shown in Fig. 14 to 17. This phase nucleates and grows due to the constant dissolution of tungsten carbide in the liquid cobalt; its presence is controlled by the amount of carbon present in the cobalt. When properly etched, the phase develops a spectrum of colors (white, gold, green, blue, and red, but predominantly gold or brown), probably as a result of crystal orientation effects. Figures 16 and 17 show that the tungsten carbide grains have become rounded and that grain boundaries are present within the η phase.

The second stable form of η phase is shown in Fig. 18. The $(Co_6W_6)C$ form $(M_{12}C)$ is seen only at the substrate/CVD coating interface. Its appearance is caused by the gettering action of titanium atoms selectively removing carbon from the available cobalt, a reaction thermodynamically favored even in the presence of atmospheric carbon during coating deposition. Because the CVD process occurs at temperatures below the liquidus of the Co-W-C alloy, the reactions occur in the solid state and do not change the geometry of the binder. As a result, the η phase is discon-

tinuous and occupies only that volume formerly occupied by the cobalt. Both forms are hard, brittle cubic compounds that deteriorate the fracture toughness of the cemented carbide and must therefore be controlled or eliminated.

**Representative Micrographs.** The micrographs shown in this article represent the variety of cemented carbides now available. They cover the range of cobalt concentration from 1.5 to 25% and complex carbide contents from 0 to 55%. (See the article "Superhard Tool Materials" in Volume 3 of the 9th Edition of *Metals Handbook* for uses and physical properties.) The Rockwell A scale hardness (HRA) value is given for each of the included micrographs, because this is one of the most important properties of cemented carbides. The hardness value obtained is a complex function of the amount of binder, the composition of the phases, and the particle size of the constituents. Generally, hardness increases with decreasing binder volume and decreasing particle size.

## Quantitative Metallography

The current quantitative metallography of cemented carbides is presented in Ref 8 and 9. The important parameters to be measured are pore volume, binder volume fraction, binder mean free path, carbide grain size and shape, and the contiguity, which is the particle-to-particle grain-boundary ratio to total surface area. Using well-established stereological techniques, microstructural parameters such as the volume fraction of binder, the tungsten carbide mean linear intercept grain size, the carbide contiguity, and the binder mean linear intercept distance can be measured or calculated from appropriate micrographs (Ref 9).

The precision and accuracy with which this can be accomplished, however, depends on the particular carbide structure being investigated and has led to the use of many imaging techniques and contrasting methods. Because the quantities to be measured vary in size from 20-$\mu$m particles to less than 0.1-$\mu$m-thick binder layers, no single imaging technique is suitable. Research laboratories report the use of heat tinting (Ref 10), electrolytic etching (Ref 11), interference vapor-deposited films (Ref 12), and ion etching (Ref 13), as well as chemical etchants other than Murakami's. Each has particular advantages for certain grades and compositions of carbide or for particular imaging methods.

Imaging methods other than bright-field optical microscopy include differential interference microscopy, scanning electron microscopy (SEM), transmission electron microscopy (TEM) (replication techniques), photoemission electron microscopy (Ref 14-16), and scanning auger microscopy (Ref 17). Of these, scanning electron microscopy and photoemission microscopy seem to be emerging as the most useful techniques, especially

when used in conjunction with automatic image analyzers. The cited references will provide sufficient information to evaluate the techniques for specific applications. More information on quantitative metallography can be found in the article "Quantitative Metallography" in this Volume.

## REFERENCES

1. "Metallographic Procedures for Sintered Carbide," Report 01.84, Struers Inc., Cleveland

2. G. Vander Voort, *Metallography Principles and Practice*, McGraw-Hill, 1984

3. "Standard Test Method for Apparent Porosity in Cemented Carbides," B 276, *Annual Book of ASTM Standards*, Vol 02.05, ASTM, Philadelphia, 1984, p 105-109

4. "Standard Practice for Evaluating Apparent Grain Size and Distribution of Cemented Tungsten Carbides," B 390, *Annual Book of ASTM Standards*, Vol 02.05, ASTM, Philadelphia, 1984, p 203-207

5. "Standard Method for Metallographic Determination of Microstructure in Cemented Carbides," B 657, *Annual Book of ASTM Standards*, Vol 02.05, ASTM, Philadelphia, 1984, p 538-542

6. E. Breval and V. Sakari, Structure and Hardness of Titanium Carbide Coatings on Hard Metals, in *International Chalmers Symposium on Surface Problems in Materials Science and Technology*, Sweden, 1979

7. L. Akesson, An Experimental and Thermodynamic Study of the Co-W-C System in the Temperature Range 1470-1700 K, in *Science of Hard Materials*, R.K. Viswanadham, *et al.*, Ed., Plenum Press, 1983, p 71-82

8. H.E. Exner, Qualitative and Quantitative Interpretation of Microstructures in Cemented Carbides, in *Science of Hard Materials*, R.K. Viswanadham, *et al.*, Ed., Plenum Press, 1983, p 233-259

9. J. Gurland, Application of Quantitative Microscopy to Cemented Carbides, in *Practical Applications of Quantitative Metallography*, STP 839, J.L. McCall and J.H. Steele, Jr., Ed., ASTM, Philadelphia, 1984, p 65-84

10. H. Grewe, Structural Investigation on Hard Metals, *Prakt. Metallog.*, Vol 5, 1969, p 411-419

11. W. Mader and K.F. Muller, Determination and Comparison of Structural Parameters of Hard Metal Alloys Using Electron and Optical Micrographs, *Prakt. Metallog.*, Vol 5, 1968, p 616-625

12. W. Peter, E. Kohlhaas, and O. Jung, Revealing of Hard Metal Structures by Interference Vapor-Deposition, *Prakt. Metallog.*, Vol 4, 1967, p 288-290

13. A. Doi, T. Nishikawa, and A. Hara, Ion-Etching Techniques for Microstructural Characterization of Cemented Carbides

# 276/Metallographic Techniques and Microstructures

and Ceramics, in *Science of Hard Materials*, R.K. Viswanadham, *et al.*, Ed., Plenum Press, 1983, p 329-339

14. H. Gahm, S. Karagoz, and G. Kompek, Metallographic Methods for the Characterization of the Microstructure of Cemented Carbides, *Pract. Metallog.*, Vol 18, 1981, p 14-30

15. E.M. Vyger, Metallography and Microstructural Characterization of Some Hardmetal Grades by Optical and Electron Microscopy, *Prakt. Metallog.*, Vol 19, 1982, p 592-604, 639-649

16. B. Egg, Experiences with Quantitative Automatic Scanning Electron Microscopy, *Pract. Metallog.*, Vol 22, p 78-87

17. D.T. Quinto, G.J. Wolfe, and M.N. Haller, Low-Z Element Analysis in Hard Materials, in *Science of Hard Materials*, R.K. Viswanadham, *et al.*, Ed., Plenum Press, 1983, p 947-971

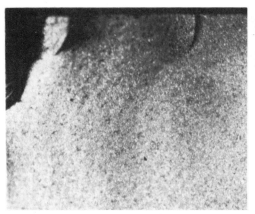

**Fig. 1** Free (excess) carbon appears as clustered dark spots on this fracture surface of a cemented carbide. As-polished. 21×

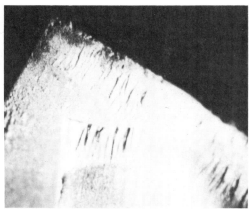

**Fig. 2, 3** Carbon deficiency (η phase) on a fracture surface of cemented carbide. Fig. 2: before etching, η phase appears as shiny stringers, dots, and clusters. Fig. 3: after etching 5 s in Murakami's reagent, η phase is black.

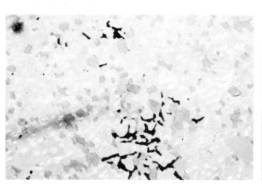

**Fig. 4** 86WC-8(Ta,Ti,Nb,W)C-6Co alloy, 91.6 HRA. An example of C-porosity (see Ref 5). Black areas are porosity, some of which still contain graphite (dark gray) distributed at grain boundaries of tungsten carbide particles (light gray, angular) and mixed carbides (darker gray, irregular, and rounded). Cobalt binder is white. As-polished. 1500×

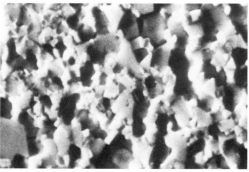

**Fig. 5** Scanning electron micrograph of 79WC-14(Ta,Ti,Nb,W)C-7Co alloy, 92.2 HRA. Raised areas are cobalt binder; gray particles in intermediate areas are tungsten carbide; rounded, deeply etched particles are mixed carbides. Murakami's reagent (see Table 2), 2 min. 3000×

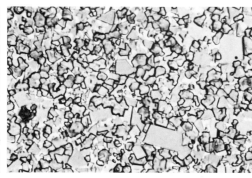

**Fig. 6** 80WC-13(Ta,Ti,Nb,W)C-7Co alloy, 92.2 HRA. White matrix is cobalt binder; light gray, angular areas are tungsten carbide; darker gray, rounded particles are mixed carbides. Murakami's reagent, 2 min. 1500×

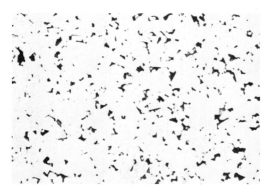

**Fig. 7** Same specimen as Fig. 6, except etched to remove only the cobalt binder phase. Black areas are the removed binder phase. The photographic printing technique used suppresses the unetched tungsten carbide and mixed carbide particles. FeCl₃ (see Table 2), 10 s. 1500×

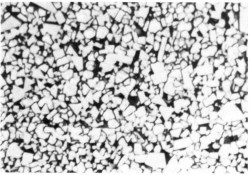

**Fig. 8** Same specimen as Fig. 6. Binder and grain boundaries are black; angular, light gray particles are tungsten carbide; rounded, gray particles are mixed carbides. Murakami's reagent, 2 min, followed by FeCl₃, 10 s. 1500×

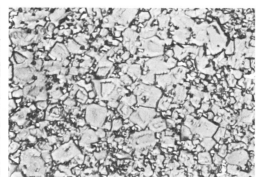

**Fig. 9** 5WC-8Mo-79TiC-8Ni alloy, 93.8 HRA. Irregular, gray shapes are complex carbides, many of which have a central core of unreacted titanium carbide. The fine, dark particles are overetched tungsten carbide and complex carbides; the nickel binder is white. Hot H₂O₂, 4 min (see Table 2). 1500×

 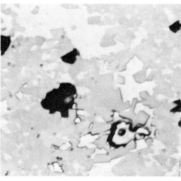 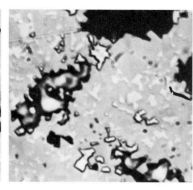 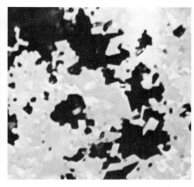

**Fig. 10, 11, 12, 13** 89WC-10(Ta,W)C-1Co alloy, 94 HRA. Four micrographs of the same field showing progressive etching of W₂C. Fig. 10: black areas are porosity, and white phase is W₂C. Fig. 11: some W₂C (white) is deeply etched, and some is unetched, depending on orientation of the grains. Fig. 12: deeply etched W₂C (white); black areas are porosity or completely removed W₂C. Fig. 13: white areas are unetched W₂C or cobalt binder; black areas are completely removed W₂C or porosity. Gray, angular WC particles remain unetched throughout. Fig. 10: as-polished. Fig. 11: dilute (¹/₁₀ strength) Murakami's reagent, 10 s. Fig. 12: dilute Murakami's reagent, 30 s. Fig. 13: full-strength Murakami's reagent, 30 s. 2000×

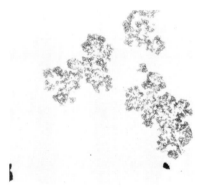 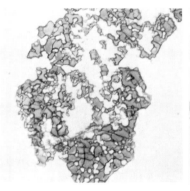 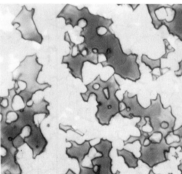 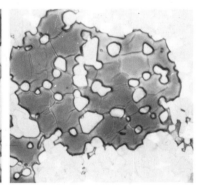

**Fig. 14** 85WC-8(Ta,Ti,Nb,W)C-7Co alloy, 90.3 HRA. Typical dendritic structure of η phase ((Co₃W₃)C). The composition of the phase was confirmed using x-ray diffraction techniques. Murakami's reagent, 3 s. 100×

**Fig. 15** Same alloy and etch as Fig. 14. Micrograph shows preserved (Co₃W₃)C (M₆C) on an undifferentiated cemented carbide background. The (Co₃W₃)C phase is highly colored under bright-field illumination. 500×

**Fig. 16** Same alloy and etch as Fig. 14. (Co₃W₃)C phase is dark gray with black etch boundaries. The varying shades of gray are due to the different colors of the phase. Background consists of angular, gray tungsten carbide particles, rounded, gray mixed carbides, and white cobalt binder. 1500×

**Fig. 17** Same alloy and etch as Fig. 14. Micrograph shows (Co₃W₃)C η phase detail. Eta phase is various shades of gray with clear grain boundaries; light gray tungsten carbide particles surrounded by η phase are rounded due to solubility of the binder. 1500×

 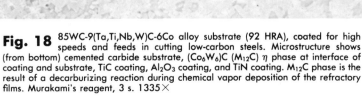 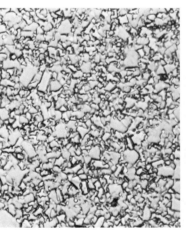 

**Fig. 18** 85WC-9(Ta,Ti,Nb,W)C-6Co alloy substrate (92 HRA), coated for high speeds and feeds in cutting low-carbon steels. Microstructure shows (from bottom) cemented carbide substrate, (Co₆W₆)C (M₁₂C) η phase at interface of coating and substrate, TiC coating, Al₂O₃ coating, and TiN coating. M₁₂C phase is the result of a decarburizing reaction during chemical vapor deposition of the refractory films. Murakami's reagent, 3 s. 1335×

**Fig. 19** 97WC-3Co alloy, 93.2 HRA. Gray particles are WC, dark, overetched spots are mixed carbides; white particles are cobalt binder. Using ASTM standard B 390, this microstructure would be classified type 3-F (3, cobalt content; F, fine-grained structure). Murakami's reagent, 2 min. 1500×

**Fig. 20** 92WC-2(Ta,W)C-6Co alloy, 92.7 HRA. Gray particles are tungsten carbide, and white areas are cobalt binder. The increased cobalt content is apparent when this figure is compared with Fig. 19. Murakami's reagent, 2 min. 1500×

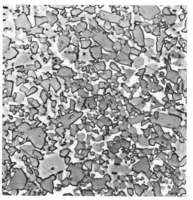

**Fig. 21** 89WC-11Co alloy, 89.8 HRA. Gray particles are tungsten carbide; white particles are cobalt binder in this medium-size grain structure. Note how HRA decreases as cobalt concentration increases (compare with Fig. 19 and 20). Murakami's reagent, 2 min. 1500×

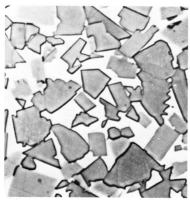

**Fig. 22** 85WC-15Co alloy, 84.9 HRA. This is a coarse structure, with tungsten carbide particles (gray, faceted particles in the white cobalt binder phase). Again, HRA has decreased as cobalt content has increased. Murakami's reagent, 2 min. 1500×

**Fig. 23** 75WC-25Co alloy, 79.3 HRA. Another coarse structure, with gray tungsten carbide particles in the white cobalt matrix. Compare HRA and cobalt content with the previous four figures. Murakami's reagent, 2 min. 1500×

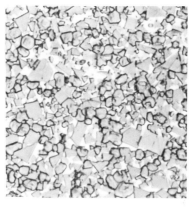

**Fig. 24** 83WC-10(Ta,Ti,Nb,W)C-8Co alloy, 90.3 HRA. Angular, gray particles are tungsten carbide; rounded, dark particles are mixed carbides; white particles are cobalt binder. Murakami's reagent, 2 min. 1500×

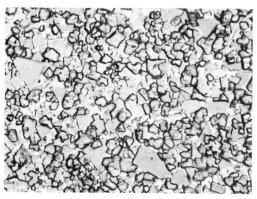

**Fig. 25** 78WC-15(Ta,Ti,Nb,W)C-7Co alloy, 92.2 HRA. Angular, gray particles are tungsten carbide; heavily etched, rounded particles are mixed carbides. The cobalt binder is white. Murakami's reagent, 2 min. 1500×

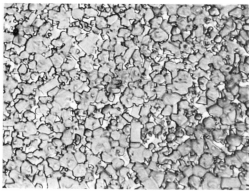

**Fig. 26** 73WC-21(Ta,Ti,Nb,W)C-6Co alloy, 92.9 HRA. This fine-grain microstructure consists of angular tungsten carbide, rounded mixed carbides, and white cobalt matrix. Murakami's reagent, 2 min. 1500×

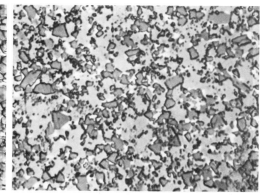

**Fig. 27** 43WC-50(Ta,Ti,Nb,W)C-6Co alloy, 90.0 HRA. Small, dark gray particles are tungsten carbide, larger, irregularly shaped, light gray areas are mixed carbides; white areas are the cobalt binder phase. Murakami's reagent, 2 min. 1500×

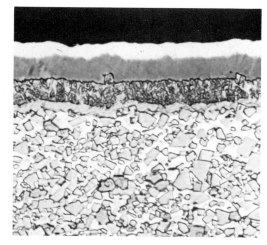

**Fig. 28** 86WC-8(Ta,Ti,Nb,W)C-6Co alloy, 91.6 HRA, with chemical vapor deposited coatings (from top) TiN, TiCN, and TiC. Angular, gray particles in the substrate are tungsten carbide; rounded particles are mixed carbides; and cobalt binder is white. Murakami's reagent, 2 min. 1500×

**Fig. 29** Back-scattered scanning electron micrograph of 90WC-10Co alloy, 89.8 HRA. Gray particles are tungsten carbide; cobalt binder phase is black. Compare this microstructure with that in Fig. 21. As-polished. 1500×

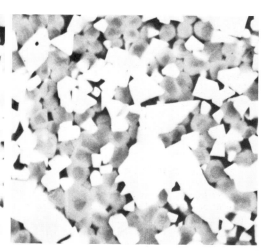

**Fig. 30** Back-scattered scanning electron micrograph of 76WC-16(Ta,Ti,Nb,W)C-8Co alloy, 92.2 HRA. Light gray, angular particles are tungsten carbide, dark gray, rounded particles are mixed carbides; and cobalt binder is black. Compare this structure with Fig. 25. Murakami's reagent, 2 min. 1500×

# Wrought Stainless Steels

By George F. Vander Voort
Supervisor
Applied Physics Research & Development
Carpenter Technology Corporation

and

Hughston M. James
Senior Metallurgist
Metal Physics Research
Carpenter Technology Corporation

WROUGHT STAINLESS STEELS are complex alloys containing a minimum of 11% Cr plus other elements to produce ferritic, martensitic, austenitic, duplex, or precipitation-hardenable grades. Procedures used to prepare wrought stainless steels for macroscopic and microscopic examination are similar to those used for carbon and alloy steels and for tool steels (see the articles "Carbon and Alloy Steels" and "Tool Steels" in this Volume). However, certain types require careful attention to prevent artifacts. Because the austenitic grades work-harden readily, cutting and grinding must be carefully executed to minimize deformation. The high-hardness martensitic grades that contain substantial undissolved chromium carbide are difficult to polish while fully retaining the carbides. The most difficult of such grades to prepare is AISI 440C, particularly in the annealed or annealed and quenched condition. For the most part, preparation of stainless steels is reasonably simple if the basic rules for metallographic preparation are followed. However, unlike carbon, alloy, and tool steels, etching techniques are more difficult due to the high corrosion resistance of stainless steels and the various second phases that may be encountered. Nominal compositions of grades illustrated in this article are given in Table 1.

## Macroexamination

The procedures used to select and prepare stainless steel disks for macroetching are identical to those used for carbon, alloy, and tool steels. Because these grades are more difficult to etch, all surfaces to be etched must be smooth ground or polished. Saw-cut surfaces will yield little useful information if they are macroetched.

Macroetchants for stainless steels are listed in Table 2. Heated macroetchants are used with stainless steels in the same manner as carbon, alloy, or tool steels. Etchant compositions are often more complex and more aggressive. In the study of weld macrostructures, it is quite common to polish the section and use one of the general-purpose microetchants.

The standard sulfur print technique (Ref 1) can be used to reveal the distribution of manganese sulfide (MnS) inclusions in stainless steels. However, if the manganese content of the grade is low, chromium will substitute for manganese in the sulfides, and the sulfur print intensity will decrease. As the manganese content decreases below approximately 0.60%, chromium substitutes for manganese. At manganese contents below approximately 0.20%, pure chromium sulfides will form. These produce no image in the sulfur print test.

## Microexamination

**Sectioning** techniques for stainless steels are identical to those used for carbon, alloy, or tool steels. Grades softer than approximately 35 HRC can be cut using a band saw or power hacksaw. However, such cutting produces substantial deformation and should be avoided with the deformation-sensitive austenitic grades. Deformation will be greatly reduced if cutting is performed using abrasive cutoff wheels with the proper degree of bonding. Shearing can be used with the ferritic grades, but should be avoided with the austenitics.

**Mounting** procedures, when required, are also identical to those used for carbon, alloy, and tool steels. If edge preservation is required for near-surface examination, compression-mounting epoxy can be used, or specimens can be plated with electroless nickel. For specimens with surface cracks, it may be useful to vacuum impregnate the specimen in cold-setting epoxy; epoxy will be drawn into the cracks, minimizing bleedout problems after etching.

**Grinding** is performed using 120-, 240-, 320-, 400-, then 600-grit water-cooled silicon carbide papers. Care must be taken, particularly when grinding austenitic grades, to remove the cold work from cutting and from each grinding step. In general, speeds of approximately 300 rpm and moderate, firm pressure are used. Grinding times are 1 to 2 min per step. If grinding is carried out by hand, the specimen should be rotated 45 to 90° between each step. Automatic grinding devices produce omnidirectional grinding patterns.

**Polishing.** After grinding, specimens are usually rough polished using 6- or 3-μm diamond as a paste, spray, or slurry on napless, low-nap, or medium-nap cloths. Edge flatness and inclusion retention are usually improved by using napless cloths, although scratch removal may not be as complete as with medium-nap cloths. A lubricant extender compatible with the diamond abrasive should be used to moisten the cloth and reduce drag. A wheel speed of approximately 150 rpm is usually adequate. Pressure should be moderate and firm; specimen rocking should be avoided if polishing is carried out by hand.

For hand polishing, rotate the specimen around the wheel in the direction opposite to wheel rotation while moving from center to edge. Automatic devices generally produce better edge flatness than hand polishing. After this step, the specimen may be polished using 1-μm diamond abrasive on a medium-nap cloth. For routine examination, a 1-μm diamond finish may be adequate, particularly for the hardenable grades.

To produce high-quality, scratch-free surfaces suitable for photomicroscopy, specimens should be final polished using one or more fine abrasives. The most commonly used final abrasives are 0.3-μm α-alumina ($Al_2O_3$) or 0.05-μm γ-$Al_2O_3$. Medium-nap

**Table 1  Compositions of wrought stainless steels(a)**

| Grade | C | Cr | Ni | Mn | Si | P | S | Others |
|---|---|---|---|---|---|---|---|---|
| | | | | Composition, % | | | | |
| **Austenitic grades** | | | | | | | | |
| 201 . . . . . . . . . . 0.15 | 16.00-18.00 | 3.50-5.50 | 5.50-7.50 | 1.0 | 0.060 | 0.030 | 0.25N |
| 301 . . . . . . . . . . 0.15 | 16.00-18.00 | 6.00-8.00 | 2.0 | 1.0 | 0.045 | 0.030 | . . . |
| 302 . . . . . . . . . . 0.15 | 17.00-19.00 | 8.00-10.00 | 2.0 | 1.0 | 0.045 | 0.030 | . . . |
| 303 . . . . . . . . . . 0.15 | 17.00-19.00 | 8.00-10.00 | 2.0 | 1.0 | 0.20 | 0.15 min | 0.60Mo(b) |
| 304 . . . . . . . . . . 0.08 | 18.00-20.00 | 8.00-10.00 | 2.0 | 1.0 | 0.045 | 0.030 | 0.10N |
| 308 . . . . . . . . . . 0.08 | 19.00-21.00 | 10.00-12.00 | 2.0 | 1.0 | 0.045 | 0.030 | . . . |
| 310 . . . . . . . . . . 0.25 | 24.00-26.00 | 19.00-22.00 | 2.0 | 1.5 | 0.045 | 0.030 | . . . |
| 316 . . . . . . . . . . 0.08 | 16.00-18.00 | 10.00-14.00 | 2.0 | 1.0 | 0.045 | 0.030 | 2.0-3.0Mo, 0.10N |
| 316L . . . . . . . . 0.03 | 16.00-18.00 | 10.00-14.00 | 2.0 | 0.75 | 0.045 | 0.030 | 2.0-3.0Mo, 0.10N |
| 321 . . . . . . . . . . 0.08 | 17.00-19.00 | 9.00-12.00 | 2.0 | 1.0 | 0.045 | 0.030 | 0.10N, 5 $\times$ C+N min Ti |
| 20Cb-3 . . . . . . . 0.07 | 19.00-21.00 | 32.00-38.00 | 2.0 | 1.0 | 0.045 | 0.035 | 2.0-3.0Mo, 3.0-4.0Cu 8 $\times$ C min Nb (1.0 max) |
| 22-13-5 . . . . . . . 0.06 | 20.5-23.5 | 11.5-13.5 | 4.0-6.0 | 1.0 | 0.040 | 0.030 | 1.5-3.0Mo, 0.2-0.4N, 0.1-0.3Nb, 0.1-0.3V |
| **Ferritic grades** | | | | | | | | |
| 409 . . . . . . . . . . 0.08 | 10.50-11.75 | . . . | 1.0 | 1.0 | 0.045 | 0.045 | 6 $\times$ C Ti (0.75 max) |
| 430 . . . . . . . . . . 0.12 | 16.00-18.00 | . . . | 1.0 | 1.0 | 0.040 | 0.030 | . . . |
| 430F . . . . . . . . . 0.12 | 16.00-18.00 | . . . | 1.25 | 1.0 | 0.040 | 0.060 | 0.60Mo(b) |
| 446 . . . . . . . . . . 0.20 | 23.00-27.00 | . . . | 1.5 | 1.0 | 0.040 | 0.030 | 0.25N |
| 182-FM . . . . . . . 0.08 | 17.50-19.50 | . . . | 2.5 | 1.0 | 0.040 | 0.15 min | . . . |
| E-Brite . . . . . . . . 0.01 | 25.0-27.5 | 0.50 | 0.40 | 0.40 | 0.020 | 0.020 | 0.75-1.5Mo, 0.015N, 0.2 max Cu (0.5 max Cu + Ni) |
| **Martensitic grades** | | | | | | | | |
| 403 . . . . . . . . . . 0.15 | 11.50-13.00 | . . . | 1.0 | 0.5 | 0.040 | 0.030 | . . . |
| 410 . . . . . . . . . . 0.15 | 11.50-13.50 | . . . | 1.0 | 1.0 | 0.040 | 0.030 | . . . |
| 416 . . . . . . . . . . 0.15 | 12.00-14.00 | . . . | 1.25 | 1.0 | 0.060 | 0.15 min | 0.60Mo(b) |
| 420 . . . . . . . . . . 0.15 min | 12.00-14.00 | . . . | 1.0 | 1.0 | 0.040 | 0.030 | . . . |
| 420F . . . . . . . . . 0.15 min | 12.00-14.00 | . . . | 1.25 | 1.0 | 0.060 | 0.15 min | 0.60Mo(b) |
| 431 . . . . . . . . . . 0.20 | 15.00-17.00 | 1.25-2.50 | 1.0 | 1.0 | 0.040 | 0.030 | . . . |
| 440A . . . . . . . . . 0.60-0.75 | 16.00-18.00 | . . . | 1.0 | 1.0 | 0.040 | 0.030 | 0.75Mo |
| 440B . . . . . . . . . 0.75-0.95 | 16.00-18.00 | . . . | 1.0 | 1.0 | 0.040 | 0.030 | 0.75Mo |
| 440C . . . . . . . . . 0.95-1.20 | 16.00-18.00 | . . . | 1.0 | 1.0 | 0.040 | 0.030 | 0.75Mo |
| **Precipitation-hardenable grades** | | | | | | | | |
| 630 . . . . . . . . . . 0.07 (17-4PH) | 15.50-17.50 | 3.0-5.0 | 1.0 | 1.0 | 0.040 | 0.030 | 3.0-3.5Cu, 0.15-0.45Nb + Ta |
| 631 . . . . . . . . . . 0.09 (17-7PH) | 16.00-18.00 | 6.5-7.75 | 1.0 | 1.0 | 0.040 | 0.030 | 0.75-1.50Al |
| 633 . . . . . . . . . . 0.07-0.11 (AM-350) | 16.00-17.00 | 4.00-5.00 | 0.5-1.25 | 0.5 | 0.040 | 0.030 | 2.5-3.25Mo, 0.07-0.13N |
| 634 . . . . . . . . . . 0.10-0.15 (AM355) | 15.00-16.00 | 4.00-5.00 | 0.5-1.25 | 0.5 | 0.040 | 0.030 | 2.5-3.25Mo |
| 635 . . . . . . . . . . 0.08 (Stainless W) | 16.00-17.50 | 6.00-7.50 | 1.0 | 1.0 | 0.040 | 0.030 | 0.4Al, 0.4-1.2 Ti |
| 15-5PH . . . . . . . 0.07 | 14.00-15.5 | 3.5-5.5 | 1.0 | 1.0 | 0.040 | 0.030 | 2.5-4.5Cu, 0.15-0.45Nb + Ta |
| PH13-8mo . . . . . 0.05 | 12.25-13.25 | 7.5-8.5 | 0.10 | 0.10 | 0.010 | 0.008 | 2.0-2.5Mo, 0.90-1.35Al, 0.01N |
| Custom 450 . . . . 0.05 | 14.00-16.00 | 5.0-7.0 | 1.0 | 1.0 | 0.030 | 0.030 | 1.25-1.75Cu, 0.5-1.0Mo, 8 $\times$ C min Nb (1.0 max) |
| Custom 455 . . . . 0.05 | 11.00-12.50 | 7.5-9.5 | 0.5 | 0.5 | 0.040 | 0.030 | 0.5Mo, 1.5-2.5Cu, 0.8-1.4Ti, 0.1-0.5Nb |
| **Duplex stainless steel** | | | | | | | | |
| 312 . . . . . . . . . . 0.15 | 30.0 (nominal) | 9.0 (nominal) | 2.0 | 1.0 | 0.045 | 0.030 | . . . |

(a) Maximum, unless range is given or unless otherwise noted. (b) Optional

cloths are usually used. Polishing with these abrasives, mixed as a water slurry, is performed in the same manner as diamond polishing. Specimens should be carefully cleaned between each rough and final polishing step to avoid contamination at the next step. Colloidal silica is a highly suitable final abrasive for stainless steels.

Stainless steels, particularly the austenitic grades, are often polished electrolytically. In most cases, electropolishing is performed after grinding to a 600-grit silicon carbide finish. Table 3 lists recommended procedures. Electropolishing usually produces high-quality, deformation-free surfaces; however, in-

## Table 2 Macroetchants for stainless steels

| Etchant | Comments |
|---|---|
| 1. 50 mL HCl, 10 g CuSO$_4$ (copper sulfate), 50 mL H$_2$O(a) | Marble's reagent. General-purpose macroetch; can be heated |
| 2. 50 mL HCl, 50 mL H$_2$O, 20 mL 30% H$_2$O$_2$ | Mix HCl and H$_2$O, heat to 70-75 °C (160-170 °F). Immerse specimen and add H$_2$O$_2$ in steps when foaming stops; do not mix |
| 3. (a) 15 g (NH$_4$)$_2$S$_2$O$_8$ (ammonium persulfate) and 75 mL H$_2$O (b) 250 g FeCl$_3$ and 100 mL H$_2$O (c) 30 mL HNO$_3$ | Lepito's No. 1 etch. Combine (a) and (b), then add (c); immerse specimen at room temperature; use fresh |
| 4. 1 part HCl and 1 part H$_2$O | Standard hot-etch. Use at 70-80 °C (160-180 °F), 15-45 min; desmut by dipping in warm 20% aqueous HNO$_3$ solution to produce a bright surface |
| 5. 10-40 mL HNO$_3$, 3-10 mL 48% HF, 25-50 mL H$_2$O | Use at 70-80 °C (160-180 °F); immerse until the desired degree of contrast is obtained |
| 6. 50 mL HCl and 25 mL saturated CuSO$_4$ in H$_2$O | Use at 75 °C (170 °F); immerse until the desired degree of contrast is obtained |

(a) When water is specified, use distilled water.

clusion attack is encountered, and second phases may be attacked preferentially.

**Etching.** For inclusion examination, etching is not required, although it is necessary for examining the microstructure. Although the stainless steels are reasonably easy to polish, etching is generally a more difficult step. The corrosion resistance of stainless steels and the potential microstructural complexity of these alloys makes selection of the best etchant a more difficult problem than for carbon and alloy steels.

Stainless steel etchant ingredients are dissolved in water, methanol or ethanol, glycerol, or a mixture of these solvents. Reagents with alcohol or glycerol as the solvent provide better wetting of the surface than water-base reagents and generally provide more uniform etching. Because alcohol reduces dissociation, alcohol-base reagents can be made more concentrated without becoming too powerful for controlled etching. Stainless steel surfaces passivate; therefore, reducing conditions are preferred to oxidizing conditions that promote passivity. Consequently, stainless steel etchants often contain hydrochloric (HCl), sulfuric (H$_2$SO$_4$), or hydrofluoric (HF) acid, although nitric acid (HNO$_3$) may be used alone or mixed with HCl to produce aqua regia or a modified aqua regia. Swabbing, instead of immersion, may be desired to obtain more uniform etch results. Electrolytic etching is also very popular, because it produces uniform etching, is easier to control, and gives reproducible results. Numerous etchants have been proposed for

stainless steels; each has advantages and disadvantages.

Etching the 400-series ferritic or martensitic grades is simpler than the 200- or 300-series austenitics or the 600-series precipitation-hardenable grades. Vilella's reagent (4% picral + HCl) or superpicral is commonly used with ferritic and martensitic grades. Etching of the extra-low-interstitial-content ferritic grades to observe the grain boundaries, however, is much more difficult than the ordinary ferritics. Examples are illustrated in the accompanying micrographs. Microetchants are listed in Table 4.

Etching of the austenitic grades to examine the grain structure is difficult with most standard reagents. As shown in the illustrations, most of the standard reagents reveal only some of the grain boundaries. Tint etching, which requires a high-quality polish for good results, reveals all of the grains by color contrast. To measure the grain size when a more accurate value is required than can be obtained by a comparison chart rating, all the boundaries must be revealed. Twin boundaries are ignored.

Sensitizing the specimen by heating it for 1 to 6 h at 650 °C (1200 °F) will facilitate revealing the grain boundaries. An alternate technique (Ref 2, 3) involves electrolytically etching the solution-annealed specimen in 60% aqueous HNO$_3$ (see Table 4). With this procedure, twin boundaries are not revealed. This etch will also bring out prior-austenite grain boundaries in solution-annealed, but not aged, precipitation-hardened grades. For structure-property correlations, the mean lineal intercept value for grain and twin boundaries should be measured, because the twin boundaries also contribute to strengthening.

## Table 3 Electropolishing procedures for stainless steels

| Electrolyte composition | Comments |
|---|---|
| 1. 50 mL HClO$_4$ (perchloric acid), 750 mL ethanol, 140 mL H$_2$O(a) | Add HClO$_4$ last, with care. Use at 8-20 V dc, 0.3-1.3 A/cm$^2$ (1.9-8.4 A/in.$^2$), 20 °C (70 °F), 20-60 s. Rinse immediately after polishing |
| 2. 78 mL HClO$_4$, 90 mL H$_2$O, 730 mL ethanol, 100 mL butyl cellusolve | Add HClO$_4$ last, with care. Use at 0.5-1.5 A/cm$^2$ (3.2-9.7 A/in.$^2$), 20 °C (70 °F) max |
| 3. 62 mL HClO$_4$, 700 mL ethanol, 100 mL butyl cellusolve, 137 mL H$_2$O | Add HClO$_4$ last, with care. Use at 1.2 A/cm$^2$ (7.7 A/in.$^2$), 20 °C (70 °F), 20-25 s |
| 4. 25 g CrO$_3$, 133 mL acetic acid, 7 mL H$_2$O | Use at 20 V dc, 0.09-0.22 A/cm$^2$ (0.58-1.4 A/in.$^2$), 17-19 °C (63-66 °F), 6 min. Dissolve CrO$_3$ in solution heated to 60-70 °C (140-160 °F) |
| 5. 37 mL H$_3$PO$_4$, 56 mL glycerol, 7 mL H$_2$O | Use at 0.78 A/cm$^2$ (5.0 A/in.$^2$) 100-120 °C (212-250 °F), 5-10 min |
| 6. 6 mL HClO$_4$ and 94 mL ethanol | Use at 35-40 V dc, 24 °C (75 °F), 15-60 s |

(a) When water is specified, use distilled water.

Such a measurement should not be converted to a grain size value.

Various alkaline ferricyanide reagents, such as Murakami's reagent, have been widely used to etch austenitic stainless steels for phase identification. The colors produced by these etchants vary with etchant composition, temperature, time, and phase orientation. When using a particular reagent in the prescribed manner, the colors obtained may differ from those reported in the literature. However, the etch response, that is, what is attacked and what is not attacked, is highly reproducible.

When using the standard formulation of Murakami's reagent at room temperature, for example, the carbides will be attacked in 7 to 15 s; σ phase will be only lightly attacked after 3 min. If higher concentrations of potassium hydroxide (KOH) or sodium hydroxide (NaOH) and potassium ferricyanide (K$_3$Fe(CN)$_6$) are used at room temperature, σ phase will be attacked instead of the carbides. Used boiling, the standard formulation attacks ferrite, carbide, and σ phase, although some evidence indicates that σ will not be attacked. Therefore, when using this reagent or one of its numerous modifications, directions should be followed carefully. Experimentation with specimens of known constitution is also recommended.

Electrolytic reagents, which are used often with austenitic and duplex grades, provide greater control of the etching process and are highly reproducible. Perhaps the most commonly used electrolytic reagent is 10% aqueous oxalic acid, which will reveal carbides after a short etch if they are present (see Table 4). When carbides are not present, the austenite grain boundaries will be revealed in 15 to 60 s. If ferrite is present, it will be outlined after 10 to 15 s.

Electrolytic reagents are generally quite simple in composition. The selectivity of electrolytic reagents based on various hydroxide solutions has been demonstrated (Ref 4). Strong hydroxide solutions attack σ phase preferentially to carbides; weak hydroxide solutions attack carbides much more readily than σ phase. Therefore, to reveal σ phase, 10 N KOH is employed, and to reveal carbides, concentrated ammonium hydroxide (NH$_4$OH) is used. For intermediate-strength hydroxide solutions, etching response is altered by a change in the applied potential.

Several sequential etching procedures have been suggested for phase identification in austenitic stainless steels. One procedure (Ref 4) involves etching first with Vilella's reagent to outline the phases present. Next, the specimen is electrolytically etched with 10 N KOH at 3 V dc for 0.4 s to color σ phase, if present, but not carbides. The specimen is then electrolytically etched with concentrated NH$_4$OH at 6 V dc for 30 s to color any carbides present. Another procedure (Ref 5) also begins with Vilella's reagent to reveal the constituents. Next, Murakami's reagent is used at room temperature to stain the carbides present. Any σ phase or δ-ferrite present is unaffected. Finally, the specimen is electrolytically etched with aqueous chromium trioxide ($CrO_3$), which will attack carbides and σ phase, but not δ-ferrite. Murakami's reagent does not attack carbides in titanium- or niobium-stabilized stainless steels. These carbides are attacked slowly in electrolytic $CrO_3$.

Delta-ferrite in martensitic, austenitic, or precipitation-hardenable grades can be preferentially colored by electrolytic etching with 20% aqueous NaOH at 20 V dc for 5 to 20 s. This procedure outlines and uniformly colors tan δ-ferrite. Although the color varies with orientation, 10 N KOH also colors δ-ferrite.

Potentiostatic etching (Ref 1) is frequently used for selective etching of constituents in stainless steels. This technique is similar to electrolytic etching, except a third electrode is included to monitor the etch potential, which is controlled using a potentiostat. This technique affords the greatest possible control over etching.

Heat tinting is a useful technique with austenitic stainless steels. Phase delineation is improved by first etching with a general-purpose reagent, such as Vilella's. The specimen is then heated in air at 500 to 700 °C (930 to 1290 °F); 650 °C (1200 °F) has been most commonly used with times to 20 min. Austenite is colored more readily than ferrite (see Fig. 20), and carbides resist coloration longest. After 20 min at 650 °C (1200 °F), austenite is blue-green, σ phase is orange, ferrite is light cream, and carbides are uncolored.

Magnetic colloids have also been used to detect ferromagnetic constituents in austenitic stainless steels. This technique has been extensively applied using a ferromagnetic colloid solution containing very fine magnetic particles (Ref 6). Delta-ferrite and strain-induced martensite are readily identified by this method.

**Electron Microscopy.** Scanning electron-microscopy (SEM) and transmission electron microscopy (TEM) are used to examine the fine structure of stainless steels and for phase identification. Scanning electron microscopy examination uses the same specimens as optical microscopy. As-polished specimens often can be examined, although etching is more common. Many second-phase constituents can be observed using backscattered electron detectors due to the adequate atomic number contrast between these phases and the matrix. However, secondary electron images produced from topographic contrast and atomic number contrast are most often used. Energy-dispersive x-ray analysis (EDXA) is prevalent for chemical analysis of second phases, although lightweight elements, such as carbon and nitrogen, cannot be detected unless thin-window or windowless EDXA detectors or wavelength-dispersive detectors are used.

Transmission electron microscopy requires preparation of replica or thin-foil specimens (see the article "Transmission Electron Microscopy" in this Volume). Replicas may be

**Table 4  Microetchants for stainless steel**

| Etchants | Comments | Etchants | Comments |
|---|---|---|---|
| 1. 1 g picric acid, 5 mL HCl, 100 mL ethanol | Vilella's reagent. Use at room temperature to 1 min. Outlines second-phase particles (carbides, σ phase, δ-ferrite), etches martensite | 12. 30 g KOH, 30 g $K_3Fe(CN)_6$, 100 mL $H_2O$ | Modified Murakami's reagent. Use at 95 °C (203 °F) for 5 s. Colors σ phase reddish brown, ferrite dark gray, austenite unattacked, carbide black. Use under a hood. |
| 2. 1.5 g $CuCl_2$ (cupric chloride), 33 mL HCl, 33 mL ethanol, 33 mL $H_2O$(a) | Kalling's No. 1 reagent for martensitic stainless steels. Use at room temperature. Martensite dark, ferrite colored, austenite not attacked | 13. 10 g oxalic acid and 100 mL $H_2O$ | Popular electrolytic etch, 6 V dc, 25-mm spacing. 15-30 s reveals carbides; grain boundaries revealed after 45-60 s; σ phase outlined after 6 s. Lower voltages (1-3 V dc) can be used. Dissolves carbides. Sigma strongly attacked, austenite moderately attacked, ferrite not attacked |
| 3. 5 g $CuCl_2$, 100 mL HCl, 100 mL ethanol | Kalling's No. 2 reagent. Use at room temperature. Ferrite attacked rapidly, austenite slightly attacked, carbides not attacked | | |
| 4. 5 g $CuCl_2$, 40 mL HCl, 30 mL $H_2O$, 25 mL ethanol | Fry's reagent. For martensitic and precipitation-hardenable grades. Use at room temperature | 14. 10 g NaCN (sodium cyanide) and 100 mL $H_2O$ | Electrolytic etch at 6 V dc, 25-mm spacing, 5 min, platinum cathode. Sigma darkened, carbides light, ferrite outlined, austenite not attacked. Good for revealing carbides. Use with care under a hood. |
| 5. 4 g $CuSO_4$, 20 mL HCl, 20 mL $H_2O$ | Marble's reagent. Used primarily with austenitic grades. Use at room temperature to 10 s. Attacks σ phase | | |
| 6. 3 parts glycerol, 2-5 parts HCl, 1 part $HNO_3$ | Glyceregia. Popular etch for all stainless grades. Higher HCl content reduces pitting tendency. Use fresh, never store. Discard when reagent is orange colored. Use with care under a hood. Add $HNO_3$ last. Immerse or swab a few seconds to a minute. Attacks σ phase, outlines carbides. Substitution of water for glycerol increases attack rate | 15. 10 mL HCl and 90 mL methanol | Electrolytic etch at 1.5 V dc, 20 °C (70 °F) to attack σ phase. Use at 6 V dc for 3-5 s to reveal structure. |
| | | 16. 60 mL $HNO_3$ and 40 mL $H_2O$ | Electrolytic etch to reveal austenite grain boundaries (but not twins) in austenitic grades. With stainless steel cathode, use at 1.1 V dc, 0.075-0.14 A/$cm^2$ (0.48-0.90 A/$in.^2$), 120 s. With platinum cathode, use at 0.4 V dc, 0.055-0.066 A/$cm^2$ (0.35-0.43 A/$in.^2$), 45 s. Will reveal prior-austenite grain boundaries in solution-treated (but not aged) martensitic precipitation-hardenable alloys |
| 7. 45 mL HCl, 15 mL $HNO_3$, 20 mL methanol | Methanolic aqua regia. Used with austenitic grades to reveal grain structure, outline ferrite and σ phase | | |
| 8. 15 mL HCl, 5 mL $HNO_3$, 100 mL $H_2O$ | Dilute aqua regia for austenitic grades. Uniform etching of austenite, outlines carbides, σ phase, and ferrite (sometimes attacked) | 17. 50 g NaOH and 100 mL $H_2O$ | Electrolytic etch at 2-6 V dc, 5-10 s to reveal σ phase in austenitic grades. |
| 9. 4 g $KMnO_4$ (potassium permanganate), 4 g NaOH, 100 mL $H_2O$ | Groesbeck's reagent. Use at 60-90 °C (140-195 °F) to 10 min. Colors carbides dark, σ phase gray, ferrite and austenite not affected | 18. 56 g KOH and 100 mL $H_2O$ | Electrolytic etch at 1.5-3 V dc for 3 s to reveal σ phase (red-brown) and ferrite (bluish). Chi colored same as sigma |
| 10. 30 g $KMnO_4$, 30 g NaOH, 100 mL $H_2O$ | Modified Groesbeck's reagent. Use at 90-100 °C (195-212 °F) for 20 s to 10 min to color ferrite dark in duplex alloys. Austenite not affected | 19. 20 g NaOH and 100 mL $H_2O$ | Electrolytic etch at 20 V dc, for 5-20 s to outline and color δ-ferrite tan. |
| 11. 10 g $K_3Fe(CN)_6$, 10 g KOH or 7 g NaOH, 100 mL $H_2O$ | Murakami's reagent. Use at room temperature to 60 s to reveal carbides; σ phase faintly revealed by etching to 3 min. Use at 80 °C (176 °F) to boiling to 60 min to darken carbides. Sigma may be colored blue, ferrite yellow to yellow-brown, austenite not attacked. Use under a hood. | 20. $NH_4OH$ (conc) | Electrolytic etch at 1.5-6 V dc for 10-60 s. Very selective. At 1.5 V, carbide completely etched in 40 s; sigma unaffected after 180 s. At 6 V, σ phase etched after 40 s |
| | | 21. 10 g $(NH_4)_2S_2O_8$ and 100 mL $H_2O$ | Use at 6 V dc for 10 s to color carbide dark brown |

(continued)

**Table 4** (continued)

| Etchants | Comments | Etchants | Comments |
|---|---|---|---|
| 22. 200 mL HCl and 1000 mL H$_2$O | Beraha's tint etch for austenitic, duplex, and precipitation-hardenable grades. Add 0.5-1.0 g K$_2$S$_2$O$_5$ per 100 mL of solution (if etching is too rapid, use a 10% aqueous HCl solution). Immerse at room temperature (never swab) for 30-120 s until surface is reddish. Austenite colored, carbides not colored. Longer immersion colors ferrite lightly. If coloration is inadequate, add 24 g NH$_4$F · HF (ammonium bifluoride) to stock reagent at left. | 24. Saturated aqueous Ba(OH)$_2$ (barium hydroxide) | Attacks carbides well before σ phase in austenitic grades when used at 1.5 V dc, but attacks both equally when used at 3-6 V dc. Has been used to differentiate χ phase and Laves phase (use at 4.3 V dc, platinum cathode, 20 s). Chi is stained mottled-purple, Laves is not colored, ferrite is stained tan |
| | | 25. 50 mL each H$_2$O, ethanol, methanol, and HCl; plus 1 g CuCl$_2$, 3.5 g FeCl$_3$, 2.5 mL HNO$_3$ | Ralph's reagent. Use by swabbing. Can be stored. General purpose etch for most stainless steels. Does not attack sulfides in free-machining grades |
| 23. 20 g picric acid and 100 mL HCl | Etch by immersion. Develops grain boundaries in austenite and δ-ferrite in duplex alloys | | |

(a) When water is specified, use distilled water.

made to reveal the outline and topography of the phases, or if the specimen is deeply etched, second-phase particles may be extracted. Extraction replicas permit analysis of second phases by electron diffraction and by EDXA. Thin-foil specimens can also be analyzed by these methods, although interference from the matrix is possible. Table 5 lists electropolishing procedures for producing stainless steel thin foils.

**Bulk Extractions.** Although bulk samples can be directly analyzed by x-ray diffraction for phase identification, it is quite common to extract the second phases chemically and analyze the extracted particles. This eliminates the matrix and concentrates the second phase, facilitating identification of small amounts of the second-phase constituents. Bulk extraction of phases from wrought stainless steels is performed using the same procedures as for wrought heat-resistant grades (see the article "Wrought Heat-Resistant Alloys" in this Volume).

## Microstructures of Wrought Stainless Steels

The microstructures of wrought stainless steels can be quite complex. Matrix structures vary according to the type of steel, such as ferritic, austenitic, martensitic, precipitation hardenable, or duplex. A wide range of second-phase constituents (see Table 6) can be observed; welding or high-temperature exposure increases the complexity. Additional information is available in Ref 7.

**Austenitic Stainless Steels.** The most commonly used stainless steels are the austenitic grades, of which AISI 302 and 304 are the most popular. These grades contain 16% or more Cr, a ferrite-stabilizing element, and sufficient austenite-stabilizing elements, such

as carbon, nitrogen, nickel, and manganese, to render austenite stable at room temperature. The grades containing silicon, molybdenum, titanium, or niobium—AISI 302B, 316, 317, 321, and 347, for example—will sometimes include a minor amount of δ-ferrite because of the ferrite-stabilizing influence of these elements. Alloys with substantial nickel are fully austenitic, for example, AISI 310 or 330. For alloys susceptible to δ-ferrite stabilization, the amount present will depend on the composition, chemical homogeneity, and hot working. Alloys with especially low carbon contents to minimize susceptibility to sensitization during welding (AISI 304L, 316L, or 317L, for example) will have a greater tendency toward δ-ferrite stabilization.

Numerous studies have been conducted to predict matrix phases based on chemical composition. Most of these studies have concentrated on predicting weldment microstructures (Ref 8-15); others have concentrated on predicting cast microstructures (Ref 16-18) or predicting structures at the hot-working temperature (Ref 19) or after hot working (Ref 20). Measurement of the δ-ferrite content of stainless steels, particularly weldments, has been widely studied (Ref 21-24).

The austenite in these grades is not stable, but metastable. Martensite can be formed, particularly in the leaner grades, by cooling specimens to very low temperatures or by extensive plastic deformation. Nonmagnetic, hexagonal close-packed (hcp) ε-martensite and magnetic, body-centered cubic (bcc) α'-martensite have been observed. Empirical relationships have been developed to show how composition influences the resistance of such steel to deformation-induced martensite (Ref 25, 26).

Carbon content limits are generally 0.03, 0.08, or 0.15% in the austenitic grades. Solution annealing will usually dissolve all or most of the carbides present after hot rolling. Rapid quenching from the solution-annealing temperature of generally 1010 to 1065 °C (1850 to 1950 °F) will retain the carbon in solution, producing a strain-free, carbide-free austenitic microstructure.

The most widely observed carbide type in austenitic stainless steels is M$_{23}$C$_6$, which is often referred to as Cr$_{23}$C$_6$, but more properly is (Cr,Fe)$_{23}$C$_6$ or (Cr,Fe,Mo)$_{23}$C$_6$. The precipitation of this carbide at grain boundaries during welding produces intergranular corrosion. To counter "sensitization" during welding, carbon contents are reduced or strong carbide formers are added, as in AISI 321 and 347.

Precipitation of M$_{23}$C$_6$ carbide occurs as a result of heating solution-annealed grades to 500 to 950 °C (930 to 1740 °F); the fastest rate of precipitation takes place from 650 to 700 °C (1200 to 1290 °F). Precipitation occurs first at austenite/δ-ferrite phase boundaries, when present, followed by precipitation at other noncoherent interfaces (grain and twin boundaries), and finally by precipitation at coherent twin boundaries. In addition, M$_{23}$C$_6$ may precipitate at inclusion/matrix-phase boundaries.

The appearance of M$_{23}$C$_6$ varies with the precipitation temperature and time. It is most

**Table 5 Electropolishing procedures for preparing thin-foil stainless steel specimens**

| Solution composition | Comments |
|---|---|
| 1. 5 or 10 mL HClO$_4$ and 95 or 90 mL acetic acid at 20 V dc | Popular electropolish for stainless steels. Used for window technique or for perforation of disk specimens. Keep solution cool |
| 2. (a) 10 mL HNO$_3$ and 90 mL H$_2$O(a) at 50 V dc (b) 10 mL HClO$_4$, 20 mL glycerol, 70 mL ethanol at 65 V dc | Popular procedures for austenitic grades. Use (a) to electrodish specimens, then (b) for perforation. |
| 3. 10 mL HClO$_4$ and 90 mL ethanol at 12 V dc, 0 °C (32 °F) | Popular electropolish for stainless steels. Use for perforation. |
| 4. 40 mL H$_2$SO$_4$ and 60 mL H$_3$PO$_4$ at 35 V dc, 0.3 A/cm$^2$ (1.9 A/in.$^2$) | Electropolish for stainless steels for perforation |
| 5. 25 g CrO$_3$, 133 mL acetic acid, 7 mL H$_2$O at 20 °C (70 °F) | Electropolish for stainless steels. Good for window method. Opacity of solution makes it difficult to use for jet perforation. |
| 6. (a) 40 mL acetic acid, 30 mL H$_3$PO$_4$, 20 mL HNO$_3$, 10 mL H$_2$O at 80-120 V dc, 0.1 A/cm$^2$ (0.65 A/in.$^2$) (b) 54 mL H$_3$PO$_4$, 36 mL H$_2$SO$_4$, 10 mL ethanol at 6 V dc | Procedure for austenitic grades. Jet electrodish disks prior to final thinning with (b) to perforation. |
| 7. 45 mL H$_3$PO$_4$, 30 mL H$_2$SO$_4$, 25 mL H$_2$O at 6 V dc | Procedure for austenitic grades for perforation |

(a) When water is specified, use distilled water.

**Table 6  Second-phase constituents observed in stainless steels**

| Phase | Crystal structure | Lattice parameters, nm | Reported compositions | Comments |
|---|---|---|---|---|
| $M_{23}C_6$ | fcc | $a_0 = 1.057-1.068$ | $(Cr_{16}Fe_5Mo_2)C_6$ $(Cr_{17}Fe_{4.5}Mo_{1.5})C_6$ $(Fe,Cr)_{23}C_6$ | Most commonly observed carbide in austenitic stainless steels. Precipitates from 500-950 °C (930-1740 °F), fastest at 650-700 °C (1200-1290 °F) |
| $M_6C$ | fcc | $a_0 = 1.085-1.111$ | $(Cr,Co,Mo,Ni)_6C$ $(Fe_3Mo_3)C$ $Fe_3Nb_3C$ $(Fe,Cr)_3Nb_3C$ | Observed in austenitic grades containing substantial molybdenum or niobium after long time exposure |
| $M_7C_3$ | Hexagonal | $a_0 = 1.398$ $c_0 = 0.4523$ | $Cr_7C_3$ | Observed in martensitic grades |
| MC | Cubic | $a_0 = 0.430-0.470$ | TiC NbC | Observed in alloys with additions of titanium or niobium. Very stable carbide. Will usually contain some nitrogen |
| Sigma ($\sigma$) | Tetragonal | $a_0 = 0.8799-0.9188$ $c_0 = 0.4544-0.4599$ | FeCr FeMo Fe(Cr,Mo) $(Fe,Ni)_x(Cr,Mo)_y$ | Formation from $\delta$-ferrite is much more rapid than from austenite. Potent embrittler below 595 °C (1105 °F). Forms with long time exposure from 650-900 °C (1200-1650 °F) |
| Chi ($\chi$) | bcc ($\alpha$-Mn structure) | $a_0 = 0.8862-0.892$ | $Fe_{36}Cr_{12}Mo_{10}$ $(Fe,Ni)_{36}Cr_{18}Mo_4$ $M_{18}C$ | Observed in alloys containing substantial molybdenum. Chi precipitates with exposure to 730-1010 °C (1345-1850 °F) (varies with alloy composition) |
| Laves ($\eta$) | Hexagonal | $a_0 = 0.470-0.4744$ $c_0 = 0.772-0.7725$ | $Fe_2Mo$ $(Ti_{21}Mo_9)$ $(Fe_{50}Cr_5Si_5)$ | Forms in austenitic alloys with substantial amounts of molybdenum, titanium, or niobium after long time exposure from 600-1100 °C (1110-2010 °F) |

easily studied using extraction replicas. At the lower precipitation temperatures, $M_{23}C_6$ has a thin, continuous, sheetlike morphology. When the precipitation temperature is 600 to 700 °C (1110 to 1290 °F), feathery dendritic particles form at boundary intersections. With time, these precipitates coarsen and thicken. At still higher precipitation temperatures, $M_{23}C_6$ forms at grain boundaries as discrete globular particles whose shape is influenced by the boundary orientation, degree of misfit, and temperature (Ref 27). The $M_{23}C_6$ that precipitates at noncoherent twin boundaries is lamellar or rodlike; that which precipitates at coherent twin boundaries is platelike. The $M_{23}C_6$ that forms at the lower precipitation temperatures is most detrimental to intergranular corrosion resistance.

Alloys given deliberate minor additions of titanium or niobium—AISI 321 and 347, for example—form titanium or niobium carbides, rather than $M_{23}C_6$. To take full advantage of these additions, solution-annealed specimens are subjected to a stabilizing heat treatment to precipitate the excess carbon as titanium or niobium carbides. This treatment is commonly used with AISI 321 and involves holding the specimen several hours at 845 to 900 °C (1550 to 1650 °F). These MC-type carbides will precipitate intragranularly at dislocations or stacking faults within the matrix. Some may also precipitate on grain boundaries.

Additions of titanium or niobium must be carefully controlled to neutralize the carbon in solution. In practice, titanium and niobium carbides can contain some nitrogen, and both can form rather pure nitrides. Titanium nitrides usually appear as distinct, bright yellow cubic particles. Titanium carbide is grayish, with a less regular shape. Ti-

tanium carbonitride will have an intermediate appearance that varies with the carbon/nitrogen ratio. Chromium nitrides are not usually observed in the austenitic grades, unless the service environment causes substantial nitrogen surface enrichment or they are nitrogen strengthened.

Carbides of the $M_6C$ type are observed in austenitic grades containing substantial molybdenum or niobium additions. It usually precipitates intragranularly. For example, in AISI 316 with 2 to 3% Mo, $M_6C$ will form after approximately 1500 h at 650 °C (1200 °F). Several types of $M_6C$ have been observed, including $Fe_3Mo_3C$, $Fe_3Nb_3C$, and $(Fe,Cr)_3Nb_3C$.

Several types of sulfides have been observed in austenitic grades. The most common form is MnS. However, if the manganese content is low, chromium will replace some of the manganese in the sulfide. At manganese contents less than approximately 0.20%, pure chromium sulfides will form. Because these are quite hard, machinability (tool life) will be poor. Some free-machining grades have additions of selenium to form manganese selenides, rather than manganese sulfides. In grades with substantial titanium, several forms of titanium sulfides have been observed, including $Ti_2S$, $Ti_2SC$, and $Ti_4C_2S_2$.

Several intermetallic phases may be formed by high-temperature exposure. These phases form from titanium, vanadium, and chromium ("A" elements) and from manganese, iron, cobalt, and nickel ("B" elements). Some of these phases are stoichiometric compounds. Probably the most important is $\sigma$ phase, first observed in 1927. The leaner austenitic grades free of $\delta$-ferrite are relatively immune to $\sigma$-phase formation, but the higher alloy grades and those containing $\delta$-ferrite are

prone to its formation. Sigma is frequently described as FeCr, although its composition can be quite complex and variable, ranging from $B_4A$ to $BA_4$.

Certain elements, such as silicon, promote $\sigma$-phase formation. Cold working also enhances subsequent $\sigma$-phase formation. Empirical equations based on composition have been developed to predict the tendency toward $\sigma$-phase formation (Ref 28, 29). Sigma is a very potent embrittler whose effects are observable at temperatures below approximately 595 °C (1100 °F). Sigma also reduces resistance to strong oxidizers. The morphology of $\sigma$ phase varies substantially. Etching techniques (Ref 30-33) have been widely used to identify $\sigma$ phase in stainless steels, but x-ray diffraction is more definitive. Because its crystal structure is tetragonal, $\sigma$ phase responds to crossed polarized light.

Chi phase (Ref 34-39) is observed in alloys containing substantial additions of molybdenum subjected to high-temperature exposure. Chi can dissolve carbon and exist as an intermetallic compound or as a carbide ($M_{18}C$). It is often observed in alloys susceptible to $\sigma$-phase formation and has a bcc, $\alpha$-manganese-type crystal structure. Several forms of the intermetallic phase have been identified, as shown in Table 6. Chi nucleates first at grain boundaries, then at incoherent twin boundaries, and finally intragranularly (Ref 39). Chi varies in shape from rodlike to globular. As with $\sigma$ phase, cold work accelerates nucleation of $\chi$ phase.

Laves phase ($\eta$ phase) can also form in austenitic stainless steels after long-term high-temperature exposure (Ref 38, 39). Alloys containing molybdenum, titanium, and niobium are most susceptible to Laves formation. Precipitation occurs from 650 to 950 °C (1200 to 1740 °F). Laves is a hexagonal intermetallic compound of $AB_2$ form. Several types have been observed, as shown in Table 6. Laves phase precipitates intragranularly and exists as globular particles.

Other phases have been observed in stainless steels, but less often than those discussed above. Among these is R phase (Ref 40-42), which has been observed in a Fe-12Cr-Co-Mo alloy and in welded AISI 316. A globular nickel-titanium silicide, G phase, was observed in a 26Ni-15Cr heat-resistant A-286 type alloy and was attributed to grain-boundary segregation (Ref 43). A chromium-iron-niobide phase, Z phase (Ref 44), was detected in an 18Cr-12Ni-1Nb alloy after creep testing at 850 °C (1560 °F). Table 6 summarizes the more common second-phase constituents observed in stainless steels.

**The ferritic stainless steels** (Ref 45) are basically iron-chromium alloys with enough chromium and other elements to stabilize bcc ferrite at all temperatures. Carbon and nitrogen contents must be minimized. The microstructure of these alloys consists of ferrite plus small amounts of finely dispersed $M_{23}C_6$, but other phases may form due to high-temperature exposure. However, because of severe embrittlement problems, these alloys are generally not used for elevated-temperature service.

The ferritic grades depend on solid-solution strengthening, because heat treatment cannot be used to harden the alloys or produce grain refinement. Quenching ferritic alloys from high temperatures produces only very slight increases in hardness.

Three forms of embrittlement can occur in ferritic stainless steels: σ-phase embrittlement, 475 °C embrittlement, and high-temperature embrittlement. Sigma is difficult to form in alloys with less than 20% Cr, but forms readily in alloys with 25 to 30% Cr when heated between 500 and 800 °C (930 and 1470 °F). Molybdenum, silicon, nickel, and manganese additions shift the σ-forming tendency to lower chromium contents. As with the austenitic grades, σ phase severely reduces ductility and toughness below approximately 600 °C (1110 °F). Sigma can be re-dissolved by holding for a few hours above 800 °C (1470 °F).

Ferritic stainless steels are susceptible to embrittlement when heated from 400 to 540 °C (750 to 1005 °F), a condition referred to as 475 °C or 885 °F embrittlement. Embrittlement, which increases with time at temperature, is caused by production of chromium-rich and iron-rich ferrites, but can be removed by heating above approximately 550 °C (1020 °F). Under identical aging conditions, embrittlement increases with increasing chromium content.

High-temperature embrittlement occurs in alloys with moderate to high interstitial carbon and nitrogen contents heated above 950 °C (1740 °F) and cooled to room temperature, resulting in severe embrittlement and loss of corrosion resistance. This has been attributed to chromium depletion adjacent to precipitated carbides and nitrides. The properties of such a sensitized specimen can be improved by heating to 700 to 950 °C (1290 to 1740 °F), which allows chromium to diffuse to the depleted areas. A better procedure, however, is to reduce the carbon and nitrogen contents to very low levels, which also improves toughness and weldability. Strong carbide-forming elements, such as titanium and niobium, may also be added.

**Martensitic Stainless Steels.** The hardenable martensitic stainless steels contain more than 10.5% Cr plus other austenite-stabilizing elements, such as carbon, nitrogen, nickel, and manganese, to expand the austenite phase field and permit heat treatment. The composition must be carefully balanced to prevent δ-ferrite formation at the austenitizing temperature. Delta-ferrite in the hardened structure should be avoided to attain the best mechanical properties. Empirical formulas have been developed to predict δ-ferrite formation based on the composition (Ref 46, 47). Temperature control during austenitization is also important for preventing δ-ferrite formation. The martensitic grades are generally immune from σ-phase formation.

Increases in strength when martensitic stainless steels are heat treated depend primarily on the carbon content, which can vary widely in these grades, and on the stability of δ-ferrite at the austenitizing temperature. The hardenability of these grades is very high due to the high chromium content. All these grades can be martempered to reduce the risk of quench cracking in complex shapes. The heat treatment of these grades is very similar to that of highly alloyed tool steels.

The appearance of martensite in these grades varies with carbon content. With increasing carbon content, the martensite becomes finer, changing from lath to plate morphology, and the amount of residual retained austenite increases, but will not cause problems unless excessively high austenitizing temperatures are used.

Tempering reactions are similar to those observed in the high-alloy tool steels. For example, when as-quenched AISI 410 is tempered, $M_3C$ is present at tempering temperatures to approximately 480 °C (900 °F), but is not present at approximately 650 °C (1200 °F). At approximately 480 °C (900 °F), $M_{23}C_6$ forms. It becomes the predominant carbide at 540 °C (1005 °F) and above. At approximately 480 °C (900 °F), $M_7C_3$ also forms, but decreases in quantity with higher tempers. Because $M_7C_3$ seriously degrades corrosion resistance, its presence at tempering temperatures of 480 to 650 °C (900 to 1200 °F) precludes using this tempering range. Tempers below approximately 480 °C (900 °F) are also avoided due to low toughness. Overtempering must be avoided, particularly in those grades containing nickel, because of formation of reverted austenite.

Martensitic stainless steels are also susceptible to surface decarburization during heat treatment if the furnace atmosphere is not properly controlled. However, with their high chromium content, they are less susceptible than many of the low-alloy tool steels.

**Precipitation-Hardenable Grades.** The precipitation-hardenable stainless steels (Ref 48-51) were developed in the 1940s when the first alloy of this type, Stainless W, was introduced. Three types of precipitation-hardenable grades have been developed: austenitic, semiaustenitic, and martensitic. All are hardened by a final aging treatment that precipitates very fine second-phase particles from a supersaturated solid solution. Precipitation introduces strain into the lattice, which produces the strengthening. Maximum strengthening occurs well before visible precipitates are produced. Increasing the aging temperature reduces the aging time for maximum strength, but a lower strength is obtained. As shown in Table 1, precipitation-hardenable grades contain additions of aluminum, copper, titanium, and, occasionally, molybdenum and niobium to produce the precipitates.

The semiaustenitic grades have an austenitic matrix with up to 20% δ-ferrite that persists throughout heat treatment. These grades

are austenitic (plus δ-ferrite) in the solution-annealed condition, but can be transformed to martensite by a series of thermal or thermomechanical treatments. Because they are complex alloys, the chemical composition must be carefully balanced.

Heat treatment of the semiaustenitic grades requires conditioning of the austenite matrix, transformation to martensite, then precipitation hardening. The austenite conditioning treatment removes carbon from solution as $Cr_{23}C_6$ beginning at the austenite/δ-ferrite interfaces. This is accomplished by heating to between 705 and 815 °C (1300 and 1500 °F). The austenite is unstable and transforms to martensite upon cooling. The martensite start temperature, $M_s$, is approximately 65 to 93 °C (150 to 200 °F); the martensite finish temperature, $M_f$, is approximately 15 °C (60 °F). The alloy is then aged, usually between 480 and 650 °C (900 and 1200 °F), to relieve stress produced during martensite formation and increase toughness, ductility, and corrosion resistance. Aging at 565 °C (1050 °F) or above results in overaging, with the occurrence of precipitation of the strengthening intermetallic second phase, tempering of the martensite, and partial reversion of martensite to austenite ("reverted" austenite). Cold working can also be used to produce martensite, which is followed by aging.

Commercial examples of semiaustenitic precipitation-hardenable stainless steels include types 17-7PH, PH15-7Mo, and PH14-8Mo. Also classed as semiaustenitic precipitation-hardenable grades are AM-350 and AM-355, but they do not have true precipitation reactions. These grades are embrittled by long-term exposure above approximately 550 °C (1020 °F) due to continued precipitation of the intermetallic strengthening phase.

The martensitic grades are the most popular precipitation-hardenable stainless grades. They are martensitic after solution annealing and do not retain austenite. Stainless W is a martensitic precipitation-hardenable type. Other more recently developed martensitic precipitation-hardenable grades are 17-4PH, 15-5PH, PH13-8Mo, Custom 450, and Custom 455, which are capable of strengths to 1380 MPa (200 ksi) or above.

Stainless W and 17-4PH contain δ-ferrite stringers in the martensitic matrix; the other grades are essentially free of δ-ferrite and so have better through-thickness properties. After solution annealing, they are aged at 425 to 455 °C (795 to 850 °F) or at 675 °C (1250 °F). High aging temperatures will produce reaustenitization, which transforms to untempered martensite upon cooling to room temperature.

The austenitic precipitation-hardenable grades have the lowest usage. The austenite matrix in these alloys is very stable, even after substantial cold working. These grades are the forerunners of superalloys. The most common austenitic precipitation-hardenable grade is A-286.

The duplex stainless steels (Ref 52-54) were developed as a result of studies of superplasticity. They are usually very fine-grained microduplex structures with a composition centered around 26Cr-6.5Ni (IN-744). The very fine grain size improves strength and toughness, and their superplastic nature promotes hot workability. They exhibit good strength and corrosion resistance.

Thermomechanical processing is required to produce the fine duplex structure. During soaking for hot working, the second phase is dissolved. During hot working, it precipitates and stabilizes the grain size of the recrystallized matrix. The microduplex structure results only when second-phase precipitation precedes or occurs during recrystallization.

Service exposure at 370 to 540 °C (700 to 1005 °F) results in an increase in strength but loss of toughness. Sigma phase will form in IN-744 from exposure to temperatures between 550 and 800 °C (1020 and 1470 °F). Cold working enhances subsequent $\sigma$-phase formation. Other examples of duplex stainless steels include AISI 329, Alloy 2205, 7-Mo PLUS, Ferralium Alloy 255, and 44LN.

## REFERENCES

1. G.F. Vander Voort, *Metallography: Principles and Practice*, McGraw-Hill, 1984
2. F.C. Bell and D.E. Sonon, Improved Metallographic Etching Techniques for Stainless Steel and for Stainless Steel to Carbon Steel Weldments, *Metallography*, Vol 9, 1976, p 91-107
3. J.M. Stephenson and B.M. Patchett, Grain-Boundary Etches for Austenitic and Ferritic Ni-Cr-Mo Corrosion-Resistant Alloys, *Sheet Met. Ind.*, Vol 56, 1979, p 45-50, 57
4. J.J. Gilman, Electrolytic Etching—The Sigma Phase Steels, *Trans. ASM*, Vol 44, 1952, p 566-600
5. E.J. Dulis and G.V. Smith, Identification and Modes of Formation and Re-Solution of Sigma Phase in Austenitic Chromium-Nickel Steels, in *STP 110*, ASTM, Philadelphia, 1951, p 3-37
6. R.J. Gray, Magnetic Etching with Ferrofluid, in *Metallographic Specimen Preparation*, Plenum Press, 1974, p 155-177
7. D. Peckner and I.M. Bernstein, Ed., *Handbook of Stainless Steels*, McGraw-Hill, 1977
8. A.L. Schaeffler, Constitution Diagram for Stainless Steel Weld Metal, *Met. Prog.*, Vol 56 (No. 5), Nov 1949, p 680-680B
9. W.T. DeLong *et al.*, Measurement and Calculation of Ferrite in Stainless Steel Weld Metal, *Weld. J.*, Vol 35 (No. 11), Nov 1956, p 521s-528s
10. W.T. DeLong, A Modified Phase Diagram for Stainless Steel Weld Metals, *Met. Prog.*, Vol 77, Feb 1960, p 98-100B
11. H.F. Reid and W.T. DeLong, Making Sense Out of Ferrite Requirements in Welding Stainless Steels, *Met. Prog.*, Vol 103, June 1973, p 73-77
12. C.J. Long and W.T. DeLong, The Ferrite Content of Austenitic Stainless Steel Weld Metal, *Weld. J.*, Vol 52, July 1973, p 281s-297s
13. St. Mayerhofer and H. Kohl, Statistical Analysis of the Delta Ferrite Content of Austenitic Steels, *Berg-Hüttenmänn. Monatsh.*, Vol 111 (No. 9), BISI 5304, 1966, p 443-453
14. W.T. DeLong, Ferrite in Austenitic Stainless Steel Weld Metal, *Weld. J.*, Vol 53, July 1974, p 273s-286s
15. H.A. Meijer, Quantitative Analysis of Ferrite in Austenitic Stainless Steel, *Br. Weld. J.*, Vol 13, Jan 1966, p 12-17
16. F.C. Hull, Delta Ferrite and Martensite Formation in Stainless Steels, *Weld. J.*, Vol 42 (No. 5), May 1973, p 193s-203s
17. L.S. Aubrey *et al.*, Ferrite Measurement and Control in Cast Duplex Stainless Steels, in *STP 756*, ASTM, Philadelphia, 1982, p 126-164
18. M.T. Leger, Predicting and Evaluating Ferrite Content in Austenitic Stainless Steel Castings, in *STP 756*, ASTM, Philadelphia, 1982, p 105-125
19. L. Pryce and K.W. Andrews, Practical Estimation of Composition Balance and Ferrite Content in Stainless Steels, *J. Iron Steel Inst.*, Vol 195, Aug 1960, p 415-417
20. C.M. Hammond, The Development of New High-Strength Stainless Steels, in *STP 369*, ASTM, Philadelphia, 1965, p 47-53
21. R.B. Gunia and G.A. Ratz, The Measurement of Delta Ferrite in Austenitic Stainless Steel, *Weld. Res. Council Bull.*, No. 132, Aug 1968
22. L.A. Brough, The Effects of Processing on Delta Ferrite Measurement, *J. Mater. Energy Syst.*, Vol 5 (No. 1), June 1983, p 36-42
23. W.L. Johns *et al.*, Percent Delta Ferrite Determination in Type 304 Stainless Steel Weldments, *Microstruc. Sci.*, Vol 2, 1974, p 13-22
24. G.M. Goodwin *et al.*, A Study of Ferrite Morphology in Austenitic Stainless Steel Weldments, *Weld. J.*, Vol 51, Sept 1972, p 425s-429s
25. C.B. Post and W.S. Eberly, Stability of Austenite in Stainless Steels, *Trans. ASM*, Vol 39, 1947, p 868-890
26. A.J. Griffiths and J.C. Wright, Mechanical Properties of Austenitic and Metastable Stainless Steel Sheet and their Relationships with Pressforming Behaviour, *Iron Steel Inst. Pub. 117*, 1969, p 51-65
27. R. Stickler and A. Vinckier, Morphology of Grain-Boundary Carbides and Its Influence on Intergranular Corrosion of 304 Stainless Steel, *Trans. ASM*, Vol 54, 1961, p 362-380
28. J.T. Gow and O.E. Harder, Balancing the Composition of Cast 25 Per Cent Chromium—12 Per Cent Nickel Type Alloys, *Trans. ASM*, Vol 30, 1942, p 855-935
29. F.C. Hull, Effects of Composition on Embrittlement of Austenitic Stainless Steels, *Weld. J.*, Vol 52, 1973, p 104s-113s
30. E.J. Dulis and G.V. Smith, Identification and Mode of Formation and Re-Solution of Sigma Phase in Austenitic Chromium-Nickel Steels, in *STP 110*, ASTM, Philadelphia, 1951, p 3-37
31. R. Franks *et al.*, Experiments on Etching Procedures for the Identification of the Sigma Phase in Austenitic Chromium-Nickel Stainless Steels, *Proc. ASTM*, Vol 53, 1953, p 143-169, 177-180
32. A.J. Lena, Sigma Phase—A Review, *Met. Prog.*, Vol 66, Sept 1954, p 122-128
33. W.E. White and I. LeMay, Metallographic Observations on the Formation and Occurrence of Ferrite, Sigma Phase, and Carbides in Austenitic Stainless Steels, *Metallography*, Vol 3, 1970, p 35-50, 51-60
34. K.W. Andrews and P.E. Brookes, Chi Phase in Alloy Steels, *Met. Treatment Drop Forg.*, July 1951, p 301-311
35. P.K. Koh, Occurrence of Chi Phase in Molybdenum-Bearing Stainless Steels, *Trans. AIME*, Vol 197, 1953, p 339-343
36. J.S. Kasper, The Ordering of Atoms in the Chi-Phase of the Iron-Chromium-Molybdenum System, *Acta Metall.*, Vol 2, May 1954, p 456-461
37. J.G. McMullin et al., Equilibrium Structure in Fe-Cr-Mo Alloys, *Trans. ASM*, Vol 46, 1954, p 799-811
38. F.L. Ver Snyder and H.J. Beattie, The Laves and Chi Phases in a Modified 12Cr Stainless Alloy, *Trans. ASM*, Vol 47, 1955, p 211-230
39. B. Weiss and R. Stickler, Phase Instabilities During High Temperature Exposure of 316 Austenitic Stainless Steel, *Met. Trans.*, Vol 3, April 1972, p 851-866
40. H. Hughes and S.R. Keown, Precipitation of a Transition Intermetallic Compound (R-Phase) in Steels, *J. Iron Steel Inst.*, Vol 206, March 1968, p 275-277
41. D.J. Dyson and S.R. Keown, A Study of Precipitation in a 12% Cr-Co-Mo Steel, *Acta Metall.*, Vol 17, 1969, p 1095-1107
42. J.K. Lai and J.R. Haigh, Delta-Ferrite Transformation in a Type 316 Weld Metal, *Weld. J.*, Vol 58, Jan 1979, p 1s-6s
43. H.T. Beattie and W.C. Hagel, Intermetallic Compounds in Titanium-Hardened Alloys, *Trans. AIME*, Vol 209, July 1957, p 911-917
44. K.W. Andrews and H. Hughes, discussion of paper "Aging Reaction in Certain Superalloys," *Trans. ASM*, Vol 49, 1957, p 999
45. J.J. Demo, *Structure, Constitution, and General Characteristics of Wrought Ferritic Stainless Steels*, STP 619, ASTM, Philadelphia, 1977
46. R.H. Thielemann, Some Effects of Composition and Heat Treatment on the

High Temperature Rupture Properties of Ferrous Alloys, *Proc. ASTM*, Vol 40, 1940, p 788-804

47. K.J. Irvine *et al.*, The Physical Metallurgy of 12% Chromium Steels, *J. Iron Steel Inst.*, Vol 195, Aug 1960, p 386-405

48. K.J. Irvine *et al.*, Controlled-Transformation Stainless Steels, *J. Iron Steel Inst.*, Vol 192, July 1959, p 218-238

49. A. Kasak *et al.*, Development of Precipitation Hardening Cr-Mo-Co Stainless Steels, *Trans. ASM*, Vol 56, 1963, p 455-467

50. B.R. Banerjee *et al.*, Structure and Properties of PH15-7Mo Stainless, *Trans. ASM*, Vol 57, 1964, p 856-873

51. H.L. Marcus *et al.*, Precipitation in 17-7PH Stainless Steel, *Trans. ASM*, Vol 58, 1965, p 176-182

52. R.C. Gibson *et al.*, Properties of Stainless Steels with a Microduplex Structure, *Trans. ASM*, Vol 61, 1968, p 85-93

53. S. Floreen and H.W. Hayden, The Influence of Austenite and Ferrite on the Mechanical Properties of Two-Phase Stainless Steels Having Microduplex Structures, *Trans. ASM*, Vol 61, 1968, p 489-499

54. H.D. Solomon and T.M. Devine, Duplex Stainless Steels—A Tale of Two Phases, paper 8201-089, presented at the 1982 ASM Metals Congress, St. Louis, MO, 1982

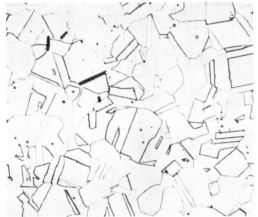

**Fig. 1** Type 201 stainless steel strip, annealed 5 min at 1065 °C (1950 °F) and rapidly cooled to room temperature. The structure is equiaxed austenite grains and annealing twins. 10 mL HNO₃, 10 mL acetic acid, 15 mL HCl, and 2 drops glycerol. 250×

**Fig. 2** Type 301 stainless steel, mill annealed at 1065 °C (1950 °F) and cold worked. Some martensite (dark) has formed in the austenitic matrix. Electrolytic: HNO₃-acetic acid, then 10% oxalic acid. 200×

**Fig. 3** Type 301 sheet cold rolled to 10% reduction (quarter hard), showing martensite formation in deformed austenite grains. Stringers and pits are etched-out inclusions. Electrolytic: 10% oxalic acid. 250×

**Fig. 4** Type 301 sheet, cold rolled to 40% reduction (full hard), showing almost complete transformation to martensite in severely deformed austenite grains. Electrolytic: 10% oxalic acid. 250×

**Fig. 5** Type 302 stainless steel strip, 1.6 mm (0.06 in.) thick, annealed at 1065 °C (1950 °F) and rapidly cooled to room temperature. The structure consists of ferrite pools (globules) in an austenitic matrix. Electrolytic: 10% NaCN. 500×

**Fig. 6** Type 304 stainless steel strip, annealed 5 min at 1065 °C (1950 °F), cooled in air. Structure consists of equiaxed austenite grains and annealing twins. 10 mL HNO₃, 10 mL acetic acid, 15 mL HCl, and 2 drops glycerol. 250×

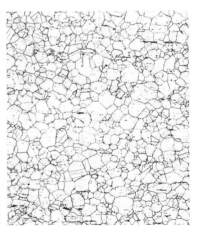

**Fig. 7** Type 304 strip, annealed 2 min at 1065 °C (1950 °F) and air cooled. Structure is equiaxed austenite grains, annealing twins, and small stringer inclusions. Electrolytic: HNO₃-acetic acid, then 10% oxalic acid. 100×

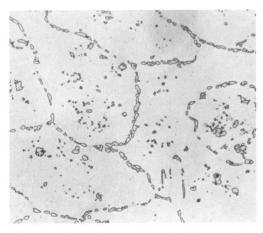

**Fig. 8** Type 310 stainless steel plate, hot rolled and annealed at 1065 °C (1950 °F), water quenched in less than 3 min, exposed 27 months at 760 °C (1400 °F), and slowly air cooled. Structure is σ-phase precipitates in an austenitic matrix. Electrolytic: saturated NaOH, 1.5 V dc, 6 s. 250×

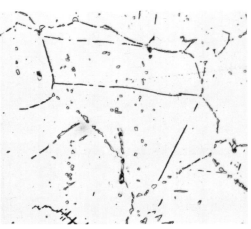

**Fig. 9** Type 316 stainless steel, annealed 30 min at 1080 °C (1975 °F) and exposed 3000 h at 815 °C (1500 °F). Prolonged exposure at temperature has resulted in the formation of islands of σ and χ phases at austenite grain boundaries. Picral and HCl. 500×

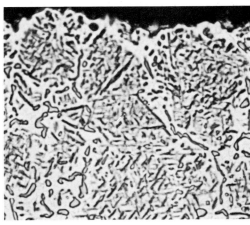

**Fig. 10** Type 316 tubing, packed with boron nitride powder and held 2285 h at 840 °C (1540 °F). The gray phase at grain boundaries and Widmanstätten platelets within grains are chromium nitride. The matrix is austenite. 12 mL lactic acid, 38 mL HCl, and 2 mL HNO₃. 500×

**Fig. 11** Type 316 stainless steel, solution annealed at 1035 °C (1900 °F) and water quenched. Etching has revealed most of the austenite grain and annealing twin boundaries. 10 mL HNO₃, 10 mL acetic acid, 15 mL HCl, and 5 mL glycerol. 100×

**Fig. 12** Same steel and processing as Fig. 11, etched electrolytically to reveal austenite grain boundaries. Not all of the boundaries are visible. Electrolytic: 10% aqueous oxalic acid, 6 V dc, 15 s. 100×

**Fig. 13** Same steel and processing as Fig. 11, etched to reveal austenite grain boundaries. Not all of the boundaries are revealed. Compare with Fig. 12 and 14. Marble's reagent. 100×

**Fig. 14** Same steel and processing as Fig. 11, etched to reveal austenite grain boundaries. Not all of the boundaries are visible. Compare with Fig. 12 and 13. Equal parts H₂O, HCl, and HNO₃. 100×

**Fig. 15** Same steel and processing as Fig. 11, etched to reveal austenite grain boundaries. Note that twins are not etched. Electrolytic: 60% aqueous HNO₃, 0.6 V dc, 2 min (platinum cathode). 100×

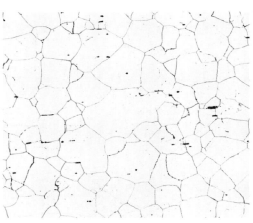

**Fig. 16** Same steel as Fig. 11, solution annealed and sensitized. Twins are not etched, because no carbide was precipitated at the twins. Equal parts H₂O, HCl, and HNO₃. 100×

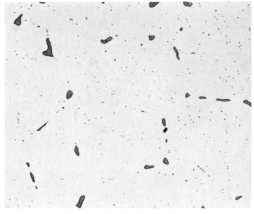

**Fig. 17** Annealed type 321 stainless steel furnace part, after 16 months service at 900 °C (1650 °F) in hydrogen. Sigma-phase islands at austenite grain boundaries and fine, dispersed chromium carbide. Electrolytic: 40% aqueous NaOH. 300×

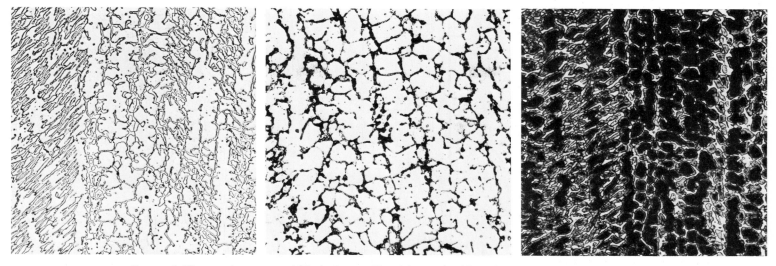

**Fig. 18, 19, 20** The use of different etchants to reveal δ-ferrite in austenitic stainless steel weld metal. Fig. 18: etched in Vilella's reagent. Fig. 19: etched 15 s in modified Murakami's reagent (30 g K₃Fe(CN)₆, 30 g KOH, and 150 mL H₂O) at 95 °C (200 °F) to color δ-ferrite brown. Fig. 20: heat tinted at 595 °C (1100 °F) to color austenite red and δ-ferrite cream. See also Fig. 21 to 23. 500×

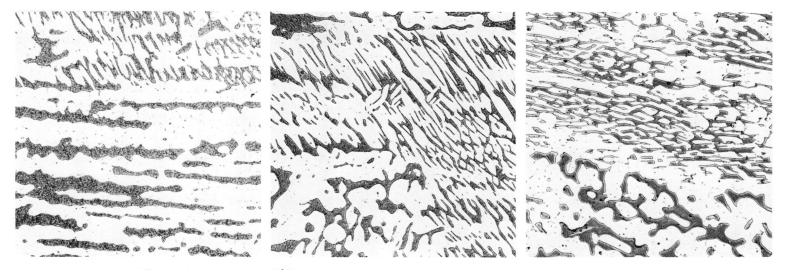

**Fig. 21, 22, 23** Different etchants used to reveal δ-ferrite in austenitic stainless steel weld metal. Fig. 21: electrolytic etch 10 s in 10 N KOH, 2.5 V dc. Fig. 22: electrolytic etch 25 s in 20% aqueous NaOH, 20 V dc. Fig. 23: etched 15 min in boiling Murakami's reagent. 500×

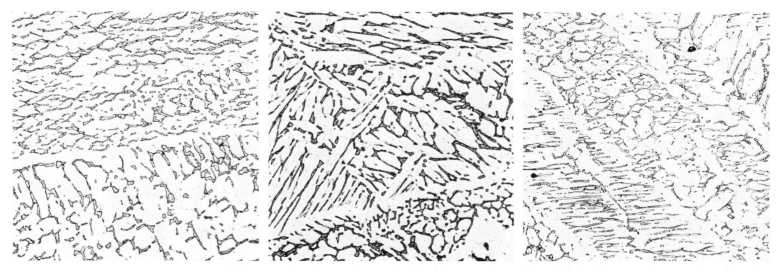

**Fig. 24, 25, 26** Austenitic stainless steel weld metal, etched using different reagents to reveal σ phase. Fig. 24: electrolytic etch in 10 N KOH, 2.5 V dc, 10 s. Fig. 25: electrolytic etch in 20% aqueous NaOH, 20 V, 25 s. Fig. 26: etched 3 min in Murakami's reagent, room temperature. 500×

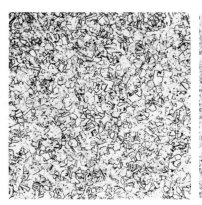
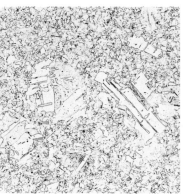
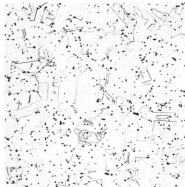

**Fig. 27** 22-13-5 austenitic stainless steel (400 HV), solution annealed and cold drawn. Note the uniform grain structure. 10 mL HNO$_3$, 10 mL acetic acid, 15 mL HCl, and 2 drops glycerol. 200×

**Fig. 28** 22-13-5 stainless steel, solution annealed and cold drawn as in Fig. 27. In this case, a duplex grain structure developed. 10 mL HNO$_3$, 10 mL acetic acid, 15 mL HCl, and 2 drops glycerol. 100×

**Fig. 29** Type 308 stainless steel, solution annealed and cold worked. The grain structure is difficult to reveal by chemical etching. 10 mL HNO$_3$, 10 mL acetic acid, 15 mL HCl, and 2 drops glycerol. 400×

**Fig. 30** Same material and processing as Fig. 29, examined under differential interference contrast illumination to reveal surface topography. 10 mL HNO$_3$, 10 mL acetic acid, 15 mL HCl, and 2 drops glycerol. 400×

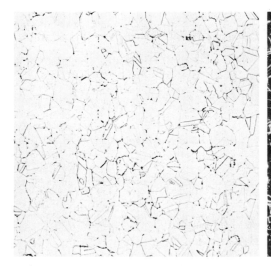
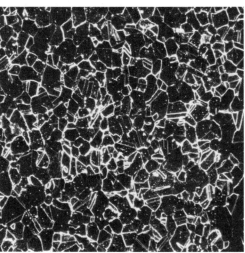
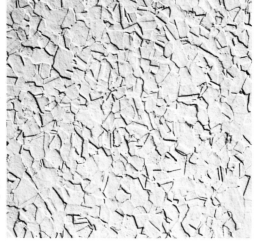

**Fig. 31, 32, 33** 20Cb-3 austenitic stainless steel, solution annealed. The use of different illumination modes to reveal the chemically etched grain structure. Fig. 31: bright-field illumination. Fig. 32: dark-field illumination. Fig. 33: differential interference contrast. 10 mL HNO$_3$, 10 mL acetic acid, 15 mL HCl, and 2 drops glycerol. 400×

**Fig. 34, 35, 36** Type 316L stainless steel, cold drawn, using different illumination modes. The structure is revealed more clearly with dark-field illumination and differential interference contrast than with bright-field illumination. Fig. 34: bright-field illumination. Fig. 35: dark-field illumination. Fig. 36: differential interference contrast. 10 mL HNO$_3$, 10 mL acetic acid, 15 mL HCl, and 2 drops glycerol. 100×

**Fig. 37, 38, 39** Proprietary austenitic stainless steel, not recrystallized after hot working. The structure is revealed more clearly using dark-field illumination and differential interference contrast than by bright-field illumination. Fig. 37: bright-field illumination. Fig. 38: dark-field illumination. Fig. 39: differential interference contrast. 10 mL $HNO_3$, 10 mL acetic acid, 15 mL HCl, and 2 drops glycerol. 100×

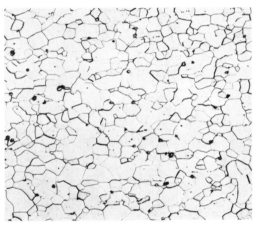

**Fig. 40** Stringer-type manganese sulfide inclusions in resulfurized type 303 stainless steel. Free-machining additives such as MnS permit higher machining speeds, lower power consumption, and promote longer tool life. See also Fig. 41. As-polished. 500×

**Fig. 41** Mixed manganese sulfide and manganese selenide inclusions in type 303 selenium-treated stainless steel (0.21% Se). Selenium has beneficial effects similar to sulfur (see Fig. 40), but also imparts greater ductility to free-machining stainless steels than does sulfur. As-polished. 500×

**Fig. 42** Muffler-grade type 409 stainless steel (0.045C-11Cr-0.50Ti) strip, annealed 1 h per inch of thickness at 870 °C (1600 °F) and air cooled to RT. Equiaxed ferrite grains and dispersed titanium carbide particles. 10 mL $HNO_3$, 10 mL acetic acid, 15 mL HCl, and 2 drops glycerol. 100×

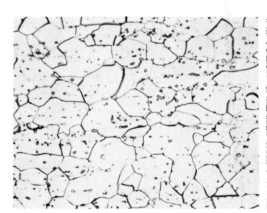

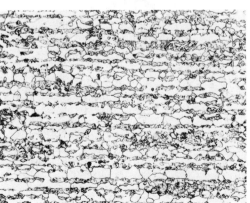

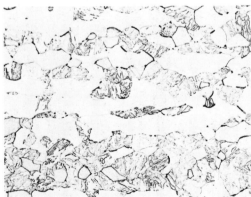

**Fig. 43** Type 430 stainless steel strip, annealed at 845 °C (1550 °F) and cooled in air. The structure consists of equiaxed ferrite grains and randomly dispersed chromium carbide particles. Vilella's reagent. 500×

**Fig. 44** Type 430 ferritic stainless steel. This grade can sometimes be partially hardenable, depending on composition balance and amount of segregation. The structure in this longitudinal section is streaks of martensite (dark) and ferrite (white). See Fig. 45. Glyceregia. 100×

**Fig. 45** Same as Fig. 44, but a higher magnification to resolve the structure more clearly. Ferrite (white constituent) is approximately 235 HV; martensite (dark), 360 HV. Same etchant as Fig. 44. 400×

**Fig. 46** Type 430F (resulfurized free-machining 430, 254 HV) ferritic stainless steel. Longitudinal section shows dispersed manganese sulfide stringers in a ferrite matrix. As-polished. 200×

**Fig. 47** 182-FM (18Cr-2Mo) resulfurized free-machining stainless steel (230 HV). The structure is carbide and sulfides in a ferritic matrix. Ralph's reagent. 200×

**Fig. 48** Type 434 modified free-machining ferritic stainless steel (260 HV). Longitudinal section shows carbides and sulfide stringers in a matrix of ferrite. Ralph's reagent. 100×

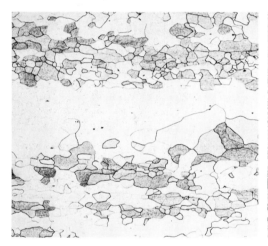

**Fig. 49** E-Brite (26Cr-1Mo) ferritic stainless steel plate (180 HV), 6 mm (0.25 in.) thick. Longitudinal section shows ferrite grains. 10 mL HNO₃, 10 mL acetic acid, 15 mL HCl, and 2 drops glycerol. 50×

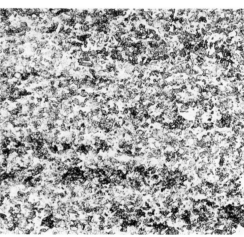

**Fig. 50** Type 403 martensitic stainless steel (320 HV) in the quenched and tempered condition. Longitudinal section shows a structure of tempered martensite. Vilella's reagent. 400×

**Fig. 51** Type 410 stainless steel (300 HV), with sulfur added for machinability, in the quenched and tempered condition. Structure is tempered martensite with some manganese sulfide stringers. Vilella's reagent. 400×

**Fig. 52** Type 420 stainless steel, quenched and tempered. Structure is tempered martensite. Vilella's reagent. 100×

**Fig. 53** Type 420 stainless steel (306 HV), quenched and tempered with sulfur added to improve machinability. Tempered martensite with some sulfide inclusions. Vilella's reagent. 400×

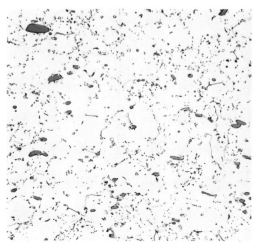

**Fig. 54** Free-machining type 416 stainless steel (160 HV), annealed. The gray particles are sulfides. Vilella's reagent. 400×

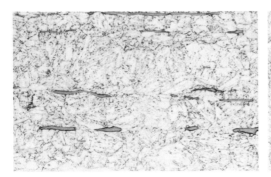

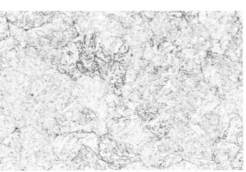

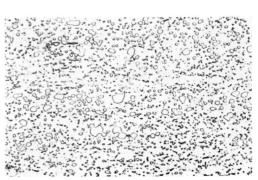

**Fig. 55** Same free-machining stainless steel as shown in Fig. 54, but in the quenched and tempered condition. Longitudinal section shows δ-ferrite stringers (white), tempered martensite, and sulfides. Vilella's reagent. 400×

**Fig. 56** Type 431 stainless steel (335 HV) in the quenched and tempered condition. Structure is tempered martensite. This martensitic alloy has a nickel addition (1.25-2.50%) for enhanced corrosion resistance. Vilella's reagent. 200×

**Fig. 57** Type 440A stainless steel in the annealed condition. Longitudinal section shows chromium carbide particles in a ferritic matrix. See Fig. 58 for effects of austenitizing/air cooling/tempering heat treatment on the structure of this alloy. 5% picric acid and 3% hydrochloric acid in alcohol. 500×

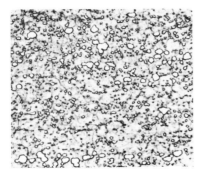

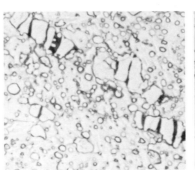

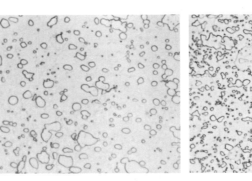

**Fig. 58** Type 440A stainless steel, austenitized 30 min at 1010 °C (1850 °F), air cooled and tempered 30 min at 595 °C (1100 °F). The structure is partly spheroidized particles of chromium carbide in a martensitic matrix. Compare with the annealed structure shown in Fig. 57. 1% picric acid and 5% HCl in alcohol. 500×

**Fig. 59, 60** Type 440B martensitic stainless steel (245 HV) in the spheroidize annealed condition. Fig. 59: specimen was polished incorrectly; note resulting cracks in and around the carbide particles. Fig. 60: same specimen as shown in Fig. 59 but polished properly. No cracking is evident in this specimen. See the article "Mechanical Grinding, Abrasion, and Polishing" in this Volume for detailed information on procedures. Vilella's reagent. 1000×

**Fig. 61** Type 440C stainless steel (255 HV) in the spheroidize annealed condition. Structure is chromium-rich carbide particles in a ferrite matrix. See also Fig. 62 and 63 for the effects of alternate heat treatments on the structure of this martensitic alloy. Vilella's reagent. 1000×

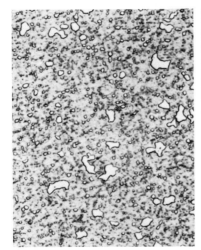

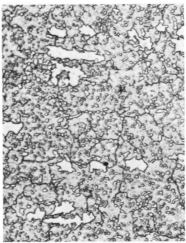

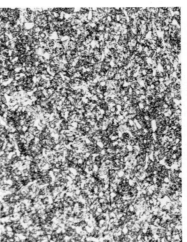

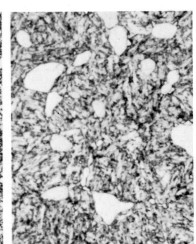

**Fig. 62** Type 440C martensitic stainless steel, austenitized 1 h at 1010 °C (1850 °F), air cooled, and tempered 2 h at 230 °C (450 °F). The structure is carbide particles in a martensitic matrix. Vilella's reagent. See also Fig. 63. 500×

**Fig. 63** Type 440C stainless steel bar, preheated 30 min at 760 °C (1400 °F), austenitized 30 min at 1025 °C (1875 °F), air cooled to 65 °C (150 °F), and double tempered (2 h each) at 425 °C (800 °F). Primary and secondary carbides (islands and particles) in tempered martensite. Superpicral. 500×

**Fig. 64, 65** AM350 semiaustenitic precipitation-hardenable stainless steel, containing a small amount of ferrite (white patches) in a martensitic matrix. Some retained austenite is also present. This grade and AM355 (see Fig. 66 to 68), while classed as precipitation-hardenable alloys, do not have true precipitation reactions. Fry's reagent. Fig. 64: 100×. Fig. 65: 1000×

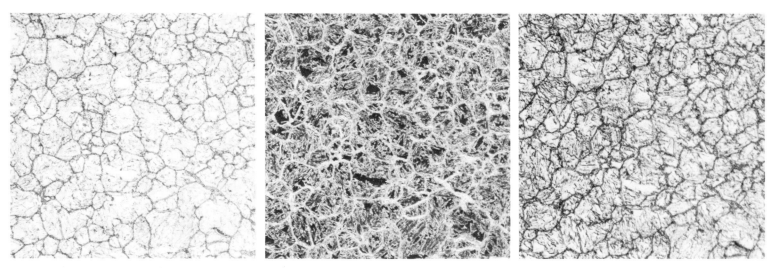

**Fig. 66, 67, 68** AM355 precipitation-hardenable stainless steel (525 HV), heat treated. The structure is martensite, but etching has revealed prior austenite grain boundaries. Fig. 66: bright-field illumination. Fig. 67: dark-field illumination. Fig. 68: Differential interference contrast. Vilella's reagent. 400×

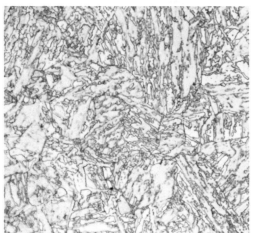

**Fig. 69** PH13-8Mo precipitation-hardenable stainless steel (475 HV), solution annealed and aged. The structure is tempered martensite. Fry's reagent. 1000×

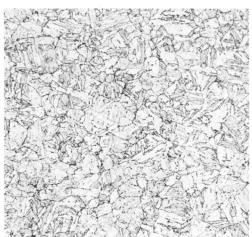

**Fig. 70** 17-4PH stainless steel, solution annealed and aged. Structure is tempered martensite (no δ-ferrite). Compare with Fig. 81 to 84. Fry's reagent. 200×

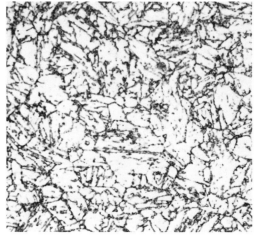

**Fig. 71** Custom 450 precipitation-hardenable stainless steel (360 HV), solution annealed and aged (H1050). The structure is tempered martensite. Fry's reagent. 1000×

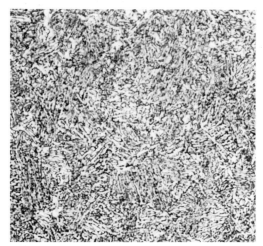

**Fig. 72** Custom 450 precipitation-hardenable stainless steel (320 HV), solution annealed and aged (H1150). The structure is tempered martensite and reverted austenite. Fry's reagent. 1000×

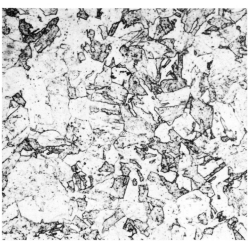

**Fig. 73** Custom 455 precipitation-hardenable stainless steel (51 HRC), solution annealed and aged (H850). The structure is martensitic. Fry's reagent. 1000×

**Fig. 74** Custom 455 precipitation-hardenable stainless steel (36 HRC) in the solution annealed and aged condition (H1100). The structure is martensitic. Fry's reagent. 1000×

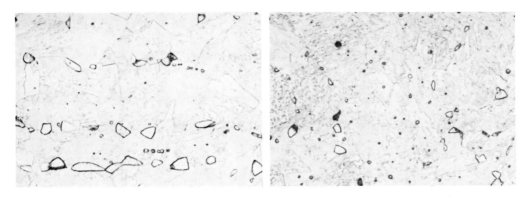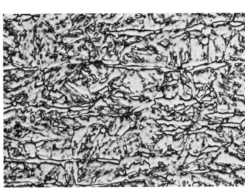

**Fig. 75, 76** 17-7PH semiaustenitic precipitation-hardenable stainless steel (165 HV) that was hot rolled and annealed. The outlined particles shown in this photomicrograph are δ-ferrite. Fig. 75: a longitudinal section. Fig. 76: a transverse section. Figures 77 and 78 show this alloy in the solution-annealed/air-cooled condition. Figure 79 illustrates a heat-treated, cold-rolled structure. Vilella's reagent. 1000×

**Fig. 77** 17-7PH stainless, solution annealed at 1065 °C (1950 °F), then held 10 min at 955 °C (1750 °F), air cooled, held 8 h at −75 °C (−100 °F), held 1 h at 510 °C (950 °F), and air cooled. Ferrite stringers in a martensitic matrix. Vilella's reagent. 1000×

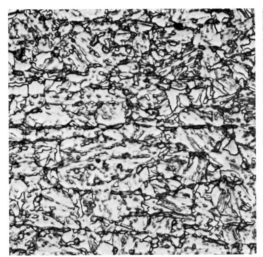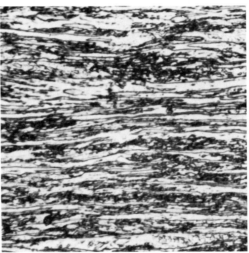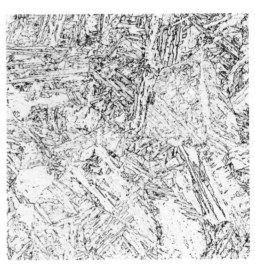

**Fig. 78** Same as Fig. 77, but reheated and held 1.5 h at 760 °C (1400 °F), air cooled to 15 °C (60 °F) and held 30 min, heated to 565 °C (1050 °F) and held 1.5 h, and air cooled. The structure is the same as Fig. 77, but this steel is more ductile. Vilella's reagent. 1000×

**Fig. 79** 17-7PH stainless steel, cold rolled at the mill, then held 1 h at 480 °C (900 °F) and air cooled. Structure is essentially martensite; austenite was transformed by cold rolling. Electrolytic: $HNO_3$-acetic acid, then 10% aqueous oxalic acid. 1000×

**Fig. 80** 15-5PH martensitic precipitation-hardenable stainless steel (41 HRC), solution annealed and aged. Structure is tempered martensite. Vilella's reagent. 200×

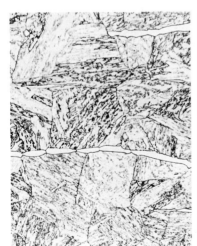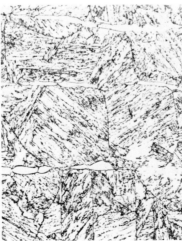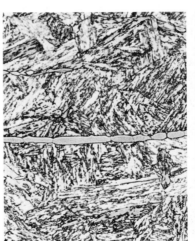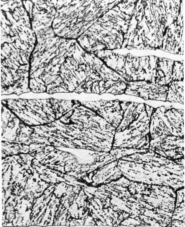

**Fig. 81, 82, 83, 84** 17-4PH precipitation-hardenable stainless steel, heat treated. The effect of different etchants in revealing the structure, which consists of δ-ferrite stringers in a martensitic matrix. Fig. 81: etched using Fry's reagent. Fig. 82: etched using Vilella's reagent. Fig 83: etched using Marble's reagent. Fig. 84: etched using superpicral. 500×

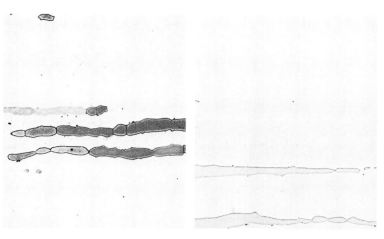

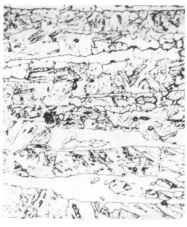

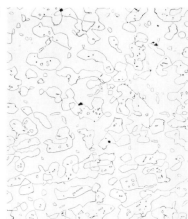

**Fig. 85, 86** Same stainless steel as Fig. 81 to 84, etched electrolytically to reveal δ-ferrite stringers. Fig. 85: etched 10 s in 10 N KOH at 2.5 V dc. Fig. 86: etched 21 s in 20% aqueous NaOH at 20 V dc. 500×

**Fig. 87** Stainless W in the solution annealed and aged condition; δ-ferrite stringers in tempered martensite elongated in the rolling direction. Superpicral. 500×

**Fig. 88** Type 312 duplex stainless steel (250 HV) in the solution annealed and aged condition. Transverse section shows austenite in a matrix of ferrite. Glyceregia. 200×

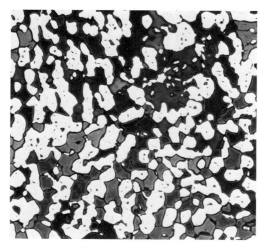

**Fig. 89** Same stainless steel and processing as Fig. 88, but tint etched to color the ferrite phase. The austenite remains white. 10% aqueous HCl and 1% aqueous $K_2S_2O_5$. 200×

**Fig. 90** Proprietary duplex stainless steel (250 HV). The specimen has been etched to reveal carbide phase; the matrix is only faintly visible in this longitudinal section. Vilella's reagent. 200×

**Fig. 91** Same duplex stainless steel as in Fig. 90, tint etched. Ferrite in the matrix is colored; austenite is unaffected. 10% aqueous HCl and 1% aqueous $K_2S_2O_5$. 200×

# Stainless Steel Casting Alloys

STAINLESS STEEL casting alloys are widely used to resist corrosion by aqueous solutions at or near room temperature and by hot gases and liquids at elevated temperatures to 650 °C (1200 °F). These alloys, identified by Alloy Casting Institute (ACI) designations, contain more than 11% Cr and up to 30% Ni. Additional information on the properties and selection of stainless steel casting alloys can be found in the articles "Corrosion-Resistant Steel Castings" and "Properties of Cast Stainless Steels" in Volume 3 of the 9th Edition of *Metals Handbook*.

## Specimen Preparation

The techniques and equipment used for mounting, grinding, and polishing specimens of stainless steel casting alloys for metallographic examination are similar to those described in the article "Wrought Stainless Steels" in this Volume.

**Grinding and Polishing.** Coarse grinding is generally performed with 80-, 100-, and 120-grit papers, followed by fine grinding with 240-, 320-, 400-, and 600-grit papers. Rough polishing involves the use of rotating disks covered with napless cloth impregnated with pastes of diamond dust or slurries of alumina ($Al_2O_3$) with 9-, 6-, then 3-$\mu$m particle sizes. Rotating disks covered with soft cloth of medium to long nap and slurries of 0.3- and 0.05-$\mu$m $Al_2O_3$ are used for fine polishing. Throughout grinding and polishing, care should be exercised to minimize the occurrence of disturbed metal.

**Etching.** The etchants used to delineate the microstructure of stainless steel casting alloys are given in Table 1. Also in Table 1, several alloys are listed with the etchants used to reveal their general microstructure, or to emphasize a microconstituent of interest, such as ferrite or carbide. The presence of ferrite in the austenitic CF-type alloys improves weldability, as well as resistance to intergranular corrosion and stress-corrosion cracking. The distribution of carbide is important, because carbide precipitation at the austenite grain boundaries lessens resistance to intergranular corrosion. Properly solution-treated CF and CG (modified CF alloys containing 3 to 4% Mo) castings have a structure essentially free of precipitated carbide.

The intermetallic $\sigma$ phase in austenitic-ferritic alloys is important, because the presence of $\sigma$ reduces corrosion resistance and imparts ambient-temperature brittleness. Etchants used in detecting $\sigma$ phase also are listed in Table 1.

## Microstructures of Cast Stainless Steels

The stainless steel casting alloys depicted in micrographs in this article (Table 2) are iron-chromium and iron-chromium-nickel alloys similar to some of the martensitic, ferritic, and austenitic wrought stainless steels.

**Table 1 Compositions and applications of etchants for stainless steel casting alloys**

| Etchant | Composition |
|---|---|
| 1. Oxalic acid (electrolytic, 6 V) | 10 g oxalic acid, 100 mL $H_2O$ |
| 2. Vilella's reagent | 5 mL HCl, 1 g picric acid, 100 mL ethanol (95%) or methanol (95%) |
| 3. Kalling's reagent 2 | 100 mL HCl, 5 g $CuCl_2$ (cupric chloride), 100 mL ethanol (95%) |
| 4. Murakami's reagent (unheated) | 1-4 g $K_3Fe(CN)_6$ (potassium ferricyanide), 10 g KOH (or 7 g NaOH), 100 mL $H_2O$ |
| 5. Murakami's reagent (boiling) | Same composition as etchant 4, but heated to boiling temperature for use |
| 6. Chromic acid (electrolytic, 6 V) | 10 g $CrO_3$, 100 mL $H_2O$ |
| 7. 10N potassium hydroxide (electrolytic, 6 V) | 560 g KOH (potassium hydroxide) diluted with distilled $H_2O$ to a volume of 1000 mL |
| 8. HCl, $HNO_3$, acetic acid | 15 mL HCl, 10 mL $HNO_3$, 10 mL acetic acid |
| 9. Acid ferric chloride | Saturated solution of $FeCl_3 \cdot 6H_2O$ in HCl (conc); add few drops $HNO_3$ |
| 10. Glyceregia | 10 mL $HNO_3$, 20-50 mL HCl, 30 mL glycerol |
| 11. Sodium cyanide (electrolytic, 6 V) | 10 g NaCN (sodium cyanide), 90 mL $H_2O$. *Caution:* Avoid skin contact or inhalation of vapors. |

| Alloy | Condition | General microstructure | Ferrite | Carbide | Sigma phase |
|---|---|---|---|---|---|
| | | | Etchants for revealing: | | |
| CA-6NM | Hardened and tempered(a) | 2 | 3 | 4 | ... |
| CA-15 | Hardened and tempered(a) | 2 or 9 | 3 | 4 | ... |
| CB-7CU-1 | Solution treated(b) | 2 | 2 | ... | ... |
| CD-4MCu | Solution treated(b) | 1, 2, or 6 | ... | ... | 2, then 7 |
| CE-30 | As-cast | 2 | 3 | 4 | 2, then 7; or 11 |
| CF-3 | Solution treated(c) | 7 | 3 | 1, 4 | 2, then 7 |
| CF-3M | Solution treated(c) | 8 | 3 | 1, 4 | 2, then 7; or 11 |
| CF-8 | Solution treated(d) | 7 or 10 | 3 | 1, 4 | 2, then 7 |
| CF-8C | Solution treated(d) | 1 or 6 | 3 | 1, 4 | 2, then 7; or 11 |
| CF-8M | Solution treated(d) | 9 | 3 | 1, 4 | 2, then 7 |
| CF-20 | Solution treated(d) | 1 | 3 | 1, 4 | ... |
| CG-8M | Solution treated(d) | 1 | 3 | 1, 4 | 5; or 7, then 11 |
| CN-7M | Solution treated(e) | 1 or 6 | ... | ... | ... |

(a) Heat to 955 °C (1750 °F) min, air cool, and temper at 595 °C (1100 °F) min. (b) Heat to 1040 °C (1900 °F) min, quench in water or oil. (c) Heat to 1040 °C (1900 °F) min, rapid cool. (d) Heat to 1040 °C (1900 °F) min, water quench. (e) Heat to 1120 °C (2050 °F) min, water quench.

Revised by C.R. Bird, Chief Metallurgist, Stainless Foundry & Engineering, Inc.

**Table 2   Compositions of stainless steel casting alloys**

| ACI type | UNS designation | Wrought alloy type(a) | Composition, % | | | | | | | | | |
|---|---|---|---|---|---|---|---|---|---|---|---|---|
| | | | C (max) | Mn (max) | Cr | Ni | Si (max) | P (max) | S (max) | Mo | Others |
| CA-6NM ........ | J91540 | ... | 0.06 | 1.00 | 11.5-14.0 | 3.5-4.5 | 1.00 | 0.04 | 0.03 | 0.4-1.0 | ... |
| CA-15 ........... | J91150 | 410 | 0.15 | 1.00 | 11.5-14.0 | 1.0 max | 1.50 | 0.04 | 0.03 | 0.5 max(b) | ... |
| CB-7Cu-1 ........ | J92110 | 17-4 PH | 0.07 | 0.70 | 15.5-17.7 | 3.6-4.6 | 1.00 | 0.04 | 0.03 | ... | 2.5-3.2 Cu 0.20-0.35 Nb 0.05 max Ni |
| CD-4MCu ....... | J93370 | ... | 0.04 | 1.00 | 24.5-26.5 | 4.75-6.00 | 1.00 | 0.04 | 0.04 | 1.75-2.25 | 2.75-3.25 Cu |
| CF-3 ........... | J92700 | 304L | 0.03 | 1.50 | 17.0-21.0 | 8.0-12.0 | 2.00 | 0.04 | 0.04 | ... | ... |
| CF-3M ......... | J92800 | 316L | 0.03 | 1.50 | 17.0-21.0 | 9.0-13.0 | 1.50 | 0.04 | 0.04 | 2.0-3.0 | ... |
| CF-8 ........... | J92600 | 304 | 0.08 | 1.50 | 18.0-21.0 | 8.0-11.0 | 1.50 | 0.04 | 0.04 | ... | ... |
| CF-8C .......... | J92710 | 347 | 0.08 | 1.50 | 18.0-21.0 | 9.0-12.0 | 1.50 | 0.04 | 0.04 | ... | Nb(c) |
| CF-8M ......... | J92900 | 316 | 0.08 | 1.50 | 18.0-21.0 | 9.0-12.0 | 1.50 | 0.04 | 0.04 | 2.0-3.0 | ... |
| CF-16F ........ | J92701 | 303 | 0.16 | 1.50 | 18.0-21.0 | 9.0-12.0 | 1.50 | 0.17 | 0.04 | 1.5 max | 0.20-0.35Se(d) |
| CF-20 ........... | J92602 | 302 | 0.20 | 1.50 | 18.0-21.0 | 8.0-11.0 | 1.50 | 0.04 | 0.04 | ... | ... |
| CK-20 .......... | J94202 | 310 | 0.20 | 2.00 | 23.0-27.0 | 19.0-22.0 | 2.00 | 0.04 | 0.04 | ... | ... |
| CN-7M ......... | J95150 | ... | 0.07 | 1.50 | 19.0-22.0 | 27.5-30.5 | 1.50 | 0.04 | 0.04 | 2.0-3.0 | 3.0-4.0 Cu |

(a) Type numbers of wrought alloys are listed only for nominal identification of corresponding wrought grades. Composition ranges of cast alloys are not the same as for corresponding wrought alloys; cast alloy designations should be used for castings only. (b) Molybdenum not intentionally added. (c) Nb, 8 × %C min (1.0% max); or Nb + Ta, 9 × %C (1.1% max)

The microstructures of stainless steel casting alloys depend primarily on composition and heat treatment. The hardenable ferritic-martensitic alloys such as CA-15, are austenitized, cooled, and tempered, usually to enhance mechanical properties. The non-hardenable austenitic alloys, such as CF-8, are solution treated to increase resistance to corrosion. Normal heat treatments for the most widely used casting alloys are given in Table 1.

**Classification.** Of the alloys listed in Table 2, CA-6NM and CA-15 are essentially martensitic when cooled from the austenitizing temperature (approximately 980 °C, or 1800 °F). The martensitic structure of CA-6NM depends on a proper balance of low carbon content (0.06% maximum) and nickel content (nominally 4%). These alloys develop maximum strength and corrosion resistance in the hardened and tempered condition. They are normally tempered at a temperature safely above the maximum recommended service temperature—approximately 540 °C (1000 °F).

Alloy CB-7Cu-1 is a precipitation-hardening alloy similar to wrought 17-4 PH (see Table 2). It is essentially martensitic in the solution-treated and the aged conditions. It is generally solution treated at approximately 1040 °C (1900 °F) and aged at 480 to 620 °C (900 to 1150 °F) for maximum strength and resistance to corrosion.

Alloy CD-4MCu is a duplex-phase alloy that in the solution-treated condition consists of up to 65% ferrite and 35% austenite. It contains molybdenum and copper. It is normally used only in the solution-treated condition. After solution treating at temperatures above 1040 °C (1900 °F) and quenching in

water, oil, or air (depending on casting shape and intended service), it has excellent corrosion resistance and about twice the strength of CF-8, an austenitic alloy that normally contains less than 15% ferrite.

Alloys CF-3 through CF-16F in Table 2 are austenitic, with limited amounts of ferrite; alloys CF-20, CK-20 and CN-7M are completely austenitic. They exhibit maximum corrosion resistance in the solution-treated condition. The corrosion resistance of certain alloys is enhanced by extra-low carbon content (as in CF-3), a molybdenum addition (as in CF-3M and CF-8M), or the addition of niobium (as in CF-8C). Alloy CF-16F contains 0.20 to 0.35% Se for improved machinability.

**Carbide Precipitation and Corrosion Resistance.** The austenitic alloys are widely used to resist attack by corrosive aqueous solutions at or near room temperature and hot gases and liquids at temperatures to 650 °C (1200 °F). In general, the corrosion resistance of these alloys is optimum when all carbide is in solution, a condition achieved by rapid cooling from the solution-treating temperature. However, carbide in solution will precipitate at grain boundaries when these alloys are exposed to temperatures in the sensitizing range, 425 to 870 °C (800 to 1600 °F), which may occur in service or during welding. Unless the alloy is stabilized by adding a preferential carbide former, such as niobium, or carbide formation is inhibited by extra-low carbon content, the precipitation of chromium-containing carbide at grain boundaries will intensify grain-boundary attack.

**Carbide-Formation Rate in CF Alloys.** When carbon content is 0.03% (CF-3), no carbide forms in 30 min at 425 or 540 °C (800

or 1000 °F), or in 15 min at 870 °C (1600 °F). At 650 °C (1200 °F), carbide forms within 1 min. Carbide also forms at 760 °C (1400 °F). However, at this low carbon level, the corrosion rate based on nitric acid tests is low.

When carbon content is 0.08% (CF-8), carbide forms at 540 °C (1000 °F) after 15 min, but the amount of precipitate is too small to affect corrosion behavior. At 650 °C (1200 °F), carbide is precipitated within 1 min, and corrosion rate and intensity of intergranular attack increase with time at temperature. Carbide also forms at 760 and 870 °C (1400 and 1600 °F). Maximum sensitization is reached in 15 min at 760 °C (1400 °F) and in 5 min at 870 °C (1600 °F), and increased time at temperature *lowers* the corrosion rate.

The behavior of a 0.12% carbon alloy is similar to that of a 0.08% carbon alloy. Carbide formation begins at 425 °C (800 °F), however, and is most intense at 650 °C (1200 °F). At 870 °C (1600 °F), corrosion rate declines with time after reaching a maximum.

**Molybdenum and Niobium Additions.** Molybdenum increases the ferrite content of the structure, providing more opportunity for carbide to form at ferrite-austenite boundaries rather than grain boundaries, resulting in increased resistance to intergranular attack, an effect shared by other ferrite-promoting elements.

Niobium contributes to general corrosion resistance and resistance to intergranular attack. By forming niobium carbide preferentially throughout the sensitizing range, it inhibits depletion of chromium from the austenite matrix and precipitation of chromium-containing carbide at grain boundaries.

**Fig. 1** CA-6NM alloy, normalized 1 h at 1010 °C (1850 °F) and tempered 2 h at 650 °C (1200 °F). Structure consists of tempered martensite. Vilella's reagent. 400×

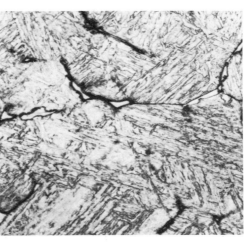

**Fig. 2** CA-6NM alloy, 75-mm (3-in.) thick section, as-cast. Cooling rate was very slow (casting was made in a sand mold). Precipitated chromium carbide particles (dark) and ferrite (white) are present at grain boundaries in a matrix of low-carbon martensite. See also Fig. 3. Vilella's reagent. 200×

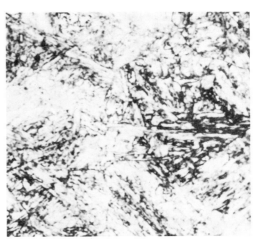

**Fig. 3** Same alloy and section thickness as for Fig. 2, but heated to 1040 °C (1900 °F) and held 4 h, air cooled, tempered 5 h at 635 °C (1175 °F). The carbide particles at grain boundaries have dissolved during austenitizing; matrix consists of ferrite-free tempered martensite. Vilella's reagent. 500×

**Fig. 4** CA-6NM alloy, 75-mm (3-in.) thick section, heated to 1050 °C (1925 °F) and held 3 h, air cooled, tempered 1 h at 605 °C (1125 °F). Ferrite-free tempered martensite, but coarser than in Fig. 3. See also Fig. 5. Vilella's reagent. 500×

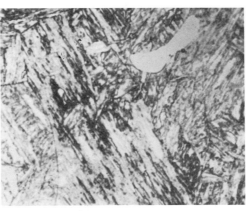

**Fig. 5** Same alloy and heat treatment as for Fig. 4, but a section 150-mm (6-in.) thick. Some ferrite (note pool in upper right corner) is present in the tempered martensite matrix. Vilella's reagent. 500×

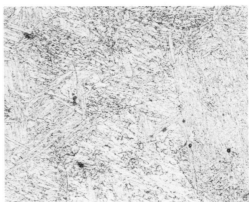

**Fig. 6** CA-15 alloy, normalized 4 h at 980 °C (1800 °F) and tempered 6 h at 705 °C (1300 °F). Structure consists of tempered martensite. Vilella's reagent. 400×

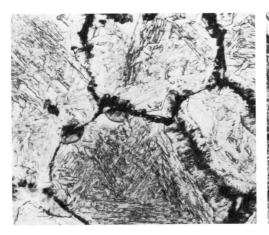

**Fig. 7** CA-15 alloy, 75-mm (3-in.) thick section, as-cast. Structure consists of islands of ferrite and dark-etching particles of chromium carbide at prior austenite grain boundaries in a matrix of martensite. See also Fig. 8 and 9. Vilella's reagent. 200×

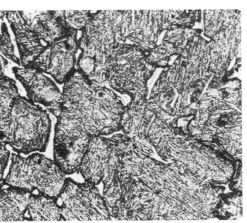

**Fig. 8** Same alloy, section thickness, and condition as Fig. 7, but a different casting, etchant, and magnification. Structure consists of islands of ferrite and grain-boundary carbide (dark) in martensite matrix. See Fig. 9. Ferric chloride. 100×

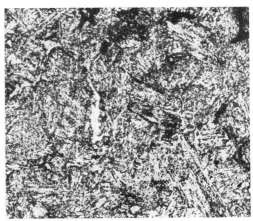

**Fig. 9** Same alloy and section thickness as for Fig. 8, but heated to 1040 °C (1900 °F) and held for 3 h, air cooled, tempered at 690 °C (1275 °F) for 4 h. Ferrite islands have blended with the tempered martensite matrix. Ferric chloride. 100×

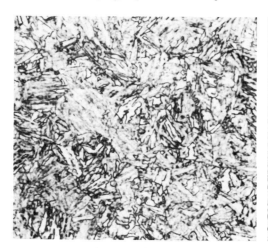

**Fig. 10** CA-15 alloy, 75-mm (3-in.) thick section, austenitized at 1010 °C (1850 °F), air cooled, tempered at 675 °C (1250 °F) for 4 h. The structure shows traces of ferrite in a matrix of tempered martensite. See also Fig. 11. Vilella's reagent. 200×

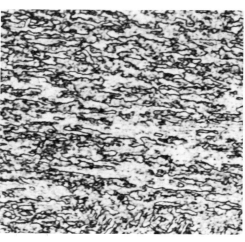

**Fig. 11** Same alloy, section thickness, and heat treatment as for Fig. 11, but at a higher magnification to emphasize the traces of ferrite in the tempered martensite matrix. Hardness of casting, 223 HB. Vilella's reagent. 500×

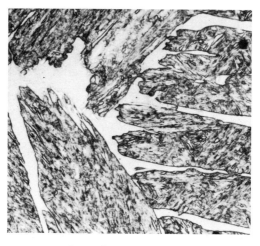

**Fig. 12** Same alloy and heat treatment as in Fig. 10, but for a 150-mm (6-in.) thick section, showing the effect of section thickness on structure. Islands of ferrite appear in the matrix of tempered martensite. See also Fig. 13. Vilella's reagent. 200×

**Fig. 13** Same alloy, section thickness, and heat treatment as for Fig. 12, but at a higher magnification to reveal dispersed ferrite particles and massive ferrite stringers in the tempered martensite matrix. Vilella's reagent. 500×

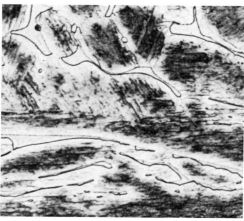

**Fig. 14** CB-7Cu-1 alloy, as-cast. The structure consists of elongated pools of ferrite (light gray constituent) in a matrix of martensite, which varies in carbon content (as indicated by the response to etching). See also Fig. 15. Vilella's reagent. 500×

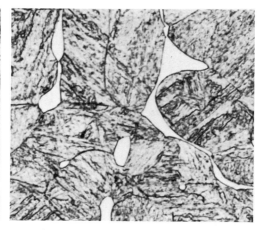

**Fig. 15** Same alloy as Fig. 14, but austenitized at 1050 °C (1925 °F) for 1 h and aged at 495 °C (925 °F). The matrix, tempered martensite, still contains ferrite pools (light), but shows less variation in carbon content. Vilella's reagent. 500×

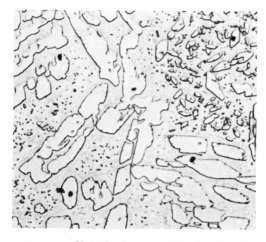

**Fig. 16** CD-4MCu alloy, as-cast. Structure: jagged pools and particles of austenite in ferrite. Black specks are nonmetallic inclusions. Electrolytic: 10% $CrO_3$ at 6 V for 5 to 60 s. 500×

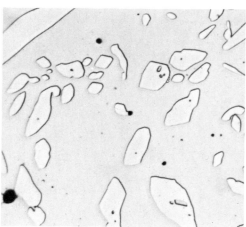

**Fig. 17** Same alloy as for Fig. 16, but solution treated at 1065 °C (1950 °F) for 1 h and water quenched. Shows effect of homogenization. Electrolytic: 10% $CrO_3$ at 6 V for 5 to 60 s. 500×

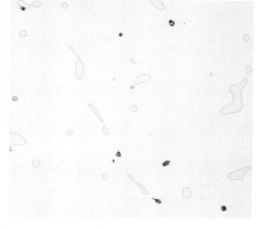

**Fig. 18** CF-3 alloy, solution treated 1 h at 1120 °C (2050 °F) and water quenched. Structure is austenite, with ferrite pools and inclusions. See also Fig. 19. Glyceregia. 400×

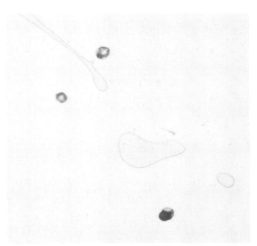

**Fig. 19** Same alloy and processing as Fig. 18. Higher magnification of ferrite pools and inclusions in austenite matrix. Glyceregia. 1000×

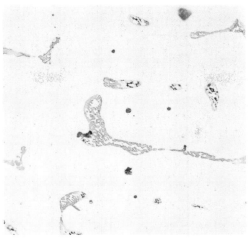

**Fig. 20** CF-3M alloy, solution treated 1 h at 1120 °C (2050 °F), water quenched and reheated 100 h at 760 °C (1400 °F). Structure is austenite matrix with some σ-phase present. See also Fig. 21. Electrolytic: NaCN. 400×

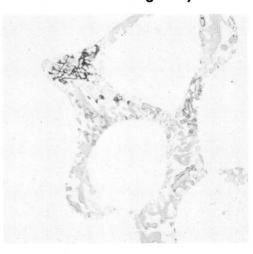

**Fig. 21** Same alloy and processing as Fig. 20. Higher magnification of σ-phase in austenite. Electrolytic: NaCN. 1000×

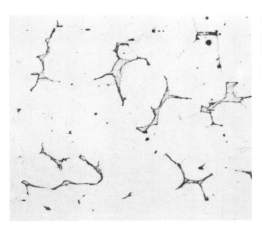

**Fig. 22** CF-3 alloy, 150-mm (6-in.) thick section, as-cast, showing dispersed islands of ferrite (5% by volume) and grain-boundary carbide particles in an austenite matrix. See also Fig. 23. HCl, HNO₃, acetic acid. 100×

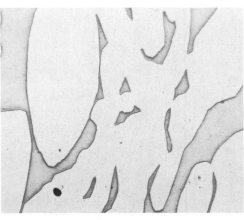

**Fig. 23** Same alloy and section thickness as for Fig. 22, but solution treated at 1120 °C (2050 °F) and water quenched. Specimen was taken from center of section. Elongated pools of ferrite in an austenite matrix (light). Electrolytic: 10N KOH. 250×

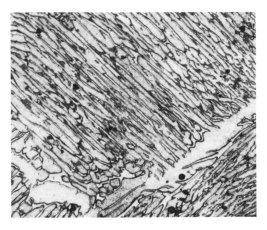

**Fig. 24** CF-3M alloy, as-cast. Specimen taken from a 25-mm (1-in.) thick section. Structure consists of a complex network of elongated ferrite in a matrix of austenite. Ferrite content is estimated at 22%. HCl, HNO₃, acetic acid. 100×

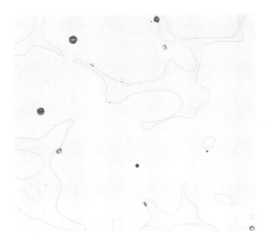

**Fig. 25** CF-8M alloy, solution treated 1 h at 1120 °C (2050 °F) and water quenched. Structure is austenite with ferrite and oxide inclusions. See also Fig. 26. Kalling's reagent. 400×

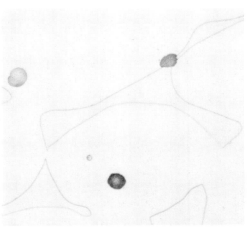

**Fig. 26** Same alloy and processing as Fig. 25, but a higher magnification view of the microstructure. Kalling's reagent. 1000×

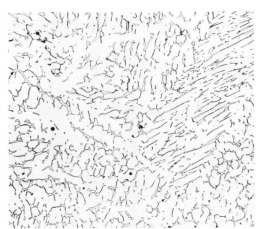

**Fig. 27** CF-8 alloy, 25-mm (1-in.) thick section, as sand cast. Structure contains 15 to 20% ferrite in an austenite matrix. Fig. 28 shows the sand cast alloy after solution treatment; Fig. 29 shows another as-cast structure. Electrolytic: oxalic acid. 80×

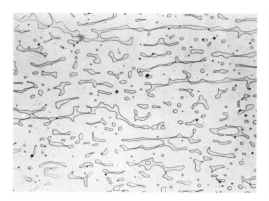

**Fig. 28** Same sand cast alloy and section thickness as Fig. 26, but solution treated 1 h at 1120 °C (2050 °F) and water quenched. Structure: pools of ferrite (outlined) in austenite; dendritic pattern has been altered. Glyceregia. 100×

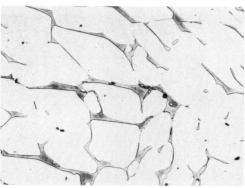

**Fig. 29** CF-8 alloy, 25-mm (1-in.) thick section, as-cast. The structure consists of a network of ferrite (dark-etching islands) and some precipitated particles of carbide (dark spots) in a matrix of austenite (light gray background). Electrolytic: KOH; 3 V, 3 s. 200×

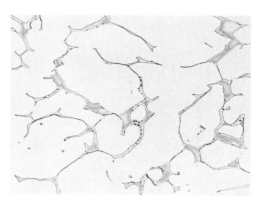

**Fig. 30** CF-8 alloy, 150-mm (6-in.) thick section, as-cast. Similar in ferrite distribution to Fig. 29. Note that chromium carbide particles have precipitated at the ferrite-austenite boundaries. Matrix is austenite. See also Fig. 31. Electrolytic: KOH. 200×

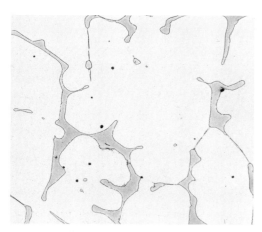

**Fig. 31** Same alloy and section thickness as for Fig. 30, but solution treated at 1075 °C (1970 °F) for 6 h and water quenched. Carbide particles have dissolved, but traces of ferrite network remain. Electrolytic: KOH. 300×

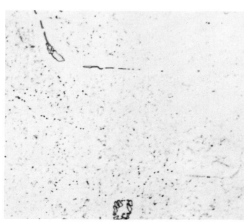

**Fig. 32** CF-8C alloy, solution treated at 1120 °C (2050 °F) for 1 h, water quenched, stabilized at 925 °C (1700 °F) for 1 h. Niobium carbide particles (black) precipitated during stabilization treatment at 925 °C (1700 °F). Remaining structure: ferrite in austenite matrix. Electrolytic: 10% CrO₃; 6 V, 5 to 60 s. 500×

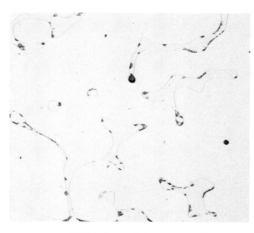

**Fig. 33** CF-8M alloy, solution treated 1 h at 1120 °C (2050 °F) and water quenched, sensitized 1 h at 650 °C (1200 °F) and air cooled. Structure is austenite, with ferrite and carbide precipitates along the austenite-ferrite interface. See also Fig. 34. Glyceregia. 400×

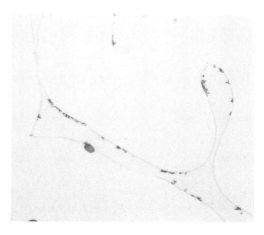

**Fig. 34** Same alloy and processing as Fig. 33. Higher magnification of austenite, ferrite and carbide precipitates at interface. Kalling's reagent. 1000×

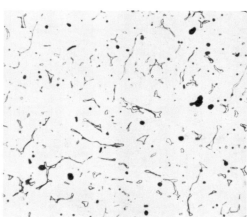

**Fig. 35** CF-16F alloy, a 25-mm (1-in.) bar, as-cast. The structure consists of selenide particles (black), precipitated carbide particles, and fine ferrite islands in a matrix of austenite. Dispersed selenide particles of this type improve the machining characteristics of the steel. Electrolytic: oxalic acid. 100×

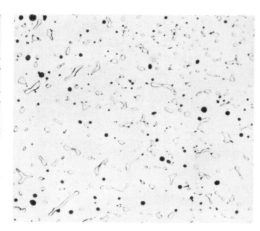

**Fig. 36** Same alloy and bar size as for Fig. 35, but solution treated at 1120 °C (2050 °F) and water quenched. The precipitated carbide particles have dissolved, and the ferrite islands have re-formed. Selenide particles (black) were relatively unaffected by the solution treatment. Electrolytic: oxalic acid. 100×

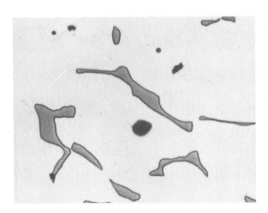

**Fig. 37** CF-16F alloy, solution treated at 1120 °C (2050 °F) and water quenched. The structure consists of selenide particles (dark spots) and islands of ferrite in a matrix of austenite. Electrolytic: 10N KOH. 500×

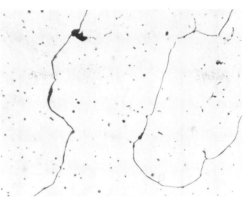

**Fig. 38** CF-20 alloy, a 25-mm (1-in.) bar, as-cast. The structure consists of fine particles of carbide dispersed in a matrix of austenite with precipitated carbide particles at grain boundaries. Oxalic acid. 100×

**Fig. 39** CK-20 alloy, 25-mm (1-in.) thick section, as-cast. Primary carbide, precipitated carbide, and globular inclusions (silicate and manganese sulfide) in an austenite matrix. See also Fig. 40. Glyceregia. 200×

**Fig. 40** Same alloy and section thickness as for Fig. 39, but solution treated at 1120 °C (2050 °F) for 1 h and water quenched. Most precipitated carbide particles have dissolved. Electrolytic: oxalic acid. 100×

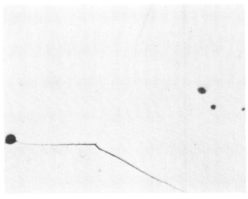

**Fig. 41** CN-7M alloy, 25-mm (1-in.) thick section, as-cast. Precipitated chromium carbide ($M_{23}C_6$) at grain boundaries of the austenite matrix. Black dots are inclusions. See also Fig. 42. Electrolytic: 10% $CrO_3$; 6 V, 5 to 60 s. 500×

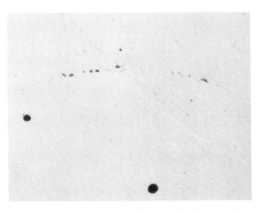

**Fig. 42** Same alloy and section thickness as for Fig. 41, but solution treated 1 h at 1120 °C (2050 °F) and water quenched. Structure shows traces of carbide at grain boundaries of the austenite matrix; black dots are inclusions. Electrolytic: 10% $CrO_3$; 6 V, 5 to 60 s. 500×

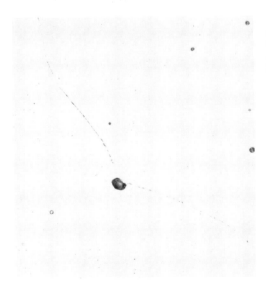

**Fig. 43** CN-7M alloy, solution treated 1 h at 1175 °C (2150 °F) and water quenched. Structure consists of austenite with dispersed inclusions. See also Fig. 44. Electrolytic: oxalic acid. 400×

**Fig. 44** Same alloy and processing as Fig. 43. Higher magnification of dispersed inclusions in austenite matrix. Electrolytic: oxalic acid. 1000×

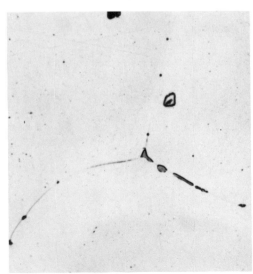

**Fig. 45** CN-7M alloy, 75-mm (3-in.) thick section, as-cast. The structure consists of $M_{23}C_6$ carbides (predominantly, chromium carbide) precipitated at the grain boundaries of the austenite matrix. See also Fig. 46. Electrolytic: oxalic acid. 500×

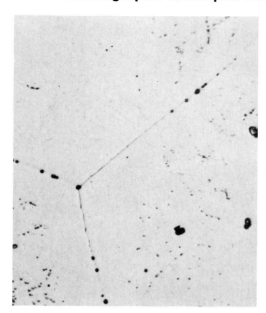

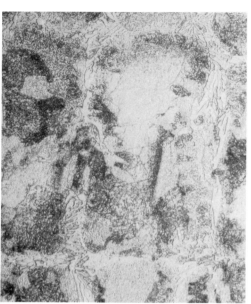

**Fig. 46** Same alloy and section thickness as for Fig. 45, but solution treated at 1120 °C (2050 °F) for 1 h and water quenched. Small discrete chromium carbide particles at grain boundaries of the etch-pitted austenite matrix. Electrolytic: oxalic acid. 500×

**Fig. 47** 440C stainless (Fe-17Cr-0.5Mo-1.0C), investment cast in a 5 mm (0.19 in.) section and annealed. Dendritic structure with interdendritic carbide network. See also Fig. 48. Vilella's reagent. 500×

**Fig. 48** Same alloy and processing as Fig. 47. Higher magnification view of Fig. 47, showing interdendritic carbide particles and very fine carbide particles in the matrix. Vilella's reagent. 1000×

# Wrought Heat-Resistant Alloys

By George F. Vander Voort
Supervisor
Applied Physics Research and Development
Carpenter Technology Corporation

and

Hughston M. James
Senior Metallurgist
Metal Physics Research
Carpenter Technology Corporation

WROUGHT HEAT-RESISTANT ALLOYS cover a wide range of chemical compositions, microstructural constituents, and mechanical properties. This article summarizes metallographic techniques and microstructural constituents of three types of wrought heat-resistant alloys: iron-base, nickel-base, and cobalt-base. The metallographic methods discussed also are suitable for preparing the equivalent cast heat-resistant alloys; microstructural constituents are quite similar except for obvious differences in homogeneity and porosity (see the article "Heat-Resistant Casting Alloys" in this Volume).

## Specimen Preparation

The procedures used to prepare metallographic specimens of wrought heat-resistant grades are quite similar to those for iron-base alloys and for most metals (see the Section "Metallographic Techniques" in this Volume). Aspects particularly significant to the preparation of wrought superalloys will be emphasized. Table 1 lists the nominal compositions of alloys illustrated in this article.

**Macroetching.** Wrought heat-resistant alloys are examined for macrostructure in the same manner as tool steels and stainless steels. Disks are cut (usually from billet samples) at representative locations, such as the top and bottom of ingots or remelted stock, and are ground before macroetching. Macroetchants for the wrought austenitic iron-nickel-chromium heat-resistant alloys are the same as those recommended for wrought austenitic stainless steels (see the article "Wrought Stainless Steels" in this Volume). Macroetchants for wrought nickel-base and cobalt-base heat-resistant alloys are given in Table 2.

Macroetched features in consumable-electrode remelted superalloys are different from those observed in ingot cast steels. Unique macroetch features observed in these remelted alloys include freckles, radial segregation, and ring patterns (Ref 1-7). Freckles are dark-etching spots due to localized segregation or to enrichment of carbides or Laves phase. They are detrimental to material quality. Radial segregation appears as dark-etching elongated spots in a radial or spiral pattern. Ring patterns are concentric rings that etch lighter (usually) or darker than the matrix. They are revealed only by macroetching. The nature of ring patterns remains obscure. Examination has revealed little difference between ring and matrix areas and no measurable influence on mechanical properties.

**Sectioning.** Various sectioning devices have been used with superalloys. The usual precautions regarding excessive heating should be followed. For austenitic grades, which are sensitive to deformation, the more vigorous sectioning techniques, such as band sawing or power hacksawing, may introduce excessive distortion or work hardening, depending on the alloy and heat-treatment condition. Such methods are suitable for initial sectioning of large pieces, but final cutting of specimens is best performed using abrasive cutoff machines. Heavy deformation introduced by sawing may be difficult to remove by subsequent grindings and polishings. Abrasive cutoff wheels used are usually the consumable type. Abundant coolant should be used; submerged cutting is preferred.

**Mounting.** Many bulk specimens can be ground and polished without mounting. Some automatic grinding and polishing devices require a mounted specimen, which is usually 25, 32, or 38 mm (1, 1¼, or 1½ in.) in diameter; others do not. Mounting facilitates polishing of small or irregularly shaped specimens.

It may sometimes be necessary to view the microstructure at the extreme edge of a specimen. Optimum results are obtained when the edge of interest is plated with electroless or electrolytic nickel before mounting (see the article "Mounting of Specimens" in this Volume). Good results can be obtained without plating if the specimen is mounted using a compression-molded epoxy resin, particularly if automatic polishing is used.

When edge retention is not a primary requirement, specimens can be mounted using any of the popular compression-mounting materials or castable resins. Most produce acceptable results; each resin has advantages and disadvantages. The selection of a particular resin is often based on familiarity.

**Grinding** of specimens takes place by hand or by use of automatic devices. Grinding is performed using water-cooled silicon carbide paper at 150 to 600 rpm. The usual grit-size sequence is 120, 240, 320, 400, and 600 grit; finer grits are occasionally used. Grit sizes finer than 600 can be useful for preparing nickel-base superalloys. This eliminates coarse diamond paste polishing and may improve retention of carbides and intermetallic phases and reduce relief.

Moderately heavy pressure is used for hand grinding. The specimen must be held flat against the paper. After each grinding, the specimen is rinsed, wiped clean, and rotated 45 to 90° before grinding with the next paper. Grinding should proceed for approximately twice as long as needed to remove all the scratches from the previous step; 1 to 2 min per step is usually adequate. Automatic grinding produces omnidirectional scratch patterns. Wrought superalloys are not susceptible to embedding of silicon carbide from the

**Table 1  Nominal compositions of wrought heat-resistant alloys**

| Alloy | C | Fe | Ni | Co | Cr | Ti | Mo | Others |
|---|---|---|---|---|---|---|---|---|
| **Iron-nickel-base alloys** | | | | | | | | |
| A-286 (AISI 660) ........ 0.05 | bal | 26.0 | ... | 15.0 | 2.15 | 1.25 | 0.3V, 0.2Al, 0.003B |
| Discaloy (AISI 662) ...... 0.04 max | bal | 25.0 | ... | 13.5 | 1.75 | 3.0 | 0.1Al |
| Incoloy 800 ............. 0.05 | bal | 32.5 | ... | 21.0 | 0.38 | ... | 0.38Al |
| Incoloy 901 ............. 0.05 | bal | 42.7 | ... | 13.5 | 2.5 | 6.2 | 0.25Al |
| N-155 (AISI 661) ........ 0.15 | bal | 20.0 | 20.0 | 21.0 | ... | 3.0 | 2.5W, 1.0Nb + Ta, 0.15N |
| AISI 330 ............... 0.05 | bal | 36.0 | ... | 19.0 | ... | ... | ... |
| 16-25-6 (AISI 650) ....... 0.08 max | bal | 25.0 | ... | 16.0 | ... | 6.0 | 0.15N |
| Hastelloy X (AISI 680) ... 0.10 max | 18.5 | bal | 1.5 | 22.0 | ... | 9.0 | 0.6W |
| Pyromet 31 ............. 0.04 | bal | 55.5 | ... | 22.7 | 2.5 | 2.0 | 1.5Al, 1.1Nb, 0.005B |
| Alloy 718 .............. 0.04 | 18.5 | bal | ... | 19.0 | 0.9 | 3.05 | 5.13Nb + Ta, 0.5Al |
| **Nickel-base alloys** | | | | | | | | |
| Astroloy ............... 0.06 | ... | bal | 17.0 | 15.0 | 3.5 | 5.25 | 4.0Al, 0.03B |
| Hastelloy C ............ 0.07 | 5.0 | bal | 2.5 max | 16.0 | ... | 17.0 | 4.0W |
| Hastelloy C-276 ........ 0.02 | 5.5 | bal | 2.5 max | 15.5 | ... | 16.0 | 3.75W, 0.35V |
| Hastelloy W ........... 0.12 max | 5.5 | bal | 2.5 | 5.0 | ... | 24.5 | 0.6 V |
| Alloy 600 ............. 0.1 max | 8.0 | bal | ... | 15.5 | ... | ... | ... |
| Alloy 625 ............. 0.1 max | 5.0 max | bal | 1.0 max | 21.5 | 0.4 max | 9.0 | 3.65 Nb + Ta, 0.4 Al max |
| Alloy X-750 ........... 0.04 | 7.0 | bal | ... | 15.5 | 2.5 | ... | 0.95 Nb + Ta, 0.7Al |
| Nimonic 80 ........... 0.10 max | 5.0 max | bal | 2.0 max | 19.5 | 2.25 | ... | 1.13Al |
| René 41 .............. 0.09 | ... | bal | 11.0 | 19.0 | 3.1 | 10.0 | 1.5Al, 0.010 B max |
| René 95 .............. 0.15 | ... | bal | 8.0 | 14.0 | 2.5 | 3.5 | 3.5Al, 3.5W, 3.5 Nb |
| TD-Nickel ............ | ... | bal | ... | ... | ... | ... | 2ThO$_2$ |
| U-700 ................ 0.15 max | 1.0 max | bal | 18.5 | 15.0 | 3.5 | 5.2 | 4.25Al, 0.05B |
| U-710 ................ 0.07 | ... | bal | 15.0 | 18.0 | 5.0 | 3.0 | 2.5Al, 1.5W, 0.02B |
| 50Cr-50Ni ............ 0.06 | ... | bal | ... | 50.0 | 1.0 | ... | ... |
| Waspaloy ............. 0.07 | ... | bal | 13.5 | 19.5 | 3.0 | 4.3 | 1.4Al, 0.07 Zr, 0.006B |
| **Cobalt-base alloys** | | | | | | | | |
| Elgiloy ............... 0.15 | 15.0 | 15.0 | bal | 20.0 | | 7.0 | 2.0 Mn |
| Haynes 25 (L-605) ..... 0.10 | ... | 10.0 | bal | 20.0 | ... | ... | 15.0W, 1.5Mn, 0.55i |
| Haynes 188 ........... 0.10 | 1.5 | 22.0 | bal | 22.0 | ... | ... | 14.0W, 0.08La |
| Stellite 6B ........... 1.1 | 3.0 max | 3.0 max | bal | 30.0 | | | 4.5W |
| S-816 ................ 0.38 | 4.0 | 20.0 | bal | 20.0 | ... | 4.0 | 4.0W, 4.0Nb |
| MP35N ............... 0.025 max | 1.0 max | 35.0 | bal | 20.0 | 1.0 max | 10.0 | 0.010 B max |

grinding paper, but if the specimen contains cracks or pores, it should be cleaned ultrasonically. For most specimens, a simple wash under running water will remove any loose abrasive or grinding debris. Specimens should be washed in alcohol (preferably ethanol) and dried in hot air.

**Rough polishing** often begins using 6- or 3-$\mu$m diamond abrasive, generally as a paste,

although aerosols or slurries are also used. The use of 5-$\mu$m alumina (Al$_2$O$_3$) for rough polishing has been largely replaced by the more efficient diamond abrasives.

Although a wide range of cloths is available, low-nap or napless cloths are generally used for rough polishing. Canvas, which is quite popular, provides economical durability. Synthetic napless chemotextile cloths are

also used. Billiard cloth and red felt are sometimes preferred. A lubricant/extender fluid should always be added to reduce friction and drag and to promote more efficient cutting. Wheel speeds are 150 to 300 rpm. Moderate pressure is applied.

During hand polishing, the specimen should be rotated counter to wheel rotation while it is moved slowly from center to edge. Again, the specimen must be held firmly against the wheel to avoid rocking. Polishing should continue until grinding scratches are removed; 1 to 2 min is usually adequate.

A second diamond polishing step generally using 1-$\mu$m diamond is often performed. A synthetic suede medium-nap cloth is commonly used, but other cloths may also yield good results. This step is carried out in the same manner as the initial diamond polishing. After each diamond polishing, the specimen should be carefully cleaned to remove abrasive, extender oil, and polishing debris. Ultrasonic cleaning produces excellent results, but is not always required.

**Final polishing** may involve one or more steps, depending on the need to remove all scratches. For routine inspection, polishing to

**Table 2  Macroetchants for wrought heat-resistant alloys**

| Composition(a) | Comments |
|---|---|
| 1. 1 part 30% H$_2$O$_2$, 2 parts HCl, 2 or 3 parts H$_2$O | Recommended for nickel-chromium alloys; use fresh solution; reveals grain structure; if the surface is stained, remove with 50% aqueous HNO$_3$; etch approximately 2 min |
| 2. (a) 15 g (NH$_4$)$_2$S$_2$O$_8$ (ammonium persulfate) and 75 mL H$_2$O (b) 250 g FeCl$_3$ and 100 mL HCl (c) 30 mL HNO$_3$ | Lepito's macroetch for general macrostructure and weldments; mix a and b, add c; immerse 30-120 s at room temperature |
| 3. 200 g FeCl$_3$, 200 mL HCl, H$_2$O to 1000 mL | For nickel-base superalloys; etch to 90 min at 100°C (212°F) |
| 4. HCl saturated with FeCl$_3$ | For cobalt-base superalloys; add 5% HNO$_3$ before use at room temperature; clean surface by dipping in 50% aqueous HCl |
| 5. (a) 21 mL H$_2$SO$_4$, 15 mL HCl, 21 mL HNO$_3$, 21 mL HF, 22 mL H$_2$O (b) 40 mL 20% aqueous CuCl$_2$ (copper chloride), 40 mL HCl, 20 mL HF | For cobalt-base superalloys; etch 5 min in (a), then 5 min in (b) |
| 6. 50 mL saturated aqueous CuSO$_4$ (copper sulfate) and 50 mL HCl | For iron-nickel- and nickel-base alloys; swab or immerse, room temperature |

(a) Whenever water is specified, use distilled water.

a 1-$\mu$m diamond finish may be adequate. When photomicroscopy is anticipated, additional steps are usually required. A wide range of final polishing abrasives may be used. Alumina slurries are quite common, using 0.3-$\mu$m and/or 0.05-$\mu$m $Al_2O_3$. Colloidal silica ($SiO_2$) (Ref 1) produces exceptional results with these alloys.

Final polishing is generally performed using synthetic suede medium-nap cloths at approximately 150 rpm. During hand polishing, the specimen should be rotated counter to wheel rotation while it is moved from center to edge. The slurry is occasionally added to the cloth during polishing. Moderate pressure is used, and care must be taken to avoid rocking the specimen. A polishing time of 1 to 2 min is usually adequate. After polishing, the specimen should be carefully cleaned and dried to avoid staining. When hand polishing, the operator's hands must be cleaned after each rough and final polishing to prevent contamination.

Automatic polishing machines are quite useful for final polishing. A wide variety of devices is available. The time required using these units ranges from a few minutes to approximately 30 min for vibratory polishing.

Mechanical polishing is sometimes followed with a brief electropolish to remove any smeared or flowed metal without introducing preferential attack of the second phase constituents. Extended electropolishing should be avoided. Table 3 lists appropriate electropolishing solutions for wrought nickel-base and cobalt-base heat-resistant alloys. Electropolishing solutions for wrought iron-nickel-cobalt austenitic alloys are the same as those used for wrought austenitic stainless steels.

**Etching.** Some minor phases in superalloys can be observed easily in the as-polished condition. Minimal relief can be introduced during final polishing to accentuate these particles. They can be observed in bright-field illumination by color contrast, which is useful for phase identification[2]. The nitrides, carbonitrides, borides, and metal carbides are readily observed without etching.

The wrought iron-nickel-base heat-resistant alloys are basically austenitic stainless steels. Therefore, the techniques for etching and identifying phases in wrought austenitic stainless steels apply to these alloys.

Glyceregia is one of the most prevalent reagents for revealing the general structure of iron-nickel and nickel-base heat-resistant alloys. It should always be mixed fresh and discarded when it turns orange. Glyceregia will etch all the heat-resistant grades, except some of the high cobalt content superalloys. For etching solution-annealed nickel-base alloys, glycerol content is often decreased, and nitric acid ($HNO_3$) content is often increased. The standard composition is ideal for solution-annealed and aged specimens, which are easier to etch. The mixture of hydrochloric acid, sulfuric acid, and nitric acid ($HCl$-$H_2SO_4$-$HNO_3$) (95-5-3) is also quite popular for these alloys and is used similarly. For grain size examination in aged specimens, etching with waterless Kalling's or Marble's reagents is quite common. Several electrolytic reagents are also commonly used. Color etchants, though not widely used for these alloys, produce very good results (see the article "Color Metallography" in this Volume).

Table 4 lists some of the more commonly used reagents for etching iron-nickel-, nickel-, and cobalt-base heat-resistant alloys. Additional information regarding the etching of wrought heat-resistant alloys can be found in Ref 1 and 8 to 15.

Some electropolishing procedures are useful for microstructural examination using scanning electron microscopy (SEM) or transmission electron microscopy (TEM) (replicas). The electropolish sometimes produces attack of the $\gamma'$ phase, and subsequent etching is unnecessary. For replica examination, it is often helpful to use a reagent or an electropolish that attacks $\gamma'$ so that this phase is readily distinguished from other phases (Ref 16-18). In such cases, the $\gamma'$ is recessed, but other second phases are in relief.

Selective etchants and heat tinting have been commonly used to differentiate various carbide types and to identify $\sigma$ phase. Borides, which are similar in appearance to metal carbides, can be discriminated by selective etching. Metal carbides are selectively colored; borides are unaffected (Ref 19).

## Microexamination

**Transmission Electron Microscopy.** Because some of the important constituents in wrought heat-resistant alloys, such as $\gamma'$ phase, are generally too small to observe using the optical microscope, considerable use has been made of transmission electron microscopy. Besides affording greater resolution and higher magnification, TEM provides means for phase identification by electron diffraction and, when equipped with x-ray detectors, can provide chemical analysis data. Such analytical procedures are necessary to understand the strengthening mechanisms for heat-resistant alloys.

Several types of specimens can be prepared for TEM examination; each type has advantages and disadvantages. The replica method, which had been prevalent, is being replaced by use of the scanning electron microscope (Ref 17, 18). A well-polished and properly etched specimen can be examined by SEM at magnifications of 50 000$\times$ or more. Therefore, much of the structural examination role of TEM replicas can be accomplished without replica preparation and the complication of replica interpretation or artifact control.

In addition, the contrast mechanisms operable in the scanning electron microscope are valuable for structural examination. Because chemical analysis using SEM is limited to features larger than a few microns, TEM examination and analysis of extracted constituents remains an important procedure. Procedures for preparing structural and extraction replicas are discussed in the article "Transmission Electron Microscopy" in this Volume and in Ref 20 to 28. Direct examination of the fine structure of wrought heat-resistant alloys is also performed by TEM examination of thin foils. As with extraction replicas, electron diffraction and chemical analysis can be performed.

Because the beam size in a transmission electron microscope or a scanning transmission microscope is much smaller than in a scanning electron microscope, much finer particles can be analyzed using thin foils without interference from the surrounding matrix. Extremely small particles are difficult

**Table 3  Electropolishing techniques for wrought heat-resistant alloys**

| Electrolyte composition | Comments |
| --- | --- |
| 1. 37 mL $H_3PO_4$, 56 mL glycerol, 7 mL $H_2O$ | For Inconel 625, use 1.2–1.6 A/cm² (8–10 A/in.²); for Incoloy 800, use 3.1 A/cm² (20 A/in.²); platinum cathode |
| 2. 25 mL $H_3PO_4$, 25 mL $HNO_3$, 50 mL $H_2O$ | For Inconel 600 and X-750, use 17.8 A/cm² (115 A/in.²), 5–10 s; platinum cathode |
| 3. 144 mL ethanol, 10 g $AlCl_3$ (anhydrous aluminum chloride), 45 g $ZnCl_2$ (anhydrous zinc chloride), 16 mL N-butyl alcohol, 32 mL $H_2O$ | For cobalt-base superalloys; use 23–25 V dc at room temperature with successive 1-min periods |
| 4. 40 mL $HClO_4$ (perchloric acid), 450 mL acetic acid, 15 mL $H_2O$ | For Nimonic alloys; use 15 V dc, 0.1 A/cm² (0.65 A/in.²) below 25 °C (77 °F) |
| 5. 10 mL $HClO_4$ and 90 mL acetic acid | For nickel-base alloys, use at 0.5–0.9 A/cm² (3–6 A/in.²), 30 s for aged specimens, longer for solution-annealed ones; keep cool (10–15 °C, or 50–60 °F); best results by polishing in 5-s intervals |
| 6. 70 mL methanol and 10 mL $H_2SO_4$ | For nickel-base superalloys, use at 20–25 V dc, 0.3–0.8 A/cm² (2–5 A/in.²), room temperature; 10–15 s after a 600-grit finish or 5 s after a 0.3-$\mu$m $Al_2O_3$ finish; $\gamma'$ slightly etched |
| 7. 60 mL methanol, 10 mL $H_2SO_4$, 5 mL HCl | Use same as No. 6; produces more etching of $\gamma'$ phase; if $HNO_3$ is substituted for HCl, the surface will be smooth without relief or attack |
| 8. 7 mL ethanol, 20 mL $HClO_4$, 10 mL glycerol | Use same as No. 6; mix carefully, keep cool; produces smooth surfaces |
| 9. 15 mL HCl and 85 mL methanol | For nickel-base superalloys, use at 30–40 V dc, 0.3–1.2 A/cm² (2–8 A/in.²), at room temperature for 5–10 s after a 600-grit silicon carbide finish or 2–5 s after a 0.3-$\mu$m $Al_2O_3$ finish; produces strong carbide relief, etches $\gamma'$; very good for SEM examination |

**Table 4  Microetchants for wrought heat-resistant alloys**

| Composition | Comments |
|---|---|
| 1. 3 parts glycerol, 2–3 parts HCl, 1 part $HNO_3$ | Glyceregia; mix fresh, do not store; discard when solution is orange; use by immersion or swabbing 5–60 s; very popular general etch for structure of iron-base and nickel-base superalloys; $\gamma'$ in relief |
| 2. 5 mL HF, 10 mL glycerol, 85 mL ethanol | Electrolytic etch at 0.04–0.15 $A/cm^2$ (0.25–1.0 $A/in.^2$), 6–12 V dc; for nickel-base alloys, $\gamma'$ in relief; stop etch when edges are brownish; excellent etch for TEM replica work |
| 3. 12 mL $H_3PO_4$, 47 mL $H_2SO_4$, 41 mL $HNO_3$ | Electrolytic etch, 6 V dc, 0.12–0.15 $A/cm^2$ (0.75–1.0 $A/in.^2$), a few seconds; add to 100 mL $H_2O$ to slow etch; for nickel-base alloys; use under hood; mix $H_3PO_4$ and $HNO_3$, then add $H_2SO_4$; stains matrix when $\gamma'$ is present; good for revealing segregation and for examining $\gamma'$ with TEM replicas; attacks Bakelite; stop etch when edge of specimen is brownish |
| 4. 30 mL lactic acid, 20 mL HCl, 10 mL $HNO_3$ | For nickel-base superalloys |
| 5. 5 g $CuCl_2$ 100 mL HCl, 100 mL ethanol | Waterless Kalling's reagent; immerse or swab to a few minutes; for iron-base and nickel-base superalloys |
| 6. 10 g $CuSO_4$, 50 mL HCl, 50 mL $H_2O$(a) | Marble's reagent for iron-nickel and cobalt-base superalloys; immerse or swab 5–60 s; a few drops of $H_2SO_4$ will increase etch activity; reveals grain boundaries and second-phase particles |
| 7. 5 mL $H_2SO_4$, 3 mL $HNO_3$, 92 mL HCl | For iron-base and nickel-base alloys; add $H_2SO_4$ to HCl, stir, allow to cool, add $HNO_3$; discard when orange; swab 10–30 s; use under hood; do not store |
| 8. 20 mL $HNO_3$ and 60 mL HCl | Aqua regia; for iron-base and nickel-base superalloys; use under hood, do not store; immerse or swab 5–60 s; attacks $\sigma$ phase, outlines carbides, reveals grain boundaries |
| 9. 50 mL HCl and 1–2 mL 30% $H_2O_2$ | For nickel-base alloys; attacks $\gamma'$-phase; immerse 10–15 s |
| 10. 5 mL $H_2SO_4$ 8 g $CrO_3$, 85 mL $H_3PO_4$ | Electrolytic etch at 10 V dc, 0.2 $A/cm^2$ (1.3 $A/in.^2$), 5–30 s; reveals inhomogeneities in nickel-base alloys |
| 11. 10 mL $HNO_3$, 10 mL acetic acid, 15 mL HCl, 2–5 drops glycerol | Use fresh, same precautions as glyceregia; used for hard to etch solution-treated nickel-base alloys |
| 12. (a) 33 mL HCl and 67 mL $H_2O$<br>(b) 50 mL HCl and 50 mL $H_2O$ | Beraha's tint etch for nickel-base alloys; add 0.6–1 g $K_2S_2O_5$ (potassium metabisulfite) to 100 mL stock solution (a); immerse (never swab) 60–150 s, slowly agitate; if colors are not developed, add 1–1.5 g $FeCl_3$ or 2–10 g $NH_4 \cdot HF$ (ammonium bifluoride) to 100 mL stock solution (b); immerse 60-150 s, agitate gently; colors matrix |
| 13. 10 g $K_3Fe(CN)_6$ (potassium ferricyanide), 10 g KOH, 100 mL $H_2O$ | Murakami's reagent; for iron-base and nickel-base superalloys; use hot (75 °C, or 170 °F) to darken $\sigma$ phase; use at room temperature to darken carbides; better results may be obtained if the specimen is first etched in 50% aqueous $HNO_3$ at 8 V dc; use under a hood |
| 14. 10 g $CrO_3$ and 100 mL $H_2O$ | Electrolytic etch, 6 V dc, 10–30 s; for iron-base and nickel-base superalloys; $\sigma$ attacked, carbides outlined or attacked |
| 15. 80 mL $H_3PO_4$ and 10 mL $H_2O$ | Electrolytic etch for nickel-base superalloys at 3 V dc (closed-circuit), 0.11–0.12 $A/cm^2$ (0.7–0.8 $A/in.^2$), 7–9 s; if the surface is stained, swab with the electrolyte; use fresh solution; used to determine the degree of carbide continuity at the grain boundaries |
| 16. 25 g $CrO_3$, 130 mL acetic acid, 7 mL $H_2O$ | Electrolytic etch for nickel-base superalloys at 10 V dc (closed circuit) for 2 min; the current density will drop during the first 20 s; use fresh; used to reveal prior grain boundaries |
| 17. 30 mL HCl, 7 mL $H_2O$, 3 mL 30% $H_2O_2$ | Popular etch for cobalt-base superalloys |
| 18. 100 mL HCl and 5 mL 30% $H_2O_2$ | Popular etch for cobalt-base superalloys; up to 20% $H_2O_2$ has been used; mix fresh; immerse 1–10 s |
| 19. 5–10 mL HCl and 95–90 mL $H_2O$ | Electrolytic etch for cobalt-base superalloys; use at 3 V dc, 1–5 s, carbon cathode |
| 20. 2 mL $H_2SO_4$ and 98 mL $H_2O$ | Etch first with glyceregia to dissolve matrix uniformly; then etch electrolytically at 6–12 V dc, 0.12–0.15 $A/cm^2$ (0.75–1.0 $A/in.^2$) until edge of specimen is brownish; good for TEM replica studies |
| 21. 5 mL HF, 10 mL glycerol, 10–50 mL ethanol, $H_2O$ to 100 mL total volume | Etch first with glyceregia to dissolve matrix uniformly; then etch with solution at left to dissolve $\gamma'$; use at 6–12 V dc, 0.12–0.15 $A/cm^2$ (0.75–1.0 $A/in.^2$) for less than 1 s; good for TEM replica work or SEM examination |

(a) When water is specified, use distilled water

**Table 5  Electropolishing solutions for TEM thin foils of wrought heat-resistant alloys**

| Composition | Comments |
|---|---|
| 1. 950 mL acetic acid and 50 mL $HClO_4$ | Popular electropolish for wrought superalloys for perforation; use at 70–80 V dc, 100–120 mA, 15 °C (60 °F) |
| 2. 133 mL acetic acid, 25 g $CrO_3$, 7 mL $H_2O$ | Best for window method; opacity makes jet thinning difficult; use at 10–12 V dc, 20 °C (70 °F) |
| 3. 77 mL acetic acid and 23 mL $HClO_4$ | For cobalt-base superalloys; keep temperature below 30 °C (85 °F), stainless steel cathode; used with the window method; use at 22 V dc, 0.08 $A/cm^2$ (0.5 $A/in.^2$) |
| 4. 600 mL methanol, 250 mL butanol, 60 mL $HClO_4$ | Two step procedure:<br>(a) 0.13-mm (0.005-in.) disk, polished 15–30 min at 30 V<br>(b) final thinning at 16–24 V; use at −60 to −70 V (−75 to −95 °F) |

to analyze, even with a scanning transmission electron microscope. Extraction replicas are useful, because matrix effects can be eliminated. In addition, using a scanning transmission electron microscope, microdiffraction patterns are obtainable from individual particles rather than many particles. The microdiffraction pattern is of great value in basic structural studies of the constituents.

Thin foils are prepared by the window method or the disk method described in Ref 20 to 22 and 28 to 31. These methods involve careful sectioning to obtain a relatively thin slice of the material free of artifacts, followed by mechanical, chemical, or electrolytic thinning until a small area is thin enough for electron transmission. Table 5 lists several popular electropolishing procedures for preparing thin foils of wrought heat-resistant alloys.

**Bulk Extractions.** X-ray diffraction studies of phases extracted electrolytically is a widely practiced, important tool for phase identification in wrought heat-resistant alloys (Ref 32-40). Because of the complex nature of these alloys, such techniques must be carefully controlled to ensure good results. Qualitative identification of the phases by this method is considerably easier than quantitative evaluations. The extraction method must be designed to permit separation of the carbides, nitrides, $\gamma'$, and topologically close-packed (tcp) phases. Once separated, the phases can be analyzed using x-ray diffraction, chemical analysis (elemental), and optical and electron microscopy procedures.

Considerable research has been conducted to establish reliable procedures for bulk extraction in wrought heat-resistant alloys (Ref 32-40). Anodic dissolution using 10% HCl in methanol, which dissolves $\gamma'$ and the austenitic matrix, is implemented to extract carbides, borides, nitrides, and tcp phases. If the alloy to be digested contains substantial amounts of tungsten, tantalum, or niobium, 1% tartaric acid is added to prevent contamination of the residue.

To extract $\gamma'$ from nickel-base alloys, two electrolytes have been used: (1) 20% aqueous phosphoric acid ($H_3PO_4$) or (2) an aqueous solution containing 1% ammonium sulfate [$(NH_4)_2SO_4$] and 1% citric acid or tartaric acid. The latter electrolyte produces better recovery of $\gamma'$. When the ammonium sulfate/citric or tartaric acid electrolyte is used, the residue will also contain carbides, nitrides, and borides (if present in the alloy). All the $\gamma'$ morphologies are extracted using this electrolyte. Details concerning the use of these electrolytes, and others given in Table 6, are provided in Ref 32 to 40.

## Microstructures of Wrought Heat-Resistant Alloys

Wrought heat-resistant alloys are designed for use above approximately 540 °C (1000 °F). In general, they have an austenitic ($\gamma$ phase) matrix and contain a wide variety of secondary phases. The most common second

**Table 6  Techniques for bulk electrolytic extractions**

| Solution | Comments |
|---|---|
| 1. 10% HCl in methanol | For extraction of carbides, borides, topologically close-packed phases, and geometrically close-packed phases from nickel-base and iron-nickel-base alloys; solution may dissolve $Ni_3Ti$; maintain bath at 0–30 °C (32–85 °F); for alloys containing tungsten, niobium, tantalum, or hafnium, add 1% tartaric acid; use 0.05–0.1 $A/cm^2$ (0.33–0.65 $A/in.^2$) for 4 h or longer (additional details in ASTM E 963) |
| 2. 0.5–2% citric acid and $(NH_4)_2SO_4$ in $H_2O$ (1% of each is most common) | Used to extract $\gamma'$ phase in nickel-base Udimet 700; use at 0.03 $A/cm^2$ (0.2 $A/in.^2$) for 3 h at room temperature; minor amounts of carbides and borides will also be extracted (additional details in Ref 35–38) |
| 3. 10 or 20% $H_3PO_4$ in $H_2O$ | Used to extract $\gamma'$ in nickel-base alloys; may etch the $\gamma'$ phase, although results have been contradictory |
| 4. 50 mL $HNO_3$, 20 mL $HClO_4$, 1000 mL $H_2O$ | For extraction of $\gamma'$ and $\eta$ in nickel-base superalloys; use at 0.1 $A/cm^2$ (0.65 $A/in.^2$), 25 °C (75 °F) |
| 5. 300 g KCl (potassium chloride), 30 g citric acid, 50 mL HCl, 1000 mL $H_2O$ | For extraction of carbides from nickel-base superalloys; use at 0.1 $A/cm^2$ (0.65 $A/in.^2$), 25 °C (75 °F) |

phases are metal carbides ($MC$, $M_{23}C_6$, $M_6C$, and $M_7C_3$) and $\gamma'$, the ordered face-centered cubic (fcc) strengthening phase [$Ni_3(Al,Ti)$] found in iron-nickel- and nickel-base superalloys. In alloys containing niobium or niobium and tantalum, the primary strengthening phase is $\gamma''$, a body-centered tetragonal (bct) phase. Other phases, generally undesirable, may be observed due to variations in composition or processing or due to high-temperature exposure. Included in this group are orthorhombic $\delta$ phase ($Ni_3Nb$), $\sigma$ phase, Laves, and the hexagonal close-packed (hcp) $\eta$ phase ($Ni_3Ti$). Nitrides are also commonly observed, and borides may be present in some alloys.

The physical metallurgy of these systems is extremely complex, perhaps more challenging than that of any other alloy system. In addition, as demonstrated in Table 1, the compositions of these alloys are complex as well. References 41 to 52 provide basic review articles on the metallography and physical metallurgy of these alloys. Table 7 summarizes the functions of elements in superalloys. In general, the iron-nickel-base alloys tend toward formation of tcp phases, such as $\sigma$, $\mu$, Laves,

and $\chi$ phase. The nickel-base alloys are prone to precipitation of ordered geometrically close-packed (gcp) phases, such as $\gamma'$ and $\eta$. Such phases are not common in cobalt-base alloys, because $\gamma'$ is not a suitable strengthening agent. The cobalt-base alloys contain various carbides, nitrides, $\sigma$, and $\mu$, depending on composition, processing, and exposure conditions.

**Iron-Nickel-Base Alloys.** Several types of iron-nickel-base alloys have been developed. These alloys contain at least 10% Fe, but generally 18% to approximately 55%. The most important iron-nickel-base alloys are those with an austenitic matrix that are strengthened by $\gamma'$, such as A-286. Some of these alloys are quite similar to wrought austenitic stainless steels with the addition of the $\gamma'$ strengthening agent; therefore, metallographic procedures for these alloys are identical to those for wrought austenitic stainless steels. Other iron-nickel-base alloys, such as Inconel 718, contain less iron plus additions of niobium and tantalum to obtain strengthening from $\gamma''$. Another group of iron-nickel-base alloys contains rather high carbon contents and is strengthened by carbides, ni-

trides, carbonitrides, and solid-solution strengthening. Other iron-nickel-base alloys, such as Hastelloy X, derive most of their strength from solid-solution alloying, with a minor influence from carbide precipitation.

**Nickel-Base Alloys.** Nickel-base high-temperature alloys are basically of two types: solid solution and precipitation hardenable. The solid-solution alloys contain little or no aluminum, titanium, or niobium; the precipitation-hardenable alloys contain several percent aluminum and titanium, and a few contain substantial niobium.

The age-hardenable alloys are strengthened by $\gamma'$ precipitation by the addition of aluminum and titanium, by carbide, and by solid-solution alloying. The nature of the $\gamma'$ is of primary importance in obtaining optimum high-temperature properties. Compositionally, the aluminum and titanium content and the aluminum/titanium ratio are very important, as is heat treatment. Increasing the aluminum/titanium ratio improves high-temperature properties. The volume fraction, size, and spacing of $\gamma'$ are important parameters to control. Alloys with low amounts of $\gamma'$ require greater attention to $\gamma'$ spacing than alloys with high amounts. Other factors, such as coherency strain due to the lattice mismatch between $\gamma$ and $\gamma'$, appear to be important in certain alloys, such as Waspaloy.

Grain size is an important microstructural parameter. Fine grain sizes normally provide superior room-temperature properties, such as toughness, strength, and fatigue resistance. Coarse grain sizes generally yield better creep resistance at elevated temperatures, although properties under other types of loading may suffer. Duplex grain structures generally are undesirable. Grain size also affects carbide precipitation at the grain boundaries. Coarse grain sizes have less grain-boundary surface area; therefore, carbide precipitation will be more continuous and thicker, thus impairing properties. Due to these problems, a uniform, intermediate grain size is generally preferred.

**Cobalt-Base Alloys.** Cobalt-base superalloys are strengthened by solid-solution alloying and carbide precipitation. The grain-boundary carbides inhibit grain-boundary sliding. Unlike the iron-nickel- and nickel-base alloys, no intermetallic phase has been found that will strengthen cobalt-base alloys to the same degree that $\gamma'$ or $\gamma''$ strengthens the other superalloys. Gamma is not stable at high temperatures in cobalt-base alloys. The carbides in cobalt-base superalloys are the same as those in the other systems.

## Phases in Wrought Heat-Resistant Alloys

The microconstituents observed in iron-nickel and nickel-base wrought heat-resistant superalloys are identical, with a few exceptions. The cobalt-base alloys are not strengthened by precipitated intermetallics, but share many common features. All the alloys have an austenitic ($\gamma$ phase) matrix that is strengthened by solid-solution alloying and

**Table 7  Role of elements in superalloys**

| Effect(a) | Iron-base | Cobalt-base | Nickel-base |
|---|---|---|---|
| Solid-solution strengtheners | Cr, Mo | Nb, Cr, Mo, Ni, W, Ta | Co, Cr, Fe, Mo, W, Ta |
| fcc matrix stabilizers | C, W, Ni | Ni | ... |
| Carbide form: | | | |
|   MC | Ti | Ti | W, Ta, Ti, Mo, Nb |
|   $M_7C_3$ | ... | Cr | Cr |
|   $M_{23}C_6$ | Cr | Cr | Cr, Mo, W |
|   $M_6C$ | Mo | Mo, W | Mo, W |
| Carbonitrides: M(CN) | C, N | C, N | C, N |
| Promotes general precipitation of carbides | P | ... | ... |
| Forms $\gamma'$ $Ni_3(Al,Ti)$ | Al, Ni, Ti | ... | Al, Ti |
| Retards formation of hexagonal $\eta$ ($Ni_3Ti$) | Al, Zr | ... | ... |
| Raises solvus temperature of $\gamma'$ | ... | ... | Co |
| Hardening precipitates and/or intermetallics | Al, Ti, Nb | Al, Mo, Ti(b) W, Ta | Al, Ti, Nb |
| Oxidation resistance | Cr | Al, Cr | Al, Cr |
| Improve hot corrosion resistance | La, Y | La, Y, Th | La, Th |
| Sulfidation resistance | Cr | Cr | Cr |
| Improves creep properties | B | ... | B |
| Increases rupture strength | B | B, Zr | B(c) |
| Causes grain-boundary segregation | ... | ... | B, C, Zr |
| Facilitates working | ... | $Ni_3Ti$ | ... |

(a) Not all these effects necessarily occur in a given alloy. (b) Hardening by precipitation of $Ni_3Ti$ also occurs if sufficient Ni is present. (c) If present in large amounts, borides are formed.

by carbide precipitation. Most of the phases discussed below have some degree of solubility for other elements; therefore, their true compositions will vary from alloy to alloy and may be altered by heat treatment and thermal exposure. Not all phases permit substitution, however. Eta phase ($Ni_3Ti$) has no significant solubility for other elements. Table 8 summarizes data on the commonly encountered constituents in these alloys.

**Gamma prime,** a gcp phase, has an ordered fcc $L1_2$ crystal structure and is $Ni_3Al$ or $Ni_3(Al,Ti)$, although considerable elemental substitution occurs. For example, cobalt and chromium will replace some of the nickel, and titanium will replace part of the aluminum. Iron can replace nickel or aluminum. The lattice parameters of $\gamma$ and $\gamma'$ are similar, resulting in coherency, which accounts for the value of $\gamma'$ as the principal strengthening agent in iron-nickel- and nickel-base superalloys.

Gamma prime is spherical in iron-nickel-base and in some of the older nickel-base alloys, such as Nimonic 80A and Waspaloy. In the more recently developed nickel-base alloys, $\gamma'$ is generally cuboidal. Experiments have shown that variations in molybdenum content and in the aluminum/titanium ratio can change the morphology of $\gamma$. With increasing $\gamma/\gamma'$ mismatch, the shape changes in the following order: spherical, globular, blocky, cuboidal (Ref 53). When the $\gamma/\gamma'$ lattice mismatch is high, extended exposure above 700 °C (1290 °F) causes undesirable $\eta$ ($Ni_3Ti$) or $\delta$ ($Ni_3Nb$) phases to form.

The volume fraction, size, and distribution of $\gamma'$ are important parameters for control of properties. The volume fraction of $\gamma'$ increases with the addition of aluminum and titanium, but the amounts of each must be carefully controlled. Gamma prime contents

**Table 8    Constituents observed in wrought heat-resistant alloys(a)**

| Phase | Crystal structure | Lattice parameter, nm(b) | Formula | Comments |
|---|---|---|---|---|
| $\gamma'$ | fcc (ordered $L1_2$) | 0.3561 for pure $Ni_3Al$ to 0.3568 for $Ni_3(Al_{0.5}Ti_{0.5})$ | $Ni_3Al$ $Ni_3(Al,Ti)$ | Principal strengthening phase in many nickel- and nickel-iron-base superalloys; crystal lattice varies slightly in size (0 to 0.5%) from that of austenite matrix; shape varies from spherical to cubic; size varies with exposure time and temperature |
| $\eta$ | hcp ($D0_{24}$) | $a_0 = 0.5093$ $c_0 = 0.8276$ | $Ni_3Ti$ (no solubility for other elements) | Found in iron-, cobalt-, and nickel-base superalloys with high titanium/aluminum ratios after extended exposure; may form intergranularly in a cellular form or intragranularly as acicular platelets in a Widmanstätten pattern |
| $\gamma''$ | bct (ordered $D0_{22}$) | $a_0 = 0.3624$ $c_0 = 0.7406$ | $Ni_3Nb$ | Principal strengthening phase in Inconel 718; $\gamma''$ precipitates are coherent disk-shaped particles that form on the {100} planes (avg diam approximately 600 Å, thickness approximately 50 to 90 Å); metastable phase |
| $Ni_3Nb$ ($\delta$) | orthorhombic (ordered $Cu_3Ti$) | $a_0 = 0.5106-0.511$ $b_0 = 0.421-0.4251$ $c_0 = 0.452-0.4556$ | $Ni_3Nb$ | Observed in overaged Inconel 718; has an acicular shape when formed between 815 and 980 °C (1500 and 1800 °F); forms by cellular reaction at low aging temperatures and by intragranular precipitation at high aging temperatures |
| MC | cubic | $a_0 = 0.430-0.470$ | TiC NbC HfC | Titanium carbide has some solubility for nitrogen, zirconium, and molybdenum; composition is variable; appears as globular, irregularly shaped particles that are gray to lavender; "M" elements can be titanium, tantalum, niobium, hafnium, thorium, or zirconium |
| $M_{23}C_6$ | fcc | $a_0 = 1.050-1.070$ (varies with composition) | $Cr_{23}C_6$ $(Cr,Fe,W,Mo)_{23}C_6$ | Form of precipitation is important; it can precipitate as films, globules, platelets, lamellae, and cells; usually forms at grain boundaries; "M" element is usually chromium, but nickel-cobalt, iron, molybdenum, and tungsten can substitute |
| $M_6C$ | fcc | $a_0 = 1.085-1.175$ | $Fe_3Mo_3C$ $Fe_3W_3C-Fe_4W_2C$ $Fe_3NB_3C$ $Nb_3Co_3C$ $Ta_3Co_3C$ | Randomly distributed carbide; may appear pinkish; "M" elements are generally molybdenum or tungsten; there is some solubility for chromium, nickel-niobium, tantalum, and cobalt |
| $M_7C_3$ | hexagonal | $a_0 = 1.398$ $c_0 = 0.4523$ | $Cr_7C_3$ | Generally observed as a blocky intergranular shape; observed only in alloys such as Nimonic 80A after exposure above 1000 °C (1830 °F), and in some cobalt-base alloys |
| $M_3B_2$ | tetragonal | $a_0 = 0.560-0.620$ $c_0 = 0.300-0.330$ | $Ta_3B_2$ $V_3B_2$ $Nb_3B_2$ $(Mo,Ti,Cr,Ni,Fe)_3B_2$ $Mo_2FeB_2$ | Observed in iron-nickel- and nickel-base alloys with about 0.03% B or greater; borides appear similar to carbides, but are not attacked by preferential carbide etchants; "M" elements can be molybdenum, tantalum, niobium, nickel, iron, or vanadium |
| MN | cubic | $a_0 = 0.4240$ | TiN $(Ti,Nb,Zr)N$ $(Ti,Nb,Zr)(C,N)$ ZrN NbN | Nitrides are observed in alloys containing titanium, niobium, or zirconium; they are insoluble at temperatures below the melting point; easily recognized as-polished, having square to rectangular shapes and ranging from yellow to orange |
| $\mu$ | rhombohedral | $a_0 = 0.475$ $c_0 = 2.577$ | $Co_7W_6$ $(Fe,Co)_7(Mo,W)_6$ | Generally observed in alloys with high levels of molybdenum or tungsten; appears as coarse, irregular Widmanstätten platelets; forms at high temperatures |
| Laves | hexagonal | $a_0 = 0.475-0.495$ $c_0 = 0.770-0.815$ | $Fe_2Nb$ $Fe_2Ti$ $Fe_2Mo$ $Co_2Ta$ $Co_2Ti$ | Most common in iron-base and cobalt-base superalloys; usually appears as irregularly shaped globules, often elongated, or as platelets after extended high-temperature exposure |
| $\sigma$ | tetragonal | $a_0 = 0.880-0.910$ $c_0 = 0.450-0.480$ | FeCr FeCrMo CrFeMoNi CrCo CrNiMo | Most often observed in iron- and cobalt-base superalloys, less commonly in nickel-base alloys; appears as irregularly shaped globules, often elongated; forms after extended exposure between 540 and 980 °C (1005 to 1795 °F) |

(a) For more information on this subject, see the article "Crystal Structure of Metals" in this Volume. (b) 1 nm = 10Å

above approximately 45% render the alloy difficult to deform by hot or cold working. In the iron-nickel-base alloys, the volume fraction of $\gamma'$ phase is less than 0.2%, and it is usually spherical. Optimum strength results when the $\gamma'$ is in the size range of 0.01 to 0.05 $\mu$m, much too small to be seen using the optical microscope. If the aluminum/titanium ratio is equal to or greater than 1, extended high-temperature exposure results in replacement of $\gamma'$ by $Ni_2AlTi$, $NiAl$, or $Ni(Al,Ti)$. These phases overage rapidly at moderately high temperatures, forming massive platelike precipitates.

Alloys with $\gamma'$ contents below 20%, such as Nimonic 80A, are heat treated using a simple two-step process of solution annealing and aging. The solution anneal recrystallizes the austenite matrix and dissolves any $\gamma'$ and $M_{23}C_6$ carbides present. Aging precipitates $\gamma'$ uniformly throughout the matrix and precipitates $M_{23}C_6$ carbides at grain and twin boundaries. Alloys with $\gamma'$ contents of approximately 30%, such as Waspaloy or Udimet 500, are solution treated, then given two aging treatments. Alloys with 40 to 45% $\gamma'$, such as Udimet 700, are solution treated, then given three aging treatments.

Positive identification of $\gamma'$ is usually performed by x-ray diffraction of the residue of bulk extractions or by electron diffraction using extraction replicas. Some of the electrolytes that selectively attack $\gamma'$ can be quite useful, because the $\gamma'$ will be recessed below the matrix, and the other second phases will be in relief or plane with the surface depending on the preparation procedure.

**Gamma double prime** has an ordered bct $D0_{22}$ crystal structure with an $Ni_3Nb$ composition and is found in iron-nickel-base alloys containing niobium. It gained prominence as the strengthening phase with the introduction of Inconel 718 (Ref 54). Early studies of the strengthening mechanism produced conflicting results until the precise details of $\gamma''$-phase formation, composition, crystallography, and stability were determined (Ref 55-60).

Gamma double prime has a disk-shaped morphology and precipitates with a well-defined relationship to the austenite matrix: $[001]_{\gamma''} \parallel \langle 001 \rangle_{\gamma}$ and $\{100\}_{\gamma''} \parallel \{100\}_{\gamma}$. Strengthening is due to the coherency strains produced by the low degree of $\gamma/\gamma''$ lattice mismatch. Although $\gamma''$ and $\gamma'$ are present in Inconel 718 after aging, the amount of $\gamma'$ is much less, and $\gamma''$ is the primary strengthening agent. Other alloys strengthened by $\gamma''$ include Inconel 706 and Udimet 630.

Because $\gamma''$ is not a stable phase, application of alloys such as Inconel 718 is restricted to below 700 °C (1290 °F). Above this temperature, extended exposure produces a loss of strength due to rapid coarsening of $\gamma''$, solutioning of $\gamma''$ and $\gamma'$, and formation of the stable orthorhombic form of $Ni_3Nb$, which has an acicular, platelike shape.

Positive identification of bct $\gamma''$ is more difficult than $\gamma'$, because x-ray diffraction of bulk extraction residues will not detect $\gamma''$. The failure to detect bct $\gamma''$ is attributed to line broadening due to the very fine particle size that obscures the peaks of interest (Ref 57). Electron diffraction will, however, detect the superlattice lines of bct $\gamma''$. Bright-field TEM examination is unsatisfactory for resolving $\gamma''$ due to the high density of the precipitates and the strong contrast from the coherency strain field around the precipitates. However, dark-field TEM examination provides excellent imaging of the $\gamma''$ by selective imaging of precipitates that produce specific superlattice reflections (Ref 57). In addition, $\gamma''$ can be separated from $\gamma'$ using the dark-field mode, because the $\gamma''$ dark-field image is substantially brighter than that of $\gamma'$ (Ref 57).

**Eta phase** has a hexagonal $D0_{24}$ crystal structure with a $Ni_3Ti$ composition. Eta can form in iron-nickel-, nickel-, and cobalt-base superalloys, especially in grades with high titanium/aluminum ratios that have had extended high-temperature exposure. Eta phase has no solubility for other elements and will grow more rapidly and form larger particles than $\gamma'$, although it precipitates slowly. Coarse $\eta$ can be observed using the optical microscope.

Two forms of $\eta$ may be encountered. The first develops at grain boundaries as a cellular constituent similar to pearlite, with alternate lamellae of $\gamma$ and $\eta$; the second, intragranularly as platelets with a Widmanstätten pattern (Ref 61-63). The cellular form is detrimental to notched stress-rupture strength and creep ductility, and the Widmanstätten pattern impairs stress-rupture strength but not ductility. Eta phase is relatively easy to identify due to its characteristic appearance. Most of the general-purpose reagents will reveal $\eta$, as will x-ray diffraction of bulk-extracted residues.

**Carbides,** which are important constituents, are present in all the wrought heat-resistant superalloys. Four basic types are encountered: MC, $M_{23}C_6$, $M_6C$, and $M_7C_3$ (where M represents one or more metallic elements). Carbides in these alloys serve three principal functions. First, grain-boundary carbides, when properly formed, strengthen the grain boundary, prevent or retard grain-boundary sliding, and permit stress relaxation. Second, if fine carbides are precipitated in the matrix, strengthening results. This is important in cobalt-base alloys that cannot be strengthened by $\gamma'$. Third, carbides can tie up certain elements that would otherwise promote phase instability during service. Carbide precipitation in nickel-base alloys has a stronger tendency to form at grain boundaries than in iron-nickel- or cobalt-base alloys. Although grain-boundary carbides, depending on their morphology, can degrade properties, reducing carbon content to low levels substantially reduces creep life and ductility in nickel-base alloys.

Aging of iron-nickel- and nickel-base superalloys causes $M_{23}C_6$ to form at the grain boundaries. The optimum situation is a chain of discrete globular $M_{23}C_6$ particles at the grain boundaries. This form benefits creep-rupture life. However, if the carbides precipitate as a continuous grain-boundary film, properties will be seriously degraded. It is not uncommon to observe zones around the grain boundaries that are devoid of $\gamma'$. Such precipitate-free zones can significantly influence stress-rupture life, depending on the width of the zones (Ref 64).

In these alloys, MC-type carbide is most frequently titanium carbide; other types, such as niobium carbide, tantalum carbide, or hafnium carbide, are less common. Titanium carbide has some solubility for other elements, such as nitrogen, zirconium, and molybdenum. They are large, globular particles observable on the as-polished surface, particularly if some relief is introduced during final polishing. Metal carbides usually are irregular in shape or cubic. They can be preferentially colored by certain etchants.

The most important carbide in superalloys is $M_{23}C_6$, because it forms at the grain boundaries during aging and, when properly formed, increases the strength of the grain boundaries to balance the matrix strength. Although chromium is the primary "M" element, other metallic elements, such as nickel, cobalt, iron, molybdenum, and tungsten, can substitute for it. The discrete globular form is the most desirable morphology; films, platelets, lamellae, and cells have also been observed.

The $M_6C$ carbide is generally rich in molybdenum or tungsten, but other elements, such as chromium, nickel, or cobalt, may substitute for it to some degree. It is the most commonly observed carbide in the cobalt-base superalloys and in nickel-base alloys with high molybdenum and/or tungsten contents. In these alloys, $M_6C$ is often observed in the as-cast condition randomly distributed throughout the matrix. In wrought alloys, it will usually be dissolved during heating before hot working. It may precipitate at the grain boundaries in a blocky form or intragranularly in a Widmanstätten pattern and can be preferentially stained by certain etchants.

Although $M_7C_3$ is not widely observed in superalloys, it is present in some cobalt-base alloys and in Nimonic 80A, a nickel-chromium-titanium-aluminum superalloy, when heated above 1000 °C (1830 °F). Additions of such elements as cobalt, molybdenum, tungsten, or niobium to nickel-base alloys prevents formation of $M_7C_3$. Massive $Cr_7C_3$ is formed in Nimonic 80A in the grain boundaries after heating to 1080 °C (1975 °F). Subsequent aging at 700 °C (1290 °F) to precipitate $\gamma'$ impedes precipitation of $M_{23}C_6$ due to the previously formed $Cr_7C_3$, which generally exhibits a blocky shape when present at grain boundaries.

**Borides.** Boron is added in small amounts to many superalloys to improve stress-rupture and creep properties or to retard formation of $\eta$ phase, which would impair creep strength. Boron retards formation of the cellular grain boundary form of $\eta$, but has no influence on the intragranular Widmanstätten $\eta$. Consequently, boron influences grain-boundary structures. Boron also reduces the solubility of carbon in austenite, which increases precipitation of finer-sized MC and $M_{23}C_6$ carbides. If the boron addition is sufficiently high, detrimental borides will form. Borides are hard and brittle and precipitate at the grain boundaries. Borides are generally of $M_3B_2$ composition with a tetragonal structure (Ref 65). Molybdenum, tantalum, niobium, nickel, iron, or vanadium can be "M" elements. The identification of borides in Udimet 700 has been documented (Ref 65).

**Laves phase,** a tcp phase, has a $MgZn_2$ hexagonal crystal structure with a composition of the $AB_2$ type. Typical examples include $Fe_2Ti$, $Fe_2Nb$, and $Fe_2Mo$, but a more general formula is $(Fe,Cr,Mn,Si)_2(Mo,Ti,Nb)$. They are most commonly observed in the iron-nickel-base alloys as coarse intergranular particles; intragranular precipitation may also occur. Silicon and niobium promote formation of Laves phase in Inconel 718. Excessive amounts will impair room-temperature tensile ductility; creep properties are not significantly affected. Laves phases have been observed in certain cobalt-base alloys and have been identified as $Co_2W$, $Co_2Ti$, or $Co_2Ta$.

**Sigma phase** is a tetragonal intermetallic tcp phase that forms with a wide range of compositions. Various morphologies may be encountered, some of which are quite detrimental to properties. However, the presence of $\sigma$ in superalloys is not necessarily damaging to properties. Sigma in the form of platelets or as a grain-boundary film is detrimental, but globular intragranular precipitation can improve creep properties.

Considerable effort has been devoted to determining how composition influences $\sigma$-phase formation, particularly in nickel-base superalloys. References 66 to 70 present examples of the many studies that have been conducted. This work has substantially influenced alloy development.

Sigma can be preferentially attacked or stained by a number of reagents. However, because of the wide range of alloy compositions that may contain $\sigma$ and the variable nature of its composition, positive identification by etching is not always possible. X-ray diffraction of bulk extraction residues is a more reliable technique. Etching procedures are best applied when they can be tested for response on specimens of the alloy known to contain $\sigma$ phase.

**Mu phase** is a rhombohedral (triagonal) intermetallic tcp phase with a $W_6Fe_7$ structure (Ref 71). In general, it has little influence on properties. Mu precipitates as coarse, irregularly shaped platelets in a Widmanstätten pattern. A general formula for $\mu$ is $(Fe,Co)_7(Mo,W)_6$. Nickel can substitute for part of the iron or the cobalt.

**Nitrides** are commonly observed in superalloys containing titanium or niobium as titanium nitride (most common) or niobium nitride. Nitrides are not influenced by heat treatment and are insoluble to the melting point. Nitrides are easily identified in the as-polished condition or after etching due to their regular, angular shapes and distinct yellow-to-orange color. Nitrides are quite hard and will appear in relief after polishing. They have some solubility for carbon and may be referred to as $Ti(C,N)$, $Nb(C,N)$, and so on. They should not be confused with carbonitrides, which are much richer in carbon and lower in nitrogen. Nitrides, often duplex, include an embedded phase or a surrounding film; this second phase is generally a darker colored nitride containing considerable carbon. The usual amounts present in superalloys generally have little influence on properties.

**Other Phases.** A few other phases are less frequently observed in wrought heat-resistant alloys. For example, a few cobalt-base alloys have been developed that attain some degree of strengthening by precipitation of intermetallic phases, such as $CoAl$, $Co_3Mo$, or $Co_3Ti$. In alloys similar to A-286, G phase ($Ni_{18}Ti_8Si_6$) has been observed (Ref 72, 73). This phase has a globular shape and precipitates in grain boundaries. It is detrimental to stress-rupture life. A chromium-iron niobide, Z phase, has been observed in an Fe-18Cr-12Ni-1Nb alloy after creep testing at 850 °C (1560 °F) (Ref 74). Inclusions, some of which are similar to those found in steels, can also be found in these alloys. However, in the nickel-base alloys, titanium sulfides may be observed. Oxides, such as $Al_2O_3$ or magnesia, may also be present. Oxides and sulfides may be observed at the surface of components due to environmental effects. Coatings are also used on some alloys, and their microstructures may be of interest (Ref 75, 76).

## REFERENCES

1. G.F. Vander Voort, *Metallography: Principles and Practice*, McGraw-Hill, 1984
2. C.E. Smeltzer, Solve Steel "Freckle" Mystery, *Iron Age*, Vol 184, 10 Sept 1959, p 188-189
3. G.C. Gould, Freckle Segregation in Vacuum Consumable-Electrode Ingots, *Trans. AIME*, Vol 233, July 1965, p 1345-1351
4. J. Preston, Segregation in Vacuum-Arc-Melted Alloy Steel Ingots, *Int. Trans. Vacuum Metallurgy Conf. 1967*, American Vacuum Society, New York, 1968, p 569-588
5. R.C. Buehl and J.K. McCauley, Processing Improvement in Vacuum-Arc Remelting of Ingots, *Int. Trans. Vacuum Metallurgy Conf. 1967*, American Vacuum Society, New York, 1968, p 695-709
6. A.F. Giamei and B.H. Kear, On the Nature of Freckles in Nickel Base Superalloys, *Met. Trans.*, Vol 1, Aug 1970, p 2185-2192
7. R. Schlatter, Electrical and Magnetic Interactions in Vacuum-Arc Remelting and Their Effect on the Metallurgical Quality of Specialty Steels, *J. Vac. Sci. Technol.*, Vol 11, Nov/Dec 1974, p 1047-1054
8. R.L. Anderson, "Revealing Microstructures in Metals," Westinghouse Research Laboratory Scientific Paper 425-C000-P2, 22 Dec 1961
9. G. Petzow, *Metallographic Etching*, American Society for Metals, 1978
10. C.H. Lund and H.J. Wagner, "Identification of Microconstituents in Superalloys," DMIC Memorandum 160, Battelle Memorial Institute, Columbus, OH, 15 Nov 1962
11. H.J. Beattie and F.L. Ver Snyder, Microconstituents in High Temperature Alloys, *Trans. ASM*, Vol 45, 1953, p 397-428
12. J.W. Weeton and R.A. Signorelli, Effect of Heat Treatment Upon Microstructures, Microconstituents, and Hardness of Wrought Cobalt Base Alloy, *Trans. ASM*, Vol 47, 1955, p 815-852
13. H. Meisel *et al.*, Metallographic Development of the Structure of Nickel Based Alloys, *Pract. Metallog.*, Vol 17, 1980, p 261-272
14. F.R. Morral, Metallography of Cobalt-Base and Cobalt-Containing Alloys, *Pract. Metallog.*, Vol 10, 1973, p 398-413
15. E. Kohlhaas and A. Fischer, The Metallography of Superalloys, *Pract. Metallog.*, Vol 8, Jan 1971, p 3-25
16. W.C. Bigelow *et al.*, Electron Microscopic Identification of the $\gamma'$ Phase of Nickel-Base Alloys, *Proc. ASTM*, Vol 56, 1956, p 945-953
17. L. Bartosiewicz, Preferential Electrolytic Etching Technique to Reveal the $\gamma'$ Phase in Nickel Base Alloys, *Pract. Metallog.*, Vol 10, 1973, p 450-461
18. P.K. Footner and B.P. Richards, A Rapid Method for Measurement of $\gamma'$ Size Distribution in Nickel-Base Superalloys, *Pract. Metallog.*, Vol 17, 1980, p 489-496
19. C.P. Sullivan, The Metallographic Identification of Borides in Udimet 700, *Trans. ASM*, Vol 58, 1965, p 702-705
20. G.N. Maniar and A. Szirmae, Ed., *Manual on Electron Metallography Techniques*, STP 547, ASTM, Philadelphia, 1973
21. I.S. Brammar and M.A.P. Dewey, *Specimen Preparation for Electron Metallography*, Blackwell Scientific, 1966
22. G. Thomas, *Transmission Electron Microscopy of Metals*, John Wiley & Sons, 1964
23. J.R. Mihalisin, The Selective Identification of Constituents in Nimonic 80 by Extraction-Replica Technique, *Trans. AIME*, Vol 212, June 1958, p 349-350
24. E. Kohlhaas and A. Fischer, The Use of the Carbon-Extraction Technique in Investigations of Superalloys, *Pract. Metallog.*, Vol 6, 1969, p 291-298
25. R.J. Seher and G.N. Maniar, Analytical-

Preshadowed Extraction Replica Technique, *Metallography*, Vol 5, 1972, p 409-414

26. W.L. Mankins, Chromic Acid as an Electrolytic Etchant and Electrolyte for the Extraction of γ' in Nickel-Base Superalloys, *Metallography*, Vol 9, 1976, p 227-232

27. A.J. Portner and B. Ralph, A Technique for the Replication of γ' in Nickel-Base Superalloys, *Pract. Metallog.*, Vol 16, 1979, p 592-601

28. K.C. Thompson-Russell and J.W. Edington, *Electron Microscope Specimen Preparation Techniques in Materials Science*, Part 5, *Practical Electron Microscopy in Materials Science*, Philips Electronic Instruments, Eindhoven, Holland, 1977

29. L. Bartosiewicz, Improved Techniques of Thin Foil Preparation of Ni Base Alloys for Electron Microscopy, *Pract. Metallog.*, Vol 9, 1972, p 525-534

30. C. Hays and D.A. Nail, Transmission Electron Microscopy of Incoloy Alloy 901, *Metallography*, Vol 7, 1974, p 59-68

31. R.E. Schafrik and M. Henry, Transmission Electron Microscopy Foil Preparation and Results for Incoloy 901, *Metallography*, Vol 13, 1980, p 157-165

32. T.P. Hoar and K.W.J. Bowen, The Electrolytic Separation and Some Properties of Austenite and Sigma in 18-8-3-1 Chromium - Nickel - Molybdenum - Titanium Steel, *Trans. ASM*, Vol 45, 1953, p 443-474

33. J.F. Brown *et al.*, The Extraction of Minor Phases from Austenitic Steel, *Metallurgia*, Vol 56, Nov 1957, p 215-223

34. K.W. Andrews and H. Hughes, The Isolation, Separation, and Identification of Microconstituents in Steels, in *STP 393*, ASTM, Philadelphia, 1966, p 3-21

35. O.H. Kriege and C.P. Sullivan, The Separation of Gamma Prime from Udimet 700, *Trans. ASM*, Vol 61, 1968, p 278-282

36. O.H. Kriege and J.M. Baris, The Chemical Partitioning of Elements in Gamma Prime Separated from Precipitation-Hardened, High-Temperature Nickel-Base Alloys, *Trans. ASM*, Vol 62, 1969, p 195-200

37. M.J. Donachie and O.H. Kriege, Phase Extraction and Analysis in Superalloys—Summary of Investigations by ASTM Committee E-4 Task Group 1, *J. Mater.*, Vol 7, Sept 1972, p 269-278

38. O.H. Kriege, Phase Separation as a Technique for the Characterization of Superalloys, in *STP 557*, ASTM, Philadelphia, 1974, p 220-234

39. E. Kny, On the Methodology of Phase Extraction in Ni-Base Superalloys, *Pract. Metallog.*, Vol 13, Nov 1976, p 549-564

40. "Practice for Electrolytic Extraction of Phases from Ni and Ni-Fe Base Superalloys Using a Hydrochloric-Methanol Electrolyte, E 963, *Annual Book of ASTM Standards*, ASTM, Philadelphia, 1984

41. C. Razim, Metallography of Heat Resistant and High Temperature Alloys, *Pract. Metallog.*, Vol 5, May 1968, p 225-241; June 1968, p 299-309

42. G.P. Sabol and R. Stickler, Microstructure of Nickel-Base Superalloys, *Phys. Stat. Sol.*, Vol 35 (No. 1), 1968, p 11-52

43. P.S. Kotval, The Microstructure of Superalloys, *Metallography*, Vol 1, 1969, p 251-285

44. F.R. Morral *et al.*, Microstructure of Cobalt-Base High-Temperature Alloys, *ASM Met. Eng. Q.*, Vol 9, May 1969, p 1-16

45. J.F. Radavich and W.H. Couts, Metallography of the Superalloys, *Rev. High-Temp. Mater.*, Vol 1, Aug 1971, p 55-96

46. C.P. Sullivan and M.J. Donachie, Some Effects of Microstructure on the Mechanical Properties of Nickel-Base Superalloys, *ASM Met. Eng. Q.*, Vol 7, Feb 1967, p 36-45

47. R.F. Decker, Strengthening Mechanisms in Nickel-Base Superalloys, in *Symposium: Steel-Strengthening Mechanisms*, 5-6 May 1969, Zurich, 1970, p 147-170

48. C.T. Sims and W.C. Hagel, Ed., *The Superalloys*, John Wiley & Sons, 1972

49. C.P. Sullivan *et al.*, Relationship of Properties to Microstructure in Cobalt-Base Superalloys, *ASM Met. Eng. Q.*, Vol 9, May 1969, p 16-29

50. C.P. Sullivan and M.J. Donachie, Microstructures and Mechanical Properties of Iron-Base (-Containing) Superalloys, *ASM Met. Eng. Q.*, Vol 11, Nov 1971, p 1-11

51. D.R. Muzyka, Controlling Microstructure and Properties of Superalloys Via Use of Precipitated Phases, *ASM Met. Eng. Q.*, Vol 11, Nov 1971, p 12-20

52. D.R. Muzyka and G.N. Maniar, Microstructure Approach to Property Optimization in Wrought Superalloys, in *STP 557*, ASTM, Philadelphia, 1974, p 198-219

53. W.T. Loomis *et al.*, The Influence of Molybdenum on the γ' Phase in Experimental Nickel-Base Superalloys, *Met. Trans.*, Vol 3, April 1972, p 989-1000

54. J.F. Barker, A Superalloy for Medium Temperatures, *Met. Prog.*, Vol 81, May 1962, p 72-76

55. I. Kirman and D.H. Warrington, Identification of the Strengthening Phase in Fe-Ni-Cr-Nb Alloys, *J. Iron Steel Inst.*, Vol 205, Dec 1967, p 1264-1265

56. P.S. Kotval, Identification of the Strengthening Phase in "Inconel" Alloy 718, *Trans. AIME*, Vol 242, Aug 1968, p 1764-1765

57. D.F. Paulonis *et al.*, Precipitation in Nickel-Base Alloy 718, *Trans. ASM*, Vol 62, 1969, p 611-622

58. W.J. Boesch and H.B. Canada, Precipitation Reactions and Stability of Ni$_3$Cb in Inconel Alloy 718, *J. Met.*, Vol 21, Oct 1969, p 34-38

59. I. Kirman and D.H. Warrington, The Precipitation of Ni$_3$Nb Phases in a Ni-Fe-Cr-Nb Alloy, *Met. Trans.*, Vol 1, Oct 1970, p 2667-2675

60. R. Cozar and A. Pineau, Morphology of γ' and γ'' Precipitates and Thermal Stability of Inconel 718 Type Alloys, *Met. Trans.*, Vol 4, Jan 1973, p 47-59

61. J.R. Mihalisin and R.F. Decker, Phase Transformations in Nickel-Rich Nickel-Titanium-Aluminum Alloys, *Trans. AIME*, Vol 218, June 1960, p 507-515

62. B.R. Clark and F.B. Pickering, Precipitation Effects in Austenitic Stainless Steels Containing Titanium and Aluminum Additions, *J. Iron Steel Inst.*, Vol 205, Jan 1967, p 70-84

63. L.K. Singhal and J.W. Martin, Precipitation Processes in an Austenitic Stainless Steel Containing Titanium, *J. Iron Steel Inst.*, Vol 205, Sept 1967, p 947-952

64. E.L. Raymond, Effect of Grain Boundary Denudation of Gamma Prime on Notch-Rupture Ductility of Inconel Nickel-Chromium Alloys X-750 and 718, *Trans. AIME*, Vol 239, Sept 1967, p 1415-1422

65. H.J. Beattie, The Crystal Structure of a M$_3$B$_2$-Type Double Boride, *Acta Crystallogr.*, Vol 11, 1958, p 607-609

66. L.R. Woodyatt *et al.*, Prediction of Sigma-Type Phase Occurrence from Compositions in Austenitic Superalloys, *Trans. AIME*, Vol 236, 1966, p 519-527

67. E.O. Hall and S.H. Algie, The Sigma Phase, *Met. Rev.*, Vol 11, 1966, p 61-88

68. J.R. Mihalisin *et al.*, Sigma—Its Occurrence, Effect, and Control in Nickel-Base Superalloys, *Trans. AIME*, Vol 242, Dec 1968, p 2399-2414

69. R.G. Barrows and J.B. Newkirk, A Modified System for Predicting σ Formation, *Met. Trans.*, Vol 3, Nov 1972, p 2889-2893

70. E.S. Machlin and J. Shao, SIGMA-SAFE: A Phase Diagram Approach to the Sigma Phase Problem in Ni Base Superalloys, *Met. Trans. A*, Vol 9, April 1978, p 561-568

71. A. Raman, The μ Phases, *Z. Metallkd.*, Vol 57, April 1966, p 301-305

72. H.J. Beattie and F.L. Ver Snyder, A New Complex Phase in a High-Temperature (Iron - Nickel - Chromium - Molybdenum) Alloy, *Nature*, Vol 178 (No. 4526), 1956, p 208-209

73. H.J. Beattie and W.C. Hagel, Intermetallic Compounds in Titanium-Hardened Alloys, *Trans. AIME*, Vol 209, July 1957, p 911-917

74. K.W. Andrews and H. Hughes, discussion of Aging Reactions in Certain Superalloys, *Trans. ASM*, Vol 49, 1957, p 999

75. G.F. Slattery, Microstructural Aspects of Aluminized Coatings on Nickel-Base Alloys, *Met. Tech.*, Vol 10, Feb 1983, p 41-51

76. G.W. Goward *et al.*, Formation and Degradation Mechanisms of Aluminide Coatings on Nickel-Base Superalloys, *Trans. ASM*, Vol 60, 1967, p 228-241

**Fig. 1** Alloy A-286 (AISI 660, 195 HV), solution annealed 2 h at 900 °C (1650 °F) and oil quenched. Specimen has a very fine austenite grain size. Glyceregia. 100×

**Fig. 2** Same alloy and processing as Fig. 1, but showing an area near the surface of the specimen with a duplex grain structure. Tint etch: 20 mL HCl, 100 mL H$_2$O, 2.4 g NH$_4$F · HF, and 0.8 g K$_2$S$_2$O$_5$. 100×

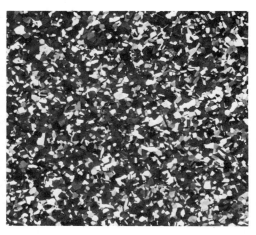

**Fig. 3** Same alloy and processing as Fig. 1, showing the very fine austenite matrix grains. Tint etch: 20 mL HCl, 100 mL H$_2$O, 1 g NH$_4$F · HF, 0.5 g K$_2$S$_2$O$_5$. 200×

**Fig. 4** Alloy A-286 (AISI 660, 357 HV), solution annealed 2 h at 900 °C (1650 °F), oil quenched, and held 16 h at 720 °C (1325 °F). A very fine-grained structure similar to that shown in Fig. 1. Glyceregia. 100×

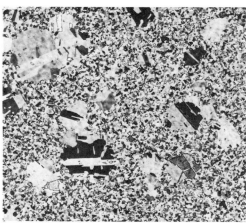

**Fig. 5** Same alloy and processing as Fig. 4, but showing a region near the surface of the specimen with a fine grain structure. Tint etched same as Fig. 2. 100×

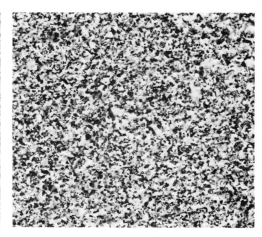

**Fig. 6** Same alloy and processing as Fig. 4, showing the very fine matrix grain structure. Tint etched same as Fig. 2. 100×

**Fig. 7** Alloy A-286 (AISI 660, 150 HV), solution annealed 1 h at 980 °C (1800 °F) and oil quenched, showing a coarser grain structure than in Fig. 1 to 6 due to the higher solutionizing temperature. Glyceregia. 100×

**Fig. 8** Same alloy and processing as Fig. 7, but tint etched using 20 mL HCl, 100 mL H$_2$O, 1 g NH$_4$F · HF, and 0.5 g K$_2$S$_2$O$_5$. 100×

**Fig. 9** Alloy A-286 (AISI 660, 318 HV), solution annealed 1 h at 980 °C (1800 °F), oil quenched, aged 16 h at 720 °C (1325 °F), and air cooled. Glyceregia. 100×

**Fig. 10** Same alloy and processing as Fig. 9, but tint etched. Only the matrix phase has been colored. 20 mL HCl, 100 mL H$_2$O, 1 g NH$_4$F · HF, and 0.5 g K$_2$S$_2$O$_5$. 100×

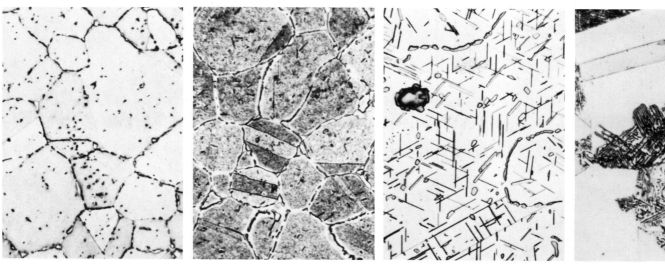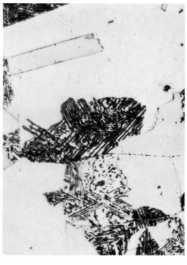

**Fig. 11, 12, 13** A-286 (AISI 660), solution annealed 1 h at 980 °C (1800 °F) and aged 16 h at 720 °C (1325 °F), then air cooled and creep tested to rupture. Fig. 11: tested 7131 h at 650 °C (1200 °F). Matrix and grain-boundary precipitates have coalesced. 31.5 HRC. Fig. 12: tested 1232 h at 730 °C (1350 °F). Grain-boundary precipitates have coalesced; the matrix is darkened by $\gamma'$ precipitation. HRC 25.5. Fig. 13: tested 546 h at 815 °C (1500 °F). Grain-boundary precipitates have coalesced, and the overaged matrix contains needlelike $\eta$ phase (Ni$_3$Ti). HRB 88.5. 15 mL HCl, 10 mL HNO$_3$, and 10 mL acetic acid. 1000×

**Fig. 14** A-286 (AISI 660), showing lamellar or cellular precipitation of $\eta$ phase (Ni$_3$Ti) caused by overaging or by insufficient boron. Cold working accelerates the response to aging. 15 mL HCl, 10 mL HNO$_3$, and 10 mL acetic acid. 1000×

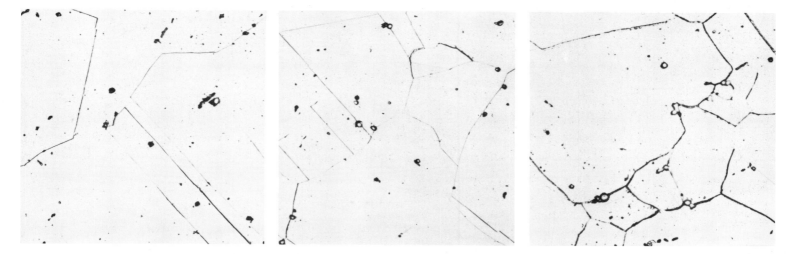

**Fig. 15, 16, 17** Discaloy iron-nickel-base alloy (AISI 662), solution annealed 1 h at 1065 °C (1950 °F), showing the effects of different aging processes. Fig. 15: oil quenched; 139 HV. Fig. 16: aged 64 h at 650 °C (1200 °F); 249 HV. Fig. 17: aged 512 h at 650 °C (1200 °F); 315 HV. Glyceregia. 500×. (R.L. Anderson)

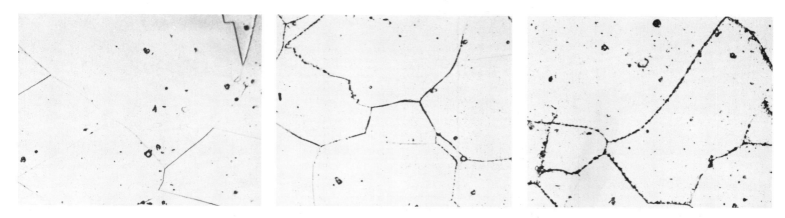

**Fig. 18, 19, 20** Same material and solution annealing treatment as Fig. 15 to 17. Fig. 18: aged 2 h at 705 °C (1300 °F); 223 HV. Fig. 19: aged 64 h at 705 °C (1300 °F); 292 HV. Fig. 20: aged 272 h at 705 °C (1300 °F); 295 HV. Glyceregia. 500×. (R.L. Anderson)

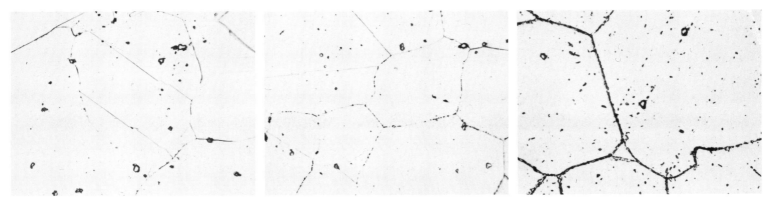

**Fig. 21, 22, 23** Same material and solution annealing as Fig. 15 to 17. Fig. 21: aged 1 h at 760 °C (1400 °F); 248 HV. Fig. 22: aged 8 h at 760 °C (1400 °F); 258 HV. Fig. 23: aged 128 h at 760 °C (1400 °F); 253 HV. Glyceregia. 500×. (R.L. Anderson)

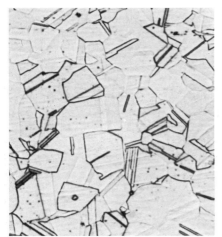

**Fig. 24** Incoloy 800 strip, in the mill-annealed condition. The microstructure consists of a solid-solution matrix in which some grains are delineated by precipitated carbide particles at the boundaries and by twinning lines. Glyceregia. 250×

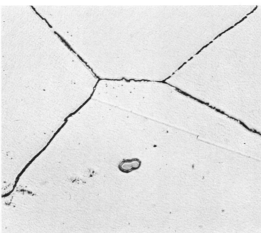

**Fig. 25** Incoloy 901, solution annealed 2 h at 1065 °C (1950 °F), water quenched, aged 2 h at 800 °C (1475 °F), air cooled, aged 24 h at 730 °C (1350 °F), and air cooled. Structure is grain-boundary envelope and MC carbide (large particle) in a γ matrix. See also Fig. 26. 1:1 HCl and H₂O. 1000×

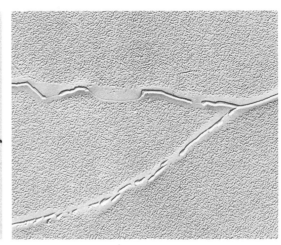

**Fig. 26** Replica electron micrograph of the specimen in Fig. 25. The grain-boundary constituents (MC, M₃B₂, or both) contributed to low ductility. Note the grain-boundary depleted zone. The γ matrix contains γ′ precipitate. Electrolytic: H₂SO₄, H₃PO₄, and HNO₃. 10 000×

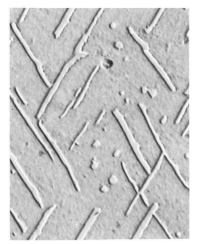

**Fig. 27** Negative replica electron micrograph of Incoloy 901, creep tested to rupture at 138 MPa (20 ksi) for 7380 h at 730 °C (1350 °F). The needlelike constituent is η phase (Ni₃Ti); the remainder of the structure is γ′ in a γ matrix. Glyceregia. 15 000×

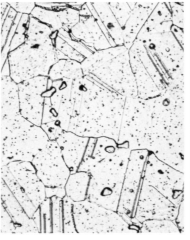

**Fig. 28** N-155 (AISI 661), solution annealed 1 h at 1150 °C (2100 °F) and water quenched. Primary carbide particles are mostly dispersed within grains; some are at grain boundaries. 1:1 HCl and H₂O. 500×

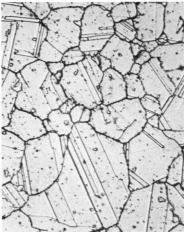

**Fig. 29** N-155 (AISI 661), solution annealed same as Fig. 28, then aged 5 h at 760 °C (1400 °F) and air cooled. Precipitated secondary carbide (M₆C or M₂₃C₆) at grain boundaries and within grains. 20% HCl, methanol, and 1% H₂O₂, 5 s. 500×

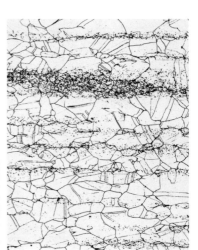

**Fig. 30** 16-25-6 (AISI 650) alloy, after forging between 650 and 705 °C (1200 and 1300 °F) and stress relieving. The solid-solution matrix exhibits banding because of carbide segregation. See also Fig. 31 and 32. Marble's reagent. 100×

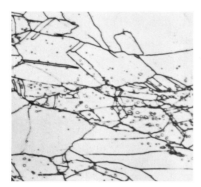

**Fig. 31** Same alloy, forging temperature, and stress-relief treatment as Fig. 30, but at a higher magnification to reveal the carbide segregation in banding. The matrix is austenitic solid solution. Marble's reagent. 500×

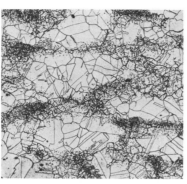

**Fig. 32** Same alloy and processing as Fig. 30. Here the carbide segregation is dispersed, not banded, in the solid-solution matrix. Compare with Fig. 30. Marble's reagent. 100×

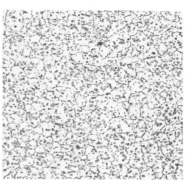

**Fig. 33** Hastelloy X (AISI 680), solution annealed at 1065 °C (1950 °F) and aged 100 h at 760 °C (1400 °F). The structure is mixed carbide particles in a γ matrix. Electrolytic: oxalic acid. 500×

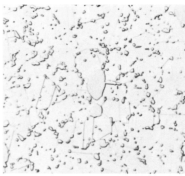

**Fig. 34** Same alloy and processing as Fig. 33, shown at twice the magnification to reveal more clearly the carbide particles in the γ matrix. Electrolytic: oxalic acid. 1000×

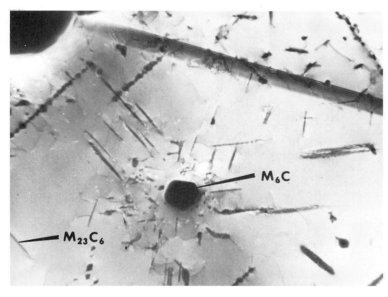

**Fig. 35** Thin-foil transmission electron micrograph of Hastelloy X, solution annealed 1 h at 1175 °C (2150 °F), water quenched, and aged 500 h at 705 °C (1300 °F). The structure is primary $M_6C$ and needlelike $M_{23}C_6$ carbides that have precipitated at dislocations generated around primary carbide. The matrix is γ solid solution. Not polished, not etched. 11 000×

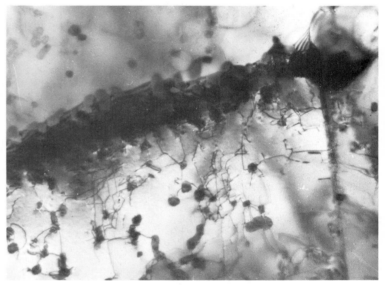

**Fig. 36** Thin-foil transmission electron micrograph of Hastelloy X, solution annealed 1 h at 1175 °C (2150 °F), water quenched, deformed 2% by reduction at room temperature, and aged 144 h at 705 °C (1300 °F). Structure is a band of high dislocation density and precipitated $M_{23}C_6$ carbide at sites of high dislocation density and adjacent locations. Not polished, not etched. 40 000×

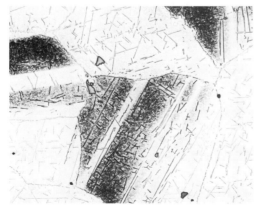

**Fig. 37** Pyromet 31 alloy (325 HV), heat treated 1500 h at 815 °C (1500 °F) to form coarse needles of η (Ni₃Ti) phase. See also Fig. 38. Glyceregia. 400×

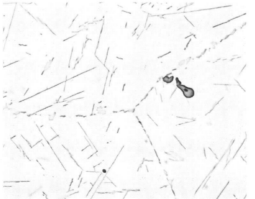

**Fig. 38** Same as Fig. 37, but at a higher magnification. Parts of only a few grains are visible. Glyceregia. 1000×

**Fig. 39** Pyromet 31 (260 HV), heat treated 4 h at 955 °C (1750 °F) to form needles of η (Ni₃Ti) phase. See also Fig. 37, 38, and 40. Glyceregia. 1000×

**Fig. 40** Same alloy and processing as Fig. 39, but shown with dark-field illumination. See also Fig. 37 and 38. Glyceregia. 1000×

**Fig. 41** Pyromet (40 HRC), solution annealed and aged. The specimen was tint etched with 66 mL HCl, 33 mL $H_2O$, and 1 g $K_2S_2O_5$. See also Fig. 42. 100×

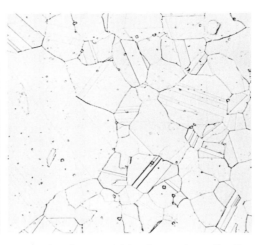

**Fig. 42** Same material and processing as Fig. 41, but etched using Kalling's reagent 2 ("waterless" Kalling's). See also Fig. 41. 100×

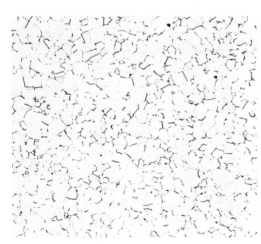

**Fig. 43** Alloy 718 (89 HRB), solution annealed 1 h at 955 °C (1750 °F) and air cooled. Large particles are MC carbides. See also Fig. 44. Glyceregia. 100×

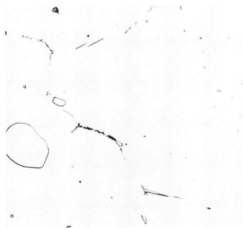

**Fig. 44** Same alloy and processing as Fig. 43, but at a higher magnification, showing large MC carbides and fine δ phase (Ni₃Nb) at the austenite grain boundaries. Glyceregia. 1000×

**Fig. 45** Alloy 718 (37 HRC), solution annealed 1 h at 955 °C (1750 °F), air cooled, aged 8 h at 720 °C (1325 °F), and air cooled. Structure is MC carbides in an austenite matrix. Glyceregia. 100×

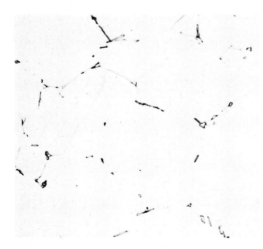

**Fig. 46** Same alloy and processing as Fig. 45, but at a higher magnification, showing a cube-shaped nitride, large MC carbides, and fine δ phase at the austenite grain boundaries. Glyceregia. 1000×

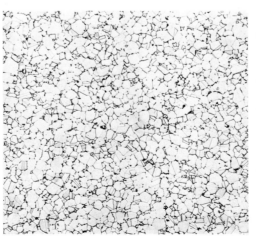

**Fig. 47** Alloy 718 (40 HRC), solution annealed 1 h at 955 °C (1750 °F), air cooled, aged 8 h at 720 °C (1325 °F), cooled 55 °C (100 °F) per hour to 620 °C (1150 °F), held 8 h, and air cooled. Structure is carbides in an austenite matrix. Glyceregia. 100×

**Fig. 48** Same alloy and processing as Fig. 47, but at higher magnification to show MC carbides and fine δ phase at the austenite grain boundaries. Glyceregia. 1000×

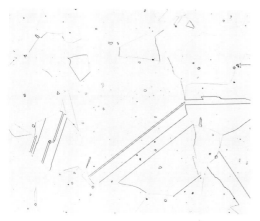

**Fig. 49** Alloy 718 (80 HRB), solution annealed 2 h at 1065 °C (1950 °F) and air cooled. Nitrides and MC carbides are visible. Compare grain size to that in Fig. 43. Glyceregia. 100×

**Fig. 50** Alloy 718 (29 HRC), solution annealed 2 h at 1065 °C (1950 °F), air cooled, aged 8 h at 720 °C (1325 °F), and air cooled. Compare with Fig. 51. Glyceregia. 100×

**Fig. 51** Same alloy (37 HRC) and annealing treatment as Fig. 50, but aged 8 h at 720 °C (1325 °F), cooled 55 °C (100 °F) per hour to 620 °C (1150 °F), held 8 h, and air cooled. Glyceregia. 100×

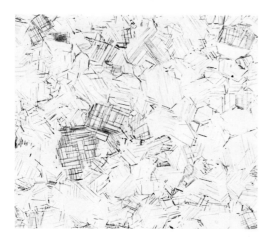

**Fig. 52** Alloy 718, solution annealed 1 h at 955 °C (1750 °F), air cooled, and aged 100 h at 870 °C (1600 °F) to form coarse δ (Ni₃Nb) needles. See also Fig. 53. Glyceregia. 200×

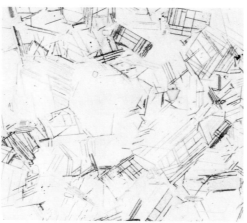

**Fig. 53** Same alloy and processing as Fig. 52, but at a higher magnification. See also Fig. 54. Glyceregia. 400×

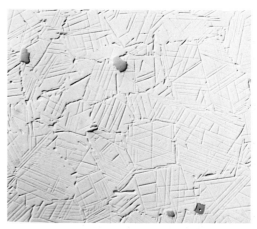

**Fig. 54** Same alloy and processing as Fig. 52, but shown using differential interference contrast. Delta needles are recessed, MC carbides stand in relief, and nitrides (lower right) are flush with the matrix. As-polished. 400×

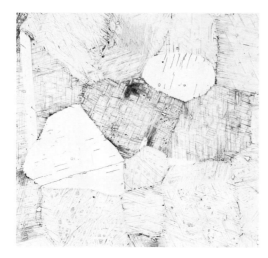

**Fig. 55** Alloy 718 (21.5 HRC), solution annealed 1 h at 1150 °C (2100 °F), air cooled, and aged 100 h at 870 °C (1600 °F) to form coarse needles of δ phase (Ni₃Nb). See also Fig. 54. Glyceregia. 100×

**Fig. 56** Same alloy and processing as Fig. 55, but using differential interference contrast illumination to show δ phase in four austenite grains. Hard MC carbide is in relief. As-polished. 400×

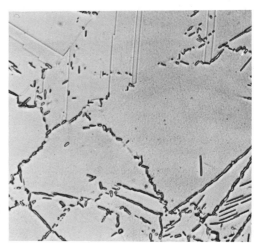

**Fig. 57** Alloy 718, solution annealed 1 h at 955 °C (1750 °F), air cooled, aged 8 h at 720 °C (1325 °F), and furnace cooled in 10 h to 620 °C (1150 °F). Structure is δ phase (Ni₃Nb) in a γ matrix. See also Fig. 59. Electrolytic: H₂SO₄, H₃PO₄, and H₂CrO₄. 1000×

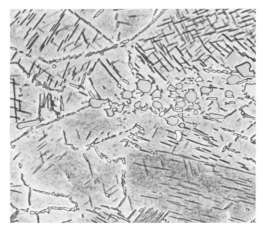

**Fig. 58** Alloy 718, solution annealed 1 h at 955 °C (1750 °F), air cooled, and aged 10 h at 760 °C (1400 °F) and at 650 °C (1200 °F). Structure is Laves phase (light gray particles), MC carbide (dark), and needlelike δ. The matrix is γ phase. See also Fig. 60. Electrolytic: $H_2SO_4$, $H_3PO_4$, and $H_2CrO_4$. 1000×

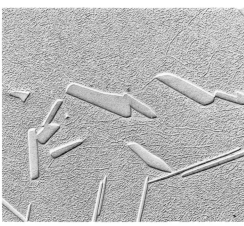

**Fig. 59** Replica electron micrograph of same alloy and processing as Fig. 57, showing details of δ-phase crystals. γ′ precipitate is visible in the γ matrix. Electrolytic: $H_2SO_4$, $H_3PO_4$, and $HNO_3$. 10 000×

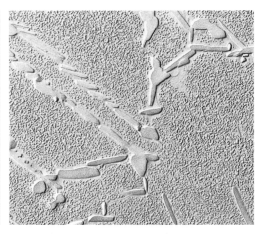

**Fig. 60** Replica electron micrograph of same alloy and processing as Fig. 58, showing precipitated carbide and needlelike $Ni_3Nb$ as well as γ′ in the γ matrix. Electrolytic: $H_2SO_4$, $H_3PO_4$, and $HNO_3$. 10 000×

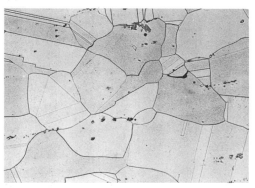

**Fig. 61** Astroloy forging, solution annealed 1 h at 1150 °C (2100 °F) and air cooled, showing grain boundaries and fine MC carbides in a γ-phase matrix. See also Fig. 62. Kalling's reagent 2. 100×

**Fig. 62** Replica electron micrograph of same alloy and processing as Fig. 61, showing a clean grain boundary (diagonal). γ′ precipitate is visible in the γ matrix. Electrolytic: $H_2SO_4$, $H_3PO_4$, and $HNO_3$. 10 000×

**Fig. 63** Astroloy forging, solution annealed 4 h at 1150 °C (2100 °F), air cooled, aged 4 h at 1080 °C (1975 °F), oil quenched, aged 4 h at 845 °C (1550 °F), air cooled, aged 16 h at 760 °C (1400 °F), and air cooled. See Fig. 64 for identification of constituents. Kalling's reagent 2. 100×

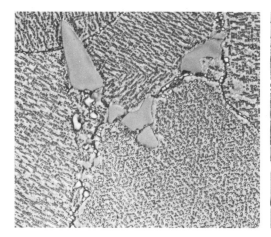

**Fig. 64** Same alloy and processing as Fig. 63, but at a higher magnification. MC carbides are precipitated at grain boundaries; the solid-solution matrix contains γ′ particles. See also Fig. 65. Kalling's reagent 2. 1000×

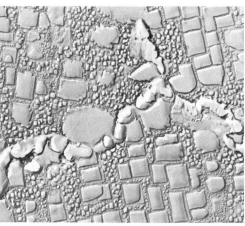

**Fig. 65** Replica electron micrograph of same alloy and processing as Fig. 63, showing intergranular γ′ precipitated at 1080 °C (1975 °F) as well as fine γ′ precipitated at 845 °C (1550 °F) and 760 °C (1400 °F). Carbide particles are visible at grain boundaries. Electrolytic: $H_2SO_4$, $H_3PO_4$, and $HNO_3$. 10 000×

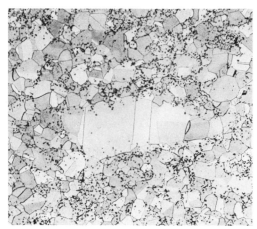

**Fig. 66** Astroloy forging, solution annealed 4 h at 1115 °C (2040 °F), air cooled, aged 8 h at 870 °C (1600 °F), air cooled, aged 4 h at 980 °C (1800 °F), air cooled, aged 8 h at 650 °C (1200 °F), air cooled, aged 8 h at 760 °C (1400 °F), and air cooled. The γ matrix contains some undissolved γ′. See also Fig. 67 and 68. Kalling's reagent 2. 100×

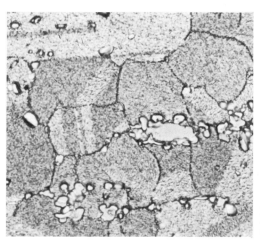

**Fig. 67** Same alloy and processing as Fig. 66, but at a higher magnification to delineate MC carbides (large, white particles) and undissolved γ′ (small, white particles). Kalling's reagent 2. 1000×

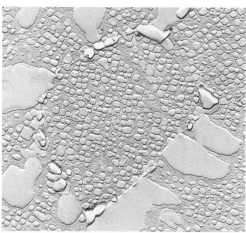

**Fig. 68** Replica electron micrograph of same alloy and processing as Fig. 66, showing $M_{23}C_6$ carbides (white, irregular) and γ′ precipitates. Electrolytic: $H_2SO_4$, $H_3PO_4$, and $HNO_3$. 10 000×

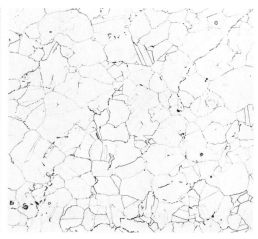

**Fig. 69** Alloy 600 (202 HV), as-forged. Specimen is from the center of a 305-mm (12-in.) diam bar. Glyceregia. 100×

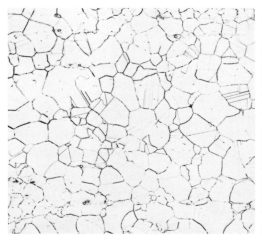

**Fig. 70** Alloy 625 (190 HV), solution annealed 30 min at 980 °C (1800 °F) and air cooled. Specimen is a longitudinal section from the mid-radius of a 140-mm (5.5-in.) diam bar. 15 mL HCl, 10 mL acetic acid, 5 mL $HNO_3$, and 2 drops glycerol. 100×

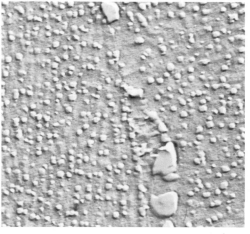

**Fig. 71** Replica electron micrograph of Inconel X-750, solution annealed 2 h at 1150 °C (2100 °F) and air cooled, then aged 24 h at 815 °C (1500 °F). Structure is small, uniformly dispersed γ′ precipitate and large, discontinuous $M_{23}C_6$ carbide at the grain boundary. Glyceregia. 15 000×

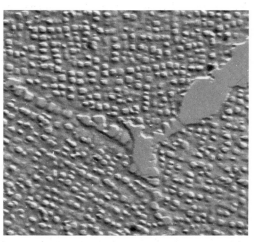

**Fig. 72** Replica electron micrograph of same alloy and annealing treatment as Fig. 71, but aged 24 h at 845 °C (1550 °F), then 24 h at 705 °C (1300 °F). Grain-boundary $M_{23}C_6$ carbide is stabilized, and precipitation of fine γ′ particles has increased. Glyceregia. 15 000×

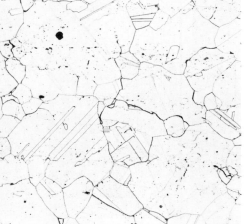

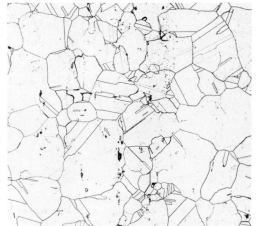

**Fig. 73, 74, 75** The effects of different etchants on solution-annealed and aged alloy X-750. Fig 73: tint etched in 50 mL HCl, 50 mL $H_2O$, and 1 g $K_2S_2O_5$. Fig. 74: etched using Kalling's reagent 2. Fig. 75: etched using glyceregia. See also Fig. 76 to 78. All 100×

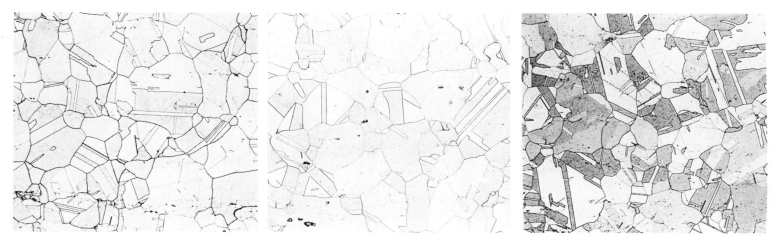

**Fig. 76, 77, 78** Different etchants used to delineate the structure of solution-annealed and aged alloy X-750. Fig. 76: etched using Marble's reagent. Fig. 77: etched using aqua regia. Fig. 78: etched using HCl + 1% $Na_2O_2$. All 100×

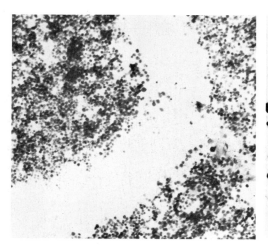

**Fig. 79** Extraction replica electron micrograph of Nimonic 80, solution annealed 8 h at 1075 °C (1965 °F) and aged 16 h at 705 °C (1300 °F). The structure is extracted γ′ phase. Electrolytic: 2% $H_2SO_4$ and $H_2O$. 15 000×

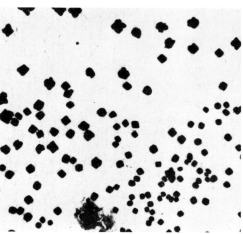

**Fig. 80** Extraction replica electron micrograph of Nimonic 80, solution annealed 1 h at 1205 °C (2200 °F) and aged 16 h at 900 °C (1650 °F). Structure is extracted cubes of γ′ phase. Electrolytic: 10% $H_2SO_4$ and $H_2O$. 15 000×

**Fig. 81** Negative replica electron micrograph of Nimonic 80, solution annealed 8 h at 1075 °C (1965 °F) and aged 16 h at 705 °C (1300 °F). Structure is grain-boundary carbide ($M_{23}C_6$) and uniformly dispersed γ′ in a matrix of γ solid solution. Glyceregia, then electrolytic: 2% $H_2SO_4$ and $H_2O$. 15 000×

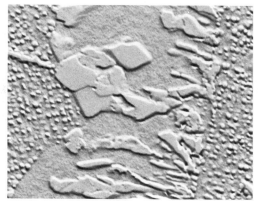

**Fig. 82** Negative replica electron micrograph of Nimonic 80, solution annealed same as Fig. 80, furnace cooled to 980 °C (1800 °F) and held 8 h, water quenched, and aged 168 h at 750 °C (1380 °F). Discontinuous precipitation of $M_{23}C_6$ carbide at grain boundaries and γ′ in the matrix. Glyceregia, then electrolytic: 1% $H_2SO_4$ and $H_2O$. 15 000×

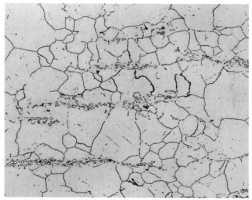

**Fig. 83** René 41, solution annealed 4 h at 1065 °C (1950 °F) and air cooled. Structure consists of stringers of carbide in a γ solid-solution matrix. See also Fig. 84 for a higher magnification of this structure. Kalling's reagent 2. 100×

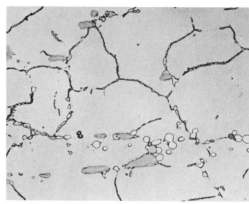

**Fig. 84** Same alloy and processing as Fig. 83, but at a higher magnification. Light, globular particles are $M_6C$; gray particles are MC carbide; grain-boundary envelopes are $M_6C$ or $M_{23}C_6$. See also Fig. 85 and 86. Kalling's reagent 2. 500×

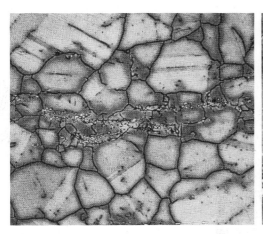

**Fig. 85** René 41, solution annealed 4 h at 1065 °C (1950 °F), air cooled, aged 16 h at 760 °C (1400 °F), and air cooled. Particles of mixed carbides are present in the γ solid-solution matrix, which was darkened by the formation of γ' at 760 °C (1400 °F). See also Fig. 86. Kalling's reagent 2. 110×

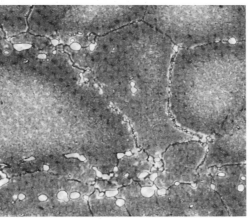

**Fig. 86** Same as Fig. 85, but at a higher magnification, showing particles of $M_6C$ (white), MC (gray), and $M_{23}C_6$ (at grain boundaries). Grain-boundary borders are darkened by γ'. Kalling's reagent 2. 540×

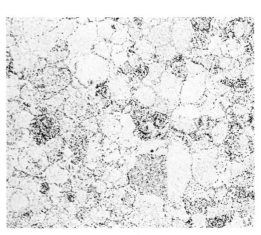

**Fig. 87** Powder-made René 95, hot isostatically pressed. Structure includes large, coarse γ'. Prior particle boundaries are also visible. See also Fig. 88 and 89. Glyceregia. 200×

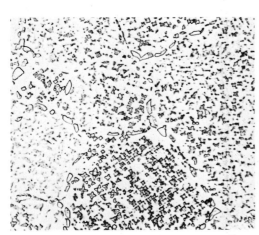

**Fig. 88, 89** The use of different illumination modes to delineate the structure of the same alloy and processing as Fig. 87. Fig. 88: bright-field illumination. Fig. 89: dark-field illumination. Some carbide networks are visible at this magnification. Glyceregia. 1000×

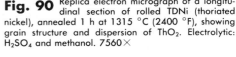

**Fig. 90** Replica electron micrograph of a longitudinal section of rolled TDNi (thoriated nickel), annealed 1 h at 1315 °C (2400 °F), showing grain structure and dispersion of $ThO_2$. Electrolytic: $H_2SO_4$ and methanol. 7560×

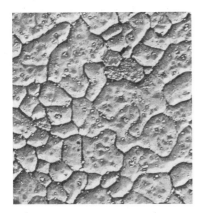

**Fig. 91** Same as Fig. 90, but this replica electron micrograph shows the grain structure and the dispersion of $ThO_2$ in a transverse section of the rolled, annealed alloy. Electrolytic: $H_2SO_4$ and methanol. 7000×

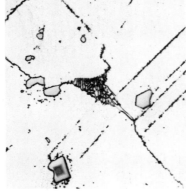

**Fig. 92** U-700, as forged. Structure is nickel-rich solid-solution matrix, eutectic with $M_3B_2$ formed by fusion at 1205 °C (2200 °F), large crystals of MC carbide, and $M_{23}C_6$ carbide at grain and twin boundaries. Kalling's reagent. 500×

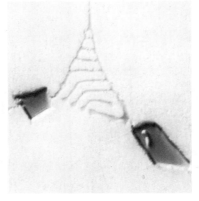

**Fig. 93** Same alloy and condition as Fig. 92, but at a higher magnification. The lamellar constituent is a boride ($M_3B_2$) formed by incipient fusion. The two large crystals are MC carbide. As-polished. 1500×

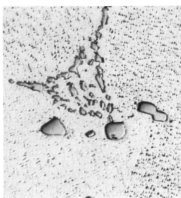

**Fig. 94** U-700, solution annealed 4 h at 1175 °C (2150 °F) and aged 4 h at 1080 °C (1975 °F). $M_{23}C_6$ has dissolved, and borides have been spheroidized. Large crystals are MC carbide; the oriented precipitate is γ'. Kalling's reagent. 1000×

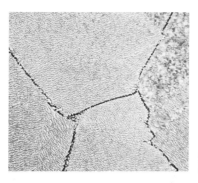

**Fig. 95** U-700, solution annealed 4 h at 1175 °C (2150 °F), aged 4 h at 1080 °C (1975 °F), aged 24 h at 845 °C (1550 °F), and aged 16 h at 760 °C (1400 °F). Carbide and boride particles are present at grain boundaries; remaining structure is MC carbide and γ′ in a γ matrix. Kalling's reagent 2. 500×

**Fig. 96** U-700, processed the same as Fig. 95, then held 500 h at 870 °C (1600 °F). Light, acicular σ phase has formed in the γ-γ′ matrix; some σ is also visible at boundaries of the platelets. Kalling's reagent 2. 500×

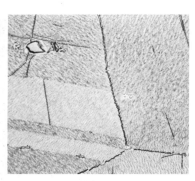

**Fig. 97** U-700, heat treated same as Fig. 95, then held 1500 h at 870 °C (1600 °F). Needles of σ phase are longer and better resolved than in Fig. 96. Sigma formation adversely affects high-temperature tensile properties. Kalling's reagent 2. 500×

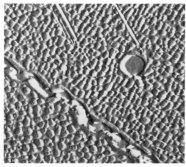

**Fig. 98** Replica electron micrograph of U-700, solution annealed same as Fig. 97 and aged 1500 h at 815 °C (1500 °F). Structure is acicular σ phase, $M_{23}C_6$ carbide at grain boundary, and γ′ within the γ matrix grains. HCl, ethanol, and $H_2O_2$. 4500×

**Fig. 99** Replica electron micrograph of U-700, solution annealed same as Fig. 97 and aged 24 h at 980 °C (1800 °F). Precipitated carbide at grain boundaries and γ′ within grains of the γ solid-solution matrix. HCl, ethanol, $CuCl_2$, and $H_2O_2$. 4500×

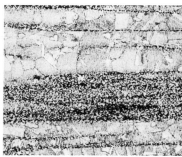

**Fig. 100** U-710 bar, solution annealed 2 h at 1120 °C (2050 °F), aged 1.5 h at 1040 °C (1900 °F), and air cooled. Longitudinal section shows recrystallized bands (light) and bands containing residual primary γ′. Kalling's reagent. 100×

**Fig. 101** U-710 bar, solution annealed 4 h at 1175 °C (2150 °F) and air cooled. Structure is dispersed primary MC carbide and $M_3B_2$ boride in a γ matrix. γ′ is in solution. Kalling's reagent. 100×

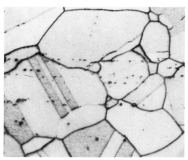

**Fig. 102** U-710 bar, solution annealed same as Fig. 101, aged 24 h at 845 °C (1550 °F), air cooled, aged 16 h at 760 °C (1400 °F), and air cooled. $M_{23}C_6$ precipitate along grain and twin boundaries. Kalling's reagent. 100×

**Fig. 103** 50Cr-50Ni sheet, 3.2 mm (0.125 in.) thick, annealed at 980 °C (1800 °F) for 1 h. Structure contains particles of chromium-rich phase (dark) and a nickel-rich phase (light). Electrolytic: 1% $H_2CrO_4$. 500×

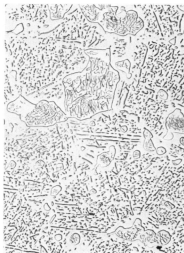

**Fig. 104** Same alloy as Fig. 103, annealed at 980 °C (1800 °F) for 120 h. Structure has same constituents as Fig. 103, but shows effects of long-time annealing on phase distribution. Electrolytic: 1% $H_2CrO_4$. 500×

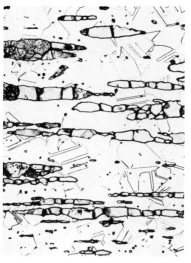

**Fig. 105** 50Cr-50Ni, hot rolled, annealed at 1205 °C (2200 °F), and water quenched. Chromium-rich phase (dark) is elongated in the rolling direction. The light matrix is a nickel-rich phase. Electrolytic: 1% $H_2CrO_4$. 200×

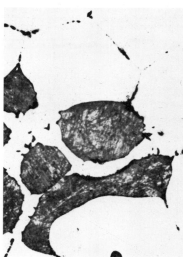

**Fig. 106** Same material as Fig. 105, hot rolled and annealed at 1315 °C (2400 °F), then water quenched. High annealing temperature caused agglomeration of chromium-rich phase (dark). Nickel-rich phase is light. Electrolytic: 1% $H_2CrO_4$. 200×

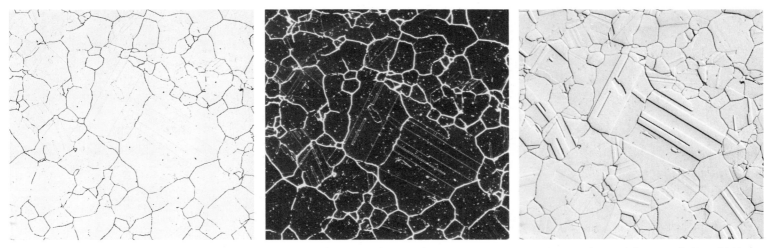

**Fig. 107, 108, 109** Waspaloy (37 HRC), solution annealed 4 h at 1035 °C (1900 °F), water quenched, aged 4 h at 845 °C (1550 °F), air cooled, aged 16 h at 760 °C (1400 °F), and air cooled. Fig. 107: bright-field illumination. Fig. 108: dark-field illumination. Fig. 109: differential interference contrast. Glyceregia. 100×

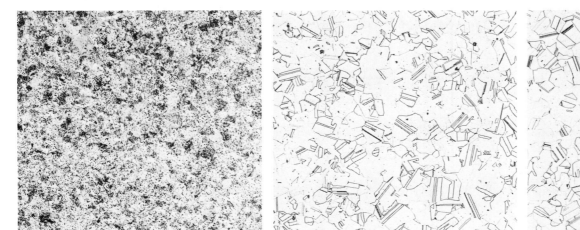

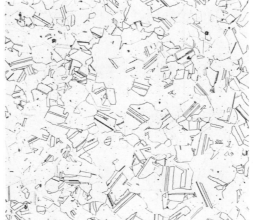

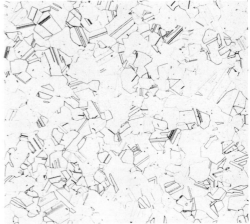

**Fig. 110** Waspaloy (265 HV), solution annealed 4 h at 1010 °C (1850 °F) and water quenched. Compare with Fig. 111 and 112. Glyceregia. 200×

**Fig. 111** Same material as Fig. 110, solution annealed 4 h at 1035 °C (1900 °F) and water quenched. 223 HV. Compare with Fig. 112. Glyceregia. 100×

**Fig. 112** Waspaloy, solution annealed 4 h at 1065 °C (1950 °F) and water quenched. Higher temperatures caused increased grain size, complete solutioning, and decreased hardness. Compare with Fig. 110 and 111. Glyceregia. 100×

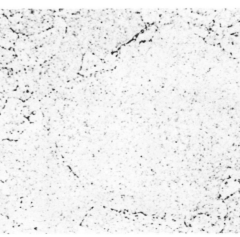

**Fig. 113** Waspaloy (42 HRC), solution annealed 4 h at 1010 °C (1850 °F), water quenched, aged 4 h at 845 °C (1550 °F), air cooled, aged 16 h at 760 °C (1400 °F), and air cooled. Glyceregia. 200×

**Fig. 114** Same alloy and processing as Fig. 113, but at a higher magnification showing residual γ' from hot working that was not dissolved. Glyceregia. 1000×

**Fig. 115** Same material and processing as Fig. 113, but tint etched to color matrix phase. See also Fig. 114. 50 mL HCl, 50 mL $H_2O$, and 1 g $K_2S_2O_5$. 100×

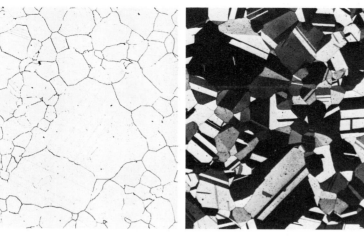

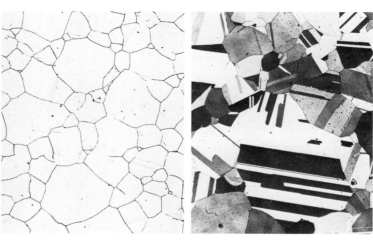

**Fig. 116, 117** Waspaloy (37 HRC), solution annealed 4 h at 1035 °C (1900 °F), water quenched, aged 4 h at 845 °C (1550 °F), air cooled, aged 16 h at 760 °C (1400 °F), and air cooled. Fig. 116: etched in glyceregia. Fig. 117: tint etched in 50 mL HCl, 50 mL $H_2O$, and 1 g $K_2S_2O_5$. Both 100×

**Fig. 118, 119** Waspaloy (35 to 36 HRC), solution annealed 4 h at 1065 °C (1950 °F), water quenched, aged 4 h at 845 °C (1550 °F), air cooled, aged 16 h at 760 °C (1400 °F), and air cooled. Fig. 118: etched in glyceregia. Fig. 119: tint etched using 50 mL HCl, 50 mL $H_2O$, 3 g $NH_4F \cdot HF$, and 1.5 g $K_2S_2O_5$. Both 100×

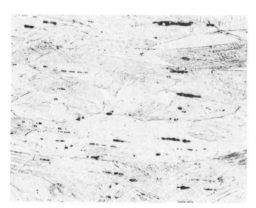

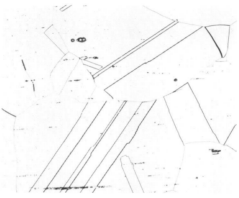

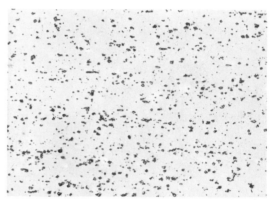

**Fig. 120** Elgiloy, cold drawn to 50 to 55% reduction, showing grains and dispersed stringers of carbide elongated in the rolling direction. Compare with Fig. 121. HCl, $HNO_3$, and $FeCl_3$. 250×

**Fig. 121** Same material and drawing process as Fig. 120, solution annealed 1 h at 1230 °C (2250 °F) and air cooled. The cold-worked grains have been fully recrystallized. HCl, $HNO_3$, and $FeCl_3$. 250×

**Fig. 122** S-816 alloy as-forged bar. The randomly dispersed carbide particles in the solid-solution matrix are primarily NbC. The high hardness of the carbides has caused them to show in relief. See also Fig. 123 to 125. As-polished. 100×

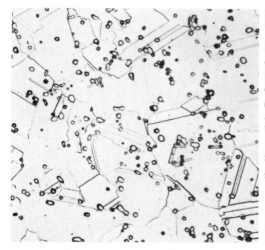

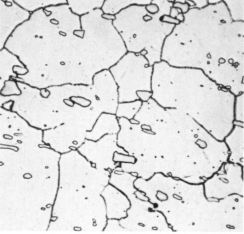

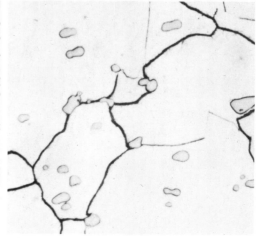

**Fig. 123** S-816 (20 HRC), solution annealed 1 h at 1175 °C (2150 °F) and water quenched. Particles of NbC are dispersed in the fcc matrix. There is no grain-boundary precipitate. 92 mL HCl, 5 mL $H_2SO_4$, and 3 mL $HNO_3$. 500×

**Fig. 124** Same material and annealing treatment as Fig. 123, but aged 16 h at 760 °C (1400 °F) and air cooled. Grain-boundary precipitate (primarily $Cr_{23}C_6$) and dispersed NbC particles in the fcc matrix. 30 HRC. 92 mL HCl, 5 mL $H_2SO_4$, and 3 mL $HNO_3$. 500×

**Fig. 125** S-816 (35 HRC), solution annealed 1 h at 1290 °C (2350 °F), water quenched, aged 16 h at 760 °C (1400 °F), and air cooled. Structure is dispersed NbC particles and grain-boundary $Cr_{23}C_6$ in the fcc matrix. See also Fig. 126 to 128. 92 mL HCl, 5 mL $H_2SO_4$, and 3 mL $HNO_3$. 1000×

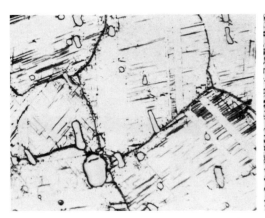

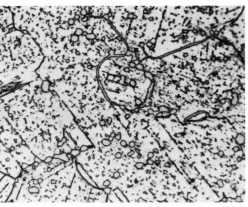

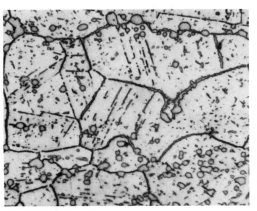

**Fig. 126** Same alloy and condition as Fig. 125, creep-rupture tested at 650 °C (1200 °F) for 3992 h at 276 MPa (40 ksi). Precipitation of $M_{23}C_6$ at grain boundaries and within grains has increased. The dispersed large particles are NbC. 39 HRC. 92 mL HCl, 5 mL $H_2SO_4$, and 3 mL $HNO_3$. 1000×

**Fig. 127** Same alloy and condition as Fig. 125, creep-rupture tested 25 500 h at 730 °C (1350 °F) and 172 MPa (25 ksi). Particles of $M_{23}C_6$ at grain boundaries and within grains have coalesced. Dispersed large particles are NbC. 38.5 HRC. 92 mL HCl, 5 mL $H_2SO_4$, and 3 mL $HNO_3$. 1000×

**Fig. 128** Same alloy and condition as Fig. 125, creep-rupture tested 19 650 h at 815 °C (1500 °F) and 86 MPa (12 500 psi). Coalescence of $M_{23}C_6$ at grain boundaries and within grains has increased. Large particles are NbC. 34 HRC. 92 mL HCl, 5 mL $H_2SO_4$, and 3 mL $HNO_3$. 1000×

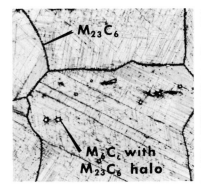

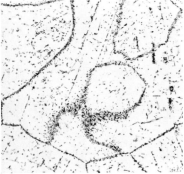

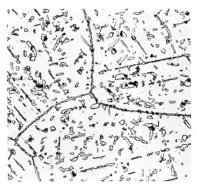

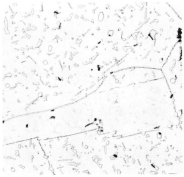

**Fig. 129** Haynes 25 (L-605), solution annealed at 1205 °C (2200 °F) and aged 3400 h at 650 °C (1200 °F). Structure is $M_6C$ and $M_{23}C_6$ carbides in a mixed fcc and hcp matrix. Electrolytic: HCl and $H_2O_2$. 500×

**Fig. 130** Haynes 25 (L-605), solution annealed same as Fig. 129 and aged 3400 h at 815 °C (1500 °F). Structure is precipitates of $M_6C$ and "$Co_2W$" intermetallic in a fcc matrix. Electrolytic: HCl and $H_2O_2$. 500×

**Fig. 131** Haynes 25 (L-605), solution annealed same as Fig. 129 and aged 3400 h at 870 °C (1600 °F). Structure is the same as Fig. 130. Electrolytic: HCl and $H_2O_2$. 500×

**Fig. 132** Haynes 25 (L-605), solution annealed same as Fig. 129 and aged 3400 h at 925 °C (1700 °F). Structure consists of $M_6C$ (primary) and "$Co_2W$" intermetallic (secondary) in a fcc matrix. Electrolytic: HCl and $H_2O_2$. 500×

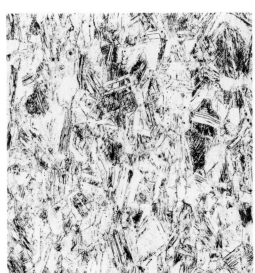

**Fig. 133, 134, 135** Haynes 25 (L-605, 486 HV), solution annealed and cold worked to 35% reduction. Longitudinal section. Fig. 133: bright-field illumination. Fig. 134: dark-field illumination. Fig. 135: differential interference contrast. All etched with 15 mL HCl, 10 mL acetic acid, 5 mL $HNO_3$, and 2 drops glycerol. 100×

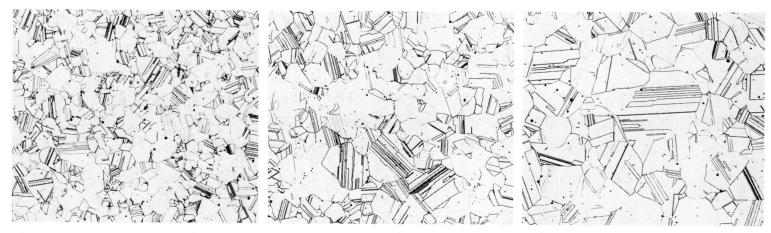

**Fig. 136, 137, 138** Haynes 25 (L-605), cold worked same as Fig. 133 to 135 and given different solution-annealing treatments. Grain size increases with increasing annealing temperature and time. Fig. 136: solution annealed 2.5 min at 1150 °C (2100 °F); 261 HV. Fig. 137: solution annealed 4.25 min at 1150 °C (2100 °F); 254 HV. Fig. 138: solution annealed 2.5 min at 1205 °C (2200 °F); 246 HV. 15 mL HCl, 10 mL acetic acid, 5 mL HNO₃, and 2 drops glycerol. 100×

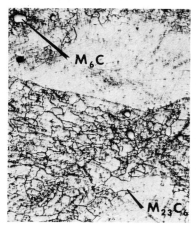

**Fig. 139** Haynes 188, cold rolled 50%, heated to 815 °C (1500 °F) for 1 h and water quenched. The partly recrystallized structure contains M₆C and M₂₃C₆ carbides in a fcc matrix. Electrolytic: HCl and H₂O₂. 1000×

**Fig. 140** Haynes 188, cold rolled 20% and solution annealed at 1175 °C (2150 °F) for 10 min, then water quenched. The fully annealed structure consists of M₆C particles in a fcc matrix. Electrolytic: HCl and H₂O₂. 500×

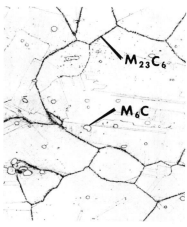

**Fig. 141** Haynes 188, solution annealed at 1175 °C (2150 °F) and aged 3400 h at 650 °C (1200 °F). Structure is M₆C and M₂₃C₆ particles in a fcc matrix. Electrolytic: HCl and H₂O₂. 500×

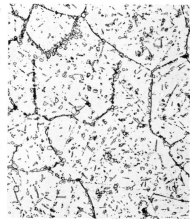

**Fig. 142** Haynes 188, solution annealed at 1175 °C (2150 °F) and aged 6244 h at 870 °C (1600 °F). Structure is M₂₃C₆, Laves phase, and probably M₆C in a fcc matrix. Electrolytic: HCl and H₂O₂. 500×

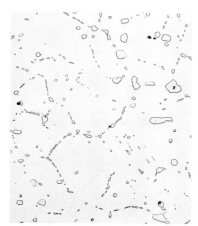

**Fig. 143** Haynes 188, solution annealed at 1175 °C (2150 °F), aged 6244 h at 980 °C (1800 °F). Structure consists of M₆C and M₂₃C₆, and probably Laves phase, in a fcc matrix. Electrolytic: HCl and H₂O₂. 500×

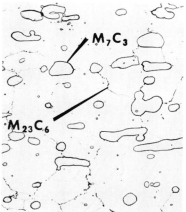

**Fig. 144** Stellite 6B, solution annealed at 1230 °C (2250 °F) and aged 8 h at 900 °C (1650 °F). Structure is M₇C₃ and M₂₃C₆ carbides in a fcc matrix. Electrolytic: HCl and H₂O₂. 500×

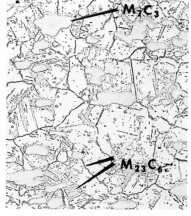

**Fig. 145** Stellite 6B, solution annealed at 1230 °C (2250 °F) and aged 8 h at 900 °C (1650 °F). M₇C₃ and M₂₃C₆ carbides in a predominantly fcc matrix with some hcp crystals. Electrolytic: HCl and H₂O₂. 500×

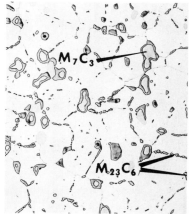

**Fig. 146** Stellite 6B, solution annealed at 1230 °C (2250 °F) and aged 8 h at 1150 °C (2100 °F). Dark areas around primary M₇C₃ show it changing to M₂₃C₆. Matrix is fcc. Electrolytic: 2% H₂CrO₄; KMnO₄ stain. 500×

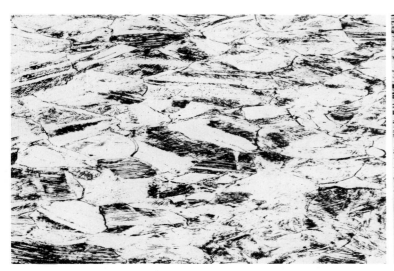 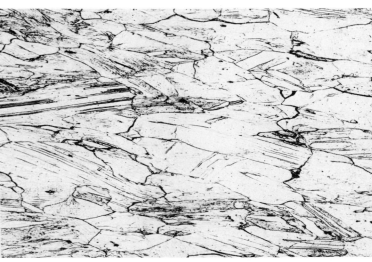

**Fig. 147** MP35N (492 HV), solution annealed 1 h at 1065 °C (1950 °F), air cooled, and cold worked to 51% reduction. Longitudinal section. See also Fig. 148. 15 mL HCl, 10 mL acetic acid, 5 mL HNO₃, and 2 drops glycerol. 100×

**Fig. 148** MP35N (565 HV), solution annealed same as Fig. 147, then aged 4 h at 535 °C (1000 °F) to increase hardness. Longitudinal section. 15 mL HCl, 10 mL acetic acid, 5 mL HNO₃, and 2 drops glycerol. 100×

# Heat-Resistant Casting Alloys

HEAT-RESISTANT CASTING ALLOYS discussed in this article include iron-, nickel-, and cobalt-base alloys that contain enough chromium to provide oxidation and sulfidation resistance. The more common grades of iron- and nickel-base alloys have been given Alloy Casting Institute (ACI) designations in the H-series (Table 1). Nominal compositions of cobalt-base and additional nickel-base heat-resistant alloys for which micrographs are presented in this article are given in Table 2. Additional information on the properties and selection of these materials can be found in Volume 1 (Fe-Cr-Ni) and Volume 3 (nickel- and cobalt-base) of the 9th Edition of *Metals Handbook*.

## Specimen Preparation

Although the three classes of materials discussed in this article cover a wide range of chemical compositions, microstructural constituents, and mechanical properties, the metallographic preparation procedures are similar. These methods are the same as those used for equivalent wrought grades and are explained in detail in the article "Wrought Heat-Resistant Alloys" in this Volume.

The following procedure is typical and has proved acceptable. First, the specimen is removed from the casting using an abrasive cutoff wheel, without allowing the specimen to overheat during cutting. The surfaces are smoothed on a belt grinder, taking precaution against overheating of the specimen. The specimen is then mounted in compression-mounting materials or cold-setting resins (see the article "Mounting of Specimens" in this Volume). It may be necessary to view the microstructure at the extreme edge of the specimen. Optimum results can be achieved when the edge to be examined is plated with nickel before mounting.

Grinding proceeds using water-cooled 120-, 320-, 400-, then 600-grit silicon carbide paper at 150 to 160 rpm. The specimen should be washed with alcohol and dried using hot air. Rough polishing is performed using 6-$\mu$m diamond paste, a napless nylon cloth, and an oil-base lubricant. The specimen is then washed thoroughly with liquid soap and water and rinsed with propanol (isopropyl alcohol). Final polish is carried out using 1-$\mu$m diamond paste on a medium-nap

synthetic suede cloth, followed by 0.05-$\mu$m $\gamma$-Al$_2$O$_3$ on a medium-nap synthetic suede cloth on a wheel or a vibratory polisher. Electropolishing can also be used for final polishing.

Etchants used when examining cast nickel- and cobalt-base alloys are the same as those used for wrought alloy examination (see Tables 2 and 4 in the article "Wrought Heat-Resistant Alloys" in this Volume). The etchants used for the Fe-Cr-Ni alloys are given in Table 3. They are classified as (1) delineating etchants (usually acid), which provide contrast and reveal general structure, (2) staining or film-forming etchants (alkaline), and (3) solutions for electrolytic etching.

**Delineating Etchants.** The effects of 19 etchants on 11 Fe-Cr-Ni alloys containing 0.02 to 0.18% C have been documented (Ref 1). Vilella's reagent proved superior for removing disturbed metal (using several etch and polish cycles) and for outlining $\sigma$ phase, carbide particles, and ferrite. Etching for 1 min at room temperature was recommended.

Vilella's reagent will serve the same purposes when applied to the higher-carbon heat-resistant casting alloys (see Fig. 3 to 5).

Glyceregia, the most widely used delineating etchant, is also used for etch and polish cycles. Marble's reagent and aqua regia are sometimes used, but to a far lesser extent than glyceregia. Hydrochloric acid (HCl) (50%) is sometimes used for outlining ferrite. It may be followed by etching with a staining etchant (see Fig. 6 and 7).

**Staining etchants,** or tint etchants, form films of reaction products on the surface of the specimen. The color of these films depends in part on film thickness, which is controlled by etching time, temperature, and the etchant used. The etchants are generally aqueous solutions of potassium hydroxide (KOH) or sodium hydroxide (NaOH) with an oxidizing agent added. Picrates, potassium permanganate (KMnO$_4$), hydrogen peroxide (H$_2$O$_2$), and ferricyanides are used as oxidizing agents.

## Table 1  Compositions of Fe-Cr-Ni heat-resistant casting alloys
See Fig. 3 to 59 for representative microstructures

| Grade | Type | C | Mn, max | Si, max | P, max | S, max | Cr | Ni | Mo, max(a) |
|---|---|---|---|---|---|---|---|---|---|
| HF | 19 chromium, 9 nickel | 0.20-0.40 | 2.00 | 2.00 | 0.04 | 0.04 | 18.0-23.0 | 8.0-12.0 | 0.50 |
| HH | 25 chromium, 12 nickel | 0.20-0.50 | 2.00 | 2.00 | 0.04 | 0.04 | 24.0-28.0 | 11.0-14.0 | 0.50 |
| HI | 28 chromium, 15 nickel | 0.20-0.50 | 2.00 | 2.00 | 0.04 | 0.04 | 26.0-30.0 | 14.0-18.0 | 0.50 |
| HK | 25 chromium, 20 nickel | 0.20-0.60 | 2.00 | 2.00 | 0.04 | 0.04 | 24.0-28.0 | 18.0-22.0 | 0.50 |
| HE | 29 chromium, 9 nickel | 0.20-0.50 | 2.00 | 2.00 | 0.04 | 0.04 | 26.0-30.0 | 8.0-11.0 | 0.50 |
| HT | 15 chromium, 35 nickel | 0.35-0.75 | 2.00 | 2.50 | 0.04 | 0.04 | 15.0-19.0 | 33.0-37.0 | 0.50 |
| HU | 19 chromium, 39 nickel | 0.35-0.75 | 2.00 | 2.50 | 0.04 | 0.04 | 17.0-21.0 | 37.0-41.0 | 0.50 |
| HW | 12 chromium, 60 nickel | 0.35-0.75 | 2.00 | 2.50 | 0.04 | 0.04 | 10.0-14.0 | 58.0-62.0 | 0.50 |
| HX | 17 chromium, 66 nickel | 0.35-0.75 | 2.00 | 2.50 | 0.04 | 0.04 | 15.0-19.0 | 64.0-68.0 | 0.50 |
| HC | 28 chromium | 0.50 max | 1.00 | 2.00 | 0.04 | 0.04 | 26.0-30.0 | 4.0 max | 0.50 |
| HD | 28 chromium, 5 nickel | 0.50 max | 1.50 | 2.00 | 0.04 | 0.04 | 26.0-30.0 | 4.0-7.0 | 0.50 |
| HL | 29 chromium, 20 nickel | 0.20-0.60 | 2.00 | 2.00 | 0.04 | 0.04 | 28.0-32.0 | 18.0-22.0 | 0.50 |
| HN | 20 chromium, 25 nickel | 0.20-0.50 | 2.00 | 2.00 | 0.04 | 0.04 | 19.0-23.0 | 23.0-27.0 | 0.50 |
| HP | 26 chromium, 35 nickel | 0.35-0.75 | 2.00 | 2.50 | 0.04 | 0.04 | 24-28 | 33-37 | 0.50 |

(a) Castings having a specified molybdenum range agreed upon by the manufacturer and the purchaser may also be furnished under these specifications.
Source: ASTM A 297

**Table 2  Nominal compositions of nickel-base and cobalt-base heat-resistant casting alloys**
See Fig. 60 to 118 for nickel-base cast microstructures and Fig. 119 to 142 for cobalt-base castings

| Alloy | C | Cr | Mo | Nb | Ti | Al | B | Zr | Fe | W | V | Ta | Re | Hf | Ni | Co |
|---|---|---|---|---|---|---|---|---|---|---|---|---|---|---|---|---|
| **Nickel-base alloys** | | | | | | | | | | | | | | | | |
| Alloy 713C . . . . . . . . | 0.12 | 12.5 | 4.2 | 2 | 0.80 | 6.1 | 0.012 | 0.10 | 2.5 max | . . . | . . . | . . . | . . . | . . . | rem | . . . |
| Alloy 718 . . . . . . . . . | 0.04 | 19 | 3.05 | 5.13 + Ta | 0.90 | 0.50 | . . . | . . . | 18.5 | . . . | . . . | . . . | . . . | . . . | rem | . . . |
| B-1900 . . . . . . . . . . . | 0.10 | 8 | 6 | 0.1 max | 1 | 6 | 0.015 | 0.08 | 0.35 max | 0.1 max | . . . | 4.3 | . . . | . . . | rem | 10 |
| Hastelloy B . . . . . . . | 0.10 | 0.6 | 28 | . . . | . . . | . . . | . . . | . . . | 5 | . . . | 0.30 | . . . | . . . | . . . | rem | 2.5 max |
| Hastelloy C . . . . . . . | 0.07 | 16 | 17 | . . . | . . . | . . . | . . . | . . . | 5 | 4 | . . . | . . . | . . . | . . . | rem | 2.5 max |
| IN-100 . . . . . . . . . . . | 0.15 | 10 | 3 | . . . | 4.7 | 5.5 | 0.015 | 0.06 | . . . | . . . | 1 | . . . | . . . | . . . | rem | 15 |
| IN-738 . . . . . . . . . . . | 0.17 | 16 | 1.75 | 0.9 | 3.4 | 3.4 | 0.01 | 0.10 | 0.50 max | 2.6 | . . . | 1.75 | . . . | . . . | rem | 8.5 |
| MAR-M 246 . . . . . . . | 0.15 | 9 | 2.5 | . . . | 1.5 | 5.5 | 0.015 | 0.05 | . . . | 10 | . . . | 1.5 | . . . | . . . | rem | 10 |
| TRW-NASA VIA . . . | 0.13 | 6.1 | 2 | 0.5 | 1 | 5.4 | 0.02 | 0.13 | . . . | 5.5 | . . . | 9 | 0.2 | 0.43 | rem | 7.5 |
| U-700 . . . . . . . . . . . . | 0.15 max | 15 | 5.2 | . . . | 3.5 | 4.25 | 0.05 max | . . . | 1 max | . . . | . . . | . . . | . . . | . . . | rem | 18.5 |
| **Cobalt-base alloys** | | | | | | | | | | | | | | | | |
| Haynes 21 . . . . . . . . | 0.25 | 27 | 5 | . . . | . . . | . . . | . . . | . . . | 1 | . . . | . . . | . . . | . . . | . . . | 3 | rem |
| Haynes 31 . . . . . . . . | 0.50 | 25.5 | . . . | . . . | . . . | . . . | 0.01 | . . . | 2 | 7.5 | . . . | . . . | . . . | . . . | 10.5 | rem |
| Haynes 151 . . . . . . . | 0.50 | 20 | . . . | . . . | . . . | . . . | 0.05 | . . . | . . . | 12.7 | . . . | . . . | . . . | . . . | . . . | rem |
| MAR-M 302 . . . . . . | 0.85 | 21.5 | . . . | . . . | . . . | . . . | 0.005 | 0.20 | . . . | 10 | . . . | 9 | . . . | . . . | . . . | rem |
| MAR-M 509 . . . . . . | 0.60 | 24 | . . . | . . . | 0.20 | . . . | . . . | 0.50 | . . . | 7 | . . . | 3.5 | . . . | . . . | 10 | rem |
| WI-52 . . . . . . . . . . . | 0.45 | 21 | . . . | 2 | . . . | . . . | . . . | . . . | 2 | 11 | . . . | . . . | . . . | . . . | 1.0 max | rem |
| 98 M2 Stellite . . . . . . . . . . | 1.7-2.2 | 28-32 | . . . | . . . | . . . | . . . | 0.7-1.5 | . . . | . . . | 17-20 | 3.7-4.7 | . . . | . . . | . . . | 2-5 | rem |

Murakami's reagent, which contains KOH with potassium ferricyanide [$K_3Fe(CN)_6$] as the oxidizing agent, is a versatile staining etchant. By staining in different tints, it permits differentiation of several types of carbide and σ phase. Murakami's reagent is used cold, warm, or boiling to obtain various effects, but it must be used with discrimination. Because the response of the reagent indicates sensitivity to the composition of the phase being stained, a given constituent does not respond identically when it appears in alloys of different composition.

Murakami's reagent has several modifications (Ref 1-3). Emmanuel's version (Ref 2) contains 30 g $K_3Fe(CN)_6$, 30 g KOH, and 60 mL $H_2O$. It will attack σ phase with little effect on carbide particles; Murakami's reagent stains carbide particles, but does not always stain σ phase.

Stain films can crack. Crack indications should be checked by repolishing the specimen lightly or by giving it an acid dip to see if the cracks are removed along with the stain. Detailed information on staining etchants can be found in the article "Color Metallography" in this Volume.

**Electrolytic etching,** when controlled by an electronic timer, offers precision and reproducibility. The specimen to be etched is usually made the anode; stainless steel, the cathode. The current can be supplied by one or more dry-cell batteries wired in series to provide outputs of 1.5, 3.0, 4.5, and 6.0 V. Current density will range from less than 0.16 to 2 A/cm² or more (<1 to ≥13 A/in.²).

Unmounted specimens are held with stainless steel tongs. If the specimen is mounted in a nonconducting material, the electrical connection can be conveniently made using a brass machine screw that contacts the underside of the specimen through a tapped hole. The electric current at the anode surface promotes oxidation and therefore serves in place of the oxidizing agents that are added to hydroxide solutions.

A study was made of various solutions for electrolytic etching of alloys in which σ phase is found. The final recommendation was to outline the structure by etching with Vilella's reagent, then to etch electrolytically in 10 N KOH just long enough to color the σ phase, but not the carbide particles, and finally to etch electrolytically in concentrated ammonium hydroxide ($NH_4OH$).

In a laboratory (Ref 5, 6) where the Fe-Cr-Ni alloys were investigated, glyceregia was preferred for revealing general structure, followed by electrolytic etching in 10% sodium cyanide (NaCN) at a current density of 0.16 A/cm² (1 A/in.²). After 1 s, carbide particles were outlined, but σ phase was not revealed; after 5 s, carbide particles were heavily outlined, and σ phase was stained blue or tan. Oxalic acid (10%) was also investigated. After 1 to 5 s with a 6-V current, carbides and σ phase were outlined. Ten percent chromic acid ($CrO_3$), when used at 2.0 A/cm² (13 A/in.²), extracted σ phase in 2 s and heavily outlined the carbides. Potassium hydroxide (1 N) used for up to 1 s with a 1.5-V current blackened σ without outlining other phases.

**Etching Procedure.** A safe procedure for etching the Fe-Cr-Ni casting alloys begins by repeating the etch and polish cycle until disturbed metal has been removed. If Vilella's reagent is used, a hood is not needed. Etching should proceed for 15 s in cold 50% HCl to reveal ferrite. This should be repeated if necessary until ferrite is clearly outlined or until it is evident that there is no ferrite. If the ferrite present contains precipitated carbide particles, it may become rough or mottled. Sigma phase and carbide particles will not be attacked, although σ phase will sometimes become evident because it will appear white and shiny against the faintly stained austenite.

If the HCl etch has indicated the possible presence of ferrite, a magnetic etch should be used (see the section "Identification of Ferrite by Magnetic Etching" in this article). After the etch in HCl or after repolishing and a dip in HCl acid, the specimen is etched in fresh Murakami's reagent for 15 s at room temperature. Following inspection, the etch should be repeated if necessary until carbides are satisfactorily colored. Several fields should be observed and indexed so that they can be found again.

Etching in hot Murakami's reagent (70 °C, or 160 °F, to boiling, as indicated by experience) then proceeds for 15 s, after which the specimen is rinsed in water, then alcohol, and then dried in a blast of warm air to ensure uniform staining. The same fields mentioned previously should be observed. Further etching may be necessary. Overexposing the specimen to the etchant can make the films too thick and can result in the deposition of small crystals on the surface.

Some of the above steps can be omitted in etching specimens of certain alloys. For example, in etching alloys HN, HP, HT, HU,

**Table 3   Etchants for microscopic examination of Fe-Cr-Ni heat-resistant casting alloys**

| Etchant | Composition | Comments |
|---|---|---|
| **Etchants for delineating general structure** | | |
| Aqua regia . . . . . . . . . . . . . . . . . . . . . . . . . . . . . . . . . . | 20 mL HNO$_3$ and 60 mL HCl | Immerse specimen. |
| Glyceregia . . . . . . . . . . . . . . . . . . . . . . . . . . . . . . . . | 10 mL HNO$_3$, 20-50 mL HCl, 30 mL glycerol | Immerse specimen; use a hood. |
| Hydrochloric acid (50%) . . . . . . . . . . . . . . . . . . . . | 50 mL HCl and 50 mL H$_2$O | Outlines ferrite; immerse specimen |
| Marble's reagent . . . . . . . . . . . . . . . . . . . . . . . . . . | 10 g CuSO$_4$ (copper sulfate), 50 mL HCl, 50 mL H$_2$O | Immerse specimen. |
| Vilella's reagent . . . . . . . . . . . . . . . . . . . . . . . . . . . | 1 g picric acid, 5 mL HCl, 100 mL ethanol | Immerse specimen. |
| Kalling's reagent . . . . . . . . . . . . . . . . . . . . . . . . . . | 1.5 g CuCl$_2$ (copper chloride), 33 mL ethanol, 33 mL H$_2$O, 33 mL HCl | Immerse or swab specimen. |
| Kalling's reagent 2 . . . . . . . . . . . . . . . . . . . . . . . . . | 5 g CuCl$_2$, 100 mL ethanol, 100 mL HCl | Same as above |
| HCl, ethanol, CuCl$_2$, H$_2$O$_2$ . . . . . . . . . . . . . . . | 35 mL HCl, 65 mL ethanol, 1 g CuCl$_2$, 7 drops 30% H$_2$O$_2$ | Same as above |
| HCl, ethanol, H$_2$O$_2$ . . . . . . . . . . . . . . . . . . . . . | 35 mL HCl, 65 mL ethanol, 7 drops 30% H$_2$O$_2$ | Same as above |
| HCl, methanol, CuCl$_2$ . . . . . . . . . . . . . . . . . . . . | 2 g CuCl$_2$, 40 mL HCl, 40-80 mL methanol | Same as above |
| HCl, methanol, FeCl$_3$ . . . . . . . . . . . . . . . . . . . . | 5 g FeCl$_3$ (ferric chloride), 15 mL HCl, 60 mL methanol | Same as above |
| **Etchants for staining or film-forming** | | |
| Alkaline hydrogen peroxide . . . . . . . . . . . . . . . . | 25 mL NH$_4$OH, 50 mL 3% H$_2$O$_2$, 25 mL H$_2$O | Ordinarily used after a delineating etchant; immerse specimen |
| Alkaline potassium ferricyanide . . . . . . . . . . . . | 10 g K$_3$Fe(CN)$_6$, 10 g NaOH, 100 mL H$_2$O | Same as above |
| Alkaline potassium permanganate . . . . . . . . . . | 4 g NaOH, 10 g KMnO$_4$, 85 mL H$_2$O | Same as above |
| Alkaline sodium picrate . . . . . . . . . . . . . . . . . . . | 2 g picric acid, 25 g NaOH, 100 mL H$_2$O | Same as above |
| Emmanuel's reagent . . . . . . . . . . . . . . . . . . . . . . | 30 g K$_3$Fe(CN)$_6$, 30 g KOH, 60 g H$_2$O | Attacks $\sigma$ phase with little or no effect on carbide particles; immerse specimen |
| Murakami's reagent . . . . . . . . . . . . . . . . . . . . . . | 10 g K$_3$Fe(CN)$_6$, 10 g KOH, 100 mL H$_2$O | Stains carbide particles without staining $\sigma$ phase(a); immerse specimen |
| **Solutions for electrolytic etching** | | |
| Ammonium hydroxide . . . . . . . . . . . . . . . . . . . . | Concentrated NH$_4$OH | Final electrolytic etch after etching in Vilella's reagent and in 10 $N$ KOH (electrolytic) |
| Cadmium acetate . . . . . . . . . . . . . . . . . . . . . . . . | 10 g cadmium acetate and 100 mL H$_2$O | Attacks (Cr,Fe) $_{23}$C$_6$ carbide particles |
| Chromic acid . . . . . . . . . . . . . . . . . . . . . . . . . . . . | 2-10 g CrO$_3$ and 100 mL H$_2$O | Outlines carbide particles; extracts $\sigma$ phase |
| HCl . . . . . . . . . . . . . . . . . . . . . . . . . . . . . . . . . . . . . | 5-10 mL HCl and 100 mL H$_2$O | Use at 3 V, 2-10 s. |
| HCl and CrO$_3$ . . . . . . . . . . . . . . . . . . . . . . . . . . | 1 g CrO$_3$ and 140 mL HCl | Add HCl to CrO$_3$; use under hood at 3 V, 2-10 s. |
| HNO$_3$ . . . . . . . . . . . . . . . . . . . . . . . . . . . . . . . . . | 50 mL HNO$_3$ and 50 mL H$_2$O | Use at 2 V. |
| H$_3$PO$_4$ . . . . . . . . . . . . . . . . . . . . . . . . . . . . . . . | 4-12 mL H$_3$PO$_4$ and 100 mL H$_2$O | Use at 1-8 V, 5-10 s. |
| Lead acetate (2 $N$) . . . . . . . . . . . . . . . . . . . . . . . | 38 g Pb(C$_2$H$_3$O$_2$)$_2$ · 3H$_2$O and distilled H$_2$O to make 100 mL | Stains austenite, then $\sigma$ phase, then carbide particles; 1.5 V for 30 s |
| Oxalic acid . . . . . . . . . . . . . . . . . . . . . . . . . . . . . . | 10 g oxalic acid and 100 mL H$_2$O | Outlines carbide and $\sigma$; 6 V, 1 to 5 s |
| Potassium hydroxide (1 $N$) . . . . . . . . . . . . . . . | 5.6 g KOH and 100 mL H$_2$O | Blackens $\sigma$ phase without outlining other phases; 1.5 V for 1 s |
| Potassium hydroxide (10 $N$) . . . . . . . . . . . . . . | 56 g KOH and 100 mL H$_2$O | Intermediate etch between Vilella's and NH$_4$OH (electrolytic) |
| Sodium cyanide(b) . . . . . . . . . . . . . . . . . . . . . . . | 10 g NaCN and 100 mL H$_2$O | Used after glyceregia; outlines carbide particles, stains $\sigma$ phase; use at 0.16 A/cm$^2$ (1 A/in.$^2$) for 1-5 s, under hood |

(a) Sometimes $\sigma$ phase is stained. Behavior must be established on a given composition. (b) Use extreme caution; avoid skin contact, ingestion, or inhalation of vapors.

HW, and HX, it is usually adequate to etch and polish until the disturbed metal has been removed and to etch in hot Murakami's reagent. The specimen should be rinsed in water, then alcohol, and then dried in a warm air blast (see Fig. 54 to 59).

## Identification of Constituents

Identification of secondary phases in Fe-Cr-Ni alloys may be quite difficult without the appropriate constitutional diagram, a complete chemical analysis, and the thermal history of the alloy. Even with this information, if a phase appears as a fine dustlike or dotlike precipitate or if the amount is so low that x-ray diffraction techniques are ineffective, identification will be uncertain. Fine precipitates, which in these alloys could be one of the carbides or $\sigma$ phase, are identified by inference. In identifying $\sigma$ phase, the sensitivity of the x-ray diffraction method can be increased somewhat by etching the matrix to

make $\sigma$ stand in relief. However, for these alloys, x-ray diffraction often fails to give positive identification, because the two common types of carbide particles and $\sigma$ phase have many diffraction lines that overlap or coincide (Ref 7).

If the constituents are large enough to show staining, they can be distinguished using microscopy. It is helpful to have a series of reference specimens of known composition and heat treatment to be used for confirming response to etching.

The Cr$_7$C$_3$ carbide is likely to appear in the higher-carbon Fe-Cr-Ni alloys as spinelike crystals of roughly hexagonal cross section, frequently with a hole in the center. It stains well with Murakami's reagent. In the alloys with 0.20 to 0.75% C, the Cr$_7$C$_3$ carbide is likely to be the eutectic carbide.

Although the cubic (Fe,Cr)$_{23}$C$_6$ carbide usually precipitates as fine particles, it can occur also in the form of grain-boundary films, lamellae, platelets, and spheroids.

The acicular constituent that occurs near creep fractures is likely to be chromium nitride, which originates by diffusion of nitrogen from the atmosphere. The acicular pattern is the result of precipitation on crystallographic planes. However, nitrides are not always acicular, and acicular platelets are not necessarily nitrides; $\sigma$ phase (see Fig. 32) and even carbides can exhibit an acicular pattern. A frequently encountered lamellar constituent that resembles pearlite has been identified as an aggregate of austenite with carbonitride, chromium nitride, or chromium carbide. Etching in Murakami's reagent at room temperature for approximately 10 s will stain the carbide, but not the nitrides or carbonitrides.

Chi phase may be encountered in Fe-Cr-Ni heat-resistant casting alloys containing molybdenum. Chi phase has a composition similar to that of $\sigma$ phase, coexists with $\sigma$ (Ref 8), and is hard and brittle. Ternary diagrams have been developed at 815 and 900 °C (1500 and 1650 °F) for the Fe-Cr-Mo system that identify χ phase as containing approximately 18% Cr, 28% Mo, and 54% Fe by weight, approximating Fe₃CrMo (Ref 9). The phase was revealed after brief etching in Vilella's reagent followed by electrolytic etching in concentrated NaOH at 1.5 V. Chi phase was first stained light brown, but after approximately 10 s, it developed a blue-gray tint, distinguishing it from σ phase, which etched brown. A brief electrolytic etch in NaCN will show χ phase before σ phase is well defined; further etching extracts χ phase (Ref 10).

## Identification of Ferrite by Magnetic Etching

Because of the low contrast, or lack of contrast, after etching, it is sometimes difficult to differentiate the ferrite contained in an austenite matrix. A technique using a magnetic field and magnetic particles (smaller than 30 nm) in an organic or an aqueous colloidal suspension can be used in conjunction with the optical microscope to identify ferrite positively (Ref 11-15). Details of the magnetic technique are described below. Additional information can be found in the article "Etching" in this Volume.

**Procedure for Examination.** A drop (5 μL measured in a micropipette) of the suspension is deposited on the surface of a specimen that has been polished and lightly etched with HCl. A thin cover is placed over the suspension. If the specimen is contained in a 25-mm (1-in.) diam plastic mount, a cover glass of the same diameter is ideal.

The specimen is placed in an inverted metallographic microscope. When the specimen is face down, its weight plus the spring pressure applied will press on the suspension under the glass, keeping it thin and relatively uniform in thickness.

An electromagnet or a permanent magnet can be used to apply a magnetic field to the specimen. The magnetic field will cause a visible concentration of the colloid particles over the magnetic areas. Figure 8 shows the magnetic pattern produced. Comparison of

Fig. 8 with Fig. 6 shows that the magnetic pattern identifies the ferrite in the specimen.

If an electromagnet is used for applying the magnetic field, it is a solenoid placed around the specimen, as shown in Fig. 1. It has a winding of 2300 A turn and operates on batteries or on direct current rectified from alternating current. The field can be cut off or reversed readily using switches. A variable autotransformer between the line and rectifier input or a rheostat in series with a battery source controls the intensity of the magnetizing field.

For cursory ferrite identification, it is simpler to use a permanent magnet. Various shapes are available. A cylindrical Alnico permanent magnet can be placed on top of the inverted specimen, as shown in Fig. 2(a) and (b), or an Alnico horseshoe magnet can be placed alongside, as shown in Fig. 2(c). The horseshoe magnet provides a horizontal and a vertical field. The field is most intense through that part of the specimen closest to the pole pieces of the magnet.

## Microstructures of Fe-Cr-Ni Alloy Castings

Except for alloy 9Cr-1Mo, which is ferritic, the heat-resistant casting alloys illustrated in this article are high-chromium-nickel-iron alloys that generally are austenitic and nonmagnetic (see Fig. 3 to 59). The austenite in the matrix of these alloys provides useful high-temperature strength (creep strength or creep-rupture strength) if it is adequately reinforced with particles of carbide and nitride. Without carbide and nitride, the austenitic casting alloys would lose their superiority in elevated-temperature strength over the 300 series wrought stainless steels (see the article "Wrought Stainless Steels" in this Volume).

**Ferrite.** The austenite must contain no ferrite to reach maximum strength. The nickel-predominant alloys, such as HN, HT, and HW, are stably austenitic over their entire composition ranges. However, in the chromium-predominant alloys, such as HF, HH,

and HK, the formation of ferrite is favored if the ratio of chromium to nickel is near the upper limit of the specification range and conversely is suppressed if the ratio is near the lower limit.

Carbon, nitrogen, and silicon also influence the occurrence of ferrite. Chromium combined in the carbide or nitride phases is not free to influence the effective chromium-to-nickel ratio of the alloy. In this sense, a low level of carbon (or nitrogen) content means a higher effective chromium content aside from the inherent characteristics of low carbon to promote ferrite formation and of high carbon to stabilize austenite. Silicon, like chromium, promotes the formation of ferrite.

Ferrite at elevated temperature is much weaker than austenite and reduces the creep-rupture strength of the alloy, but it does provide greater ductility as long as it is stable ferrite and not a source of σ phase. For optimum strength properties, therefore, the composition of each alloy grade should be controlled at the most favorable balance of the available chromium-to-nickel ratio, with these provisions: (1) although high nickel stabilizes austenite, it also makes the alloy vulnerable to sulfidation attack, (2) although high chromium encourages the formation of ferrite, it also improves the resistance to oxidation and sulfidation, and (3) although silicon also favors ferrite, it can contribute significantly to resistance to carburization.

**Carbides.** Although the carbon content of these casting alloys is markedly higher than that of the wrought grades with similar chromium and nickel contents, the compositions are nevertheless hypoeutectic; in freezing, dendrites of austenite form first and particles of carbide form last, occupying the interstices between the dendrites. The carbide exists, therefore, as massive chains of particles following the austenite grain boundaries. When the alloys are reheated to service temperatures, additional carbide particles are precipitated from the matrix in very fine form, usually delineating patterns of high-carbon segregation within the austenite.

The predominant carbide phase is most appropriately designated M₂₃C₆, in which M (metal) represents the sum of carbide-forming elements involved. A second carbide form, M₆C, is discussed below in relation to the lamellar constituent.

**Nitrides** contribute to high creep strength of these alloys, as do the carbide phases discussed above.

**The lamellar constituent** with the appearance of pearlite consists of alternate plates of austenite and carbide. High nitrogen content promotes the formation of this constituent, perhaps by lowering the solubility limit of the austenite for carbon. In the lamellar constituent found in alloys of higher nickel and chromium content than those discussed here, the carbide has been identified as M₆C; therefore, it is likely that the lamellar constituent in the structures illustrated here is also M₆C.

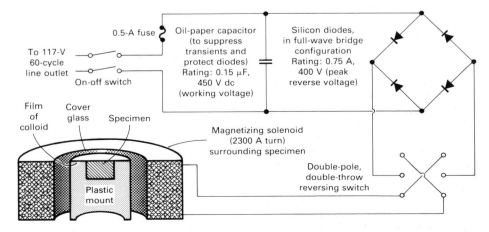

**Fig. 1** Electromagnet setup for identification of ferrite in Fe-Cr-Ni alloys

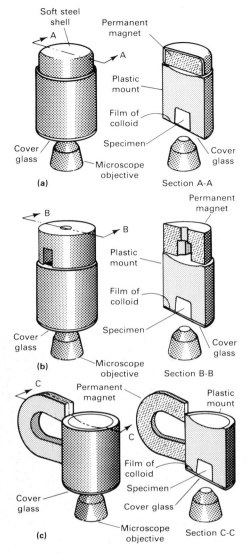

**Fig. 2** Permanent-magnet setups for identification of ferrite in an austenite matrix. (a) and (b) Use of cylindrical magnets. (c) Use of horseshoe magnet

**Sigma phase** is a hard and brittle compound usually formed from ferrite (but sometimes directly from austenite) between approximately 650 °C (1200 °F) and slightly above 870 °C (1600 °F). It develops most rapidly near 870 °C (1600 °F). In the alloys shown in this article, the compound approximates FeCr, but has a variable composition. The addition of silicon promotes the formation of σ, and a ternary composition of 43Fe-43Cr-14Si (at.%) has been suggested. Because σ imparts ambient-temperature brittleness and a loss of creep-rupture strength, its presence is generally undesirable.

## Microstructures of Nickel- and Cobalt-Base Casting Alloys

The nickel- and cobalt-base heat-resistant casting alloys illustrated in this article are re-lated to the wrought nickel and cobalt-base alloys presented in the article "Wrought Heat-Resistant Alloys" in this Volume. Representative microstructures of cast nickel-base alloys can be found in Fig. 60 to 118. Cobalt-base cast microstructures are shown in Fig. 119 to 142.

**Nickel-base alloys,** wrought and cast, derive their strength from the mechanisms of solid-solution hardening and precipitation hardening, singly and in combination. With the exception of Hastelloy B, all nickel-base alloys presented here contain 6 to 23% Cr, primarily for oxidation resistance and sulfidation resistance at elevated temperature, but also for solid-solution hardening.

The matrix of the nickel-rich solid solution is designated γ. The predominantly solid-solution alloys do not contain significant amounts of aluminum, titanium, or niobium, which promote precipitation, but are additionally strengthened by the dispersion of noncoherent carbides (MC, $M_6C$, $M_{23}C_6$) and the addition of refractory metal elements, such as molybdenum and tungsten, as well as interstitials, such as carbon and boron.

The strengthening of the precipitation-hardening alloys depends on the formation of a coherent dispersed second phase within the γ matrix. In the wrought alloys, the desired dispersion is obtained by hot working, solution annealing (heating the solid solution above the γ' solvus temperature), cooling at a rate that will result in retention of the solid-solution structure, then aging at one or more lower temperatures that favor formation of the dispersed second phase (or phases)—notably γ', which is designated $Ni_3(Al,Ti)$, and η ($Ni_3Ti$). Other elements are soluble in these basic phases.

Formation of the second phase in many of the cast alloys begins in the liquid state; therefore, solution annealing is impossible. Casting conditions (degree of superheating, mold temperature, pouring time, and cooling rate) largely control microstructure and subsequent properties. In many of the casting alloys, precipitation of the second phase is essentially complete when the casting is removed from its mold, and further heat treatment is often ineffective. Other alloys are heat treated to homogenize, to nullify effects of diffusion-coating cycles, or to enhance strength or ductility. Because complete re-solution does not occur in the cast alloys, the dispersed second phase and its strengthening effect are retained in these alloys at high service temperatures.

**Cobalt-Base Alloys.** Pure cobalt is allotropic and has a phase change from the low-temperature ε (hexagonal close-packed) to the high-temperature α (face-centered cubic) at 427 °C (801 °F). However, cobalt-base superalloys are designed to have a stabilized face-centered cubic matrix at all temperatures, and any reversion of the matrix to hexagonal close-packed crystal structure is undesirable. The alloys are characterized by chromium contents of 18 to 35%, principally to provide resistance to oxidation and sulfidation and secondarily as a carbide ($Cr_7C_3$ and $M_{23}C_6$) former and solid-solution strengthener.

Other elements common to the alloys are carbon, tungsten, tantalum, titanium, and zirconium for solid-solution strengthening and carbide (MC and $M_6C$) formation; small amounts of silicon and manganese for improved oxidation resistance; and boron for solid-solution strengthening and boride formation. The carbides are seldom binary compositions; chromium, tungsten, tantalum, silicon, zirconium, nickel, and cobalt may be present in a single particle of carbide. Molybdenum, although used extensively in nickel alloys, is used only sparingly in cobalt-base alloys (Haynes 21); in cobalt alloys, tungsten is more effective and less detrimental.

Compared to the wrought alloys, cobalt-base casting alloys have higher contents of high-melting metals, such as chromium, tungsten, tantalum, titanium, and zirconium, and higher carbon contents. Wrought and cast alloys, however, derive their strength from the dispersion of complex carbides in a highly alloyed matrix.

Depending on chemical composition and heat treatment, the microstructure of cobalt-base alloys consists of a cobalt-rich solid-solution matrix containing carbide within grains and at grain boundaries. In the cobalt-chromium-carbon system, $M_7C_3$ and $M_{23}C_6$ are common. The ratio of chromium to carbon in this ternary system is important in determining which carbide will predominate. In more complex alloy systems, cobalt, tungsten, and molybdenum replace some of the chromium in the carbide phases.

Niobium and tantalum (8 to 10%) as well as titanium and zirconium (less than 0.5%) form carbides of the MC type. Molybdenum and tungsten form $M_6C$ in the cobalt-chromium-carbon alloys when the content of either element is great enough to preclude substitution for chromium in $M_{23}C_6$.

## REFERENCES

1. E.J. Dulis and G.V. Smith, Identification and Mode of Formation and Re-solution of Sigma Phase in Austenitic Chromium-Nickel Steels, in *Symposium on the Nature, Occurrence and Effects of Sigma Phase*, STP 110, ASTM, Philadelphia, 1951
2. G.N. Emmanuel, Metallographic Identification of Sigma Phase in a 25-20 Austenitic Alloy, *Met. Prog.*, Vol 52, 1947, p 78-79
3. J.H. Jackson, The Occurrence of the Sigma Phase and Its Effect on Certain Properties of the Cast Fe-Ni-Cr Alloys, in *Symposium on the Nature, Occurrence and Effects of Sigma Phase*, STP 110, ASTM, Philadelphia, 1951
4. J.J. Gilman, Electrolytic Etching—The Sigma Phase Steels, *Trans. ASM*, Vol 44, 1952, p 566-596

5. L. Dillinger, R.D. Buchheit, and J.L. McCall, Phase Identification Etchants for Iron-Chromium-Nickel Alloys, in *Proceedings of the International Metallographic Society*, 1971, p 57-64

6. L. Dillinger and D.B. Roach, The Metallography of Cast Heat-Resistant Alloys, in *Proceedings NACE, 26th Conference*, 1970, p 356-365

7. P. Duwez and S.R. Baen, X-Ray Study of the Sigma Phase in Various Alloy Systems, in *Symposium on the Nature, Occurrence and Effects of Sigma Phase*, STP 110, ASTM Philadelphia, 1951

8. K.W. Andrews, A New Intermetallic Phase in Alloy Steels, *Nature*, Vol 164, 1949, p 1015

9. J.G. McMullin, S.F. Reiter, and D.G. Ebeling, Equilibrium Structures in Fe-Cr-Mo Alloys, *Trans. ASM*, Vol 46, 1954, p 799-806

10. P.K. Koh, Occurrence of Chi Phase in Molybdenum-Bearing Stainless Steels, *J. Metals*, Vol 5, Section 2, Feb 1953; *Trans. AIME*, Vol 197, 1953, p 339-343

11. H.S. Avery, V.O. Homerberg, and E. Cook, Metallographic Identification of Ferro Magnetic Phases, *Met. Alloys*, Vol 10, 1939, p 353-355

12. H.S. Avery, "Cast Heat-Resistant Alloys for High-Temperature Weldments," Bulletin 143, Welding Research Council, Aug 1969

13. A New Way to Reveal Magnetic Domains at High Magnifications, *Met. Prog.*, Vol 100, Dec 1971, p 82

14. W.C. Elmore, Ferromagnetic Colloid for Studying Magnetic Structures, *Phys. Rev.*, Vol 54, 1938, p 309-310

15. R.J. Gray, "Revealing Ferromagnetic Microstructures with Ferrofluid," Report RNL-TM-3681, Oak Ridge National Laboratory, Oak Ridge, TN, March 1972

**Fig. 3** 9Cr-1Mo alloy, as sand cast; center of cast section. Structure consists of a matrix of acicular ferrite containing scattered globular carbide. See also Fig. 4. Vilella's reagent. 200×

**Fig. 4** Same as Fig. 3, but taken from the end of the cast section (near surface) to show the finer structure resulting from the chilling effect of the sand mold. Vilella's reagent. 200×

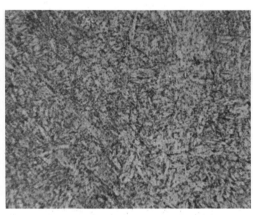

**Fig. 5** 9Cr-1Mo alloy, air cooled from 1010 °C (1850 °F) and tempered at 690 °C (1275 °F). Structure is a dispersion of spheroidized carbide particles in a ferrite matrix. Vilella's reagent. 600×

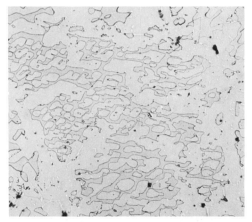

**Fig. 6** HE-14 alloy, creep tested at 4.5 MPa (650 psi) and 980 °C (1800 °F) for 336 h. Structure: islands of ferrite (darker gray) in an austenite matrix (lighter gray). White constituent is carbide particles. Compare appearance of carbide in Fig. 7, and of ferrite in Fig. 8. 50% HCl. 100×

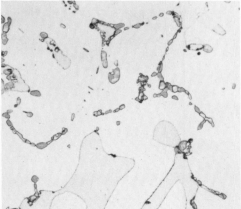

**Fig. 7** Same alloy and condition as in Fig. 6, but after a staining second etch, which darkened carbide particles, and shown at higher magnification. Structure: carbide particles (darkest gray) and ferrite islands (middle gray) in a matrix of austenite (lightest gray). 50% HCl, then Murakami's reagent. 400×

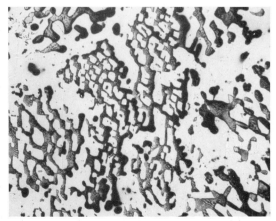

**Fig. 8** Same alloy and condition as in Fig. 6, showing the magnetic pattern (dark) on ferrite as influenced by a vertical magnetic field from a concentric solenoid. Dark areas with diffuse edges and no mosaic pattern indicate subsurface ferrite. Striped pattern shows magnetic domains. 50% HCl. 100×

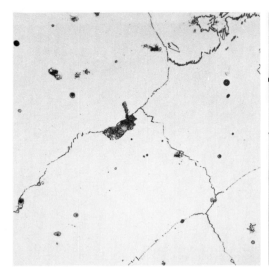

**Fig. 9** Alloy HF-33, as cast. Austenite matrix contains eutectic carbide chains (at grain boundaries) and scattered carbide particles. Note the patch of lamellar constituent at a grain boundary. The globular inclusions are chiefly sulfide and silicate. Glyceregia. 250×

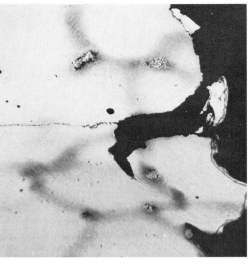

**Fig. 10** Structure at fracture in an alloy HF-33 creep-test specimen that fractured after 340 h at 650 °C (1200 °F) and 207 MPa (30 ksi). Cored structure of fine carbide precipitate has begun to form. Eutectic carbide at grain boundaries. See also Fig. 11 and 12. Glyceregia. 250×

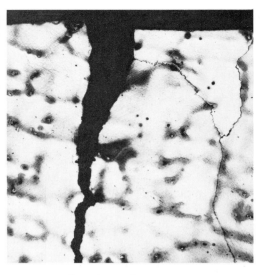

**Fig. 11** Same fractured creep-test specimen as in Fig. 10, but a lower-magnification micrograph of an area at the surface. Cored structure of fine carbide precipitate is more pronounced. A secondary crack has begun to follow carbide at grain boundary. See also Fig. 12. Glyceregia. 100×

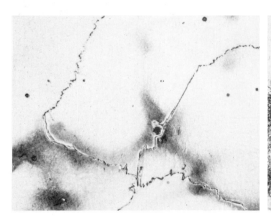

**Fig. 12** Same alloy HF-33 creep-test specimen as Fig. 10 and 11, but a view of the structure at the interior. Traces of fine carbide precipitation are evident at slip regions in the austenite matrix. Glyceregia. 250×

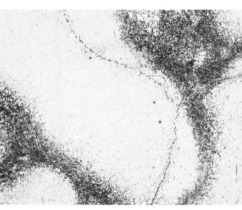

**Fig. 13** Interior of an alloy HF-33 creep-test specimen fractured after 13 690 h at 650 °C (1200 °F) and 110 MPa (16 ksi). Cored structure is more fully developed than in Fig. 10; eutectic carbide is unchanged. See also Fig. 14. Glyceregia. 250×

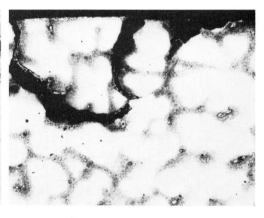

**Fig. 14** Same as Fig. 13, but at the surface of the specimen. The cored structure is clearly more sharply defined than in Fig. 11. Secondary creep-rupture cracks have begun to penetrate along the dendrite boundaries. Glyceregia. 100×

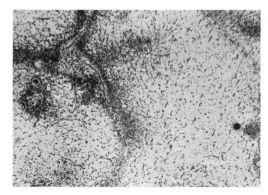

**Fig. 15** Interior of an alloy HF-33 creep-test specimen fractured after 13 680 h at 760 °C (1400 °F), 41 MPa (6 ksi). Carbide precipitation is more general than in Fig. 13 (coalescence of precipitates has begun); eutectic carbide is essentially unchanged. Glyceregia. 250×

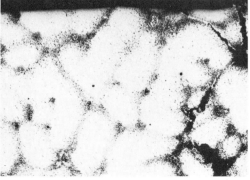

**Fig. 16** Same specimen as in Fig. 15, but showing surface structure, which is also typical of the fracture. Structure shown is similar to that of specimen in Fig. 14, but deeper penetration of creep-rupture cracks following the cored structure is evident. Glyceregia. 100×

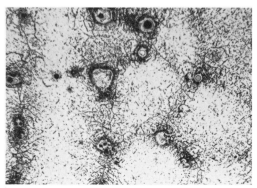

**Fig. 17** Fracture in alloy HF-33, produced after 1210 h at 870 °C (1600 °F) and 28 MPa (4 ksi). Secondary-carbide precipitation throughout, especially near particles of eutectic carbide and dendrite boundaries; some coalescence. Subgrain boundaries are prominent. Glyceregia. 250×

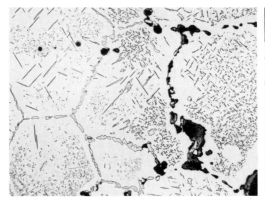

**Fig. 18** Fracture in alloy HF-33, produced after 13 300 h at 870 °C (1600 °F) and 17 MPa (2.5 ksi). Eutectic and secondary carbides have coalesced to form a nearly continuous network and paths for subsurface oxidation. Some nitride platelets. See also Fig. 19 and 20. Glyceregia. 250×

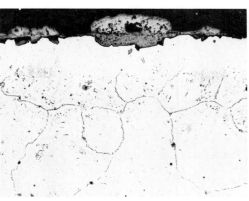

**Fig. 19** Same as Fig. 18, but at the surface, where marked decarburization is evident. Carbide at grain boundaries is coarser near the decarburized layer than farther from the surface. Some nitride is visible just below the decarburized zone. See also Fig. 20. Glyceregia. 100×

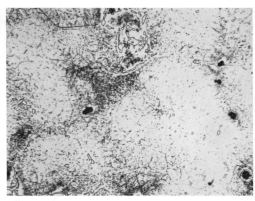

**Fig. 20** Same as Fig. 18, but at the interior of the specimen. The cored structure is much less marked than in Fig. 15, and the carbide network is less continuous than in Fig. 18. Some coalescence of carbide has occurred but, again, less than in Fig. 18. Glyceregia. 250×

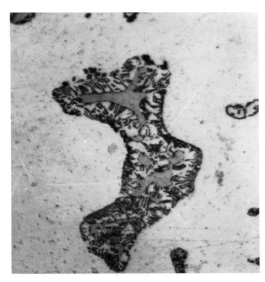

**Fig. 21** Complex ferrite-σ-carbide island in austenite matrix of as-cast alloy HF-25. Small, white areas within the margin of the island are ferrite; uniformly gray shapes in the island are σ; dark, coalesced particles around and within the island are carbide. 50% HCl, then $K_3Fe(CN)_6$. 1000×

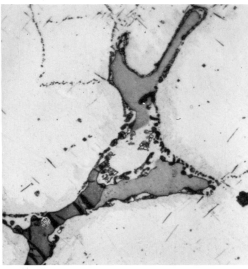

**Fig. 22** Ferrite-σ-carbide island in alloy HF-25 creep-test specimen tested for 1002 h at 760 °C (1400 °F) and 21 MPa (3 ksi). Constituents are the same as in Fig. 21. Cracks in lower arm of σ particle were induced by creep (0.10% total deformation). 50% HCl, then $K_3Fe(CN)_6$. 1000×

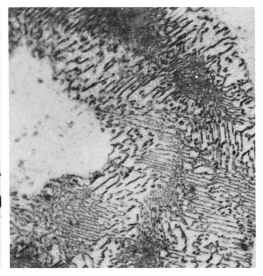

**Fig. 23** Lamellar structure in an alloy HF-34 creep-test specimen tested 1001 h at 650 °C (1200 °F) and 103 MPa (15 ksi). The lamellar constituent resembles pearlite in appearance and consists of alternate plates of austenite and carbide. 50% HCl, then $K_3Fe(CN)_6$. 1000×

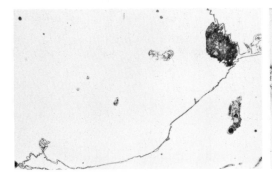

**Fig. 24** Alloy HH, as-cast. Austenite matrix grains are surrounded by nearly continuous envelopes of primary carbide. Primary carbide also occurs as interdendritic islands. Patches of lamellae, such as the one at upper right, are not clearly resolved at this magnification. Glyceregia. 250×

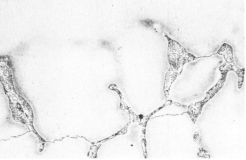

**Fig. 25** Interior of an alloy HH creep-test specimen that fractured after 250 h at 650 °C (1200 °F) and 207 MPa (30 ksi). Finely precipitated carbide has begun to delineate the cored structure. Primary carbide is more prominent than in Fig. 24. Glyceregia. 250×

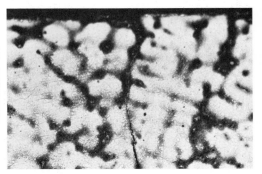

**Fig. 26** Surface of an alloy HH creep-test specimen that fractured after 6160 h at 650 °C (1200 °F) and 103 MPa (15 ksi). Carbide precipitates clearly define cored structure. Note secondary creep-rupture fissure along the carbide network. See also Fig. 27. Glyceregia. 100×

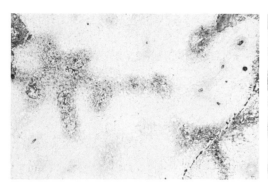

**Fig. 27** Interior of the specimen in Fig. 26, shown at a higher magnification. The lamellar patches near grain boundaries are not resolved at this magnification. Little coalescence of primary or secondary carbide has occurred with this combination of time, temperature, and strain. Glyceregia. 250×

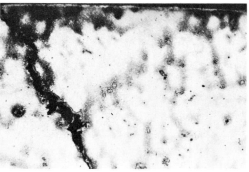

**Fig. 28** Surface of an alloy HH creep-test specimen that fractured after 12 500 h at 650 °C (1200 °F), 86 MPa (12.5 ksi). Carbide precipitation is essentially the same as in Fig. 26 and 27 and presumably is complete for this temperature. The deep crack (at left side of micrograph) is evidence of creep damage. Glyceregia. 100×

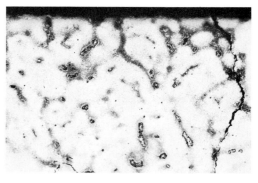

**Fig. 29** Surface of an alloy HH creep-test specimen that fractured after 550 h at 760 °C (1400 °F) and 69 MPa (10 ksi). Carbide precipitation defining high-carbon zones of the structure has begun. Note coalesced carbide and creep-rupture fissure. A sodium cyanide etch would reveal some σ. Glyceregia. 100×

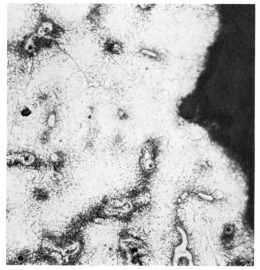

**Fig. 30** Fracture surface in an alloy HH creep-test specimen that fractured after 1230 h at 760 °C (1400 °F) and 48 MPa (7 ksi). Similar to structure in Fig. 29, but with more carbide precipitation in matrix. Primary eutectic carbide is unchanged. Glyceregia. 250×

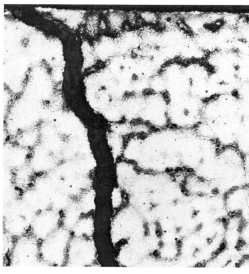

**Fig. 31** Structure at surface of the specimen in Fig. 30. Very little decarburization has occurred at the surface. The secondary creep-rupture fissure is much larger than in the specimen in Fig. 29, which fractured in slightly less than half the time at the same temperature. Glyceregia. 100×

**Fig. 32** Surface of an alloy HH creep-test specimen fractured after 10 270 h at 760 °C (1400 °F), 28 MPa (4 ksi). Platelets of σ, irregular islands of σ, some decarburization, and oxide that has formed in a creep-damage crack. Glyceregia. 100×

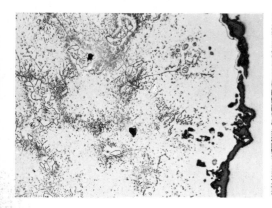

**Fig. 33** Alloy HH that fractured after 5260 h at 870 °C (1600 °F) and 21 MPa (3 ksi). Decarburization and oxidation are evident at the fracture surface. No evidence of σ. Glyceregia 250×

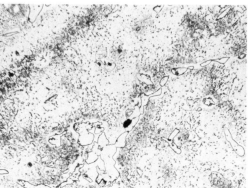

**Fig. 34** Fracture structure of an alloy HH specimen that ruptured after 9850 h at 870 °C (1600 °F) and 15 MPa (2.2 ksi). More precipitation and coalescence of carbide than in Fig. 33. A significant amount of σ is present, but not revealed by this etchant. See also Fig. 35. Glyceregia. 250×

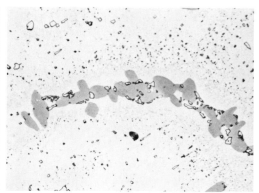

**Fig. 35** Same as Fig. 34, but etched electrolytically to reveal σ. Large, gray σ masses are associated with eutectic carbide. Electrolytic etch: 5 s in 10% NaCN. 500×

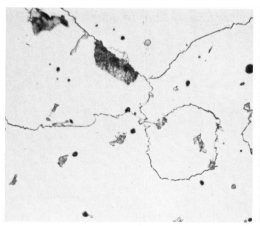

**Fig. 36** Alloy HK-35, as-cast. Scattered eutectic carbide in austenite matrix and at grain boundaries; patches of the lamellar constituent also are associated with grain boundaries. No fine particles of carbide have precipitated during freezing and mold cooling. Glyceregia. 250×

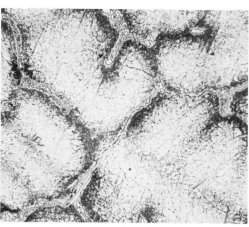

**Fig. 37** Interior of alloy HK-44 creep-test specimen fractured after 270 h at 760 °C (1400 °F), 103 MPa (15 ksi). Secondary-carbide precipitation outlines cored structure. Coarse eutectic carbide along dendrite boundaries; carbide precipitates at slip planes. Glyceregia. 250×

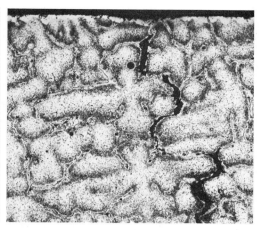

**Fig. 38** Surface of alloy HK-44 specimen fractured after 6060 h at 760 °C (1400 °F), 62 MPa (9 ksi). Trace of decarburization at surface. More carbide precipitation and coalescence than in Fig. 37. Some σ is present, but not revealed by this etchant. Glyceregia. 100×

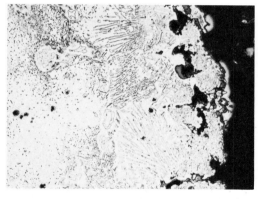

**Fig. 39** Alloy HK-35 specimen fractured after 2120 h at 870 °C (1600 °F), 31 MPa (4.5 ksi). Lamellar constituent along fracture, with nitride platelets (not fully resolved) adjacent to it. Glyceregia. 250×

**Fig. 40** Fracture in an alloy HK-44 specimen that ruptured after 2000 h at 980 °C (1800 °F) and 17 MPa (2.5 ksi). Coarsened eutectic network consists of carbonitride. An area containing many nitride platelets underlies a decarburized zone at the fracture. Glyceregia. 250×

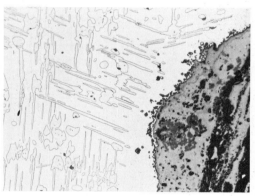

**Fig. 41** Fracture in an alloy HK-35 specimen that ruptured after 9230 h at 980 °C (1800 °F) and 9 MPa (1.3 ksi). Carbide particles and nitride platelets have coarsened appreciably. No lamellar constituent. Considerable oxidation and decarburization at the surface. Glyceregia. 250×

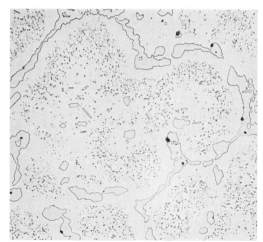

**Fig. 42** Interior of an alloy HK-44 specimen that fractured after 21 670 h at 980 °C (1800 °F) and 12 MPa (1.7 ksi). Carbide particles have coarsened. Cored structure has been virtually eliminated. Primary eutectic carbide islands are clearly outlined. Glyceregia. 250×

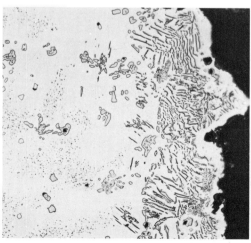

**Fig. 43** Fracture in an alloy HK-35 specimen ruptured after 760 h at 1040 °C (1900 °F) and 12 MPa (1.7 ksi). A zone of coarse lamellae borders the fracture, and there is evidence of some decarburization. The gray, internal particles are probably carbonitride. Glyceregia. 250×

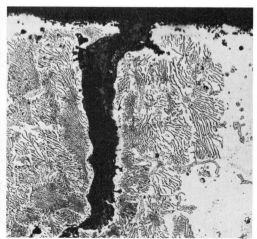

**Fig. 44** Same as Fig. 43, but at the surface of the specimen. Note the predominance of the lamellar structure adjacent to the secondary creep-rupture cracks. Some oxidation has occurred at the surface. In other respects, the structure is the same as that in Fig. 43. Glyceregia. 100×

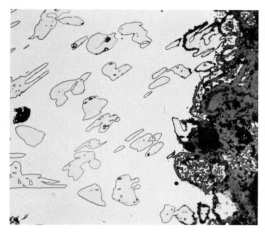

**Fig. 45** Fracture in an alloy HK-35 specimen ruptured after 8120 h at 1095 °C (2000 °F), 4.6 MPa (670 psi). Micrograph shows thick platelets, agglomerated carbide particles, subsurface oxide (mixed with metal), and scale. Glyceregia. 250×

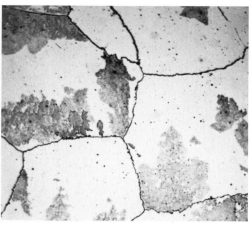

**Fig. 46** Structure of alloy HK-28 heated at 1290 °C (2350 °F) for 12 h and furnace cooled. The lamellae (25% of as-cast structure) dissolve at 1290 °C (2350 °F) and are suppressed if water quenched. Slow cooling regenerates them, as seen here. See also Fig. 47. 50% HCl, then $K_3Fe(CN)_6$. 50×

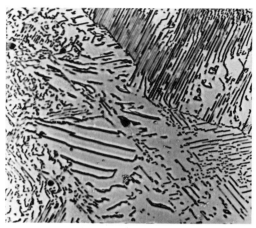

**Fig. 47** Same lamellar structure as in Fig. 46, but shown at higher magnification. All of the carbide of this alloy was dissolved by the heat treatment at 1290 °C (2350 °F); however, during furnace cooling from that temperature, some carbon precipitated as lamellae. 50% HCl, then $K_3Fe(CN)_6$. 500×

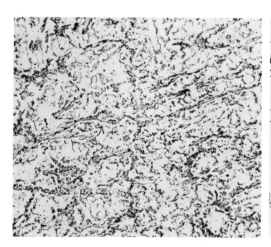

**Fig. 48** Alloy HW, as-cast, showing pattern of interdentritic eutectic carbide segregation. See Fig. 49 for same structure at higher magnification and identification of constituents. 5 mL conc HCl and 1 mL conc $HNO_3$. 50×

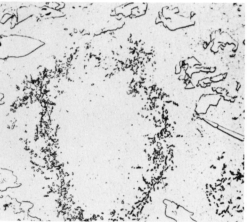

**Fig. 49** Same as Fig. 48, except at higher magnification. Austenite matrix containing massive interdendritic eutectic carbide and some small precipitated carbide particles. 5 mL conc HCl and 1 mL conc $HNO_3$. 500×

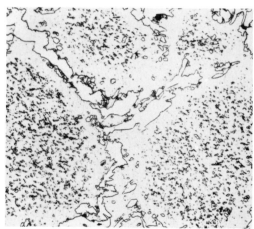

**Fig. 50** Alloy HW after aging 48 h at 870 °C (1600 °F). The aging resulted in considerable precipitation of carbide in the austenite matrix. Compare with Fig. 49. 5 mL conc HCl and 1 mL conc $HNO_3$. 500×

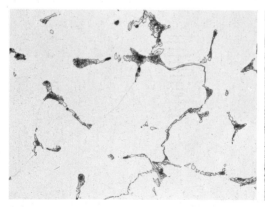

**Fig. 51** Alloy HN, as-cast. The microstructure consists of an austenite matrix containing chains of eutectic carbide between the dendrites. Note that in some portions of the eutectic carbide a duplex or lamellar structure is present. Glyceregia. 250×

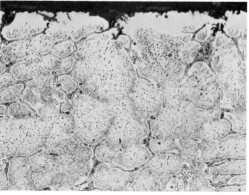

**Fig. 52** Surface of an alloy HN specimen fractured after 320 h at 980 °C (1800 °F) and 31 MPa (4.5 ksi). Secondary-carbide precipitates outlining the cored structure and throughout the matrix. Some coalescence has occurred. Surface decarburization is evident. Glyceregia. 100×

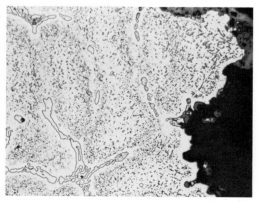

**Fig. 53** Fracture in an alloy HN specimen ruptured after 1840 h at 980 °C (1800 °F), 21 MPa (3 ksi). Carbide coalescence has coarsened the structure, producing carbide-depleted zones along eutectic networks. Some platelets are present near the fracture surface. Glyceregia. 250×

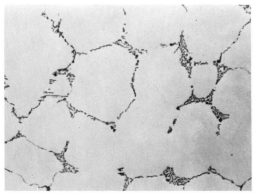

**Fig. 54** Alloy HT-44, as cast. The austenite matrix contains a complex network of eutectic carbide that outlines the boundaries of the original dendrites. Note that the larger patches of primary carbide have a lamellar structure. Compare with Fig. 58. $K_3Fe(CN)_6$. 250×

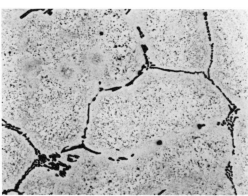

**Fig. 55** Interior of alloy HT-44 after creep-testing 1005 h at 760 °C (1400 °F) and 41 MPa (6 ksi). General precipitation of fine carbide has occurred, with some coarsening of particles. Slight carbide depletion along the eutectic network. See also Fig. 56 and 57. $K_3Fe(CN)_6$. 250×

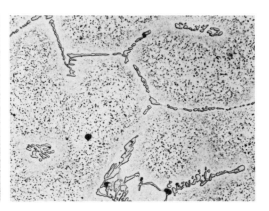

**Fig. 56** Interior of an alloy HT-44 specimen after creep-testing 1001 h at 870 °C (1600 °F) and 28 MPa (4 ksi). Eutectic carbide and fine precipitates have coarsened. As in Fig. 55, carbide-depleted zones are visible along eutectic-carbide chains. See also Fig. 57. $K_3Fe(CN)_6$. 250×

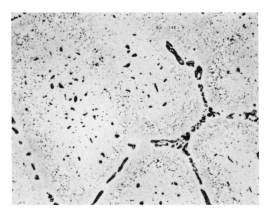

**Fig. 57** Interior of alloy HT-44 that was creep tested 1013 h at 980 °C (1800 °F) and 14 MPa (2 ksi). Carbide shows further agglomeration than in Fig. 56, with fewer precipitates remaining. Coalescence has made the eutectic-carbide chains less continuous. $K_3Fe(CN)_6$. 250×

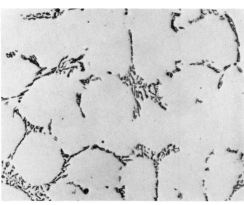

**Fig. 58** Alloy HT-57, as-cast. This structure is similar to that shown in Fig. 54 (as-cast alloy HT-44), but the higher carbon content has caused additional primary eutectic carbide to form. Also, the larger carbide shapes are coarser than those in Fig. 54. $K_3Fe(CN)_6$. 250×

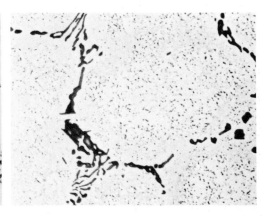

**Fig. 59** Interior of alloy HT-56 after creep-testing 1002 h at 760 °C (1400 °F) and 69 MPa (10 ksi). Primary carbide in the eutectic network is more particulated than that in Fig. 55. Many secondary carbide particles have precipitated uniformly within the grains. $K_3Fe(CN)_6$. 250×

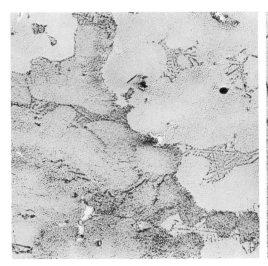

**Fig. 60** B-1900 nickel-base alloy, as-cast. Structure consists of nickel-rich γ solid-solution matrix containing a few light-etching carbide particles and dispersed γ' (see also Fig. 61 and 62 for details of the structure). Kalling's reagent. 100×

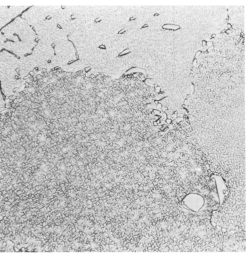

**Fig. 61** Same alloy and condition as Fig. 60, but at a higher magnification. The light-etching carbide particles are dispersed and at grain boundaries. The fine constituent within grains is γ'. See also Fig. 62. Kalling's reagent 2. 500×

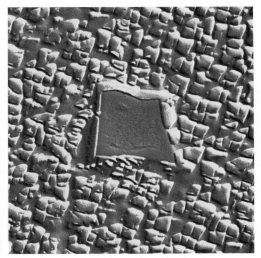

**Fig. 62** Same alloy and condition as Fig. 60, but at a higher magnification and a replica electron micrograph showing details of a large MC carbide particle and particles of γ' in the γ matrix. HCl, ethanol, $CuCl_2$, and $H_2O_2$. 7500×

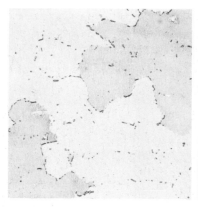

**Fig. 63** B-1900 shell mold casting, as-cast. The structure consists of nickel-rich solid-solution matrix containing dispersed and grain-boundary (Ta,Mo)C and γ' (barely visible). See also Fig. 64. Kalling's reagent. 100×

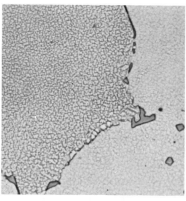

**Fig. 64** Same alloy and condition as Fig. 63, but at a higher magnification. Precipitated primary (Ta,Mo)C is at grain boundaries and within grains; precipitated γ' Ni₃(Al,Ti) is within grains. Kalling's reagent. 600×

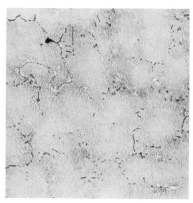

**Fig. 65** B-1900 shell mold casting, solution annealed 4 h at 1080 °C (1975 °F), aged 10 h at 900 °C (1650 °F). Grain-boundary carbide and boride and precipitated γ' in γ matrix. Black spots are voids. See also Fig. 66. Kalling's reagent. 100×

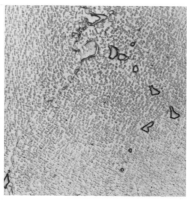

**Fig. 66** Same alloy and heat treatment as Fig. 65, but at a higher magnification, which reveals details of particles of MC and M₃B₂ at grain boundary and primary precipitated γ' Ni₃(Al,Ti) in the matrix. Kalling's reagent. 600×

**Fig. 67** Hastelloy B, as-cast. Structure consists of M₆C at grain boundaries and as islands in the γ matrix. Electrolytic etch: HCl and CrO₃. 300×

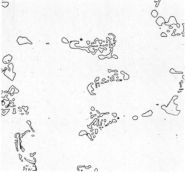

**Fig. 68** Hastelloy B casting, annealed at 1175 °C (2150 °F) for 2 h and water quenched. M₆C islands in the matrix. Electrolytic etch: HCl and CrO₃. 300×

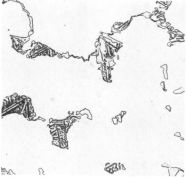

**Fig. 69** Hastelloy C, as-cast. Structure consists of M₆C at grain boundaries and as islands in the γ matrix. Electrolytic etch: CrO₃. 300×

**Fig. 70** Hastelloy C casting, annealed at 1230 °C (2250 °F) for 2 h and water quenched. M₆C in γ matrix. Electrolytic etch: CrO₃. 300×

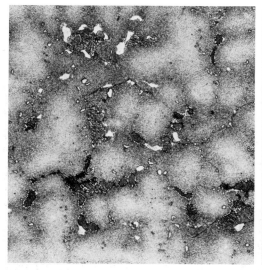

**Fig. 71** IN-100, as-cast. Small, white islands are primary (eutectic) γ'; peppery gray constituent is precipitated γ'; black constituent is probably perovskite, a complex carbide. Ni₃(Al,Ti)C; matrix is nickel-rich γ. See also Fig. 72 and 73. Marble's reagent. 100×

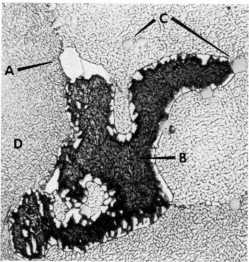

**Fig. 72** Same as Fig. 71, but at higher magnification. Light constituent (A) is primary (eutectic) γ'; dark (B), probably perovskite, Ni₃(Al,Ti)C. Dispersed carbide particles are shown at C. Gamma matrix contains precipitated (D). See also Fig. 73. Marble's reagent. 500×

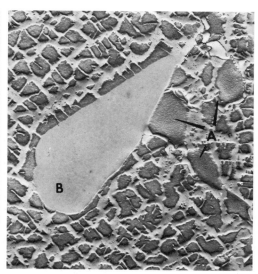

**Fig. 73** Same casting as for Fig. 71 and 72, but at higher magnification and a replica electron micrograph showing islands of primary γ' (A), a large particle of primary carbide (B), and dispersed particles of precipitated γ' in γ matrix. Marble's reagent. 5000×

**Fig. 74** IN-100, as-cast. The white islands are primary, or eutectic, γ'. Precipitated γ' is barely visible in the γ matrix. See also Fig. 75. Marble's reagent. 100×

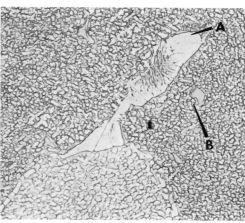

**Fig. 75** Same as Fig. 74, but at higher magnification. Island of primary (eutectic) γ' (A), dispersed carbide (B), and precipitated γ' in γ matrix. Marble's reagent. 500×

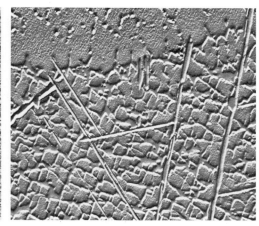

**Fig. 76** IN-100 casting, held at 760 °C (1400 °F) for 5000 h. Replica electron micrograph. Platelets of σ and primary and precipitated γ' in γ matrix. HCl, ethanol, and $H_2O_2$. 4500×

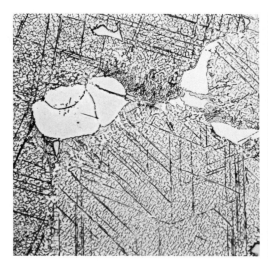

**Fig. 77** IN-100 casting, held at 815 °C (1500 °F) for 5000 h. Structure consists of massive MC particles, platelets of σ phase, and primary and precipitated γ' in the γ matrix. See also Fig. 78. HCl, ethanol, and $H_2O_2$. 500×

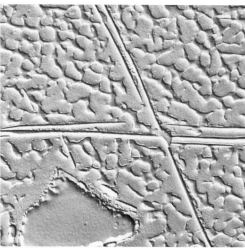

**Fig. 78** IN-100 casting, held at 815 °C (1500 °F) for 5000 h. Replica electron shows a massive particle of MC, Widmanstätten platelets of σ phase, and γ' in the γ matrix. HCl, ethanol, and $H_2O_2$. 4500×

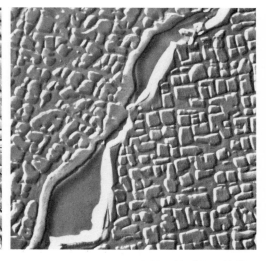

**Fig. 79** IN-100 casting, held at 925 °C (1700 °F) for 36 h. Replica electron micrograph. No σ formed at this temperature. The structure is grain-boundary carbide and γ' in the γ matrix. HCl, ethanol, $CuCl_2$, and $H_2O_2$. 4500×

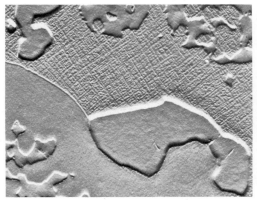

**Fig. 80** IN-100 casting, held at 925 °C (1700 °F) for 5000 h. Replica electron micrograph. No σ formed at this temperature. The structure is grain-boundary $M_{23}C_6$ and γ' in the γ matrix. HCl, ethanol, and $H_2O_2$. 4500×

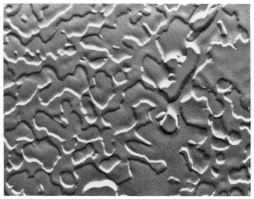

**Fig. 81** IN-100 casting, held at 1040 °C (1900 °F) for 16 h. A replica transmission electron micrograph. Note the absence of σ phase in this structure and the presence of coarsened γ' in the γ matrix. HCl, ethanol, $CuCl_2$, and $H_2O_2$. 4500×

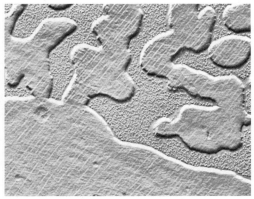

**Fig. 82** IN-100 casting, held at 1040 °C (1900 °F) for 5000 h. A replica transmission electron micrograph. Structure consists of blocky γ' and fine precipitated γ' in a matrix of γ solid solution. HCl, ethanol, and $H_2O_2$. 4500×

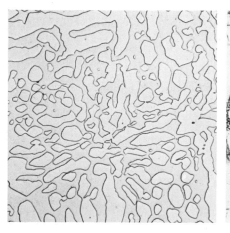

**Fig. 83** IN-100 casting, held at 1095 °C (2000 °F) for 5000 h. Optical micrograph shows random dispersion of large and small islands of γ′ in the γ matrix. HCl, ethanol, and H₂O₂. 500×

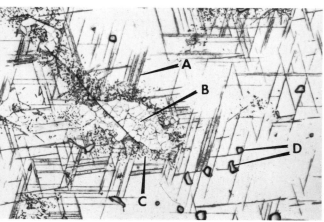

**Fig. 84** IN-100 casting, creep-rupture tested at 815 °C (1500 °F) for 1113.6 h at 276 MPa (40 ksi). The structure consists of Widmanstätten σ phase (A), primary (eutectic) γ′ (B), precipitated γ′ (C), and particles of carbide (D), in the γ matrix. Glyceregia. 500×

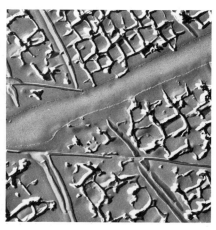

**Fig. 85** Same as Fig. 84, but at higher magnification and a replica electron micrograph showing platelets of σ emerging from carbide and precipitated γ′ in the γ matrix. Electrolytic etch: H₂SO₄ and methanol. 10 000×

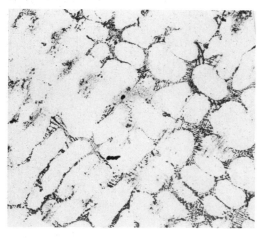

**Fig. 86** Alloy 713C ingot, 250 mm (10 in.) diam, as-cast. Structure is a matrix of γ solid solution containing "script" MC carbide in a characteristic dendritic arrangement. HCl, methanol, and CuCl₂. 100×

**Fig. 87** Alloy 713C, as-cast. The MC arrangement is in a "script" pattern (see Fig. 88 for a random pattern of carbide particles). The matrix is γ solid solution. As-polished. 100×

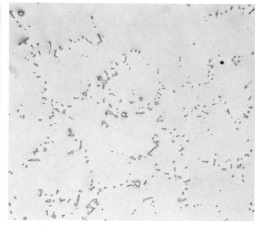

**Fig. 88** Alloy 713C, as-cast. A random pattern of MC particles appears in this structure (see Fig. 87 for a "script" pattern of carbide). The matrix is γ solid solution. As-polished. 100×

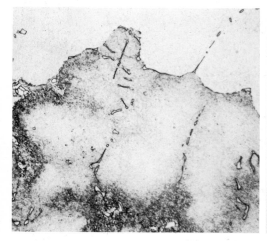

**Fig. 89** Alloy 713C, as-cast. Note the dendritic pattern. The dark areas contain carbide particles and some primary γ′ (white plates). Matrix is γ solid solution. Marble's reagent. 500×

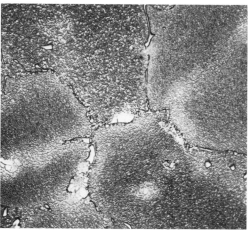

**Fig. 90** Alloy 713C, as-cast. The massive white particles are primary γ′; the grain-boundary film is MC particles. Gamma matrix contains γ′. Glyceregia. 500×

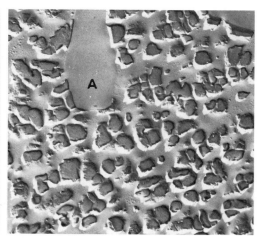

**Fig. 91** Alloy 713C, as-cast. Replica electron micrograph. Structure shown consists of large particles of carbide (A) and γ′ in the matrix of γ solid solution. Marble's reagent. 5000×

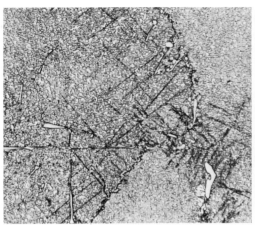

**Fig. 92** Alloy 713C casting, held 5000 h at 760 °C (1400 °F). Widmanstätten σ phase, grain-boundary carbide, and precipitated γ' in the γ matrix. See also Fig. 93. HCl, ethanol, and H₂O₂. 500×

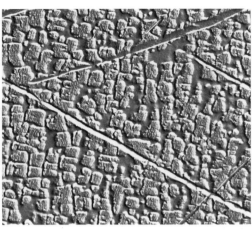

**Fig. 93** Same as Fig. 92, but at higher magnification and a replica electron micrograph showing Widmanstätten pattern of σ platelets and γ' in the γ matrix. HCl, ethanol, and H₂O₂. 4500×

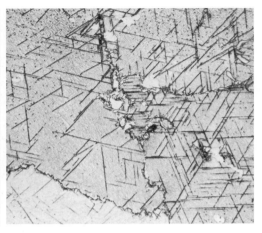

**Fig. 94** Alloy 713 casting, held at 845 °C (1550 °F) for 1000 h, air cooled. Note Widmanstätten pattern of phase and grain-boundary carbide (white) in γ matrix. Marble's reagent. 500×

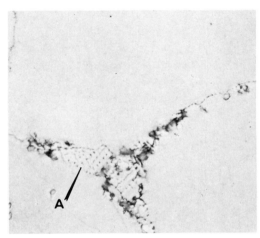

**Fig. 95** Alloy 713C casting, heated to 1260 °C (2300 °F). The grain-boundary eutectic structure (A) indicates incipient melting. Matrix is γ. See also Fig. 96. Marble's reagent. 500×

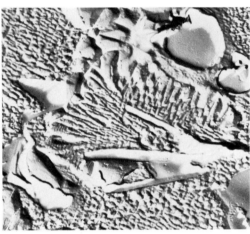

**Fig. 96** Same as Fig. 95, but at higher magnification and a replica electron micrograph showing eutectic structure at area of incipient melting and γ' in γ matrix. Marble's reagent. 5000×

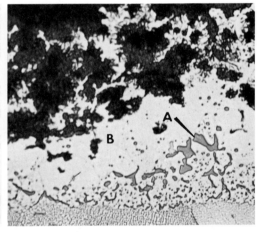

**Fig. 97** Alloy 713C, exposed to sulfidation at elevated temperature. Sulfur-rich surface layer (dark, at top), chromium sulfide particles (A), and alloy-depleted zone (B). HCl, methanol, and FeCl₃. 500×

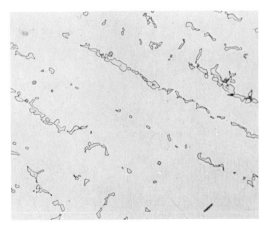

**Fig. 98** Alloy 718, vacuum cast, solution annealed 2 h at 1095 °C (2000 °F), air cooled, reannealed 1 h at 980 °C (1800 °F), air cooled, aged 16 h at 720 °C (1325 °F), air cooled. Structure: chainlike precipitate of M₂(Cb,Ti) Laves phase in the γ matrix. Compare with Fig. 99. HCl, methanol, and FeCl₃. 250×

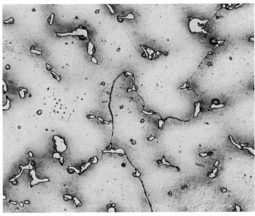

**Fig. 99** Alloy 718, vacuum cast and heat treated as for Fig. 98, except solution annealing at 1095 °C (2000 °F) was for only 1 h, and all furnace heating was done under a protective atmosphere of argon. Laves phase (white islands) has precipitated at dendrites in the γ matrix. HCl, methanol, and FeCl₃. 250×

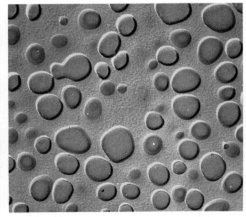

**Fig. 100** IN-738 casting, after holding at 815 °C (1500 °F) for 1000 h. A replica electron micrograph. Structure consists of rounded γ' particles in γ matrix. Compare with Fig. 103. Electrolytic etch: H₂SO₄ and methanol. 20 000×

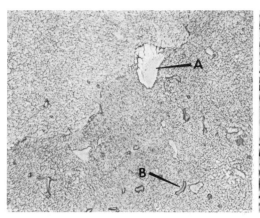

**Fig. 101** IN-738, as-cast. The structure consists of primary, or eutectic, γ′ islands (shown at A), dispersed carbide particles (shown at B), and precipitated γ′ in the matrix of γ solid solution. See also Fig. 102. Marble's reagent. 500×

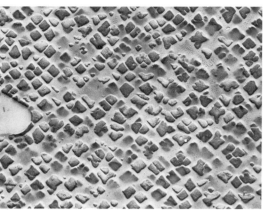

**Fig. 102** Same as Fig. 101, except at higher magnification and a replica electron micrograph showing randomly distributed precipitated γ′, Ni₃(Al,Ti) and a carbide particle (at right edge) in matrix of γ solid solution. Marble's reagent. 5000×

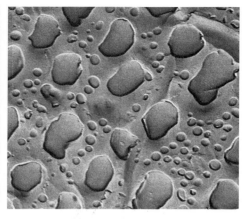

**Fig. 103** IN-738 solution annealed 2 h at 1120 °C (2050 °F), held 24 h at 845 °C (1550 °F), replica electron micrograph. Gamma-prime particles in γ; the smaller particles formed in cooling. Electrolytic etch: H₂SO₄ and methanol. 25 000×

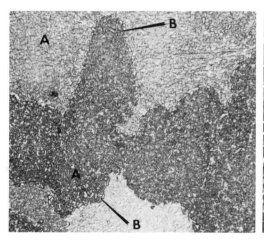

**Fig. 104** MAR-M 246, as-cast. Structure consists of precipitated γ′ in the γ matrix (A) and fine particles of carbide or primary γ′ at grain boundaries (B). See also Fig. 105. Marble's reagent. 500×

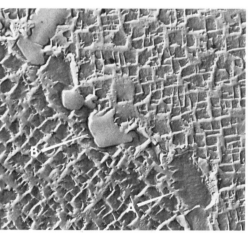

**Fig. 105** Same as Fig. 104, but at higher magnification and a replica electron micrograph showing primary γ′ (A) and carbide (B) at a grain boundary and randomly dispersed γ′ in the γ matrix. Marble's reagent. 5000×

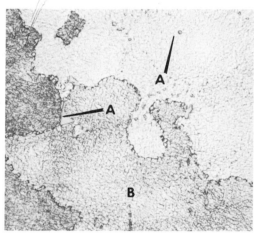

**Fig. 106** MAR-M 246 casting held 50 h at 845 °C (1550 °F), air cooled. Grain-boundary and matrix carbide (A) and dispersed γ′ in γ matrix (B). Compare with Fig. 107, a casting cooled more slowly from liquidus. Marble's reagent. 500×

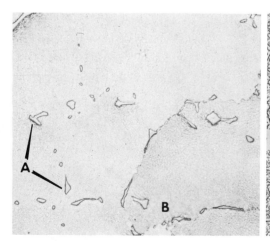

**Fig. 107** MAR-M 246 casting cooled more slowly from liquidus than that in Fig. 106, then given same heat treatment. Grain-boundary and matrix carbide (A) and a dispersion of fine γ′ in the γ matrix (B). Marble's reagent. 500×

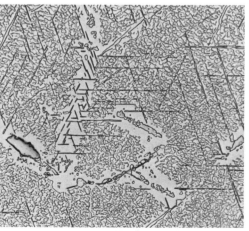

**Fig. 108** MAR-M 246 casting, held at 980 °C (1800 °F) for 5000 h. The structure consists of needlelike particles of M₆C and γ′ in the γ matrix. See Fig. 109 for better resolution of constituents. HCl, ethanol, and H₂O₂. 500×

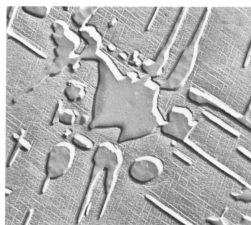

**Fig. 109** Same alloy and treatment as Fig. 108, but at a higher magnification. A replica transmission electron micrograph. Structure consists of needlelike particles of M₆C, and γ′ in the γ matrix. HCl, ethanol, and H₂O₂. 4500×

**Fig. 110** MAR-M 246 casting, exposed to temperatures above 980 °C (1800 °F). Chainlike $M_{23}C_6$ particles at grain boundaries and needlelike $M_6C$ within grains. Matrix is $\gamma$. Marble's reagent. 500×

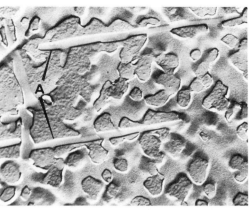

**Fig. 111, 112** Same as Fig. 110, but at higher magnification and replica electron micrographs. Fig. 111: needles of $M_6C$ (A), $M_{23}C_6$ at grain boundaries, and $\gamma'$ $Ni_3(Al,Ti)$. Fig. 112: a large particle of $M_{23}C_6$ and a connecting carbide (B), and a $\gamma'$ envelope (C). The matrix is $\gamma$. Marble's reagent. 5000×

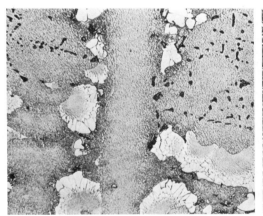

**Fig. 113** TRW-NASA VIA, as-cast. Blocky, light constituent is primary $\gamma'$; the black spots are carbide particles; the mottled gray areas are precipitated $\gamma'$ in a matrix of $\gamma$ solid solution. See also Fig. 114. Electrolytic etch: $H_2SO_4$ and methanol. 250×

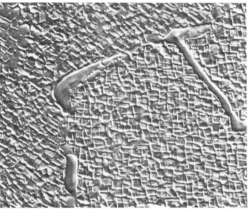

**Fig. 114** Same alloy and condition as Fig. 113, but at higher magnification. Replica electron micrograph. Large particles are MC carbide; primary (eutectic) $\gamma'$ is at lower right; remainder is $\gamma'$ in $\gamma$ matrix. Electrolytic etch: $H_2SO_4$ and methanol. 3000×

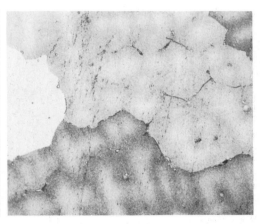

**Fig. 115** U-700 as-cast. Small, white crystals are carbide particles; darkened areas include primary (eutectic) $\gamma'$; matrix is $\gamma$ solid solution. Kalling's reagent. 100×

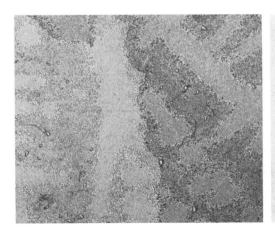

**Fig. 116** U-700 casting, solution annealed and furnace cooled to 1080 °C (1975 °F), then aged at 760 °C (1400 °F) for 16 h and air cooled. Small, white crystals are carbide; mottled gray areas include $\gamma'$. See also Fig. 117. Kalling's reagent. 100×.

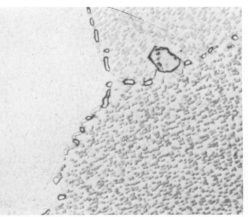

**Fig. 117** Same alloy and heat treatment as Fig. 116, but at a higher magnification. $M_{23}C_6$ has precipitated along grain boundaries. Large carbide particles dispersed within grains. Remainder is $\gamma'$ in $\gamma$ matrix. Kalling's reagent. 1000×

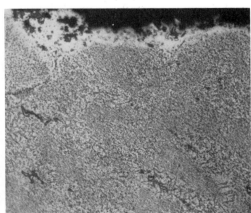

**Fig. 118** U-700 cast blade after 190-h cyclic sulfidation-erosion testing using turbine fuel and 3.5 ppm synthetic sea salt. Note erosive attack and sulfur-rich corrosion products at surface (top). Kalling's reagent. 250×

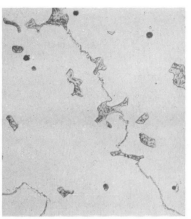

**Fig. 119** Haynes 21 cobalt-base alloy, as-cast. Structure consists of primary $M_7C_3$ particles in an $\alpha$ (fcc) matrix. See Fig. 120 to 122 for effects of heat treatment. Electrolytic etch: HCl. 200×

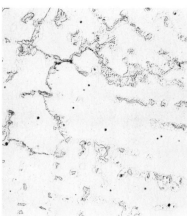

**Fig. 120** Haynes 21 casting aged 24 h at 760 °C (1400 °F). $M_7C_3$ (large particles) and precipitated $M_{23}C_6$ at grain boundaries and in grains of fcc matrix. See also Fig. 121. Electrolytic etch: HCl. 500×

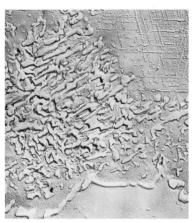

**Fig 121** Same as Fig. 120, but at higher magnification; replica electron micrograph. $M_7C_3$ particles, and $M_{23}C_6$ at grain boundaries and within grains of matrix. See also Fig. 122. Electrolytic etch: HCl. 3000×

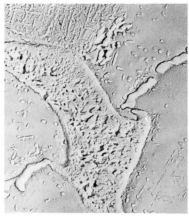

**Fig. 122** Same as Fig. 121, but showing a massive particle of primary $M_7C_3$ and secondary $M_{23}C_6$ in the fcc matrix. Carbides were determined by diffraction analysis. Electrolytic etch: HCl. 3000×

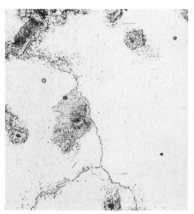

**Fig. 123** Haynes 21 casting aged 24 h at 870 °C (1600 °F). $M_7C_3$ particles and precipitated $M_{23}C_6$ at grain boundaries and in grains of fcc matrix. See also Fig. 124. Electrolytic etch: HCl. 500×

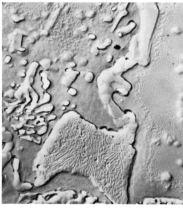

**Fig. 124** Replica electron micrograph of Fig. 123. Massive primary $M_7C_3$ particle and secondary precipitate of $M_{23}C_6$ at grain boundaries and within grains. Electrolytic etch: HCl. 3000×

**Fig. 125** Haynes 31, as-cast. Structure consists of large, primary $M_7C_3$ particles and grain-boundary $M_{23}C_6$ in an $\alpha$ (fcc) matrix. See also Fig. 126 and 127. Electrolytic etch: 2% $CrO_3$. 400×

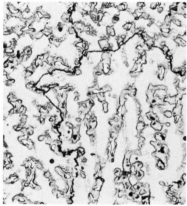

**Fig. 126** Haynes 31, as-cast thin section, aged 22 h at 730 °C (1350 °F). Precipitated $M_{23}C_6$ at grain boundaries and adjacent to primary carbide ($M_7C_3$) particles. Electrolytic etch: 2% $CrO_3$. 400×

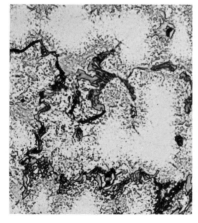

**Fig. 127** Haynes 31, as-cast thick section, aged 22 h at 730 °C (1350 °F). Large particles are $M_7C_3$; grain-boundary and mottled dispersions are $M_{23}C_6$; fcc matrix. Electrolytic etch: 2% $CrO_3$. 500×

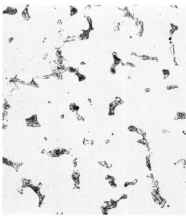

**Fig. 128** Haynes 151, as-cast. Structure consists of dispersed islands of large primary carbide ($M_6C$) in the $\alpha$ (fcc) matrix. See also Fig. 129. Electrolytic etch: HCl and $CrO_3$. 200×

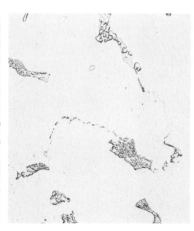

**Fig. 129** Same as Fig. 128, but at higher magnification, which reveals details of the $M_6C$ (note the lamellar form) in the $\alpha$ (fcc) matrix. Electrolytic etch: HCl and $CrO_3$. 500×

**Fig. 130** Haynes 151 casting aged 16 h at 760 °C (1400 °F) $M_6C$ particles and precipitated $M_{23}C_6$ at grain boundaries and next to $M_6C$ particles in the fcc matrix. Electrolytic etch: HCl and $CrO_3$. 500×

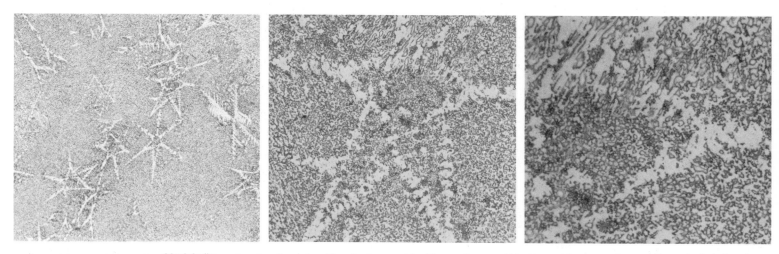

**Fig. 131, 132, 133** 98M2 Stellite, as-investment-cast ring. Microstructure consists of large primary carbides in a matrix of secondary carbides and cobalt-chromium-tungsten solid solution. Some primary carbides have solidified in a star-like array. Electrolytic etch: 50% $HNO_3$. Fig. 131: 100$\times$; Fig. 132: 500$\times$; Fig. 133: 1000$\times$. (S.E. Wall and R.L. Snyder)

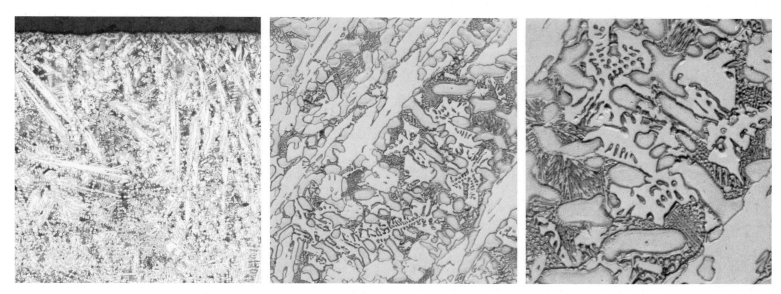

**Fig. 134, 135, 136** 98M2 Stellite, as-investment-cast bar. Very large primary carbides in a matrix of smaller secondary carbides and cobalt-chromium-tungsten solid solution. Electrolytic etch: 50% $HNO_3$. Fig. 134: 100$\times$; Fig. 135: 500$\times$; Fig. 136: 1000$\times$. (S.E. Wall and R.L. Snyder)

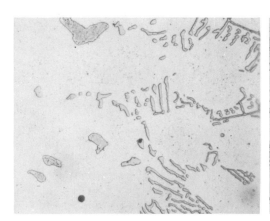

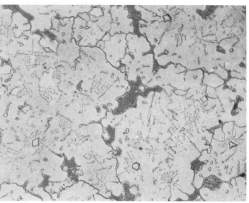

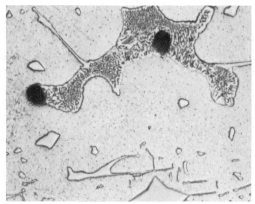

**Fig. 137** WI-52, as-cast. The solid gray islands are complex chromium-tungsten carbide; particulated islands are niobium carbide. The dark dots are silicate inclusions in the matrix of cobalt-chromium solid solution. Electrolytic etch: 5% $H_3PO_4$. 500$\times$

**Fig. 138** MAR-M 302, as-cast. Structure consists of primary, or eutectic, $M_6C$ particles (dark gray) and MC particles (small white crystals) in the matrix of cobalt-chromium-tungsten solid solution. See Fig. 139 for better resolution of constituents. Kalling's reagent. 100$\times$

**Fig. 139** MAR-M 302, as-cast, at a higher magnification than Fig. 138. The mottled gray islands are primary eutectic carbide; the light crystals are MC particles; the peppery constituent within grains of the matrix is $M_{23}C_6$. Kalling's reagent. 500$\times$

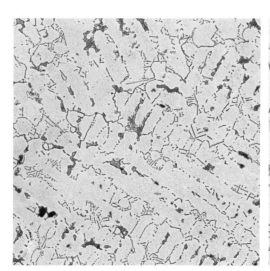

**Fig. 140** MAR-M 509, as-cast. The structure consists of MC particles in script form and $M_{23}C_6$ particles in eutectic form (gray areas) and precipitate form in the dendritic $\alpha$ solid-solution matrix (fcc). Kalling's reagent. 100×

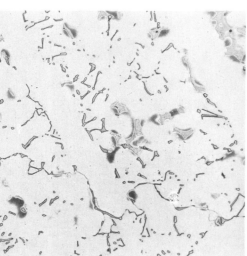

**Fig. 141** Same as Fig. 140, but at a higher magnification to reveal morphology of MC script particles, primary eutectic particles ($M_{23}C_6$), and precipitated $M_{23}C_6$ (shadowy constituent) in the $\alpha$ (fcc) matrix. Electrolytic etch: 5% $H_3PO_4$. 500×

**Fig. 142** MAR-M 509, aged at 705 °C (1300 °F). Thin-foil electron micrograph. Top left to bottom right: precipitated $M_{23}C_6$; $\alpha$ (fcc) matrix; blocky $M_{23}C_6$ with cobalt; cobalt with internal precipitate; lamellar $M_{23}C_6$ in matrix. As-polished. 10 000×

# Aluminum Alloys

ALUMINUM ALLOYS encompass a wide range of chemical compositions and thus a wide range of hardnesses. Therefore, the techniques required for metallographic preparation and examination vary considerably. Softer alloys generally are more difficult to prepare by mechanical polishing, because (1) deformation caused by cutting and grinding extends to a greater depth, (2) the embedding of abrasive particles in the metal during polishing is more likely, and (3) relief between the matrix and second-phase particles, which are considerably harder than the matrix, develops more readily during polishing. Harder alloys, although easier to prepare, present a greater variety of phases and complexities of structure. However, methods exist for circumventing the difficulties of preparing and examining soft and hard alloys. Many methods are general and apply to all metals, but some have been developed specifically for aluminum alloys.

Many recovery and precipitation processes in aluminum alloys can occur at relatively low temperatures, such as 150 to 250 °C (300 to 480 °F), which are readily produced in such operations as cutting, grinding, and mounting. These operations rarely produce changes visible by optical microscopy, although they may do so in extreme cases. However, they can produce changes in structure that are visible with an electron microscope. The metal must not overheat during specimen preparation: extra care must be taken when using unconventional methods or materials.

Aluminum is a chemically active metal that derives its stability and corrosion resistance from a protective film of oxide that prevents as-polished and etched surfaces from deteriorating rapidly. Oxide films thicker than normal can be formed in a controlled manner by making the specimen the anode of an electrolytic cell. These films can be used to reveal microstructural features.

When some types of anodic films are formed on a polished surface and when the surface is examined with reflected plane-polarized light passed through an analyzer, striking contrast effects are produced that reveal grain size and shape and orientation differences (Ref 1). Anodic film replicas have also proved useful in electron microscopy.

## Preparation for Macroscopic Examination

Aluminum alloys require the same principles of preparation for macroscopic examination as most metals. Careful and thorough visual inspection of the part or shape to be examined should precede cutting or etching. Fracture surfaces should be carefully preserved to guard against abrasion or contamination. If the part is to be sectioned, selection of the cutting plane is determined by directionality or fibering due to the working process by which the part was formed, by the suspected or known form of defect, and by the general form or nature of the part (for example, casting, forging, extrusion, or weldment).

**Mechanical Preparation.** The purpose of the examination and the type of etchant to be used determine the proper preparation of a cut surface for etching. Most macroetchants can reveal some details of macrostructure on a rough cut surface, but the overetching necessitated by the lack of initial smoothness can easily obscure significant details. Generally, a smoother or more highly polished surface requires less etching to reveal the same amount of gross detail; it also reduces the chance of losing fine detail.

Machined surfaces frequently are acceptable for macroetching and examination. However, machining with a dull tool or at unfavorable speed and feed can distort the surface and misrepresent grain structure or degree of porosity. This is particularly important when using dye penetrant and developer for revealing density, shrinkage, or gas porosity in a cast material. A shaper or milling machine is preferred to a lathe, which does not provide a constant cutting speed on a flat surface.

**Chemical Preparation.** Removal of cutting oils and other greasy contaminants from aluminum surfaces before etching is helpful, but not always necessary. Table 1 lists several etchants and etching methods that will adequately prepare specimens for macroexamination. Other combinations of concentration, proportions or dilution, temperature, and time often can be used without greatly altering the end effects.

The caustic etch (etchant 1 in Table 1) is an excellent degreaser. The acidic etchants are more likely than the caustic etch to act unevenly if the surface is not precleaned. Thorough degreasing should precede dye penetrant testing. Before the dye penetrant is applied, a very light caustic etch (etchant 1 in Table 1) can be used to remove any minor sealing of porosity by smeared metal. These precautions ensure a surface free from smeared metal and are particularly important in evaluating direct-chill cast ingots, in which the dimensions of individual pores may be quite small.

Customary safety precautions in handling strong reagents, including proper ventilation, should always be observed. Etchant containers should be chosen for their resistance to reaction with hydrofluoric acid (HF) or caustic. Final rinsing in warm or hot tap water facilitates drying. Blowing dry with clean compressed air lessens the chances of staining.

## Preparation for Microscopic Examination

The optimum procedure for microscopic examination is determined using the same considerations as for macroscopic examination, although the area to be examined usually is smaller.

**Sectioning.** Aluminum alloys can be sectioned by any standard cutting method; however, the cutting must not alter the structure or the configuration of the specimen in the plane to be examined. Because many aluminum alloys are soft, sawing or shearing

Revised by Richard H. Stevens, Technologist, Aluminum Company of America

**Table 1  Etchants for macroscopic examination of aluminum alloys**
See Table 2 for applicability to specific alloys

| Etchant | Composition | Procedure for use |
|---|---|---|
| 1 (caustic etch) . . . . . . . . . . | 10 g NaOH to each 90 mL $H_2O$ | Immerse specimen 5–15 min in solution heated to 60–70 °C (140–160 °F)(a), rinse in water, dip in 50% $HNO_3$ solution to desmut, rinse in water, dry. |
| 2 (Tucker's reagent) . . . . . . | 45 mL HCl (conc), 15 mL $HNO_3$ (conc), 15 mL HF (48%), 25 mL $H_2O$ | Mix fresh before using. Immerse or swab specimen for 10–15 s, rinse in warm water, dry, and examine for desired effect. Repeat until desired effect is obtained. |
| 3 . . . . . . . . . . . . . . . . . . . . . | 1 mL HF (48%), 9 mL $H_2O$ | Requires fairly smooth surface. Immerse until desired effect is obtained, hot water rinse, dry. |
| 4 (Poulton's reagent) . . . . . . | 12 mL HCl (conc), 6 mL $HNO_3$ (conc), 1 mL HF (48%), 1 mL $H_2O$ | May be premixed and stored(b) for long periods. Etch by brief immersion or by swabbing. Rinse in cool water, and do not allow the etchant or the specimen to heat during etching. |
| 5 . . . . . . . . . . . . . . . . . . . . . | 50 mL HCl (conc), 15 mL $HNO_3$ (conc), 3 mL HF (48%), 5 mL $FeCl_3$ solution (conc) | Mix fresh before using. Cool solution to 10–15 °C (50–60 °F) with jacket of cold water. Immerse a few seconds, rinse in cold water; repeat until desired effect is obtained. |
| 6 . . . . . . . . . . . . . . . . . . . . . | 10 mL HCl (conc), 30 mL $HNO_3$ (conc), 20 mL $H_2O$, 5 g $FeCl_3$ | Mix fresh before using. Add HCl last. Use at room temperature. Immerse a few seconds, rinse in cold water; repeat until desired effect is obtained. Can also use by swabbing. |
| 7 . . . . . . . . . . . . . . . . . . . . . | 60 mL HCl (conc), 40 mL $HNO_3$ (conc) | Mix fresh before using. Immerse or swab for a few seconds, rinse in cold water, dry, examine. Repeat until desired effect is obtained. |
| 8 . . . . . . . . . . . . . . . . . . . . . | 20 g $CuCl_2$ (cupric chloride), 100 mL $H_2O$ | Immerse specimen for a few seconds. Remove copper deposit with a mixture of 6 parts $HNO_3$ (conc) and 1 part HF (conc). Repeat until desired effect is obtained, cleaning with $HNO_3$-HF mixture and rinsing in water between steps. |

(a) This etchant may be used without being heated, but etching action will be slower. (b) Solution should be stored in a vented container, preferably under a fume hood, to prevent buildup of gas pressure. The container should be made of polyethylene or be lined with wax.

should be done at a distance from the plane to be polished and then the intervening deformed material removed by wet grinding and polishing. An abrasive saw permits cutting closer to the plane of polishing.

The temperature of the metal must not increase sufficiently during cutting to affect adversely the results of the examination. Because the grains in wrought aluminum alloys are rarely equiaxed, sections for determining grain size must be defined regarding the principal direction of working.

**Mounting** in a plastic medium to form a cylindrical piece is the accepted procedure, unless the specimen is large enough to be hand held for subsequent grinding and polishing. Standard mounting materials and methods are described in the article "Mounting of Specimens" in this Volume.

Special problems relating to the selection of mounting method or material may be caused by (1) inclusion of alloys of dissimilar hardnesses in the same mount, (2) the need to maintain flatness to the edge, (3) the need to mount thin sheet specimens for polishing in a plane perpendicular to the rolled surface, and (4) the need to connect electrical leads to one or more specimens for subsequent electropolishing or electrolytic etching. The mounting medium should not be so hard that it inhibits polishing of the softest aluminum contained in the mount or so soft that it allows rounding of the metal edges. Specimen edges whose flatness must be preserved should not be placed near the outer edge of the mounting ring.

Thin sheet specimens can be bent or clamped in various ways, but it is most convenient to pack mount them by bolting layers together. The bolted pack can be mounted in plastic or cut to a convenient shape and size for polishing. If a bolt material other than an aluminum alloy is used, it should be coated or insulated before etching to prevent galvanic corrosion.

Entrapment and seepage of liquid between layers can be minimized by immersing the pack mount in a bath of molten wax for a few minutes, removing it from the bath and cooling it until the wax has solidified, then wiping off the excess wax. Interleaving with a soft aluminum foil or thin sheet helps distinguish the interface between similar alloys, aids in revealing the thickness of anodic films, and minimizes entrapment and seepage of liquid between layers. Pack mounts are also convenient when multiple-sheet specimens are to be electropolished or electrolytically etched.

Various methods are used for making electrical connections to metal mounted in plastic. One method is to make the mount electrically conductive by preparing it from an approximately equal mixture of plastic mounting powder with clean, dry aluminum chips from a band saw.

When the heat or pressure of mounting must be avoided, various castable plastics can be used at room temperature. They can be used to fill in crevices and cracks by vacuum impregnation, even when thermal mounting is to be used.

**Grinding.** Aluminum alloys can be ground using the same general techniques for all metals. Because aluminum alloys can be ground readily with various abrasives, selection is made on an individual basis. Generally, grinding is performed in successive steps using silicon carbide abrasive papers of 180,

220, 320, 400, and 600 grit. The starting grit size depends on the type of cut surface being removed. If the specimen has been cut with a hacksaw or band saw, 180- or 220-grit paper should be used. If the specimen has been cut with a jeweler's saw or a fine abrasive or diamond wheel, initial grinding can be performed using 320-, 400-, or 500-grit paper.

Silicon carbide papers in grit sizes of 800 and 1000 are available from some suppliers; these are equivalent to 10 and 5 $\mu m$, respectively. Using 800- and 1000-grit silicon carbide papers, fine grinding can be achieved without using diamond abrasives. These finer grit sizes cause less surface deformation and produce a more uniform surface finish than diamond abrasives, thus facilitating subsequent polishings. If these papers are used, the number of grinding steps can often be reduced to five: 220, 400, 600, 800, then 1000 grit.

Motor-driven belt grinders or disk-shaped laps hasten grinding, but care must be taken to prevent overheating of the specimen. Running water suffices as a coolant and lubricant at all stages when used with a water-resistant backing for abrasive materials. The specimen should be thoroughly washed after each grinding to prevent carryover of abrasive particles to the next stage.

Abrasive particles embed easily into softer aluminum alloys. Therefore, kerosene, with or without dissolved paraffin, may be applied periodically to metallographic emery papers while hand grinding. During wet grindings with silicon carbide papers, however, less pressure should be applied to the specimen and adequate water should be used to flush away loose abrasive particles.

## Mechanical Polishing

Mechanical polishing can be accomplished in two steps: rough and finish polishing.

**Rough polishing** is performed using a suspension of 600-grit alumina ($Al_2O_3$) powder in distilled water (50 g/500 mL $H_2O$) on a billiard cloth fixed to a rotating wheel. Diamond abrasive of 6, 3, or 1 $\mu m$ (depending on the final grinding step used) on a short-nap cloth disk can also be used. The 600-grit $Al_2O_3$ is excellent for removing the thin layer of metal that smears over fine cracks and porosity during rough grinding; however, excessive time and pressure will result in rounded specimen edges and constituents in relief.

These problems can be addressed with a subsequent step using 1-$\mu m$ diamond on a short-nap cloth. The diamond can be applied as a paste or as spray and replenished as needed to provide continued cutting action. During diamond polishing, a lubricant of kerosene or a propylene glycol solution should be added to the rotating wheel. Propylene glycol solutions are the most commonly used lubricant.

Considerable hand pressure is used initially, then gradually reduced. Wheel speeds of 500 to 700 rpm are typical. For rough polishing to be successful, polishing times should range from 1 to 2 min, and short-nap cloths should be used. Specimens should be thoroughly washed or ultrasonically cleaned to remove all abrasive after rough polishing.

**Final polishing** of aluminum alloys is generally performed using a pure, heavy grade of magnesium oxide (MgO) powder with distilled or deionized water on a uniformly textured medium- or short-nap cloth. A suspension of silicon dioxide ($SiO_2$) in distilled water is also available commercially. This medium has a slightly basic pH and a grit size of 0.04 $\mu$m. An advantage of $SiO_2$ is its ability to remain in suspension; therefore, it can be purchased in the liquid form, then used without preparation.

The same guidelines for cleanliness apply to $SiO_2$ as to MgO; the polishing cloth must be cleaned carefully immediately after each use to prevent the compound from hardening, thus rendering the polishing cloth ineffective. The mouth of the container in which the suspension of $SiO_2$ is stored should be wiped clean before pouring any material on the polishing cloth so that the hard particles that have formed around the mouth are not carried onto the cloth. The MgO should be kept in tight, dry containers. It can also be reclaimed by sifting through a 200-mesh screen or by baking for a few minutes at 800 to 1000 °C (1470 to 1830 °F).

When final polishing with MgO, a teaspoon of the abrasive is applied near the center of the cloth, moistened with distilled or deionized water, then worked into a paste. A variable-speed wheel is preferred for final polishing; however, a two-speed wheel is satisfactory if the speeds are approximately 350 rpm or less.

Considerable hand pressure and frequent rotation of the specimen are used for the first few minutes, and only enough water is added to avoid dryness and pulling of the specimen by the cloth. Gradually, pressure is reduced, and more water is added to wash away excess abrasive. Toward the end of the polish, copious water can be used to remove all abrasive, and the polishing cloth in effect wipes the specimen clean.

Residual abrasive may be removed by lightly applying a clean, wet cotton swab. Final rinsing can be done with warm or hot tap water, and the specimen should be blown dry. The operation requires 5 to 15 min, depending on the skill of the operator, the alloy, and prior preparation.

A similar procedure is followed when using the suspension of $SiO_2$, except that a small to medium quantity of abrasive is poured onto the cloth, then spread around manually before starting the wheel. During polishing, additional small quantities of abrasive are added occasionally to the wheel for replenishment, finishing with distilled or deionized water to rinse the specimen.

When 1-$\mu$m diamond abrasive has been used in rough polishing, only a very brief and light touch-up on a MgO or $SiO_2$ cloth lap may be required to remove the last traces of polishing scratches. This procedure helps preserve the flatness of the microconstituents.

Alumina suspensions are particularly useful on aluminum alloys containing copper, because corrosion and plating of constituents may occur in these alloys during prolonged polishing with MgO. Whenever the volume of work warrants, multispecimen vibratory or automatic polishing methods can be used successfully for aluminum alloys.

Artifacts, or misleading microstructural features, can be produced by mechanical polishing. Failure to completely remove all metallographic paper scratches during rough polishing can leave isolated pits that falsely appear as porosity. Embedded abrasive appears as pitting or a second phase. In the presence of slightly acidic water, magnesium-rich phases can tarnish and pit; these conditions are exacerbated by overly long final polishing times or excessive water.

Very soft phases, such as lead and bismuth, are easily torn out during polishing. If there is any doubt concerning the testing results, a complete repolish is recommended. Some polishing conditions can be varied in a direction that would eliminate possible artifacts. For minimum tarnishing or minimum removal of soft phases, the 1.0-$\mu$m diamond polish, followed by a brief cleanup with MgO or $SiO_2$, is recommended.

## Chemical and Electrolytic Polishing

Although chemical and electrolytic polishing can eliminate many of the tedious hand operations of mechanical polishing, good definition of second-phase particles is less likely to be obtained than with mechanical polishing, and it is almost impossible to preserve a level polish out to an edge or within a crack or crevice. Both techniques are useful for preparing very pure alloys containing little or no second phase, or for preparing very soft alloys, which are difficult to polish mechanically. Other uses include applications in which general grain structure is the main feature of interest or where it is undesirable to cut a large surface down to a manageable size for mechanical polishing. In the latter case, a small area is masked off for chemical or electrolytic polishing.

**Chemical polishing** does not level rough surfaces as efficiently as electropolishing and so generally requires a smoother starting surface. However, it is more convenient for large areas. Solutions similar to those for commercial bright dip finishing can be used.

One method of chemical polishing is:

- *Solution*: 1 part concentrated nitric acid ($HNO_3$), 1 part ethanol; add 1% or less of a 30% solution of hydrogen peroxide ($H_2O_2$). Optimum concentration of $H_2O_2$ depends on the alloy being polished.
- *Temperature*: 0 °C (32 °F); maintain with ice bath
- *Time*: 10 to 30 min (use mechanical stirring)

- *Comments*: Start with the equivalent of a 600-grit polished surface

**Electrolytic polishing** can be performed using commercially available equipment and polishing solutions. Typical conditions for polishing are:

- *Electrolyte*: 62 mL of a 70% solution of perchloric acid ($HClO_4$), 700 mL ethanol, 100 mL 2-butoxyethanol (also known as butyl cellosolve and ethanol glycol monobutyl ether), and 137 mL distilled $H_2O$
- *Current density*: 3.85 A/cm$^2$ (24.8 A/in.$^2$); specimen is anode
- *Time*: 20 s; from 3/0 emery-paper finish
- *Comments*: Rinse in warm water, alcohol, dry in warm air. To prevent or minimize overheating of the specimen, polish in 10-s intervals, allowing specimen to cool during "off" periods.

Another commonly used electrolyte is a solution of 25 mL concentrated $HNO_3$ in 75 mL methanol. Both solutions present the usual hazards associated with the use of acids; in addition, the $HClO_4$ electrolytes pose special hazards. Electrolytes of $HClO_4$ and acetic anhydride are extremely dangerous to prepare and use and can explode if improperly handled. However, the $HClO_4$ electrolyte described above is safe to mix and to use if the precautions given in the article "Electrolytic Polishing" in this Volume are observed. For additional information, see the article "Etching" in this Volume.

The time required to produce a good electrolytic polish depends on the surface finish obtained in previous mechanical grinding or polishing—the finer the finish, the shorter the time. Heating of the specimen may occur when high currents or large contact resistances are encountered. Therefore, the size of the area to be polished should be restricted; a diameter of 10 mm (0.4 in.) is typical. Moreover, good electrical contact should be established with the specimens. The point of contact and the contacting wire should be isolated from the electrolyte and any dissimilar metals, such as copper and steel. Continuous cooling of specimen or electrolyte offers additional control.

## Macroexamination

Macroexamination of aluminum alloys is accomplished using techniques similar to those used for other metals. Much can be learned from low-magnification examination of fractures and macroetched sections. Macroexamination of cast products can reveal the degree of refinement and/or modification of silicon in silicon-containing alloys; grain size, evidence of abnormally coarse constituents, oxide inclusions, porosity, and, in many cases, type of failure, can also be studied. Fractures of forgings, extrusions, sheet, and plate can show oxide stringers, bright flakes, dark flakes, porosity, segregation of phases that have limited solubility in aluminum, flow patterns, an indication of grain size, changes in plastic deformation, overheating (eutectic melting), and type of failure.

Grain size, grain flow, and fabricating or casting defects can be observed from cut, machined, and macroetched sections. If machining does not provide a surface fine enough for adequate resolution of the macrostructure after etching, grinding with a fine silicon carbide abrasive grit paper may be necessary.

**Macroetching.** Caution must be exercised when assessing the grain size of wrought aluminum alloy products by macroetching the outer surfaces. In sheet materials, the surface grains may be deceptively fine; in forgings or extrusions, there may be a very shallow surface layer of coarse grains. Therefore, it is advisable to have some correlation with grain structure in the interior, as shown in a cross section (see Fig. 62).

Table 2 indicates the etchants in Table 1 that apply to various classes of alloys. Table 2 presents a choice between caustic and mixed-acid etching; selection should be based on the primary purpose of the examination. Mixed-acid etchants are excellent for revealing grain size, shape, and contrast, but may obscure such defects as fine cracks, inclusions of oxide skin, or porosity.

Caustic etchant is preferred for revealing defects, exaggerating fine cracks, and showing flow lines or fibering. Although grain structure in alloys with high silicon content is difficult to reveal by macroetching, etchant 8 in Table 1 and hydrofluoric acid (HF) etchant have proved useful.

The 6xxx series alloys are difficult to macroetch for grain size or grain flow; however, etchant 6 in Table 1 has proved successful. This etchant can also be used on most other alloys, particularly the 2xxx and 7xxx series alloys. Etchant 7 in Table 1 satisfactorily reveals grains and grain flow in aluminum-lithium alloys.

Examination or photography of macrospecimens requires proper illumination. It is often advisable to try alternate types of illumination or to rotate the surface being examined. This is particularly true of fracture surfaces. Features that appear black with one

**Table 3  Etchants for use in microscopic examination of aluminum alloys**
See Table 4 for applicability to specific alloys.

| Etchant | Composition | Procedure for use |
|---|---|---|
| 1 (HF etch) | 1 mL HF (48%), 200 mL $H_2O$ | Swab for 15 s or immerse for 30–45 s |
| 2 | 1 g NaOH, 100 mL $H_2O$ | Swab for 5–10 s |
| 3A (Keller's reagent) | 2 mL HF (48%), 3 mL HCl (conc), 5 mL $HNO_3$ (conc), 190 mL $H_2O$ | Immerse for 8–15 s, wash in stream of warm water, blow dry. Do not remove etching products from surface. |
| 3B (dilute Keller's reagent) | 20 mL etchant 3A, 80 mL $H_2O$ | Mix fresh before using. Immerse specimen for 5–10 s. |
| 4 (modified Keller's reagent) | 2 mL HF (48%), 3 mL HCl (conc), 20 mL $HNO_3$ (conc), 175 mL $H_2O$ | Immerse for 10–60 s, wash in stream of warm water, blow dry. Do not remove etching products from surface. |
| 5 (Barker's reagent) | 4 to 5 mL $HBF_4$ (48%), 200 mL $H_2O$ | Electrolytic: use aluminum, lead, or stainless steel for cathode; specimen is anode. Anodize 40–80 s at approximately 0.2 A/cm² (1.3 A/in.², or about 20 V dc). Check results on microscope with crossed polarizers. |
| 6 | 25 mL $HNO_3$ (conc), 75 mL $H_2O$ | Immerse in solution at 70 °C (160 °F) for 45–60 s. |
| 7 | 20 mL $H_2SO_4$ (conc), 80 mL $H_2O$ | Immerse at 70 °C (160 °F) for 30 s; rinse in cold water. |
| 8 | 10 mL $H_3PO_4$ (85%), 90 mL $H_2O$ | Immerse at 50 °C (120 °F) 1 min or 3–5 min (see Table 4). |
| 9 | 5 mL HF (48%), 10 mL $H_2SO_4$, 85 mL $H_2O$ | Immerse for 30 s. |
| 10 | 4 g $KMnO_4$, 2 g $Na_2CO_3$, 94 mL $H_2O$, a few drops wetting agent | Specimen surface must be well polished and precleaned in 20% $H_3PO_4$ at 95 °C (205 °F) for uniform wettability. After precleaning, rinse in cold water and immediately immerse in etchant for 30 s. |
| 11 | 2 g NaOH, 5 g NaF, 93 mL $H_2O$ | Immerse for 2–3 min. |
| 12 | 50 mL Poulton's reagent (etchant 4 in Table 1), 25 mL $HNO_3$ (conc), 40 mL of solution of 3 g chromic acid per 10 mL of $H_2O$ | Put a few drops on as-rolled or as-extruded surface for 1–4 min, rinse, and swab to desmut. Examine on microscope with crossed polarizers to show grains. Repeat etching, if necessary. For some 5xxx alloys, increase $HNO_3$ in solution to 50 mL. |
| 13 | 8 mL $HNO_3$ (conc), 2 mL HCl (conc), 45 mL $H_2O$, 45 mL methanol | Immerse for 10 s. |
| 14 | 5 mL acetic acid (glacial), 1 mL $HNO_3$ (conc), 94 mL $H_2O$ | Immerse for 20–30 min. |
| 15 (Graff/Sargent reagent) | 15.5 mL $HNO_3$ (conc), 0.5 mL HF (48%), 3.0 g $CrO_3$, 84.0 mL $H_2O$ | Mix fresh before using. Use at room temperature. Immerse sample and agitate mildly for 20–60 s. A second etching in Keller's reagent may further develop the structure. |

type of illumination may actually have bright specular surfaces that reflect light away from the viewing lens or objective. Thus, what appears to be a dark inclusion may actually be a brittle cleavage fracture. Linear features or defects that are parallel to the plane of incidence of the illumination are difficult to see, but they become less difficult to detect when the specimen is rotated regarding the plane of incidence.

## Microexamination

Microscopic examination and photomicrography of the polished specimen before etching is often advisable, because etching can obscure as well as reveal important details, such as incipient melting, fine cracks, and nonmetallic inclusions. Table 3 lists etchants that encompass the conventional purposes of microscopic examination of commercial aluminum alloys. Table 4 describes these purposes and suggests etchants that are best suited to the various classes of alloys.

It is often possible to apply a second etch directly over the first without repolishing, as dictated by experience. Generally, the etch-

ants that reveal grain structure are the most aggressive and should be applied last. When use of more than one etchant is anticipated and when these etchants cannot be used together, valuable repolishing time can be saved by immersing a portion of the polished specimen area, keeping the remainder for another etchant.

**Etching to reveal grain structure** cannot be easily performed on all alloys. On alloys with low alloy content, chemical etching of grains produces relief effects and steps at the grain boundaries, which do not provide well-defined grain structure. In these instances, an anodic film should be applied (using etchant 5 in Table 3), and the specimen should be viewed with plane-polarized illumination passed through an analyzer (Ref 1, 2). A properly applied film can rotate the plane of polarization regarding the orientation of the underlying grain, thus producing various shades of black, gray, or white; the specimen should be rotated to provide maximum color contrast. The contrast effects can be converted to striking color contrast by inserting a sensitive tint or quarter-wave plate.

Grain structure in more highly alloyed materials can be revealed in two ways. Alloys

**Table 2  Applicability of etchants in Table 1 to macroexamination of aluminum alloys**

| Alloy | Etchant |
|---|---|
| High-purity aluminum | 4 or 5 |
| Commercial-purity aluminum: | |
| 1xxx series | 1, 2, or 4 |
| All high-copper alloys: | |
| 2xxx series and casting alloys | 1, 6, or 7 |
| Al-Mn alloys: | |
| 3xxx series | 1, 2, 4, or 6 |
| Al-Si alloys: | |
| 4xxx series and casting alloys(a) | 2, 3, 4, or 8 |
| Al-Mg alloys: | |
| 5xxx series and casting alloys | 1, 2, 4, or 6 |
| Al-Mg-Si alloys: | |
| 6xxx series and casting alloys | 1, 2, 4, or 6 |
| Al-Cu-Mg-Zn alloys: | |
| 7xxx series and casting alloys | 1 or 6 |

(a) Also welds and brazed joints made with the use of these alloys as filler metals

**Table 4  Applicability of etchants in Table 3 to microscopic examination of aluminum alloys**

| Alloy | Etchant | Evidence revealed |
|---|---|---|
| **Examination for grain size and shape** | | |
| 1xxx, 3xxx, 5xxx, 6xxx series; most casting alloys | 5 or 12 | Grain contrast when using crossed polarizers, with or without sensitive tint |
| 2xxx, 7xxx series; aluminum-copper or aluminum-zinc casting alloys | 3A or 11, 15 | Grain contrast or grain-boundary lines |
| 5xxx series alloys with more than 3% Mg | 8 (3–5 min) | Precipitation in grain boundaries |
| **Examination for cold working** | | |
| 1xxx, 3xxx, 5xxx, 6xxx series alloys | 5 or 12 | Deformation bands or markings that cause streaked effect when using crossed polarizers |
| 2xxx, 7xxx series alloys | 3A or 11 | Deformation bands or markings that accompany relatively great amounts of cold working |
| xxx series alloys with more than 3% Mg | 8 (3–5 min) | Precipitation in bands of slip |
| **Examination for incomplete recrystallization** | | |
| 1xxx, 3xxx, 5xxx, 6xxx series alloys | 5 or 12 | Even-toned, well-outlined grains that are recrystallized, otherwise streaked, or banded |
| 2xxx series alloys, hot worked and heat treated | 3A or 11, 15 | Unrecrystallized grains of multiple, very fine subgrains |
| 6xxx series alloys, hot worked and heat treated | 9, 15 | Unrecrystallized grains of multiple, very fine subgrains |
| 7xxx series alloys, hot worked and heat treated | 8 (3–5 min) or 14, 15 | Unrecrystallized grains of multiple, very fine subgrains |
| **Examination for preferred orientation** | | |
| 1xxx, 3xxx, 5xxx, 6xxx series alloys | 5 or 12 | Predominance of certain gray tones when crossed polarizers are used; lack of randomness |
| 2xxx series alloys in T4 temper | 3A or 11, 15 | Lack of randomness in grain contrast |
| **Examination for identification of constituents** | | |
| xxx series alloys | 1 or 7 | See Table 5. |
| 2xxx, 3xxx series; aluminum-copper and aluminum-manganese casting alloys | 8 (1 min) | See Table 5. |
| 7xxx series; aluminum-zinc casting alloys | 3B | See Table 5. |
| **Examination for overheating (partial melting)** | | |
| 2xxx series alloys | 8 (1 min) | Rosettes and grain-boundary eutectic |
| 6xxx series alloys | 2 | Grain-boundary eutectic formations |
| 7xxx series alloys | 3B | Rosettes and grain-boundary eutectic formations |
| **Examination for general constituent size and distribution** | | |
| All wrought alloys and casting alloys | 1, 8, 15 (1 min) or any etchant that does not pit solid-solution matrix | Coarse insoluble particles and fine precipitate particles. Longer etching time exaggerates size of fine particles. |
| **Examination for distinction between solution-heat-treated (T4) and artificially aged (T6) tempers** | | |
| 2xxx series alloys | 3A or 11 | Loss of grain contrast, general darkening, in T6 compared with T4 |
| 6061 | 9 | Clear outlining of grain boundaries in T6; faint outlining in T4 |
| 7075, recrystallized | 4 | More grain contrast, sharper grain-boundary outlining, in T4 |
| **Examination for overaging or poor quench of solution-heat-treated alloy** | | |
| 2017 and 2024, in T4 temper | 6 | Faint dark precipitate at grain boundaries |
| **Examination for cladding thickness** | | |
| Alclad 2014, 2024, 7075 | 3A or 11 | Boundary between high grain contrast or outlining of alloy core and lighter-etching cladding |
| Brazing sheet | 1 (swab) or 13 | Boundary of high-silicon cladding alloy |
| Other clad alloys | 1 (immerse), 2, 3A, 5, or 11 | Any differences in structure that demarcate one layer from another |
| **Examination for solid-solution coring or segregation and diffusion effects** | | |
| 3xxx, 5xxx series; aluminum-magnesium casting alloys | 10 | Interference colors due to differences in thickness of tarnish films laid down on the surface |
| 2xxx series alloys and others with more than 1% Cu | 3A or 11 | Brownish-colored films due to redeposition of copper |

containing more than about 1 wt% Cu will etch pit and simultaneously form redeposited copper films, which produce a grain color contrast. In other alloys, grain-boundary precipitates may delineate the grain boundaries upon chemical etching if the metallurgical treatments have been favorable for this effect. A very dense precipitate, as in annealed or hot-worked heat-treatable alloys, makes it difficult or impossible to produce any grain contrast or to delineate grain boundaries by etching (see Fig. 47, 74, and 75).

**Etching for identification of phases** should be attempted only after a preliminary examination of the as-polished specimen to determine the natural colors of the phases. Table 5 lists etchants that have recognized effects on the second phase, particularly in certain classes of alloys. Etching may produce one of the following effects:

1. None—the etchant does not attack the second phase or the matrix.
2. Outlining of the second phase by virtue of unequal rate of attack between it and the matrix, but no change in color
3. Darkening due to roughening or pitting of

**Table 5 Metallographic identification of phases in aluminum alloys(a)**

| Basic and alternative phase designations(b) | Elements that enter in solution | External shape(c) | Appearance before etching(d) | Birefringence(e) | Etchants that aid identification(f) |
|---|---|---|---|---|---|
| Si | … | Cubic habit; primary particles form isometric polygons; eutectic may form script, blades or very fine lamellae | Light bluish-gray | None | Generally best identified without etching. Etchant 1 (swab) outlines particles and appears to lighten the color. |
| $Mg_2Si$ | … | Cubic habit; eutectic forms script that easily coalesces on heating | Natural color is darker bluish-gray than silicon, but usually tarnishes to bright blue, black, or vari-colored | None (when not roughened or tarnished) | Easily identified without etching. Caustic Etchant 2 will not attack and may enhance blue color. Acid etchants will attack and dissolve readily. |
| $MgZn_2$ or $\eta$ (Mg-Zn) | Isomorphous series with CuMgAl | Usually well rounded or irregular, except in lamellar eutectic or precipitated from solid solution | White, watery; does not polish in relief | Slight change from light to dark gray | Etchant 3B gives a smooth, dark-gray to black color. |
| $CrAl_7$ | Iron as $(Cr,Fe)Al_7$ Manganese as $(Cr,Mn)Al_7$ | Primary crystals form elongated polygons. | Light metallic gray | Weak, but will reveal twinning in large crystals | Resists attact by all common etchants |
| $CuAl_2$ or $\theta$ (Al-Cu) | … | Usually well rounded or irregular, except when precipitated from solid solution | Pale pinkish color | Strong, orange to greenish-blue Some orientations show little change. | Remains light and clear in etchants 1 (swab), 3A and 8 (1 min). Etchant 6 will darken and is good for detecting barely visible grain-boundary precipitate. |
| $FeAl_3$ | Chromium as $(Fe, Cr)Al_3$ Manganese as $(Fe, Mn)Al_3$ Possibly copper | Elongated blades or star-shaped clusters when eutectic. Resists coalescence | Light metallic gray; slightly darker than $Fe_3SiAl_{12}$ | Weak and not easily detectable | Etchant 7 will dissolve and blacken. In high-copper alloys, etchant 8 (1 min) will color it dark-brown to bluish-black. In aluminum-copper-magnesium-zinc alloys, etchant 3B will color it medium brown or gray; rough and outlined |
| $FeAl_6$ | A metastable phase in absence of manganese or copper (see $MnAl_6$) | Isomorphous with $MnAl_6$, but usually found only under conditions of high solidification rate; forms fine lamellar eutectic | Not easily defined, because of fine particle size | Same as $MnAl_6$ | Not attacked by etchant 7, but darkened by etchant 1 (swab) |
| $Mg_2Al_3$ or $Mg_5Al_8$, $\beta$ (Al-Mg) | … | Usually well rounded or irregular | White; lighter than aluminum, but may tarnish to yellow or tan; not in relief | None (when not tarnished) | Caustic etchant such as 2 will not attack or color. Acid etchants generally pit and dissolve it with varying rapidity. |
| $MnAl_6$ | Iron as $(Fe,Mn)Al_6$. Isomorphous with $(Fe,Cu)(Al,Cu)_6$ or $(Fe,Cu)Al_6$ | Primary or coarse eutectic forms solid or hollow parallelograms. Fine eutectic may form script. | Light metallic gray | Strong; light to dark gray. Does not twin | Etchant 8 (1 min) will not attack or darken this phase; however, it will attack companion phases such as $(Fe,Mn)Al_3$ or $(Fe,Mn)_3SiAl_{12}$. |
| $Cr_2Mg_3Al_{18}$ or T (Al-Cr-Mg), E (Al-Cr-Mg) | … | Usually forms by precipitation or by peritectic reaction from $CrAl_7$ | Very light metallic gray; not much in relief | None | Strongly attacked by etchants 6 and 7 |
| $(Fe,Cu)(Al,Cu)_6$ or $(Fe,Cu)Al_6$, $\alpha$ (Al-Cu-Fe) | ———————————— (See $MnAl_6$) ———————————— | | | | |
| $Cu_2FeAl_7$ or $\beta$ (Al-Cu-Fe) N (Al-Cu-Fe) | … | Elongated blades when formed eutectically. Also forms peritectically from $(Fe,Mn)_3SiAl_{12}$ and other iron-rich phases | Very light metallic gray; only slightly darker than $CuAl_2$ | Moderate; light to dark gray | Outlined, but not colored, by etchants 3B and 8 (1 min); hence, can be distinguished from other iron-rich phases with which it is associated. |
| $CuMgAl_2$ or $Cu_2Mg_2Al_5$, S (Al-Cu-Mg) | … | Very much resembles $CuAl_2$ | Slightly grayer than $CuAl_2$. Tarnishes to brown or black very readily during polishing | Very strong; yellowish to purple or greenish-blue | Roughened and darkened to varying degrees by etchants 3B and 8 (1 min), depending on polish. Etchant 3A darkens this phase, leaving $CuAl_2$ uncolored. Etchant 6 reveals barely visible grain-boundary precipitate. |
| CuMgAl | ———————————— (See $MgZn_2$) ———————————— | | | | |
| $Cr_4Si_4Al_{13}$ or $\alpha$ (Al-Cr-Si) | ———————————— (See $Fe_3SiAl_{12}$)(g) ———————————— | | | | |
| $CuMg_4Al_5$ or T (Al-Cu-Mg), c (Al-Cu-Mg) | Isomorphous series with $Mg_3Zn_3Al_2$ | Irregular rounded | Very light or slightly yellow | None | Behaves like other magnesium-rich phases, attacked rapidly by acidic etchants, not attacked by caustic etchants |
| $Fe_3SiAl_{12}$ or $Fe_3Si_2Al_{12}$, $\alpha$ (Al-Fe-Si), c (Al-Fe-Si); also $(Fe,Cu)_3SiAl_{12}$ or $\alpha$ (Al-Fe,Cr-Si); $(Fe,Mn)_3SiAl_{12}$ or $\alpha$ (Al-Fe,Mn-Si) | See footnote (g). Besides the apparent interchangeability of Fe, Cr, and Mn, this phase can probably also contain Cu. | Usually well-defined script when formed eutectically, especially when silicon is not low. May also form polyhedrons or irregular shapes, or precipitate as Widmanstätten type | Light metallic gray, slightly lighter than either $FeAl_3$ or $Fe_2Si_2Al_9$; often polishes in relief | None | This phase and its variants give various etching responses for a given etch, depending on its composition and that of the matrix. It is rarely attacked strongly, but it can darken to shades of brown when copper is present, using etchant 8 (1 min). In the absence of copper, etchant 8 (1 min) will roughen and outline it, distinguishing it from $MnAl_6$. Chromium makes it more resistant to etching. |

(continued)

**Table 5 (continued)**

| Basic and alternative phase designations(b) | Elements that enter in solution | External shape(c) | Appearance before etching(d) | Birefringence(e) | Etchants that aid identification(f) |
|---|---|---|---|---|---|
| $Fe_2Si_2Al_9$ or $FeSiAl_5$, $\beta$ (Al-Fe-Si) | ... | Bladelike when formed eutectically; retains flat shape in wrought alloys | Light metallic gray, intermediate between $Fe_3SiAl_{12}$ and Si | Moderate; light to dark gray | Etchant 1 (immerse) will attack and darken to varying degrees, depending on iron-silicon ratio. Etchant 7 will attack and dissolve it out. In both cases, $Fe_3SiAl_{12}$ is outlined but not appreciably darkened. |
| $Mg_3Zn_3Al_2$ or T (Al-Mg-Zn) | | ———————— (See $CuMg_4Al_5$) ———————— | | | |
| $Mn_3SiAl_{12}$ or $\alpha$ (Al-Mn-Si) | | ———————— (See $Fe_3SiAl_{12}$)(g) ———————— | | | |
| $Cu_2Mg_8Si_6Al_5$ or Q (Al-Cu-Mg-Si), $\lambda$ (Al-Cu-Mg-Si), h (Al-Cu-Mg-Si) | ... | This is a true quaternary phase; forms irregular shapes in eutectics | Light metallic gray; darker than $CuAl_2$ | Strong; changes from orange to blue | Etchant 8 (1 min) does not attack it, but the color distinction between it and $CuAl_2$ remains the same as when not etched. |
| $FeMg_3Si_6Al_8$ or Q (Al-Fe-Mg-Si), $\pi$ (Al-Fe-Mg-Si), h (Al-Fe-Mg-Si) | ... | This is a true quaternary phase; forms irregular shapes in eutectics; sometimes shows hexagonal symmetry | Very light metallic gray; not much in relief | Strong; changes from yellow to light blue | Not attacked by etchant 1 (immerse); hence, distinguished from $Fe_2Si_2Al_9$, with which it is usually associated |

(a) There are some phases other than those listed in this table that are less common or that appear in such small amount or as such fine particulate that identification can be made only indirectly. These include $TiAl_3$, $AlB_2$ and $TiB_2$, lead and bismuth, $NiAl_3$, $Ni_2Al_3$, $FeNiAl_9$, $Cu_3NiAl_6$, and $Cu_2Mn_3Al_{20}$. Other phases that do not normally come into equilibrium with aluminum may occasionally be encountered as a result of incomplete melting or some other abnormality in practice. (b) There is no widely accepted manner of naming or designating phases as they are encountered in equilibrium phase diagrams or in descriptions of alloy constitution. Even composition formulas are inexact, because many phases have broad homogeneity ranges or their actual composition may not coincide exactly with the ideal atomic arrangement upon which crystal structure is based. Phragmen (Ref 3) advocated using a lower-case letter prefix indicating the basic crystal structure (c = cubic, h = hexagonal, etc.). Otherwise, Greek letters and upper-case English letters have been arbitrarily used, although "T" usually denotes a ternary phase and "Q" a quaternary phase. (c) Applies mainly to case forms or to wrought alloys that have not been extensively worked. However, some iron-rich phases that resist coalescence or spheroidization will retain dimensional ratios that indicate crystalline symmetry. (d) Applies to appearance after mechanical polishing. Electrolytic polishing is rarely suitable for making phase identification. (e) An exceptional flat polish with no tarnishing is required, because any element of the surface not parallel to the plane of the surface (that is, normal to the optical axis) will cause an apparent birefringence that is not due to crystal structure. The sensitivity of this technique will also vary with the quality of the optical system. A rotating stage is necessary. (f) Etchant numbers referred to in this column correspond to etchants that are identified by number in column 1 of Table 3. (g) There are two crystal forms of $\alpha$ (Al-Fe-Si)—namely, $Fe_3SiAl_{12}$ (cubic, also called $\alpha_1$ and $Fe_2SiAl_8$) and $Fe_3Si_2Al_{12}$ (hexagonal, also called $\alpha_2$). It was believed at one time that cubic $Fe_3SiAl_{12}$ was isomorphous with analogous ternary phases $Cr_4Si_4Al_{13}$ and $Mn_3SiAl_{12}$, but the latter at least has since been found to be hexagonal. Nevertheless, the presence of even very small amounts of manganese, chromium, and copper in $\alpha$(Al-Fe-Si) seems to favor the cubic form normally encountered in commercial alloys. Metallographic distinction between the cubic and the hexagonal forms is very difficult to detect. When etched in etchant 3B (Table 3), complex alloys containing chromium and manganese (such as 5083 and 7075) may show etching contrasts within the scriptlike phase normally taken to be cubic $Fe_3SiAl_{12}$, but no separate identity has yet been established.

the surface of the second phase and, in the extreme, complete dissolution, leaving a hole that appears black or watery

4. Combined with effects 2 or 3—a tarnish or plated-out film on the second phase completely alters its color.

The quality of the polish and variations in composition, purity, or temperature of the etchant and time of etching also affect the exact polishing response. When more than one etchant is to be used for identifying phases in aluminum alloys, complete repolishing is recommended before the new etch is applied.

Other etching methods include thin film deposition for coloring phases or selective oxidation. However, phase identification is best accomplished using x-ray analysis, electron microprobe analysis, or a scanning electron microscope with an energy or wavelength dispersive system.

## Microstructures of Aluminum Alloys

Aluminum and its alloys are divided into two general categories: cast and wrought. Each of these categories is further divided into classes according to composition:

**Cast alloys**
- 1xx.x: Aluminum, 99.00% minimum and greater
- 2xx.x: Copper
- 3xx.x: Silicon, with added copper and/or magnesium
- 4xx.x: Silicon
- 5xx.x: Magnesium
- 7xx.x: Zinc
- 8xx.x: Tin
- 9xx.x: Other element

**Wrought alloys**
- 1xx.x: Aluminum, 99.00% minimum and and greater
- 2xxx: Copper
- 3xxx: Manganese
- 4xxx: Silicon
- 5xxx: Magnesium
- 6xxx: Magnesium and silicon
- 7xxx: Zinc
- 8xxx: Other element

**Aluminum-lithium alloys** are currently being developed, and to date, two alloys have been registered. Their nominal compositions are:

| | Alloy | |
|---|---|---|
| | 2090 | 8090 |
| Lithium | 2.2 | 2.4 |
| Copper | 2.7 | 1.2 |
| Magnesium | 0.0 | 0.7 |
| Zirconium | 0.12 | 0.12 |
| Iron | $\leq 0.12$ | $\leq 0.50$ |
| Silicon | $\leq 0.10$ | $\leq 0.30$ |
| Aluminum | rem | rem |

Experience suggests that these alloys are suited to conventional metallographic preparation techniques. For optical metallographic study, aluminum-lithium alloys can be etched for 30 to 45 s in Graff-Sargent etchant, followed by 7 to 8 s in Keller's etch. Alternatively, these alloys can be electropolished satisfactorily for viewing under polarized light.

When cast into ingots and hot worked to the final product form, these alloys generally exhibit unrecrystallized structures. Constituents can be identified optically and usually are aluminum-copper-iron. Particularly for alloy 2090, however, these constituents are small and widely spaced as a result of the very low iron and silicon contents.

**Dendrite cell size** or dendrite arm spacing is an important consideration in cast aluminum alloy microstructures, as discussed in the article "Solidification Structures of Aluminum Alloy Ingots" in this Volume. From the results of these measurements, information can be obtained regarding the rate of solidification of the material and therefore some indication of the strength of the material. For example, the finer the dendrite cell size, the higher the strength, all other features being equal. Measurement of dendrite cells or arm spacing is accomplished in the same manner as grain size measurement, that is, usually by the intercept method. For a discussion of the intercept method, see the article "Quantitative Metallography" in this Volume.

**Grain Size.** Because grains are seldom completely equiaxed in most wrought aluminum alloys, they must be measured in three dimensions using standardized section planes, and require some auxiliary expression of grain shape. A complete procedure for measuring the size of nonequiaxed grains is described in ASTM E 112 (Ref 4); however, this procedure does not apply to heavily worked materials or partially recrystallized alloys. It is difficult to alter manufacturing practices within normal limits such that a reproducible, specified measurable grain size can be repeatedly obtained, although processes are designed to avoid undesirable grain-size ranges.

Measured grain sizes usually are expressed in the number of grains per square millimeter, mean area per grain, or mean diameter per grain (Ref 4). The mean grain diameter is commonly used for cast alloys. Grain elongation or flattening may be expressed as a ratio of length to thickness, as observed in a longitudinal cross section. Shortcut methods employing comparison photomicrographs or grids are used in many laboratories; however, the intercept method is generally accepted.

**Temper.** The temper of work-hardened alloys or heat-treated alloys must be identified. None of the metallographic means for doing this is reliable. The degree of cold working theoretically can be estimated from the length-to-thickness ratio of cold-worked grains, but only if the dimensions of the annealed starting grains are equal in all directions.

Partly annealed tempers of work-hardened alloys are obtained by using heavy cold-work reductions, then heating the alloy in a temperature range that produces recovery but little or no recrystallization. Although recrystallization is observable, it is usually difficult to determine metallographically if recovery has occurred. When heat-treatable alloys are etched, there are subtle differences in appearance between the solution-heat-treated (T4) temper and the solution-heat-treated and artificially aged (T6) temper. Methods, such as those described in Table 4, have been devised for distinguishing between these two tempers, but they require experience and reproducibility of specimen preparation to be successful.

**Porosity** in aluminum alloy castings generally appears as round or rounded pores associated with gas or as elongated interdendritic pores referred to as "shrinkage." This occurs when there is inadequate feeding of the casting during solidification. In wrought material, pores are usually round or rounded, depending on the amount of working. In very thick plate or forgings, some residual ingot shrinkage may be present, because of the small amount of working. An approximately constituent-sized porosity heavier at the surfaces of the wrought product and diminishing in amount toward the quarter plane or center of the product occurring along the grain boundaries is known as "hydrogen deterioration" or, more commonly, as "HTO." This type of porosity results from diffusion of hydrogen, usually during a high-temperature thermal operation, such as an ingot homogenization or solution heat treatment. Use of a protective compound in these furnaces protects the material from HTO. Gas porosity in the ingot generally is not closed entirely during working of the metal, resulting in an elongated void, referred to as "bright flake," when viewed in a fracture through the metal.

**Eutectic melting** is detected in the microstructure by the presence of small, round islands of eutectic material in a fine, dendritic pattern within the rosettes, which occur whenever the eutectic melting temperature is exceeded. If the temperature during a thermal operation rises beyond the eutectic melting temperature, solid-solution melting will occur. This condition is present as a dendritic eutectic structure along grain boundaries, usually observed starting at the junction of three grains.

Eutectic melting and solid-solution melt-

ing generally are undesirable conditions that drastically affect the mechanical properties of the material and can cause quench cracking. However, partial melting, which occurs in an early thermal operation, such as ingot preheat, can be repaired in a later operation, such as solution heat treating, by dissolving the soluble phases in the rosettes.

**Powder Metallurgy Parts.** Examination of aluminum powders and blends is an important feature in the structural interpretation of aluminum powder metallurgy parts. When two parts of the powder blend are mixed with three parts of lucite powder, mounted, then prepared in the usual method for metallographic examination of metals, the dendritic structure of the individual grains can be observed after etching. A measurement of the dendrite cell size provides a measure of the chill rate for the individual particles. In addition, particles of copper, magnesium, and silicon can be identified and their distribution determined. The shape and size of the powder particles can also be approximated; however, the best technique for evaluating particle shape and size is scanning electron microscopy.

Examination of cross sections from powder metallurgy parts can provide information regarding density (porosity) and, for sintered parts, the degree of sintering and diffusion within powder particles and the presence of undissolved constituents and oxides. Hot-worked structures of aluminum powder metallurgy parts can also be evaluated; however, because of their extremely fine microstructures, they are not suitable for easy phase identification by optical microscopy. Etchant 15 in Table 3 is preferred for hot-worked powder metallurgy material. New high-strength powder metallurgy aluminum alloys 7090 and 7091 have the following nominal compositions:

| | Alloy | |
|---|---|---|
| | 7090 | 7091 |
| Copper | 1.0 | 1.5 |
| Magnesium | 2.5 | 2.5 |
| Zinc | 8.0 | 6.5 |
| Cobalt | 1.5 | 0.4 |
| Aluminum | rem | rem |

The typical hot-worked microstructure of these alloys is shown in the article "P/M Lightweight Metals" in Volume 7 of the 9th Edition of *Metals Handbook*.

**Phase identification** in aluminum alloys is an important aspect of metallography. The metallographer should recognize certain standard alloys or classes of alloys by the identifying characteristics of well-known, second-phase particles, although a chemical analysis always benefits any metallographic examination. When the alloy type is known, major abnormalities can be detected in composition or in metallurgical processing. The presence or absence of certain phases in a given alloy or their external shape provides information for tracing the metallurgical history of an alloy during manufacture or service.

All commercial wrought and cast alloys contain some insoluble particles in the aluminum matrix. In unalloyed aluminum (1xxx series), the particles consist of phases that contain impurity elements, mainly iron and silicon. In 3xxx series alloys, primary and eutectic particles of intermetallic phases of manganese with aluminum, silicon, and iron may be present. Alloys of the 5xxx series sometimes contain particles of $Mg_2Al_3$, $Mg_2Si$, and intermetallic phases with chromium and manganese.

Heat-treatable wrought and cast alloys contain soluble phases, which appear in various amounts and at various locations in the microstructure, depending on the thermal history of the specimen. In 2xxx series wrought alloys, the soluble phase is $CuAl_2$ or $CuMgAl_2$. In 6xxx series alloys, the most common intermetallic phase is $Mg_2Si$; particles of excess silicon may also be present. In 7xxx series alloys, $MgZn_2$ is the principal soluble phase, but others may also be present. The precipitate formed in these alloys is usually extremely fine. In some of the 7xxx series alloys, chromium-containing phases or $Mg_2Si$ particles are also visible ($Mg_2Si$ is insoluble in the presence of excess magnesium).

Most commercial aluminum casting alloys are hypoeutectic, and micrographs show dendrites of aluminum solid solution as the primary phase, with a eutectic mixture filling the interdendritic spaces. The eutectic in aluminum alloy castings is often of the divorced type—particles of a second phase in a solid solution. The second phase can be an intermetallic or an alloying element, such as silicon, depending on the composition of the alloy. Eutectic silicon particles can be changed from the normal large, angular shape to a finer, rounded shape by a modifying addition to the melt (usually sodium).

The phases that appear in aluminum alloys may be the alloying elements themselves (silicon, lead, or bismuth), compounds that do not necessarily contain aluminum ($Mg_2Si$ or $MgZn_2$), or compounds that contain aluminum and one or more alloying elements. Table 5 lists the phases that are most common to commercial alloys and provides information that aids in their identification.

The basic characteristics that differentiate phases are crystal structure and atomic arrangement. From this point of view, there are fewer truly distinct phases than were thought to exist. However, the many possible variations in composition, as described in Table 5, cause corresponding variations in chemical activity or in electrochemical relationships regarding the matrix and other phases. Therefore, the etching characteristics of a given basic type of phase may vary considerably with composition of the alloy. This variation has caused conflicting descriptions of the etching effects.

Another source of confusion in phase identification is the many English and Greek letters and chemical formulas that describe relatively few individual phases. In the absence of any standard phase nomenclature or designation system, many choices are found in the literature. Table 5 lists alternate designations. The chemical formula is preferred in which a crystallographic unit cell can be described by such an ideal stoichiometric ratio. Deviations from this composition are caused by broad homogeneity ranges, common in ternary or quaternary phases, or by limited or complete substitution of one element for another. In the case of complete substitution, an isomorphous series is formed, as noted in Table 5. Two elements in combination are sometimes required to substitute for a single element. For example:

$$MgZn_2 \longleftrightarrow CuMgAl_2$$
$$MnAl_6 \longleftrightarrow (Fe,Cu)Al_6$$

The basic crystal structure of a phase can influence its external shape, particularly when the phase is grown from the melt, as in a casting. The external shape in turn influences the shape of the cross section in a metallographically sectioned specimen. Phases with noncubic symmetry will more frequently form elongated shapes. The term "Chinese script," or simply "script," applies to solidified phases that form dendrite skeletons with a fine filigree appearance in section (see the article "Solidification Structures of Eutectic Alloys" in this Volume). Cubic phases are more likely to be scriptlike in shape; in section, they may show twofold, threefold, or fourfold symmetry when well formed. Noncubic phases may show predominantly only twofold symmetry.

The shape of Widmanstätten precipitates grown from solid solutions is not a reliable index of basic crystal structure. Heating of a cast or wrought structure can change the general shape of a phase by coalescence and spheroidization. The low solubility and diffusivity of the iron- and nickel-rich phases cause them to resist changing shape, unless heating is prolonged. Some phases form by delayed peritectic reactions that proceed toward completion when the solidified alloy is reheated. A peritectically formed phase may take on the external shape of the parent phase from which it grew.

The natural (unetched) color of some phases provides a reliable means of identification. This is particularly true of such phases as silicon, $Mg_2Si$, $Mg_2Al_3$, and $CuAl_2$.

## Table 6 Possible phases in various aluminum alloy systems

| Alloy system | Examples of alloy | Alloy form | Phases |
|---|---|---|---|
| Al-Fe-Si | 1100, EC | Ingot | $FeAl_3$, $FeAl_6$, $Fe_3SiAl_{12}$, $Fe_2Si_2Al_9$, Si |
| | | Wrought | $FeAl_3$, $Fe_3SiAl_{12}$ |
| Al-Fe-Mn-Si | 3003 | Ingot | $(Fe,Mn)Al_6$, $\alpha(Al\text{-}Fe\text{-}Mn\text{-}Si)$, Si |
| | | Wrought | $(Fe,Mn)Al_6$, $\alpha(Al\text{-}Fe\text{-}Mn\text{-}Si)$ |
| Al-Fe-Mg-Si (Mg:Si $\simeq$ 1.7:1) | 6063 | Ingot | $FeAl_3$, $FeAl_6$, $Fe_3SiAl_{12}$, $Mg_2Si$ |
| | | Wrought | $FeAl_3$, $Fe_3SiAl_{12}$, $Mg_2Si$ |
| Al-Fe-Mg-Si (high silicon) | 356 | Cast | $Fe_2Si_2Al_9$, $Mg_2Si$, Si |
| Al-Fe-Mg-Si (high magnesium) | 520 | Cast | $FeAl_3$, $Fe_3SiAl_{12}$, $Mg_2Si$, $Mg_2Al_3$ |
| Al-Cu-Fe-Si | 295 | Cast | $FeAl_3$, $Fe_3SiAl_{12}$, $CuAl_2$, $Cu_2FeAl_7$ |
| Al-Cu-Mg-Si-Cr | 6061 | Ingot | $(Fe,Cr)_3SiAl_{12}$, $Fe_2Si_2Al_9$, $Fe,Mg_3Si_6Al_8$, $Mg_2Si$, Si |
| | | Wrought | $(Fe,Cr)_3SiAl_{12}$, $Mg_2Si$ |
| Al-Cu-Fe-Si-Mg-Mn | 2014 | Ingot | $(Fe,Mn)_3SiAl_{12}$, $CuAl_2$, $Cu_2Mg_5Si_6Al_5$, Si |
| | | Wrought | $(Fe,Mn)_3SiAl_{12}$, $CuAl_2$, $Cu_2Mg_8Si_6Al_5$ |
| | 2024 | Ingot | $(Fe,Mn)Al_6$, $(Fe,Mn)Al_3$, $(Fe,Mn)_3SiAl_{12}$, $Mg_2Si$, $CuAl_2$, $CuMgAl_2$, $Cu_2FeAl_7$ |
| | | Wrought | $(Fe,Mn)_3SiAl_{12}$, $Mg_2Si$, $CuAl_2$, $Cu_2FeAl_7$, $Cu_2Mn_3Al_{20}$(a) |
| Al-Cu-Mg-Ni-Fe-Si | 2218, 2618 | Ingot and wrought | In addition to others, nickel may cause $NiAl_3$, $Ni_2Al_3$, $Cu_3NiAl_6$ or $FeNiAl_9$ to appear |
| Al-Fe-Mg-Si-Mn-Cr | 5083, 5086, 5456 | Ingot | $(Fe,Mn,Cr)Al_6$, $(Fe,Mn,Cr)_3SiAl_{12}$, $Mg_2Al_3$, $(Cr,Mn,Fe)Al_7$(b) |
| | | Wrought | $(Fe,Mn,Cr)_3SiAl_{12}$, $Mg_2Si$, $Mg_2Al_3$, $Cr_2Mg_3Al_{18}$(a) |
| Al-Cu-Mg-Zn-Fe-Si-Cr | 7075 | Ingot | $(Fe,Cr)Al_3$, $(Fe,Cr)_3SiAl_{12}$, $Mg_2Si$, $Mg(Zn_2AlCu)$, $CrAl_7$(b) |
| | | Wrought | $(Fe,Cr)_3SiAl_{12}$, $Cu_2FeAl_7$, $Mg_2Si$, $CuMgAl_2$, $Mg(Zn_2AlCu)$, $Cr_2Mg_3Al_{18}$(a) |

(a) May be identity of fine precipitate which comes out at elevated temperatures; not positively identified. (b) Only when chromium content is near high side of range

## Table 7 Nominal compositions of aluminum alloys

| Alloy | Nominal composition, % | Alloy | Nominal composition, % | Alloy | Nominal composition, % |
|---|---|---|---|---|---|
| **Wrought aluminum alloys(a)** | | 7039 | Al-0.27Mn-2.8Mg-0.2Cr-4.0Zn | 380 (380) | Al-9.0Si-3.5Cu |
| | | 7072 | Al-1.0Zn | 384 (384) | Al-12.0Si-3.8Cu |
| 1100 | 0.12Cu-99.00Al (min) | 7075 | Al-1.6Cu-2.5Mg-0.3Cr-5.6Zn | 392 (392) | Al-19.0Si-0.6Cu-0.4Mn-1.0Mg |
| 1230 | 99.30Al (min) | 7079 | Al-0.6Cu-0.2Mn-3.3Mg-0.2Cr-4.3Zn | 413 (13) | Al-12.0Si |
| 2014 | Al-0.8Si-4.4Cu-0.8Mn-0.5Mg | 7178 | Al-2.0Cu-2.7Mg-0.3Cr-6.8Zn | 443 (43) | Al-5.0Si |
| 2024 | Al-4.4Cu-1.5Mg | | | B443 (43) | Al-5.0Si-0.3Cu max |
| 2025 | Al-0.8Si-4.5Cu-0.8Mn | | | C443 (A43) | Al-5.0Si-2.0Fe max |
| 2117 | Al-2.6Cu-0.35Mg | **Aluminum casting alloys(b)** | | 520 (220) | Al-10.0Mg |
| 2218 | Al-4.0Cu-1.5Mg-2.0Ni | | | D712 (D612, 40E) | Al-0.6Mg-5.3Zn-0.5Cr |
| 2219 | Al-6.3Cu-0.3Mn-0.06Ti-0.1V-0.18Zr | 201 (KO-1) | Al-4.7Cu-0.6Ag-0.3Mg-0.2Ti | 850 (750) | Al-1.0Cu-1.0Ni-6.5Sn |
| 2618 | Al-2.3Cu-1.6Mg-1.0Ni-1.1Fe-0.07Ti | 222 (122) | Al-10.0Cu-0.2Mg | | |
| 3003 | Al-0.12Cu-1.2Mn | 224 (···) | Al-5.0Cu-0.4Mn | | |
| 5052 | Al-2.5Mg-0.25Cr | 238 (138) | Al-10.0Cu-4.0Si-0.3Mg | **Aluminum alloy filler metals and brazing alloys** | |
| 5083 | Al-0.6Mn-4.45Mg-0.15Cr | A240 (A140) | Al-8.0Cu-0.5Mn-6.0Mg-0.5Ni | | |
| 5086 | Al-0.45Mn-4.0Mg-0.15Cr | 242 (142) | Al-4.0Cu-1.5Mg-2.0Ni | ER2319 | Al-6.2Cu-0.30Mn-0.15Ti |
| 5454 | Al-0.8Mn-2.7Mg-0.12Cr | 295 (195) | Al-4.5Cu-0.8Si | ER4043 | Al-5.2Si |
| 5456 | Al-0.8Mn-5.1Mg-0.12Cr | 308 (A108) | Al-4.5Cu-5.5Si | ER5356 | Al-0.12Mn-5.0Mg-0.12Cr-0.13Ti |
| 5457 | Al-0.3Mn-1.0Mg | 319 (319) | Al-3.5Cu-6.0Si | 5456 | Al-0.8Mn-5.1Mg-0.12Cr |
| 5657 | Al-0.8Mg | A332 (A132) | Al-12.0Si-0.8Cu-1.2Mg-2.5Ni | R-SG70A | Al-7Si-0.30Mg |
| 6061 | Al-0.6Si-0.27Cu-1.0Mg-0.2Cr | 354 (354) | Al-9.0Si-1.8Cu-0.5Mg | 4047 (BAlSi-4) | Al-12Si |
| 6063 | Al-0.4Si-0.7Mg | 355 (355) | Al-1.3Cu-5.0Si-0.5Mg | 4245 | Al-10Si-4Cu-10Zn |
| 6151 | Al-0.9Si-0.6Mg-0.25Cr | 356 (356) | Al-7.0Si-0.3Mg | 4343 (BAlSi-2) | Al-7.5Si |
| 6351 | Al-1.0Si-0.6Mn-0.6Mg | A356 (A356) | Al-7.0Si-0.3Mg-0.2Fe max | No. 12 brazing sheet | 3003 alloy, 4343 cladding on both sides |
| 7004 | Al-0.45Mn-1.5Mg-4.2Zn-0.15Zr | A357 (A357) | Al-7.0Si-0.5Mg-0.15Ti | | |

(a) Wrought alloys are identified by Aluminum Association designations. (b) Casting alloys are identified first by Aluminum Association designations (without decimal suffixes) and then, parenthetically, by industry designations.

When not distinct enough for exact identification, color differences can be used to determine if the presence of more than one phase is likely. Good, flat, tarnish-free polishes are required, and magnification should generally be at least 500 diameters.

Another useful optical property that can assist phase identification is birefringence. This is the restoration of light from the complete extinction that crossing of polarizer and analyzer should produce on a perfectly plane, optically inactive surface. Phases with cubic crystal structures, including aluminum, are nonbirefringent. Noncubic phases show varying degrees of birefringence, and in some cases, the effect is too weak to be used with certainty. The limitations and precautions necessary in using this method are listed in Table 5.

Table 6 lists the main classes of aluminum alloys and gives the possible phases that might appear in a cast structure or a wrought structure. Some phases that appear in the cast structure are unstable and quickly or gradually disappear during subsequent thermal treatments. They dissolve completely or are replaced by another phase in a diffusion-controlled reaction. The phases that appear in a cast structure depend on the rate of solidification. Therefore, all of the phases mentioned in Table 6 may not appear simultaneously in a given alloy.

The aluminum alloys for which micrographs are presented in this article are listed in Table 7. For additional information, see the articles "Properties of Wrought Aluminums and Aluminum Alloys" and "Properties of Cast Aluminum Alloys" in Volume 2 of the 9th Edition of *Metals Handbook*. Heat treatments used to produce the standard tempers referred to in this article are defined in the articles "Heat Treatment of Aluminum Alloys" in Volume 2 and "Heat Treating of Aluminum Alloys" in Volume 4 of the 9th Edition of *Metals Handbook*.

## REFERENCES

1. P. Lacombe and M. Mouflard, "Les Applications de la Micrographie en Couleurs par Formation des Pellicules Minces Epitaxiques à Teintes d'interference à l'Étude de l'Aluminium, du fer et du Cuivre," Editions Métaux Saint Germain en Laye; extract from *Métaux (Corrosion Ind.)*, Vol 28 (No. 340), Dec 1953, p 471-488
2. L.J. Barker, A Metallographic Study of Aluminum Alloy 3S, *Iron Age*, Vol 163 (No. 21), May 1949, p 74-78
3. G. Phragmén, On the Phases Occurring in Alloys of Aluminium with Copper, Magnesium, Manganese Iron and Silicon, *J. Inst. Metals*, Vol 77, 1950, p 489-552
4. "Standard Methods for Estimating the Average Grain Size of Metals," E 112, *Annual Book of ASTM Standards*, Vol 03.03, ASTM, Philadelphia, 1984, p 120-152

## SELECTED REFERENCES

- J.E. Hatch, Ed., *Aluminum—Properties and Physical Metallurgy*, American Society for Metals, 1984
- E.H. Hollingsworth, G.R. Frank, Jr., and R.E. Willet, Identification of a New Al-Fe Constituent, FeAl$_6$, *Trans. Met. Soc. AIME*, Vol 224, 1962, p 188-189
- R.F. Lynch and J.D. Wood, Nonequilibrium and Equilibrium Constituents in an Al-1.0 pct Mg Alloy (5657), *Trans. Met. Soc. AIME*, Vol 245, 1969, p 1029-1034
- D. Munson, A Clarification of the Phases Occurring in Aluminium-Rich Aluminium-Iron-Silicon Alloys, with Particular Reference to the Ternary Phase α-AlFeSi, *J. Inst. Metals*, Vol 95, 1967, p 217-219; also, discussion by C.Y. Sun and L.F. Mondolfo, p 384
- H.W.L. Philips, Ed., "Equilibrium Diagrams of Aluminium Alloy Systems," Information Bulletin 25, Aluminium Development Association, London, 1961
- L.E. Samuels, *Metallographic Polishing by Mechanical Methods*, 3rd ed., American Society for Metals, 1982
- K.R. Van Horn, Ed., *Aluminum: Properties, Physical Metallurgy, and Phase Diagrams*, Vol I, American Society for Metals, 1967
- "Standard Methods of Preparation of Metallographic Specimens," E 3, *Annual Book of ASTM Standards*, Vol 03.03, ASTM, Philadelphia, 1984, p 5-11
- "Standard Method for Macroetching Metals and Alloys," E 340, *Annual Book of ASTM Standards*, Vol 03.03, ASTM, Philadelphia, 1984, p 330-346

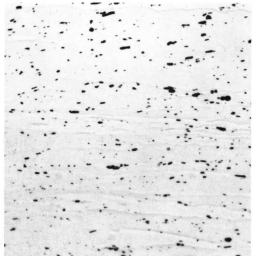

**Fig. 1** Alloy 1100-H18 sheet, cold rolled. Note metal flow around insoluble particles of FeAl$_3$ (black). Particles are remnants of scriptlike constituents in the ingot that have been fragmented by working. See also Fig. 2. 0.5% HF. 500×

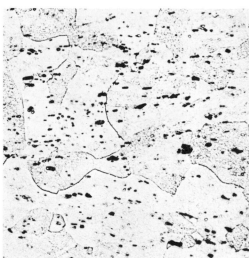

**Fig. 2** Alloy 1100-O sheet, cold rolled and annealed. Recrystallized, equiaxed grains and insoluble particles of FeAl$_3$ (black). Size and distribution of Fe-Al$_3$ in the worked structure were unaffected by annealing (see also Fig. 1). 0.5% HF. 500×

**Fig. 3** Alloy 3003-F tube, extruded through a two-port bridge die. The bands of fine precipitate show pattern of metal flow and the areas where the metal entering through the two ports was welded together in the die. Caustic fluoride. 5×

**Fig. 4** Alloy 3003-F sheet, hot rolled. Longitudinal section shows stringer of oxide from an inclusion in the cast ingot and particles of phases that contain manganese, both primary (large, angular) and eutectic (small). As-polished. 500×

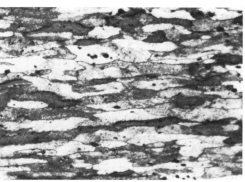

**Fig. 5** Alloy 3003-O sheet, annealed. Longitudinal section shows recrystallized grains. Grain elongation indicates rolling direction, but not the crystallographic orientation within each grain. Polarized light. Barker's reagent. 100×

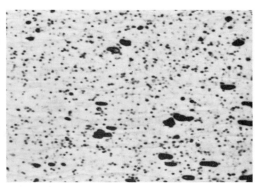

**Fig. 6** Same alloy and condition as for Fig. 5, but shown at a higher magnification. Dispersion of insoluble particles of $(Fe,Mn)Al_6$ (large) and aluminum-manganese-silicon (both large and small) was not changed by annealing. 0.5% HF. 750×

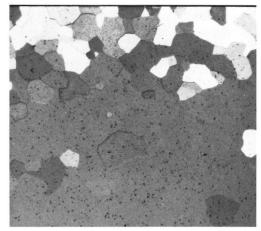

**Fig. 7** Alloy 5457-F extrusion. A transverse section, photographed with polarized light. Surface grains (top) show random reflection, indicating random crystallographic orientation; interior grains show uniform reflection, indicating a high degree of preferred orientation. Barker's reagent. 100×

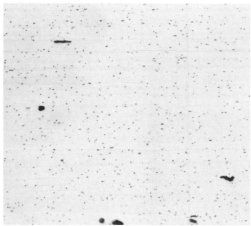

**Fig. 8** Alloy 5457-F plate 6.4-mm (0.25-in.) thick, hot rolled. Fine particles of $Mg_2Si$ precipitated during the rolling. If carried through to final sheet, this amount of precipitate would cause an objectionable milky appearance in a subsequently applied anodic coating. 0.5% HF. 500×

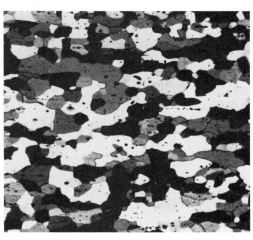

**Fig. 9** Alloy 5457-O plate 10-mm (0.4-in.) thick, longitudinal section. Annealed at 345 °C (650 °F). Polarized light. The grains are equiaxed. See also Fig. 10, 11, and 12. Barker's reagent. 100×

 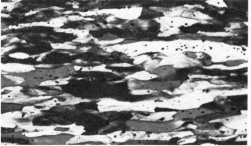 

**Fig. 10, 11, 12** Effect of cold rolling on alloy 5457-O plate, originally 10-mm (0.4-in.) thick, annealed at 345 °C (650 °F). Polarized light. See Fig. 9 for annealed structure. Fig. 10: 10% reduction. Fig. 11: 40% reduction. Fig. 12: 80% reduction. Barker's reagent. 100×

**Fig. 13** Alloy 5657-F sheet, cold rolled (85% reduction). Longitudinal section. Polarized light. Grains are greatly elongated and contribute to high strength, but ductility is lower than for specimen in Fig. 15. Barker's reagent. 100×

**Fig. 14** Same alloy and reduction as Fig. 13, stress relieved at 300 °C (575 °F) for 1 h. Polarized light. Structure shows onset of recrystallization, which improves formability. Barker's reagent. 100×

**Fig. 15** Same alloy and reduction as Fig. 13, annealed at 315 °C (600 °F) for 1 h. Polarized light. Recrystallized grains and bands of unrecrystallized grains. Barker's reagent. 100×

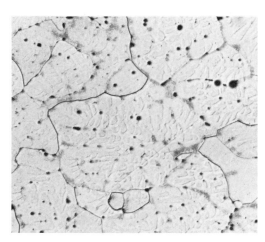

**Fig. 16** Alloy 5657 ingot. Dendritic segregation (coring) of titanium. Black spots are etch pits. Anodized coating from Barker's reagent was stripped with 10% $H_3PO_4$ at 80 °C (180 °F). 200×

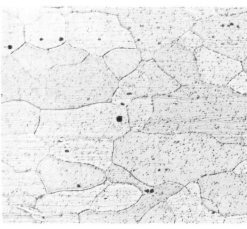

**Fig. 17** Alloy 5657 sheet. Banding from dendritic segregation (coring) of titanium in the ingot (see Fig. 16). Anodized coating from Barker's reagent was stripped with 10% $H_3PO_4$ at 80 °C (180 °F). 200×

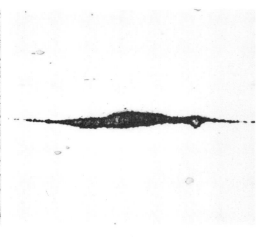

**Fig. 18** Alloy 5454, hot-rolled slab, longitudinal section. Oxide stringer from an inclusion in the cast ingot. The structure also shows some particles of $(Fe,Mn)Al_6$ (light gray). As-polished. 500×

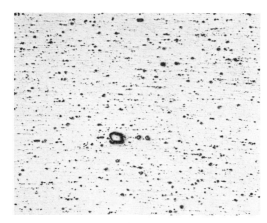

**Fig. 19** Alloy 5083-H112 plate, cold rolled. Longitudinal section shows particles of primary $MnAl_6$ (gray, outlined). Small, dark areas may be particles of insoluble phases, such as phases that contain magnesium (for example, $Mg_2Si$) or that contain manganese. Keller's reagent. 50×

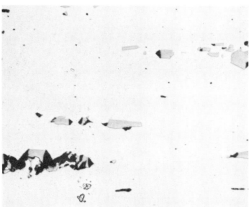

**Fig. 20** Alloy 5083 plate, cold rolled. The coarse, gray areas are particles of insoluble $(Fe,Mn)_3SiAl_{12}$; adjacent black areas are voids caused by breakup of the brittle $(Fe,Mn)_3SiAl_{12}$ particles during cold rolling. Separate black areas may be insoluble particles of $Mg_2Si$. As-polished. 500×

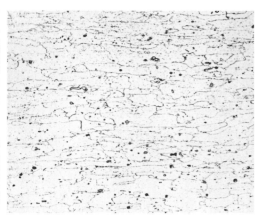

**Fig. 21** Alloy 5086-H34 plate, 13-mm (0.5-in.) thick, cold rolled and stabilized at 120 to 175 °C (250 to 350 °F) to prevent age softening. Undesirable continuous network of $Mg_2Al_3$ particles precipitated at grain boundaries; large particles are insoluble phases. See also Fig. 23. 25% $HNO_3$. 250×

**Fig. 22** Alloy 5456 plate, hot rolled. Longitudinal section. Polarized light. Partial recrystallization occurred immediately after hot rolling from residual heat. This type of recrystallization is frequently referred to as "dynamic recrystallization." Barker's reagent. 100×

**Fig. 23** Alloy 5456 plate, 6.4 mm (0.25 in.) thick, cold rolled and stress relieved below the solvus at 245 °C (475 °F). Particles are $(Fe,Mn)Al_6$ (gray), $Mg_2Si$ (black), and $Mg_2Al_3$ (fine precipitate). In contrast to Fig. 21, there is no continuous network of precipitate at grain boundaries. 25% $HNO_3$. 500×

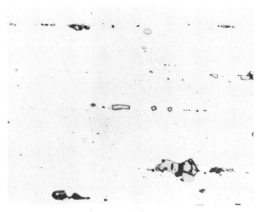

**Fig. 24** Alloy 5456-O plate, 13 mm (0.5 in.) thick, hot rolled, and annealed above the solvus. Rapid cooling resulted in retention of $Mg_2Al_3$ in solid solution. The light, outlined particles are insoluble $(Fe,Mn)Al_6$; the dark particles are insoluble $Mg_2Si$. 25% $HNO_3$. 500×

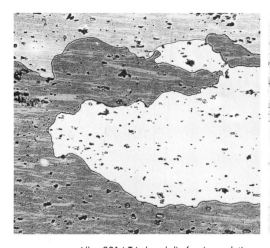

**Fig. 25** Alloy 2014-T4 closed die forging, solution heat treated at 500 °C (935 °F) for 2 h and quenched in water at 60 to 70 °C (140 to 160 °F). Longitudinal section. Structure contains particles of $CuAl_2$ (white, outlined) and insoluble $(Fe,Mn)_3SiAl_{12}$ (dark). Keller's reagent. 100×

**Fig. 26** Alloy 2014-T6 closed-die forging, solution heat treated, then aged at 170 °C (340 °F) for 10 h. Longitudinal section. Fragmented grain structure; constituents are same as for Fig. 25, but very fine particles of $CuAl_2$ have precipitated in the matrix. Keller's reagent. 100×

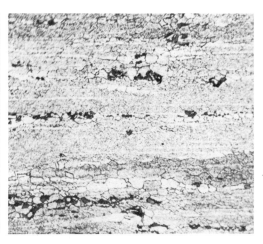

**Fig. 27** Alloy 2014-T6 closed-die forging, overaged. Solution heat treatment was sufficient, but specimen was overaged. Fragmented grain structure; constituents are same as for Fig. 26, but more $CuAl_2$ has precipitated. Note lack of grain contrast. Keller's reagent. 100×

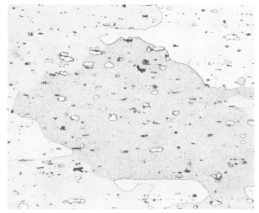

**Fig. 28** Alloy 2014-T4 closed-die forging that received insufficient solution heat treatment. Longitudinal section. Constituents are the same as for Fig. 25, but more $CuAl_2$ is visible, because less is in solution. Keller's reagent. 250×

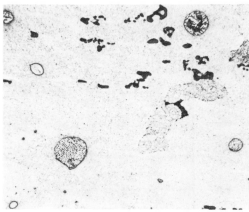

**Fig. 29** Alloy 2014-T6 closed-die forging, showing rosettes formed by eutectic melting. Solidus temperature (510 °C, or 950 °F) was exceeded during solution heat treating. Other constituents are the same as in Fig. 26. Keller's reagent. 500×

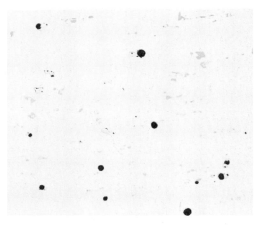

**Fig. 30** Alloy 2014-T6 closed-die forging. Hydrogen porosity (black), and particles of $(Fe,Mn)_3SiAl_{12}$ (gray) and $CuAl_2$ (gray, speckled) are visible. As-polished. 250×

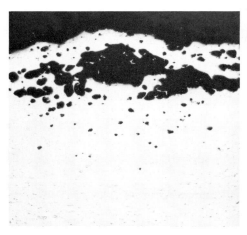

**Fig. 31** Alloy 2014-T61 closed-die forging. Blister on surface is associated with hydrogen porosity. As-polished. 50×

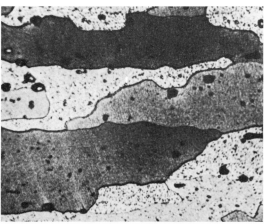

**Fig. 32** Alloy 2024-T3 sheet, solution heat treated at 495 °C (920 °F) and quenched in cold water. Longitudinal section. Dark particles are CuMgAl$_2$, Cu$_2$MnAl$_{20}$, and Cu$_2$FeAl$_7$. Keller's reagent. See also Fig. 33. 500×

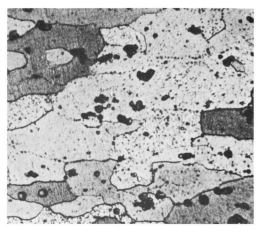

**Fig. 33** Same alloy and solution heat treatment as Fig. 32, but quenched in boiling water. The lower quenching rate resulted in precipitation of CuMgAl$_2$ at grain boundaries. Keller's reagent. 500×

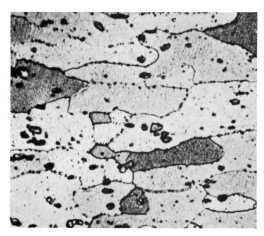

**Fig. 34** Same alloy and solution heat treatment as Fig. 32, but cooled in an air blast. The lower cooling rate resulted in increased precipitation of CuMgAl$_2$ at grain boundaries. Keller's reagent. 500×

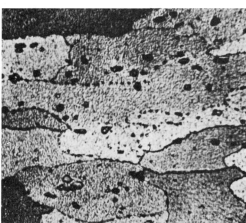

**Fig. 35** Same alloy and solution heat treatment as Fig. 32, but cooled in still air. The slow cooling resulted in intragranular and grain-boundary precipitation of CuMgAl$_2$. Keller's reagent. 500×

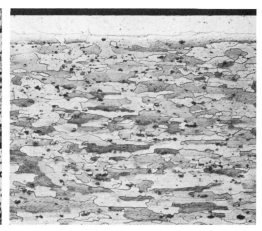

**Fig. 36** Alloy 2024-T3 sheet clad with alloy 1230 (5% per side), solution heat treated. Normal amount of copper and magnesium diffusion from base metal into cladding (top). Keller's reagent. 100×

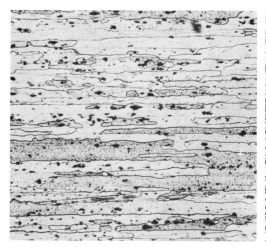

**Fig. 37** 2024-T6 sheet, 6.4 mm (0.25 in.) thick (reduced from 406-mm, or 16-in. thick ingot), stretched 2%. Longitudinal section. Note absence of strain lines in structure. See also Fig. 38 and 39. Keller's reagent. 100×

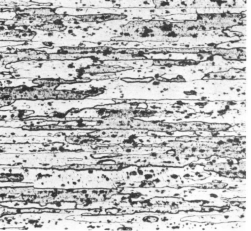

**Fig. 38** Same as Fig. 37, but stretched 6%. Longitudinal section. Some faint strain lines have formed. See also Fig. 39. Keller's reagent. 100×

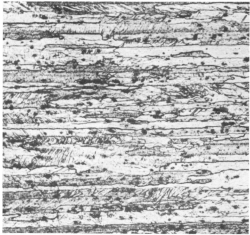

**Fig. 39** Same as Fig. 37, but stretched 20%. Longitudinal section. Many strain lines have formed. See also Fig. 38. Keller's reagent. 100×

**Fig. 40** Alloy 2024-T851 plate, 150 mm (6 in.) thick, cold rolled, solution heat treated, stretched and artificially aged. Section was taken in the rolling plane (long transverse) from an area near the surface showing elongated grains. Keller's reagent. 200×

**Fig. 41** Same alloy and condition as Fig. 40, but a longitudinal section showing the edge view of an area near the surface of the plate. Grains are flattened and elongated in the direction of rolling. See also Fig. 42. Keller's reagent. 200×

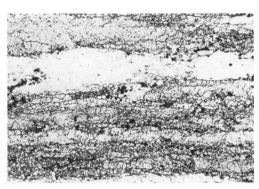

**Fig. 42** Same alloy and condition as Fig. 40, but a short transverse section showing the end view of an area near the surface of the plate. Grains are flattened, but are not as elongated as grains in Fig. 41. Keller's reagent. 200×

**Fig. 43** Same alloy, condition, and orientation as Fig. 40, but specimen was from the center of the plate thickness, which received less cold working than the surface. Keller's reagent. 200×

**Fig. 44** Same alloy, condition, and orientation as Fig. 41, but specimen was from the center of the plate thickness. There is less flattening and elongation of the grains. Keller's reagent. 200×

**Fig. 45** Same alloy, condition, and orientation as Fig. 42, but specimen was taken from the center of the plate thickness. Less coldworking resulted in less deformation. Keller's reagent. 200×

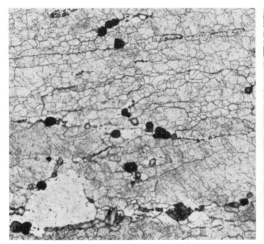

**Fig. 46** Alloy 2024-T851 plate, 100 mm (4 in.) thick, hot rolled, solution heat treated, stretched, and artificially aged. Fragmented grain structure; one small recrystallized grain. High rolling temperature limited strain and recrystallization. 10% $H_3PO_4$. 500×

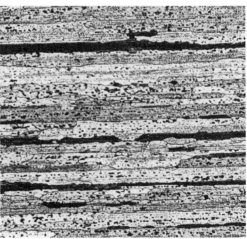

**Fig. 47** Alloy 2024-O plate, 13 mm (1/2 in.) thick, hot rolled and annealed. Longitudinal section. Elongated recrystallized grains and unrecrystallized stringers resulting from polygonization that occurred during the hot water working. $KMnO_4$, $Na_2CO_3$. 100×

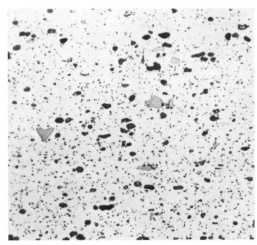

**Fig. 48** Alloy 2024-O sheet. Structure consists of light gray particles of insoluble (Cu, Fe,Mn)$Al_6$, large black particles of undissolved $CuMgAl_2$, and fine particles of $CuMgAl_2$ that precipitated during annealing. 25% $HNO_3$. 500×

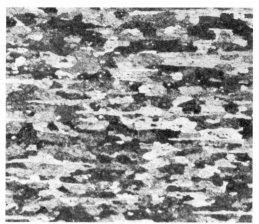

**Fig. 49** Alloy 2025-T6 closed-die forging, solution heat treated and artificially aged. Longitudinal section. Complete recrystallization resulted from high residual strain in the forging before solution treatment. See also Fig. 50. Keller's reagent. 100×

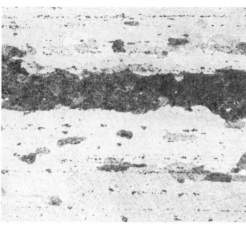

**Fig. 50** Same alloy and heat treatment as Fig. 49, but worked structure is only partly recrystallized. Incomplete recrystallization occurred because forging had lower residual strain before solution heat treatment than in Fig. 49. Keller's reagent. 100×

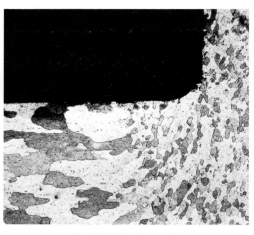

**Fig. 51** Alloy 2117-T4 rivet, cold upset, solution heat treated at 500 °C (935 °F) for 35 min, quenched in water at 25 °C (75 °F) max. The small recrystallized grains are in the rivet head, and the large grains are in the shank. Keller's reagent. 60×

**Fig. 52** Alloy 2218-T61 closed-die forging, solution heat treated and artificially aged. Fine, recrystallized structure. The dark particles of insoluble FeNiAl₉ phase show banding, which resulted from the working during forging. Keller's reagent. 100×

**Fig. 53** Alloy 2219-T6 closed-die forging, solution heat treated and artificially aged. Longitudinal section. Worked structure contains some recrystallized grains. See Fig. 54 for a totally unrecrystallized structure. Keller's reagent. 100×

**Fig. 54** Same alloy and heat treatment as Fig. 53, but showing no recrystallization of the worked structure. Note the large amount of slip (light parallel lines) that has occurred on two sets of slip planes. Keller's reagent. 100×

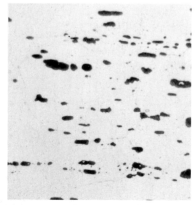

**Fig. 55** Alloy 2618-T4 closed-die forging, solution heat treated at 530 °C (985 °F) for 2 h, quenched in boiling water. Small particles of CuMgAl₂ precipitated at grain boundaries; larger particles are insoluble FeNiAl₉ phase. 0.5% HF. 500×

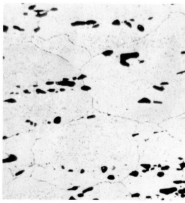

**Fig. 56** Alloy 2618-T4 forging, solution heat treated at 530 °C (985 °F) for 2 h and cooled in still air. Same constituents as Fig. 55, but slower cooling resulted in an increase of CuMgAl₂ at grain boundaries and within grains. 0.5% HF. 500×

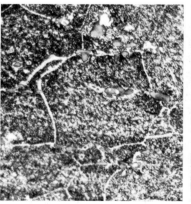

**Fig. 57** Alloy 2618-T61 forging, solution heat treated, quenched in boiling water, aged at 200 °C (390 °F) for 20 h, stabilized at 230 °C (450 °F) for 7 h. Constituents same as Fig. 55; CuMgAl₂ has also precipitated in grains. 0.5% HF. 500×

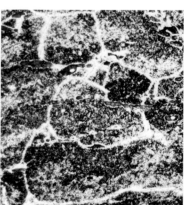

**Fig. 58** Alloy 2618-T61 forging, solution heat treated, cooled in still air, aged, and stabilized as described for Fig. 57. Constituents are same as for Fig. 57. Note increase in precipitation and alloy depletion near light grain boundaries. 0.5% HF. 500×

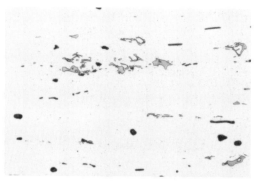

**Fig. 59** Alloy 6061-F plate, 38 mm (1.5 in.) thick, as hot rolled (91% reduction). Longitudinal section from center of plate thickness. Particles are Fe₃SiAl₁₂ (gray, scriptlike) and Mg₂Si (black). See also Fig. 60 and 61. 0.5% HF. 250×

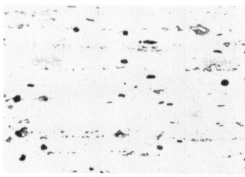

**Fig. 60** Same alloy and condition as Fig. 59, but a longitudinal section from near plate surface. Particles of Fe₃SiAl₁₂ and Mg₂Si are more broken up and uniformly distributed than in Fig. 59 (midthickness) See also Fig. 61. 0.5% HF. 250×

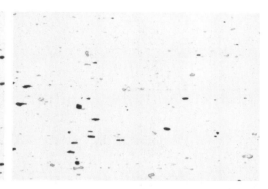

**Fig. 61** Alloy 6061-F 6.4-mm (0.25-in.) sheet, hot rolled (reduced 98%); midthickness longitudinal section. Fe₃SiAl₁₂ and Mg₂Si particles more broken and dispersed than in Fig. 60. Most Mg₂Si will dissolve during solution treating. 0.5% HF. 250×

**Fig. 62** Alloy 6063-T5 extrusion. Transverse section. Grains at surface of extrusion have recrystallized because of more working and heating. Grains in the interior of the extrusion are unrecrystallized. Tucker's reagent. Actual size

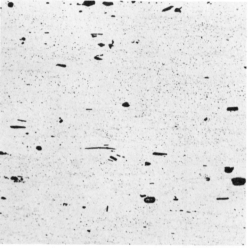

**Fig. 63** Alloy 6151-T6 closed-die forging showing large particles of Mg₂Si (rounded) and (Fe,Mn)₃SiAl₁₂ (angular or scriptlike), and a fine, banded dispersion of extremely small particles of a chromium intermetallic phase. Keller's reagent. 250×

**Fig. 64** Alloy 6351-T6 extruded tube, 1.5-mm (0.06-in.) wall. Longitudinal section. Polarized light. Coarse, recrystallized grains at top are near surface; polygonized subgrains are in unrecrystallized interior. Barker's reagent. 100×

**Fig. 65** Alloy 7079-T6 forging, reduced 40%, solution heat treated and artificially aged. Precipitation of Al-Cr-Mn phase (darker areas in structure) occurred during homogenization and is evidence of dendritic coring. NaOH,NaF. 50×

**Fig. 66** Alloy 7079-T6 forging, reduced 70%, solution heat treated and artificially aged. Grains are more elongated and thinned than in Fig. 65 because of greater amount of work. Dendritic coring is still evident. NaOH,NaF. 50×

**Fig. 67** Alloy 7079-T6 forging, reduced 85%, solution heat treated, and artificially aged. No recrystallization has occurred, because high forging temperature resulted in low residual strain. Note dendritic coring. NaOH,NaF. 50×

**Fig. 68** Alloy 7039 ingot 305 mm (12 in.) thick. Polarized light. Structure shows equiaxed grains with interdendritic areas of $Mg_2Si$ and $Fe_3SiAl_{12}$. See also Fig. 71. Barker's reagent. 50×

**Fig. 69** Alloy 7039-F plate, 150 mm (6 in.) thick, as hot rolled (50% reduction). Polarized light. Grains are elongated and thinned by working. See also Fig. 72. Barker's reagent. 50×

**Fig. 70** Alloy 7039-F plate, 50 mm (2 in.) thick, as hot rolled (83% reduction). Polarized light. Grains are greatly elongated and thinned. See also Fig. 73. Barker's reagent. 50×

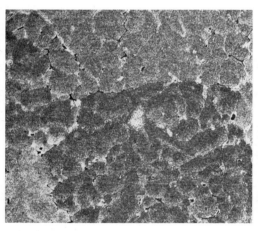

**Fig. 71** Alloy 7039 ingot, 305 mm (12 in.) thick. Dendritic cells are more evident than in Fig. 68 because of the higher magnification and the etchant used. Dendritic cells also show precipitate formed during homogenization. 10% $H_3PO_4$. 100×

**Fig. 72** Alloy 7039-F plate, 150 mm (6 in.) thick, as hot rolled (50% reduction). Dendritic cells are elongated and thinned by working. See also Fig. 69. 10% $H_3PO_4$. 100×

**Fig. 73** Alloy 7039-F plate, 50 mm (2 in.) thick, as hot rolled (83% reduction). Dendritic cells are elongated and thinned by working. See also Fig. 70. 10% $H_3PO_4$. 100×

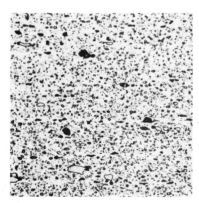

**Fig. 74** Alloy 7075-O sheet, annealed. The fine particles of $MgZn_2$ (dark) were precipitated at lower temperatures during heating to or cooling from the annealing temperature. The insoluble particles of $FeAl_3$ (light gray, outlined) were not affected by the annealing treatment. See also Fig. 75. 25% $HNO_3$. 500×

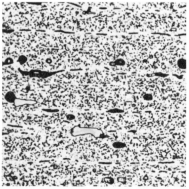

**Fig. 75** Alloy 7075-O sheet, annealed, cooled more slowly from annealing temperature than specimen in Fig. 74. Constituents are the same as for Fig. 74. Platelets of $MgZn_2$ precipitated at grain boundaries during slow cooling. 25% $HNO_3$. 500×

**Fig. 76** Alloy 7075-T7352 forging, solution heat treated, cold reduced, and artificially aged. Particles are insoluble $(Fe,Mn)Al_6$ (dark gray). Some unresolved $Mg_2Si$ may be present. This is a normal structure. See also Fig. 77. Keller's reagent. 250×

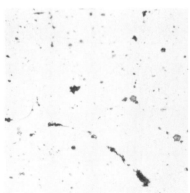

**Fig. 77** Same alloy and condition as Fig. 76, but eutectic melting temperature was exceeded during solution heat treatment. Fusion voids (black areas) and agglomeration of insoluble phases (dark gray). Keller's reagent. 250×

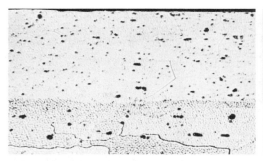

**Fig. 78** Alloy 7075-T6 sheet clad with 0.07 mm (0.0027 in.) of alloy 7072 for 1.6-mm (0.064-in.) total thickness. Particles in cladding (top) are $Fe_3SiAl_{12}$; those in core are $Cr_2Mg_3Al_{18}$ and $(Fe,Mn)Al_6$. Keller's reagent. 350×

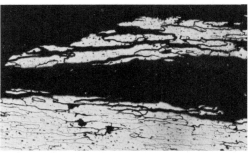

**Fig. 79** Alloy 7178-T76 sheet, 3.2 mm (0.125 in.) thick, exposed in a test chamber containing a fog of 5% NaCl for two weeks. Note exfoliation of the sheet. See also Fig. 80. Keller's reagent. 75×

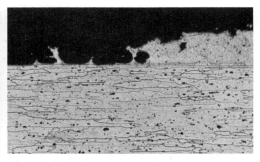

**Fig. 80** Same alloy as in Fig. 79, but clad with 0.127 mm (0.005 in.) of alloy 7072 (3.2-mm, or 0.125-in. total thickness). Sacrificial corrosion of cladding prevented exfoliation of sheet during testing. Keller's reagent. 75×

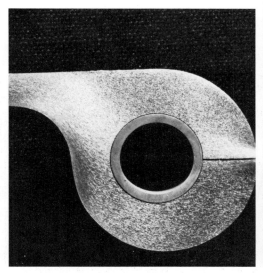

**Fig. 81** Parting-plane fracture in an alloy 7075-T6 forging that contained a bushing in a machined hole. Fracture was caused by excessive assembly stress. See also Fig. 82 and 83. Keller's reagent. 1.5×. (J.M. Van Orden, E. Walden)

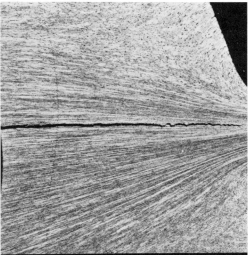

**Fig. 82** Detail of parting-plane fracture in Fig. 81. The fracture started at the machined hole and progressed parallel to the flow lines of the forging. See also Fig. 83. Keller's reagent. 8×. (J.M. Van Orden, E. Walden)

**Fig. 83** Fracture surface of parting-plane fracture in Fig. 81 (machined hole at bottom). Woody, brittle fracture pattern is typical of parting-plane fracture in this alloy. Not polished, not etched. 4×. (J.M. Van Orden, E. Walden)

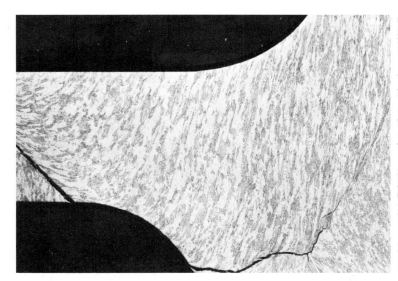

**Fig. 84** Fold, or lap, at a machined fillet in a 7075-T6 forging. Defect was continuous before machining. See also Fig. 85 for details of a small area of the portion of the defect at lower right. Keller's reagent. 8×. (J.M. Van Orden, E. Walden)

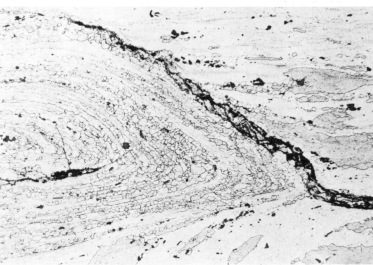

**Fig. 85** Enlarged view of an area of the fold, or lap, at lower right in Fig. 84. Defect contains nonmetallic particles, oxides, and voids, which prevented it from welding, or healing, during forging. Keller's reagent. 200×. (J.M. Van Orden, E. Walden)

**Fig. 86** Surface appearance of a lap (at trough, center) in an alloy 7075-T6 forging. Forging flow lines bend in the vicinity of the lap, indicating that the defect occurred during forging. See also Fig. 87. Not polished, not etched. 10×. (J.M. Van Orden, E. Walden)

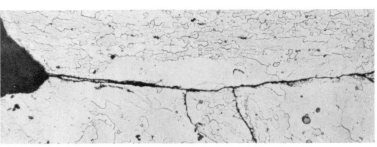

**Fig. 87** Section through the forging lap shown in surface view in Fig. 86. The trough at the surface is at the left. The grains near the lap are deformed, which indicates that the defect occurred during forging. Keller's reagent. 500×. (J.M. Van Orden, E. Walden)

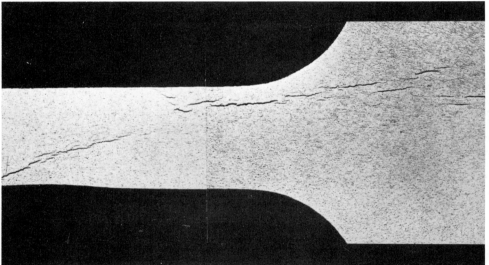

**Fig. 88** Band of shrinkage cavities and internal cracks in an alloy 7075-T6 forging. The cracks developed from the cavities, which were produced during solidification of the ingot and which remained during forging because of inadequate cropping. See Fig. 90 and 92 for higher magnification views of this defect. Keller's reagent. 9×. (J.M. Van Orden, E. Walden)

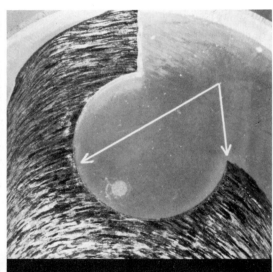

**Fig. 89** Fractured lug of an alloy 7075-T6 forging. Arrows illustrate sites at machined hole where stress-corrosion cracks originated because of stress acting across the short transverse grain direction. See also Fig. 91. Keller's reagent. 2.75×. (J.M. Van Orden, E. Walden)

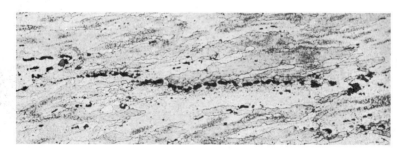

**Fig. 90** Area of the forging in Fig. 88 that contains rows of unhealed shrinkage cavities (black), shown at higher magnification. No cracks have developed from the cavities in this particular area. See Fig. 92 for view of cracked area. Keller's reagent. 200×. (J.M. Van Orden, E. Walden)

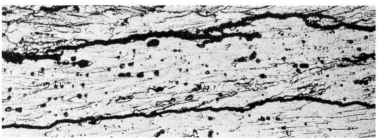

**Fig. 91** Higher magnification view of area of the fractured lug in Fig. 89 that contains intergranular cracks caused by stress corrosion, which resulted when assembly of a pin in the machined hole produced excessive residual hoop stress in the lug. Keller's reagent. 200×. (J.M. Van Orden, E. Walden)

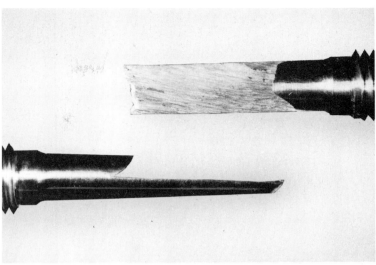

**Fig. 92** Area of the forging in Fig. 88 that contains intergranular and connecting transgranular cracks shown at a higher magnification. The cracks developed from shrinkage cavities. See also Fig. 90. Keller's reagent. 200×. (J.M. Van Orden, E. Walden)

**Fig. 93** Brittle fracture surfaces in a tension-test specimen machined from an alloy 7075-T6 forging that contained a defect of the type shown in Fig. 88 (shrinkage cavities and internal cracks). Not polished, not etched. 3×. (J.M. Van Orden, E. Walden)

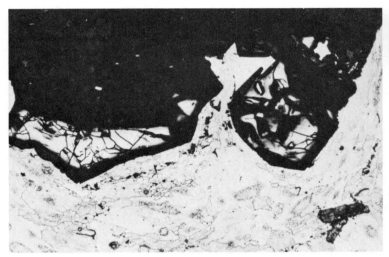

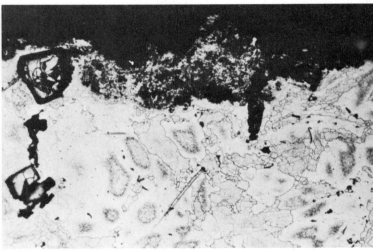

**Fig. 94** Fracture in an alloy 7075-T6 extrusion, showing segregation of chromium particles (light gray, fractured). Segregation originated in the ingot and persisted through to the final product. Keller's reagent. 200×. (J.M. Van Orden, E. Walden)

**Fig. 95** Fracture in an alloy 7075-T6 extrusion, showing a spongy inclusion of dross (center) and some segregation of chromium particles (left) at fracture surface, both of which originated in the ingot. Keller's reagent. 200×. (J.M. Van Orden, E. Walden)

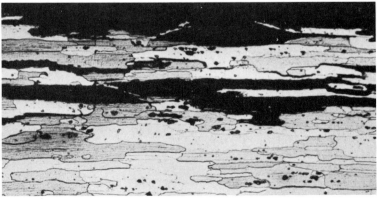

**Fig. 96** Pitting-type corrosion (dark area) in the surface of an aircraft-wing plank machined from an alloy 7075-T6 extrusion. Keller's reagent. 200×. (J.M. Van Orden, E. Walden)

**Fig. 97** Intergranular corrosion in alloy 7075-T6 plate. Grain boundaries were attacked, causing the grains to separate. Keller's reagent. 200×. (J.M. Van Orden, E. Walden)

**Fig. 98** Exfoliation-type corrosion in an alloy 7075-T6 extrusion. Rapid attack was parallel to the surface of the extrusion and along the grain boundaries or along striations within elongated grains. See also Fig. 99. Keller's reagent. 20×. (J.M. Van Orden, E. Walden)

**Fig. 99** Higher magnification view of Fig. 98 (rotated 90°), showing how the corrosion product caused the uncorroded, recrystallized skin of the extrusion to split away, resulting in a leafing action. Keller's reagent. 200×. (J.M. Van Orden, E. Walden)

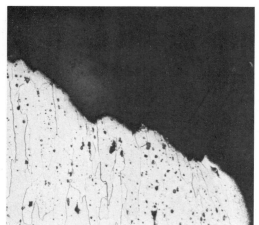

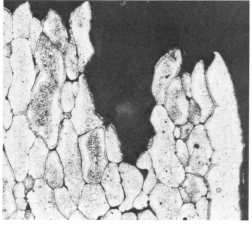

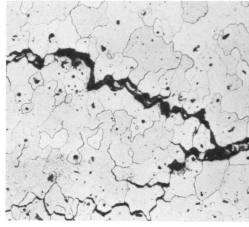

**Fig. 100** Typical ductile fracture in alloy 7075-T6 alclad sheet, showing the deformed grains and necking at the fracture. Keller's reagent. 200×. (J.M. Van Orden, E. Walden)

**Fig. 101** Brittle fracture in overheated alloy 7075-T6 alclad sheet, caused by solid-solution melting at the grain boundaries. Keller's reagent. 200×. (J.M. Van Orden, E. Walden)

**Fig. 102** Typical branched intergranular stress-corrosion cracks in an alloy 7075-T6 extruded bar. Transverse section. Keller's reagent. 200×. (J.M. Van Orden, E. Walden)

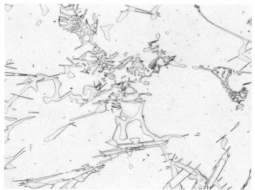

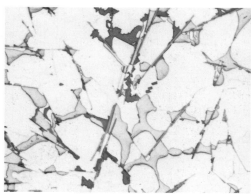

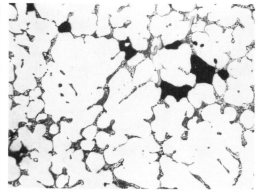

**Fig. 103** Alloy 222-T61, sand cast, solution heat treated, and artificially aged. The structure consists of an interdendritic network of rounded $CuAl_2$ containing blades of $Cu_2FeAl_7$, and some $Fe_3SiAl_{12}$ (dark-gray script). 0.5% HF. 250×

**Fig. 104** Alloy 238-F, as permanent mold cast. The structure consists of an interdendritic network of rounded $CuAl_2$ (light gray) containing blades of $Cu_2FeAl_7$ (medium gray), and some particles of silicon (dark gray). 0.5% HF. 500×

**Fig. 105** Alloy A240-F, as investment cast. The microstructure contains large shrinkage voids (black), an interdendritic network of Al-Cu-Mg eutectic (mottled), and some interdendritic particles of $CuMgAl_2$ (gray). As-polished. 50×

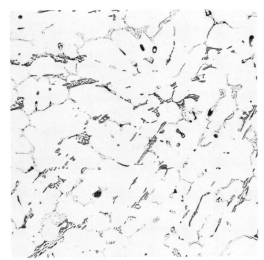

**Fig. 106** Alloy 242-F, as permanent mold cast. Structure consists of interdendritic network of particles of CuAl$_2$ (light, speckled), Cu$_3$NiAl$_6$ (medium-gray script), NiAl$_3$ (dark-gray blades), and Mg$_2$Si (black script). 0.5% HF. 100×

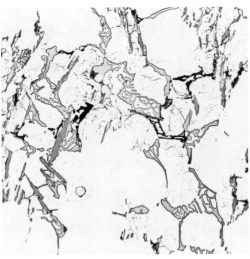

**Fig. 107** Alloy 242-T571, permanent mold cast and artificially aged. Structure contains blades of NiAl$_3$ (dark gray) in the medium-gray Cu$_3$-NiAl$_6$ script. CuAl$_2$ particles (light) and scriptlike Mg$_2$Si (black) also are present. 0.5% HF. 250×

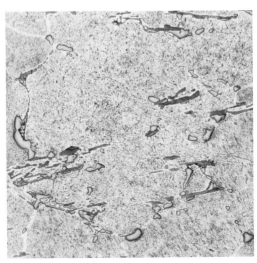

**Fig. 108** Alloy 242-T77, sand cast and heat treated. Constituents are the same as Fig. 107, but particles of NiAl$_3$ and Cu$_3$NiAl$_6$ have been rounded by solution heat treatment. Precipitation is caused by overaging treatment. 0.5% HF. 250×

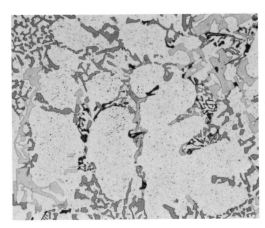

**Fig. 109** Alloy A332-F, as investment cast. Interdendritic network of eutectic silicon (medium-gray script), Mg$_2$Si (black script), Cu$_3$NiAl$_6$ (light-gray script), and NiAl$_3$ (dark-gray particles). See also Fig. 110 and 111. 0.5% HF. 250×

**Fig. 110** Alloy A332-T551, sand cast and artificially aged. Constituents are same as those of the structure in Fig. 109; but there is less Cu$_3$-NiAl$_6$, and the particles of NiAl$_3$ are more massive. See also Fig. 111. 0.5% HF. 250×

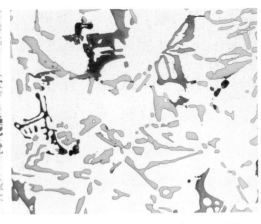

**Fig. 111** Alloy A332-T65, sand cast, solution heat treated, and artificially aged. Constituents are same as in Fig. 109, but the particles of silicon in the eutectic have been made more rounded by the solution heat treatment. 0.5% HF. 250×

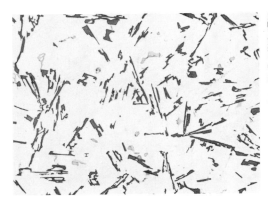

**Fig. 112** Alloy 354-F, as investment cast. Structure consists of a network of silicon particles (dark gray, angular) in a divorced interdendritic aluminum-silicon eutectic and particles of Cu$_2$Mg$_8$Si$_6$Al$_5$ phase (light gray, scriptlike). 0.5% HF. 250×

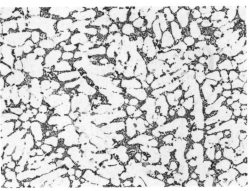

**Fig. 113** Alloy 354-F, as investment cast with two chills adjacent to the area shown. Constituents are the same as for Fig. 112; but dendritic cells are finer, and silicon particles in eutectic are smaller and less angular. 0.5% HF. 250×

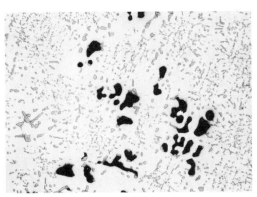

**Fig. 114** A 354-T4 investment casting with fusion voids (black) caused by eutectic melting when solidus was exceeded in solution heat treatment. Surface of casting is blistered. Gray particles are eutectic silicon. 0.1% HF. 50×

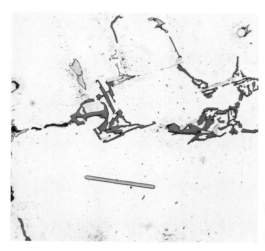

**Fig. 115** Alloy 355-F, as investment cast. Structure consists of an interdendritic network of eutectic silicon (dark gray, sharp), Cu₂Mg₈Si₆Al₅ (light-gray script), Fe₂Si₂Al₉ (medium-gray blades), and Mg₂Si (black, at left). 0.5% HF. 250×

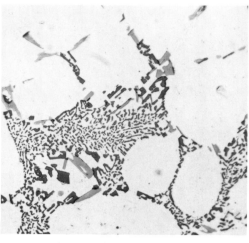

**Fig. 116** Alloy 355-F modified by the addition of Al-10Sr alloy to the melt, as investment cast. Constituents are the same as in Fig. 115, but the particles of silicon (dark gray) are less sharply angular. 0.5% HF. 250×

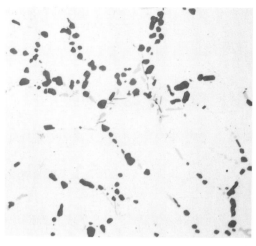

**Fig. 117** Alloy 355-T6, permanent mold cast, solution heat treated, and artificially aged. Constituents are the same as in Fig. 115, but eutectic silicon particles have been rounded by the solution heat treatment. 0.5% HF. 500×

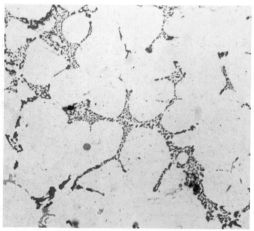

**Fig. 118** Alloy 356-F, as investment cast with sodium-modified ingot. Interdendritic structure: particles of silicon (dark gray), FeMg₃Si₆Al₈ (light-gray script), Fe₂Si₂Al₉ (medium-gray blades), and Mg₂Si (black). 0.5% HF. 250×

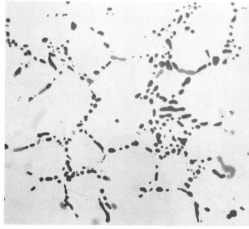

**Fig. 119** Alloy 356-T6, investment cast with sodium-modified ingot, solution heat treated, artificially aged. Solution treatment has rounded and agglomerated the particles of silicon, compared with those in Fig. 118. 0.5% HF. 250×

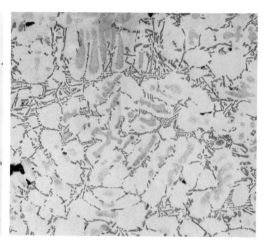

**Fig. 120** Alloy 356-T6, investment cast in a hot mold (650 °C, or 1200 °F) and heat treated. Inverse coring, large dendrite-arm spacing, and large particles of silicon that resulted from the slow cooling; also, shrinkage cavities. Keller's reagent. 50×

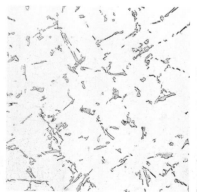

**Fig. 121** Alloy 356-F, as sand cast. Structure consists of a network of silicon particles (gray, sharp), which formed in the interdendritic aluminum-silicon eutectic. See also Fig. 122 and 123. 0.5% HF. 100×

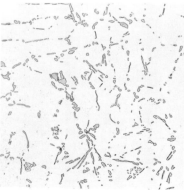

**Fig. 122** Alloy 356-T4, sand cast, solution heat treated at 540 °C (1000 °F) for 12 h, quenched in boiling water. Heat treatment caused silicon particles to be rounder than in Fig. 121 (as-cast). 0.5% HF. 100×

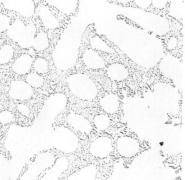

**Fig. 123** Alloy 356-F, modified by addition of 0.025% Na to the melt, as sand cast. Constituents same as for Fig. 121, but the particles of silicon in the eutectic are smaller and less angular. 0.5% HF. 100×

**Fig. 124** Alloy 356-T4, modified by addition of 0.025% Na, sand cast and heat treated as described in Fig. 122. Silicon particles are rounded and agglomerated. See also Fig. 121 to 123. 0.5% HF. 100×

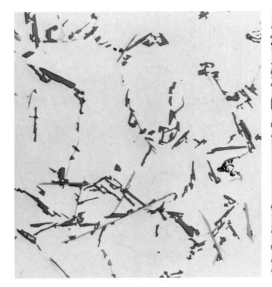

**Fig. 125** Alloy 356-T51, sand cast, artificially aged. The angular, dark gray constituent is silicon. Black script is $Mg_2Si$. Blades are $Fe_2Si_2Al_9$. Light script is $FeMg_3Si_6Al_8$. 0.5% HF. 250×

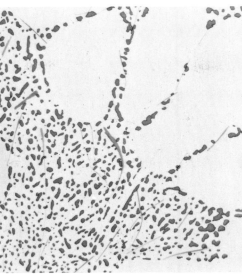

**Fig. 126** Alloy 356-T7, modified by sodium addition, sand cast, solution heat treated, and stabilized. Structure: rounded particles of silicon and blades of $Fe_2Si_2Al_9$. 0.5% HF. 250×

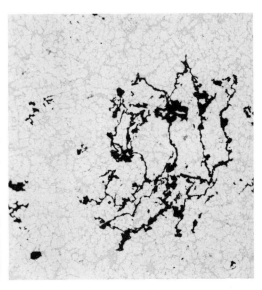

**Fig. 127** $Al_2O_3$ inclusions (black) in alloy 356-F, as investment cast with sodium-modified ingot. Light gray interdendritic network consists of particles of silicon. As-polished. 50×

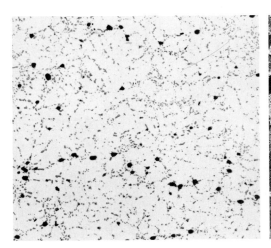

**Fig. 128** Hydrogen porosity (black) in a 356-T6 permanent mold casting that had been solution heat treated and artificially aged. 0.5% HF. 100×

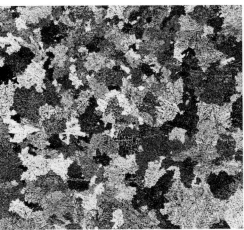

**Fig. 129** Alloy A356-F sand casting to which no grain refiner was added. The macrograin size is 5 mm (0.20 in.). See also Fig. 130. Tucker's reagent. 2×

**Fig. 130** Alloy A356-F sand casting with 0.05% Ti and 0.005% B added as grain refiners. Macrograin size is 1 mm (0.04 in.). Tucker's reagent. 2×

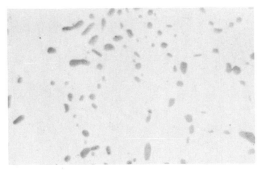

**Fig. 131** Alloy A357-T61, permanent mold cast, solution heat treated at 540 °C (1000 °F) for 12 h, quenched in water at 60 to 80 °C (140 to 180 °F), aged at 155 °C (310 °F) for 10 h. A desirable structure: rounded silicon particles and no undissolved $Mg_2Si$. See also Fig. 132. 0.5% HF. 500×

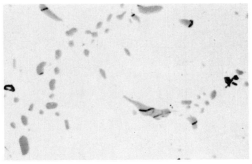

**Fig. 132** Alloy A357-T61, permanent mold cast, insufficiently solution heat treated and artificially aged. Structure contains undissolved $Mg_2Si$ (black), and some of the particles of silicon are more angular than those in the desirable structure shown in Fig. 131. 0.5% HF. 500×

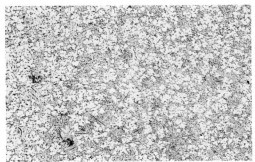

**Fig. 133** Alloy 413-F, as die cast. The structure consists of eutectic silicon (gray constituent), blades of $Fe_2Si_2Al_9$, and some light-gray particles that probably are $Fe_3SiAl_{12}$ in a matrix of aluminum solid solution. Note extreme fineness of all particulate constituents. 0.5% HF. 100×

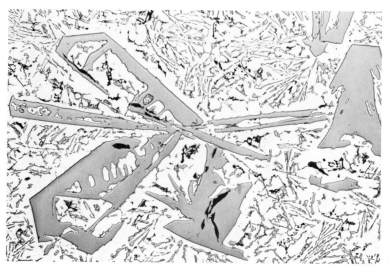

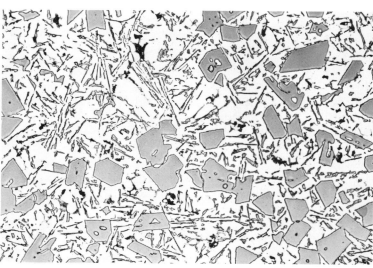

**Fig. 134** Alloy 392-F, as permanent mold cast. The structure consists of silicon (small, angular, gray particles in eutectic, and large, unrefined primary particles) and Mg$_2$Si (black constituent). See also Fig. 135. 0.5% HF. 100$\times$

**Fig. 135** Alloy 392-F, as permanent mold cast same as for Fig. 134, but phosphorus was added to the melt. This addition refined the size of the particles of primary silicon. 0.5% HF. 100$\times$

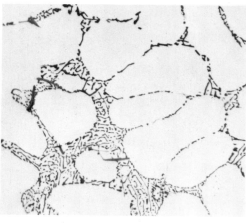

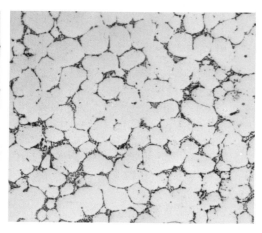

**Fig. 136** Alloy 443-F, as sand cast. Large dendrite cells resulted from slow cooling in the sand mold. Interdendritic structure: silicon (dark gray), Fe$_3$SiAl$_{12}$ (medium gray script), and Fe$_2$Si$_2$Al$_9$ (light gray needles). 0.5% HF. 500$\times$

**Fig. 137** Alloy B443-F, as permanent mold cast. The constituents are the same as those in Fig. 136 (a sand casting), but dendrite cells are smaller because of faster cooling in the metal permanent mold. See also Fig. 138. 0.5% HF. 500$\times$

**Fig. 138** Alloy C443-F, as die cast, Same constituents as in Fig. 136 and Fig. 137, but dendrite cells are smaller because of the very rapid cooling obtained in the water-cooled die-casting die. 0.5% HF. 500$\times$

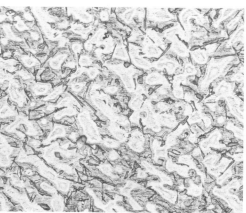

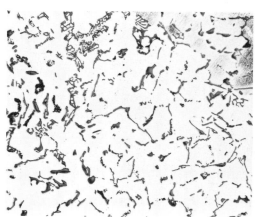

**Fig. 139** Alloy 308-F, as permanent mold cast. Structure consists of an interdendritic network of silicon particles (dark gray, angular) and rounded particles of CuAl$_2$ (light gray) that contain blades of Fe$_2$Si$_2$Al$_9$. 0.5% HF. 250$\times$

**Fig. 140** Alloy 319-F, as permanent mold cast. Dendrites of aluminum solid solution show segregation (coring). Other constituents are interdendritic network of silicon (dark gray) rounded CuAl$_2$, and (Fe,Mn)$_3$SiAl$_{12}$ script. Keller's reagent. 100$\times$

**Fig. 141** Alloy 319-T6, permanent mold cast, solution heat treated, and artificially aged. Segregation in dendrites of solid solution was eliminated by diffusion, and CuAl$_2$ was dissolved during solution heat treating. Keller's reagent. 100$\times$

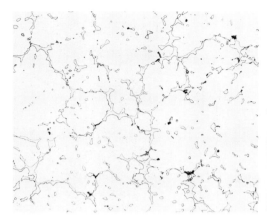

**Fig. 142** Alloy 520-F, as sand cast. Structure is insoluble particles of FeAl₃ (black) and an interdendritic network of Mg₂Al₃ phase (gray). See Fig. 143 and 144 for the effect of solution heat treatment. 0.5% HF. 100× ·

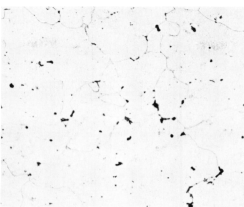

**Fig. 143** Alloy 520-T4, sand cast, solution heat treated at 425 °C (800 °F). Constituents are the same as in Fig. 142, but the solution heat treating has dissolved most of the Mg₂Al₃ phase (gray). See also Fig. 144. 0.5% HF. 100×

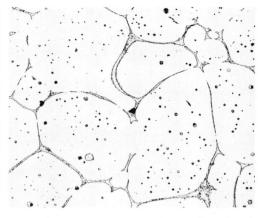

**Fig. 144** Alloy 520-T4, sand cast, solution heat treated. Solidus was exceeded during solution heat treating, and melting of the eutectic has formed a lacy network and rosettes of Mg₂Al₃ phase (gray). See also Fig. 143. 0.5% HF. 500×

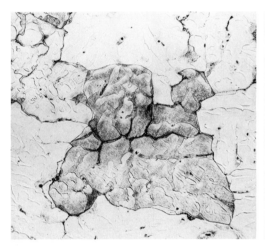

**Fig. 145** Alloy D712-F, as sand cast. Interdendritic network: particles of CrAl₇, Fe₃SiAl₁₂, and FeAl₆. Note the segregation (coring) of magnesium and zinc in the grains. See also Fig. 146. Keller's reagent. 100×

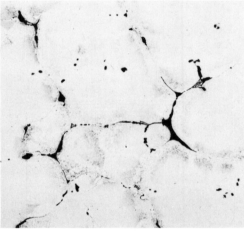

**Fig. 146** Alloy D712-F, as investment cast. Same constituents as in Fig. 145. Intergranular fusion voids (black) were caused by eutectic melting as a result of exceeding the solidus temperature during dip brazing. Keller's reagent. 100×

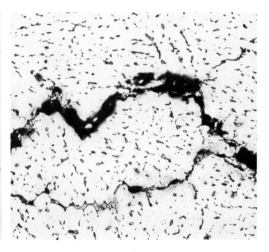

**Fig. 147** Alloy 850-F, as permanent mold cast. Note hot tear, which occurred at or above the solidus, and some Al-CuAl₂ eutectic (gray) back filling of tear. Particles of tin (rounded), NiAl₃, and FeNiAl₉ (both irregular). 0.5% HF. 100×

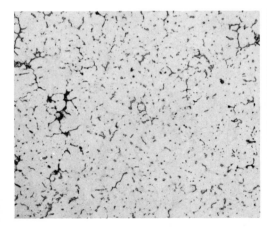

**Fig. 148** Alloy 201-F, as premium quality cast. Structure consists of an interdendritic network of undissolved eutectic CuAl₂ (gray, outlined); some shrinkage cavities (black). See Fig. 149 and 150 for the effect of solution heat treatment and stabilization. 0.5% HF. 100×

**Fig. 149** Alloy 201-T7, premium quality cast, solution heat treated, and stabilized. Structure is a fine precipitate of CuAl₂ in grains and at grain boundaries; no undissolved eutectic CuAl₂; some shrinkage cavities (black). See Fig. 150 for structure at higher magnification. 0.5% HF. 100×

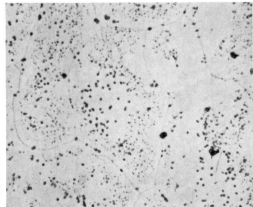

**Fig. 150** Higher magnification view of Fig. 149 showing the pattern of CuAl₂ precipitate that resulted from segregation of copper (coring). Note that the presence of silver in the alloy has resulted in some agglomeration of the precipitate. See also Fig. 153. 0.5% HF. 500×

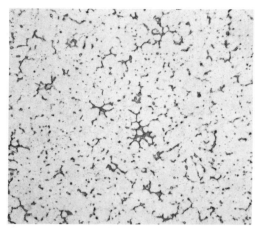

**Fig. 151** Alloy 224-F, as premium quality cast. The structure consists of an interdendritic network of undissolved eutectic CuAl₂ (gray, outlined). See Fig. 152 and 153 for the effect of heat treatment on the structure. 0.5% HF. 100×

**Fig. 152** Alloy 224-T7, premium quality cast, solution heat treated, and stabilized. Structure: fine CuAl₂ precipitate; almost all of the eutectic CuAl₂ present in Fig. 151 has been dissolved. See also higher magnification view in Fig. 153. 0.5% HF. 100×

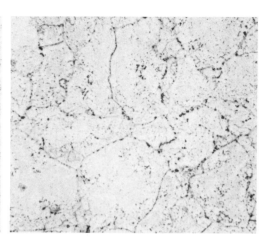

**Fig. 153** Enlarged view of structure in Fig. 152 showing a fairly even pattern of very fine particles of CuAl₂ precipitate in the aluminum grains and slightly larger particles of the precipitate at grain boundaries. 0.5% HF. 500×

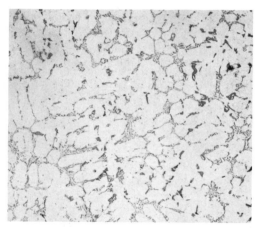

**Fig. 154** Alloy A357-F, as premium quality cast. The structure consists of an interdendritic network of eutectic silicon (gray); some particles of Mg₂Si (black). See Fig. 155 and 156 for the effect of solution heat treatment and artificial aging. 0.5% HF. 100×

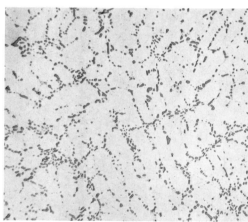

**Fig. 155** Alloy A357-T6, premium quality cast, solution heat treated, and artificially aged. Compared with Fig. 154, the silicon particles in the eutectic have been rounded and agglomerated by solution heat treatment. See Fig. 156 for a higher magnification view. 0.5% HF. 100×

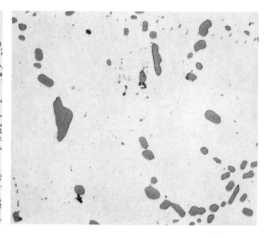

**Fig. 156** Structure in Fig. 155 at higher magnification, which shows that very little undissolved Mg₂Si (black particles) remained after solution heat treatment. No silicon precipitate is visible. See Fig. 132 for the effect of insufficient solution heat treatment. 0.5% HF. 500×

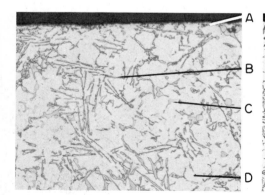

**Fig. 157** Alloy 380-F die casting. Area near a machined surface (A) shows structure typical of a casting that has desirable properties: interdendritic particles of eutectic silicon (B) and CuAl₂ (C) in a matrix of aluminum solid solution (D). See also Fig. 158. 0.5% HF. 260×. (G.L. Armstrong)

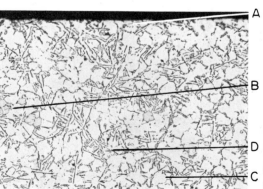

**Fig. 158** Alloy 380-F die casting. Area near a machined surface (A) illustrates some primary crystals of sludge (B) in the aluminum matrix (C) that contains eutectic silicon (D). Sludge is a high-melting iron-manganese-chromium phase that forms in high-silicon aluminum alloys. 0.5% HF. See also Fig. 157. 130×. (G.L. Armstrong)

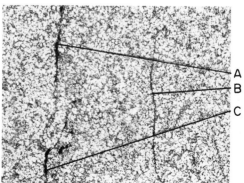

**Fig. 159** Flow lines (A, B, and C) in an alloy 384-F die casting. These may have been caused by incorrect gating, incorrect die lubrication, or incorrect injection and back pressures. 0.5% HF. 65×. (G.L. Armstrong)

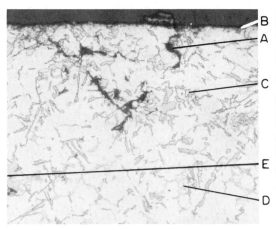

**Fig. 160** Fine Al₂O₃ (A), which should not cause machining difficulties, near the machined surface (B) of an alloy 380-F die casting. Eutectic silicon is indicated by (C); CuAl₂ by (D); and sludge, by (E). See also Fig. 161. 0.5% HF. 260×. (G.L. Armstrong)

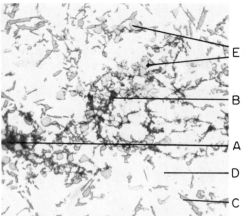

**Fig. 161** Same material as Fig. 160, but at a higher magnification. Aluminum oxide particles are indicated by (A) and (B); particles of eutectic silicon, by (C); aluminum matrix, by (D); and particles of sludge, by (E). 0.5% HF. 520×. (G.L. Armstrong)

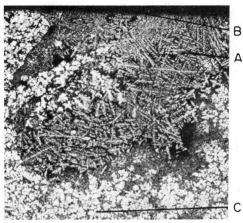

**Fig. 162** Hard area (A) at a machined surface (B) of an alloy 380-F die casting. See Fig. 163 and 164 for details of the microstructure in the hard area, which differs from the normal microstructure (C). 0.5% HF. 65×. (G.L. Armstrong)

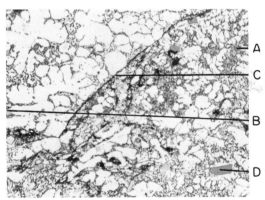

**Fig. 163** Edge of hard area in Fig. 162 shown at a higher magnification. Hard area (A) is separated from the area of normal structure (B) by a "flow line" (C) where two streams of liquid alloy met. Some sludge (D) in hard area. 0.5% HF. 425×. (G.L. Armstrong)

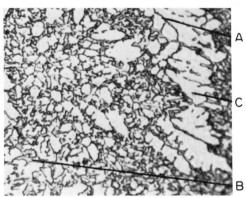

**Fig. 164** Hard area in Fig. 162 shown at a higher magnification. Structure consists of a heavy concentration of eutectic silicon (A) and CuAl₂ (B) in the aluminum matrix (C). The hard area caused difficulty in machining. 0.5% HF. 1300×. (G.L. Armstrong)

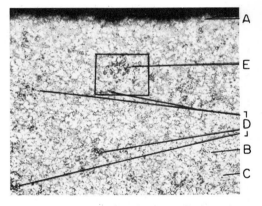

**Fig. 165** Alloy 384-F die casting. Region near a cast surface (A) has the desired structure, which consists of interdendritic particles of eutectic silicon (B) in an aluminum matrix (C), but also has some Al₂O₃ particles (D, and in outlined area E). For a higher magnification view of area (E), see Fig. 166. 0.5% HF. 65×. (G.L. Armstrong)

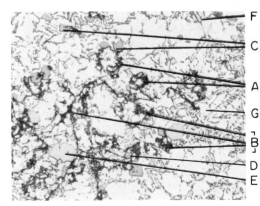

**Fig. 166** Area (E) in Fig. 165 at higher magnification, which shows that the Al₂O₃ particles (A and B) are fine and may not cause machining problems. Small particles of sludge (C, D, and E) are associated with the Al₂O₃ particles. (F) is eutectic silicon; (G) is matrix of aluminum solid solution. 0.5% HF. 520×. (G.L. Armstrong)

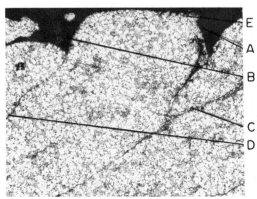

**Fig. 167** Cold-shut voids (A, B) and flow lines (C, D), both caused by failure of the streams of molten metal to merge, at the cast surface (E) of an alloy 384-F die casting. 0.5% HF. 55×. (G.L. Armstrong)

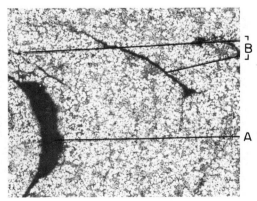

**Fig. 168** Void (A), which was caused by poor filling of the mold and associated flow lines (B) in an alloy 384-F die casting. See Fig. 169 for flow lines without voids. 0.5% HF. 65×. (G.L. Armstrong)

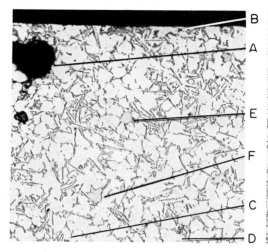

**Fig. 169** Gas porosity (A), caused by entrapped air, near the machined surface (B) of an alloy 380-F die casting. Eutectic silicon particles (C) in aluminum matrix (D), and particles of sludge (E and F). 0.5% HF. 130×. (G.L. Armstrong)

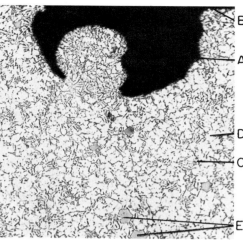

**Fig. 170** Gas-porosity cavity (A), which was caused by entrapped air, at a machined surface (B) of an alloy 384-F die casting. Microstructure is eutectic silicon (C) in an aluminum matrix (D); some sludge (E) is present. 0.5% HF. 130×. (G.L. Armstrong)

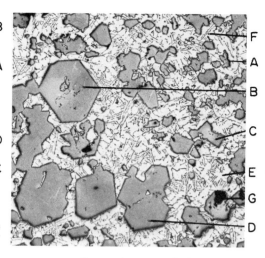

**Fig. 171** Coarse primary crystals of sludge (A, B, C, and D) removed from molten alloy 384 prior to die casting. The remainder of the structure consists of aluminum matrix (E), eutectic silicon (F), and Al₂O₃ (G). 0.5% HF. 40×. (G.L. Armstrong)

**Fig. 172** Alloy 413-F die casting. The gate area (A) of the casting has the desired structure, which consists of interdendritic particles of eutectic silicon (B) and the light-etching matrix of aluminum solid solution (C). 0.5% HF. 41×. (G.L. Armstrong)

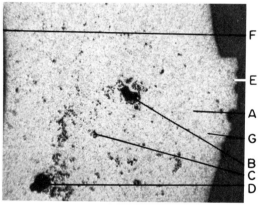

**Fig. 173** Gate area (A) of an alloy 413-F die casting, showing gas porosity (B, C, and D) scattered from the outside wall (E) to the inside wall (F). See Fig. 174 for details of (G), a sound region. 0.5% HF. 11×. (G.L. Armstrong)

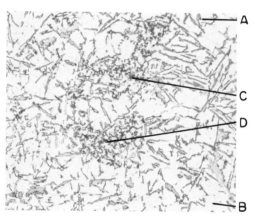

**Fig. 174** Area (G) in Fig. 173 at a higher magnification. Angular eutectic silicon (A) in matrix of aluminum solid solution (B) in normal structure and rounded silicon in undesirable structures (C and D). 0.5% HF. 520×. (G.L. Armstrong)

**Fig. 175** Gate area (A) of an alloy 413-F die casting. There are areas of undesirable silicon structure (B) and a gas pore (C), which was caused by air entrapment, in a region that otherwise exhibits a normal structure (D). 0.5% HF. 41×. (G.L. Armstrong)

**Fig. 176** Gate area (A) of an alloy 413-F die casting that has a cold-shut void (B) and a region of undesirable structure (C and D) surrounded by areas of normal structure (E and F). See also Fig. 177, 178, and 179. 0.5% HF. 11×. (G.L. Armstrong)

**Fig. 177** Area of cold-shut void (A) in Fig. 176. The void resulted when two streams of molten metal failed to merge and interdiffuse. One of the streams produced a normal structure (B), and the other produced an undesirable structure (C). See also Fig. 178 and 179. 0.5% HF. 35×. (G.L. Armstrong)

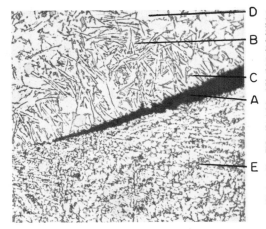

**Fig. 178** Inner end of cold-shut void (A) in Fig. 177 showing start of flow line between region of normal structure (B), with eutectic silicon (C) of normal shape in matrix of aluminum solid solution (D), and region of undesirable structure (E). See also Fig. 179. 0.5% HF. 520×. (G.L. Armstrong)

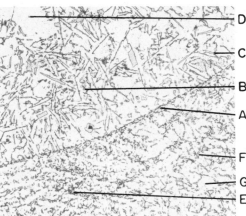

**Fig. 179** Continuation of flow line (A) in Fig. 178, separating normal structure (B), with angular silicon (C) in aluminum matrix (D), from undesirable structure (E), with rounded silicon (F) in aluminum matrix (G). Line extends across entire section thickness. 0.5% HF. 520×. (G.L. Armstrong)

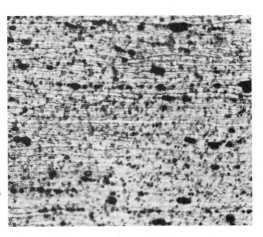

**Fig. 180** Alloy 5052-O sheet, 10 mm (0.40 in.) thick, used for weld shown in Fig. 181 to 183. Structure shows particles of $CrAl_7$ (coarse, black). Rounded, outlined areas are pits, where etchant removed $Mg_2Si$. Keller's reagent. 500×

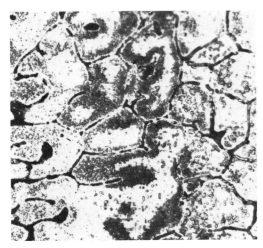

**Fig. 181** Heat-affected zone of the weld shown in Fig. 183. Weld bead (see also Fig. 182) was to the right. Structure: equiaxed dendrites of aluminum with much $Mg_2Al_3$ precipitate near dendrite boundaries forming the dark band in Fig. 183. Keller's reagent. 500×

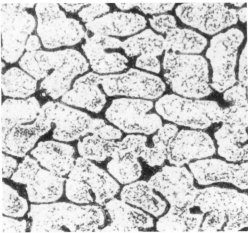

**Fig. 182** Bead of the weld shown in Fig. 183. Filler metal was alloy ER5356. The structure consists of equiaxed dendrites of aluminum with a fine precipitate of $Mg_2Al_3$ (dark) in the dendrites and at dendrite boundaries. Keller's reagent. 500×

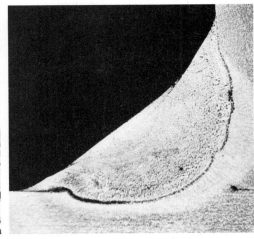

**Fig. 183** Gas tungsten-arc fillet weld in alloy 5052-O sheet. Filler metal was alloy ER5356. See also Fig. 180, 181, and 182. Tucker's reagent. 15×

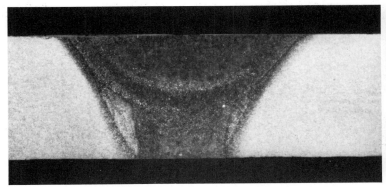

**Fig. 184** Gas tungsten-arc weld in a butt joint in alloy 6061-T6 plate, 6.4 mm (0.250 in.) thick. Alternating current and ER4043 filler metal were used. See also Fig. 186 and 188 for other views of the weld. Keller's reagent. 5.5×

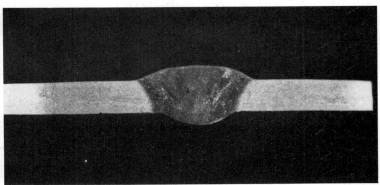

**Fig. 185** Gas tungsten-arc weld in a butt joint in alloy 6061-T6 sheet, 1.6 mm (0.063 in.) thick. Alternating current and ER4043 filler metal were used. Note the extent of the heat-affected zone. See also Fig. 187 and 189. Keller's reagent. 5.5×

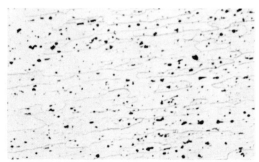

**Fig. 186** Structure of 6.4-mm (0.250-in.) thick 6061-T6 plate used in making the weld shown in Fig. 184. Elongated grains of aluminum solid solution contain particles of Mg₂Si (black). See also Fig. 187. Keller's reagent. 100×

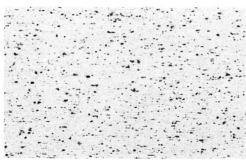

**Fig. 187** Structure of 1.6-mm (0.063-in.) thick 6061-T6 sheet used in making the weld shown in Fig. 185. The microstructure is the same as Fig. 186, but contains more Mg₂Si. See Fig. 189 for structure of edge of fusion zone. Keller's reagent. 100×

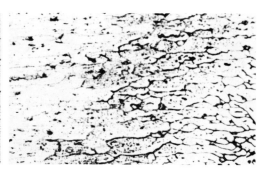

**Fig. 188** Edge of fusion zone of a weld made in 6.4-mm (0.250-in.) thick 6061-T6, using alternating current. Interdendritic network of aluminum-silicon eutectic (dark) in weld bead (right); dark band of Al-Mg₂Si eutectic in the heat-affected zone. Keller's reagent. 100×

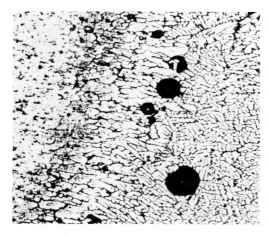

**Fig. 189** Edge of fusion zone of a weld made in 1.6-mm (0.063-in.) thick 6061-T6, using alternating current. The base metal is located on the left and the weld bead is located on the right. The structure is the same as that in Fig. 188, but some porosity (large, black areas) is evident. Keller's reagent. 100×

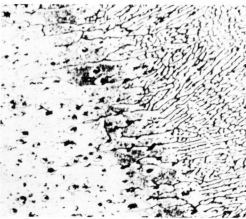

**Fig. 190** Edge of fusion zone of a weld made in 6.4-mm (0.250-in.) thick 6061-T6, using straight-polarity direct current. Dark band of Al-Mg₂Si eutectic in heat-affected zone, next to weld bead (right), is narrower and more pronounced than in Fig. 188 (weld made with alternating current). Keller's reagent. 100×

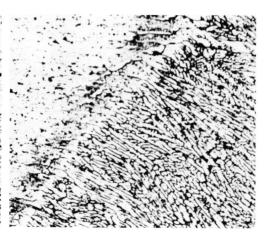

**Fig. 191** Edge of fusion zone of a weld made in 1.6-mm (0.063-in.) thick 6061-T6, using straight-polarity direct current. The microstructure is the same as for the 6.4-mm (0.250-in.) thick plate in Fig. 190, but the amount of interdendritic aluminum-silicon eutectic in the weld bead is greater. Keller's reagent. 100×

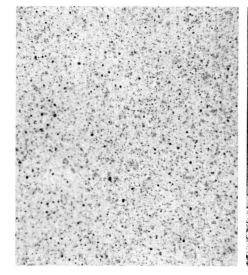

**Fig. 192** Structure of the 6061-T6 extruded tube (extrusion direction vertical) used for the weld shown in Fig. 193. Black dots are Mg₂Si particles. Keller's reagent. 50×

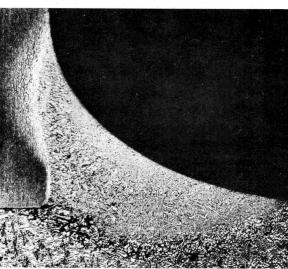

**Fig. 193** Gas tungsten-arc fillet weld joining a 6061-T6 tube (upper left) and an A356-T6 investment casting; ER4043 filler metal. Keller's reagent. 15×

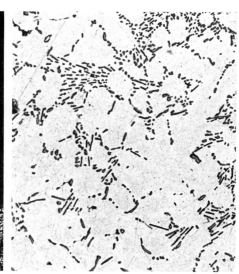

**Fig. 194** Structure of A356-T6 investment casting (sodium-modified; grain-refined) used for the weld shown in Fig. 193. Interdendritic network is eutectic silicon. Keller's reagent. 50×

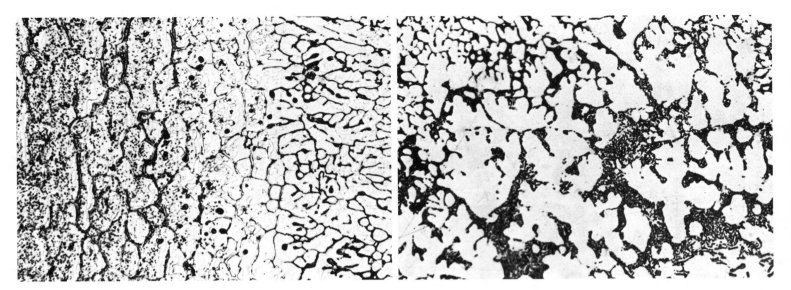

**Fig. 195** Edge of the fusion zone of the weld shown in Fig. 193, with the tube at the left and the weld bead at the right. Aluminum-silicon eutectic is present between the dendrites of the weld bead; Al-Mg₂Si eutectic is between the grains of the heat-affected zone of the tube. Keller's reagent. 50×

**Fig. 196** Edge of the fusion zone of the weld shown in Fig. 193, with the weld bead at top and left and the casting at bottom and right. Interdendritic aluminum-silicon eutectic is present; some in the weld bead, and a large amount in the heat-affected zone of the casting. Keller's reagent. 50×

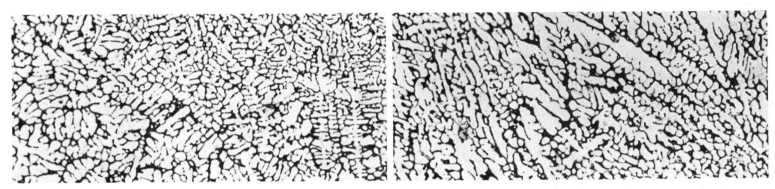

**Fig. 197** Bead (near tube) of the weld in Fig. 193. Interdendritic network of aluminum-silicon eutectic is present in the matrix solid solution. Keller's reagent. 50×

**Fig. 198** Bead (near casting) of the weld in Fig. 193. Dendrites of solid solution are less equiaxed, more columnar than in Fig. 197. Keller's reagent. 50×

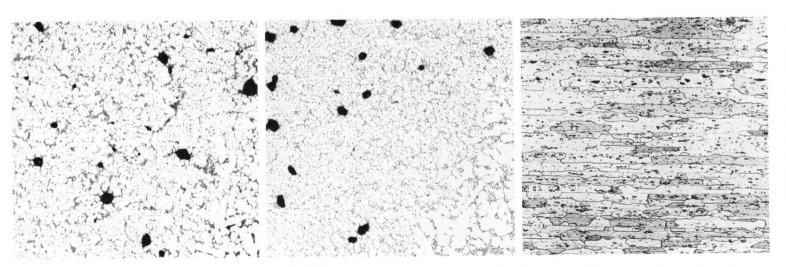

**Fig. 199** Edge of fusion zone of a gas tungsten-arc repair weld in a 356-F investment casting. Alternating current and R-SG70A filler metal were used. Interdendritic aluminum-silicon eutectic (gray); porosity (black). See also Fig. 200. Keller's reagent. 50×

**Fig. 200** Same material as Fig. 199, but after solution heat treatment. Particles of eutectic silicon have become rounded and agglomerated. Zone between weld bead and heat-affected zone is less clearly defined than in Fig. 199; porosity remains. Keller's reagent. 50×

**Fig. 201** Structure of 2219-T37 sheet, 3.2 mm (0.125 in.) thick, used for the weld shown in Fig. 202 and 203. Longitudinal section. Elongated grains of solid solution with particles of CuAl₂ (light) and (Fe,Mn)₃SiAl₁₂ (dark). Keller's reagent. 100×

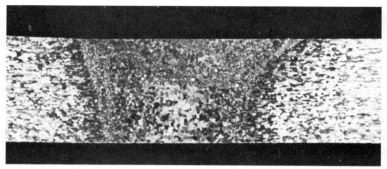

**Fig. 202** Gas tungsten-arc weld in a butt joint in alloy 2219-T37 sheet; alloy ER2319 filler metal. See also Fig. 204. Keller's reagent. 10×

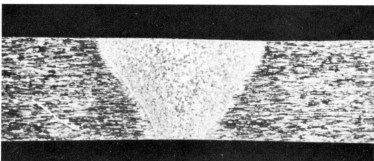

**Fig. 203** Electron beam weld in a butt joint in alloy 2219-T37 sheet; alloy ER2319 filler metal. See also Fig. 205. Keller's reagent. 10×

**Fig. 204** Edge of the fusion zone of the gas tungsten-arc weld shown in Fig. 202. The base metal is on the left. See also Fig. 205. Keller's reagent. 100×

**Fig. 205** Edge of the fusion zone of the electron beam weld shown in Fig. 203. The base metal is on the left. Keller's reagent. 100×

**Fig. 206** Electron beam weld in a butt joint in alloy 5456-H321 plate, 25 mm (1 in.) thick. No filler metal was used. See Fig. 207 for details of the edge of the fusion zone. Keller's reagent. 10×

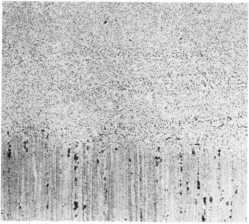

**Fig. 207** Edge of fusion zone (base metal is at bottom) of the electron beam weld in Fig. 206. Keller's reagent. 100×

**Fig. 208** Electron beam weld in alloy 6061-T6 sheet, 3.2 mm (0.125 in.) thick. No filler metal was used. See Fig. 209 and 210 for details of the edge of the fusion zone. Keller's reagent. 10×

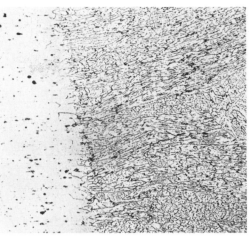

**Fig. 209** Edge of the fusion zone (base metal is at left) of the electron beam weld in Fig. 208. Note abrupt change from structure of base metal to that of weld bead. See also Fig. 210. Keller's reagent. 100×

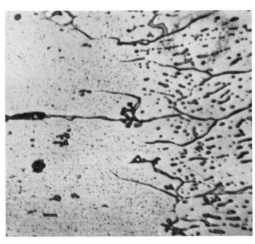

**Fig. 210** Same material as Fig. 209, but at a higher magnification. Particles of Mg$_2$Si (black) and Fe$_3$SiAl$_{12}$ (gray) in base metal (left) and interdendritic Al-Mg$_2$Si eutectic in weld metal. Keller's reagent. 500×

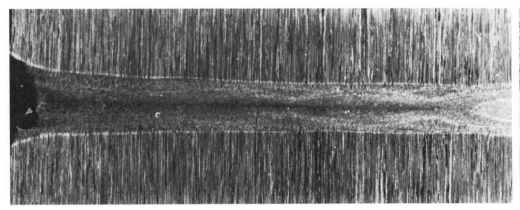

**Fig. 211** Electron beam weld in a butt joint in alloy 7039-T63 plate, 25 mm (1 in.) thick. No filler metal was used. See Fig. 212 for details of the edge of the fusion zone. Keller's reagent. 10×

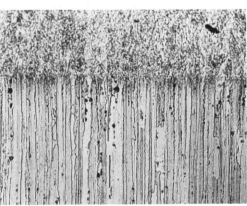

**Fig. 212** Edge of fusion zone (base metal is at bottom) of the electron beam weld in Fig. 211. Keller's reagent. 100×

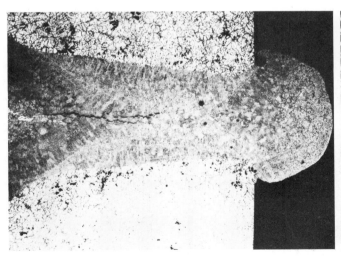

**Fig. 213** Electron beam weld in an alloy 295-T6 investment casting. Weld was made without filler metal. Overheating during welding resulted in a considerable amount of dropthrough (right), with accompanying longitudinal shrinkage cracks in the center of the weld metal. See also Fig. 214. Tucker's reagent. 5×

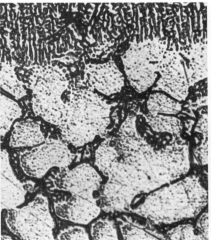

**Fig. 214** Edge of fusion zone of weld shown in Fig. 213 (base metal at bottom). Large dendrites of solid solution in base metal, small dendrites in weld bead; Al-CuAl$_2$-Si eutectic in both. Keller's reagent. 150×

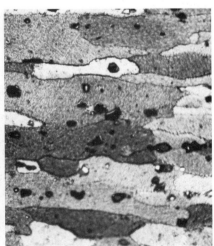

**Fig. 215** Core of alclad 2024-T4 sheet used in resistance spot weld shown in Fig. 216. The dark particles are CuMgAl$_2$, Cu$_2$MnAl$_{20}$, and Cu$_2$FeAl$_7$; light particles, CuAl$_2$. See also Fig. 217 to 220. Keller's reagent. 500×

**Fig. 216** Resistance spot weld in 2024-T4 sheets clad with alloy 1230. Oval nugget has zone of columnar grains surrounding equiaxed grains. See also Fig. 217 to 220. Tucker's reagent. 10×

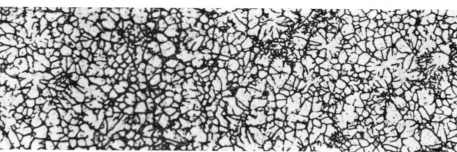

**Fig. 217** Inner zone of nugget of the resistance spot weld shown in Fig. 216. The structure consists of small equiaxed grains. This inner zone is surrounded by an outer zone that consists of columnar grains. See also Fig. 218. Keller's reagent. 500×

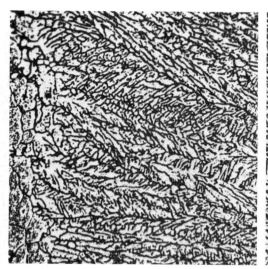

**Fig. 218** Outer zone of nugget of the weld shown in Fig. 216. Columnar grains are normal to the edge of the nugget. See also Fig. 217, which shows inner zone of nugget. Keller's reagent. 550×

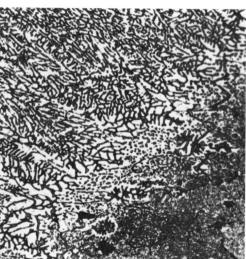

**Fig. 219** Transition zone of the weld in Fig. 216 showing eutectic segregation—depletion (light band) at edge of nugget and concentration (dark band) in the base metal. Keller's reagent. 550×

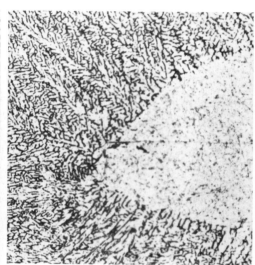

**Fig. 220** Outer zone of nugget (at interface) of resistance spot weld made in alclad 2024-T4 sheets. Unfused cladding (right) projects into the weld nugget. See also Fig. 216. Keller's reagent. 550×

**Fig. 221** Explosive welded joint between aluminum sheet (top) and steel showing characteristic ripples at the interface. A ripple is shown at a higher magnification in Fig. 222. As-polished. 6×

**Fig. 222** Ripple at interface of explosive welded joint between aluminum sheet (top) and steel. Cracks have appeared in the dark-gray phase (which probably is $FeAl_3$). As-polished. 60×

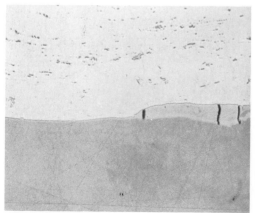

**Fig. 223** Explosive welded joint between aluminum sheet (top) and copper. Cracks (black) have appeared in the aluminum-copper phase (light gray) at the relatively smooth interface. As-polished. 225×

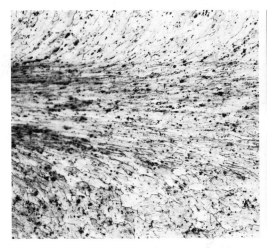

**Fig. 224** Pressure weld (cold) in alloy 2014-T6 bar. The flow lines at the joint show the movement of metal toward the edge of the bar during weld upsetting. 0.5% HF. 150×

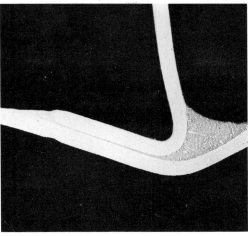

**Fig. 225** Brazed joint between 6063-O sheets, made with 4047 (BAlSi-4) filler metal. See Fig. 226 for details of structure of the smaller fillet. As-polished. 5×

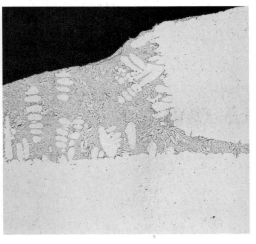

**Fig. 226** Smaller fillet of brazed joint shown in Fig. 225. Structure consists of dendrites of aluminum solid solution (light gray) and aluminum-silicon eutectic matrix (dark). As-polished. 50×

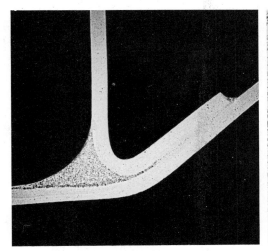

**Fig. 227** Brazed joint between alloy 7004-O sheets, made with alloy 4245 filler metal. See Fig. 228 for details of the microstructure of the larger fillet. As-polished. 5×

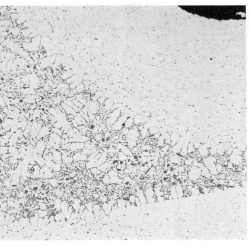

**Fig. 228** Larger fillet of brazed joint shown in Fig. 227. Structure consists of dendrites of aluminum solid solution (light), matrix of aluminum-silicon eutectic (mottled), and particles of primary silicon (dark). As-polished. 50×

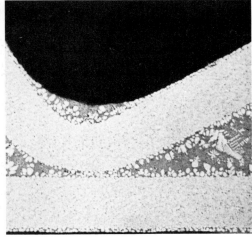

**Fig. 229** Brazed joint in 12-O brazing sheets (alloy 3003 clad on both sides with alloy 4343 filler metal). Fillets show dendrites of solid solution (light) in aluminum-silicon eutectic matrix. 0.5% HF. 30×

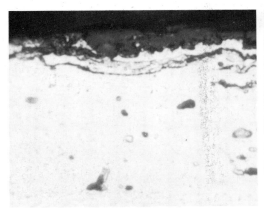

**Fig. 230** Surface fretting (dark gray) on 3.2-mm (0.125-in.) thick alloy 7075-T651 sheet that was fayed to a 4130 steel strap in a fatigue test. Fretting corrosion product is $Al_2O_3$. Keller's reagent. 1050×

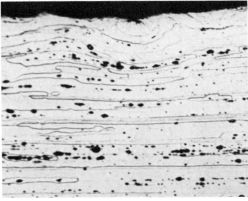

**Fig. 231, 232** Alloy 7075-T651 sheet showing the effect of saturation peening. Fig. 231: longitudinal section. Fig. 232: transverse section. The sheet was peened with S230 cast steel shot to an Almen-gage intensity of 0.006 to 0.008 A. The surface of the sheet (at the top) shows deformation and roughening. Keller's reagent. 150×

**Fig. 233** Surface at top of electrochemically machined hole in 25-mm (1-in.) thick 7075-T651 plate, showing roughness. Keller's reagent. 50×

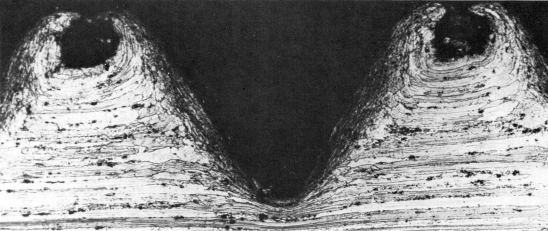

**Fig. 234** Section through machined threads in an alloy 2024-T4 extruded bar, 25 mm (1 in.) diam, showing a typical degree of surface roughness on thread flanks. Machining burrs have been left on the crests of the threads. Microstructure is essentially unworked. See also Fig. 236. Keller's reagent. 100×

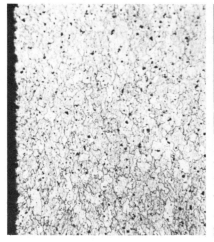
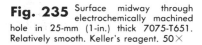

**Fig. 235** Surface midway through electrochemically machined hole in 25-mm (1-in.) thick 7075-T651. Relatively smooth. Keller's reagent. 50×

**Fig. 236** Section through cold-rolled threads in an alloy 2024-T4 extruded bar, 25 mm (1 in.) diam, showing highly worked structure in metal at thread flanks. Deformed metal almost completely encloses a cavity at crest of each thread; this is an undesirable condition. Compare machined threads in Fig. 234. Keller's reagent. 100×

# Beryllium

By James M. Marder
Supervisor, Beryllium Metal
Research & Development
Brush Wellman Inc.

and

R. Batich
Senior Metallographer
Brush Wellman Inc.

BERYLLIUM is prepared and examined metallographically in much the same way as other more common metals; however, the toxicity of beryllium necessitates the use of extreme care. Procedures and equipment must be designed to contain the harmful dust that can be produced during metallographic preparation. Examination usually is performed to determine grain size, distribution of second-phase oxide particles, voids, inclusions, the presence of machine-damaged surfaces, and, in the case of rolled sheet, the state of cold work. These microstructural characteristics can be important in determining the performance of a beryllium component.

Polarized light is generally used for metallographic examination instead of chemical etchants, although grain-boundary etchants have been used in some investigations. The fine grain size of the most common commercial forms of beryllium (vacuum hot-pressed block and rolled sheet) limits the value of magnifications less than 250×.

Beryllium is considered extremely hazardous to health when sufficient quantities of dust, mists, or fumes containing particles small enough to enter the lungs (typically 10 $\mu$m or less) are inhaled. Sectioning, grinding, and polishing operations that produce dusts or fumes should be performed under adequately vented hoods equipped with special filters. Metallographic preparation equipment and laboratory work surfaces should be damp wiped periodically to prevent accumulation of dry particles. For additional information, see the article "Toxicity of Metal Powders" in Volume 7 of the 9th Edition of *Metals Handbook*.

## Specimen Preparation

Metallographic preparation begins with standard sectioning and mounting techniques. Wet rough grinding contains and carries away dust generated during this operation. Disks of waterproof silicon carbide grinding paper are mounted on a wheel rotating at approximately 1150 rpm. Grit sizes of 120, 240, 320, 400, and 600 are used. Care must be taken to prevent deformation twinning, and ample time must be allowed at each grinding step to remove damage caused by previous operations.

Another mechanical grinding procedure that has proved successful for beryllium uses 120-, 240-, and 400-grit silicon carbide papers on a wheel rotating at 1750 rpm. Kerosene is used as the lubricant. Grinding pressures should be extremely light. Fresh papers are used to minimize surface deformation and chipping. More information on this and other grinding techniques can be found in Ref 1.

Rough polishing is performed using a 550-rpm wheel, a chemotextile cloth with adhesive backing, and a medium-light concentration 8- to 22-$\mu$m diamond compound. The specimen should be frequently rotated counter to the direction of wheel rotation. Heavy pressure is used to maximize material removal. Polishing time is approximately 2 min.

Fine polishing is carried out using a 550-rpm wheel, an adhesive-backed rayon cloth, and a medium-light concentration 1- to 5-$\mu$m diamond compound. The mount should be frequently rotated counter to the direction of wheel rotation. Heavy to medium hand pressure is used to maximize removal of material. Polishing time is approximately 3 min.

The final fine polishing is performed using a 550-rpm wheel, an adhesive-backed rayon cloth, and a 0.05-$\mu$m deagglomerated $\gamma$-alumina ($Al_2O_3$) and water slurry. Final polishing takes approximately 3 to 5 min. The specimen should appear flat and free of most scratches.

An attack-polish procedure may also be used. Initial polishing is performed using $Al_2O_3$ abrasive on a short-nap cloth at 1750 rpm. A 5 to 10% aqueous oxalic acid solution is used with the $Al_2O_3$ to achieve a simultaneous chemical attack and mechanical polish. Final polishing is then performed using $\gamma$-$Al_2O_3$ and the aqueous oxalic acid solution on a medium-nap cloth at 1750 rpm. Water, instead of oxalic acid solution, is used to keep the wheel moist during the last few seconds of final polishing. Care must be taken to maintain the proper balance between chemical attack and abrasive action to achieve optimum polishing conditions. Polishing times are approximately 1 min for each wheel. Vibratory polishing and electrolytic polishing of beryllium have also been used (Ref 1).

## Macroexamination

Commercially available beryllium is predominantly a powder metallurgy (P/M) product. Structural castings have poor strength and ductility because of their coarse grain size, and forgings tend to be highly anisotropic. Therefore, macroexamination is seldom used for beryllium, because vacuum hot pressing does not produce substantial flow, and the grain size is too small for macroexamination to be a valuable tool. For additional information on production of beryllium powders and properties and applications of beryllium P/M parts, see Volume 7 of the 9th Edition of *Metals Handbook*.

## Microexamination

Microexamination of beryllium is generally carried out using polarized light. Polarized light techniques cause color differences between grains as a result of crystallographic orientation differences. Polarized light also shows the positions from which oxide particles have been "pulled out" of the structure during polishing. These locations generally appear bright white.

An etchant that is sometimes used, known as 2-2-2 etch, consists of 2% concentrated sulfuric acid ($H_2SO_4$), 2% diluted (48%) hydrofluoric acid (HF), 2% concentrated nitric acid ($HNO_3$), and the remainder distilled water. The specimen should be swabbed 5 to 10 s at (preferably) 20 °C (70 °F). Although strongly temperature dependent and not as widely used as the polarized light observation mode, this method can reveal grain boundaries and oxides. Other etchants used for beryllium are listed in Table 1.

## Microstructures of Beryllium

The microstructure of vacuum hot-pressed beryllium has grains of beryllium and particles of beryllium oxide (BeO) as major constituents. The microstructural differences between grades are subtle; grain size and oxide content are the only distinguishing characteristics.

Rolled beryllium sheet begins as a hot-pressed block, which is subsequently subjected to warm rolling. The final microstructure consists of the usual elongated grains; aspect ratios depend on the actual reduction performed.

Intentional alloying does not occur in the production of pure beryllium, because beryllium has low solubility for most elements and the introduction of alloying elements generally compromises the desirable density and modulus of this metal. Microalloying, which is essentially performed by controlling the proportions of iron and aluminum, is used primarily to prevent the formation of grain-boundary films.

The predominant second-phase constituent is BeO, which has the hexagonal close-packed (hcp) crystal structure and acts as a grain-boundary pinning agent. Because the strength of beryllium is strongly dependent upon grain size, there is a strong correlation among oxide content, grain size, and strength.

The amount of oxide also correlates inversely with ductility. Therefore, a high-strength, low-ductility grade, such as I-400, has a high oxide level of 4.2% minimum. High-ductility structural grades, such as S-65

**Table 1   Etchants used for beryllium(a)**

| Etchant | Remarks |
|---|---|
| **Chemical etchants** | |
| 90 mL ethanol, 10 mL HF | Immerse specimen 10-30 s; increases contrast between inclusions or constituent particles and the matrix |
| 100 mL $H_2O$, 0.5-2 mL HF | Same as above; HF can also be used in glycerol |
| 95 mL $H_2O$, 5 mL $H_2SO_4$ | Immerse 1-15 s to reveal grain boundaries |
| 100 mL $H_2O$, 3-20 g oxalic acid | Use boiling; immerse specimen 2 min to reveal precipitates, up to 16 min to reveal grain boundaries |
| **Electrolytic etchants** | |
| 2 mL HCl, 2 mL $HNO_3$, 2 mL $HClO_4$ (perchloric acid), 94 mL ethylene glycol | Etch at 5 V dc for 5-7 s, stainless steel cathode; solution can be used for electropolishing at 10-16 V dc, 0.1 A/cm² (0.65 A/in.²) |
| 2 mL HCl, 98 mL ethylene glycol | Etch at ∼ 70 V dc, 1-4 min, stainless steel cathode at 10-15 °C (50-60 °F); if structure not etched, reduce to 6-8 V dc for 3-5 s; stir solution, wash specimen in boiling water; specimen can be examined under bright-field illumination |
| 100 mL $H_3PO_4$, 30 mL glycerol, 30 mL ethanol, 2.5 mL $H_2SO_4$ | Grain-boundary etch; cathode covered with cotton, and specimen swabbed lightly in a circular pattern; use stainless steel cathode, 25 V dc for 1-3 min (30-s cycles) at 10 °C (50 °F); polarized light improves contrast |

(a) Source: Ref 1

**Table 2   Grades of vacuum hot-pressed beryllium**

| Chemical composition | S-65B | S-200F | I-220A | I-400 |
|---|---|---|---|---|
| Be, % (min) | 99.0 | 98.5 | 98.0 | 94.0 |
| BeO, % (max) | 1.0 | 1.5 | 2.2 | 4.2(a) |
| Al, ppm (max) | 600 | 1000 | 1000 | 1600 |
| C, ppm (max) | 1000 | 1500 | 1500 | 2500 |
| Fe, ppm (max) | 800 | 1300 | 1500 | 2500 |
| Mg, ppm (max) | 600 | 800 | 800 | 800 |
| Si, ppm (max) | 600 | 600 | 800 | 800 |
| Other, ppm (max) | 400 | 400 | 400 | 1000 |

(a) BeO specified is minimum in this instance.

and S-200F, have oxide levels of 1 and 1.5%, respectively. Particles of BeO appear in polarized light photomicrographs as bright spots, which are actually locations from which the particles have "pulled out" during metallographic preparation.

The typical commercial grades of vacuum hot-pressed beryllium fall into two categories. Instrument grades are designated "I"; structural grades, "S." Instrument grades typically find application in gyroscopes, in inertial navigation systems, and as precision satellite and airborne optical components. Typical structural-grade applications are satellite superstructures, antenna booms, and optical

support structures. The microstructures of four grades of vacuum hot-pressed beryllium and an example of rolled sheet are illustrated in the micrographs that follow. The chemical compositions of these materials are given in Table 2.

## REFERENCE

1. C.W. Price and J.L. McCall, A Review of Metallographic Preparation Procedures for Beryllium and Beryllium Alloys, DMIC Memorandum 237, Defense Metals Information Center, Batelle Memorial Institute, Columbus, OH, 1968

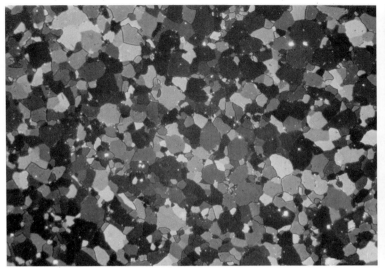

**Fig. 1** S-65B vacuum hot-pressed block; billet consolidated from impact-ground powder. Polarized light micrograph shows substantially equiaxed grains with particles of BeO. Bright areas are locations where BeO has been "pulled out" during metallographic preparation. As-polished. 250×

**Fig. 2** S-200F vacuum hot-pressed block; billet consolidated from impact-ground powder. Seen under polarized light, the microstructure consists of equiaxed grains with particles of BeO. Average grain size is 8 to 10 μm; bright areas show where oxide has been "pulled out" during preparation. As-polished. 250×

**Fig. 3** I-220 vacuum hot-pressed block; billet consolidated from impact-ground powder. Polarized light photomicrograph shows substantially equiaxed grains with BeO particles. Average grain size is 8 to 9 μm; bright areas are locations where BeO was "pulled out" during preparation. The relatively high oxide content of I-220 produces the greater number of oxide particles present. As-polished. 250×

**Fig. 4** I-400 vacuum hot-pressed block; billet consolidated from ball-milled powder. Under polarized light, microstructure shows substantially equiaxed grains with particles of BeO, along with bright areas where BeO was "pulled out" during preparation. Average grain size is 5 μm or less. The relatively high (4.2% min) BeO content of I-400 is apparent in this micrograph. As-polished. 250×

**Fig. 5** SR-200 sheet, rolled at elevated temperature from S-200E vacuum hot-pressed block. Under polarized light, longitudinal section shows grains elongated in the rolling direction. This structure is typical of beryllium sheet, which often has reduced ductility if it is recrystallized after rolling. As-polished. 500×

# Beryllium-Copper and Beryllium-Nickel Alloys

By John C. Harkness
Supervisor
Alloy Research and Development
Brush Wellman Inc.

and

Amitava Guha
Senior Metallurgist
Alloy Research and Development

BERYLLIUM-COPPER AND BERYL-LIUM-NICKEL ALLOYS are selected as representative metallographic specimens depending on product form. Edge and interior samples are important in castings, forgings, and hot- or cold-finished rod, bar, tube, and plate. Longitudinal and transverse sections, which should be examined in strip and wire, are equally important in heavy-section wrought products. Strip may also be examined by electropolishing and etching a small spot on the rolled surface, although this approach is generally not used by commercial suppliers. Care should be taken when examining components manufactured from these alloys to select sections that reveal the microstructural effects of the parts-fabrication process (stamping and forming, machining, plating) and the undisturbed structure of the raw material. Age hardening of these beryllium-containing alloys by the parts fabricator can produce distinct changes in matrix etching response, but does not alter the grain size or intermetallic-compound particle distribution that are characteristic of the mill production process. Components should be examined before and after fabricator heat treatment.

## Health and Safety

Despite low concentrations of beryllium in commercial beryllium-copper and beryllium-nickel alloys (nominally 2 wt% or less), these materials can be hazardous to health if excessive quantities of dust, mists, or fumes containing particles of alloy small enough to enter the lungs (typically 10 $\mu$m or less) are inhaled. Precautions are not required for metallographic sectioning, grinding, or polishing performed wet or for shearing of clean, thin-section strip or wire. Adequate ventilation should be provided for dry sectioning, grinding, or polishing operations, which produce dust or fumes. Metallographic preparation equipment and laboratory work surfaces should be damp wiped periodically to remove accumulation of dry alloy particles. Beryllium-containing alloys are not harmful in contact with skin or wounds, or if swallowed. For additional information, see the article "Toxicity of Metal Powders" in Volume 7 of the 9th Edition of *Metals Handbook*.

## Specimen Preparation

Metallographic equipment and procedures for beryllium-containing alloys are much the same as those recommended for general metallurgical laboratory use.

**Sectioning** of specimens is carried out by sawing, abrasive cutting, or shearing, depending on section thickness and strength. Abrasive wheels formulated for nonferrous or medium-hardness materials and general-purpose use are satisfactory for beryllium copper. Wheels formulated for hard materials and heavy sections are better for beryllium nickel. Abrasive cutting should be performed wet to avoid thermal damage to the specimen and to guard health and safety. Sufficient surface metal is then removed from the sectioned face of the specimen by wet rough grinding to eliminate any deformed material introduced during sectioning.

**Mounting** is usually required for specimens too small to be hand held while polishing or for those requiring edge preservation. Flat strip or transverse sections of small-diameter rod and wire may be stacked and gripped in reusable metal screw clamps for unembedded preparation. Alternatively, samples may be embedded with cold-mounting or compression-molding resins; commercial metal or plastic sample clips are used to stand the sample upright in the mold. Transparent mounting resins are preferred for delicate fabricated parts, such as electrical contacts, to help locate features of interest in the final plane of polish. When distortion of the sample under pressure is to be avoided, cold mounting is preferred over compression molding.

Edge protection may be enhanced by nickel plating prior to mounting or by using hard compression-molding resins formulated for edge preservation. Glass beads or alumina ($Al_2O_3$) granules added to cold-mounting resins for the same purpose will likely contaminate the polishing wheel and cause undesirable specimen scratching, particularly in the softer forms of beryllium copper.

**Grinding.** Coarse grinding is performed wet on a belt or disk grinder using 120- or 180-grit abrasive paper to remove any deformed metal layer. Fine grinding is also performed wet, either by hand on strips of abrasive paper or mechanically on 300-rpm or faster disks using 240-, 320-, 400-, then 600-grit abrasives. The sample is rotated 90° between each grinding. Silicon carbide or $Al_2O_3$ abrasives may be used.

**Mechanical polishing** is usually accomplished in rough and final stages. Rough polishing is performed using a 6-$\mu$m diamond on a wheel covered with a hard, napless chemotextile cloth. Extender oil is applied sparingly, and the wheel is rotated at approximately 300 rpm or less. The specimen is initially positioned so that the direction of polishing is perpendicular to the 600-grit grinding scratches. Maintaining this orientation, it is moved radially back and forth between center and edge of the polishing wheel under moderate pressure until these scratches are removed. The specimen is then briefly rotated counter to the rotation of the wheel to distribute the rough polishing scratches randomly.

Final polishing is performed using 0.05-μm $Al_2O_3$ in distilled water suspension and a wheel covered with low-nap rayon cloth. Speeds are the same as those used for coarse polishing. The wheel is kept moderately saturated with polishing suspension, and the specimen is counterrotated to vary the direction of final polishing. An exception to this procedure is the case of the softer annealed or lightly cold-worked tempers of beryllium copper, in which unidirectional final polishing, parallel to the specimen long axis, helps to minimize scratching. The specimen is washed under running water after each polishing step with mild soap and a cotton swab, then rinsed with alcohol and dried under a warm air blast.

**Automatic Grinding and Polishing.** Several automatic metallographic preparation machines are available that provide rapid and reproducible grinding and polishing of multiple specimens through the use of preset pressure control and a cycle timer. These machines use metal sample holder disks that accommodate 4 to 12 or more cylindrical metallographic mounts or various numbers and sizes of unembedded samples. The holders are rotated by the sample mover head of the machine at approximately 150 rpm and are mechanically pressed against the rotating work wheel, which can be a coarse grinding stone, a wheel accepting successively finer grades of abrasive paper, or cloth-covered polishing wheels. Some systems also employ lapping techniques. Work wheels must be manually changed between preparation steps, but the specimens are never removed from the holder until they are ready to be etched. This preserves a common plane of polish and maintains flatness of the prepared surfaces. Due to the high pressures and short cycle times typically used, these automatic machines increase metallographic laboratory productivity and improve edge preservation and inclusion retention.

Automatic metallographic preparation techniques vary according to the machine used and materials being prepared, but the following procedures have been successfully used for beryllium-containing alloys and can be adapted to any automatic system.

Holders containing mounted specimens or relatively square cut, unembedded specimens are rough ground on 120- or 240-grit paper and fine ground on 240-, 320-, 400-, then 600-grit papers. Very uneven, unembedded specimens may require coarse 60- or 80-grit stone or paper grinding to bring all the samples in a holder to a single plane of polish. A copious flow of recirculated water-base coolant is applied to the work wheel during each grinding

step; it is not necessary to wash the samples in the holder between grindings. Wheel speeds of 150 rpm, pressures of 150 N (35 lbf), and times of approximately 30 s per grinding are usually sufficient. Zirconia ($ZrO_2$) abrasive papers will last longer than silicon carbide or $Al_2O_3$ under these grinding conditions. The loaded sample holder is then ultrasonically cleaned in alcohol, dried in an air blast, and returned to the machine for polishing.

Two or three polishings may be employed. One approach, which applies primarily to holders containing up to six 30-mm (1.25-in.) mounts, begins with 6-μm diamond on a hard, napless chemotextile, proceeds to 3-μm diamond on a low-nap cloth, and finishes with 1-μm diamond on a soft, high-nap cloth. Wheel speed in each case is 150 rpm. The first and second polishings use a pressure of 150 N (35 lbf) for 2 min per step, the final polishing, 100 N (25 lbf) pressure for 35 s. Polishing extender is dripped sparingly on the wheels during each step, and the sample holder and work wheels should rotate in the same direction in each step.

Another approach, useful for high-volume production of embedded and unembedded samples, is to use a 9-μm diamond slurry on a lapping disk, followed by a 0.3-μm $Al_2O_3$ suspension on a low-nap rayon cloth, with an optional intermediate step of 3-μm $Al_2O_3$ suspension on a hard chemotextile. Times and pressures are varied to suit the size and number of samples.

The sample holder is ultrasonically cleaned and dried after each polishing, and the samples are then removed from the holder for etching and final examination. Specimens of different alloys and hardnesses usually may be mixed in a single holder without harming the prepared surfaces of the softer samples.

**Electropolishing.** Clean, as-rolled strip surfaces or sectioned sample faces of beryllium-copper alloys prepared through 400- to 600-grit grinding paper may be electropolished. A satisfactory all-purpose electrolyte for beryllium-copper alloys is a mixture of 1 part nitric acid ($HNO_3$) and 2 parts methanol used at a temperature of $-30$ °C ($-20$ °F), with a voltage of 25 V and a platinum cathode. An electrolyte of 40 mL phosphoric acid ($H_3PO_4$), 60 mL hydrogen peroxide, ($H_2O_2$), 40 mL methanol, and 20 mL $H_2O$ may also be used for beryllium copper in conjunction with a stainless steel cathode, a mask of 0.5 to 1 cm$^2$ (0.08 to 0.16 in.$^2$) area, 20 to 30 V, and approximately 0.2 A. This technique is applicable to general polishing, but is particularly suited to examining intermetallic phases in beryllium copper, which can be rendered in high relief. Polishing is accomplished in a few seconds to a few minutes, using a moderately pumped electrolyte.

## Macroexamination

Castings, forgings, billet, hot-rolled plate and hot-extruded rod, bar, and tube forms of

beryllium-containing alloys are frequently subjected to low-magnification macroexamination. Fracture surfaces of failed components or mechanical test specimens of these product forms may also be examined at low magnification. One purpose of macroexamination is to evaluate grain structure and metal flow patterns indicating thermomechanical processing history. The technique also applies to documentation of differential heat treatment, weld penetration, or localized structural damage due to environmental attack. Fracture surfaces indicate the relative ductility of the material and the mode of failure.

**Fracture Surface Characteristics.** Tensile fracture surfaces of wrought beryllium copper appear macroscopically ductile. Tensile fractures of annealed material typically exhibit macrocup/cone ductile behavior. Alloys heat treated at temperatures and/or times less than or equal to those required to achieve maximum precipitation hardened strength are underaged or peakaged and exhibit blocky, transgranular fractures. Alloys heat treated at higher temperatures and longer times than those required to produce maximum strength are overaged, have a ductile appearance, and show grain facets.

Fatigue fracture features in wrought beryllium copper depend on stress intensity and bending mode. Low stress intensity tends to produce ductile fracture surfaces with a mixed mode character. Higher levels of stress intensity cause a trend toward transgranular fracture. Beryllium copper resists corrosion in many environments, but can stress-corrosion crack in the presence of ammonia. Such cracks are transgranular and intergranular.

**Macroetching.** Once ground to at least 320 or 400 grit, beryllium copper is macroetched by an initial, brief immersion in concentrated $HNO_3$, followed by immersion in or flooding with dilute $HNO_3$ (1 part concentrated $HNO_3$ to 2 parts distilled $H_2O$). The etchant attack is stopped by rinsing in running water. After the etched sample is rinsed in alcohol and dried in a warm air blast, the macrostructure can be preserved by spraying on a coat of clear lacquer, preferably containing a copper tarnish inhibitor such as benzotriazol ($C_6H_4NHN$:N). Beryllium nickel can be macroetched by the same procedure, omitting the concentrated $HNO_3$ presoak.

In addition to grain structure and flow patterns, macroetched samples of beryllium coppers with 1.6 wt% or more Be reveal locally heat-affected zones as light etched areas if reannealed or unaged and as dark etched areas if aged. Light etched or reddish-colored areas adjacent to exterior or crack surfaces in uniformly aged materials usually signal environmental attack leading to local depletion of beryllium and lack of aging response. Matrix darkening on etching is not as pronounced in aged beryllium nickel and is absent in beryllium coppers containing less than 0.6 wt% Be, limiting the information revealed by macroetching of these alloys essentially to matters of grain morphology. Castings and cast billet exhibit columnar dendritic grain growth from solidification. Hot-finished, large-section forms of the beryllium-containing alloys occasionally exhibit in the macrostructure individual large grains, elongated in the direction of working.

## Microexamination

Etching procedures for beryllium-containing alloys vary with alloy type and condition or temper. Particularly for beryllium coppers with less than 0.6 wt% Be, general microstructures are more difficult to reveal in the age-hardened conditions than in the hot-finished, solution-annealed, or cold-worked conditions.

Microetchants for beryllium copper and beryllium nickel are listed in Table 1, along with their compositions, etching procedures, uses, and precautions. Nitric acid and water (etchant 9, Table 1) is a good, general-purpose etchant for all forms and tempers of beryllium nickel. Modified Marble's etchant (etchant 10, Table 1), which is especially suited to hot-worked or annealed material, provides dramatic grain-structure detail with sensitive tint illumination.

Ammonium persulfate hydroxide (etchant 1, Table 1) is a general-purpose etchant for beryllium coppers. It reveals grain structure in unaged material, although twinning may be present to complicate grain size measurement. In the case of alloys with 1.6 wt% or more Be, this etchant darkens the matrix of age-hardened material; the degree of coloration varies with the extent of precipitation in the alloy. A variation of this etchant that contains $H_2O_2$ (etchant 2, Table 1) offers improved grain-boundary delineation in unaged material.

Grains in aged, concentrated alloys of beryllium copper may be highlighted by etching with ammonium persulfate hydroxide, followed by brief swabbing with dichromate (etchant 3, Table 1) to lighten the matrix. Another reliable way to enhance grain boundaries in unaged alloys of these compositions is to age the samples for 15 to 20 min at 370 °C (700 °F), then follow with the two-stage etching procedure described above. This technique eliminates twinning, and grain size can be accurately determined from the decoration of the grain boundaries with dark etching γ precipitate.

Alloys with 0.6 wt% or less Be exhibit little microstructural difference between the aged and unaged conditions, and grain structure is frequently obscured by twinning if ammonium persulfate hydroxide is used. To enhance the general microstructure in these situations, the cyanide (etchant 6, Table 1), persulfate hydroxide/cyanide (etchant 7, Table 1), or two-step cyanide (etchant 6, Table 1)/cyanide peroxide hydroxide (etchant 8, Table 1) etchants are used. Care must be taken to observe all safety precautions of these toxic solutions.

None of the etchants listed differentially attack intermetallic compounds in beryllium copper—to distinguish cobalt or nickel beryllides from β phase, for example. This distinction must be made on the basis of appearance in the as-polished condition. Beryllides are blue gray; β phase is creamy white and surrounded by a thin, dark outline.

Any of the etchants listed, which are intended for bright-field optical microscopy, may be utilized for scanning electron microscopy examination to reveal fine structural details not optically resolvable. One such application is the resolution of the lamellar structure of grain-boundary γ precipitate in high-temperature aged beryllium coppers containing 1.60 to 2.00 wt% Be.

## Microstructures of Beryllium-Copper Alloys

The two general categories of beryllium-copper alloys are the high-strength and the high-conductivity alloys. The wrought high-strength alloys contain 1.60 to 2.00 wt% Be, with approximately 0.25 wt% Co. The addition of cobalt promotes fine grain size in the cast form, lessens grain growth during an-

**Table 1   Etching reagents for beryllium-copper and beryllium-nickel alloys**

| Etchant | Composition | Comments |
|---|---|---|
| 1. Ammonium persulfate hydroxide | 1 part $NH_4OH$ (conc) and 2 parts $(NH_4)_2S_2O_8$ (ammonium persulfate) 2.5% in $H_2O$ | All beryllium-copper alloys. General structure. Preheat sample in hot water (optional); swab etch 2–20 s; use fresh. |
| 2. Ammonium persulfate hydroxide (variation) | 2 parts 10% $(NH_4)_2S_2O_8$, 3 parts $NH_4OH$ (conc), 1 part 3% $H_2O_2$, and 5–7 parts $H_2O$(a) | All beryllium-copper alloys. Offers improved grain boundary delineation in unaged material. A, 1/4H, 1/2H, H tempers (unaged, use less $H_2O$. AT through HT and aged, use more $H_2O$). Use fresh; swab or immerse 5–60 s. Preheat specimen in hot $H_2O$ if etching rate is slow. |
| 3. Dichromate | 2 g $K_2Cr_2O_7$ (potassium dichromate), 8 mL $H_2SO_4$ (conc), 1 drop HCl per 25 mL of solution, and 100 mL $H_2O$(a). | Grain structure of wrought Cl7000, Cl7200, Cl7300. Use for AT through HT and mill hardened (aged). Etch first with ammonium persulfate hydroxide (No. 1 or 2); wipe dichromate 1–2 times over specimen to remove dark etch color. Do not overetch; sample may pit. May be used with laboratory aging of annealed or as-rolled material at 370 °C (700 °F) for 15–20 min to enhance grain boundary delineation for grain size determination |
| 4. Hydroxide/peroxide | 5 parts $NH_4OH$ (conc), 2–5 parts 3% $H_2O_2$, and 5 parts $H_2O$ | Common etchant for copper and brass, also applicable to beryllium-copper alloys. Use fresh. |
| 5. Ferric chloride | 5 g $FeCl_3$ (ferric chloride), 50 mL HCl, and 100 mL $H_2O$ | Common etchant for copper alloys, also applicable to cold rolled tempers of beryllium-copper alloys C17500 and C17510 to show grain structure. Immerse 3–12 s. |
| 6. Cyanide | 1 g KCN (potassium cyanide) and 100 mL $H_2O$ | General structure of beryllium-copper alloys C17500, C17510 (No. 6). Immerse 1–5 min; stir slowly while etching; use etchant 7 if others are too weak to bring out structure. A two-step technique for improved results on C17510 includes immersion in etchant 6 followed by swabbing with etchant 8. *Caution:* Poison fumes! Use fume hood. Do not dispose of used solutions directly into drains. Pour used solution into beaker containing chlorine bleach. Let stand 1 h, then flush down drain with plenty of running water. |
| 7. Persulfate hydroxide/cyanide | 4 parts ammonium persulfate hydroxide etchant (etchant 1 or 2) and 1 part cyanide etchant (etchant 6) | |
| 8. Cyanide peroxide hydroxide | 20 mL KCN, 5 mL $H_2O_2$, and 1–2 mL $NH_4OH$ | |
| 9. Nitric acid and water | 30 mL $HNO_3$ (conc) and 70 mL $H_2O$ | Beryllium nickel, all tempers. General structure. Swab etch. |
| 10. Modified Marble's etchant | 4 g $CuSO_4$ (copper sulfate), 20 mL HCl (conc), and 20 mL $H_2O$ | Beryllium nickel, all tempers. General structure. Swab etch. May also be used with sensitive tint illumination to reveal grain structure of hot worked or annealed material |
| 11 Phosphoric acid electrolyte | 20 mL $H_2O$ (tap, not distilled), 58 mL 3% $H_2O_2$, 48 mL $H_3PO_4$, and 48 mL ethyl alcohol | For deep etching of beryllium copper. Polish specimen through 1-μm or finer $Al_2O_3$. Use 0.5-1 cm² (0.08–0.16 in.²) mask. 0.1 A to etch (higher amperes to polish). Low to moderate flow rate. 3 to 6 s to etch, up to 60 s to polish |

(a) Use distilled water, unless otherwise noted.

nealing, and reduces the rapid softening of the alloy due to overaging. Solution annealing at temperatures of 760 to 790 °C (1400 to 1450 °F), followed by rapid quenching, retains the beryllium in solid solution at room temperature. Precipitation hardening can be accomplished by aging for 0.1 to 4 h at 260 to 400 °C (500 to 750 °F); the time and temperature depend on the composition, amount of cold work, and strength levels desired. Cold working prior to aging results in faster age hardening and higher strengths.

The most commercially important of the high-strength compositions is C17200, which contains 1.80 to 2.00 wt% Be. This is the strongest of the beryllium-copper alloys; tensile strengths range to 1520 MPa (220 ksi) in the fully age-hardened condition. A leaded version of this alloy, C17300, exhibits improved machinability. A composition slightly lower in cost, C17000, with 1.60 to 1.79 wt% Be, is available with tensile properties in the age-hardened condition approximately 10% lower than those of C17200.

The high-strength alloys are also produced as casting alloys, designated C82400, C82500, C82510, C82600, and C82800. The beryllium content is higher (up to approximately 2.75 wt%) than in wrought alloys, but the general microstructural characteristics are similar. These alloys are produced as cast ingots that can be remelted and cast by foundries using any conventional molding technique.

The high-conductivity alloys have low beryllium levels (0.2 to 0.7 wt%) and high cobalt and nickel levels. The wrought version of the alloy containing 2.4 to 2.7 wt% Co is designated C17500. The cast version is designated C82000. The wrought version containing 1.4 to 2.2 wt% Ni instead of cobalt is designated C17510, and the corresponding casting alloy is C82200. The properties of the nickel-containing alloys are very similar to the cobalt-containing alloys. The solution-annealing temperature range for the high-conductivity alloys is 900 to 955 °C (1650 to 1750 °F). Aging is performed at 425 to 565 °C (800 to 1050 °F) for 3 to 8 h, depending on the amount of cold work and combination of properties sought.

The various commercial beryllium-copper alloys illustrated in this article are listed in Table 2, which provides compositional limits. Data sheets published by the alloy producers may be consulted for detailed information, such as physical and mechanical properties and typical applications. The phases and constituents resulting from alloying elements and various heat treatments are discussed below.

**The Beryllide Phase.** Commercial beryllium-copper alloys contain cobalt or nickel or both. These alloying elements are normally in solution in the liquid metal. Because of their strong affinity for beryllium, they combine with it and separate during solidification as particles that are approximately 10-$\mu$m in the longest dimension. These constituent particles are termed "beryllides." During subsequent thermomechanical processing, the

**Table 2 Chemical compositions of beryllium-copper alloys**

| Alloy | Composition, wt% | | | | | |
|---|---|---|---|---|---|---|
| | Be | Co | Ni | Pb | Other | Cu |
| **Wrought alloys** | | | | | | |
| C17000 | 1.60-1.79 | (a) | (a) | ... | ... | rem |
| C17200 | 1.80-2.00 | (a) | (a) | ... | ... | rem |
| C17300 | 1.80-2.00 | (a) | (a) | 0.20-0.6 | ... | rem |
| C17500 | 0.40-0.7 | 2.4-2.7 | ... | ... | ... | rem |
| C17510 | 0.20-0.6 | 0.30(b) | 1.4-2.2 | ... | ... | rem |
| **Cast alloys** | | | | | | |
| C82000 | 0.45-0.8 | 2.4-2.7 | 0.20 | ... | 0.15 Si | rem |
| C82200 | 0.35-0.8 | ... | 1.0-2.0 | ... | ... | rem |
| C82400 | 1.65-1.75 | 0.20-0.40 | 0.10 | ... | 0.20 Fe | rem |
| C82500 | 1.90-2.15 | 0.35-0.7 | 0.20 | ... | 0.20-0.35 Si, 0.20 Fe | rem |
| C82510 | 1.90-2.5 | 1.0-1.2 | 0.20 | ... | 0.20-0.35 Si, 0.25 Fe | rem |
| C82600 | 2.25-2.45 | 0.35-0.7 | 0.20 | ... | 0.20-0.35 Si, 0.25 Fe | rem |
| C82800 | 2.50-2.75 | 0.35-0.7 | 0.20 | ... | 0.20-0.35 Si, 0.25 Fe | rem |

(a) Nickel + cobalt, 0.20 min.; Nickel + cobalt + iron, 0.60 max. (b) Maximum if no range given

beryllides are broken up somewhat but are not dissolved into solid solution during normal solution annealing.

The primary beryllide phase is best observed in the as-polished condition as blue-gray Chinese script in castings. The secondary beryllides forming after solidification of the major phase can have a rodlike morphology with preferred crystallographic orientation with the matrix. In wrought products, the beryllides appear as roughly spherical, blue-gray particles.

**The Beta Phase.** The $\beta$ phase forms peritectically from the liquid metal. It is observed in high-strength alloy castings as an interdendritic network surrounding the primary copper-rich $\alpha$ phase. Experiments have shown that the $\beta$ phase cannot be retained at room temperature, because it decomposes into $\alpha$ and $\gamma$ phases by a eutectoid transformation. The (transformed) $\beta$ phase stands out in relief in the as-polished state as white angular patches. In wrought metal containing 1.8 to 2.0 wt% Be, long (transformed) $\beta$ stringers may exist due to insufficient homogenization before hot working.

**The Gamma Phase.** The $\gamma$ phase forms in overaged beryllium-copper alloys as an equilibrium precipitate. In concentrated alloys of beryllium-copper, the $\gamma$-phase precipitation starts at the grain boundaries and advances into the adjoining grains, consuming the fine, metastable precipitates. This type of precipitation is termed "discontinuous precipitation" or "cellular precipitation." The $\gamma$ precipitates formed by this mechanism have a platelike morphology. In the age-hardened state, the grain boundary containing the $\gamma$ precipitate is soft compared to the hardened matrix.

Precipitation of the $\gamma$ phase can also occur in the grain boundaries in high-strength beryllium-copper alloys if the rate of quenching from the solution-annealing temperature is not fast enough to retain beryllium in solid solution. In metallographically polished specimens etched using standard procedures, the $\gamma$ phase stands out at the grain boundaries as dark nodules on a bright matrix. The lamellar morphology of the $\gamma$ phase is resolved by scanning or transmission electron microscopy.

**Hardening Precipitates.** Excellent room-temperature mechanical properties of beryllium-copper alloys are derived from the formation of a series of metastable precipitates during aging. Several such metastable phases form before the equilibrium $\gamma$ phase is observed. The precipitation sequence at large undercoolings is:

$$\text{Supersaturated solid solution} \rightarrow$$
$$\text{Guinier-Preston (GP) zones} \rightarrow \gamma'' \rightarrow \gamma' \rightarrow \gamma$$

Guinier-Preston zones are the first precipitates to form and are coherent with the matrix. They are nucleated in large densities. The coherency strain fields set up due to the misfit of the zones and the matrix strengthen the alloy. With continued aging, Guinier-Preston zones transform to more stable precipitates.

The metastable precipitates can be detected by transmission electron microscopy. They are identified by the characteristic features observed in the electron diffraction pattern. The presence of hardening precipitates can be recognized only indirectly by light microscopy as striations on the surface of a polished and etched alloy that result from the overlap of coherency strains.

## Microstructures of Beryllium-Nickel Alloys

Commercial beryllium-nickel alloys can be precipitation hardened in a manner similar to beryllium-copper alloys by solution annealing, quenching, optional cold working, and aging. These alloys usually contain 1.80 to 2.70 wt% Be; titanium, chromium, or carbon, among others, are added for grain-size control, corrosion resistance, hot workability, or machinability. Typical chemical compositions of the alloys are listed in Table 3. Solu-

**Table 3  Chemical compositions of beryllium-nickel alloys**

| Alloy | Type | Composition, wt% | | | | |
|---|---|---|---|---|---|---|
| | | Be | Ti | Cr | C | Ni |
| UNS36000 | Wrought | 1.80-2.05 | 0.4-0.6 | ... | ... | rem |
| M220C | Casting | 2.00-2.30 | ... | ... | 0.50-0.75 | rem |
| 41C | Casting | 2.7 | ... | 0.5 | ... | rem |
| 42C | Casting | 2.7 | ... | 12 | ... | rem |

tion annealing of these alloys is performed at approximately 980 to 1065 °C (1800 to 1950 °F). After quenching, tensile strengths approaching 2068 MPa (300 ksi) are obtained by aging at approximately 510 °C (950 °F) for 1 to 3 h.

Precipitation in the beryllium-nickel system is similar to the beryllium-copper system regarding the sequence and the structure of the metastable phases formed during aging. The equilibrium $\gamma$ phase (NiBe) is formed by a discontinuous reaction consuming the hardening precipitates. Nickel-beryllium compound particles containing titanium exist in the wrought alloy and assist grain refinement. Graphite nodules are present in the cast alloys containing carbon and contribute to improved machinability.

**Fig. 1** C82200 alloy casting. As-cast microstructure shows interdendritic networks of large primary beryllide phase in a matrix of $\alpha$ solid solution. Preferred orientation of small secondary beryllides is observed with the matrix. Etchant 6 (Table 1) 400×

**Fig. 2** C82500 alloy casting, solution annealed at 790 °C (1450 °F) and aged to peak hardness at 315 °C (600 °F) for 3 h. Microstructure consists of Chinese-script beryllides in a copper-rich $\alpha$ solid-solution matrix, with angular $\beta$ phase transformed to a lamellar aggregate of $\alpha$ and $\gamma$ phases. Striations are the result of metastable precipitation in the alloy. Etchant 1 (Table 1). 400×

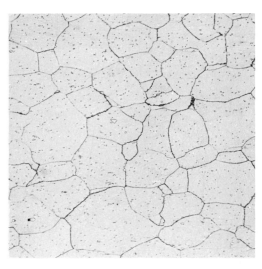

**Fig. 3** C17200 alloy strip, mill hardened to AM (TM00) temper to achieve maximum formability at moderate strength. Longitudinal section shows roughly equiaxed grains of $\alpha$ phase and cobalt beryllides. Metastable precipitates that form during hardening and increase strength and hardness are not resolved. Etchant 1 (Table 1). 400×

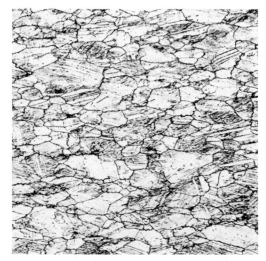

**Fig. 4** C17200 alloy strip, mill hardened to XHMS (TM08) temper for high strength and limited formability. Longitudinal section shows elongated grains of the $\alpha$ phase and cobalt beryllides. Striations result from precipitation of metastable phases not resolved by optical microscopy. Etchant 1 (Table 1). 400×

**Fig. 5** C17200 alloy strip, solution annealed at 790 °C (1450 °F) and water quenched. Longitudinal section shows equiaxed grains of supersaturated $\alpha$-phase solid solution of beryllium in copper. Cobalt beryllide particles are uniformly dispersed throughout the structure. Etchant 1 or 2 (Table 1). 400×

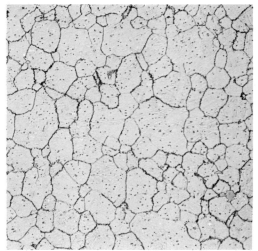

**Fig. 6** C17200 alloy strip, solution annealed at 790 °C (1450 °F), quenched rapidly to room temperature and precipitation hardened at 315 °C (600 °F) for 3 h to achieve maximum hardness. Longitudinal section shows equiaxed $\alpha$ grains and the cobalt-beryllide phase uniformly dispersed. Metastable phases are not resolved, but small quantities of equilibrium $\gamma$ phase are present in the grain boundaries. Etchant 1 (Table 1). 400×

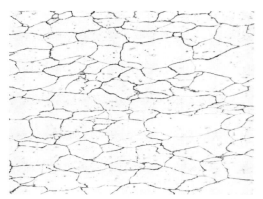

**Fig. 7** C17200 alloy strip, solution annealed at 790 °C (1450 °F) and cold rolled at 37% to full hard temper. Longitudinal section shows elongated grains of α phase and cobalt beryllides. Etchant 1 or 2 (Table 1). 400×

**Fig. 8** C17200 alloy strip, solution annealed, cold rolled full hard and precipitation hardened at 315 °C (600 °F) for 2 h to achieve maximum hardness. Longitudinal section shows elongated grains of α phase and cobalt beryllides. Striations are caused by metastable precipitates not resolved by optical microscopy. Etchant 1 (Table 1). 400×

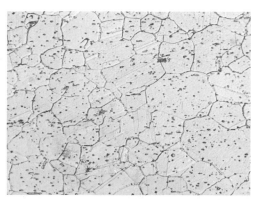

**Fig. 9** C17510 alloy strip, solution annealed at 900 °C (1650 °F), quenched rapidly to room temperature, and precipitation hardened at 480 °C (900 °F) for 3 h to achieve maximum hardness. Equiaxed grains of supersaturated solution of beryllium and nickel in copper are shown. Etchant 6 (Table 1). 400×

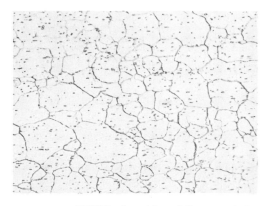

**Fig. 10** C17510 alloy strip, solution annealed, cold rolled, and precipitation hardened at 480 °C (900 °F) for 2 h to achieve maximum hardness. Structure consists of α phase and a uniform distribution of the nickel-beryllide phase. Elongated grains are the result of cold work. Metastable precipitates are not resolved. Etchant 6, followed by swabbing with etchant 8 (Table 1). 400×

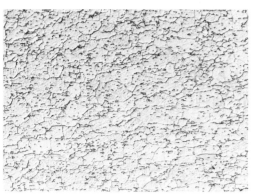

**Fig. 11** C17500 alloy strip, solution annealed at 900 °C (1650 °F), quenched rapidly to room temperature and precipitation hardened at 480 °C (900 °F) for 3 h to achieve maximum hardness. Microstructure shows equiaxed grains of supersaturated solution of beryllium and cobalt in copper. The cobalt-beryllide phase is uniformly distributed, and metastable hardening precipitates are not resolved. Etchant 6 (Table 1). 400×

**Fig. 12** C17500 alloy strip, solution annealed, cold rolled, and precipitation hardened at 480 °C (900 °F) for 2 h to achieve maximum hardness. Structure consists of the α phase and a uniform distribution of the beryllide phase. Elongated grains are the result of cold work, and metastable hardening precipitates are not resolved. Etchant 6 (Table 1). 400×

**Fig. 13** C17200 alloy strip, solution annealed and aged at 370 °C (700 °F) for 6 h to attain an overaged condition. The structure shows γ precipitates in the grain boundaries, which appear as dark nodules in a light matrix. Etchant 1 (Table 1). 400×

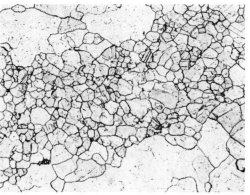

**Fig. 14** C17200 alloy plate, cast, homogenized, and hot worked. The microstructure shows nonuniform distribution of grain sizes, which is typical of a hot-worked product. Greater uniformity in grain size distribution may be achieved in the finished product by successive cold-working and annealing operations. Etchant 1 (Table 1). 700×

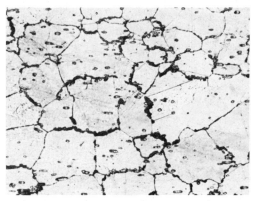

**Fig. 15** UNS 36000 alloy strip, solution annealed at 990 °C (1800 °F), water quenched, and aged at 510 °C (950 °F) for 1.5 h. The structure shows nickel-beryllium compound particles dispersed uniformly through the nickel-rich matrix. Hardening precipitates are not resolved, but equilibrium γ (NiBe) precipitates are present in grain boundaries. Etchant 10 (Table 1). 800×

**Fig. 16** C17200 alloy strip, solution annealed and age hardened. The white constituents of the structure are $\beta$ stringers. These zones of beryllium segregation are carried through from billet casting and homogenization. Etchant 1 (Table 1). 700$\times$

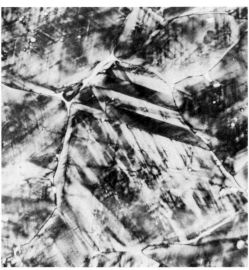

**Fig. 17** C17200 alloy strip heated to 885 °C (1625 °F) and water quenched. The microstructure shows "burned metal" caused by solution annealing at too high a temperature. Partial melting at the grain boundaries, caused by extreme temperatures, resolidifies as $\beta$ phase. Etchant 1 (Table 1). 700$\times$

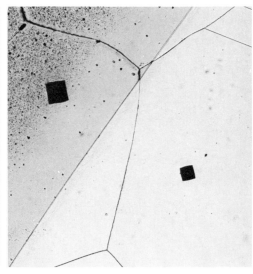

**Fig. 18** C17510 alloy rod, solution annealed in air at 980 °C (1800 °F) for 3 h , then aged at 480 °C (900 °F) for 3 h. The microstructure shows internal oxidation resulting from solution annealing without a protective atmosphere. Note the loss in hardness (as indicated by the microhardness indentations) within the internal oxidation zone. Etchant 6 (Table 1). 200$\times$

# Copper and Copper Alloys

COPPER AND COPPER ALLOY specimens, wrought and cast, are prepared for macro- and microexamination in much the same way as other metals (see the Section "Metallographic Techniques" in this Volume).

## Macroexamination

Specimens for macroscopic examination are extracted from larger masses using common cutting tools. The tools must be kept sharp to minimize cold working of the specimen.

**Surface Preparation.** Surfaces suitable for macroetching usually can be obtained in two machining operations. In the first operation, a heavy cut is taken to remove the metal that was cold worked during sectioning; in the second, a light cut is taken using a V-shape tool to remove the remaining effects of cold work.

The need for further surface preparation depends on the amount of detail required. The surface detail revealed by etching increases as the degree of surface irregularity decreases. The machined surface is often ground using 180-grit or finer abrasive—and sometimes as fine as 600 grit.

**Etching.** Deep etching removes the effects of cold work, but produces a rough surface; therefore, it is common practice to deep etch the machined or rough-ground surface, regrind it lightly, then etch it lightly.

Selection of an etchant for a macrospecimen depends primarily on the alloy to be etched and the features to be examined. Because the capabilities of two or more etchants often overlap or are the same, selection of a specific etchant is arbitrary. Table 1 lists compositions of the more commonly used macroetchants, along with etching procedures, purposes of the etchants or characteristics revealed, and alloys for which they are ordinarily used.

## Microexamination

Specimens of copper and copper alloys for microscopic examination are extracted from larger masses by sawing, shearing, filing, hollow boring, or abrasive-wheel cutting.

**Mounting.** In general, the procedures for mounting copper and copper alloy specimens are the same as those for other metals. Coppers and copper alloys are extremely susceptible to work hardening; therefore, when possible, the face used for examination should be the one that has been subjected to the least cutting.

Bakelite is the mounting material most often used. Diallyl phthalate, glass or fiber filled, is a suitable alternative to Bakelite. Methyl methacrylate is softer than Bakelite and thus is not as good for edge preservation.

However, its transparency is sometimes advantageous.

The combination of heat and pressure needed for compression-mounting materials will sometimes crush or adversely affect specimens, especially those of thin sheet or strip. Under these conditions, one of the epoxies or some other castable mounting material must be used. Edge preservation of copper and copper alloy specimens can be accomplished by the same methods used for specimens of other metals (see the article "Mounting of Specimens" in this Volume).

**Grinding.** Wet grinding is preferred for all coppers and copper alloys. Common practice involves rough grinding the specimen surface to remove metal that has been cold worked, then finish grinding to obtain a suitable surface. Finish grinding is performed using flat

## Table 1 Etchants for macroscopic examination of coppers and copper alloys

Procedure for use: immerse at room temperature, rinse in warm water, dry

| Composition | Copper or copper alloy | Comments |
|---|---|---|
| 1. 50 mL $HNO_3$, 0.5 g $AgNO_3$ (silver nitrate), 50 mL $H_2O$ | All coppers and copper alloys | Produces a brilliant, deep etch |
| 2. 10 mL $HNO_3$ and 90 mL $H_2O$ | Coppers and all brasses | Grains; cracks and other defects |
| 3. 50 mL $HNO_3$ and 50 mL $H_2O$(a) | Coppers, all brasses, aluminum bronze(b) | Same as above; reveals grain contrast |
| 4. 30 mL HCl, 10 mL $FeCl_3$, 120 mL $H_2O$ or methanol | Coppers and all brasses | Same as etchant above(c) |
| 5. 20 mL acetic acid, 10 mL 5% $CrO_3$, 5 ml 10% $FeCl_3$, 100 mL $H_2O$(d) | All brasses | Produces a brilliant, deep etch |
| 6. 2 g $K_2Cr_2O_7$, 4 mL saturated solution of NaCl, 8 mL $H_2SO_4$, 100 mL $H_2O$(e) | Coppers, high-copper alloys, phosphor bronze | Grain boundaries, oxide inclusions |
| 7. 40 g $CrO_3$, 7.5 g $NH_4Cl$ (ammonium chloride), 50 mL $HNO_3$, 8 mL $H_2SO_4$, 100 mL $H_2O$ | Silicon brass, silicon bronze | General macrostructure |
| 8. 45 mL acetic acid and 45 mL $HNO_3$ | Copper | Grain boundary and macroetch by polish attack |
| 9. Saturated $(NH_4)_2S_2O_8$ (ammonium persulfate) | Copper and copper alloys | Use after the acetic acid listed above; increases contrast of brass |
| 10. 40 mL $HNO_3$, 20 mL acetic acid, 40 mL $H_2O$ | Copper and copper alloys | Macroetch 90-10, 70-30, and leaded brass |

(a) Solution should be agitated during etching to prevent pitting of some alloys. (b) Aluminum bronzes may form smut, which can be removed by brief immersion in concentrated $HNO_3$. (c) Excellent for grain contrast. (d) Amount of water can be varied as desired. (e) Immerse specimen 15-30 min, then swab with fresh solution.

Revised by R.E. Ricksecker, director of Metallurgy, Chase Brass and Copper Co. (retired), and T.F. Bower, director of Metallurgical Process Development, Chase Brass and Copper Co. Thanks are due to Antoni Tabak, International Copper Research Association, who provided considerable help in contacting INCRA-sponsored contractors.

**Table 2  Electrolytes and conditions for electrolytic polishing of copper and copper alloys**

| Composition | Voltage | Current density A/cm² | Current density A/in.² | Cathode | Duration | Copper or copper alloy |
|---|---|---|---|---|---|---|
| 1. 825 mL H₃PO₄ and 175 mL H₂O | 1.0-1.6 | 0.02-0.1 | 0.13-0.65 | Copper | 10-40 min | Unalloyed copper |
| 2. 250 mL H₃PO₄, 250 mL ethanol, 50 mL propanol, 500 mL distilled H₂O, 3 g urea | 3-6 | 0.4-0.8 | 2.6-5.2 | Stainless steel | 50 s | Coppers and copper alloys |
| 3. 700 mL H₃PO₄ and 350 mL H₂O | 1.2-2.0 | 0.06-0.1 | 0.39-0.64 | Copper | 15-30 min | Coppers; α, β, and α-β brasses; aluminum, silicon, tin; and phosphor bronzes; beryllium, iron, lead, or chromium |
| 4. 580 g H₄P₂O₇ and 1000 mL H₂O | 1.2-1.9 | 0.08-0.12 | 0.05-0.77 | Copper | 10-15 min | Coppers, brasses |
| 5. 300 mL HNO₃ and 600 mL methanol | 20-70 / 30-50 | 0.65-3.1 / 2.5-3.1 | 4.2-20.0 / 16.1-51.0 | Stainless / Stainless | 10-60 s / 5-10 s | Coppers, brasses / Silicon bronze, phosphor bronze |
| 6. 170 g CrO₃ and 830 mL H₂O | 1.5-12 | 0.95-2.2 | 6.1-14.2 | Stainless | 10-60 s | Brasses |
| 7. 400 mL H₃PO₄ and 600 mL H₂O | 1.0-2.0 | 0.06-0.15 | 0.39-0.97 | Copper or stainless | 1-15 min | α, α-β brasses; copper-iron, copper-chromium |
| 8. 30 mL HNO₃, 900 mL methanol, 300 g Cu(NO₃)₂ (cupric nitrate) | 45-50 | 1.05-1.25 | 6.77-8.1 | Stainless | 15 s | Bronzes (have tendency to etch) |
| 9. 670 mL H₃PO₄, 100 mL H₂SO₄, and 300 mL distilled H₂O | 2-3 | 0.1 | 0.64 | Copper | 15 min | Copper; copper-tin containing up to 6% Sn |
| 10. 470 mL H₃PO₄, 200 mL H₂SO₄, 400 mL distilled H₂O | 2-2.3 | 0.1 | 0.64 | Copper | 15 min | Copper-tin up to 9% Sn |
| 11. 350 mL H₃PO₄ and 650 mL ethanol | 2-5 | 0.02-0.07 | 0.13-0.45 | Copper | 10-15 min | Copper alloys with high lead (to 30%) |
| 12. 540 mL H₃PO₄ and 460 mL H₂O | 2 | 0.065-0.075 | 0.4-0.5 | Copper | 5-15 min | Copper |
|  | 2-2.2 | 0.1-0.15 | 0.64-0.97 | Copper | 15 min | Nickel silver |

wheels and silicon carbide papers of progressively finer grit—usually 240, 320, 400, and 600. Ultrafine 800- and 1200-grit papers are sometimes used.

An acceptable alternative to wet grinding is to dry grind on belts having progressively finer grit sizes (180, 240, and 320 grit), then to hand polish on progressively finer emery papers (1, 0, 00, 000, and 0000). Wet grinding is recommended; during either procedure, the specimen should always be rotated 90° before grinding using the next finer grit size.

**Rough Polishing.** Most coppers and copper alloys are relatively soft and so require a polishing medium that provides maximum cutting with minimum rubbing. Rough polishing should be performed using diamond-impregnated nylon cloth. Duck canvas, wool broadcloth, and cotton (listed in order of decreasing preference) are also used for polishing.

The preferred abrasive for rough polishing on any of the cloths mentioned above is 3- to 9-μm diamond paste. However, 400-grit or finer alumina ($Al_2O_3$), used with distilled water as the vehicle, is usually an acceptable alternative. A wheel speed of approximately 200 rpm is generally recommended.

**Finish Polishing.** Generally, napped cloths are preferred for finish polishing. The abrasive is usually 0.3-μm α-$Al_2O_3$ or 0.05-μm γ-$Al_2O_3$; both abrasives are used with water as a vehicle. Other abrasives that have proved satisfactory for finish polishing are magnesium oxide (MgO) in distilled water, ferric oxide ($Fe_2O_3$), colloidal silica ($SiO_2$), and fine diamond paste. Recommended wheel speed is 150 to 200 rpm.

Specimen rotation during polishing elicits numerous opinions. Hand polishing necessitates developing a personal technique that may require a degree of manual dexterity; mechanical polishing gives more reproducible results and is preferred.

After polishing, the specimen is rinsed in water and dried with warm air. Automatic polishing (usually vibratory) has proved highly successful for polishing copper alloys. Automatic polishing greatly minimizes human variables. Attack polishing (combined polishing and etching) using ferric nitrate $Fe(NO_3)_3$ or ammonium hydroxide/ammonium persulfate [$NH_4OH$-$(NH_4)_2S_2O_8$] solution can be more safely performed using automatic equipment than by hand.

**Electrolytic polishing** of coppers and copper alloys alleviates many of the difficulties encountered in mechanical polishing. Additional information is available in the article "Electrolytic Polishing" in this Volume.

Apart from offering the usual advantages over mechanical polishing of saving time,

minimizing the human variable, and minimizing artifacts resulting from disturbed metal, electrolytic polishing offers some advantages for copper and copper alloys:

- It is excellent for revealing grain size and shape on all sides of specimens.
- It is especially well adapted to use on single-phase copper alloys.
- It reveals true microstructure with less difficulty than mechanical polishing.

Disadvantages of electrolytic polishing for copper and copper alloys include:

- Different rates of attack cause some phases of multiphase alloys to stand out in relief.
- The edge effect of electrolytic polishing, whereby edges of specimens are attacked and polished more than other areas, limits application of the process to examination of surfaces in from the edges.
- Attack around nonmetallic particles, voids, and inclusions in the specimen may occur at a more rapid rate than attack of the matrix and so the size of voids or inclusions may be exaggerated.

Table 2 lists compositions of some electropolishing solutions, together with electropolishing conditions that have proved satisfactory for the coppers and copper alloys shown in the last column in the table. The durations listed in Table 2 are generally based on conditions where electrolytic polishing completely replaces mechanical polishing. Useful results may be obtained when mechanical polishing is followed by electrolytic polishing. Durations for electrolytic polishing are then always under 1 min.

**Examination of As-Polished Specimens.** As-polished specimens of coppers and copper alloys are frequently examined metallographically. Characteristics revealed include the presence of oxide in as-cast copper, lead particles and cavities in cast red brass, oxides in zirconium copper, and corrosion in brazed joints. As-polished specimens are used also for microprobe examinations. Specimens are also examined under polarized light to differentiate cuprous oxide ($Cu_2O$) inclusions from other inclusions. Under polarized light, only the $Cu_2O$ inclusions appear ruby red; under white light, copper oxide and other inclusions appear blue-gray. Oxides of arsenic and antimony also are optically active under polarized light.

**Chemical Etching.** Table 3 lists chemical etchants that are used for coppers and copper alloys and includes etching procedures and the alloys to which each etchant is commonly applied. The ammonium hydroxide/hydrogen peroxide/water solution (etchant 1, Table 3) is by far the most widely used etchant. It is probably optimum for routine work and applies to most coppers and copper alloys. This etchant was used for many of the specimens shown in the micrographs in this article. This etchant is also widely used for determining the inclusion content of brass and bronze strip.

**Table 3  Etchants and procedures for microetching of coppers and copper alloys**

| Composition(a) | Procedure | Copper or copper alloy |
|---|---|---|
| 1. 20 mL NH$_4$OH, 0-20 mL H$_2$O, 8-20 mL 3% H$_2$O$_2$ | Immersion or swabbing 1 min; H$_2$O$_2$ content varies with copper content of alloy to be etched; use fresh H$_2$O$_2$ for best results(b) | Use fresh for coppers and copper alloys; film on etched aluminum bronze can be removed using weak Grard's solution, preferred for brasses |
| 2. 1 g Fe(NO$_3$)$_3$ and 100 mL H$_2$O | Immersion | Etching and attack polishing of coppers and alloys |
| 3. 25 mL NH$_4$OH, 25 mL H$_2$O, 50 mL 2.5% (NH$_4$)$_2$S$_2$O$_8$ | Immersion | Attack polishing of coppers and some copper alloys |
| 4. 2 g K$_2$Cr$_2$O$_7$, 8 mL H$_2$SO$_4$, 4 mL NaCl (saturated solution), 100 mL H$_2$O | Immersion; NaCl replaceable by 1 drop HCl per 25 mL solution; add just before using; follow with FeCl$_3$ or other contrast etch | Coppers; copper alloys of beryllium, manganese, and silicon; nickel silver; bronzes, chromium copper; preferred for all coppers to reveal grain boundaries, grain contrast, and cold deformation |
| 5. CrO$_3$ (saturated aqueous solution) | Immersion or swabbing | Coppers, brasses, bronzes, nickel silver |
| 6. 50 mL 10-15% CrO$_3$ and 1-2 drops HCl | Immersion; add HCl at time of use | Same as above; color by electrolytic etching or with FeCl$_3$ etchants |
| 7. 8 g CrO$_3$, 10 mL HNO$_3$, 10 mL H$_2$SO$_4$, 200 mL H$_2$O | Immersion or swabbing | Grain contrast etch for ETP copper, does not dissolve Cu$_2$O; use after etchant 3 when etching deoxidized high-phosphorus copper for microstructure |
| 8. 10 g (NH$_4$)$_2$S$_2$O$_8$ and 90 mL H$_2$O | Immersion; use cold or boiling | Coppers, brasses, bronzes, nickel silver, and aluminum bronze |
| 9. 10% aqueous copper ammonium chloride plus NH$_4$OH to neutrality or alkalinity | Immersion; wash specimen thoroughly | Coppers, brasses, nickel silver; darkens $\beta$ in $\alpha$-$\beta$ brass |
| 10. FeCl$_3$, g  HCl, mL  H$_2$O, mL <br> 5    50    100 <br> 20    5    100(c)(d) <br> 25    25    100 <br> 1    20    100 <br> 8    25    100 <br> 5    10    100(e)(f) | Immersion or swabbing; etch lightly or by successive light etches to required results | Coppers, brasses, bronzes, aluminum bronze; darkens $\beta$ phase in brass; gives contrast following dichromate and other etches |
| 11. 5 g FeCl$_3$, 100 mL ethanol, 5-30 mL HCl | Immersion or swabbing for 1 s to several minutes | Coppers and copper alloys; darkens $\beta$ phase in $\alpha$-$\beta$ brasses and aluminum brass |
| 12. HNO$_3$ (various concentrations) | Immersion or swabbing; 0.15-0.3% AgNO$_3$ added to 1:1 solution gives a brilliant, deep etch | Coppers and copper alloys |
| 13. NH$_4$OH (dilute solutions) | Immersion | Attack polishing of brasses and bronzes |
| 14. 50 mL HNO$_3$, 20 g CrO$_3$, 75 mL H$_2$O | Immersion | Aluminum bronze, free-cutting brass; film from polishing can be removed with 10% HF |
| 15. 5 mL HNO$_3$, 20 g CrO$_3$, 75 mL H$_2$O | Immersion | Same as above |
| 16. 59 g FeCl$_3$ and 96 mL ethanol | Immersion; heat sample first in hot H$_2$O | Macro- and microetch for annealed copper-nickel alloys |
| 17. 16 g CrO$_3$, 1.8 g NH$_4$Cl (ammonium chloride), 10 mL HNO$_3$, 200 mL H$_2$O | Immersion | Preferred etch for copper-nickel; preferential attack of copper-rich phase in castings |
| 18. 5 parts HNO$_3$, 5 parts acetic acid, 1 part H$_3$PO$_4$ | Immersion, 3 s | Coppers, brasses |
| 19. Equal parts NH$_4$Cl and H$_2$O | Immersion | Coppers and alloys |
| 20. 60 g FeCl$_3$, 20 g Fe(NO$_3$)$_3$, 2000 mL H$_2$O | Immersion | Copper-nickel alloys |
| 21. 1 part acetic acid, 1 part HNO$_3$, 2 parts acetone | Immersion | Copper-nickel alloys |

(a) The use of concentrated etchants is intended unless otherwise specified. (b) This etchant may be alternated with FeCl$_3$. (c) Grard's No. 1 etchant. (d) Plus 1 g CrO$_3$. (e) Grard's No. 2 etchant. (f) Plus 1 g CuCl$_2$ and 0.05 g SnCl$_2$ (tin chloride)

**Table 4  Electrolytes and operating conditions for electrolytic etching of copper and copper alloys**

| Composition | Operating conditions | Copper or copper alloy |
|---|---|---|
| 1. 5-14% H$_3$PO$_4$ (8%) and rem H$_2$O | Voltage range, 1-8; etching time, 5-10 s | Coppers, cartridge brass, free-cutting brass, admiralty, gilding metal |
| 2. 250 mL 85% H$_3$PO$_4$, 250 mL 95% ethanol, 500 mL H$_2$O, 2 mL wetting agent | Voltage range, 1-3; current density, 0.1-0.15 A/cm$^2$ (0.64-0.97 A/in.$^2$); etching time, 30-60 s | Coppers |
| 3. 30 g FeSO$_4$ (ferrous sulfate), 4 g NaOH, 100 mL H$_2$SO$_4$, 1900 mL H$_2$O | 0.1 A at 8-10 V for 15 s; do not swab surface after etching | Darkens $\beta$ phase in brasses and gives contrast after H$_2$O$_2$-NH$_4$OH etch; also for nickel silver and bronzes |
| 4. 1 mL CrO$_3$ and 99 mL H$_2$O | 6 V; aluminum cathode; etching time, 3-6 s | Beryllium copper and aluminum bronze |
| 5. 5 mL acetic acid (glacial), 10 mL HNO$_3$, 30 mL H$_2$O | Voltage range 0.5-1 V; current density, 0.2-0.5 A/cm$^2$ (1.3-1.9 A/in.$^2$); etching time, 5-15 s | Copper-nickel alloys; avoiding contrast associated with coring |

The potassium dichromate/sulfuric acid/sodium chloride/water etchant (usually referred to simply as potassium dichromate, K$_2$Cr$_2$O$_7$; see etchant 4 in Table 3) is also used extensively, especially for revealing structures of welded and brazed joints.

Chromic acid (H$_2$CrO$_4$, etchant 5 in Table 3) is also prevalent. For the micrographs shown in this article, it was used for electrodeposited copper, nickel silver, and brazed joints in copper. The other etchants listed in Table 3 have limited uses, although some are used for the same alloys and structures as the etchants discussed above.

**Electrolytic etching** reveals cold-worked structures of brasses, gives contrast to $\beta$ phase in brass, and, in copper-nickel alloys, reduces the contrast due to coring that usually appears with chemical etching. It is also used to bring out the general structure of beryllium copper, cartridge brass, free-cutting brass, aluminum bronze, nickel silver, and admiralty metal. Table 4 lists five electrolytes that have proved successful for electrolytic etching.

**Examination for Inclusions.** Microscopic examination has become increasingly valuable for evaluating the fabrication characteristics of certain copper alloys, particularly brass and bronze sheet and strip. A correlation exists between the number of inclusions present, as well as their length and distribution, and fabrication characteristics, especially formability. Inclusions are best revealed by swabbing the specimen quickly with NH$_4$OH-H$_2$O$_2$ (etchant 1, Table 3), then washing it in running water and drying with an air blast.

## Microstructures of Copper and Copper Alloys

Nominal compositions of the copper and copper alloys represented in the accompanying micrographs are listed in Table 5. The micrographs illustrate the effects of alloying elements, heat treatment, percentages of reduction by rolling, and corrosion and dezincification. Also shown are the structures of welds and brazed joints.

## REFERENCES

1. T.F. Bower and D.A. Granger, "Copper and Copper Alloy Ingot Structure—A Preliminary Survey," Report 70-34, The Casting Laboratory, Cleveland, 1970
2. T.J. Kelley, "Welding of Copper-Nickel Clad Steels," INCRA project 240, International Copper Research Association, New York, 1980
3. N.J. Grant, "Structure-Property Relationships in High Temperature, High Strength, High Conductivity Copper-Base Alloys," INCRA project 311, International Copper Research Association, New York, 1981

**Table 5  Nominal compositions of copper and copper alloys**

### Wrought coppers

| CDA No. | Name | Cu | P | Te |
|---|---|---|---|---|
| C10100 | Oxygen-free electronic copper (OFE) | 99.99 min | 0.0003 | 0.0010 |
| C10200 | Oxygen-free copper (OF) | 99.95 min | . . . | . . . |
| C11000 | Electrolytic tough pitch copper (ETP) | 99.90 min | . . . | . . . |
| C12200 | Phosphorus-deoxidized copper, high residual phosphorus (DHP) | 99.90 min | 0.015-0.040 | . . . |
| C12500 | Fire-refined tough pitch copper (FRTP) | 99.88 min | . . . | 0.025 |
| C14500 | Phosphorus-deoxidized copper, tellurium bearing | 99.90 min | 0.004-0.012 | 0.40-0.70 |
| C14700 | Sulfur-bearing copper | 99.90 min | . . . | . . . |
| C15000 | Zirconium copper | 99.80 min | . . . | . . . |

### Wrought high-copper alloys

| CDA No. | Name | Cu | Other |
|---|---|---|---|
| C17200 | Beryllium copper | rem | 1.80-2.00 Be, 0.20 Al, 0.20 Si |
| C18200 | Chromium copper | rem | 0.6-1.2 Cr, 0.10 Fe, 0.10 Si |
| C18700 | Leaded copper | rem | 0.8-1.5 Pb |
| C19400 | Iron-bearing copper | 97.0 min | 2.1-2.6 Fe, 0.05-0.2 Zn |

### Wrought brasses

| CDA No. | Name | Cu | Pb | Fe | Zn | Other |
|---|---|---|---|---|---|---|
| C26000 | Cartridge brass, 70% | 68.5-71.5 | 0.07 | 0.05 | rem | . . . |
| C26800 | Yellow brass, 66% | 64.0-68.5 | 0.15 | 0.05 | rem | . . . |
| C28000 | Muntz metal, 60% | 59.0-63.0 | 0.30 | 0.07 | rem | . . . |
| C31600 | Leaded commercial bronze, nickel bearing | 87.5-90.5 | 1.3-2.5 | 0.10 | rem | 0.7-1.2 Ni |
| C33500 | Low-leaded brass | 62.0-65.0 | 0.25-0.7 | 0.15 | rem | . . . |
| C35000 | Medium-leaded brass, 62% | 60.0-63.0 | 0.8-2.0 | 0.15 | rem | . . . |
| C36000 | Free-cutting brass | 60.0-63.0 | 2.5-3.7 | 0.35 | rem | . . . |
| C44300 | Arsenical admiralty | 70.0-73.0 | 0.07 | 0.06 | rem | 0.8-1.2 Sn |
| C44400 | Antimonial admiralty | 70.0-73.0 | 0.07 | 0.06 | rem | 0.8-1.2 Sn |
| C44500 | . . . . . . . . . | 70.0-73.0 | 0.07 | 0.06 | rem | 0.8-1.2 Sn, 0.02-0.10 P |
| C48500 | High-leaded naval brass | 59.0-62.0 | 1.3-2.2 | 0.10 | rem | 0.5-1.0 Sn |

### Wrought bronzes

| CDA No. | Name | Cu | Pb | Sn | Zn | Other |
|---|---|---|---|---|---|---|
| C51000 | Phosphor bronze, 5% A | rem | 0.05 | 4.2-5.8 | 0.30 | 0.10 Fe |
| C51800 | Phosphor bronze | rem | 0.02 | 4.0-6.0 | . . . | 0.01 Al |
| C63000 | Aluminum bronze, 10% | rem | . . . | 0.20 | 0.30 | 9.0-11.0 Al, 2.0-4.0 Fe, 4.0-5.5 Ni |
| C64700 | Silicon-nickel bronze | rem | 0.1 | . . . | 0.5 | 1.6-2.2 Ni |
| C67500 | Manganese bronze A | 57.0-60.0 | 0.2 | 0.5-1.5 | rem | 0.8-2.0 Fe |
| C68700 | Arsenical aluminum brass | 76.0-79.0 | 0.07 | . . . | rem | 1.8-2.5 Al 0.02-0.06 As |
| C69700 | Leaded brass | 75.0-80.0 | 0.5-1.5 | . . . | rem | 2.5-3.5 Si |

### Wrought copper-nickel alloys and nickel silvers

| CDA No. | Name | Cu | Ni | Other |
|---|---|---|---|---|
| C70600 | Copper nickel, 10% | rem | 9.0-11.0 | 1.0-1.8 Fe, 1.0 Zn |
| C71300 | Copper nickel, 25% | rem | 23.5-26.5 | 1.0 Zn, 1.0 Mn |
| C71500 | Copper nickel, 30% | rem | 29.0-33.0 | 0.50 Fe |
| C71900 | Copper nickel | rem | 28.0-33.0 | 2.2-3.0 Cr |
| C74500 | Nickel silver, 65-10 | 63.5-66.5 | 9.0-11.0 | 0.25 Fe, 0.5 Mn |
| C75200 | Nickel silver, 65-18 | 63.5-66.5 | 16.5-19.5 | 0.25 Fe, 0.5 Mn |

### Cast high-copper alloy

| CDA No. | Name | Cu | Zn | Cr | Other |
|---|---|---|---|---|---|
| C81500 | Chromium copper | 98.0 min | 0.10 | 0.40-1.5 | 0.15 Si, 0.1 Fe, 0.1 Al |

### Cast brasses, bronzes, and nickel silver

| CDA No. | Name | Cu | Sn | Zn | Al | Other |
|---|---|---|---|---|---|---|
| C83600 | Leaded red brass | 84.0-86.0 | 4.0-6.0 | 4.0-6.0 | 0.005 | 4.0-6.0 Pb |
| C86200 | Manganese bronze | 60.0-66.0 | 0.2 | 22.0-28.0 | 3.0-4.9 | 2.0-4.9 Fe, 2.5-5.0 Mn |
| C86300 | Manganese bronze | 60.0-66.0 | 0.2 | 22.0-28.0 | 5.0-7.5 | 2.5-5.0 Mn |
| C86500 | Manganese bronze | 55.0-60.0 | 1.0 | 36.0-42.0 | 0.5-1.5 | 0.4-2.0 Fe |
| C90300 | Tin bronze | 86.0-89.0 | 7.5-9.0 | 3.0-5.0 | 0.005 | 1.0 Ni |
| C92600 | Leaded tin bronze | 86.0-88.5 | 9.3-10.5 | 1.3-2.5 | 0.005 | 0.8-1.5 Pb |
| C94100 | High-leaded tin bronze | 72.0-79.0 | 4.5-6.5 | 1.0 | 0.005 | 18.0-22.0 Pb |
| C95300 | Aluminum bronze | 86.0 min | . . . | . . . | 9.0-11.0 | 0.8-1.5 Fe |
| C95400 | Aluminum bronze | 83.0 min | . . . | . . . | 10.0-11.5 | 3.0-5.0 Fe, 1.5 Ni |
| C95500 | Nickel-aluminum bronze | 78.0 min | . . . | . . . | 10.0-11.5 | 3.0-5.0 Fe, 3.0-5.5 Ni |
| C95600 | Silicon-aluminum bronze | 88.0 min | . . . | . . . | 6.0-8.0 | 1.8-3.5 Si |
| C97800 | Nickel silver | 64.0-67.0 | 4.0-5.5 | 1.0-4.0 | 0.005 | 24.0-27.0 Ni |

### Filler metals and brazing alloys

| CDA No. | Name | Cu | Ag | Zn | Other |
|---|---|---|---|---|---|
| C11000 | Electrolytic tough pitch (ETP) copper | 99.90 min | . . . | . . . | 0.04 O |
| | BCuP-5 brazing alloy | 80.0 | 14.5-15.5 | . . . | 4.8-5.2 P |
| C28580 | Copper-zinc brazing alloy | 49.0-52.0 | . . . | rem | 0.5 Pb, 0.1 Fe |
| | BAg-8a brazing alloy | 27.8 | 72.0 | . . . | 0.20 Li |
| | BAg-1 brazing alloy | 14.0-16.0 | 44.0-46.0 | 14.0-18.0 | 23.0-25.0 Cd |

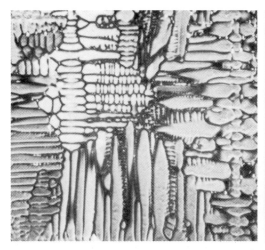

**Fig. 1** Alloy 11000 (ETP copper), static cast. Excellent definition of dendritic structure. Etchant 10, Table 3. 5×. (J. Bartholomew)

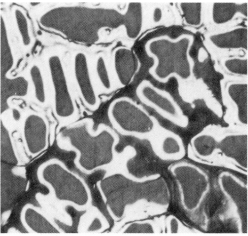

**Fig. 2** Same material as Fig. 1, but at higher magnification to show detail of dendritic structure. Etchant 4, Table 3. 75×. (J. Bartholomew)

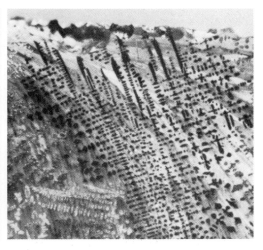

**Fig. 3** Same material as Fig. 1, static cast. Grains from the chilled bottom grew through the dendrite "skeletons," producing a mixed grain structure. Etchant 10, Table 3. 3×

**Fig. 4** Alloy 12200 (DHP copper). Longitudinal section of static-cast ingot showing columnar structure. Pouring direction was from top to bottom. Etchant 10, Table 3. 2×. (J. Dibee)

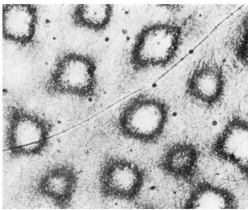

**Fig. 5** Same alloy as Fig. 4. Transverse section shows the cross section of the columnar structure and a grain boundary. Etchant 4, then etchant 1, Table 3. 50×. (J. Dibee)

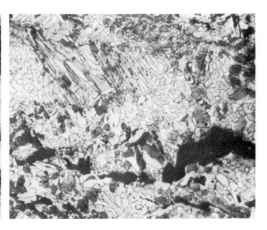

**Fig. 6** Alloy 36000 (free-cutting brass), as-cast. Solid-state transformation makes this structure appear unlike an as-cast structure. Etchant 1, Table 3. 50×. (J. Bartholomew)

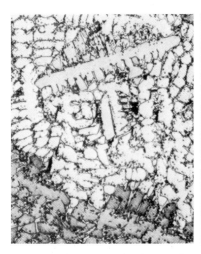

**Fig. 7** Same material as Fig. 6, with primary dendrites of α phase darkened. Lead appears as small spheroids. Etchant 1, Table 3. 50×. (J. Dibee)

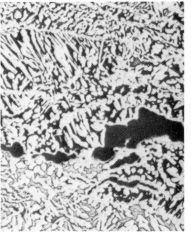

**Fig. 8** Same alloy as Fig. 6, with β phase darkened by preferential attack of the etchant. In this case, α phase is formed in the solid state during cooling. Etchant 16, Table 3. 50×. (J. Dibee)

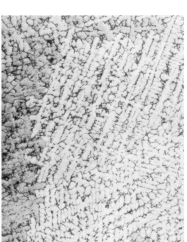

**Fig. 9, 10** Same alloy as Fig. 6, semicontinuous cast. Fig. 9: α-phase dendrites in the columnar zone near the outside edge of the ingot. Fig. 10: mixed α- and β-phase dendrites near the center of the ingot. Etchant 1, Table 3. 30×. (Ref 1)

**Fig. 11** Alloy 26000 (cartridge brass), annealed. Polarized light illumination was used to increase contrast of the microstructure. Etchant 18, then etchant 19, Table 3. 55×. (J. Dibee)

**Fig. 12** Alloy 68700 (arsenical aluminum brass), annealed. Structure is α-brass, with the aluminum in solid solution. Etchant 18, Table 3. 55×. (J. Dibee)

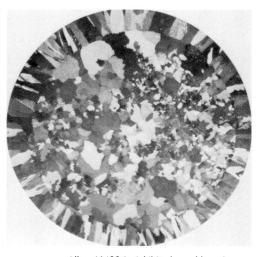

**Fig. 13** Alloy 46400 (uninhibited naval brass), as-cast. Transverse macrosection showing the columnar structure of the outer edges of the casting that result from more rapid cooling near the surface of the casting. Etchant 12, Table 3. 1.5×. (J. Dibee)

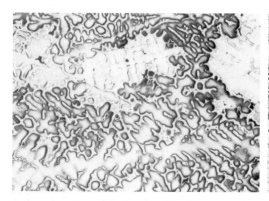

**Fig. 14** Same specimen as Fig. 13, except at higher magnification to reveal dendritic microstructure. Etchant 1, then etchant 16, Table 3. 30×. (J. Dibee)

**Fig. 15** Alloy 68700 (arsenical aluminum brass), as-cast. Macrosection showing typical dendritic structure. See Fig. 16 for detail. Etchant 18, then etchant 16, Table 3. 4×. (J. Dibee)

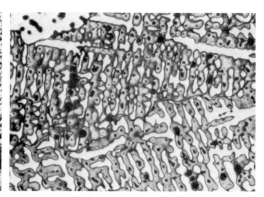

**Fig. 16** Same as Fig. 15, except at higher magnification to reveal more detail of the structure. Same etchants as Fig. 15. 75×. (J. Dibee)

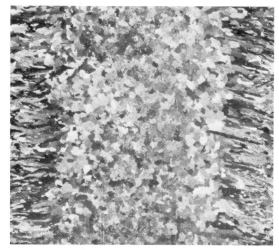

**Fig. 17** Alloy 71500 (copper nickel, 30% Ni), as-cast. Longitudinal section showing columnar structure near the surface of the billet. The grains are inclined upward from horizontal by up to 30° due to convection in the initial state of freezing. Etchant 18, then etchant 16, Table 3. 0.3×. (J. Bartholomew)

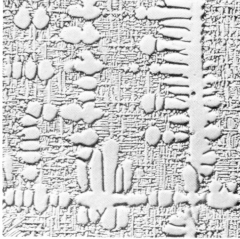

**Fig. 18** Alloy 26000 (cartridge brass), cast, slowly cooled, and quenched. Primary dendrites aligned in ⟨100⟩ crystallographic directions. The fine, quenched structure has the same orientation as the coarse dendrites. Etchant 1, Table 3, then electropolished with electrolyte 1, Table 2. 30×. (J. Dibee)

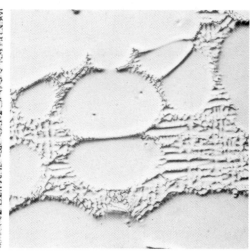

**Fig. 19** Same alloy and processing as Fig. 18. Higher magnification shows that fine dendrites originate in the coarse ones and have the same orientation. Dendrites starting in directions that are not ⟨100⟩ do not grow very far. Same etchant and electrolyte as Fig. 18. 85×. (J. Dibee)

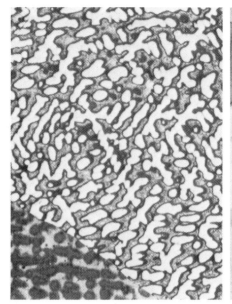

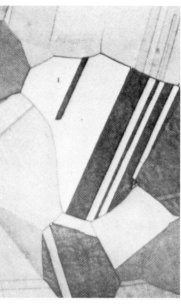

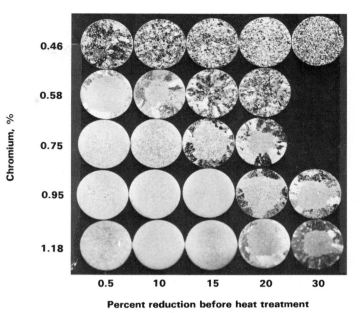

**Fig. 20** Alloy 70600 (copper-nickel, 10% Ni), semicontinuous cast. Microstructure shows the distinct segregation of the copper-rich phase (dark) and the nickel-rich phase (light). Etchant 17, Table 3. 50×. (J. Dibee)

**Fig. 21** Alloy 46400 (uninhibited naval brass), extruded, drawn, and annealed. Structure shows twinned grains resulting from annealing. Etchant 16, Table 3. 300×. (J. Dibee)

**Fig. 22** Alloy 18200 (chromium copper, 0.8% Cr), solutionized 5 min at 1010 °C (1850 °F). Solutionizing increases solubility of chromium, which gives higher hardness after quenching and aging. However, if all chromium goes into solid solution, uncontrolled grain growth results, starting where there is the most cold work before heat treatment (right). Excessive grain growth embrittles grain boundaries; temperature, chromium content, cold work, and time at temperature must be controlled to prevent complete solution of chromium and uncontrolled grain growth. 0.45×. (T. Cobb)

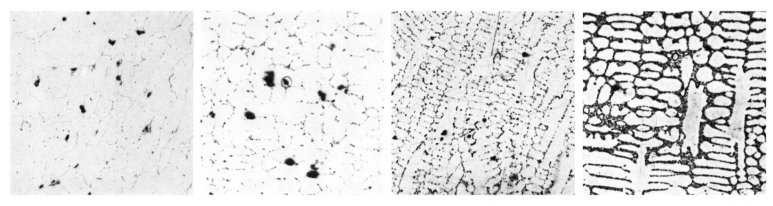

**Fig. 23, 24, 25, 26** The effect of oxygen content on the microstructure of as-cast, copper-oxygen alloys. Oxygen contents less than 0.39% result in primary dendrites of copper (light) plus eutectic (mottled areas of small, round oxide in copper). Fig. 23: 0.024% O. Fig. 24: 0.05% O. Fig. 25: 0.09% O. Fig. 26: 0.18% O. As-polished. 100×

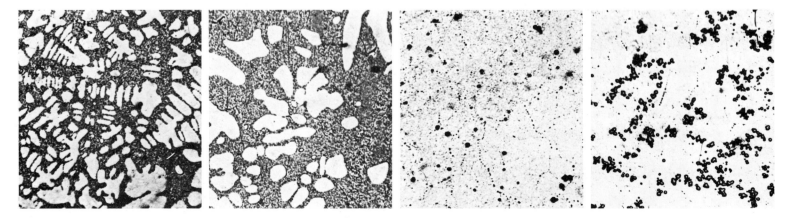

**Fig. 27, 28, 29, 30** Same as Fig. 23 to 26. Fig. 27: 0.23% O. Fig. 28: 0.32% O. Figures 29 and 30, containing more than 0.39% O, have structures consisting of particles or dendrites of oxide (dark) and eutectic. Fig. 29: 0.44% O. Fig. 30: 0.50% O. As-polished. 100×

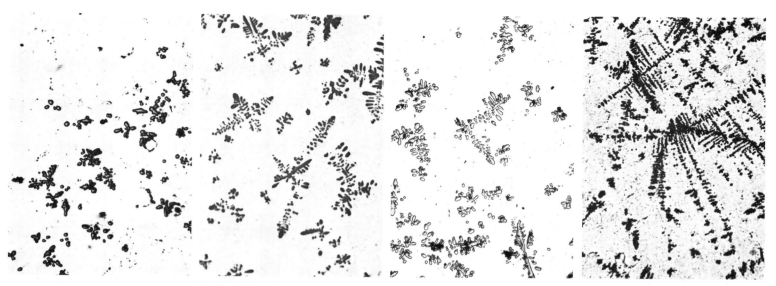

**Fig. 31, 32, 33, 34** Same as Fig. 23 to 26, with dark oxide dendrites in a eutectic matrix. Fig. 31: 0.60% O. Fig. 32: 0.70% O. Fig. 33: 0.78% O. Fig. 34: 0.91% O. As-polished. 100×

**Fig. 35** Copper 10200 (OF copper), hot-rolled bar. Large, equiaxed, twinned grains. Etchant 1, Table 3. 100×

**Fig. 36** Same as Fig. 35, cold worked, annealed 30 min at 850 °C (1560 °F). Equiaxed, recrystallized grains, containing twinned areas. Etchant 4, Table 3. 250×

**Fig. 37** Same as Fig. 35, hot-rolled bar, heated 1 h in air to 665 °C (1225 °F). Specimen from near surface shows $Cu_2O$ (dark dots) caused by oxygen penetration during heating. Etchant 1, Table 3. 250×

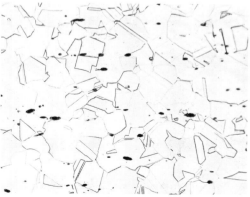

**Fig. 38** Copper 11000 (ETP copper) hot-rolled rod. Transverse section shows equiaxed grains and dispersion of $Cu_2O$ particles. Etchant 4, Table 3. 250×

**Fig. 39** Same as Fig. 38. Longitudinal section shows equiaxed grains and well-dispersed, slightly elongated $Cu_2O$ particles (dark dots). Etchant 4, Table 3. 250×

**Fig. 40** Same as Fig. 38, extruded rod. Longitudinal section showing equiaxed grains and dispersed $Cu_2O$ (dark dots). Etchant 4, Table 3. 400×

**Fig. 41** Same as Fig. 38, heated in hydrogen. Hydrogen diffused into the copper, reacted with $Cu_2O$ at the grain boundaries, formed steam, and forced the copper grains apart, causing embrittlement and porosity. See also Fig. 42. Etchant 4, Table 3. 75×

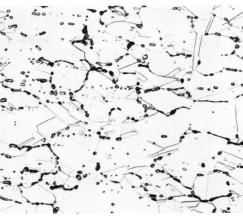

**Fig. 42** Same as Fig. 38, heated to 850 °C (1560 °F) in an atmosphere containing hydrogen. Structure shows same voids as Fig. 41. Etchant 4, Table 3. 250×

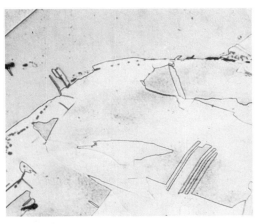

**Fig. 43** Copper 12500 (FRTP copper) hot-rolled strip 12.7 mm (0.5 in.) thick. Structure consists of twinned grains of copper, with stringers of $Cu_2O$ particles resulting from segregation of the oxide in the ingot during casting. Etchant 1, Table 3. 200×

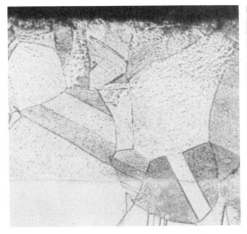

**Fig. 44** Copper 12200 (DHP copper). Internal oxidation (presence of dark dots of $P_2O_5$). Etchant 4, Table 3. 75×

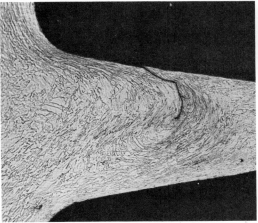

**Fig. 45** Same metal as Fig. 44. Lap defect in the fin of a condenser tube. Lap was caused by tool misalignment during the rolling of fins on the tube. Etchant 4, Table 3. 75×

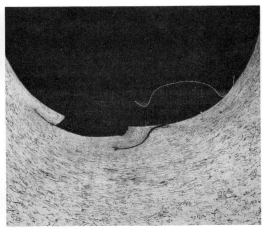

**Fig. 46** Same as Fig. 45. Lap defect between fins of a condenser tube, caused by tool misalignment during fin rolling. Etchant 4, Table 3. 75×

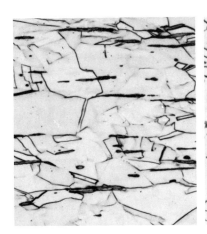

**Fig. 47** Copper 14520 (DPTE copper) hot-rolled and drawn rod. Dark particles elongated in the rolling direction are copper telluride, which improves machinability. Etchant 7, Table 1. 250×

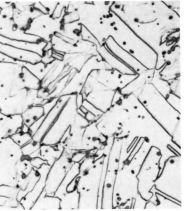

**Fig. 48** Copper 14700 (sulfur-bearing copper) rod, cold worked to 50% reduction. Transverse section shows dispersion of round particles of CuS, which improves machinability. Etchant 7, Table 1. 200×

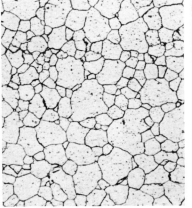

**Fig. 49** Alloy 17200 (beryllium copper), solution treated 10 min at 790 °C (1450 °F) and water quenched. Typical hardness is 62 HRB. Structure is equiaxed grains of supersaturated solid solution of beryllium in copper. Etchant 3, Table 3. 300×

**Fig. 50** Same alloy and processing as Fig. 49, but aged 3 h at 360 °C (600 °F) after solution treatment. Typical hardness is 37 HRC. Copper-beryllium precipitate at grain boundaries and within α grains. Etchant 3, Table 3. 300×

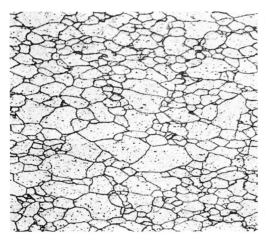

**Fig. 51** Same alloy and processing as Fig. 49, except reduced 11% by cold rolling to quarter-hard temper. Typical hardness is 79 HRB. Alpha grains are elongated in the direction of rolling. Etchant 3, Table 3. 300×

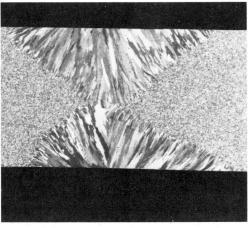

**Fig. 52** Copper 11000 (ETP copper) cold-rolled bar, annealed approximately 1 h by holding at 375 °C (705 °F), then tungsten arc welded in two passes using straight-polarity direct current and copper 11000 filler metal. See Fig. 53 for structure details at the fusion zone edge. Etchant 1, Table 3. 2×

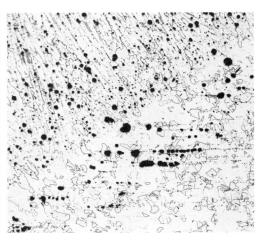

**Fig. 53** Edge of fusion zone of weld in Fig. 52. Gas porosity (dark areas) in fusion zone (upper left) and in the heat-affected zone (bottom right). Etchant 1, Table 3. 25×

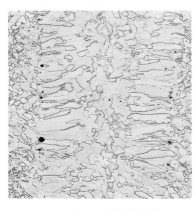

**Fig. 54** Copper 10100 (OFE copper) bar, electron beam welded without filler metal. Columnar grains in fusion zone (middle) and original equiaxed grains in base metal. The scattered black dots along the edge of the fusion zone are gas porosity. Etchant 2, Table 3. 35×

**Fig. 55** Alloy C70600 (copper nickel, 10% Ni), 2.3 mm (0.090 in.) thick. Laser welded to 1020 steel base. Weld made with 2.0 kW of laser input energy at travel speed of 17 to 25.4 mm/s (40 to 60 in./min). No melting of the steel base occurred. Etchant 21, Table 3. 15×. (Ref 2)

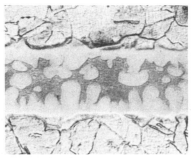

**Fig. 56** Copper 10100 (OFE copper) brazed with BCuP-5 filler metal. Silver-copper-phosphorus eutectic (mottled gray) in the joint, with large dendrites of copper solid solution (light gray) extending into the joint from the grains of unalloyed base metal. Grains of unalloyed copper in the base metal are medium size. Compare with Fig. 53. Etchant 5, Table 3. 125×

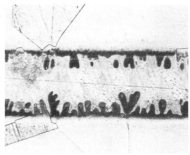

**Fig. 57** Same as Fig. 56, brazed with BAg-8a filler metal. Silver-copper eutectic (mottled gray) in the joint, with small dendrites of copper solid solution (dark) extending into the joint from the unalloyed base metal. Grains of unalloyed copper in the base metal are extremely large. Etchant 5, Table 3. 70×

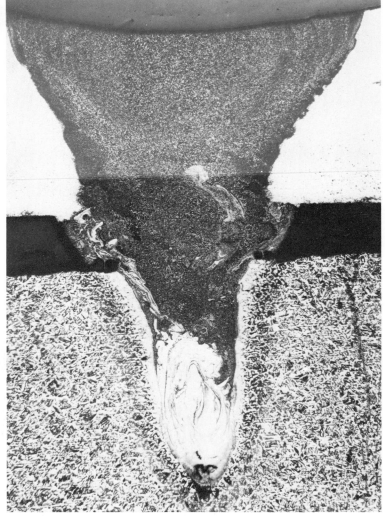

**Fig. 58** Same alloy as Fig. 55, except 2.5 mm (0.1 in.) thick. Alloy laser welded to 1020 steel, with a 0.8-mm (0.03-in.) gap between pieces. Laser input energy was 5 kW; travel speed, 17 mm/s (40 in./min). Etchant 21, Table 3. 20×. (Ref 2)

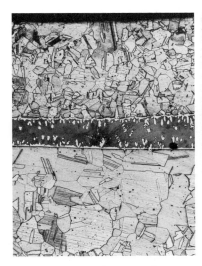

**Fig. 59** Brazed joint between tubes of copper 12200 (DHP copper). Filler metal was BAg-1. See Fig. 61 for details of structure. Etchant 4, Table 3. 75×

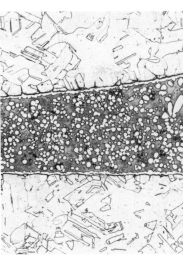

**Fig. 60** Brazed joint between tubes of copper 12200. Filler metal was BCuP-5. See Fig. 62 for details of structure. Etchant 4, Table 3. 100×

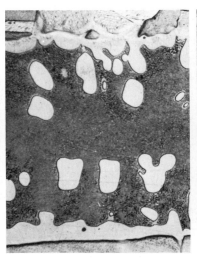

**Fig. 61** Brazed joint in Fig. 59, except at higher magnification. Filler metal (middle) has copper-rich dendrites in a matrix of silver-copper-zinc-cadmium eutectic (dark gray, mottled). Etchant 4, Table 3. 540×

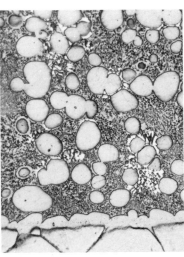

**Fig. 62** Brazed joint in Fig. 60, except at a higher magnification. Filler metal (top) has copper-rich dendrites (light gray) in a matrix of silver-copper-phosphorus. Base metal is at the bottom. Etchant 4, Table 3. 540×

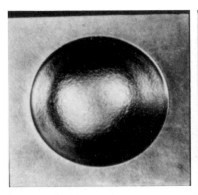

**Fig. 63** Alloy 26000 (cartridge brass) drawn cup, showing "orange peel" (rough surface). See Fig. 65 for grain structure. Etchant 1, Table 3. Actual size

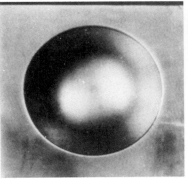

**Fig. 64** Same as Fig. 63, with a smooth surface. See Fig. 66 for structural details. Etchant 1, Table 3. Actual size

**Fig. 65** Grain structure of drawn cup in Fig. 63. The rough surface of the cup was caused by the large grain size. Etchant 1, Table 3. 85×

**Fig. 66** Structure of the drawn cup in Fig. 64. Because grains are small, the cup has a smooth surface. Etchant 1, Table 3. 85×

**Fig. 67** Copper 12200 drawn condenser tube, with a branched intergranular stress-corrosion crack starting at an outside surface. See Fig. 68 for details of a similar crack. Potassium dichromate. 100×

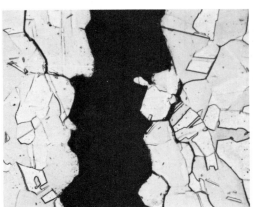

**Fig. 68** Same material and processing as Fig. 67. An intergranular stress-corrosion crack, possibly caused by amine boiler-treatment compounds in boiler condensate. Potassium dichromate. 500×

**Fig. 69** Alloy 26000 (cartridge brass) tube, drawn, annealed and cold-reduced 5%. Typical intergranular stress-corrosion crack, with some branching. $NH_4OH + H_2O_2$. 150×

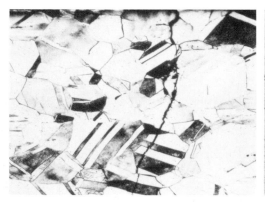

**Fig. 70** Alloy 26000 (cartridge brass), showing a transgranular corrosion crack. Note the lack of branching in the inner (fatigue) section of the crack. Etchant 1, Table 3. 130×

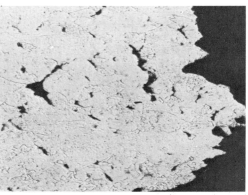

**Fig. 71** Copper 11000 (ETP copper) 16-mm (0.625-in.) diam bar, tested at 350 °C (660 °F) at an extension rate of 0.03 mm/s (0.00114 in./s). W-type void formation. Etchant 1, Table 3. 160×

**Fig. 72** Same material and processing as Fig 71. Magnetized view showing a W-type crack. 645×

**Fig. 73** Copper 10100 (OFE copper) 10-mm (0.375-in.) diam rod, rolled to 1.3-mm (0.052 in.) strip and annealed. Crack formed at the intersection of shearing grain boundary and the surface. The specimen was tested at 550 °C (1020 °F) with an extension rate of 0.03 mm/s (0.001 in./s). Etchant 1, Table 3. 910×

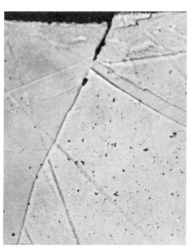

**Fig. 74** Same as Fig. 73. A small crack formed at the intersection of a grain boundary and the surface. Same testing conditions and etchant as Fig. 73. 1000×

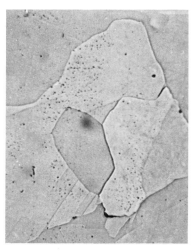

**Fig. 75** Copper 10200 (OF copper) 6.3-mm (0.25-in.) diam rod. Microstructure after testing at 550 °C (1020 °F) with an extension rate of 0.03 mm/s (0.001 in./s). Etchant 1, Table 3. 800×

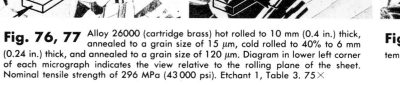

**Fig. 76, 77** Alloy 26000 (cartridge brass) hot rolled to 10 mm (0.4 in.) thick, annealed to a grain size of 15 μm, cold rolled to 40% to 6 mm (0.24 in.) thick, and annealed to a grain size of 120 μm. Diagram in lower left corner of each micrograph indicates the view relative to the rolling plane of the sheet. Nominal tensile strength of 296 MPa (43 000 psi). Etchant 1, Table 3. 75×

**Fig. 78, 79** Same alloy and processing as Fig. 76 and 77, except reduced by cold rolling from 6 mm (0.24 in.) to 4 mm (0.15 in.) thick. Hard temper; nominal tensile strength of 524 MPa (76 000 psi). Etchant 1, Table 3. 75×

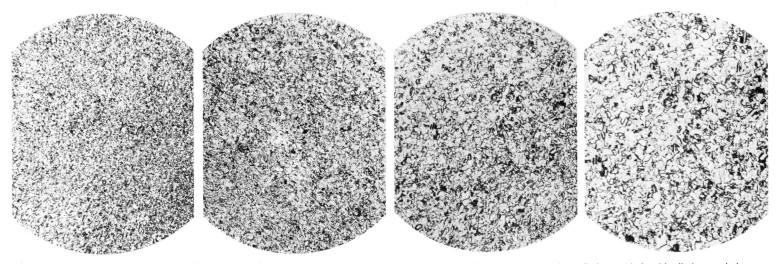

**Fig. 80, 81, 82, 83** Alloy 26000 (cartridge brass), processed to obtain various grain sizes. Preliminary processing: hot rolled, annealed, cold rolled, annealed to a grain size of 25 μm, cold rolled to 70% reduction. Final anneal temperature gives difference in grain sizes. Fig. 80: grain size is 5 μm; final annealed at 330 °C (625 °F). Fig. 81: grain size is 10 μm; final annealed at 370 °C (700 °F). Fig. 82: grain size is 15 μm; final annealed at 405 °C (760 °F). Fig. 83: grain size is 20 μm; final annealed at 425 °C (800 °F). Etchant 1, Table 3. 75×

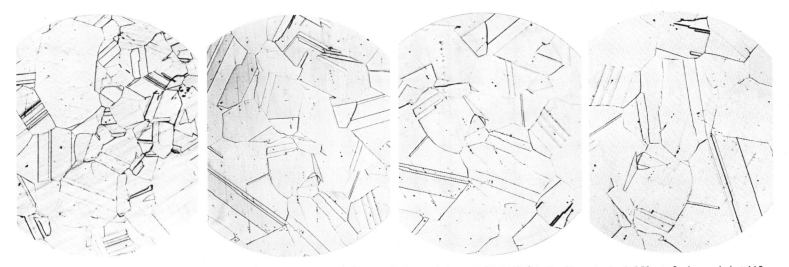

**Fig. 84, 85, 86, 87** Same as Fig. 80 to 83. Fig. 84: grain size is 125 μm; final annealed at 640 °C (1180 °F). Fig. 85: grain size is 150 μm; final annealed at 665 °C (1225 °F). Fig. 86: grain size is 175 μm; final annealed at 680 °C (1260 °F). Fig. 87: grain size is 200 μm; final annealed at 705 °C (1300 °F). Etchant 1, Table 3. 75×

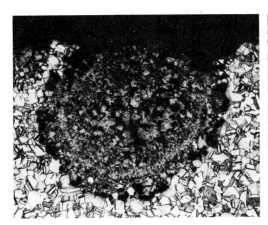

**Fig. 88** Same alloy as Fig. 80 to 87. Local (plug-type) dezincification (dark, at specimen surface) consists of a spongy mass of copper that resulted from the selective removal of zinc. Etchant 1, Table 3. 150×

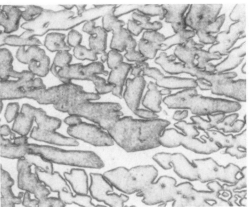

**Fig. 89** Alloy 28000 (Muntz metal) ingot, as-cast. Structure is dendrites of α phase in a matrix of β phase. Etchant 1, Table 3. 210×

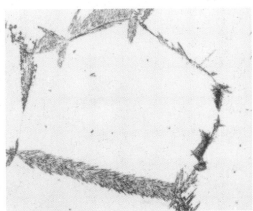

**Fig. 90** Same as Fig. 89, showing α feathers that formed at β grain boundaries during quenching of the all-β structure. Etchant 1, Table 3. 105×

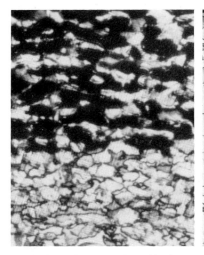

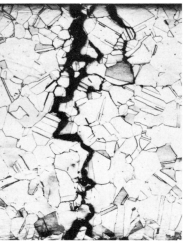

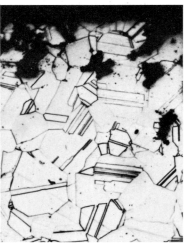

**Fig. 91** Same as Fig. 89, hot-rolled plate. Uniform (layer) dezincification. Alpha grains remain in the corroded area (top). Etchant 1, Table 3. 90×

**Fig. 92** Cu-27.5Zn-1.0Sn alloy tube. Stress-corrosion crack through the wall of the tube, probably caused by mercury or ammonia. Etchant 1, Table 3. 100×

**Fig. 93** Alloy 44300 (arsenical admiralty) tube, drawn, stress relieved, and bent 180°. Transgranular stress-corrosion crack. Etchant 1, Table 3. 200×

**Fig. 94** Same alloy as Fig. 90, drawn and annealed tube. Uniform dezincification, with α grains in the corroded area (dark at the surface). Etchant 1, Table 3. 250×

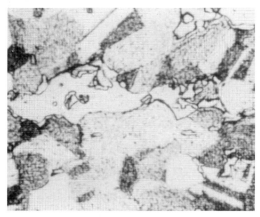

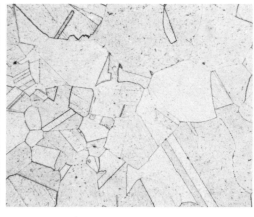

**Fig. 95** Alloy 67500 (manganese bronze A) extruded rod. Iron-rich phase (light, outlined) within β phase (smooth etching) and between α and β phases. Etchant 1, Table 3. 875×

**Fig. 96** Alloy 51000 (phosphor bronze, 5% A) rod, extruded, cold drawn, and annealed 30 min at 565 °C (1050 °F). Structure consists of recrystallized α grains with annealing twins. Etchant 4, Table 3. 500×

**Fig. 97** Alloy 64700 (silicon-nickel bronze), aged 2 h at 480 °C (900 °F) after solution treatment. Alpha grains appear hazy because of unresolved nickel-silicon precipitate. Etchant 4, Table 3. 200×

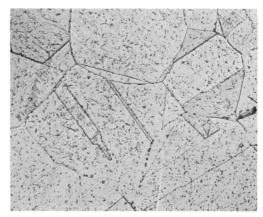

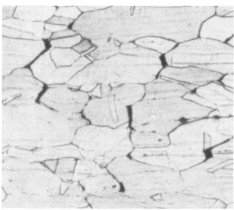

**Fig. 98** Same as Fig. 97, but at a higher magnification to reveal nickel-silicon precipitate at grain boundaries and within grains. Etchant 4, Table 3. 500×

**Fig. 99** Alloy 70600 (copper nickel, 10% Ni), showing the grain-boundary cracks (dark areas) typical of stress-rupture failure. Etchant 4, Table 3. 300×

**Fig. 100** Alloy 74500 (nickel silver, 65-10) cold-rolled sheet, 2.5 mm (0.10 in.) thick, annealed at 650 to 700 °C (1200 to 1290 °F). Longitudinal section shows equiaxed crystallized grains of α solid solution containing twin bands. Etchant 20, Table 3. 100×

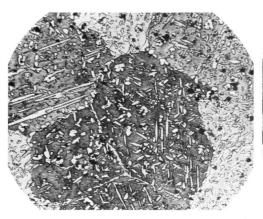

**Fig. 101** Alloy 86200 (64Cu-26Zn-3Fe-4Al-3Mn manganese bronze) as sand cast. Small needles of α solid solution in a matrix of β phase (various shades of gray). Black dots of iron-rich phase are well dispersed. Compare with Fig. 102. Etchant 1, then etchant 16, Table 3. 100×

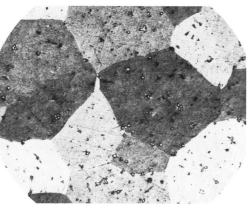

**Fig. 102** Alloy 86300 (63Cu-25Zn-3Fe-6Al-3Mn manganese bronze), as sand cast. Essentially the same composition as alloy in Fig. 101, but higher minimum strength requirements. Constituents are the same as Fig 101, except very little α solid solution is present. Same etchants as Fig 101. 100×

**Fig. 103** Dealuminized alloy 95400 (aluminum bronze), as sand cast. Voids (black) and matrix (medium gray) around α grains at top resulted from dealuminizing in salt water. Small, gray rosettes in grains are an aluminum-rich aluminum-nickel-iron phase. Alpha grains at the bottom are a matrix of eutectoid transformed β phase. Etchant 8, Table 3. 250×

**Fig. 104** Alloy 95400 (aluminum bronze), solution treated 2 h at 900 °C (1650 °F), water quenched, tempered 2 h at 650 °C (1200 °F), and water quenched. Alpha grains (white needles) are smaller than in the as-cast condition (Fig. 103). Etchant 4, Table 3. 200×

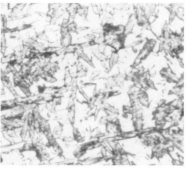

**Fig. 105** Alloy 95500 (nickel-aluminum bronze, 11.5% Al), as sand cast. Small α grains (light gray, mottled) in matrix of retained β phase (white), with some eutectoid decomposed β phase (dark gray). Compare with Fig. 106. Electrolytically etched in electrolyte 5, Table 4. 250×

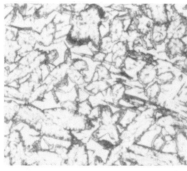

**Fig. 106** Same alloy as Fig. 105, except 11.0% Al with larger α grains and a greater amount of eutectoid decomposed β phase in the matrix. Electrolytically etched in electrolyte 5, Table 4. 250×

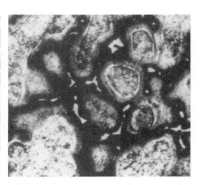

**Fig. 107** Alloy 97800 (Cu-5Sn-2Pb-2Zn-25Ni), as sand cast. Structure is dendrites of α phase (variegated gray) showing coring and interdendritic copper-nickel-tin phase (light). Etchant 4, Table 3. 75×

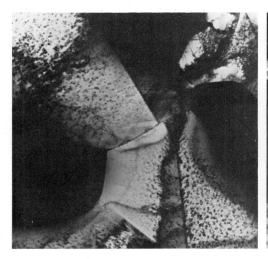

**Fig. 108** Transmission electron micrograph of a rapidly solidified Cu-5Ni-2.5Ti alloy, hot extruded at 750 °C (1380 °F), solution heat treated 1 h at 950 °C (1740 °F); air cooled. Fine precipitate is (Cu,Ni)₃Ti. As-polished. 18 000×. (Ref 3)

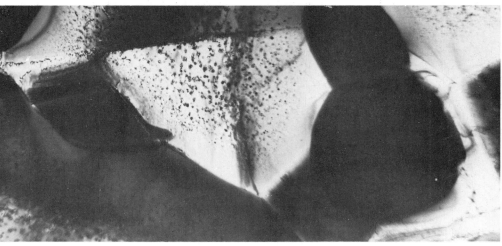

**Fig. 109** Transmission electron micrograph of same alloy as in Fig. 108, solution heat treated at 950 °C (1740 °F) for 1 h and air cooled. Grain size is less than 2 μm. The structure is primary Ni₃Ti and a fine precipitate of (Cu,Ni)₃Ti. See also Fig. 108 and 110. As-polished. 28 000×. (Ref 3)

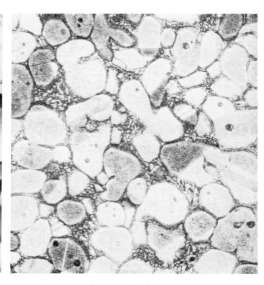

**Fig. 110** Transmission electron micrograph of same alloy and processing as Fig. 109, but higher magnification shows the very fine (~0.25 μm) aging precipitate of (Cu,Ni)$_3$Ti. See also Fig. 108 and 109. As-polished. 75 200×. (Ref 3)

**Fig. 111** Transmission electron micrograph of a copper-zirconium (0.57Zr, with 0.31ZrO$_2$) powder metallurgy product, as hot extruded. The relatively coarse dark particles are Cu$_5$Zr precipitates; the finer dark particles are probably ZrO$_2$. As-polished. 24 480×. (N. Grant)

**Fig. 112** Alloy 36000 (free cutting brass) semi-solid processed plumbing fitting. The large particles (white, light gray) are solid that was present before casting; the matrix was rapidly solidified to produce the structure shown. NH$_4$OH + H$_2$O$_2$ + H$_2$O. 310×. (K.P. Young)

# Lead and Lead Alloys

By Carl DiMartini
General Superintendent
Metals Technology
ASARCO, Inc.

LEAD AND LEAD ALLOY specimens are prepared for metallographic examination in much the same way as those of other metals (see the Section "Metallographic Techniques" in this Volume). An important and troublesome difference is that lead and lead alloys are so soft that considerable surface flow or distortion occurs during grinding and polishing. If not removed, the distorted layer obscures the true structure of the specimen. In addition, the deformation and heating caused by the preparation can be sufficient to develop a pseudostructure (recrystallization) in the specimen. It is essential, therefore, to employ techniques that minimize these effects in sample preparation.

## Specimen Preparation

**Sectioning.** Because lead and lead alloys are so soft, specimens can be extracted from large masses by any of several processes, including cutting with a knife or with a microtome, sawing, shearing, and machining. If specimens are cut by manual or power sawing, a coolant, such as water or methanol, should be used to minimize buildup of frictional heat.

A conventional metallurgical cutoff machine is the preferred means of extracting specimens from the larger mass of material. Liquid coolants minimize the possibility of overheating. The cutoff wheels in such machines produce specimens with surfaces that often are smooth enough to require only light grinding and polishing prior to microexamination.

**Mounting.** Specimens can be ground and polished unmounted, but usually it is more convenient to mount them. Mounting techniques using thermoplastic or thermosetting resins are not suitable for mounting lead and lead alloys, because use of these mounting materials requires heat and pressure. The required mounting pressure deforms the specimen, and the heat will cause recrystallization.

Therefore, the specimen should be mounted in materials that can be cast and subsequently cured at room temperature. Various materials of this type are available. The materials and the techniques for using them are described in the article "Mounting of Specimens" in this Volume.

**Grinding.** If the specimen to be examined has been extracted with an abrasive cutoff wheel or by turning on a lathe, grinding prior to polishing and etching, although useful, may not be necessary.

Grinding is not necessary for specimens that have been cut on a microtome. Using a sharp microtome and the proper technique, it is possible to remove from the specimen several layers (shavings) of material approximately 1- to 5-μm thick. The smooth cut obtained with a microtome leaves a surface that has minimum distortion and that can be polished without having been ground. Specimens with uneven and severely distorted surfaces, such as those produced by sawing, usually require grinding, which can be done automatically, by machine or by hand.

Automatic grinding of lead and lead alloys is accomplished using mounted specimens, which are loaded into a ring sample holder. These holders accommodate several specimens at once, and each specimen in the ring receives identical treatment. Specimens are wet-ground using 320-, 400-, and 600-grit silicon carbide papers in sequence with water as the lubricant. Grinding times are usually 3 min per step for this method. The specimens and the ring holder should be thoroughly cleaned—preferably ultrasonically—between each grinding step.

In machine grinding, fresh abrasive and abundant liquid (usually water) on the grinding belt or wheel, especially during grinding with finer abrasives, must be used to prevent abrasive particles from becoming embedded in the lead specimen. Machine grinding can be done with a belt-type machine or with a disk grinder using 120-grit silicon carbide paper as the abrasive. Then the specimen

should be wet ground (preferably on a disk grinder) using silicon carbide papers of progressively finer sizes through approximately 400 grit.

Hand grinding can be performed on abrasive papers lubricated with a saturated solution of paraffin in kerosene and backed by a glass plate. Water is sometimes used as a lubricant instead of paraffin in kerosene. With proper technique, hand grinding is less likely to embed abrasive particles in the specimen surface than is machine grinding.

In hand grinding, the specimen is held with firm pressure and drawn with an even, smooth stroke from the top to the bottom of the abrasive paper. At the completion of the stroke, the specimen is lifted, replaced at the top of the abrasive paper and again drawn down the length of the paper. It is important not to use a back-and-forth motion, which will smear the specimen surface excessively and increase the probability that abrasive particles will become embedded in the specimen and that the specimen surface will have a high center. During grinding, it is essential that the specimen and the paper be cleaned frequently to remove loose particles of abrasive that may become embedded in the specimen.

**Polishing.** Specimens that have been ground on automatic equipment may be polished using a similar technique. The specimens, loaded in a ring holder, are rough polished using 9-μm diamond on a canvas cloth, then 1-μm alumina on a rayon cloth. Final polishing is performed with 0.5-μm cerium oxide ($CeO_2$) on a rayon cloth followed by colloidal silica on a rayon cloth. Times of about 3 min per step are sufficient, and the specimens should be cleaned between each step. After polishing with colloidal silica, specimens are removed from the ring holder and vibratory polished using colloidal silica on rayon cloth for 20 min. If a layer of disturbed metal has formed on the specimen surface during grinding, it can be removed by deep chemical etching using a mixture of glacial acetic acid and 30% hydrogen peroxide ($H_2O_2$) or a mixture of aqueous solutions of ammonium molybdate [$(NH_4)_2MoO_4$] and nitric acid ($HNO_3$) (see etchants 3 and 4 in Table 1). The specimen is usually etched to remove the deformed metal before polishing.

For mechanical polishing, a felt wheel using a water suspension of 0.3-$\mu$m alumina ($Al_2O_3$) as the abrasive is adequate. Polishing must be done with light pressure, using clean polishing cloths to prevent extraneous materials from becoming embedded in the soft lead surface. Final polishing, if required, is generally done on a 120-rpm wheel using 0.05-$\mu$m $Al_2O_3$ suspended in water as the abrasive.

Etch-polishing is recommended for all lead and lead alloy specimens, especially for the softer lead-base metals such as unalloyed lead and low alloys of tin, bismuth, and antimony. Etch-polishing consists of alternately etching and polishing until a bright, lustrous, scratch-free surface is obtained. The specimen is then rinsed in water, dipped in a warm solvent such as ethanol, methanol, or acetone, and dried in forced air.

**Electropolishing** is not used extensively for lead and lead alloys, although good results have been obtained, especially for unalloyed lead, Several references in the literature discuss the subject.

The use of an electrolyte consisting of 3 parts glacial acetic acid and 1 part 60% perchloric acid ($HClO_4$) with a copper cathode and a current density of 100 to 200 A/cm$^2$ (650 to 1300 A/in.$^2$) for 3 to 5 min is recommended in Ref 1. To avoid the hazard of using this electrolyte (mixtures of $HClO_4$ and acetic acid can be explosive), 60% $HClO_4$ without the acetic acid can be used; however, $HClO_4$ is a very strong acid and precautions should be taken in its use.

**Etching.** Table 1 lists compositions of the etchants most often used for macroetching and microetching of lead and lead alloy specimens. Etching procedures and specific uses for the various etchants are also included in Table 1. All but two of these etchants are used by immersing or swabbing the specimen; only etchants 9 and 10 are used for electrolytic etching.

Primarily because lead and lead alloys smear so easily, etch-polishing alternated with examination under the microscope is required. Sometimes, several cycles of polishing, etching, and examination are necessary, requiring much skill and patience. In addition to smearing, lead and lead alloys are susceptible to tarnishing (or blackening) during etching. One or two light turns on the final polishing wheel, followed by flushing of the specimen with water, rinsing in warm ethanol or methanol, and drying in warm air, will often remove this tarnish and reveal the true structure. Discoloration from overetching or oxidation or both can sometimes be removed by lightly swabbing the specimen with a 2 to 3% aqueous solution of EDTA (ethylenediamine tetraacetic acid disodium salt).

The tarnishing of the lead in the polishing operation can be used to differentiate between various phases in such commercially important alloy systems as antimonial lead and lead-tin solders. With such alloys, polishing often causes the lead matrix to blacken, whereas the secondary antimony or tin-rich phases remain bright.

## Microscopic Examination

Microscopic examination of lead and lead alloys is normally done by conventional reflected-light techniques using bright-field illumination. Polarized light can be used for contrasting phases in lead alloys, particularly when the specimen contains particles of hard intermediate phases such as antimony-tin, tin-arsenic, or lead-tellurium. However, these phases can be easily identified by bright-field microscopy. No particular use is made of dark-field illumination.

If the need exists, specialized microscopic techniques can be used to advantage for studying the structure of lead alloys. For example, replica electron microscopy has been used to study the nucleation of precipitates that occurs during aging of the supersaturated solid solutions of antimony in lead.

**Table 1   Recommended etchants and procedures for macroscopic and microscopic examination of lead and lead alloys**

| Etchant | Composition (parts are by volume) | Procedure | Use |
|---|---|---|---|
| 1 | 1 part acetic acid (glacial)<br>1 part nitric acid (conc)<br>4 parts glycerol | Use freshly prepared solution at 80 °C (176 °F); discard after use. For macroetching: etch several minutes, rinse in water. For microetching: etch several seconds. For best results, alternate etching with polishing. | Macroetching of lead; development of microstructures and grain boundaries in lead, and in lead-calcium, lead-antimony, and lead-tin (low-tin) alloys |
| 2 | 100 parts acetic acid (glacial)<br>10 parts $H_2O_2$ (30%) | Etch for 10-30 min, depending on the depth of the disturbed layer. Dry and clean with concentrated nitric acid if required. | Microetching of lead-antimony alloys containing up to 2% Sb |
| 3 | 3 parts acetic acid (glacial)<br>1 part $H_2O_2$ (30%) | Etch by immersing specimen in solution for 6-15 s. Dry with alcohol. | Microetching of lead, lead-calcium alloys, and lead-antimony alloys containing more than 2% Sb. Also removes disturbed metal |
| 4 | Solution A:<br>15 g $(NH_4)_2MoO_4$<br>100 mL distilled $H_2O$<br>Solution B:<br>6 parts nitric acid (conc)<br>4 parts distilled $H_2O$ | Mix equal quantities of solutions A and B. Etch by alternately swabbing specimen and washing in running water. | Macroetching of lead. A very rapid etchant; well suited for removing thick layers of disturbed metal from specimens |
| 5 | 3 parts acetic acid (glacial)<br>4 parts nitric acid (conc)<br>16 parts distilled $H_2O$ | Use freshly prepared solution at 40-42 °C (104-108 °F). Immerse specimen for 4-30 min until disturbed layer is removed. Clean with cotton in running water. | Microetching of unalloyed lead, and lead-tin alloys containing up to 3% tin |
| 6 | 2 parts acetic acid (glacial)<br>2 parts nitric acid (conc)<br>2 parts $H_2O_2$ (30%)<br>5 parts distilled $H_2O$ | Etch for 2-10 s by swabbing. Rinse specimen in running water and dry with alcohol. | Macroetching of unalloyed lead, and of lead-bismuth, lead-tellurium, and lead-nickel alloys |
| 7 | 1 part nitric acid (conc)<br>1 part distilled $H_2O$ | Etch for 5-10 min by immersion. If thick layer of disturbed metal is to be removed, solution can be heated to boiling. Rinse in running water, rinse in alcohol and dry. | Developing macrostructure of welds and laminations in lead products |
| 8 | Solution A: 10% aqueous solution of $(NH_4)_2S_2O_8$<br>Solution B: 30% aqueous solution of tartaric acid | Mix 5 mL of solution A with 2 mL of solution B. Swab specimen for 5-10 s. Rinse in running water. | Microetching to distinguish cuboidal antimony-tin phase from antimony-rich phases in lead-antimony-tin alloys such as bearing alloys or type metals. Solution A blackens antimony-tin phase; solution B etches antimony-rich phases. |
| 9 | 6 parts $HClO_4$ (70%)<br>4 parts $H_2O$ | Immerse specimen (anode) in electrolyte; cathode is platinum spiral. Etch 45-90 s at 6 V, 4 A. | Electrolytic etching of lead-antimony alloys containing more than 2% Sb |
| 10 | 1 part HCl (conc)<br>9 parts $H_2O$ | Same as for etchant 9 | Same as for etchant 9 |
| 11 | 1 part $(NH_4)_2MoO_4$ (ammonium molybdate)<br>1 part citric acid<br>10 parts distilled $H_2O$ | | |

The scanning electron microscope and the microprobe microanalyzer have proved to be valuable tools in the structural analysis of lead alloys. The microprobe, because it can quantitatively describe constituents, is particularly helpful in identifying the phases that occur in complex alloys such as lead-tin-antimony-arsenic and lead-bismuth-tin-cadmium.

## Microstructures of Lead and Lead Alloys

Lead alloys for which micrographs are shown in this section can be grouped into five alloy systems: (1) lead-calcium (with and without tin), (2) lead-copper, (3) lead-tin (with and without silver), (4) lead-antimony, and (5) lead-antimony-tin (with and without arsenic or copper). For information on the uses and properties of these alloys, see Volume 2 of the 9th Edition of *Metals Handbook*. The article "Sleeve Bearing Materials" in this Volume shows additional micrographs of lead alloys.

**Lead-Calcium.** At 300 °C (570 °F), approximately 0.06% Ca is soluble in lead, but at room temperature, the solubility drops to about 0.01%, causing intragranular precipitation of rods of $Pb_3Ca$. If solidified slowly enough, lead alloys containing more than approximately 0.07% Ca also show primary $Pb_3Ca$, which appears as cubes or star-shaped dendrites. Small additions of tin to dilute lead-calcium alloys cause the formation of a lead-calcium-tin phase, which precipitates as acicular particles at grain boundaries.

**Lead-Copper.** Copper and lead, which are essentially insoluble in the solid state, form a eutectic at 0.06% Cu. The eutectic structure appears as small discrete particles of copper in a matrix of lead, which blends into any primary lead that is also present. Additions of copper up to the eutectic composition result in grain refinement, as well as improvement in fatigue properties.

**Lead-Tin.** A eutectic forms between tin and lead at 183 °C (361 °F). Because the eutectic composition is 61.9Sn-38.1Pb, all of the lead-base alloys in the system contain primary grains of lead-rich solid solution. Alloys that have more than 19% Sn contain some eutectic, which consists of lamellae or globules of lead-rich solid solution in a tin-rich matrix. A low solidification rate favors formation of the lamellar type of eutectic; a high rate, as in most soldering applications, favors the globular type.

Although the solubility of tin in lead at the eutectic temperature is 19%, at room temperature it is reduced to about 2%, causing considerable precipitation of tin-rich solid solution, which appears as granules and needles within the grains of lead-rich solid solution.

When silver is added to lead-tin alloys, it combines with tin to form $Ag_3Sn$, which then forms a pseudobinary eutectic with lead at 1.75% Ag and 0.7% Sn. At the eutectic temperature of 309 °C (589 °F), the solubility of $Ag_3Sn$ in lead is about 0.1%. Therefore, most silver-lead solders, which contain 0.5 to 1.5% Ag and 1 to 2% Sn, have cast microstructures comprising dendrites of lead-rich solid solution and interdendritic eutectic that consists of $Ag_3Sn$ in lead-rich solid solution. At higher tin contents, some tin-rich solid solution may also appear in the eutectic.

**Lead-Antimony.** At the eutectic temperature of 251 °C (484 °F), 3.5% Sb is soluble in lead. At room temperature, only 0.44% Sb is soluble in lead, and after cooling at a rate lower than that of air cooling, small rods of antimony precipitate from solid solution. After furnace cooling, the rods appear at the grain boundaries; after even slower cooling, they also appear within the grains. After air cooling, the antimony often is retained in solution, permitting subsequent age hardening.

The eutectic mixture has a lamellar form, with particles of antimony in a matrix of lead-rich solid solution. In hypoeutectic alloys (below 11.2% Sb), the lead-rich phase of the eutectic blends into the primary lead-rich phase that is also present, giving the eutectic a divorced appearance. Hypereutectic alloys show angular primary crystals of antimony in eutectic.

**Lead-Antimony-Tin.** One of the two peritectics in the antimony-tin system occurs at 425 °C (797 °F), where molten metal reacts with antimony-rich solid solution to form SbSn. Both antimony and tin are moderately soluble in SbSn, resulting in a phase field extending at room temperature approximately from 44 to 59% Sn.

At approximately 10% Sb, 10% Sn, and 247 °C (476 °F), the Pb-SbSn pseudobinary system contains a eutectic that has a lamellar form, with particles of SbSn-rich phase in a matrix of lead-rich solid solution. The eutectic point lies on a eutectic trough in the liquidus surface of the ternary diagram. This trough, which defines the limit for the formation of primary lead crystals, connects the lead-antimony and lead-tin eutectic points. The trough also passes through a ternary eutectic point at 11.5% Sb, 3.5% Sn, and 240 °C (464 °F). The form of the ternary eutectic mixture is also lamellar, with particles of both SbSn-rich phase and antimony-rich solid solution in a matrix of lead-rich solid solution.

A line from the lead-antimony eutectic point through the ternary eutectic point and terminating at the SbSn peritectic defines the limit for the formation of primary antimony crystals. Lines leading from the ternary eutectic point to both peritectics in the antimony-tin system define the limits for the formation of primary SbSn crystals. Because the antimony-rich side of the SbSn phase field can dissolve about 13% Pb, the boundary between the Pb-SbSn field and the Pb-Sb-SbSn field lies at an antimony-to-lead ratio of 2:1. The boundary between the lead-antimony field and the Pb-Sb-SbSn field lies at about 2% Sb.

Antimony-rich solid solution and SbSn-rich phase can often be distinguished by etching with a mixture of 5 mL ammonium persulfate [$(NH_4)_2S_2O_8$] solution (10 g in 100 mL $H_2O$) and 2 mL tartaric acid solution (30 g in 100 mL $H_2O$). The antimony-rich phase is white and remains so during etching; the SbSn-rich phase is light gray, but becomes yellowish during etching and may develop etch pits. In a fine eutectic structure, the lamellae of antimony-rich phase are unchanged by etching, but the lamellae of SbSn-rich phase develop dark edges. Primary crystals of antimony-rich phase are angular, but are usually somewhat elongated; primary crystals of SbSn-rich phase are cuboidal.

Additions of copper to lead-antimony-tin alloys usually combine with tin to form creamy-white needles of $Cu_6Sn_5$. However, the copper occasionally combines with antimony to form rods of $Cu_2Sb$ that have a purple or violet color (light gray in micrographs). Additions of arsenic dissolve in the lead, antimony, and SbSn phases and therefore are not visible in the microstructure.

## REFERENCES

1. G. Kehl, *Metallurgical Laboratory Practices*, McGraw-Hill, 1949
2. W. Hoffman, *Lead and Lead Alloys*, 2nd ed., Springer-Verlag, 1970 (in English)

**Fig. 1** Ultra-high-purity lead. Surface oxide and intergranular attack caused by simulated grid corrosion (anodizing). Anodized in $H_2SO_4$ (1.25 sp gr). 45×

**Fig. 2** High-purity lead (99.99% Pb), as-cast. Transverse section through a pig showing large equiaxed and columnar grains. Large grains result from the absence of grain-nucleating impurities and alloying elements (such as copper). Ammonium molybdate reagent. Actual size

**Fig. 3** Commercially pure lead, corrosion tested same as the higher purity specimen in Fig. 1. Surface shows same results. Anodized in $H_2SO_4$ (1.25 sp gr). 45×

**Fig. 4** Pb-0.039Ca, corrosion tested same as Fig. 1 and 3. Surface shows same results as those for unalloyed specimens. Anodized in $H_2SO_4$ (1.25 sp gr). 45×

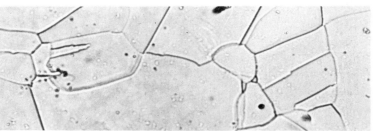

**Fig. 5** Chemical lead (Pb-0.06Cu) sheet, ¼ in. thick; rolled surface. The small grain size at high magnification in this micrograph results from the presence of grain-nucleating particles of copper (dark spots with grains). 3 parts acetic acid, 1 part 30% $H_2O_2$. 1000×

**Fig. 6** Pb-0.05Ca-0.48Sn, corrosion tested same as the more dilute alloy in Fig. 4. Surface shows same results. Anodized in $H_2SO_4$ (1.25 sp gr). 45×

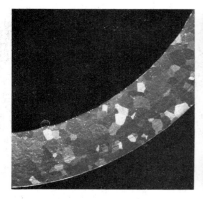

**Fig. 7** High-purity lead; cross section of cable sheath (25-mm, or 1-in., OD; 2.7-mm, or 0.105-in., wall). Recrystallized, equiaxed grains. $(NH_4)_2MoO_4$, then acetic-nitric (ASTM 114). 6×

**Fig. 8** Copper-bearing lead (0.04 to 0.08% Cu); cross section of cable sheath with 2.7-mm (0.105-in.) wall thickness. The grains contain lead-copper eutectic, which forms at a copper content of 0.06%. Same etchant as Fig. 7. 10×

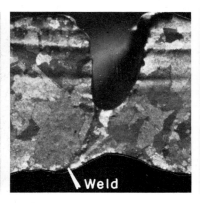

**Fig. 9** Commercially pure lead; cross section through cable sheath wall, at break in extrusion weld. Grains are larger than in the copper-bearing lead shown in Fig. 8. Same etchant as Fig. 7. 10×

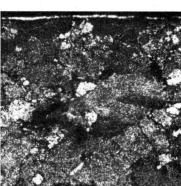

**Fig. 10** Copper-bearing lead (0.15% Cu); section through wall of cable sheath showing intergranular cracks (black areas in center) that resulted from creep. Same etchant as Fig. 7. 75×

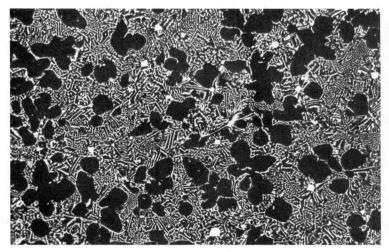

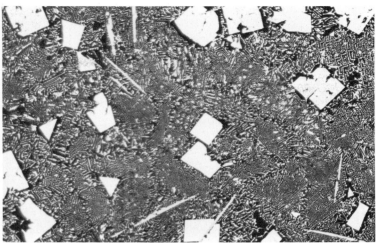

**Fig. 11** Lead-base babbitt, SAE alloy 13 (Pb-10Sb-5Sn-0.5Cu). Dendritic grains of lead-rich solid solution (black) and primary cuboids of antimony-tin intermetallic phase (white) in matrix of ternary eutectic (filigreed) consisting of antimony-rich solid solution (white), antimony-tin phase (also white), and lead-rich solid solution (black). 15 mL acetic acid, 20 mL HNO₃, 80 mL H₂O; at 42 °C (108 °F). 250×

**Fig. 12** Lead-base babbitt, SAE alloy 14 (Pb-15Sb-10Sn-0.5Cu). Primary needles of Cu₆Sn₅ phase and primary cuboids of antimony-tin intermetallic phase (both white) in a matrix of fine pseudobinary eutectic (filigreed) made up of lead-rich solid solution (dark) and antimony-tin phase (light). See also Fig. 13 to 16. Same etchant as Fig. 11. 250×

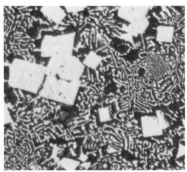

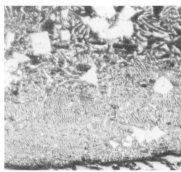

**Fig. 13, 14** Lead-base babbitt, SAE alloy 14 (Pb-15Sb-10.2Sn-0.4Cu-0.4As) as-cast in 38-mm (1.5-in.) diam by 19-mm (0.75-in.) high copper mold. Center of casting shows primary cuboids of antimony-tin phase (light) and a few small primary crystals of lead (black) in a matrix of binary eutectic (filigreed). 5% HCl. Fig. 13: 200×. Fig. 14: 500×

**Fig. 15, 16** Same material as Fig. 13 and 14, but cast in gray iron liner (at bottom). Chilled area has fine eutectic structure of lamellar antimony-tin (light) and lead-rich solid solution (dark). Fig. 15: 5% HCl, 100×. Fig. 16: 7 parts acetic acid, 3 parts 3% H₂O₂, 250×

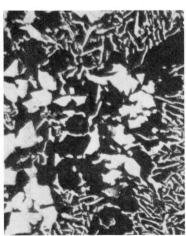

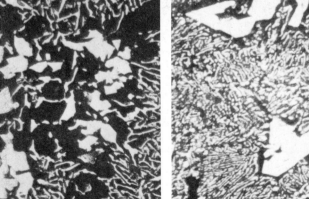
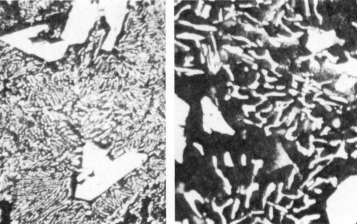

**Fig. 17, 18** Lead-base babbitt (Pb-12.5Sb-5Sn) as-cast in 32-mm (1.5-in.) diam by 19-mm (0.75-in.) high copper mold. Center of casting shows dendritic grains of lead (black) and primary crystals of antimony (light) in a ternary eutectic matrix (filigreed). 7 parts acetic acid, 3 parts 3% H₂O₂. Fig. 17: 200×. Fig. 18: 500×

**Fig. 19, 20** Same material as Fig. 17 and 18, but as-cast in gray iron liner. Fig. 19: arbor-chilled bearing surface consists of primary antimony crystals in fine ternary eutectic. Fig. 20: area between arbor and liner consists of more antimony crystals, a few lead dendrites (black), and coarse eutectic resulting from slower cooling. Same etchant as Fig. 17 and 18. 640×

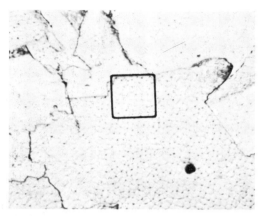

**Fig. 21** Pb-0.044Ca, etched in 5 parts acetic acid, 1 part 30% H₂O₂, then in ammonium molybdate reagent. See Fig. 22 for a close-up view of area in square. 92×

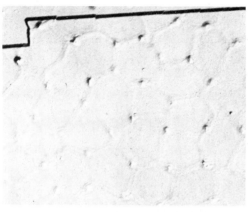

**Fig. 22** Magnified view of area outlined by square in Fig. 21. The mosaic pattern and the pits in the grains resulted from overetching with the ammonium molybdate reagent used in Fig. 21. 600×

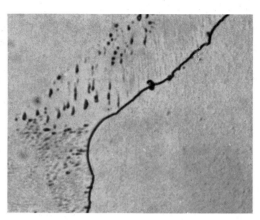

**Fig. 23** Pb-0.058Ca. Small particles of Pb₃Ca phase (dark) that precipitated near a grain boundary. 5 parts acetic acid, 1 part 30% H₂O₂, then in ammonium molybdate reagent. 1825×

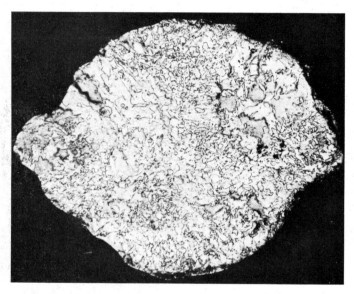

**Fig. 24** Pb-0.08Ca, as-cast. Section through a cross-member wire of a battery grid (parting line horizontal) showing fine grain structure. See Fig. 25 and 26 for details of the structure in a similar lead alloy. 15 g citric acid + 9 g ammonium molybdate in 80 mL H₂O. 50×

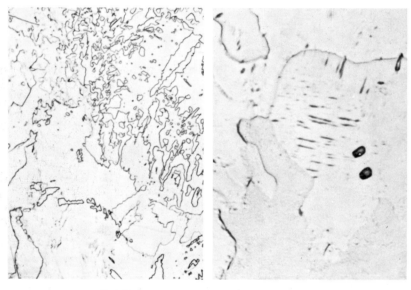

**Fig. 25, 26** Pb-0.083Ca. A higher calcium content than in Fig. 21 results in smaller grains. Fine Pb₃Ca precipitate (dark) is recognizable in Fig. 26. 15 g citric acid + 9 g ammonium molybdate in 80 mL H₂O. Fig. 25: 92×. Fig. 26: 1825×

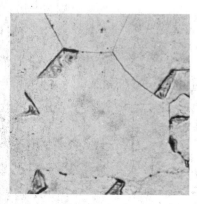

**Fig. 27** Pb-0.045Ca-0.46Sn. Large grains, similar in size to those of the lead-calcium alloy shown in Fig. 21. See Fig. 28 for a view at higher magnification. 5 parts acetic acid, 1 part 30% H₂O₂, then in ammonium molybdate reagent. 92×

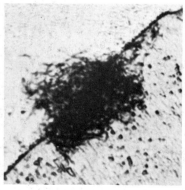

**Fig. 28** Same alloy as in Fig. 27, but at a higher magnification, which reveals a clump of dark acicular precipitate of Pb-Ca-Sn intermetallic phase. Same etchant as Fig. 27. 1825×

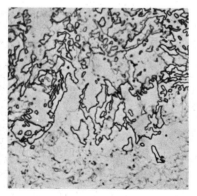

**Fig. 29** Pb-0.083Ca-0.49Sn. Small grains, similar in size to those of the lead-calcium alloy shown in Fig. 25. See Fig. 30 for view at higher magnification. Same etchant as Fig. 27. 92×

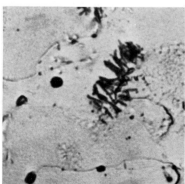

**Fig. 30** Same alloy as in Fig. 29, but at higher magnification, showing large primary particles and a clump of acicular precipitate of Pb-Ca-Sn phase (dark). Same etchant as Fig. 27. 1825×

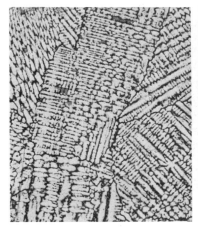

**Fig. 31** Pb-5Sb, as-cast. Section through wire of battery grid showing larger grains than in Fig. 24. See also Fig. 32 to 34. 15 g citric acid + 9 g ammonium molybdate in 80 mL $H_2O_2$. 50×

**Fig. 32** Pb-5Sb, as-cast. Section through the connection tab of a battery grid showing dendritic grains. See also Fig. 33 and 34. Same etchant as Fig. 31. 100×

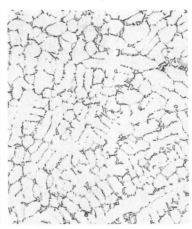

**Fig. 33** Same as Fig. 32, except not etched. Higher magnification shows dendrites of lead-rich solid solution. See also Fig. 34 and 36. As-polished. 200×

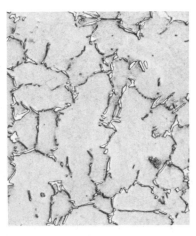

**Fig. 34** Same as Fig. 33, except at higher magnification, which shows interdendritic network of antimony (light). See also Fig. 35. As-polished. 500×

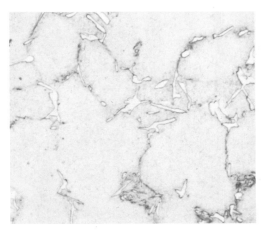

**Fig. 35** Same as Fig. 34, except at higher magnification, which shows that the eutectic in the interdendritic area (discrete particles of antimony in matrix of lead-rich solid solution) is of the divorced type. As-polished. 1000×

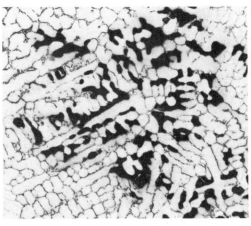

**Fig. 36** Same as Fig. 33, except showing an area that contains shrinkage porosity. The voids (black) were caused by withdrawal of molten eutectic from between the dendrites during solidification of the casting. As-polished. 200×

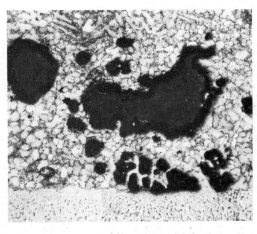

**Fig. 37** Pb-5Sb, as-cast. Section through connecting strap of battery, which shows gross porosity (black) within the strap and at the interface where the strap was cast onto a connection tab (bottom) of a grid. Same etchant as Fig. 24. 100×

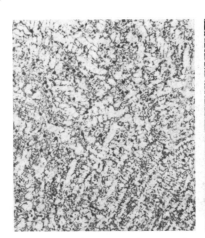

**Fig. 38** Pb-11Sb. Near-eutectic composition, containing lead dendrites (light) in a fine eutectic matrix. See also Fig. 39. Acetic acid + $H_2O_2$ (ASTM 57). 250×

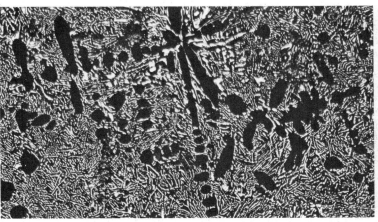

**Fig. 39** Pb-11.1Sb, as-cast. Microstructure is similar to that in Fig. 38, but different etchant used reversed appearance of constituents. Slight alloy segregation resulted in the formation of enlarged dendrites of lead (dark) and bright clusters of antimony. Acetic-nitric (ASTM 114). 100×

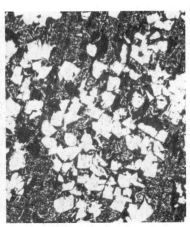

**Fig. 40** Pb-20Sb. Primary crystals of antimony (light) in a fine eutectic matrix of antimony in lead-rich solid solution. Same etchant as Fig. 39. 200×

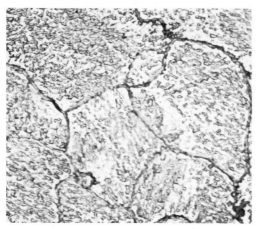

**Fig. 41** Can solder (Pb-2Sn), slowly solidified. Light gray lead-rich grains with dark gray tin precipitate in grain boundaries and within grains. 1 part acetic acid, 1 part HNO₃, 8 parts glycerol. 400×

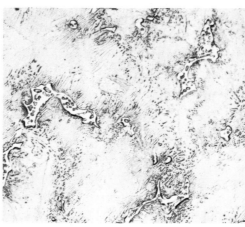

**Fig. 42** Terne metal (Pb-15Sn), slowly solidified. Alloy segregation has resulted in lead-tin eutectic between cored grains of lead that have tin precipitated at edges. Same etchant as Fig. 41. 400×

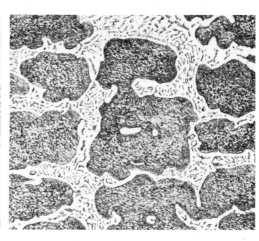

**Fig. 43** Tipping solder (Pb-30Sn), slowly solidified. Dark lead-rich dendritic grains with interdendritic lamellar eutectic consisting of tin (white) and lead (dark). Same etchant as Fig. 41. 400×

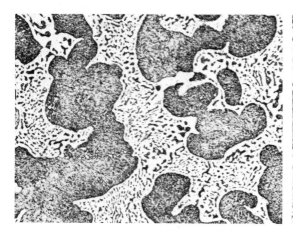

**Fig. 44** Plumber's wiping solder (Pb-40Sn) slowly solidified. Dark dendritic grains of lead-rich solid solution in a lamellar eutectic matrix of tin-rich solid solution (white) and lead-rich solid solution (dark). See also Fig. 45. 1 part acetic acid, 1 part HNO₃, 8 parts glyercol. 400×

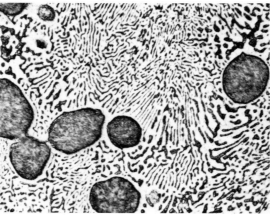

**Fig. 45** Half-and-half solder (Pb-50Sn), slowly solidified. Dark dendritic grains of lead-rich solid solution in lamellar eutectic matrix of tin-rich solid solution (white) and lead-rich solid solution (dark). See also Fig. 44 and 46. Same etchant as Fig. 44. 400×

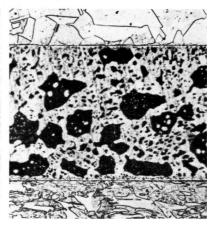

**Fig. 46** Copper parts (top and bottom) soldered with Pb-50Sn. The eutectic is globular because of faster solidification than in Fig. 45. 1 part NH₄OH, 1 part 3% H₂O₂, 1 part H₂O. 250×

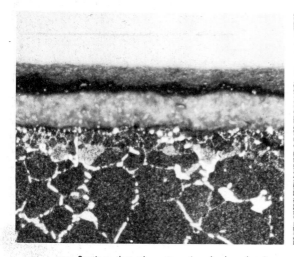

**Fig. 47** Section through automotive body, showing body solder (Pb-2.6Sn-5.25Sb-0.5As) beneath four coats of paint (top). Dark lead-rich grains and intergranular ternary eutectic of antimony-tin phase and antimony (both light) and lead (dark). 2 mL acetic acid, 98 mL methanol. 325×

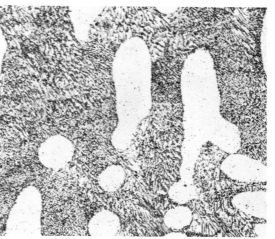

**Fig. 48** Silver lead solder (Pb-1Sn-1.5Ag), as-solidified. Light dendritic grains of lead-rich solid solution in lamellar eutectic matrix of lead-rich solid solution (light) and Ag₃Sn intermetallic phase (dark). 1 part acetic acid, 1 part HNO₃, 8 parts glycerol. 400×

**Fig. 49** Solder-brass interface of joint soldered with Pb-3.8Sn-0.5Ag. Solder (top) shows columnar dendrites of lead; dark interdendritic Pb-Ag₃Sn eutectic. 3 parts acetic acid, 1 part 9% H₂O₂, then acetic-nitric (ASTM 113). 500×

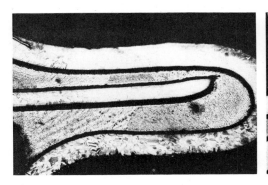

**Fig. 50** Tank-to-header joint, soldered with Pb-2Sn-0.5Ag. Large grains of solder contain dark voids that may have been caused by solidification shrinkage. Same etchant as Fig. 49. 10×

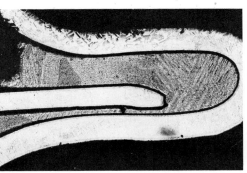

**Fig. 51** Same as Fig. 50, except a view showing a single void (black) in the narrow region of the joint. The shadow outlining the solder is caused by relief between the solder and the harder brass that formed during polishing. See also Fig. 52. Same etchant as Fig. 49. 10×

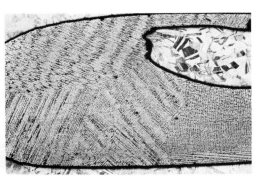

**Fig. 52** Same as Fig. 51, except higher magnification shows columnar dendrites of lead (light) and interdendritic Pb-Ag₃Sn eutectic (dark) in large grains of solder. The void (black) may have been caused by lack of wetting of the brass by the solder. Same etchant as Fig. 49. 25×

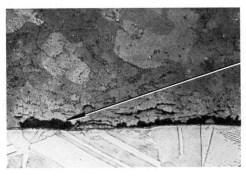

**Fig. 53** Tip of the cracked area along the interface between the solder (top) and the brass header sheet (bottom) of the joint shown in Fig. 54 (area indicated by upper circle). Note that the thin intermetallic layer at the interface was not attacked. Same etchant as Fig. 49. 250×

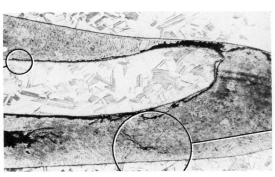

**Fig. 54** A section through a failed joint, showing cracks (black) in the solder, which may have been caused by stress corrosion. See Fig. 53 and 54 for higher magnification views of the cracks in the circled areas. Same etchant as Fig. 49. 25×

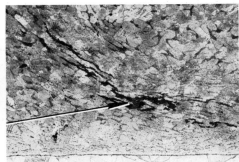

**Fig. 55** Cracked area in the solder (top) of the joint shown in Fig. 54 (area indicated by lower circle). The cracks, which may have started at solidification-shrinkage cracks, are interdendritic and are parallel to the direction of solidification. Same etchant as Fig. 49. 100×

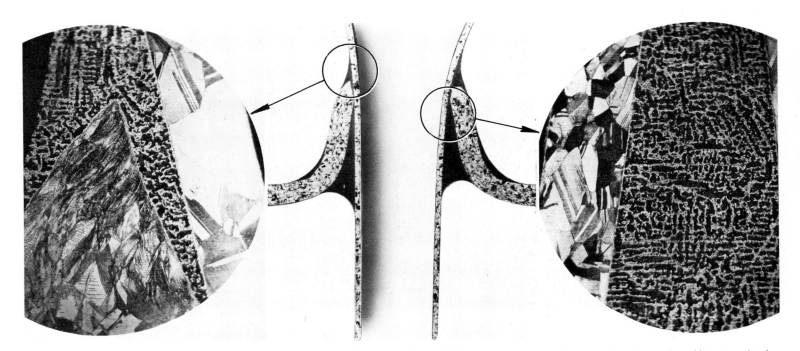

**Fig. 56, 57, 58** Radiator-tube-to-header joint soldered with Pb-35Sn. Figures 56 and 58 are enlargements of circled areas of Fig. 57, as indicated by arrows. Lead-rich solid-solution dendrites (dark) in interdendritic tin-lead eutectic. A thin layer of copper-tin intermetallic compound (light) is at solder-brass interface. 5 parts NH₄OH, 2 parts 3% H₂O₂, 5 parts H₂O. Fig. 56 and 58: 125×. Fig. 57: 10×

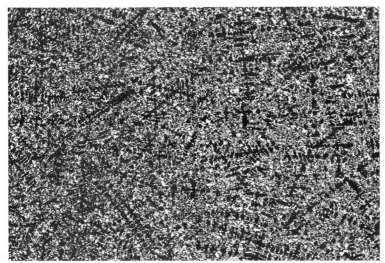

**Fig. 59** Linotype metal (Pb-11Sb-3Sn). Thin dendrites of lead-rich solid solution (dark) in a matrix of ternary eutectic consisting of antimony-tin intermetallic phase (light gray), antimony-rich solid solution (white), and lead-rich solid solution (dark). Acetic-nitric etchant (ASTM 114). 100×

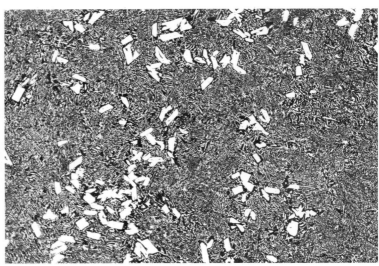

**Fig. 60** Monotype metal (Pb-16.5Sb-7Sn). Primary crystals of antimony-rich solid solution (white) in matrix of ternary eutectic consisting of antimony-tin intermetallic phase (light gray), lead-rich solid solution (dark), and antimony-rich solid solution (white). Same etchant as Fig. 59. 100×

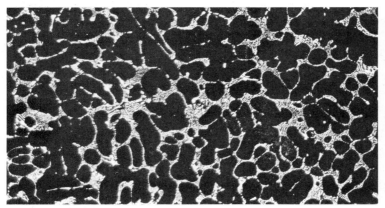

**Fig. 61** Electrotype metal (Pb-3.5Sb-3.5Sn). Dendritic grains of lead-rich solid solution (dark) in a matrix of pseudobinary eutectic (filigreed); constituents of the matrix are antimony-tin intermetallic phase (light) and lead-rich solid solution (dark). Same etchant as Fig. 59. 250×

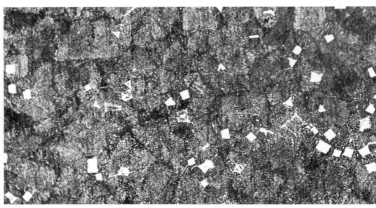

**Fig. 62** Stereotype metal (Pb-13Sb-6.5Sn). Structure is primary cuboids of antimony-tin intermetallic phase (light) in a matrix of ternary eutectic that consists of antimony-rich solid solution (light), lead-rich solid solution (dark), and antimony-tin intermetallic phase (light). Same etchant as Fig. 59. 100×

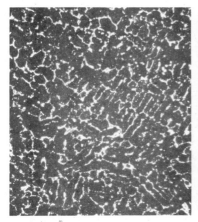

**Fig. 63** Pb-3Sb-3Sn. Dendrites of lead-rich solid solution (dark) and interdendritic pseudobinary eutectic of antimony-tin phase (light) and lead. Same etchant as Fig. 59. 200×

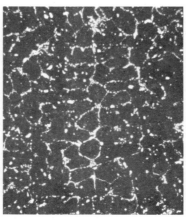

**Fig. 64** Pb-4Sb-0.75Sn. Dendrites of lead-rich solid solution (dark) and interdendritic binary eutectic of antimony (light) and lead. Same etchant as Fig. 59. 200×

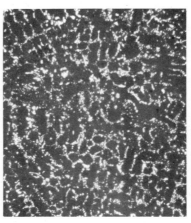

**Fig. 65** Pb-6Sb-1Sn. Microstructure is same as Fig. 64, except more interdendritic antimony-lead eutectic is present. Same etchant as Fig. 59. 200×

**Fig. 66** Pb-15Sb-15Sn-0.5Cu. Primary cuboids of antimony-tin phase (light) in a matrix of pseudobinary eutectic consisting of lead (dark) and antimony-tin (light). Same etchant as Fig. 59. 200×

# Magnesium Alloys

MAGNESIUM ALLOY specimens chosen for metallographic examination should be representative. For example, longitudinal and transverse specimens of sheet should be examined, edge and center sections of large ingots should be considered, and the mouth of a casting crack should be studied as the point of origin of the crack.

## Specimen Preparation

**Sectioning.** Specimens are removed from the metal mass by band sawing or hacksawing. Care should be exercised to prevent cold working of the metal, which can alter the microstructure and complicate interpretation of constituents.

Specimens that have been severely cold worked by rough sawing, squeezing in a vise, or heavy stamping are likely to be mechanically twinned close to the worked surface. The cold-worked surface can be removed by extending the time of each grinding and polishing step up to twice the time required for removing scratches from the preceding stage. Metal should be removed to a depth of approximately 1 mm (0.040 in.) during preparation of the specimen. Cold deformation introduced in the surface layers by grinding and polishing has little detrimental effect on the microstructure, unless the prepared specimen is subsequently heated above the recrystallization temperature.

In general, the methods and equipment for specimen preparation discussed in the article "Sectioning" in this Volume apply to magnesium alloy specimens.

**Mounting.** Specimens that are too small to be held conveniently for grinding and polishing or that have an edge that is to be studied can be mounted in one of the common plastic mounting materials. Cold-mounting materials are preferred, because the use of mounting materials that require pressure, such as Bakelite, may result in cold working of the specimen. Sheet specimens can be clamped together to form packs. Clamping or bolting must be done carefully to prevent cold working.

**Grinding.** Dry and wet grinding are performed with abrasive belts, rotating disks, or abrasive papers by hand. Abrasives used for grinding are alumina ($Al_2O_3$), silicon carbide, and emery.

For dry grinding, disks of 60-, 180-, and 320-grit $Al_2O_3$ and grade 0 emery are rotated on (preferably) vertical, 500- to 1400-rpm wheels. An oil bath below the disks catches the grinding dust. The specimen must not overheat during grinding; overheating will affect the microstructure and can produce a separation between the plastic mount and the metal specimen. Progressing from one grit size to the next, the specimen should be turned 90° and should be cleaned with a cloth saturated with a water-soluble solvent, such as industrial ethanol, to prevent coarse abrasive particles from being carried to finer grit disks. To keep the surface parallel and flat, greater pressure is applied to the trailing side of the specimen than to the leading side.

Wet grinding is preferred, because it prevents overheating of the specimen and maintains exposure of the sharp edges of the abrasive. A conventional 200-mm (8-in.) horizontal polishing wheel and disks of 240-, 320-, 400-, and 600-grit silicon carbide paper are most often used for rough through fine grinding. A small stream of water directed at the disks during grinding flushes away the abraded fragments. Samples can be rotated 90° between steps. A 32-mm (1.25-in.) diam mounted specimen can be dry or wet ground in 2 min per step.

**Mechanical polishing** is performed in two stages: rough and finish. Rough polishing removes the major part of the disturbed metal remaining after the final grinding step. Finish polishing removes the superficial scratches that remain after rough polishing.

Wheels used for both polishing stages consist of a medium-nap cloth, such as washable cotton velveteen or a bonded-pile fabric. A suspension of 600-grit $Al_2O_3$ powder in distilled water (35 g $Al_2O_3$ per 500 mL $H_2O$) is used on the wheel for rough polishing; for best results, the cloth is maintained just moist enough to prevent seizure of the specimen. The specimen is rotated counter to the wheel direction. Polishing time should be twice as long as needed to remove the scratches from the final grinding operation. Moderate pressure should be used to minimize relief polishing caused by the difference in rate of stock removal between the harder and softer microconstituents.

For finish polishing, a suspension of 10 g $\alpha$-$Al_2O_3$ per 500 mL $H_2O$ is used on the wheel. To facilitate polishing, 15 mL of filtered or other soft soap is sometimes added to the abrasive solution. The specimen is moved across the face of the wheel and rotated counter to wheel rotation to change the contact point between specimen and wheel and to distribute the abrasive. Counter-rotation also prevents the formation of "comet tails" around hard particles of manganese- or zirconium-rich phases.

Finish polishing is carried out with moderate pressure on a relatively wet wheel. Too light pressure will cause relief polishing of the constituents and a rough texture. By flooding the wheel with the abrasive suspension and using light pressure on the specimen during the last 5 s, scratches can be reduced to a minimum. The polished specimen is rapidly transferred from the wheel to running tap water and gently rubbed with a wetted finger or cotton ball to remove the fine abrasive. It is then rinsed in alcohol and dried in a blast of warm clean air.

Light scratches and cold-worked surface metal on the polished specimen can be removed by alternate light etching and light repolishing. If soap was used in the polishing slurry, it must be thoroughly rinsed away, because it can cause considerable staining if an etchant containing glycol is used.

Revised by Kenneth J. Clark, Development Engineer, Wellman Dynamics Corp.

**Chemical polishing,** though not as effective as mechanical polishing for bringing out details, is often satisfactory for routine examinations. Before chemical polishing, the specimen is ground with 000 emery paper or 600-grit silicon carbide paper. It is then swabbed for 30 to 60 s with approximately 10% nital. Often used as a slow-acting chemical polish is a glycol etchant containing 1% concentrated nitric acid ($HNO_3$). Following chemical polishing, the specimen is etched as usual. Anhydrous ethanol or methanol is preferred to prevent staining.

**Electrolytic polishing** is used when a scratch-free surface is desired for critical examination without etching. It is useful for polishing large pieces; whole test bars can be polished in 4 to 8 h. For electrolytic polishing of magnesium alloys, a conventional setup and a stainless steel cathode are used. The electrolyte consists of three parts 85% phosphoric acid ($H_3PO_4$) and five parts 95% ethanol; both are cooled to approximately 2 °C (35 °F) before mixing. Specimens should be polished through 000 emery paper using a kerosene and paraffin mixture as a lubricant, then solvent cleaned before electrolytic polishing.

The cathode and specimen are spaced 20 mm (0.8 in.) apart in a quiescent bath. A current of 3 V is applied for 30 s, then reduced to 1.5 V and maintained until the desired finish is produced. While the current is on, the specimen is removed from the electrolyte and rinsed quickly in rapidly running tap water. If the current is shut off while the specimen is in the electrolyte, chemical etching and roughening result.

More rapid electrolytic polishing is obtained with an electrolyte consisting of 10% hydrochloric acid (HCl) in cellosolve (ethylene glycol monoethyl ether). This electrolyte must be kept below 4 °C (40 °F) during polishing.

## Macroexamination

**Fracture-Surface Characteristics.** Cast forms, such as slabs, ingots, and sand castings, are fractured and examined for grain-size variations, porosity, hot tears, oxide inclusions, phases that have limited solubility in the matrix, coring, and approximate degree of solution of massive compounds. Similarly, extrusions and forgings are fractured to show flow patterns, grain-size variations, stringers of oxide, phases that have limited solubility in the matrix, laps, and variations in amount of plastic deformation.

Fractures resulting from tensile and fatigue failures and from stress corrosion exhibit distinct features. Tensile or tensile-impact failures are transcrystalline and leave a rough, striated surface contour. Failure is likely to occur along basal crystallographic planes; under these conditions, the striations change from grain to grain. If tensile failure occurs at an elevated temperature, intercrystalline grain-boundary surfaces with geometrical facets are exposed. The elevated temperature of tensile-failure occurrence referred to is commonly approximately 230 °C (450 °F), although this temperature can vary depending on the alloy content and the strain rate.

Fatigue fractures are transcrystalline but relatively smooth. Fan-shape striations radiate from one or more point origins. Stress-corrosion failures are characterized by cracks with many branches.

**Macroetching.** The macroetchant most often used for showing discontinuities in castings and flow lines in forgings is an aqueous solution containing 5 to 20% acetic acid. The etchant is swabbed on the prepared surface for 10 s to 3 min, then washed away in running water.

The dense, black deposit encountered when alloys containing appreciable amounts of zinc are etched in acetic acid solutions can be removed by immersion, immediately after rinsing, in an aqueous solution of 10 to 100% of 48% hydrofluoric acid (HF). The reactivity of this etchant is proportional to the concentration of HF. With some structures, it may be advantageous to retain the black deposit, especially if it is thin. An acetic-nitrate pickle is often preferred for macroetching magnesium alloys containing zinc, because no black deposit is formed. The part is immersed for 1 to 5 min in an aqueous solution of 20% acetic acid plus 5% sodium nitrate ($NaNO_3$), rinsed in water, and air-blast dried.

One of the acetic-picral etchants listed in Table 1 should be used for castings and to show the grain structure of impact extruded or forged parts that have a homogeneous recrystallized structure and a minimum of alloy gradients. The part is immersed in the etchant for 10 s to 1 min, transferred to a pan of ethanol to rinse the etched surface uniformly, rinsed in warm flowing ethanol, then dried in a blast of warm air.

## Microexamination

The etchants and etching times used for microexamination depend on the composition, physical condition and temper of the specimen. Time may vary from 5 to 10 s for a specimen of an alloy in the as-cast or aged condition to 60 s for one in the solution heat-treated condition. Etchants used for specimens of magnesium alloys are listed in Table 1, along with their compositions, etching procedures, characteristics, and uses.

**Table 1  Selected etchants for macroscopic and microscopic examination of magnesium alloys**

| Etchant | Composition | Etching procedure | Characteristics and use |
|---|---|---|---|
| 1 | *Nital:* 1 to 5 mL $HNO_3$ (conc), 100 mL ethanol (95%) or methanol (95%) | Swab or immerse specimen for a few seconds to 1 min. Wash in water, then alcohol and dry. | Shows general structure. |
| 2 | *Glycol:* 1 mL $HNO_3$ (conc), 24 mL water, 75 mL ethylene glycol | Immerse specimen face up and swab with cotton for 3 to 5 s for as-cast or aged metal and up to 1 min for heat treated metal. Wash in water, then alcohol and dry. | Shows general structure. Reveals constituents in magnesium/rare earth and magnesium-thorium alloys. |
| 3 | *Acetic glycol:* 20 mL acetic acid, 1 mL $HNO_3$ (conc), 60 mL ethylene glycol, 20 mL water | Immerse specimen face up with gentle agitation for 1 to 3 s for as-cast or aged metal and up to 10 s for solution-heat-treated metal. Wash in water, then alcohol and dry. | Shows general structure and grain boundaries in heat treated castings. Shows grain boundaries in magnesium/rare earth and magnesium-thorium alloys. |
| 4 | 10 mL HF (48%), 90 mL $H_2O$ | Immerse specimen face up for 1 to 2 s. Wash in water, then alcohol and dry. | Darkens $Mg_{17}Al_{12}$ phase and leaves $Mg_{32}(Al,Zn)_{49}$ phase unetched and white. |
| 5 | *Phospho-picral:* 0.7 mL $H_3PO_4$, 4 to 6 g picric acid, 100 mL ethanol (95%) | Immerse specimen face up for about 10 to 20 s or until polished surface is darkened. Wash in alcohol and dry. | For estimating the amount of massive phase. Stains matrix and leaves phase white. Staining improves as magnesium-ion content increases with use. |
| 6 | *Acetic-picral:* 5 mL acetic acid, 6 g picric acid, 10 mL $H_2O$, 100 mL ethanol (95%) | Immerse specimen face up with gentle agitation until face turns brown. Wash in a stream of alcohol; dry with a blast of air. | A universal etchant. Defines grain boundaries in most alloys and tempers by etch rate and color of stain. Reveals cold work and twinning readily. |
| 7 | *Acetic-picral:* 20 mL acetic acid, 3 g picric acid, 20 mL $H_2O$, 50 mL ethanol (95%) | Same as for etchant 6 but etch for at least 15 s to develop a heavy film. | Orientation of crackled film is parallel to trace of basal plane. Film crackles in high-alloy areas. Distinguishes between fusion voids surrounded by normal level of alloy and microshrinkage with low alloy content. |
| 8 | *Acetic-picral:* 10 mL acetic acid, 4.2 g picric acid, 10 mL $H_2O$, 70 mL ethanol (95%) | Same as for etchant 6 | Reveals grain boundaries more readily than etchant 6, especially in dilute alloys. |
| 9 | 0.6 g picric acid, 10 mL ethanol (95%), 90 mL $H_2O$ | Immerse specimen face up for 15 to 30 s. Wash in alcohol and dry. | Used after HF etchant to darken matrix to give better contrast between matrix and white ternary phase. |
| 10 | 2 mL HF (48%), 2 mL $HNO_3$ (conc), 96 mL $H_2O$ | Immerse specimen face up with gentle agitation. Do not swab. | Grain structure and coring in magnesium-zinc-zirconium alloys |

For sand, permanent mold, and die cast alloys in the as-cast condition and for virtually all the alloys in the aged condition, the glycol etchant is used; it is especially useful for the magnesium/rare earth alloys and magnesium-thorium alloys. Acetic-picral etchants are used to stain the grains selectively, especially for viewing with sensitive-tint or polarized light.

For cast metal in the solution-heat-treated condition and for most wrought alloys, the glycol, acetic-glycol, and acetic-picral etchants in Table 1 are satisfactory. Etchant 10 in Table 1 reveals the grain structure of alloys containing zinc and zirconium.

Phospho-picral with 6% picral (etchant 5 in Table 1) darkens the magnesium solid solution and leaves the other phases unchanged. The amount of staining is a function of the saturation of the solid solution. This etchant is particularly useful for quickly estimating the amount of undissolved second phase in solution-heat-treated metal, because of the extreme contrast it produces between the darkened matrix and the unetched second phase.

In etching with phospho-picral, the specimen is immersed face up for 10 to 20 s or until the polished surface darkens. Next, it is washed in ethanol and dried or washed in ethanol, then water, then ethanol and dried. Washing directly in water lightens the stain and lessens the contrast. Staining can be accelerated by immersing the specimen in the etchant, then withdrawing it into the air. The phospho-picral etchant is also useful for resolving grain boundaries and lamellar precipitate.

When alloy AZ31B and other dilute alloys normally fabricated in wrought form do not respond well to the acetic-picral etchant 6 in Table 1, the slightly different acetic-picral etchant 7 is recommended.

When etchants do not delineate grain boundaries, polarized light may be used, or the specimen may be pinched in a vise to produce twins. Grain boundaries in the AZ81 alloys are best seen after solution heat treatment. In dilute magnesium-zirconium alloys containing rare earth metals or thorium, care must be taken not to confuse cells surrounded by interdendritic $\beta$ phase with grains.

## Microstructure of Magnesium and Magnesium Alloys

Most magnesium alloys can be classified into five groups: (1) magnesium-aluminum-manganese (with or without zinc or silicon), (2) magnesium-zinc-zirconium (with or without thorium), (3) magnesium/rare earth metal/zirconium (with or without zinc or silver), (4) magnesium-thorium-zirconium (with or without zinc), and (5) magnesium-lithium-aluminum.

Magnesium alloys deform plastically by slip and twinning. As in other metals, slip lines are visible only when a polished surface is deformed or when a deformed specimen has been given a subsequent heat treatment to cause precipitation along the slip planes. Twins, however, are not destroyed by polishing; they may be recognized by their lenticular shape after etching.

Magnesium alloys are solution heat treated in a protective atmosphere—usually 0.5% sulfur dioxide or 3 to 5% carbon dioxide. Without the protective atmosphere, "high-temperature oxidation" or "burning" occurs. The eutectic deposits near the surface of the metal are attacked preferentially. This high-temperature oxidation is particularly rapid if eutectic melting is present concurrently. Eutectic melting is recognizable under a microscope as small shrinkage voids, chiefly intergranular, that are similar in appearance to microporosity, which is generally more irregular in outline.

Voids of doubtful origin in magnesium-aluminum alloys can be identified after solution heat treatment by the distribution of the precipitated $Mg_{17}Al_{12}$ constituent. If little or no precipitate is formed in the immediate vicinity of the voids, the voids are definitely attributable to microporosity. The presence of more precipitate in this location than in the surrounding area is proof that the voids are caused by eutectic melting during heat treatment.

Oxide films are occasionally found as thin, dark irregular lines in the microstructure of castings. Films formed in the crucible are usually thick and clustered and may contain entrapped manganese-rich particles. Films are thin and extended when produced by the breaking of the oxide "tube" in pouring or by turbulence in filling the mold.

Magnesium alloys for which micrographs are presented in this article are listed in Table 2. For information on the properties and temper designations of these alloys, see the articles "Selection and Application of Magnesium and Magnesium Alloys," "Properties of Magnesium Alloys," and "Corrosion Resistance of Magnesium and Magnesium Alloys" in Volume 2 of the 9th Edition of *Metals Handbook*.

**Aluminum.** A eutectic forms between the solid solution of aluminum in magnesium and the intermetallic compound $Mg_{17}Al_{12}$. With normal air cooling of castings, this eutectic takes either of two forms, depending on whether or not the alloy contains zinc. In an alloy without zinc, the eutectic forms as a massive compound, which contains islands of magnesium solid solution; in an alloy that contains zinc, it takes a completely divorced form—particles of compound in solid solution whose appearance blends into that of the adjacent primary solid solution.

The precipitation of $Mg_{17}Al_{12}$ from solid solution can be continuous or discontinuous. At aging temperatures above approximately 205 °C (400 °F), it appears in a continuous Widmanstätten pattern. Discontinuous precipitation, which starts at grain boundaries and has a lamellar form, is favored by lower

### Table 2 Nominal compositions of magnesium alloys

| Alloy | Al | Mn | Rare earths | Th | Zn | Zr |
|---|---|---|---|---|---|---|
| **Wrought alloys** | | | | | | |
| AZ31B | 3.0 | 0.5 | ... | ... | 1.0 | ... |
| AZ61A | 6.5 | 0.2 | ... | ... | 1.0 | ... |
| AZ80A | 8.5 | 0.2 | ... | ... | 0.5 | ... |
| HK31A | ... | ... | ... | 3.0 | ... | 0.7 |
| HM21A | ... | 0.5 | ... | 2.0 | ... | ... |
| HM31A | ... | 1.5 | ... | 3.0 | ... | ... |
| LA141A(a) | 1.2 | ... | ... | ... | ... | ... |
| ZE10A(b) | ... | ... | 0.2 | ... | 1.2 | ... |
| ZK21A | ... | ... | ... | ... | 2.3 | 0.6 |
| ZK60A | ... | ... | ... | ... | 5.7 | 0.6 |
| **Casting alloys** | | | | | | |
| AM60A | 6.0 | 0.2 | ... | ... | ... | ... |
| AM100A | 10.0 | 0.2 | ... | ... | ... | ... |
| AS41A(c) | 4.0 | 0.2 | ... | ... | ... | ... |
| AZ63A | 6.0 | 0.2 | ... | ... | 3.0 | ... |
| AZ91A(d) | 9.0 | 0.2 | ... | ... | 0.6 | ... |
| AZ91C | 8.7 | 0.2 | ... | ... | 0.7 | ... |
| AZ91D | 0.15–0.35 | ... | ... | ... | ... | ... |
| AZ91E | 0.17–0.35 | ... | ... | ... | ... | ... |
| AZ92A | 9.0 | 0.2 | ... | ... | 2.0 | ... |
| EZ33A(b) | ... | ... | 3.0 | ... | 2.6 | 0.6 |
| HK31A | ... | ... | ... | 3.0 | ... | 0.7 |
| HZ32A | ... | ... | ... | 3.0 | 2.1 | 0.7 |
| K1A | ... | ... | ... | ... | ... | 0.7 |
| QE22A(e) | ... | ... | 2.0 | ... | ... | 0.6 |
| ZK51A | ... | ... | ... | ... | 4.6 | 0.7 |
| ZK61A | ... | ... | ... | ... | 6.0 | 0.7 |
| ZH62A | ... | ... | ... | 1.8 | 5.7 | 0.7 |
| **Filler metals** | | | | | | |
| ER AZ61A | 6.5 | 0.2 | ... | ... | 1.0 | ... |
| ER AZ92A | 9.0 | 0.2 | ... | ... | 2.0 | ... |
| ER AZ101A | 10.0 | 0.2 | ... | ... | 1.0 | ... |

(a) Contains 14% Li. (b) Rare earth metal designated "R" in identifications of intermetallic phases, is present as mischmetal (approximately 50% Ce and 50% other rare earth metals). (c) Contains 0.75% Si. (d) Alloys AZ91A and AZ91B are identical in composition, except that residual copper to 0.35% max is allowable in AZ91B. (e) Contains 2.5% silver. Rare earth metal, designated "R" in identifications of intermetallic phases, is present as didymium (approximately 85% Nd and 15% Pr).

aging temperatures and aluminum content above 8%. At approximately 290 °C (550 °F), the lamellar precipitate begins to coalesce, and at approximately 370 °C (700 °F), it redissolves in the matrix.

**Manganese.** In magnesium alloys that contain manganese but no aluminum, the manganese appears as primary elemental particles. Manganese combines with aluminum, when present, to form the compounds MnAl, $MnAl_4$, or $MnAl_6$. These compounds may be contained in a single particle, with the ratio of aluminum to manganese increasing from the center to the surface of the particle. Solution heat treatment transforms the particle to $MnAl_6$. The presence of sufficient iron modifies the manganese-aluminum compounds to very hard manganese-aluminum-iron compounds.

Particles of manganese-aluminum compound often occur in the form of chunks and needles. The particles sometimes have irregular, sawtooth surfaces, which result from growth in the mushy and the early solid stages.

**Rare Earth Metals.** Because of the low solubility of rare earth metals in magnesium, there is usually an excess of $Mg_9R$ compound at the grain boundaries of magnesium-mischmetal and magnesium-didymium alloys.

**Silicon** is present in magnesium alloys as particles of $Mg_2Si$. These particles are distinguished by their angular outline, smooth edges, and light-blue color.

**Thorium.** At the eutectic temperature of 589 °C (1092 °F), 4.5% Th is soluble in magnesium; however, because of alloy segregation, magnesium alloys containing as little as 2% Th often contain a divorced eutectic and show massive $Mg_4Th$ compound at the grain boundaries. At temperatures below the eutectic, this compound is also precipitated from solid solution. In castings, the precipitate forms within grains and is seldom visible. In worked structures, the precipitate is often clearly visible at grain boundaries.

The addition of thorium to magnesium-zinc alloys changes the degenerate eutectic, which contains magnesium-zinc compound, to a lamellar eutectic, which contains a magnesium-thorium-zinc compound.

**Zinc.** At the eutectic temperature of 340 °C (644 °F), 6.2% Zn is soluble in magnesium, but at lower temperatures there is general precipitation of magnesium-zinc compound whose particles are not clearly resolvable by an electron microscope until the alloy is overaged.

When zinc is added to magnesium-aluminum alloys, the magnesium-aluminum eutectic takes a completely divorced form, in which massive particles of $Mg_{17}Al_{12}$ compound—or of $Mg_{32}(Al,Zn)_{49}$ compound, if the ratio of zinc to aluminum exceeds 1:3—are surrounded by magnesium solid solution. Additions of zinc to magnesium/rare earth metal alloys increase the amount and continuity of the compound at the grain bound-

aries. Zinc additions also promote the change of the magnesium/rare earth eutectic to the divorced form. By adding approximately 2% Zn to magnesium alloys containing at least 2% Th, an acicular, or platelet, form of compound develops. The acicular form entirely replaces the massive form when the zinc content is increased to approximately 3%, but it again disappears when the zinc content is further increased to above 5%.

**Zirconium,** in amounts less than 1%, is alloyed with magnesium and added to magnesium alloys containing zinc, rare earth metals, or thorium. In binary magnesium-zirconium alloys, zirconium-rich particles may occasionally be seen within grains. In the more complex alloys, zirconium may form compounds with zinc and with certain elements that are impurities in those alloys, such as aluminum, iron, silicon, and hydrogen.

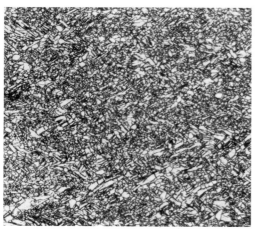

**Fig. 1** Alloy AZ31B-H24 sheet. Longitudinal edge view of worked structure, showing elongated grains, and mechanical twins, which resulted from warm rolling of the sheet. Etchant 8, Table 1. 250×

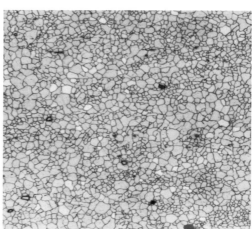

**Fig. 2** Alloy AZ31B-O sheet. Longitudinal edge view of structure recrystallized by annealing. Particles of manganese-aluminum compound (dark gray) and fragmented $Mg_{17}Al_{12}$ (outlined). Etchant 8, Table 1. 200×

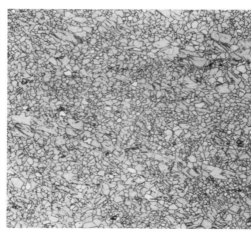

**Fig. 3** Alloy AZ31B tooling plate. Longitudinal edge view. Essentially recrystallized structure resulting from anneal flattening; outlined particles of fragmented $Mg_{17}Al_{12}$. Etchant 8, Table 1. 200×

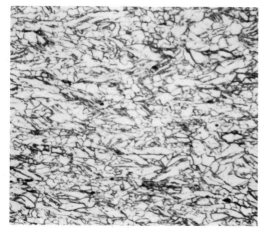

**Fig. 4** ZE10A-H24 sheet. Longitudinal edge view of worked structure similar to that in Fig. 1, showing elongated grains and mechanical twins (bounded by parallel lines), resulting from warm rolling of the sheet. Etchant 7, Table 1. 500×

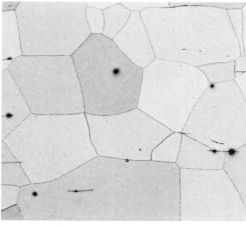

**Fig. 5** LA141A-O sheet. Longitudinal edge view of recrystallized structure that resulted from annealing for 30 min at 260 °C (500 °F). The structure is generally clean, but entrapped dross is present in some areas. Etchant 5, Table 1. 250×

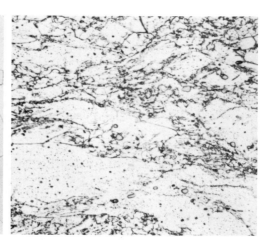

**Fig. 6** HM21A-T8 sheet. Longitudinal edge view of worked structure, showing $Mg_4Th$, both as outlined particles of fragmented massive compound and as precipitate within grains and at boundaries of the elongated grains. Etchant 5, Table 1. 500×

**Fig. 7** HK31A-H24 sheet. Longitudinal edge view, showing structure similar to Fig. 6, but with less Mg₄Th precipitated in grains and more at the elongated grain boundaries. Etchant 5, Table 1. 500×

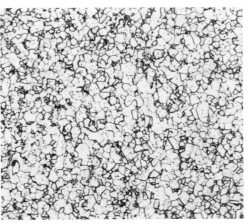

**Fig. 8** HK31A-O sheet. Longitudinal edge view of structure recrystallized by annealing. Note that most of the Mg₄Th precipitate shown in Fig. 7 has redissolved. See also Fig. 9. Etchant 5, Table 1, 10 s. 250×

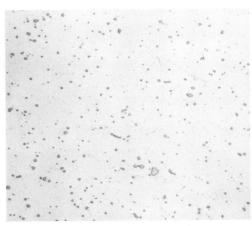

**Fig. 9** HK31A-O sheet. Same as Fig. 8, except not etched, which has made the outlined particles of fragmented massive Mg₄Th compound more easily visible. As-polished. 500×

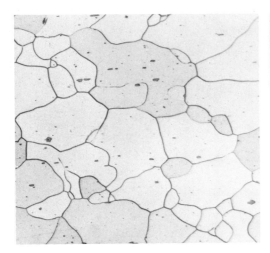

**Fig. 10** AZ31B-F extrusion. Longitudinal view of hot-worked structure. Large, equiaxed recrystallized grains; particles of manganese-aluminum compound and fragmented Mg₁₇Al₁₂. Etchant 8, Table 1. 250×

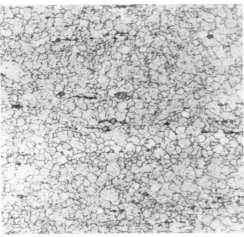

**Fig. 11** AZ61A-F extrusion. Longitudinal view of hot-worked structure. Small, equiaxed recrystallized grains; stringers of fragmented Mg₁₇Al₁₂. See also Fig. 12. Etchant 6, Table 1. 250×

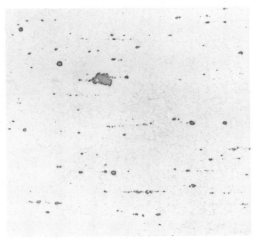

**Fig. 12** Same as Fig. 11, except this specimen has not been etched, making the stringers of fragmented Mg₁₇Al₁₂ more easily visible. As-polished. 250×

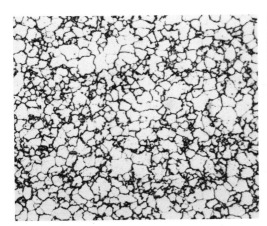

**Fig. 13** AZ80A-F extrusion. Longitudinal view of hot-worked structure. Small, equiaxed recrystallized grains; small amount of Mg₁₇Al₁₂ discontinuous precipitate at the grain boundaries. See also Fig. 14. Etchant 3, Table 1, 15 s. 250×

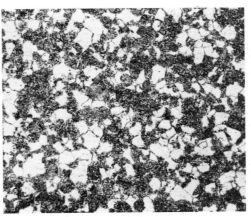

**Fig. 14** AZ80A-T5 extrusion. Longitudinal view showing much mottled Mg₁₇Al₁₂ discontinuous precipitate near the grain boundaries, resulting from the artificial aging treatment. Compare with Fig. 13. Etchant 2, Table 1, 5 s. 250×

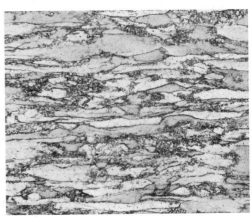

**Fig. 15** ZK21A-F extrusion. Longitudinal view of hot-worked structure. Small equiaxed recrystallized grains at the boundaries of and also within large, unrecrystallized elongated grains. Etchant 6, Table 1. 100×

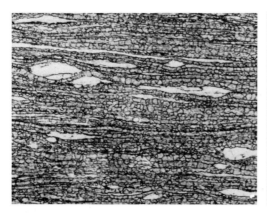

**Fig. 16** ZK60A-F extrusion. Longitudinal view of banded hot-worked structure. Small, recrystallized grains; light islands are solid solution deficient in zinc and zirconium (due to alloy segregation) and so more resistant to hot working. See also Fig. 17. Etchant 6, Table 1, then Etchant 4, Table 1. 250×

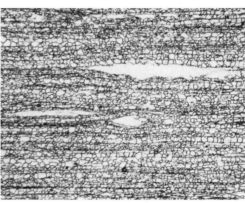

**Fig. 17** Same as Fig. 16, except artificially aged to the T5 temper. Despite higher magnification, structure appears same as Fig. 16 (precipitate formed during aging is unresolvable by microscopy). Etchant 7, Table 1, 7 s, then Etchant 6, Table 1, 1 s. 500×

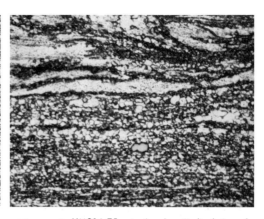

**Fig. 18** HM31A-T5 extrusion. Longitudinal view of banded hot-worked structure. Small, recrystallized grains; dark $Mg_4Th$ grain-boundary precipitate; light islands are solid solution rich in thorium and so more resistant to hot working; gray particle is manganese. Etchant 5, Table 1. 500×

**Fig. 19** AZ80A-T5 forging. Longitudinal view of hot-worked structure, showing large, recrystallized grains and spheroidized $Mg_{17}Al_{12}$ discontinuous precipitate mainly in the grains near the boundaries. Etchant 5, Table 1. 200×

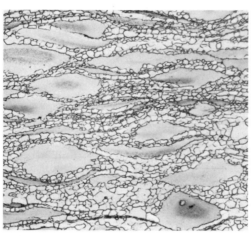

**Fig. 20** ZK60A-T5 forging. Longitudinal view. Structure same as Fig. 17, but with slightly larger grains and increased alloy segregation. Etchant 7, Table 1, 7 s, then Etchant 6, Table 1, 2 s. 500×

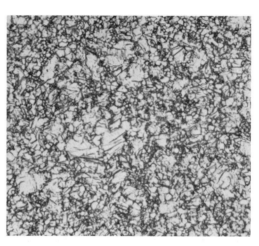

**Fig. 21** HM21A-T5 forging. Longitudinal view. Structure is similar to that of sheet shown in Fig. 6, except the forging has smaller grains. (Grain growth in sheet caused by solution heat treatment.) Etchant 5, Table 1. 250×

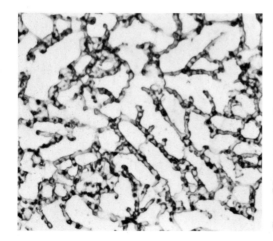

**Fig. 22** AM60A-F die casting. Small, cored grains of magnesium solid solution in which the aluminum content increases toward the boundaries; passive $Mg_{17}Al_{12}$ compound at grain boundaries. Relief polishing causes dark areas. See also Fig. 23. Etchant 3, Table 1. 500×

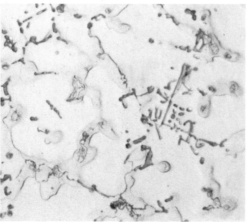

**Fig. 23** AS41A-F die casting. Same structure as that shown in Fig. 22, but with the addition of $Mg_2Si$ in Chinese script and globular forms. Etchant 3, Table 1, 5 s. 500×

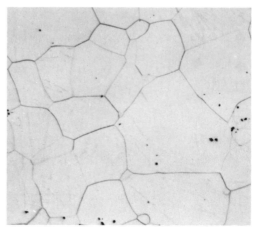

**Fig. 24** K1A-F die casting. Small crystals of zirconium randomly dispersed in grains of magnesium that are larger than those in more highly alloyed die castings (compare with Fig. 22, 23, and 25.) Etchant 2, Table 1, 10 s. 250×

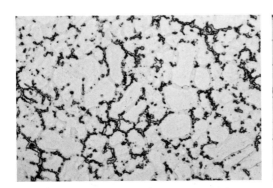

**Fig. 25** AZ91A-F die casting. Massive $Mg_{17}Al_{12}$ compound at the boundaries of small, cored grains. Segregation (coring) in the grains and absence of precipitated discontinuous $Mg_{17}Al_{12}$ are results of the rapid cooling rate of die castings. See also Fig. 26 and 27. Etchant 2, Table 1, 5 s. 500×

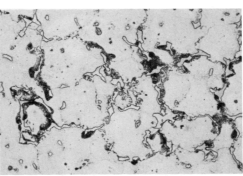

**Fig. 26** AZ92A-F permanent mold casting. $Mg_{17}Al_{12}$ compound: massive (outlined) at grain boundaries; precipitated (dark) near grain boundaries. Slower cooling rate than that of die castings has resulted in larger grains than in structure shown in Fig. 25. Etchant 2, Table 1, 5 s. 250×

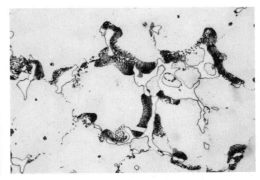

**Fig. 27** AZ92A-F sand casting. Same microstructure as that shown in Fig. 26, except the slower cooling rate, in comparison with that of permanent mold castings, has resulted in larger grains. See Fig. 32 for effects of aging. Etchant 2, Table 1, 5 s. 250×

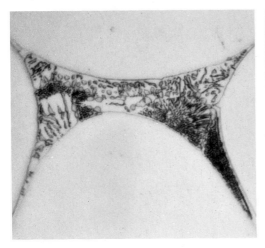

**Fig. 28** AZ92A-F sand casting. The appearance of the interdendritic eutectic, a mixture of magnesium solid solution and $Mg_{17}Al_{12}$, was retained in this form by a rapid quench from above the eutectic temperature. See also Fig. 29. Etchant 2, Table 1, 5 s. 1500×

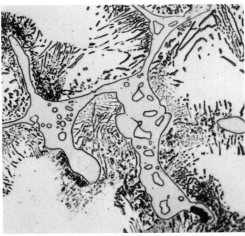

**Fig. 29** AM100A-F, as-cast. Massive $Mg_{17}Al_{12}$ compound containing globular magnesium solid solution and surrounded by lamellar $Mg_{17}Al_{12}$ precipitate. Normal air cooling produces this type of segregated eutectic. Compare with Fig. 28 and 30. Etchant 2, Table 1, 5 s. 500×

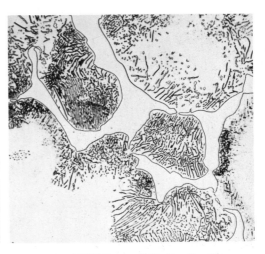

**Fig. 30** AZ92A-F, as-cast. Massive $Mg_{17}Al_{12}$ compound surrounded by lamellar $Mg_{17}Al_{12}$ precipitate. Normal air cooling of zinc-containing magnesium-aluminum alloys produces this type of completely divorced eutectic. Compare with Fig. 29. Etchant 2, Table 1. 500×

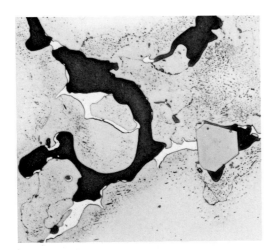

**Fig. 31** Massive $Mg_{32}(Al,Zn)_{49}$ (white) in as-cast alloy AZ63A-F. Specimen etched with 50% picral to protect $Mg_2Si$ (hexagonal particle) from HF, then with 5% HF to blacken $Mg_{17}Al_{12}$ and distinguish it from $Mg_{32}(Al,Zn)_{49}$, then with 10% picral to darken the matrix. 500×

**Fig. 32** Alloy AZ92A-T6 sand casting. Lamellar $Mg_{17}Al_{12}$ precipitate (light and dark gray) was produced throughout the grains of magnesium solid solution by artificial aging. Some isolated islands of $Mg_2Si$ (white) are also present. Etchant 2, Table 1. 100×

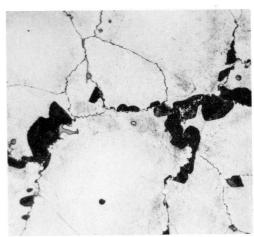

**Fig. 33** Alloy AZ63A-T6 sand casting. Lamellar $Mg_{32}(Al,Zn)_{49}$ discontinuous precipitate (dark) near some grain boundaries; some particles of $Mg_2Si$ and manganese-aluminum compounds. Note that with 6% Al there is less precipitate than with 9% Al (compare with Fig. 32). Etchant 2, Table 1, 5s. 250×

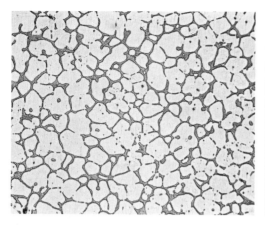

**Fig. 34** EZ33A-T5 sand casting. Interdendritic network of massive $Mg_9R$ compound. The precipitate in the dendritic grains of magnesium solid solution is not visible. Etchant 2, Table 1. 100×

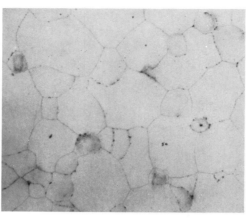

**Fig. 35** ZK51A-T5 sand casting. Fine, degenerate eutectic magnesium-zinc compound at the grain boundaries. The grains of magnesium solid solution are essentially homogeneous. Etchant 2, Table 1, 5 s. 250×

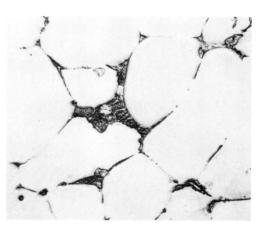

**Fig. 36** ZH62A-T5 sand casting. Characteristic lamellar, or filigree, form of eutectic magnesium-thorium-zinc compound at the boundaries of grains of magnesium solid solution. 2% nital. 250×

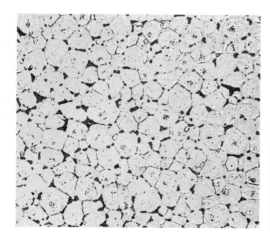

**Fig. 37** QE22A-T6 sand casting. Massive $Mg_9R$ compound is present at the boundaries of grains of magnesium solid solution, resulting from partial solution and coalescence of the magnesium-didymium eutectic. Etchant 2, Table 1. 100×

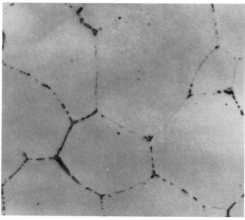

**Fig. 38** HK31A-T6 sand casting. Intergranular particles of massive $Mg_4Th$ compound (gray, outlined). The precipitate in the grains of magnesium solid solution is not visible. See Fig. 39 for effect of zinc addition. Etchant 2, Table 1, 15 s. 500×

**Fig. 39** HZ32A-T5 sand casting. Intergranular Mg-Th compounds: bunches of acicular compound (dark gray) and small areas of massive $Mg_4Th$ (see Fig. 38). The precipitate within matrix grains is not visible. 2% nital. 250×

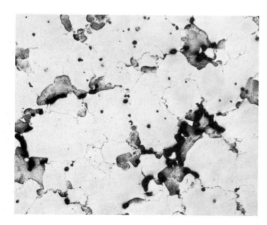

**Fig. 40** Fusion microporosity in an AZ63A-T4 sand casting. Gray lamellar precipitate, present around black voids despite solution heat treatment, indicates alloy segregation in these areas. See also Fig. 41. Etchant 2, Table 1, 10 s. 100×

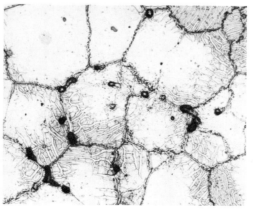

**Fig. 41** Fusion microporosity in an AZ63A-T4 sand casting. The gray crackled film, formed around the black voids by the acetic-picral etchant indicates alloy segregation in these areas. See also Fig. 40. Etchant 6, Table 1, 15 s. 100×

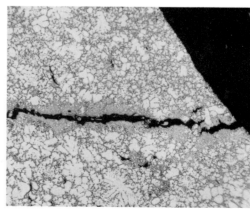

**Fig. 42** Hot tear in an AZ91A-F die casting. Tear occurred in an area of compound segregation that was last to solidify and least resistant to stress caused by mold restriction during solidification shrinkage. Etchant 2, Table 1, 5 s. 75×

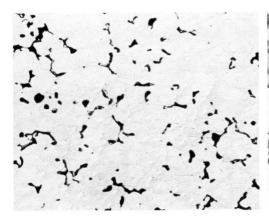

**Fig. 43** Shrinkage microporosity in an AZ92A-T6 sand casting. The uniform dispersion of voids (black) in particular areas of the casting is typical of this type of porosity, which results from improper feeding of molten metal to those areas. See also Fig. 44. Etchant 2, Table 1. 100×

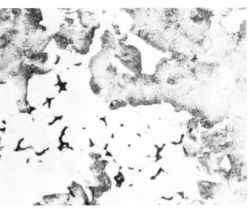

**Fig. 44** Shrinkage microporosity in an AZ92A-T6 sand casting. Voids (black), resulting from withdrawal of molten eutectic from between dendrites during solidification, are surrounded by areas low in alloying elements and containing no gray precipitate. Etchant 2, Table 1, 5 s. 100×

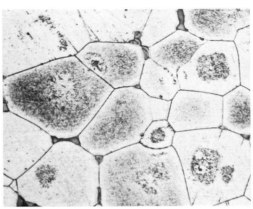

**Fig. 45** QE22A-T6 sand casting. Alloy segregation (coring), characterized by intragranular precipitation of didymium and zirconium hydrides (formed during solution treatment by reaction with water vapor) and by less Mg₉R at grain boundaries than normal. Etchant 3, Table 1. 500×

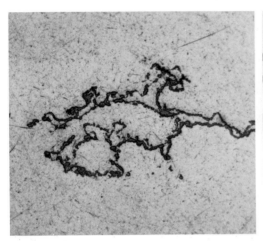

**Fig. 46** Segregation of zinc-zirconium-iron compound in a ZK61A-F sand casting. This compound and $Zr_2Zn_3$ form under similar conditions; the two can be distinguished by etching with 10% HF, which attacks $Zr_2Zn_3$ but not zinc-zirconium-iron. Etchant 2, Table 1, 10 s. 250×

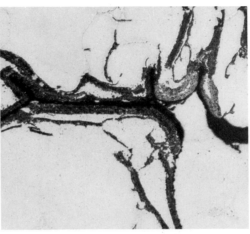

**Fig. 47** Segregation of layered oxide skin in a ZK61A-F sand casting. This type of skin forms on molten metal surfaces that are incompletely protected for several minutes. Compare with the thin oxide skin shown in Fig. 48. Etchant 2, Table 1, 10 s. 250×

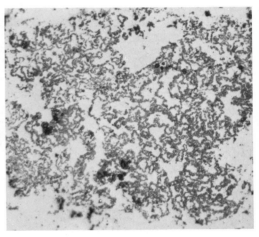

**Fig. 48** Segregation of thin oxide skin in an AZ91A-F die casting. This type of skin forms whenever molten metal surfaces are exposed to the atmosphere for a few seconds. Compare with the layered oxide skin in Fig. 47. Etchant 2, Table 1, 10 s. 250×

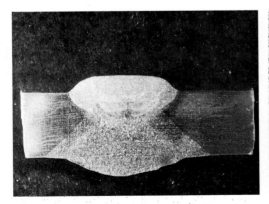

**Fig. 49** Incomplete fusion in a two-pass gas tungsten-arc butt weld in 4-mm (0.160-in.) thick AZ31B-H24 sheet. Weld was made with alloy ER AZ61A filler metal. Note the unfused area at the root of the second pass (top). Etchant 6, Table 1. 3.8×

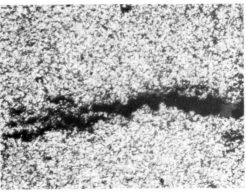

**Fig. 50** Shrinkage crack in the crater of a gas tungsten arc weld in an AZ92A-T6 casting caused by interruption of welding without first reducing current to lower the temperature of the weld pool. 2% nital. 75×

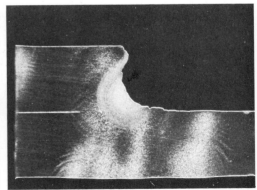

**Fig. 51** Undercutting in a gas tungsten arc fillet weld in 4-mm (0.160-in.) thick AZ31B-H24 sheet. The weld was made with ER AZ61A filler metal. Note undercut area in the edge of the top sheet of the lap joint. Etchant 6, Table 1. 3.8×

**Fig. 52** Incomplete joint penetration of a gas tungsten arc weld in a butt joint between 4-mm (0.160-in.) thick AZ31B-H24 sheets. The weld was made with ER AZ61A filler metal. Note the unfused joint at the root of the weld. Etchant 6, Table 1. 3.8×

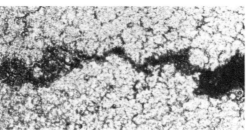

**Fig. 53** Crack in the heat-affected zone of a gas tungsten arc weld in an AZ92A-T6 casting, caused by use of excessive welding current, producing too high a temperature gradient between base metal and weld pool. 2% nital. 75×

**Fig. 54** Gross gas porosity in gas tungsten arc weld joining 5-mm (0.190-in.) thick AZ31B-H24 sheets; ER AZ61A filler metal. Causes include dirty base metal and filler metal, inadequate coverage by shielding gas, and moisture in gas. Etchant 6, Table 1. 3.8×

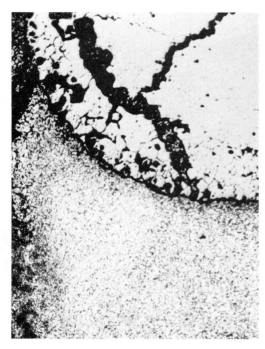

**Fig. 55** Subsurface tungsten inclusion (large, round particle at top) in a gas tungsten arc weld in an AZ92A-T6 casting. Filler metal is alloy ER AZ92A. 2% nital. 75×

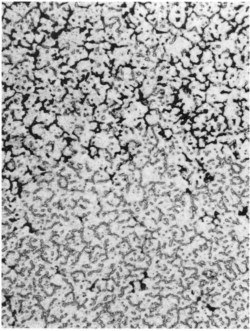

**Fig. 56** Border area between zones of profuse (top) and sparse (bottom) shrinkage microporosity in a gas tungsten arc weld deposit of ER AZ101A filler metal. Etchant 5, Table 1. 65×

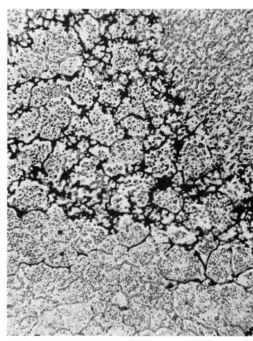

**Fig. 57** Shrinkage microporosity in heat-affected zone of gas tungsten arc weld made in an AZ91C-T6 casting with ER AZ92A filler metal. (The weld deposit is at top right.) Etchant 5, Table 1. 75×

# Nickel and Nickel-Copper Alloys

By William L. Mankins
Process Development Manager
Huntington Alloys International

THE PREPARATION of metallographic specimens and the microstructures of alloys containing 96% or more nickel (Nickel 200, Nickel 270, and Duranickel 301) and nickel-copper alloys (Monel 400, Monel R-405, and Monel K-500) are considered in this article. Micrographs of these alloys are shown in Fig. 1 to 15.

The procedures and materials for sectioning, mounting, grinding, and polishing specimens are essentially the same for all nickel alloys regardless of specimen size or sophistication of laboratory facilities. In preparing specimens for metallographic examination, it is important to prevent working of the surface.

## Preparation for Microscopic Examination

The specimen to be examined is cut to a convenient size with a silicon carbide water-cooled cutoff wheel, then mounted in a hard plastic, such as Bakelite or a hard epoxy resin. Next, the mounted specimen is ground flat on a belt grinder using 120-grit abrasive and water coolant. In general, it is preferable that the exposed area of the specimen not exceed about 1.6 cm$^2$ (0.25 in.$^2$).

**Grinding** may be performed manually or on power-driven wheels using silicon carbide paper disks, starting with 220-grit and following with 320-, 400-, and 600-grit. The specimen is then washed thoroughly and cleaned ultrasonically to remove any abrasive particles remaining on the surface.

**Polishing.** All scratches from grinding are removed by polishing on a nylon cloth charged with 6-$\mu$m diamond paste and lubricated with lapping oil. An alternate method is to polish on a broadcloth-covered wheel using 5-$\mu$m levigated alumina ($Al_2O_3$) powder suspended in water.

Final polishing may be performed in one or two stages with a polishing wheel or vibratory polisher. If a polishing wheel is used, Microcloth and $\gamma$-$Al_2O_3$ powder ($<$0.1-$\mu$m particle size) suspended in water are recommended. An alternative requires semifinal and final polishing using a vibratory polisher. Semifinal polishing employs a nylon polishing cloth and a slurry of 0.3-$\mu$m $Al_2O_3$ and distilled water. A 350-g weight is placed on the specimen throughout the polishing cycle. At the conclusion of each polishing cycle, the specimen is cleaned ultrasonically. Final polishing employs a short-nap microcloth and a slurry of 0.05-$\mu$m $Al_2O_3$ and distilled water. Polishing continues until the surface is free of scratches.

**Electropolishing.** Nickel and nickel-copper alloys can be electropolished satisfactorily, although best results are generally obtained with specimens that first have been polished mechanically through 600-grit. Recommended electrolytes and current densities for electropolishing these alloys are given in Table 1. A platinum cathode is suggested and the electrolyte should be water cooled and continuously stirred.

**Table 1   Electrolytes and current densities for electropolishing of nickel and nickel-copper alloys**

| Electrolyte composition | Applicable alloys | Current density A/cm$^2$ | A/in.$^2$ |
|---|---|---|---|
| 37 mL H$_3$PO$_4$ | Nickel 200 | 1.4-1.5 | 9-10 |
| (conc), 56 mL | Nickel 270 | 1.5-1.8 | 10-12 |
| glycerol, 7 mL | Duranickel 301 | 1.25-1.5 | 8-10 |
| H$_2$O | Monel 400 | 0.9-1 | 6-7 |
| 33 mL HNO$_3$ | Monel 400, R-405, | 1.5-2.3 | 10-15 |
| (conc), 66 mL methanol | K-500 | | |

**Etching.** The solutions and conditions for etching nickel alloys for microscopic examination are described in Table 2. The acids used should be concentrated; when water is indicated, use distilled water only.

**Table 2   Etchants for microscopic examination of nickel and nickel-copper alloys for grain boundaries and general structure**

| Composition of etchant | Conditions for use |
|---|---|
| **Etchants for Nickel 200 and 270; Permanickel; Duranickel 301; and Monel 400, R-450, and K-500** | |
| 1 part 10% aqueous solution of NaCN (sodium cyanide), 1 part 10% aqueous solution of (NH$_4$)$_2$S$_2$O$_8$ (ammonium persulfate). Mix solutions when ready to use. | Immerse or swab specimen for 5-90 s(a) |
| 1 part HNO$_3$ (conc), 1 part acetic acid (glacial). Use fresh solution. | For revealing grain boundaries. Immerse or swab specimen for 5-20 s |
| 7.5 mL HF, 2.5 mL HNO$_3$, 200 mL methanol | Immerse sample 2-4 min |
| 5 g FeCl$_3$, 50 mL HCl, 100 mL H$_2$O | Immerse or swab specimen up to a few minutes |
| **Alternate etchant for Monel K-500** | |
| Glyceregia: 10 mL HNO$_3$ (conc), 20 mL HCl (conc), 30-40 mL glycerol | Etch by immersing or swabbing the specimen for 30 s to 5 min |

(a) This cyanide-containing etchant is very hazardous in its preparation and use. Cyanide, even in small quantities, as dust, solution, or fumes may be fatal when taken into the body. A fume hood should be utilized.

## Preparation for Macroscopic Examination

Surfaces to be etched for macroscopic examination may be prepared by surface grinding to a fine finish with 180-grit and 240-grit silicon carbide paper. Finer grinding, although unnecessary, yields a finer surface before etching, which requires less severe macroetching to reveal the metal structure.

Etching of nickel alloys for macroscopic examination is performed by immersing or swabbing the ground specimen for 5 to 20 s in an etchant composed of equal parts (by volume) of concentrated nitric acid ($HNO_3$) and glacial acetic acid.

Macroetching of nickel-copper alloys is done by immersing or swabbing the ground specimen in concentrated $HNO_3$. Colorless acid should be used to avoid staining. Depending on the purpose of examination, etching time should be 3 to 5 min. Within this range, shorter etching times will reveal sulfur embrittlement and details of welds in Monel; longer times will reveal general structure, including surface and subsurface cracks, porosity, and forging flow lines. Macroetching can be hastened by warming the specimen in hot water prior to etching.

## Microstructures of Nickel and Nickel-Copper Alloys

Nickel-base alloys are widely used as high-temperature materials. Micrographs of such alloys are presented in the articles "Wrought Heat-Resistant Alloys" and "Heat-Resistant Casting Alloys" in this Volume. Micrographs of nickel-base alloys employed as magnetically soft materials are in the article "Magnetic and Electrical Materials" in this Volume. The micrographs in this article show structures of nickel alloys that are used primarily for their resistance to corrosion and for other specialized applications. As shown in Table 3, these alloys range in nickel content from 66.5% to 99.98%.

The microstructure of Nickel 200 typically contains some nonmetallic inclusions (principally oxide). Prolonged exposure to temperatures from 425 to 650 °C (800 to 1200 °F)

**Table 3  Nominal compositions of nickel and nickel-copper alloys**

| Alloy | Composition |
|---|---|
| Nickel 200 | 99.5Ni-0.08C-0.18Mn-0.20Fe |
| Nickel 270 | 99.98Ni-0.01C |
| Permanickel 300 | 98.5Ni-0.20C-0.25Mn-0.30Fe-0.35Mg-0.40Ti |
| Duranickel 301 | 96.5Ni-0.15C-0.25Mn-0.30Fe-0.63Ti-4.38Al |
| Monel 400 | 66.5Ni-31.5Cu-0.15C-1.0Mn-1.25Fe |
| Monel R-405 | 66.5Ni-31.5Cu-0.15C-1.0Mn-1.25Fe-0.043S |
| Monel K-500 | 66.5Ni-29.5Cu-0.13C-0.75Mn-1.0Fe-0.60Ti-2.73Al |

results in the precipitation of graphite from the nickel solid solution.

Although Nickel 270 (99.98% Ni) is less likely than Nickel 200 to contain nonmetallic inclusions, their structures are similar, assuming that mechanical working and thermal treatments are similar (compare Fig. 1 and 2 to Fig. 3 and 4).

Permanickel 300 is an age-hardening alloy that in the solution-annealed condition shows randomly dispersed particles of titanium nitride (TiN) and graphite when observed through an optical microscope. When subsequently age hardened, the alloy has a similar appearance (Fig. 5), but it also contains a fine granular precipitate. This phase is not resolvable by optical microscopy in material aged at a normal aging temperature (480 °C, or 900 °F), but is visible in overaged material. The phase or phases responsible for the age hardening of this alloy have not been positively identified. The mechanism appears to be complex; carbon, magnesium, and tita-

nium are required for full hardness. Precipitation of a compound such as $Ni_3(Mg,Ti)C_x$ seems likely during age hardening.

Duranickel 301, an age-hardening alloy, combines the corrosion resistance of unalloyed nickel with increased strength and hardness. After solution annealing, this alloy is age hardened by holding in the temperature range of 425 to 705 °C (800 to 1300 °F), which precipitates the phase $Ni_3(Al,Ti)$ throughout the structure. In the solution-annealed and properly aged condition (see Fig. 6), the precipitated phase is not resolved by an optical microscope. Some particles of graphite, however, are usually visible.

**Nickel-Copper Alloys.** Monel 400 is a stable solid solution of nickel and copper. Nonmetallic inclusions often appear in the microstructure (see Fig. 7).

Monel R-405 is a free-machining grade of Monel 400. The microstructures of these two alloys are similar for the same mechanical and thermal treatment, except for the sulfide particles in Monel R-405, which improve machinability (Fig. 8).

Monel K-500 is produced by adding aluminum and titanium to the basic nickel-copper composition. Solution annealing and aging produce a $\gamma'$ precipitate throughout the matrix. In material aged at the normal temperature of 595 °C (1100 °F), this precipitate is not resolvable by an optical microscope (Fig. 12 and 13). However, in material that is overaged—by holding at 705 °C (1300 °F), for example—the precipitate is visible by optical microscopy (Fig. 14 and 15). In addition to the precipitate, particles of TiN are usually present in the microstructure.

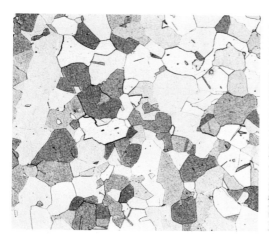

**Fig. 1** Nickel 200, cold drawn and annealed in a continuous process at 830 °C (1525 °F). Structure: nickel solid solution. See also Fig. 2. NaCN, $(NH_4)_2S_2O_8$. 100×

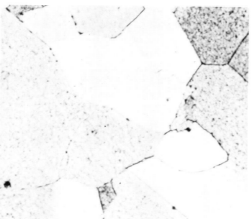

**Fig. 2** Same as Fig. 1, but at higher magnification. Variation in shade of grains is caused by variation in grain orientation. NaCN, $(NH_4)_2S_2O_8$. 500×

**Fig. 3** Nickel 270, hot rolled and annealed in a continuous process at 830 °C (1525 °F). Structure: nickel solid solution. See also Fig. 4. NaCN, $(NH_4)_2S_2O_8$. 100×

**Fig. 4** Same alloy and same processing as in Fig. 3, but shown at a higher magnification. The variation in shade of the grains (dark, gray, and white) is the result of variation in grain orientation. NaCN, $(NH_4)_2S_2O_8$. 500×

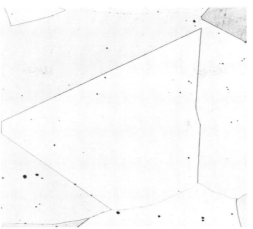

**Fig. 5** Permanickel 300, solution annealed 1 h at 1205 °C (2200 °F) and water quenched, aged 10 h at 480 °C (900 °F) and water quenched. Dispersed particles of TiN and graphite (black dots) in nickel solid solution. NaCN, $(NH_4)_2S_2O_8$. 100×

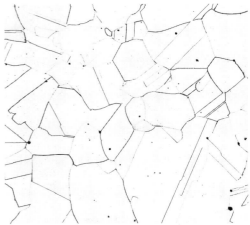

**Fig. 6** Duranickel 301, solution annealed for 30 min at 980 °C (1800 °F) and water quenched, aged for 20 h at 480 °C (900 °F) and water quenched. Microstructure: nickel solid solution; graphite particles (black dots). NaCN, $(NH_4)_2S_2O_8$. 50×

**Fig. 7** Monel 400, cold drawn and annealed in a continuous process at 830 °C (1525 °F). Nickel-copper solid solution with a few unidentified nonmetallic inclusions (black). NaCN, $(NH_4)_2S_2O_8$. 100×

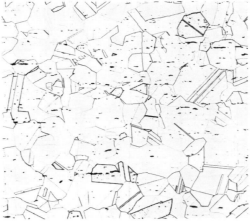

**Fig. 8** Monel R-405, cold drawn, and annealed in a continuous process at 830 °C (1525 °F). Microstructure: nickel-copper solid solution with sulfide stringers (black constituent). NaCN, $(NH_4)_2S_2O_8$. 100×

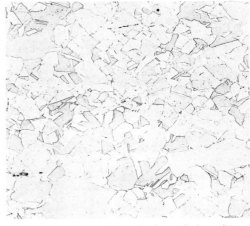

**Fig. 9** Monel K-500 in the hot rolled condition. Structure: nickel-copper solid solution. Variation in shade of grains is the result of variation in grain orientation. Glyceregia. 100×

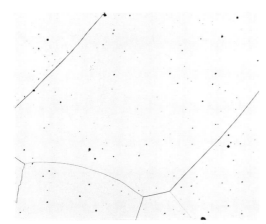

**Fig. 10** Monel K-500, solution annealed for 1 h at 1205 °C (2200 °F) and quenched in water. Nickel-copper solid-solution matrix. See also Fig. 11 to 15. NaCN, $(NH_4)_2S_2O_8$. 100×

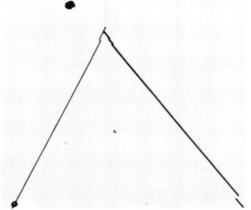

**Fig. 11** Same as Fig. 10, but at higher magnification. Portions of only three grains are visible. The black dots are nitride particles. See also Fig. 10 and 12 to 15. NaCN, $(NH_4)_2S_2O_8$. 1000×

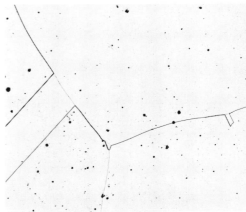

**Fig. 12** Monel K-500, held 1 h at 1205 °C (2200 °F), transferred to a furnace at 595 °C (1100 °F) and aged 4 h, water quenched. Solid-solution matrix; nitride particles. See also Fig. 10, 11, and 13 to 15. NaCN, $(NH_4)_2S_2O_8$. 100×

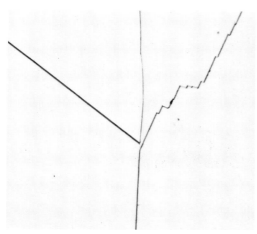

**Fig. 13** Same as Fig. 12, but at higher magnification. Structure contains precipitated $Ni_3(Al,Ti)$, resolvable only by electron microscopy unless aging temperature is higher than 595 °C (1100 °F). See also Fig. 10 to 12 and 14, 15. NaCN, $(NH_4)_2S_2O_8$. 1000×

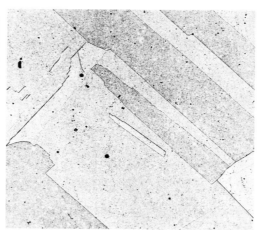

**Fig. 14** Monel K-500, held 1 h at 1205 °C (2200 °F), transferred to a furnace at 705 °C (1300 °F) and aged 4 h, water quenched. Precipitated $Ni_3(Al,Ti)$ appears as tiny particles dispersed in the matrix solid solution. See also Fig. 10 to 13 and 15. NaCN, $(NH_4)_2S_2O_8$. 100×

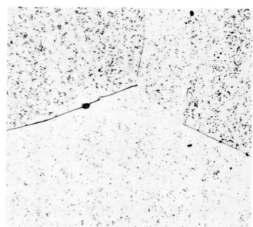

**Fig. 15** Same as Fig. 14 except at a higher magnification. The $Ni_3(Al,Ti)$ precipitate is better resolved. When this precipitate is resolvable by optical microscopy, overaging is indicated. See also Fig. 10 to 14. NaCN, $(NH_4)_2S_2O_8$. 1000×

# Refractory Metals and Alloys

By John B. Lambert
Vice President and
Corporate Technical Director
Fansteel

and

Mortimer Schussler
Senior Scientist
Fansteel

REFRACTORY METALS and their alloys are prepared similarly for metallographic examination. Slight increases in grinding, polishing, and etching times may be required for alloys, because they are generally harder than the unalloyed metals. Particular product forms, such as wire, may also necessitate special preparation techniques.

The procedures described in the section "Specimen Preparation" can be applied to metallographic preparation of niobium (columbium), tantalum, molybdenum, tungsten, and their alloys. Alternate procedures that have been used for each of these materials are also summarized. Specific etchants for these metals and their alloys are listed in Table 1.

Information on the properties and selection of refractory metals and their alloys can be found in Volume 3 of the 9th Edition of *Metals Handbook*. Production of refractory metal powders and the processing and applications of refractory powder metallurgy parts are discussed in Volume 7 of the 9th Edition of *Metals Handbook*.

## Specimen Preparation

**Sectioning.** The following abrasive wheels have been found to be efficient regarding cutting quality, cutting speed, and wheel wear:

- *Niobium and tantalum (all sizes)*: A 180 PR (rubber-bonded, 180-grit alumina, $Al_2O_3$)
- *Molybdenum (larger specimens)*: A 180 PR or A 60 MR (rubber-bonded, 60-grit $Al_2O_3$), which cuts faster at the expense of wheel wear
- *Molybdenum (thin specimens)*: A 180 PR
- *Tungsten (thicker than 3 mm, or $^{1}/_8$ in.)*: A 90 KR (rubber-bonded, 90-grit $Al_2O_3$) or C 120 KR (rubber-bonded, 120-grit silicon carbide)
- *Tungsten (thinner than 3 mm, or $^{1}/_8$ in.)*: A 180 PR (cut slowly)

- *Tungsten (general)*: A 70 TB (resinoid-bonded, 70-grit $Al_2O_3$)

Tungsten products, such as wire, can be cut using wet or dry abrasive wheels, preferably after a heavy nickel plate has been applied to the wire. Nickel plating aids edge retention and helps keep wire sections flat during polishing. Because tungsten products can delaminate, they should not be cut with shears or wire cutters.

**Initial Grinding.** Irregularly shaped specimens that are not cut can be ground flat on an 80-grit belt sander. It is generally preferable to remove excess stock in this manner before mounting.

**Mounting.** Green Bakelite, the preferred thermosetting resin, is mounted in a heated press under 690 kPa (100 psi) pressure at 150 to 180 °C (300 to 355 °F) for 2 min. The pressure is then released and the press opened. If the melted but uncured Bakelite does not rupture at the top and release moisture, the small bubbles that form should be pricked. Pressure is then reapplied at 24 to 34 MPa (3500 to 5000 psi) for 3 to 5 min at the same temperature curing cycle.

**Grinding.** Wet grinding is performed using 240- and then 400-grit silicon carbide paper on rotating brass laps, with running water as the lubricant. Grinding time depends on specimen hardness and size, but is usually twice the time required to remove scratches from the previous operation.

**Rough and intermediate polishing** is carried out in two steps using rotating brass laps covered with nylon and 30- and 9-$\mu$m diamond paste. The lubricant is kerosene. The mounts must be cleaned thoroughly with alcohol and soap between polishings.

**Final polishing** is performed using a rotating brass lap covered with a bonded synthetic rayon polishing cloth (Microcloth), 1-$\mu$m diamond paste, and kerosene. The medium nap of the synthetic rayon polishing cloth produces an excellent scratch-free finish; however, during grinding and rough polishing, refractory metals develop a disturbed surface layer that must be removed to observe the true structure. This is accomplished by a series of light etchings just enough to cloud the specimen, alternated with very light repolishings on the final lap that do not quite remove the etch (see Table 1 for etchant compositions and procedures). Four to eight etch/polish operations are usually sufficient. The true structure is revealed when two successive etchings reveal the same structure. The final etching should be much deeper than the previous etchings.

**Vibratory polishing** is an excellent alternative to the above procedures. Niobium and tantalum are polished as described above, including the 1-$\mu$m diamond lap. The mount is cleaned and placed in a 300-g holder for use in a vibratory lapping-polishing machine with a long-nap synthetic velvet (Rayvel) and an aqueous suspension of 0.3-$\mu$m $Al_2O_3$. In a freshly cleaned machine, disturbed metal can be removed in approximately 18 h. As metal sludge accumulates over a few weeks, the time required may double. After a final etch, the true structure is revealed.

For molybdenum and tungsten, the standard polishing procedure is used, through the 30-$\mu$m diamond lap. The mounts are then cleaned and placed in the vibratory lapping-polishing machine as for tantalum and niobium, except nylon cloth is used. Remaining scratches are removed, and the specimen is polished without disturbing the metal. Depending on the cleanliness of the polishing apparatus, 6 to 15 h are required. The true structure appears after one etch.

**Electropolishing.** Unmounted larger specimens of molybdenum and tungsten can be electropolished adequately for routine examination. The cutting wheels previously

**Table 1 Etchants for metallographic specimens of refractory metals(a)**

| Etchant | Composition | Comments |
|---|---|---|
| **Etchants for niobium and tantalum and their alloys** | | |
| ASTM 66 | 30 mL HF, 15 mL $HNO_3$, 30 mL HCl | Swab 3 to 10 s or immerse for 2 min |
| ASTM 158 | 10 mL HF, 10 mL $HNO_3$, 20 mL glycerol | Swab 5 to 15 s |
| ASTM 159 | 5 mL HF, 20 mL $HNO_3$, 50 mL acetic acid | Swab 10 to 30 s |
| ASTM 161 | 25 mL $HNO_3$, 5 mL HF, 50 mL $H_2O$ | Immerse 5 to 120 s |
| ASTM 163(b) | 30 mL $H_2SO_4$, 30 mL HF, 3-5 drops 30% $H_2O_2$, 30 mL $H_2O$ | Immerse 5 to 60 s; use this solution for alternate etch and polishing |
| ASTM 164 | 50 mL $HNO_3$, 30 g $NH_4HF_2$ (ammonium bifluoride), 20 mL $H_2O$ | Swab 3 to 10 s; use fume hood |
| **Additional etchants for niobium and niobium alloys** | | |
| ASTM 160 | 20 mL HF, 15 mL $H_2SO_4$, 5 mL $HNO_3$, 50 mL $H_2O$ | Immerse up to 5 min |
| ASTM 162B | 10 mL $HNO_3$, 10 mL HF, 30 mL lactic acid | Swab for 5 s; repeat if necessary |
| $HNO_3$ + HF + $H_2O$ | 25 mL $HNO_3$, 5 mL HF, 50 mL $H_2O$ | Immerse up to 2 min |
| Solution A | 50 mL lactic acid, 30 mL $HNO_3$, 2 mL HF | Swab specimen 1 to 3 min with solution A, acts as a chemical polishing agent and etchant; then |
| Solution B | 30 mL lactic acid, 10 mL $HNO_3$, 10 mL HF | swab 5 s with solution B; repeat if necessary; HF content in solution B controls etch speed |
| **Additional etchants for tantalum and tantalum alloys** | | |
| ASTM 177 | 10 g NaOH, 100 mL $H_2O$ | Swab or immerse 5 to 15 s |
| ASTM 178 | 20 mL HF, 20 mL $HNO_3$, 60 mL lactic acid | Swab for 5 to 20 s |
| Solution C | 10 mL HF, 10 mL $HNO_3$, 30 mL lactic acid | Swab specimen 2 or more min using solution C for desired surface; solution C is used as a chemical polish, though some etching will occur; if surface |
| Solution D | 10 mL HF, 90 mL $H_2SO_4$ | is not etched sufficiently, use solution D electrolytically at 0.08 to 0.16 $V/cm^2$ (0.5 to 1 V/in.$^2$) of specimen; solution D should be mixed very slowly; use carbon cathode and platinum connection to specimen; discard solution D after 1 h; use fume hood |
| ASTM 164 | 50 mL $HNO_3$, 30 g $NH_4HF_2$, 20 mL $H_2O$ | Swab 3 to 10 s; use fume hood |
| **Etchants for tungsten and molybdenum and their alloys** | | |
| Murakami's reagent (ASTM 98C) | 10 g $K_3Fe(CN)_6$ (potassium ferricyanide), 10 g KOH or NaOH, 100 mL $H_2O$ | Swab 5 to 60 s; immersion will produce a stain etch; follow with water rinse, alcohol rinse, dry |
| Murakami's reagent (modified) | 15 g $K_3Fe(CN)_6$, 2 g NaOH, 100 mL $H_2O$ | |
| Murakami's reagent (modified A) | 30 g $K_3Fe(CN)_6$, 10 g NaOH, 200 mL $H_2O$ | |
| ASTM 131 | 5 mL $H_2SO_4$, 1 mL HF, 100 mL 95% methanol | Electrolytic at 50 to 60 V for 10 to 20 s |
| ASTM 132 | 5 mL HF, 10 mL $HNO_3$, 30 mL lactic acid | Swab with heavy pressure for 5 to 10 s; water rinse, alcohol rinse, dry, then swab etch using ASTM 98C for 5 to 30 s |
| ASTM 209 | 15 mL $HNO_3$, 3 mL HF, 80 mL $H_2O$ | Immerse for 5 to 60 s |
| **Additional etchants for molybdenum and molybdenum alloys** | | |
| ASTM 129 | 10 mL HF, 30 mL $HNO_3$, 60 mL lactic acid | Swab 10 to 20 s; vary HF content to increase/decrease etching activity |
| ASTM 130 | 25 ml HCl, 10 mL $H_2SO_4$, 75 mL methanol | Electrolytic at 30 V for 30 s; *Caution:* keep below 24 °C (75 °F) |

(a) *Caution:* For all etchants that contain HF, immerse the specimen for the necessary time, rinse in water, and place in boiling 5% solution of ammonium pentaborate for 1 min. Cool the mount under cold running water, then wipe dry with a soft disposable tissue or rinse in hot water and blow dry. This procedure protects microscope optics from HF attack and minimizes stain. (b) Adjust amount of $H_2O_2$ to obtain a reaction rate that will reveal the microstructure after etching for approximately 20–40 s.

listed yield a surface smooth enough for this operation. An excellent polish, particularly with difficult-to-polish alloys such as molybdenum alloys, TZM, and TZC can be obtained using an electrolyte consisting of 12.5% sulfuric acid ($H_2SO_4$) in alcohol, with nickel as the cathode and 8 to 50 V dc. Voltage is easily monitored by inspection; an in-

tense blue layer forms on the surface of the specimen when the correct voltage is applied. Because alcohol has a relatively low boiling point, the electrolyte must be prepared carefully and must be cooled by a water bath during electrolytic polishing.

A 66% solution of chromic acid ($CrO_3$) in water is a more stable electrolyte and is used

at a high current density of approximately 2.3 $A/cm^2$ (15 A/in.$^2$). Therefore, the specimen must be removed frequently from the bath and cooled in running water. Nickel is again used as the cathode.

Electropolishing of higher quality can be obtained by first mounting the specimens, followed by grinding, and rough polishing through 30-$\mu$m diamond. The power requirements in this case are approximately 3 A at a lower voltage, and the etching time is 30 to 40 s for a typical specimen.

Aqueous electrolytes containing 1 to 10% sodium hydroxide (NaOH) or potassium hydroxide (KOH) can be used successfully for electropolishing of tungsten and tungsten alloys. Best results are obtained if half the volume of water in the solution is replaced by glycerol and the NaOH content is approximately 5%. With a 4% NaOH aqueous solution, a satisfactory polish should be obtained in 20 s using a current density of 2.3 $A/cm^2$ (15 A/in.$^2$).

Excellent polishes can be obtained over a wide range of current densities. However, if the current density is too high, pitting will occur; if too low, the specimen will etch. Heat is generated at high current densities and, if excessive, may cause uneven polishing, etching, or both. Overheating can be minimized by frequently cooling the specimen in a stream of cold water. Electropolishing also can remove inclusions. Large sections often do not polish evenly.

**Electrolytic Etching.** Molybdenum and tungsten can be electroetched with the same equipment and electrolytes used for electropolishing. Power required is approximately 0.4 A for 8 s for molybdenum and 0.4 A for 5 s for tungsten. Large specimens will etch more evenly in a chemical etchant. The specimens should be cleaned prior to examination.

**Etchants.** Etchant ASTM 163 in Table 1 is preferred for niobium and tantalum; Murakami's reagent (modified A), for molybdenum and tungsten.

## Alternate Preparation Procedures for Niobium and Tantalum

**Polishing.** A typical method of rough polishing niobium and tantalum uses a wax wheel and 15-$\mu$m levigated $Al_2O_3$. Intermediate polishing is performed using a synthetic rayon cloth-covered wheel and 1-$\mu$m $Al_2O_3$; final polishing, a synthetic rayon cloth-covered wheel and 0.3-$\mu$m $Al_2O_3$.

**Polish-etching,** also known as chemical-mechanical polishing or attack polishing, is suited to niobium, tantalum, and their alloys, but the procedure is different from that for polish-etching of tungsten and molybdenum. After grinding, the specimen is rough polished on a conventional corrosion-resistant horizontal polishing wheel covered with a chemotextile material (Pellon cloth) using 0.3-$\mu$m $Al_2O_3$. The specimen is then polish-etched on synthetic velvet cloth using a slurry of 0.05-$\mu$m $Al_2O_3$ and a solution of hydrofluoric acid (HF) (2 mL for niobium, 5 mL for tantalum), 5 mL nitric acid ($HNO_3$), and 30 mL lactic acid. Because this mixture is hazardous and extremely corrosive, and because polish-etching is time consuming, the specimen should be held in a mechanical holder rather than by hand. Initial polishing is performed for 1 to 4 h using a 160-rpm wheel and a 450-g (1-lb) weight on the holder. For final polish-etching, the weight on the holder is reduced to 225 g (0.5 lb) and held 15 min.

**Etchants** used for metallographic specimens of niobium, tantalum, and their alloys are listed in Table 1.

## Alternate Preparation Procedures for Molybdenum

Because molybdenum is relatively soft, scratches and distorted metal that develop in mechanical polishing are difficult to eliminate; therefore, electropolishing, as previously described, and electromechanical polishing are often used for molybdenum.

**Electromechanical polishing** combines electrolytic and mechanical polishing. It is excellent for retention of second phases and inclusions, for providing the most realistic representation of porosity, and for obtaining specimen flatness. Polishing time is only slightly longer than for electropolishing.

Operating conditions for electromechanical polishing of molybdenum and molybdenum alloys are not critical. The following conditions are typical. The polishing wheel must be covered with a material that will resist the electrolyte used; synthetic velvet is suggested. Polishing wheel speed should range from 255 to 1100 rpm. The abrasive/electrolyte is 0.05-$\mu$m $Al_2O_3$ dispersed in a small amount of a 30% $K_3Fe(CN)_6$ aqueous solution. The polarity of the 3 to 12 V dc power supply is slowly alternated—approximately 30 cpm—between the polishing wheel and the specimen. Polishing time is 2 to 5 min.

Electromechanical polishing is generally preferred for final polishing of large specimens and often is used as an intermediate or final polish for wire specimens. Final polishing may also be performed electrolytically. The etchants used in this technique and in polish-etching can corrode brass laps, as can the metals being polished.

**Polish-etching.** Although electropolishing and electromechanical polishing provide the most consistent results, polish-etching is also satisfactory for molybdenum specimens. Polish-etching substitutes chemical attack for the electrolytic action obtained in electromechanical polishing.

Polish-etching is recommended when the equipment required for electromechanical polishing is not available. The slurry used in polish-etching is prepared by adding 0.05-$\mu$m $Al_2O_3$ to a solution containing 3.5 g $K_3Fe(CN)_6$, 1 g NaOH, and 300 mL $H_2O$ or to a solution containing 1 g $CrO_3$ and 75 mL

$H_2O$. Results are improved by chemical polishing using a solution of 30 mL lactic acid, 10 mL $HNO_3$, and 5 mL HF, then polish-etching. The solution is used fresh (it should not be stored) and is applied by swabbing with heavy pressure.

**Etchants.** A modified Murakami's reagent, which provides good grain-boundary contrast and minimizes etch pitting, is recommended for etching molybdenum. A typical mixture contains 15 g $K_3Fe(CN)_6$, 2 g NaOH, and 100 mL of $H_2O$. Specimens are immersed 5 to 10 s. Other etchants for molybdenum and its alloys are given in Table 1.

## Alternate Preparation Procedures for Tungsten

**Mounting.** Most specimens of tungsten or tungsten alloys are mounted. In mounting wires, however, it is difficult to obtain sections that are parallel to the longitudinal axis, because wires are seldom perfectly straight. One method involves pressing the wires into a lead block, which then serves as the mounting block. For wires less than 0.15 mm (0.006 in.) in diameter, a harder solder block, such as tin-lead (Alloy Grade 50A, 50Sn-50Pb), should be used to avoid losing the wires in the mount as a result of the smearing action of unalloyed lead.

This mounting technique is also used for coils of lamp wire and electronic wire. Under pressure, the loops of a coil fold over, placing the longitudinal axis of the wire parallel to the polishing plane. Fragile specimens can be pressed with less damage and distortion into solder blocks that have been preheated to 175 °C (345 °F).

Another technique includes placing the wires in an aluminum mold 25 to 40 mm (1 to 1.5 in.) in diameter. Enough clear epoxy resin to make a thin disk is poured over the wires. The mold is then heated on a hotplate at 70 to 90 °C (160 to 190 °F) for 20 min. When the epoxy resin hardens, the disk containing the wires is removed from the mold and is cut transversely to the axis of the wires. The transverse section is then placed upright in the mold, and more epoxy resin is poured in—this time to a substantial depth. The mold is again heated as described above. When the epoxy resin has cured, the wires are held perpendicular to the plane of polish, and the section of the original epoxy-resin disk is completely fused into the new mount. Grinding, polishing, and etching can now be performed as required.

**Grinding.** Rough and finish grinding of tungsten and tungsten alloys is performed with conventional procedures using wet $Al_2O_3$ laps or papers from 60 through 600 grit. Light pressure is recommended throughout grinding, and fresh abrasive laps or papers should be used during final grinding. However, fine wire requires a less coarse initial grinding, because the depth of cold work resulting from grinding may exceed the diameter of the wire. Wires less than 25 $\mu$m in

diameter are polished using a cloth-covered lap and 0.05-$\mu$m $Al_2O_3$. Further mechanical polishing is not required if electropolishing or electromechanical polishing methods are to be used.

**Electromechanical Polishing.** Conditions for electromechanical polishing of tungsten are similar to those used for molybdenum. Voltage is increased to 5 to 15 V dc, and the speed of the polishing wheel is decreased to 160 to 550 rpm.

**Polish-etching.** Tungsten is polish-etched in the same manner as molybdenum.

**Etchants.** Murakami's reagent, conventional or modified, is most often used for etching tungsten and tungsten alloys, although other etchants are sometimes used. In addition to the etchants shown in Table 1, electrolytic etching in a 4% NaOH aqueous solution with 10 to 50 A/cm² (65 to 325 A/in.²) ac or 5 to 10 A/cm² (30 to 65 A/in.²) dc has been used to improve grain-boundary contrast.

## Microstructures of Refractory Metals and Alloys

Refractory metals illustrated in this article include niobium, tantalum, molybdenum, and tungsten. Several alloy modifications of these metals are also represented. Micrographs cover wrought structures of products developed from powder metallurgy compacts and from ingots made by melting and casting.

**Niobium** alloys were developed to provide greater oxidation resistance and elevated-temperature strength than are obtainable with the commercially pure metal. Niobium oxidizes less rapidly than the other refractory metals. Although no single element can be added to niobium to make an oxidation-resistant alloy, combinations will produce various oxidation behaviors. Many of the alloying additions that improve oxidation resistance also benefit high-temperature strength.

Combinations of molybdenum, tantalum, tungsten, and titanium serve as solid-solution strengtheners when added to niobium; the ternary and quaternary solid-solution alloys exhibit complex strength-temperature responses. Second-phase strengthening is achieved by controlled additions of zirconium, hafnium, or both. These additions develop metal-nonmetal systems in which strengthening results from the formation of zirconium oxide ($ZrO_2$) or of zirconium or hafnium carbide.

**Tantalum.** In industry, tantalum, which closely resembles niobium, is produced as a powder or sponge and is further purified in the solid or the liquid state. Solid-state purification occurs during sintering; liquid-state purification, during vacuum-arc melting or electron-beam melting in high vacuum. Consolidated high-purity tantalum has also been produced by the thermal decomposition of a halide, such as tantalum bromide ($TaBr_5$), on a hot wire. Unalloyed tantalum has limited usefulness in high-temperature applications, because it has relatively low hot strength and low resistance to oxidation even at moderate temperatures.

The elevated-temperature strength of tantalum is significantly increased by alloying. Additions of up to 10% tungsten or molybdenum are effective in solid solution. Additions of zirconium or hafnium to ternary alloys also contribute to solid-solution strengthening. Alloying, however, does not significantly increase oxidation resistance.

**Molybdenum.** Wrought products of molybdenum are developed from powders that are compacted and sintered. Sintered ingots can be fabricated directly. Purification of molybdenum is a major problem, however, and consolidation and purification are often achieved concurrently by vacuum-arc melting, electron-beam melting, zone refining, or levitation melting. Multiple melting to attain a desired level of purification is common.

The earliest alloys of molybdenum contained less than 2% alloying elements, providing higher recrystallization temperatures and higher mechanical properties at elevated temperature than could be obtained with unal-

loyed molybdenum. For several years, the development of molybdenum alloys with higher alloy content was limited by the inability of existing facilities to work the alloys. On an experimental basis, however, binary alloys of molybdenum and niobium, tantalum, titanium, tungsten, vanadium, hafnium, and zirconium were prepared as arc-cast ingots and studied primarily in the cast condition.

Binary alloys of molybdenum and tungsten have higher melting points than unalloyed molybdenum. As tungsten content increases, the melting point, hardness, and density of binary alloys increase almost linearly between those of pure molybdenum and pure tungsten; however, the workability and machinability of binary alloys decrease gradually.

**Tungsten.** Wrought products of tungsten, such as wire and sheet, are developed initially from high-purity powder that is pressed to form a compact, then sintered. The sintered compact may be fabricated directly, which is the more common practice, or it may be used as an electrode in a melting process, such as consumable-electrode vacuum-arc melting. Micrographs of sintered and wrought products are presented in this article.

Although prepared from commercially pure powders, most wrought tungsten products, especially those used in lamp and electronic-tube applications, contain one or more useful additives. "Non-sag," doped tungsten is prepared with a small amount of alkaline aluminosilicate; most of the silicate evaporates in sintering, leaving a residue of approximately 100 ppm.

Doping increases the recrystallization temperatures of tungsten by approximately 415 °C (750 °F), changes the recrystallized grains from equiaxed to elongated, and improves resistance to creep and high-temperature deformation, properties that are essential for tungsten wire used in incandescent lamps. Thoriated tungsten, an alloy normally containing a dispersion of from 0.5 to 2.0% thorium dioxide, has greater resistance to impact and vibration in lamp filaments and improved thermionic emission in tungsten cathode electronic tubes than unalloyed tungsten. Perhaps the best known solid-solution alloys are those containing rhenium. The tungsten-rhenium alloys presented in this section exhibit higher electrical resistivity than unalloyed tungsten and are widely used in filaments for photographic flashbulbs.

**Fig. 1** High-purity niobium (<10 ppm C, 30 ppm O, 20 ppm N), 1.6-mm (0.062-in.) thick sheet. Electron-beam melted, cold forged, cold rolled, 50 to 90% reductions between anneals. Final anneal in vacuum at 900 °C (1650 °F) for 1 h. Longitudinal section showing fully recrystallized structure. Etchant: ASTM 163. 250×

**Fig. 2** FS-80 niobium alloy tube 3.2-mm (1/8-in.) OD, 0.25-mm (0.010-in.) wall (after 70% reduction), vacuum annealed 1 h at 1150 °C (2100 °F). Longitudinal section. Solid-solution matrix consists of large recrystallized grains (ASTM No. 5-1/2). Intragranular precipitate is probably $ZrO_2$. 30 mL each 50% HF, $H_2SO_4$, and $H_2O$ with 3 to 5 drops 30% $H_2O_2$. 250×

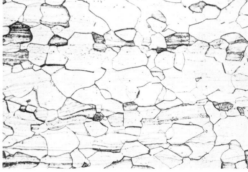

**Fig. 3** FS-85 niobium alloy (Nb-28Ta-11W-0.8Zr), 2.8-mm (0.110-in.) thick sheet. Arc melted, hot extruded, warm rolled at 705 °C (1300 °F), 50 to 75% reductions between anneals. Final anneal in vacuum at 1315 °C (2400 °F) for 1 h. Longitudinal section of fully recrystallized structure showing typical banding. ASTM grain size 7. Etchant: ASTM 163. 250×

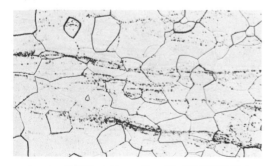

**Fig. 4** C-103 niobium alloy (Nb-10Hf-1Ti-0.5Zr), 6.4-mm (0.25-in.) thick plate, cold worked and annealed. The microstructure shows stringers, elongated in the rolling direction, of a dispersed phase consisting of $HfO_2$ and $ZrO_2$ compounds. Etchant: ASTM 163. 150×

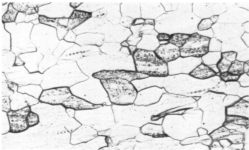

**Fig. 5** C-103 niobium alloy, 0.1-mm (0.040-in.) thick sheet. Arc melted, hot extruded, warm rolled, and annealed. Cold rolled to finished size. Final annealed in vacuum at 1290 °C (2350 °F) for 1 h. Longitudinal section showing fully recrystallized structure. ASTM grain size 7. Etchant: ASTM 163. 250×

**Fig. 6** Nb-30Ti-20W alloy sheet. Electron-beam melted ingot, arc remelted in vacuum. Forged, rolled, annealed, and gas nitrided. Scanning electron micrograph of titanium-rich nitride phase (dark) in a titanium-depleted niobium alloy matrix. Outer surface of specimen is shown at bottom of micrograph. 33% HCl and 17% HF in glycerol. 500×

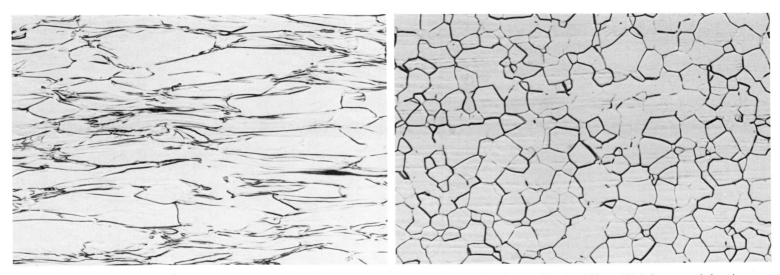

**Fig. 7, 8** Nb-46.5Ti, 13-mm (0.5-in.) diam rod. Vacuum-arc melted into 2700-kg (6000-lb) ingot, press forged, rotary forged to 150-mm (6-in.) diam, annealed, and water quenched. Extruded to 38-mm (1.5-in.) diam, annealed and quenched, surface conditioned, and drawn to size. Rough polished on silk with acidified (1 to 2% $CrO_3$) 1-μm $Al_2O_3$ slurry. Final polished on Microcloth using a slurry of 3 to 4 g $Al_2O_3$ in 150 mL $H_2O$. A 5- to 10-mL solution of 22 mL $HNO_3$ and 3 mL HF in 250 mL $H_2O$ is added to the slurry on the wheel. Fig. 7: longitudinal section of wrought as-drawn microstructure. Fig. 8: longitudinal section of equiaxed, recrystallized structure resulting from annealing after final draw. Both swab etched using 10 mL lactic acid, 10 mL $H_2O_2$, 3 mL $HNO_3$, and 3 mL HF. 400×

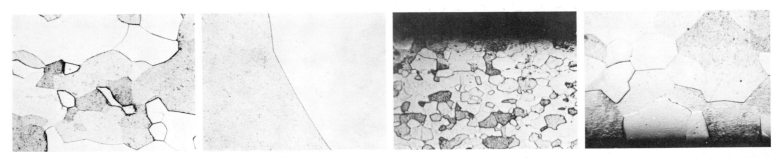

**Fig. 9, 10** Unalloyed tantalum sheet. Electron-beam melted, forged, cold reduced 60%, annealed in vacuum at 1095 °C (2000 °F) for 1 h. Fig. 9: final annealed in vacuum at 1010 °C (1850 °F) for 1 h. Longitudinal cross section showing fully recrystallized, equiaxed grains of mixed size. Average ASTM grain size 6. 250×. Fig. 10: final annealed in vacuum at 2000 °C (3630 °F) for 1 h. Longitudinal cross section of fully recrystallized structure showing effect of final annealing temperature on grain growth. ASTM grain size 00. 110×. Etchant: ASTM 163.

**Fig. 11, 12** Unalloyed tantalum powder metallurgy sheet. Bar cold rolled 85%, annealed, and finish rolled to 0.25-mm (0.010-in.) thick sheet. Longitudinal sections showing fully recrystallized structure. Fig. 11: final annealed in vacuum at 1260 °C (2300 °F) for 1 h. ASTM grain size 9. Fig. 12: same as Fig. 11, with added 30-min final anneal at 2000 °C (3630 °F). ASTM grain size 2 to 6. Compare with Fig. 9 and 10. Etchant: ASTM 163. 250×

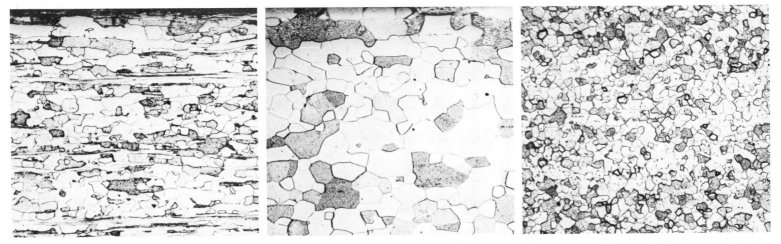

**Fig. 13, 14** Ta-250 ppm Y (added as $Y_2O_3$) powder metallurgy sheet. Bar cold rolled 85%, annealed, and finish rolled to 0.25-mm (0.010-in.) thick sheet. Final annealed in vacuum at 1260 °C (2300 °F) for 1 h. Fig. 13: longitudinal cross section showing banding from residual cold work resulting from yttria stabilization. ASTM grain size 9. Fig. 14: same as Fig. 13, with added 30-min final anneal at 2000 °C (3630 °F). Longitudinal cross section. ASTM grain size 8. Etchant: ASTM 163. 250×

**Fig. 15** Ta-150 ppm Si (silicon doped) 0.6-mm (0.023-in.) diam powder metallurgy capacitor wire. Sintered bar cold rolled up to 90% reduction between anneals, cold drawn approximately 75%. Final annealed in vacuum at 1315 °C (2400 °F) for 1 h. Longitudinal section, fully recrystallized structure. ASTM grain size 10. Etchant: ASTM 163. 250×

**Fig. 16** Ta-100 ppm V (vanadium doped) 25-$\mu$m (0.001-in.) thick powder metallurgy capacitor foil. Bar rolled to 60% reduction, annealed in vacuum 1 h, rolled to 0.45-mm (0.018-in.) thickness, final annealed, and finish rolled to final gage. Scanning electron micrograph of a longitudinal cross section showing as-rolled elongated grains. Etchant: ASTM 163. 3000×

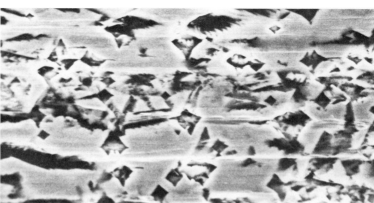

**Fig. 17** Ta-100 ppm V (vanadium doped) 25-$\mu$m (0.001-in.) thick powder metallurgy capacitor foil. Bar rolled to 60% reduction, annealed in vacuum 1 h, rolled to 0.45-mm (0.018-in.) thickness, final annealed, and finish rolled to final gage. Scanning electron micrograph showing the cold-worked through-surface structure after etching. Etched in electrolyte consisting of 30 g ammonium bromide, 5 g calcium chloride, and 18 mL deionized $H_2O$ in 1000 mL methyl alcohol. Current density: 18 mA/$cm^2$ (118 mA/$in.^2$) for 20 min. 2000×

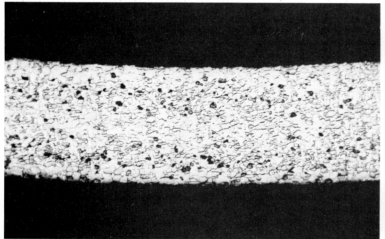

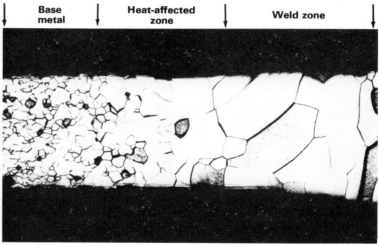

Base metal | Heat-affected zone | Weld zone

**Fig. 18, 19** Tantaloy "63" (Ta-2.5W-0.15Nb) tube, 0.6-mm (0.024-in.) thick wall, 19-mm (0.75-in.) OD. Electron-beam melted, warm forged, and cold rolled 50 to 90% between anneals from ingot to final product. Sheet annealed in vacuum at 1260 °C (2300 °F) for 1 h, press-brake formed, gas tungsten arc welded, and given final sizing pass. Fig. 18: transverse section showing fully recrystallized microstructure of base metal with some cold work resulting from the sizing operation. Fig. 19: transverse section through weld showing fine-grained base metal, coarsened grain size in heat-affected zone, and coarse-grained nondendritic weld zone. Etchant: ASTM 163. 50×

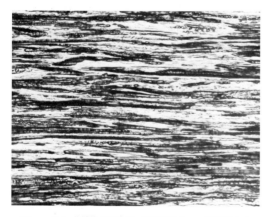

**Fig. 20** "61" metal (Ta-7.5W) 0.8-mm (0.032-in.) diam powder metallurgy spring wire. Sintered bar, square warm rolled at 315 °C (600 °F), 50 to 75% reduction, and cold drawn up to 50% between anneals. Longitudinal section showing elongated grain structure. Etchant: ASTM 163. 250×

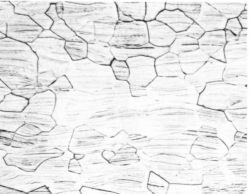

**Fig. 21** Ta-10W alloy 1.0-mm (0.040-in.) thick sheet. Electron-beam melted, warm forged, cold rolled, and annealed. Final annealed in vacuum at 1480 °C (2700 °F). Longitudinal section showing fully recrystallized structure and banding. ASTM grain size 6. Etchant: ASTM 163. 250×

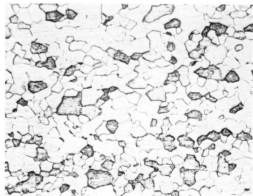

**Fig. 22** Ta-40Nb alloy 3.2-mm (0.125-in.) thick sheet. Ingot warm forged and cold rolled, with 50 to 90% reduction between anneals. Final annealed in vacuum at 1205 °C (2200 °F). Micrograph shows fully recrystallized, equiaxed grains. ASTM grain size 9. Etchant: ASTM 163. 250×

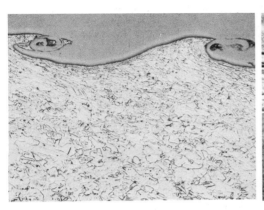

**Fig. 23** Unalloyed tantalum, phosphorus-deoxidized copper, and steel plate (not shown) that were explosively bonded, then rolled. Note irregular bond pattern. 10% ammonium persulfate. 100×

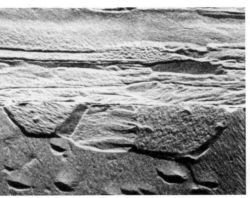

**Fig. 24** Unalloyed tantalum/Nickel 201 explosively bonded bimetal; both materials 3.2 mm (0.125 in.) thick. Cold rolled to size and annealed. Scanning electron micrograph shows fully cold-worked tantalum (top) and fully recrystallized nickel (bottom). Etchant: ASTM 163, then ASTM 24. 300×

**Fig. 25** Unalloyed 0.4-mm (0.015-in.) thick tantalum clad by explosive bonding on both sides with 5052 aluminum alloy. Roller leveled after bonding. Scanning electron micrograph of a longitudinal section showing aluminum surrounding slightly worked tantalum. Etchant: ASTM 163. 125×

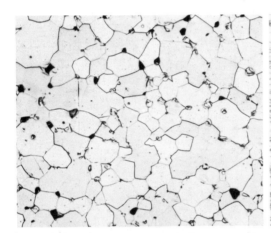

**Fig. 26** Commercially pure molybdenum, pressed from powder and sintered. The structure consists of an aggregate of molybdenum grains; the black spots are voids. Compare with Fig. 27. Murakami's reagent. 200×

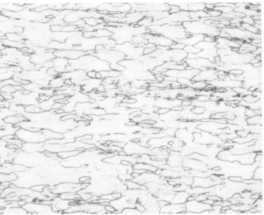

**Fig. 27** Same as Fig. 26, except extruded after sintering. Extruding has elongated the grains of molybdenum and closed most of the voids. Remaining voids (black dots) are smaller. Murakami's reagent. 200×

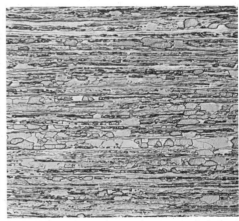

**Fig. 28** Commercially pure molybdenum, rolled to 1.0-mm (0.040-in.) thick sheet, annealed at 900 °C (1650 °F) for 1 h. Longitudinal section. Partly recrystallized. See also Fig. 29. Murakami's reagent (mod). 200×

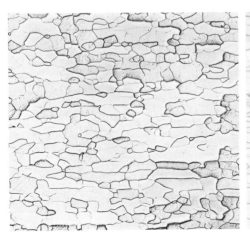

**Fig. 29** Same sheet as Fig. 28, annealed 15 min at 1350 °C (2460 °F). Completely recrystallized. No voids are visible. Murakami's reagent (mod). 200×

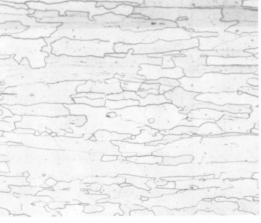

**Fig. 30** Mo-0.5Ti alloy, cold rolled and annealed by heating to 1315 °C (2400 °F). The structure consists of elongated grains. Murakami's reagent. 200×

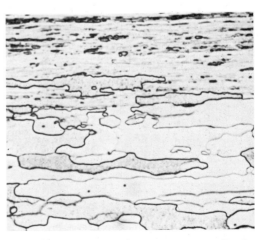

**Fig. 31** Mo-0.5Ti alloy, cold rolled; recrystallized by annealing. Surface layer (top) is unrecrystallized because of nitrogen contamination. Etchant: ASTM 129. 500×

**Fig. 32** TZM alloy, "warm" rolled at 1260 °C (2300 °F). Longitudinal section. Structure is mostly unrecrystallized solid solution. Murakami's reagent. 200×

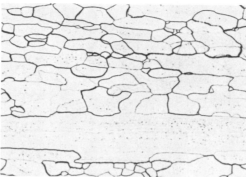

**Fig. 33** TZM alloy, hot rolled at 1595 °C (2900 °F), which resulted in a completely recrystallized structure of elongated grains. Murakami's reagent. 200×

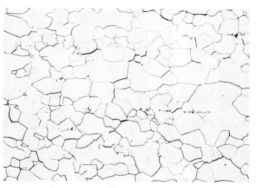

**Fig. 34** 70Mo-30W alloy, cold worked and annealed by heating to 1425 °C (2600 °F). Recrystallized, equiaxed grains of solid solution. Murakami's reagent. 200×

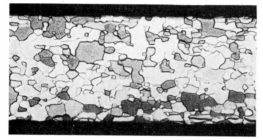

**Fig. 35** Tungsten wire (not doped), 0.2-mm (0.007-in.) diam, annealed at 2700 °C (4890 °F) for 5 min. Fully recrystallized, equiaxed grains. Murakami's reagent (mod). 200×

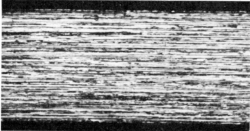

**Fig. 36** Tungsten wire (non-sag, doped lamp grade) 0.2-mm (0.007-in.) diam. As-drawn structure showing elongated grains. Murakami's reagent (mod). 200×

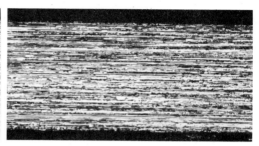

**Fig. 37** Same grade and size of tungsten wire as for Fig. 36, annealed 10 min at 1900 °C (3450 °F), showing start of recrystallization. Murakami's reagent (mod). 200×

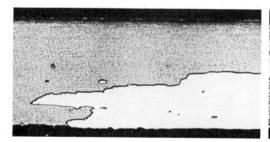

**Fig. 38** Same grade and size of tungsten wire as for Fig. 36, annealed 5 min at 2700 °C (4890 °F). The microstructure is recrystallized; grains are "finger-locked." Murakami's reagent (mod). 200×

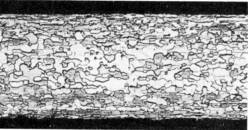

**Fig. 39** W-3Re wire (non-sag, doped lamp grade) 0.2-mm (0.007-in.) diam. Annealed 5 min at 2700 °C (4890 °F). Recrystallized structure. Murakami's reagent (mod). 200×

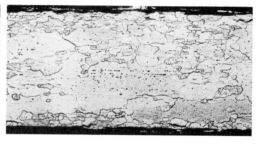

**Fig. 40** Thoriated tungsten wire (1% ThO$_2$), annealed 5 min at 2700 °C (4890 °F). A recrystallized structure of mixed grain size. The tiny black spots are ThO$_2$ inclusions. Murakami's reagent (mod). 200×

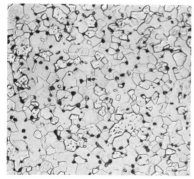

**Fig. 41** Commercially pure tungsten (not doped), pressed from powder and sintered; 95% theoretical density. The black areas among tungsten grains are voids. Murakami's reagent (mod). 400×

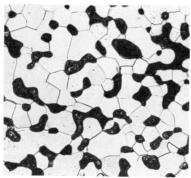

**Fig. 42** Commercially pure tungsten, sintered, then infiltrated with 20% (by volume) Cu (dark grains) to improve electrical and thermal conductivity. Murakami's reagent (mod). 400×

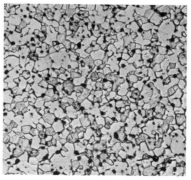

**Fig. 43** 98W-2ThO$_2$ alloy, pressed and sintered; 99% theoretical density. Light areas are tungsten grains; black dots are ThO$_2$. Murakami's reagent (mod). 400×

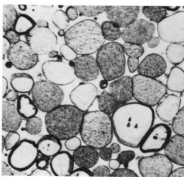

**Fig. 44** 90W-6Ni-4Cu alloy, as sintered. Structure: spheroids of tungsten embedded in a matrix of copper-nickel solid solution. Murakami's reagent (mod). 200×

# Rhenium and Rhenium-Bearing Alloys

By Jon A. Kish
Plant Manager
Rhenium Alloys, Inc.

RHENIUM is used in its pure metallic form and as an alloying element in molybdenum-rhenium and tungsten-rhenium alloys. Information on the uses of rhenium and rhenium-bearing alloys as well as the effects of alloying additions of rhenium on the ductility and tensile strength of refractory metals is available in Volume 7 of the 9th Edition of *Metals Handbook*.

Tungsten-rhenium alloys exhibit characteristics during processing that are similar to those of pure tungsten. The metallographic techniques used for pure tungsten are therefore suitable for tungsten-rhenium alloy metallography (see the article "Refractory Metals and Alloys" in this Volume).

Molybdenum-rhenium alloys display a relatively soft, ductile, equiaxed structure after recrystallization and must be treated somewhat differently than pure molybdenum. Pure molybdenum exhibits a fibrous structure because of the extensive cold working in most commercially produced mill products.

Wrought products of rhenium and rhenium-bearing alloys are produced by powder metallurgy techniques. Rhenium powder is obtained by reducing ammonium perrhenate ($NH_4ReO_4$) in hydrogen. These powders are then pressed and sintered at temperatures of approximately 90% of their melting point. Sintered ingots can be fabricated directly. Although some work has been conducted on fabrication by chemical vapor deposition and vacuum arc melting, this article discusses materials fabricated by powder metallurgy. Emphasis is placed on molybdenum-rhenium alloys, which comprise most of the rhenium metals used commercially.

## Specimen Preparation

**Sectioning** of pure rhenium and tungsten-rhenium shapes is performed using abrasive cutoff wheels or by electrical discharge machining. Because of the high work-hardening rate of rhenium, conventional mechanical sectioning is virtually impossible. Sheet and plate can be sheared, but the cold-worked area should be removed during subsequent grinding and polishing. Molybdenum-rhenium alloys can be sectioned by mechanical methods, but allowance must be made for removal of the affected area by rough grinding.

**Mounting** procedures for rhenium and rhenium-bearing alloys are identical to those used for other refractory metals (see the article "Refractory Metals and Alloys" in this Volume).

**Grinding.** The standard procedure for rough grinding rhenium and rhenium-bearing alloys consists of wet grinding with a 120-grit silicon carbide paper. Water is the preferred coolant. Subsequent grinding with water is performed using 240-, 400-, and 600-grit silicon carbide paper.

**Polishing** of rhenium and rhenium-bearing alloys is best accomplished on a nylon cloth with 15-, 6-$\mu$m diamond paste, then on a flocked twill lapping cloth with 1-$\mu$m diamond paste. Final polishing is performed using 0.01-$\mu$m alumina ($Al_2O_3$) with water. Because rhenium and molybdenum are relatively soft, an etch of modified Murakami's reagent (15 g potassium ferricyanide ($K_3Fe(CN)_6$), 2 g sodium hydroxide (NaOH), and 100 mL $H_2O$) is used to remove any distorted or flowed material (comet tails) prior to the final polish.

Another method for removing material damaged during preparation is to introduce modified Murakami's reagent (4%) to the cloth wheel during final polishing to remove flowed metal. This polish-etch process limits scratching of the sample.

Rhenium and rhenium-bearing alloys may also be polished electrolytically, or by an electromechanical process (a combination of electrolytic and mechanical polishing). (For more information on these preparation techniques, see the articles "Electrolytic Polishing" and "Mechanical Grinding, Abrasion and Polishing" in this Volume.)

## Macroexamination

Macroexamination of rhenium and rhenium-bearing alloys is useful to determine the size, shape, and volume of porosity. Because rhenium and molybdenum-rhenium alloys are normally used in the recrystallized condition, mechanical working flow lines are nonexistent. Macroexamination is also useful in observing fractured surfaces, seams, folds, and inclusions. As-polished or polish-etched specimens are best for macroexamination.

## Microexamination

Modified Murakami's reagent is the preferred etchant for microexamination of most rhenium and rhenium-bearing alloys. Grain boundaries and details of the structure usually appear within 15 to 60 s at room temperature. Longer times tend to produce etch pitting and do not provide a representative view of the microstructure. When porosity is present, care must be taken not to overly enlarge the size of the pores through etching. Evidence of mechanical twinning, if present, will be observed during the same time span. Additional polishing and etching are necessary at times to confirm the true metallurgical condition of the specimen.

With optimum processing techniques, up to 48 wt% Re is soluble in molybdenum, and up to 26 wt% Re is soluble in tungsten. Optimum processing conditions require the use of high-purity powder blends, proper sintering times and temperatures, and careful annealing practices. Molybdenum-rhenium alloys are annealed in hydrogen above the recrystallization temperature (approximately 1600 °C, or 2910 °F); tungsten-rhenium alloys are stress-relief annealed below the recrystallization temperature. All rhenium-bearing alloys should be cooled rapidly upon completion of the annealing hold time. The temperature should be dropped by 1000 °C (1800 °F) as quickly as possible in a water-jacketed cooling zone. Complete cooling takes approximately 5 to 10 min, depending on the thickness of the material.

If process conditions are not optimum, evidence of a second phase (σ phase) will be observed in the microstructure of molybdenum-rhenium alloys (Fig. 1, 2, 5, and 6). Sigma phase is a rhenium-rich phase that is hard and brittle. During polishing, it usually appears intergranularly and slightly raised from the solid solution surrounding it. Evidence of σ phase in tungsten-rhenium alloys, when present, is similar to that exhibited in molybdenum-rhenium alloys. Higher rhenium contents of both alloys are difficult to fabricate; therefore, little work has been performed to observe the microstructure that may result.

**Fig. 1, 2** Mo-48Re foil (longitudinal section). Warm worked from ingot, then cold worked to a 0.025-mm (0.001-in.) thickness. Hydrogen annealed at 1600 °C (2910 °F) and held at temperature for 2 min. Fig. 1: lamellar-type σ phase. Fig. 2: globular-type σ phase. Modified Murakami's reagent. 500×

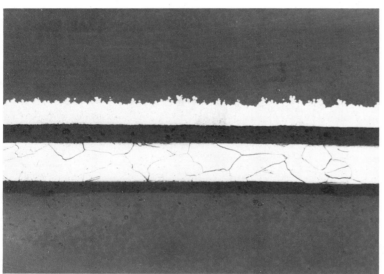
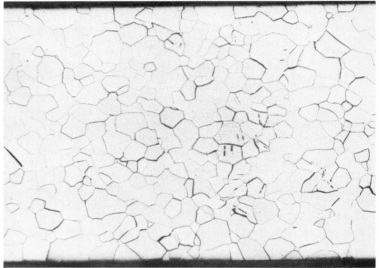

**Fig. 3** Mo-41Re foil (longitudinal section). Warm worked from 9.5-mm (3/8-in.) thick ingot, then cold worked to a 0.3-mm (0.012-in.) thickness. Hydrogen annealed at 1600 °C (2910 °F) and held at temperature for 5 min. Equiaxed structure with an average ASTM grain size of 8.0. Modified Murakami's reagent. 200×

**Fig. 4** Same as Fig. 3, but cold worked to a 0.05-mm (0.002-in.) thickness. Hydrogen annealed at 1600 °C (2910 °F) and held at temperature for 2 min. Slightly elongated structure with some grains traversing the entire thickness. The jagged border parallel to the foil sample is copper from a circuit board that was used during mounting to prevent crushing the foil. The dark layer separating the copper from the foil is epoxy. Modified Murakami's reagent. 200×

**Fig. 5** Mo-47Re rod. Warm worked from 38-mm (1.5-in.) diam ingot to 16-mm (5/8-in.) diam. Hydrogen annealed 30 min at 1600 °C (2910 °F). Microstructure exhibits some σ phase. Modified Murakami's reagent. 190×

**Fig. 6** Mo-41Re rod. Warm worked from 38-mm (1.5-in.) diam ingot to 23-mm (0.90-in.) diam. Hydrogen annealed 2 h at 1600 °C (2910 °F). Evidence of σ phase. Dark areas are porosity. Modified Murakami's reagent. 190×

**Fig. 7** Mo-41Re rod. Warm worked from 19-mm (3/4-in.) diam ingot to 9.5-mm (3/8-in.) diam. Hydrogen annealed 30 min at 1600 °C (2910 °F). 270 HV. Equiaxed structure with an average ASTM grain size of 7.0. Modified Murakami's reagent. 100×

**Fig. 8** Mo-41Re rod. Warm swaged from 38-mm (1.5-in.) diam ingot to 25-mm (1-in.) diam. Hydrogen annealed at 1600 °C (2910 °F) for 10 min. 275 HV. Equiaxed structure with an average ASTM grain size of 7.0. Modified Murakami's reagent. 100×

# Tin and Tin Alloys

By C.J. Thwaites
Research Manager
International Tin Research Institute

M.E. Warwick
Head of Metallurgy and
Tinplate Division
International Tin Research Institute

and

Brian Scott
Staff Metallurgist
International Tin Research Institute

TIN AND TIN ALLOYS are extremely soft and have low recrystallization temperatures; therefore, the preparation of tin and tin alloy specimens for metallographic examination presents special problems rarely encountered in preparing specimens of other metals. However, many of the preparation steps are similar or identical to those for other metals (see the section "Metallographic Techniques" in this Volume).

## Specimen Preparation

**Sectioning.** The use of an abrasive cutoff wheel is preferred for extracting specimens of tin and tin alloys from larger masses of material. Specimens may also be sawed. A coolant, such as water or alcohol, should be used to minimize the buildup of frictional heat.

**Mounting** of tin and tin alloy specimens should be carried out at room temperature, because elevated temperatures can induce structural changes. Thermosetting mounting compounds are therefore unsuitable. Specimens can be mounted satisfactorily at room temperature using castable mounting materials, such as the polyesters and acrylics. Care should be taken to select a material with minimum temperature rise during curing (see the article "Mounting of Specimens" in this Volume).

When examination of the edges of a specimen is required, a supporting layer is deposited on the surface by electroplating or electroless plating before mounting. The coating should be harder than the specimen; copper and nickel coatings are most often used.

**Grinding and Polishing.** Distortion of the surface layers of tin and tin alloys may cause recrystallization, which will mask the true structure. For tin alloys in a metastable state, distortion of the surface regions as a result of working may cause such structural changes as precipitation from a supersaturated solid solution.

To avoid working the surface, extreme care must be exercised during grinding and polishing because of the susceptibility to distortion during those operations. The method described below is, with slight modifications, suitable for grinding and polishing of tin and all types of tin alloys with minimum distortion.

The specimen is flattened with a file or by careful turning in a lathe, then wet ground on silicon carbide papers of successively finer grit. The papers are maintained wet by a continuous stream of lubricant, usually water, that washes away the particles of metal cut from the specimen surface. This prevents clogging of the abrasive papers, which would lead to surface flowing of the metal instead of cutting. During grinding, new sheets of abrasive papers and excessive pressure should be avoided, because loose particles of silicon carbide can easily embed in many soft tin-base alloys. For alloys with zinc-rich and aluminum-rich phases, which may be stained by water, kerosene is used as the lubricant.

A light, positive pressure is preferred during polishing. Each polishing should continue for at least twice as long as required to remove the scratches from the previous polishing stage. Polishing is usually carried out using different grades of diamond suspended in an oil- or water-base lubricant. The polishing wheels and the pads used for diamond pastes should always be free of dust, grit, and the diamond particles from the previous polishing step. Coarse grinding and fine polishing should be carried out at different locations; fine polishing requires an environment free of corrosive fumes.

Scratches from the final abrasive papers are removed by polishing for several minutes on a wheel covered with a short-nap or napless cloth impregnated with 3- to 6-$\mu$m diamond paste. Next, the specimen is polished on a wheel covered with a short-nap cloth impregnated with 0.25- to 1-$\mu$m diamond paste; the duration depends on the microstructure of the specimen. Specimens should be polished thoroughly to remove deformation from the previous stage, but excess polishing can easily result in grain or phase relief. If grain-boundary relief appears before a heavily worked layer from the previous polishing is completely removed, the diamond impregnation of the polishing cloth should be increased to maintain a rapid cutting rate. Polishing may continue using 0.25- and 0.1-$\mu$m diamond on wheels covered with short-nap cloth or may proceed to the final polishing. The commercially available lubricants may be used with all diamond polishings. After each polishing, the specimen should be thoroughly washed in a dilute solution of liquid detergent; rinsing in water and ethanol and drying in forced air is also suitable. An ultrasonic cleaner may be used, but care should be taken with specimens that may contain loose particles.

Further polishing, if necessary, is carried out by hand using a pad of long-nap cloth impregnated with $\gamma$-alumina ($Al_2O_3$) and a suitable lubricant (usually water). A plain long-nap cloth is recommended, because a dyed cloth may stain the freshly cut metal on polished surfaces. Vibratory polishing can also be employed.

**Etching.** Although the method of polishing is the same for all types of tin and tin alloys, different etchants are used for the various alloys (see Table 1 for etchant compositions).

*Pure tin* can be etched easily in an alcoholic ferric chloride ($FeCl_3$) solution or in a 2% solution of hydrochloric acid (HCl) in alcohol.

*Tin-lead alloys* have simple two-phase structures, with a eutectic occurring at 63% Sn. Primary tin phase and primary lead phase are present, respectively, in hypereutectic and hypoeutectic alloys. Alloys containing primary tin are best etched in a solution of (by volume) 1 part nitric acid ($HNO_3$), 1 part acetic acid, and 8 parts glycerol; a 5% solution of silver nitrate ($AgNO_3$) in water is most suitable for alloys containing the primary lead phase. Both etchants blacken the lead without attacking the tin.

*Tin-antimony alloys* are more difficult to etch than other tin-base alloys. Several of the etchants listed in Table 1 can be used, but 2% nital is considered optimum. Etching should be carried out as soon as possible after final polishing, because a thin, porous film forms on the surface if the specimen is left standing. This results in pitting when the specimen is immersed in the etchant. In tin-antimony-copper alloys, the tin-antimony solid solution is supersaturated at room temperature and is therefore metastable. If strain energy remains in the surface regions as a result of working during polishing, recrystallization and precipitation may occur, masking the true structure.

# Techniques for Tin and Tin Alloy Coatings

Whenever specimens of harder base metals coated with tin or tin alloys are prepared for microscopic examination, it is difficult to prevent a step from forming at the interface between the relatively soft coating and the base metal. With such coatings, it is imperative to deposit a supporting metal layer with a hardness similar to that of the base metal on top of the coating. When the base metal is copper or a copper alloy, the supporting layer should be copper; when the base metal is steel or cast iron, this layer usually is nickel. In examining the interface between a base metal and a thick coating, as in the study of bearings, using a supporting layer offers no advantage unless examination of the edge of the specimen is required.

**Mounting.** For reasons stated earlier in this article, specimens with tin or tin alloy coatings should be mounted at room temperature. In addition, thin sheet specimens may be crushed or deformed if mounted in a material that requires pressure and high temperature. Specimens usually are mounted so that a normal cross section of the coating is obtained. However, when an extremely thin coating, such as electroplated tin, is to be examined, an oblique section, called a taper section (Fig. 1), is often used. The use of taper sections increases the effective magnification in the direction normal to the interface and so offers information on small details that otherwise would not be visible. A true interface structure is obtained only along the edge adjacent to the acute angle (see Fig. 1).

The linear enlargement obtained by using taper sections, termed the distortion ratio, is equal to the cosecant of the angle between the section plane and the specimen axis. Therefore, for a distortion ratio of ten, which is often the nominal aim, the angle, $\theta$, is 5° 44' 21". For accuracy, the actual distortion ratio should be determined directly from precise measurements of the thickness of the specimen before mounting and the thickness of the taper section after mounting.

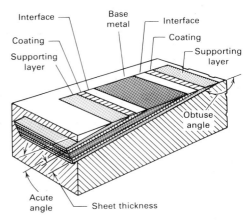

**Fig. 1** Components of a taper section of tinplate. See text for a more complete discussion.

Taper sections are obtained using the procedure illustrated in Fig. 2. First, the specimen, with the coated surface down, is mounted using an inclined-surface mounting plug, which has the face on which the specimen rests tapered to the desired angle $\theta$ (Fig. 2a). The tapered mount holding the specimen is extracted from the mounting die, and, if necessary, the back face of the mount is turned in a lathe to make it flat and normal to the axis of the mount.

The tapered mount is then inverted, placed on a straight mounting plug in the mounting die, and completely covered with an additional layer of mounting compound (Fig. 2b). After this layer has set and fused with the tapered mount and the mounted specimen has been removed from the die (Fig. 2c), the mount is carefully turned in a lathe until the edge of the specimen is exposed; that edge is then removed by grinding (Fig. 2d). The resulting exposed area is the taper section, which is subsequently polished, etched, and examined. The exposed taper section should be near the center of the mount.

**Grinding and Polishing.** In grinding and polishing tin and tin alloy coatings, the effect of differences in hardness between the coating and the base metal can be minimized and often (for thin coatings) almost eliminated by the following procedure. The specimen is carefully turned in a lathe; each cut should be shallower than the previous cut, finishing with five or six cuts 0.01 mm (0.0005 in.) deep. The specimen is then ground on successively finer grades of well-lubricated silicon carbide papers. Grinding is performed with the interface between the coating and the base metal oriented at an angle of 15° to 20° to the direction of grinding; this orientation is alternated from left to right with successive strokes, as shown in Fig. 3.

Diamond paste should be used for polishing to obtain satisfactory final results. Use of any other polishing medium, such as $Al_2O_3$, results in the formation of a considerable step, which complicates examining the interface. Even when diamond paste is used, precautions must be taken to minimize the step.

**Table 1   Etchants for tin and tin alloys**

| Etchant | Uses |
|---|---|
| 1. 2 mL HCl, 5 mL $HNO_3$, 93 mL methanol | General use for tin and tin alloys |
| 2. 2 mL HCl, 5 mL $HNO_3$, 93 mL $H_2O$ | Grain-contrast etchant for tin and pewter |
| 3. 5 mL HCl, 2 g $FeCl_3$, 30 mL $H_2O$, 60 mL 95% methanol or 95% ethanol | General use for tin and tin alloys |
| 4. 2 mL HCl and 98 mL 95% methanol or 95% ethanol | Grain-boundary etchant for pure tin |
| 5. 10 mL $HNO_3$, 10 mL acetic acid, 80 mL glycerol | Darkens the lead in the eutectic of tin-rich tin-lead alloys |
| 6. 5% $AgNO_3$ in $H_2O$ | Darkens primary and eutectic lead in lead-rich tin-lead alloys |
| 7. 2% nital (2 mL $HNO_3$ in 98 mL 95% ethanol or 95% methanol) | Recommended for etching tin-antimony alloys; darkens tin-rich matrix, leaving intermetallics unattacked. Often used for etching specimens of babbitted bearings |
| 8. Picral (4 g picric acid in 100 mL 95% methanol or 95% ethanol) | For etching tin-coated steel and tin-coated cast iron (see text) |
| 9. 1 drop concentrated $HNO_3$, 2 drops HF(a), 25 mL glycerol; then picral | For etching tin-coated steel (see text) |
| 10. $NH_4OH$ diluted with a few drops of 30% $H_2O_2$ | For etching tin-coated copper and copper alloys (polish attack) |
| 11. 3 parts acetic acid, 4 parts $HNO_3$, 16 parts $H_2O$ | General etchant for lead-tin alloys and for soldered joints |

(a) Safety requirements should be strictly observed when handling HF.

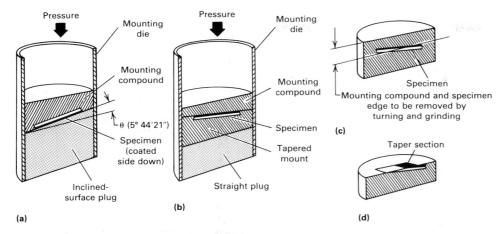

**Fig. 2** Steps in the preparation of a taper section. (a) First mount, using an inclined-surface plug. (b) Second mount, using a straight plug. (c) Mounted specimen before turning and grinding. (d) Mounted taper section after turning and grinding. See text for more information.

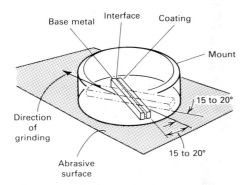

**Fig. 3** Orientations of the interface regarding the direction of grinding. Specimens with tin and tin alloy coatings are alternated 15° to 20° on either side of the direction of grinding to minimize differences in hardness between the coating and the base.

Fast cutting on the polishing wheel is necessary, and the specimen should be stationary, with the interface at an angle near 90° to the direction of motion during the final stages of polishing.

First, the specimen is polished for up to several minutes on a wheel covered with a napless cloth impregnated with 3- to 6-$\mu$m diamond paste; the specimen is rotated on the cloth to remove the unidirectional scratches resulting from the finest abrasive paper. Napless cloth allows fast and uniform cutting of the base metal and the coating, which limits the depth of any step that might subsequently form. The next polishing is performed using a short-nap cloth and 0.25- to 1-$\mu$m diamond paste; the specimen is rotated for 30 to 40 s, then polished for an additional 30 s using light pressure while holding the specimen stationary. If necessary, this procedure is repeated using 0.25- and 0.1-$\mu$m pastes. Finally, if required, the specimen may be lightly rubbed on a pad of plain long-nap cloth impregnated with $\gamma$-$Al_2O_3$ or placed on a vibratory polisher for a short time. This last operation must be of short duration, because the specimen will rapidly develop steps at the interface. This is generally true for all stages

of preparation—the longer the time spent at any stage, the more likely is the formation of a step—but is particularly true of final stages of polishing.

The harder tin alloy coatings, such as speculum metal (copper-tin) and tin-nickel, are generally deposited onto steel or copper-base alloys to provide corrosion resistance and to enhance appearance. Because of the hardness of these coatings, there is far less danger of a step forming at an interface. Such specimens may be satisfactorily polished using the methods described for bronzes (see the article "Copper and Copper Alloys" in this Volume). Sometimes in grinding tin-nickel coatings, particularly when the grinding papers are new, the extremely brittle tin-nickel compound will chip, and extensive cracks will form below the surface, which requires removing the coating to an appreciable depth to reach a truly representative region.

With thick tin alloy coatings, such as those on babbitted bearings, little can be gained by plating a supporting layer on top of the coating. The step formed during polishing is usually greater than that obtained with a thin coating. This can be minimized if grinding is carried out alternately in the directions shown in Fig. 3.

**Etching.** When tin and tin alloy coatings are examined, the interface between the coating and the base metal often is of primary interest, and the microstructure at this interface is usually revealed by etching. Hot-dip and electrodeposited tin coatings on steel are best etched in picral, which also outlines the interface between the steel and the tin-iron alloy layer without etching the tin. Another procedure to reveal this layer involves etching in a solution of 1 drop concentrated $HNO_3$, 2 drops hydrofluoric acid (HF), and 25 mL glycerol to outline the interface between the tin and the $FeSn_2$, then etching in picral to outline the interface between the $FeSn_2$ and the steel. Safety procedures for handling HF should be strictly observed.

Picral is also used to etch cast iron having a tin coating, because it does not attack the

tin. The microstructure of cast iron generally consists of graphite nodules and cementite ($Fe_3C$) in a pearlitic matrix. Because of the presence of $Fe_3C$, picral does not outline the $Fe$-$FeSn_2$ interface as it does with tin coatings on steel, but the $FeSn_2$ is still easily discerned.

Electrodeposited or hot-dip tin coatings on copper and copper alloys are readily etched by polish attack using a solution of 20 mL concentrated ammonium hydroxide ($NH_4OH$), 80 mL distilled $H_2O$, and a few drops of 30% hydrogen peroxide ($H_2O_2$). This solution etches the base metal and outlines the interface between the base metal and the alloy layer, but does not attack the tin. Polish-attack etching in a solution of 10 g ammonium persulfate [$(NH_4)_2S_2O_8$], 45 mL concentrated $NH_4OH$, and 135 mL distilled $H_2O$ yields similar results.

Specimens of steel-backed tin alloys, such as babbitted bearings, are best etched in 2% nital, which generally etches the steel and the tin alloy. With some specimens, however, the microstructure of the tin alloy is revealed before that of the steel. If this occurs, the specimen should be etched in picral, which reveals the structure of the steel without affecting the tin alloy. If etching does not immediately follow final polishing, the surface of the specimen passivates and pitting occurs upon etching.

Specimens of steel-backed aluminum-tin bearings are etched in 2% nital, which outlines the particles of tin in the aluminum-tin alloy. If the steel backing is not etched within the time required for etching the aluminum-tin alloy, it can be emphasized by subsequent etching as described above for steel-backed tin alloy specimens.

**Use of Electron Microscopy.** The following procedure is recommended for electron microscopy to determine the nature of the intermetallic compound formed by the reaction between tin or tin-lead coatings on various substrates. The overlying coating is removed using a solution of 10 parts sodium hydroxide (NaOH) plus 7 parts orthonitrophenol at 60 °C (140 °F). Thick or high-lead coatings require longer immersion times; gentle swabbing with cotton wool increases the dissolution rate of tin-lead coatings. After complete removal of the coating to expose the intermetallic surface (the surface usually appears a uniform matte gray), the specimen should be thoroughly washed in warm distilled water, then dried using acetone. The surface of the intermetallic should be examined in the optical microscope to ensure that all tin-base coating has been removed before replicating for transmission electron microscopy or gold coating for scanning electron microscopy.

Back-scattered electron imaging is also used in examination of surface microstructure and metallographically sectioned solder and solder joints. Specimen preparation is the same as for normal SEM examination. Examples of back-scattered scanning electron micrographs are shown in Fig. 43 to 45.

## Microstructures of Tin and Tin Alloys

The more important tin-rich alloys depicted in this article are based on the following systems: tin-copper, tin-lead, tin-lead-cadmium, tin-antimony, tin-antimony-copper, tin-antimony-copper-lead, tin-silver, tin-indium, tin-zinc, and tin-zinc-copper. Additional micrographs and information on tin alloys can be found in the article "Sleeve Bearing Materials" in this Volume.

**Tin-Copper.** Tin and copper form a eutectic containing 0.9% Cu that consists of fine lamellae of $Cu_6Sn_5$ in a matrix of virtually pure tin. Hypoeutectic alloys (Fig. 6) of the tin-copper system are composed of primary tin with interdendritic eutectic. In tin-copper alloys that have copper contents above the eutectic composition, large acicular crystals of primary $Cu_6Sn_5$ are present in the Sn-$Cu_6Sn_5$ eutectic matrix.

**Tin-Lead.** Alloys of this simple eutectic system (Fig. 7 to 12) are composed of primary dendrites of tin-rich or lead-rich solid solution surrounded by eutectic. The eutectic, which occurs at 61.9% Sn, consists of the lead-rich and tin-rich phases as lamellae or globules, depending on the solidification rate. In general, the higher the solidification rate, the greater the probability of formation of a globular eutectic. At the eutectic composition, chill casting normally results in a globular eutectic, and air cooling leads to the formation of the characteristic lamellar eutectic structure. Heat treatment at a temperature approaching that of the eutectic converts the lamellar structure to the globular form.

**Tin-Lead-Cadmium.** The composition of the most frequently used commercial tin-lead-cadmium alloy (Fig. 25) is close to that of the ternary eutectic, which contains approximately 52% Sn, 30% Pb, and 18% Cd. The eutectic consists of the three terminal solid solutions. In as-polished specimens, the tin-rich phase appears white, the lead-rich phase light gray, and the cadmium-rich phase nearly black.

In some regions, the structure of the eutectic is lamellar, consisting of bands of the dark cadmium-rich phase bordered on either side with bands of the light gray lead-rich phase, which are in turn bordered along their outer edges by the tin-rich phase. In other regions, the phases are more globular and form a fine cellular pattern.

**Tin-Antimony.** The solid solubility of antimony in tin is appreciable at elevated temperature, but decreases rapidly as temperature decreases. Chill-cast alloys with antimony contents to 8% normally consist of a cored solid solution of antimony in tin. Slow cooling allows some precipitation of SbSn, which is evident as white particles between the tin-rich dendrites (SbSn is an intermetallic phase, which has a fairly wide phase field, extending from 41 to 56% Sb).

Heat treatment or natural aging increases the amount of interdendritic SbSn; upon prolonged aging, an acicular precipitate of SbSn also appears within the dendrites. At antimony contents exceeding 8%, cuboids of primary SbSn are produced in a tin-rich matrix that is formed by a peritectic reaction between the melt and the primary SbSn. Finely divided particles of SbSn may again precipitate from the tin-rich matrix. At antimony contents of 30 to 40%, primary SbSn precipitates from the melt as irregularly shaped dendrites. Figures 13 to 15 show typical microstructures of tin-antimony alloys.

**Tin-Antimony-Copper.** Additions of up to 2% Cu to tin-antimony alloys containing up to 8% Sb (Fig. 16) result in the formation of needles of primary $Cu_6Sn_5$, with some finer interdendritic eutectic of $Cu_6Sn_5$ and a solid solution of antimony in tin. As copper content increases (Fig. 17 to 19), successively larger amounts of primary $Cu_6Sn_5$ crystals form. Copper contents in excess of 4 or 5% (Fig. 20 and 21) often produce long needles of $Cu_6Sn_5$ that appear in cross section as hollow hexagons, H-shapes, or chevrons arranged in hexagonal or triangular patterns or as multiple-limbed starlike configurations.

In alloys with antimony contents above 9% and copper contents of 2% or more, the SbSn cuboids that form are often nucleated by the primary $Cu_6Sn_5$ needles; the $Cu_6Sn_5$ needles then appear embedded within, or passing through, the SbSn cuboids.

After exposure to elevated temperature during service or heat treatment, the corners of the SbSn cuboids often become rounded, and irregular particles of SbSn are precipitated between the tin-rich dendrites and also on the sides of the primary $Cu_6Sn_5$ needles and SbSn cuboids.

**Tin-Antimony-Copper-Lead.** When lead is added to the tin-antimony-copper ternary system (Fig. 22 and 23), the solubility of antimony in the tin-rich solid solution is reduced, and more cuboids of SbSn, possibly containing some lead, are observed. In addition, coring of the tin-rich dendrites is reduced, and interdendritic lakes of a ternary eutectic (probably composed of SbSn and of tin-rich and lead-rich solid solutions) appear. The primary $Cu_6Sn_5$ needles are unaffected by the presence of lead.

**Tin-Silver.** A eutectic containing 3.5% Ag forms between nearly pure tin and $Ag_3Sn$. The eutectic consists of fine needles of $Ag_3Sn$ in the tin-rich matrix. In hypereutectic alloys (Fig. 24), the primary $Ag_3Sn$ appears as coarse needles in the eutectic matrix.

**Tin-Indium.** At 50.9% In, the tin-indium system forms a eutectic consisting of two intermetallic phases: a light, tin-rich solid solution and a dark, indium-rich solid solution. Cast 50Sn-50In alloy (Fig. 26) shows mainly a eutectic structure of fairly coarse, rounded particles of the tin-rich phase in a matrix of the indium-rich phase.

**Tin-Zinc.** Zinc and tin form a simple eutectic at 8.9% Zn that consists of a solid solution of zinc in tin and almost pure zinc. The eutectic consists of fine needles of zinc and a tin-rich solid solution. Alloys containing more than 8.9% Zn (Fig. 27) exhibit a network of acicular dendrites of primary zinc in a eutectic matrix.

**Tin-Zinc-Copper.** The addition of a small amount of copper to an Sn-30Zn alloy causes the zinc-rich components of the eutectic to coarsen and the zinc to appear in the form of large plates. The copper combines with tin to form $Cu_6Sn_5$ and with zinc to form a compound described as $Cu_5Zn_8$ or $CuZn_3$. The copper-tin and copper-zinc compounds occur in intimate contact, forming roughly hexagonal prisms. Prisms of $Cu_6Sn_5$ are often embedded in the copper-zinc compound, which accurately follows the original outline of the $Cu_6Sn_5$. Figures 28 and 29 show examples of microstructures of this ternary system.

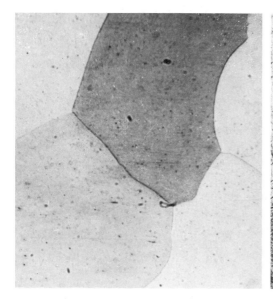

**Fig. 4** High-purity tin. The structure consists of large, equiaxed grains that show no deformation from polishing. Etchant 1, Table 1. 150×

**Fig. 5** Pure tin, showing twinned grains and recrystallized grains along original grain boundaries that result from working during polishing. Etchant 2, Table 1. 100×

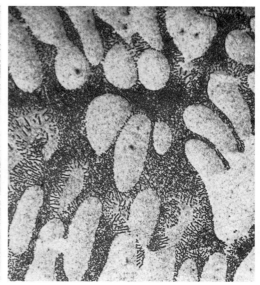

**Fig. 6** Sn-0.4Cu alloy. Structure consists of dendritic grains of tin-rich solid solution in a eutectic matrix of $Cu_6Sn_5$ (dark) in tin-rich solid solution. Etchant 1, Table 1. 150×

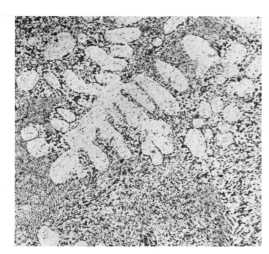

**Fig. 7** Sn-30Pb alloy (soft solder). Dendrites of tin-rich solid solution (light) in a matrix of tin-lead eutectic. Fig. 8 shows the structure of the eutectic. Etchant 2, Table 1. 150×

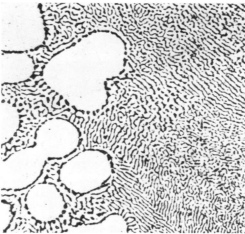

**Fig. 8** Same structure and etchant as Fig. 7, but at higher magnification to show structure of the tin-lead eutectic. Black outlines of the dendrites are formed by divorced eutectic. 375×

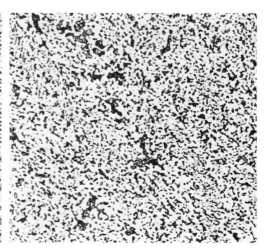

**Fig. 9** Sn-37Pb alloy (eutectic soft solder). Structure shows globules of lead-rich solid solution (dark), some of which exhibit a slightly dendritic structure, in a matrix of tin. Etchant 7, Table 1. 375×

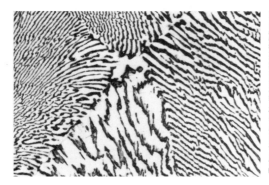

**Fig. 10** Same alloy and etchant as Fig. 9, except the mold was warmed to slow cooling. This resulted in the lamellar, rather than globular, structure of tin (light) and lead-rich solid solution (dark). 375×

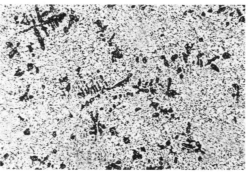

**Fig. 11** Sn-40Pb alloy (soft solder). Structure consists of small dendrites of lead-rich solid solution (dark) in a fine matrix of globular tin-lead eutectic. Etchant 7, Table 1. 150×

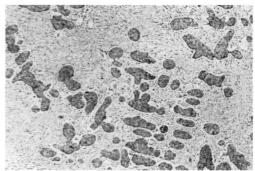

**Fig. 12** Sn-50Pb alloy. Dendrites of lead-rich solid solution (dark) in a matrix of fine lamellar eutectic consisting of lead-rich solid solution (dark) and tin (light). Etchant 7, Table 1. 150×

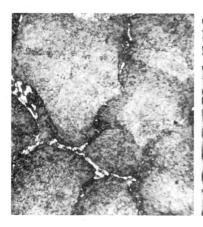

**Fig. 13** Sn-5Sb alloy. Structure consists of coarse, cored dendrites of tin-rich solid solution and precipitated interdendritic SbSn phase (light). Etchant 7, Table 1. 150×

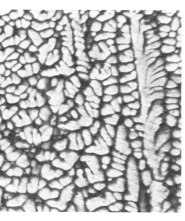

**Fig. 14** Same alloy and etchant as Fig. 13, except the casting mold was chilled for faster cooling. The structure consists of heavily cored dendrites with well-marked branches. 150×

**Fig. 15** Sn-30Sb alloy. Structure consists primarily of crystals of SbSn (light) in fine peritectic matrix of SbSn and tin-rich solid solution. Etchant 7, Table 1. 375×

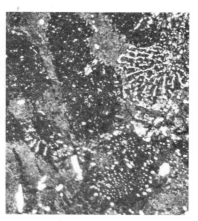

**Fig. 16** Sn-6Sb-2Cu alloy (pewter). Cored dendrites are tin-rich solid solution that contain needles of white $Cu_6Sn_5$. The matrix is coarse Sn-$Cu_6Sn_5$ eutectic. Etchant 7, Table 1. 375×

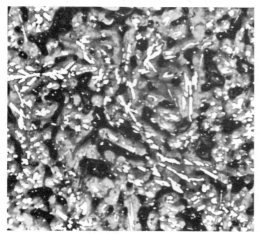

**Fig. 17** Sn-4.5Sb-4.5Cu alloy. Structure consists of fine, cored dendrites of tin-rich solid solution containing needles and small particles of $Cu_6Sn_5$ (white). Etchant 7, Table 1. 150×

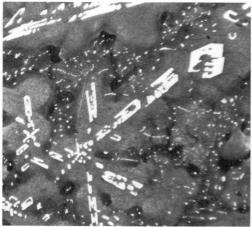

**Fig. 18** Sn-7Sb-3.5Cu alloy, with structure consisting of coarse, cored dendrites of tin-rich solid solution containing needles and small particles of $Cu_6Sn_5$ (white). Etchant 7, Table 1. 150×

**Fig. 19** Sn-9Sb-4Cu alloy. Structure consists of coarse, cored dendrites of tin-rich solution containing needles of $Cu_6Sn_5$ and cuboids of SbSn (both white). Etchant 7, Table 1. 150×

**Fig. 20** Sn-8Sb-8Cu alloy. Needles of $Cu_6Sn_5$ and cubic particles of SbSn (both white) in a matrix of tin-rich solid solution. Etchant 7, Table 1. 150×

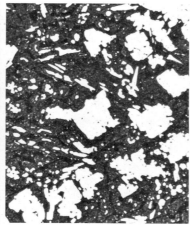

**Fig. 21** Sn-13Sb-5Cu alloy. Microstructure similar to that of Fig. 20. Etchant 7, Table 1. 150×

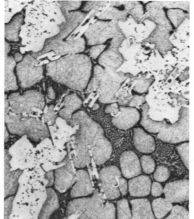

**Fig. 22** Sn-12Sb-10Pb-3Cu alloy. Structure consists of $Cu_6Sn_5$ needles and SbSn crystals (both light) in dendrites of tin-rich solid solution, along with some interdendritic eutectic. Etchant 7, Table 1. 150×

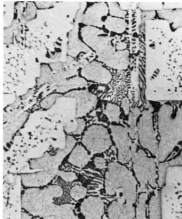

**Fig. 23** Sn-15Sb-18Pb-2Cu alloy. Structure is similar to that in Fig. 22, but contains more SbSn crystals and more, coarser interdendritic eutectic. Etchant 7, Table 1, 150×

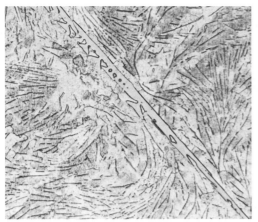

**Fig. 24** Sn-5Ag alloy. Structure consists of a large, acicular, primary crystal of Ag₃Sn in a eutectic matrix of acicular Ag₃Sn in tin. Etchant 1, Table 1. 150×

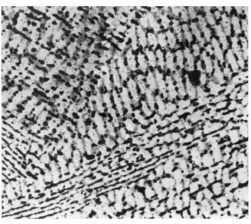

**Fig. 25** Sn-31Pb-18Cd alloy. Structure is a lamellar ternary eutectic of solid solutions of cadmium in tin (light), tin in lead (gray), and cadmium in lead (dark). Etchant 7, Table 1. 375×

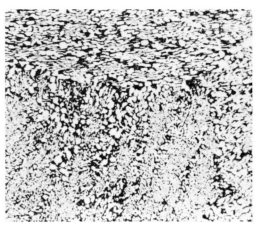

**Fig. 26** 50Sn-50In alloy. Structure is a eutectic of globular tin-rich intermetallic phase (light) in a matrix of dark indium-rich intermetallic. Etchant 1, Table 1. 150×

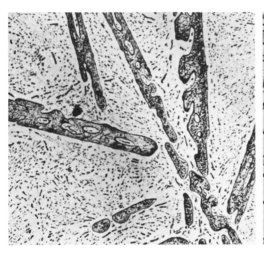

**Fig. 27** Sn-30Zn alloy. Structure consists of acicular dendritic crystals of zinc (dark, mottled) in a eutectic matrix of zinc particles (dark) in tin (light). 1% nital. 375×

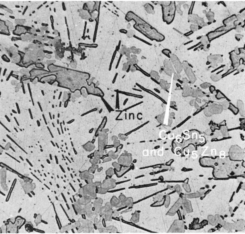

**Fig. 28** Sn-28Zn-2Cu alloy. Large and small zinc needles (dark) are intermingled with particles of Cu₆Sn₅ and Cu₅Zn₈ in a tin matrix. See Fig. 29 for an enlarged view of this structure. 1% nital. 150×

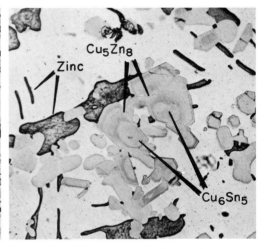

**Fig. 29** Same alloy as Fig. 28. Cu₅Zn₈ (yellow under bright-field illumination) often surrounds Cu₆Sn₅ (blue under bright-field illumination). The dark constituent is zinc. 1% nital. 375×

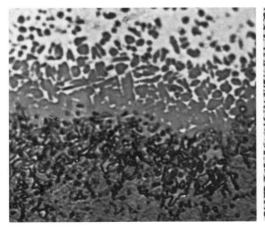

**Fig. 30** Steel-tin interface of hot-dip tinplate. A 6° taper section is shown. From bottom: steel substrate (dark gray), interface between steel and FeSn₂ (dark, mottled), gray crystals of FeSn₂ in tin, and bottom of tin coating (light). 2% picral. 22 500× vertical; 2250× horizontal

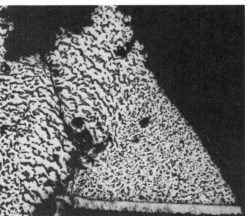

**Fig. 31** Sn-40Pb alloy, section of a wave-soldered printed circuit board joint that was thermally cycled. Structure shows a thermal fatigue crack propagating through the tin-lead fillet. The tin-lead structure has coarsened in the highly stressed region near the crack. Etchant 7, Table 1. 80×

**Fig. 32** Scanning electron micrograph of Sn-40Pb alloy wave-soldered printed circuit board joint that was thermally cycled. Micrograph shows a typical thermal fatigue crack in the joint. The crack is at a 45° angle to the circuit lead and totally encircles it. 50×

**Fig. 33** SEM of a Cu₆Sn₅ intermetallic formed beneath Sn-40Pb alloy coating. The coating was originally electrodeposited on a copper substrate and was reflowed in hot oil. Alkaline orthonitrophenol (10 parts NaOH and 7 parts orthonitrophenol) at 60 °C (140 °F) used to remove coating. 2000×

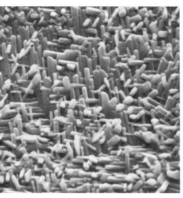

**Fig. 34** Intermetallic layer of electrolytic tinplate, with electrodeposited tin reflowed, then removed with same solution used in Fig. 33. FeSn₂ crystallites have formed at the coating/substrate interface. 5000×

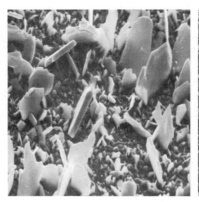

**Fig. 35** Scanning electron micrograph of tin-plated nickel specimen that was stored 11 years at room temperature. The tin coating has been removed using the same solution as Fig. 33, revealing the nickel-tin intermetallic compound formed by solid-state diffusion. 1000×

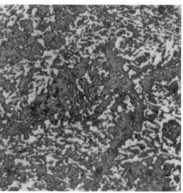

**Fig. 36** Sn-57Bi alloy, chill cast. Structure shows the coarse, globular eutectic of tin-bismuth. Bismuth-rich regions are dark; tin-rich areas are light. Etchant 7, Table 1. 350×

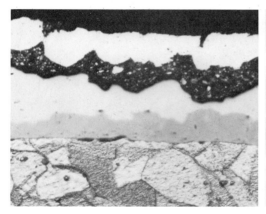

**Fig. 37** Sn-40Pb coating electrodeposited on a copper substrate and stored 200 days at 170 °C (340 °F). A layer of Cu₃Sn has formed near the copper, and on top of that a layer of Cu₆Sn₅ has formed. Attack polished using etchant 10, Table 1, then exposed to HCl vapor. 500×

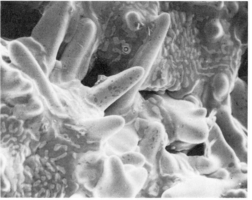

**Fig. 38** Scanning electron micrograph of Sn-48Pb-2Sb cast alloy. Surface structure of a contraction cavity in the casting. Lead-rich dendrite arms (light phase) protrude from the eutectic matrix. As-polished. 500×

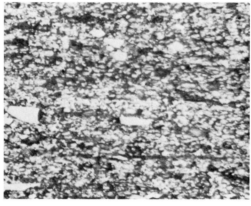

**Fig. 39** Sn-6Sb-2Cu pewter, cold rolled. This specimen was poorly prepared; the surface is scratch-free, but deformation in the surface from previous polishings has masked the true structure. Compare with Fig. 40. Etchant 2, Table 1. 500×

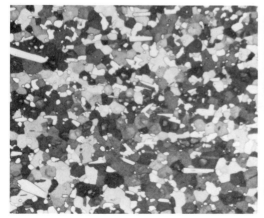

**Fig. 40** Same alloy and etchant as Fig. 39 correctly prepared so the true structure of the pewter is apparent. The tin-rich matrix is shown in contrast; SbSn and Cu₆Sn₅ intermetallic particles are unattacked. 500×

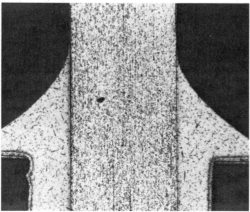

**Fig. 41** Sn-40Pb alloy, section of a wave-soldered joint on a printed circuit board. A section through the component lead shows a perfectly soldered joint. The solder fillet is concave and has a low contact angle on the component lead and on the copper pad of the circuit board. Etchant 10, Table 1. 40×

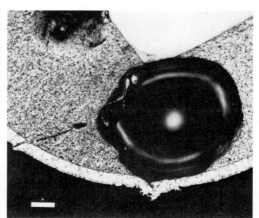

**Fig. 42** Sn-40Pb alloy section of a wave-soldered printed circuit board. Micrograph shows a large blowhole in the solder caused by outgassing through the defect visible in the copper plating. Etchant 10, Table 1. 150×

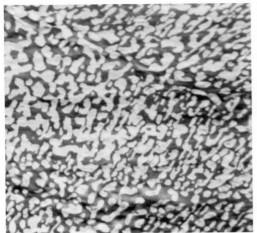

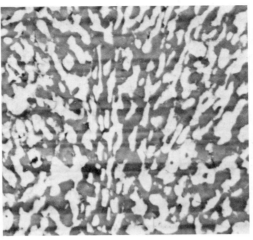

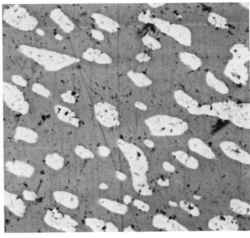

**Fig. 43** Back-scattered scanning electron micrograph of 63Sn-37Pb solder in a soldered joint. The surface structure in this near-eutectic composition consists of lead-rich phase (light) and tin-rich phase (dark). As-polished. 2000×

**Fig. 44** Back-scattered scanning electron micrograph of 63Sn-37Pb coating on a electrical terminal. The structure consists of a lead-rich phase (light) and a tin-rich phase (dark). As-polished. 2000×

**Fig. 45** Back-scattered scanning electron micrograph of 63Sn-37Pb solder in a joint that was thermally aged and cycled. Globular lead-rich phase (light) and tin-rich matrix. As-polished. 2000×

# Titanium and Titanium Alloys

By Rodney R. Boyer
Senior Research Engineer
Boeing Commercial Airplane Company

TITANIUM is an allotropic element; that is, it exists in more than one crystallographic form. At room temperature, titanium has a hexagonal close-packed (hcp) crystal structure, which is referred to as "alpha" phase. This structure transforms to a body-centered cubic (bcc) crystal structure, called "beta" phase, at 883 °C (1621 °F).

Alloying elements generally can be classified as $\alpha$ or $\beta$ stabilizers. Alpha stabilizers, such as aluminum and oxygen, increase the temperature at which the $\alpha$ phase is stable. Beta stabilizers, such as vanadium and molybdenum, result in stability of the $\beta$ phase at lower temperatures. This transformation temperature from $\alpha + \beta$ or $\alpha$ to all $\beta$ is known as the $\beta$ transus temperature. The $\beta$ transus is defined as the lowest equilibrium temperature at which the material is 100% $\beta$.

Below the $\beta$ transus temperature, titanium will be a mixture of $\alpha + \beta$ if the material contains some $\beta$ stabilizers, or it will be all $\alpha$ if it contains no $\beta$ stabilizers. The $\beta$ transus is important, because processing and heat treatment are often carried out with reference to some incremental temperature above or below the $\beta$ transus. Alloying elements that favor the $\alpha$ crystal structure and stabilize it by raising the $\beta$-transus temperature include aluminum, gallium, germanium, carbon, oxygen, and nitrogen.

Two groups of elements stabilize the $\beta$ crystal structure by lowering the transformation temperature. The $\beta$ isomorphous group consists of elements that are miscible in the $\beta$ phase, including molybdenum, vanadium, tantalum, and niobium. The other group forms eutectoid systems with titanium, having eutectoid temperatures as much as 333 °C (600 °F) below the transformation temperature of unalloyed titanium. The eutectoid group includes manganese, iron, chromium, cobalt, nickel, copper, and silicon. Two other elements that often are alloyed in titanium are tin and zirconium. These elements have extensive solid solubilities in $\alpha$ and $\beta$ phases. Although they do not strongly promote phase stability, they retard the rates of transformation and are useful as strengthening agents.

**Alloy Classes.** Titanium alloys have generally been classified as $\alpha$ alloys, $\alpha + \beta$ alloys, and $\beta$ alloys. Alpha alloys have essentially an all-$\alpha$ microstructure. Beta alloys are those alloys from which a small volume of material can be quenched into ice water from above its $\beta$ transus without martensitic decomposition of the $\beta$ phase. Alpha-beta alloys contain a mixture of $\alpha$ and $\beta$ phases at room temperature. Within the $\alpha + \beta$ class, an alloy that contains less than 2 to 3% $\beta$, such as Ti-8Al-1Mo-1V, may also be referred to as a "near-$\alpha$" or "super-$\alpha$" alloy.

The principal alloying element in $\alpha$ alloys is aluminum (oxygen is the principal alloying element in commercially pure titanium), but certain $\alpha$ alloys and most commercially pure (unalloyed) titanium contain small amounts of $\beta$-stabilizing elements. Similarly, $\beta$ alloys contain small amounts of $\alpha$-stabilizing elements as strengtheners in addition to the $\beta$ stabilizers.

The $\beta$ alloys can be further broken down into $\beta$ and "near-$\beta$." This distinction is necessary, because the phase transformations that occur, the reaction kinetics, and the processing could be different if the alloy is a near-$\beta$ (lean) alloy, such as Ti-10V-2Fe-3Al, or a rich $\beta$ alloy, such as Ti-13V-11Cr-3Al.

Preparation of metallographic specimens of unalloyed titanium, and of $\alpha$, $\alpha + \beta$, and $\beta$ titanium alloys, is described in this article, and representative micrographs for each alloy class are presented. Information on the properties and selection of titanium and titanium alloys is available in Volume 2 of the 9th Edition of *Metals Handbook*.

## Specimen Preparation

**Sectioning** of titanium and titanium alloys follows conventional procedures, but deformation and overheating must be avoided as they can both cause changes in microstructure. Deformation can result in mechanical twinning and strain-induced transformation products, and overheating can change the phase distribution or the phases present. Abrasive cutting with silicon carbide wheels is satisfactory if adequate coolant is used. Hacksawing is recommended for small specimens to avoid overheating. See the article "Sectioning" in this Volume for additional information.

**Mounting.** Titanium and its alloys are mounted in common materials such as Bakelite, Lucite, epoxy resins, and diallyl phthalate. The selection of the mounting medium depends on equipment available, specimen size, and the metallographic features of interest. For example, when edge preservation is important, Bakelite or diallyl phthalate is recommended. Nickel plating specimens before mounting also assists in edge preservation, as does adding 50 vol% of silica ($SiO_2$) or a similar hard material powder, between 200 and 325 mesh, to the epoxy resin mounting material. In general, the temperatures encountered using Bakelite, Lucite, or diallyl phthalate do not cause problems. However, when the metallographic examination involves the hydride phase it may be best to leave the specimen unmounted or to mount it in a room-temperature-setting epoxy resin, because of the increased solubility of hydrogen in titanium at only moderately increased temperatures. Mounting in a thermosetting material can sometimes cause the hydride to go back into solution and, upon cooling, re-precipitation of the hydride in an altered form, usually a fine dispersion. Care must also be exercised with epoxies. The exothermic reaction of some room-temperature-setting epoxies can generate enough heat to cause the hydride to go into solution.

**Grinding.** The procedure for grinding titanium specimens is similar to that for grinding steel specimens. The specimens are ground on successive grades of silicon carbide paper, starting with 180-grit and proceeding to 240-, 400-, and 600-grit papers, using water or kerosene to keep the specimens cool and to flush away loose particles of metal and abrasive. It is possible to start grinding with a paper as coarse as 80 grit, provided pressure is light to minimize cold working. Hand, disk, and belt grinding are used. To avoid embedding abrasive particles in the ground surface, the papers may be dressed with solid stick wax. Wax is also used in dry final grinding.

**Manual polishing** consists of three stages: rough, intermediate, and final polishing. Rough polishing is performed on a high-speed polishing wheel covered with a lintless rayon or silk cloth using medium pressure and levigated 1- or 3-$\mu$m $\alpha$-alumina ($Al_2O_3$). The levigated $Al_2O_3$ may be placed on the wheel and wetted with water or an acid solution if an etching action is desired. It may also first be mixed with the desired reagent, acid, or water and applied to the wheel as a slurry. A typical 500-mL slurry may contain 15 g levigated $Al_2O_3$, 10 mL nitric acid ($HNO_3$), 1.5 mL hydrofluoric acid (HF), with the balance consisting of water. An alternative rough polishing technique is the use of a nylon cloth and a 15- to 6-$\mu$m diamond paste.

Intermediate polishing is accomplished by proceeding to a finer abrasive, such as 0.3-$\mu$m levigated $Al_2O_3$ or 1-$\mu$m diamond paste, with a possible intermediate step of 3-$\mu$m diamond paste. Intermediate polishing begins with heavy pressure, which decreases as polishing progresses. Several cycles of polishing and etching may be needed to remove smeared metal. Etching should be light to avoid pitting. The specimen is unetched when final polishing begins.

Final polishing is performed on a low-speed wheel covered with Microcloth using 0.05-$\mu$m $Al_2O_3$, water, or an acid solution and light pressure on the specimen. Again, the $Al_2O_3$ may be placed directly on the wheel or in a slurry. A water solution would consist of 15 g 0.05-$\mu$m levigated $Al_2O_3$ and 35 mL $H_2O$. Colloidal silica is also an effective final polishing abrasive. Several cycles of polishing and etching may be necessary during final polishing.

Edge retention can be enhanced by directional polishing through each polishing stage. The specimen is held in position on the polishing wheel with the edge to be maintained as shown in Fig. 1. The mount should be rotated in place about 30 to 40° to minimize streaking the mount surface.

An alternate rough and intermediate polishing uses a wax wheel covered with 6 to 13 mm (¼ to ½ in.) of paraffin. This procedure is somewhat faster than that described above, but can cause metal smearing. Consequently,

polishing is normally performed using an acid slurry. Final polishing is accomplished as described above using the Microcloth. Rough polishing is performed using 3-$\mu$m $Al_2O_3$; intermediate, 0.3-$\mu$m $Al_2O_3$. A typical wax wheel slurry may consist of approximately 50 vol% $Al_2O_3$ and 50 vol% $H_2O$.

**Automatic polishing** provides control of the pressure exerted on the specimen. Specimens are ground through 180-, 240-, 400-, and 600-grit silicon carbide paper using water or kerosene as the coolant. Final polishing is carried out using Microcloth and 0.05-$\mu$m $\gamma$-$Al_2O_3$ for about 10 min. Several specimens can be prepared simultaneously.

**Vibratory polishing,** although a slower process than electrolytic or mechanical polishing, produces good results. It is a two-stage operation that follows grinding on abrasive papers. Preliminary polishing is performed on a canvas cloth for 2 to 4 h using a slurry of 0.05-$\mu$m $Al_2O_3$ or on a silk cloth for 30 to 45 min using a slurry of 0.3-$\mu$m $Al_2O_3$. Final polishing is performed on a short-nap cloth for 15 min to 4 h using a slurry of 0.05-$\mu$m $Al_2O_3$. Colloidal silica can also be used. Several short polishing and etching cycles may be used to remove disturbed metal.

**Electropolishing** is considerably faster than mechanical polishing. An electrolyte recommended for electropolishing contains 600 mL methanol, 360 mL ethylene glycol, and 60 mL perchloric acid ($HClO_4$). Polishing time is 15 to 25 s at a current density of 1 to 1.5 $A/cm^2$ (6.5 to 9.7 $A/in.^2$), depending on specimen size and polishing area. The electrolyte given above, having a low concentration of $HClO_4$, is nonexplosive and can be stored for several weeks. However, care should be exercised in handling concentrated $HClO_4$, because it can react explosively with organic materials.

**Etching.** Several etchants are used for macroetching and microetching of titanium and titanium alloys. The choice is often arbitrary for a given type of alloy, but if one does not succeed the other etchants should be tried. Macroetching is usually performed by immersion. Microetching is accomplished by swabbing or immersion. Etching times are usually short, ranging from 3 to 10 s. The specimen should be examined after light etching to avoid overetching.

Nearly all etchants for titanium and titanium alloys contain HF and an oxidizing agent, such as $HNO_3$. Table 1 lists the compositions and purposes of etchants suitable for use on unalloyed titanium and on titanium alloys. Kroll's reagent, a dilute aqueous solution containing HF and $HNO_3$, is the etchant most widely used for commercial titanium alloys.

## Macroexamination

Macrostructural examination of titanium alloys provides useful information about material processing, both melting and metalworking. It is used for detection of melting

defects or anomalies, qualitative assessment of grain refinement and uniformity, as well as determination of grain flow in forged products.

Three principal defects are to be found in macrosections of ingot, forged billet, or other semifinished product forms. These include high aluminum defects (HADs or Type II defects), high interstitial defects (HIDs, also referred to as Type I defects or low-density interstitial defects), and $\beta$ flecks. High aluminum defects are areas containing an abnormally high amount of aluminum. These are soft areas in the material (Fig. 80 and 81) and are also referred to as "$\alpha$ segregation." Defects referred to as "$\beta$ segregation" are sometimes associated with $\alpha$ segregation. These are areas in which aluminum is depleted. The high interstitial defects (Fig. 78 and 79) are normally high in oxygen and/or nitrogen, which stabilize the $\alpha$ phase. These defects are hard and brittle; they are normally associated with porosity, as illustrated in Fig. 28.

Beta flecks are regions enriched in a $\beta$-stabilizing element due to segregation during ingot solidification. Their occurrence in $\alpha + \beta$ alloys is uncommon. Flecking becomes more of a problem with $\beta$ alloys, which have much higher amounts of $\beta$-stabilizing additions. The problem is most prevalent in iron- and chromium-bearing alloys. This enrichment of a localized region with $\beta$ stabilizers lowers the $\beta$ transus, locally changing the microstructure and thereby enabling their detection.

This microstructural modification can take two forms. In $\alpha + \beta$ alloys, such as Ti-6Al-6V-2Sn, vanadium enrichment lowers the $\beta$ transus, but is not sufficient to stabilize the $\beta$ to room temperature. When working or heat treating the material high in the $\alpha + \beta$ phase field, the microstructure observed (after cooling back to room temperature) will consist of primary $\alpha$ and transformed $\beta$. The $\beta$ fleck region, however, forms at a temperature above the $\beta$-transus temperature, resulting in no primary $\alpha$ in this region—it is all transformed $\beta$. This condition is apparent in Fig. 97 and 98. A $\beta$ fleck could go undetected if the final processing and heat treatment are conducted at a temperature low enough that the $\beta$-transus suppression is not sufficient to cause a microstructural perturbation. The effects of $\beta$ flecks on properties in such alloys as Ti-6Al-4V and Ti-6Al-6V-2Sn are still in question, but the effect is not a major one.

Beta flecks are more of a problem with near-$\beta$ alloys; they are observed macroscopically as shiny spots or flecks. Their appearance is similar in $\alpha + \beta$ alloys (Fig. 102). The $\beta$-stabilizer enrichment in the flecked regions of $\beta$ alloys, however, is sufficient to stabilize the $\beta$ down to room temperature. To guarantee material that will be fleck-free, producers must solution heat treat samples at a temperature below the $\beta$ transus. The material will then form $\alpha$, but $\beta$-fleck regions will be above or much nearer the transus. Therefore, they

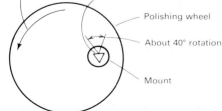

**Fig. 1** Specimen and polishing wheel setup to improve edge retention in titanium and titanium alloys

**Table 1  Etchants for examination of titanium and titanium alloys**

| Etchant | Comments | Etchant | Comments |
|---|---|---|---|
| **Macroetchants** | | **Microetchants (continued)** | |
| 50 mL HCl, 50 mL H$_2$O | General-purpose etch for $\alpha + \beta$ alloys | 10 mL HF, 10 mL HNO$_3$, 30 mL lactic acid | Chemical polish and etch for most alloys |
| 30 mL HNO$_3$, 3 mL HF, 67 mL H$_2$O (slow) to 10 mL HNO$_3$, 8 mL HF 82, mL H$_2$O (fast) | Used at room temperature to 55 °C (130 °F) for 3-5 min. Reveals grain size and surface defects | 2 mL HF, 98 mL H$_2$O | Reveals $\alpha$ case for most alloys |
| | | 98 mL saturated oxalic acid in H$_2$O, 2 mL HF | Reveals $\alpha$ case (interstitial contamination) for most alloys |
| 15 mL HNO$_3$, 10 mL HF, 75 mL H$_2$O | Etch about 2 min. Reveals flow lines and defects | 6 g NaOH, 60 mL H$_2$O, heat to 80 °C (180 °F), add 10 mL H$_2$O$_2$ | Good $\alpha$-$\beta$ contrast, general microstructures for most alloys |
| Two-stage etch (a) consisting of: (1) 8 mL HF, 10 mL HNO$_3$, 82 mL H$_2$O and (2) 18 g/L (2.4 oz/gal) of NH$_4$HF$_2$ (ammonium bifluoride) in H$_2$O | Reveals $\alpha$ and $\beta$ segregation (aluminum segregation) | 2 mL HF, 98 mL H$_2$O, then 1 mL HF, 2 mL HNO$_3$, 97 mL H$_2$O | General-purpose etch for near-$\alpha$ alloys(b) |
| | | 10 mL KOH (40%), 5 mL H$_2$O$_2$, 20 mL H$_2$O | Stains $\alpha$, transformed $\beta$ |
| | | 18.5 g benzalkonium chloride, 33 mL ethanol, 40 mL glycerol, 25 mL HF | General-purpose etch for titanium-aluminum-zirconium and titanium-silicon alloys |
| **Microetchants** | | 2 mL HF, 4 mL HNO$_3$, 94 mL H$_2$ | Reveals microstructure in aged Ti-13V-11Cr-3Al |
| 1-3 mL HF, 10 mL HNO$_3$, 30 mL lactic acid | Reveals hydrides in unalloyed titanium | 50 mL 10% oxalic acid, 50 mL 0.5% HF with H$_2$O | Etch 12–20 s. General-purpose etch for $\beta$ alloys |
| 1 mL HF, 30 mL HNO$_3$, 30 mL lactic acid | Reveals hydrides in unalloyed titanium | 10 s with Kroll's, then 10–15 s with 50 mL 10% oxalic acid, 50 mL 0.5% HF with H$_2$O | Brings out aged structure in Ti-10V-2Fe-3Al |
| Kroll's reagent: 1–3 mL HF, 2–6 mL HNO$_3$, H$_2$O to 1000 mL | General-purpose etch for most alloys | | |
| 10 mL HF, 5 mL HNO$_3$, 85 mL H$_2$O | General-purpose etch for most alloys | | |
| 1 mL HF, 2 mL HNO$_3$, 50 mL H$_2$O$_2$, 47 mL H$_2$O | Removes etchant stains for most alloys | | |

(a) Two-stage etch procedure: Degrease (if necessary) and clean, making sure the surface is water-break free. Immerse in solution (1) at 45–55 °C (110–135 °F) for 2–3 min and rinse thoroughly in clean cold water. Immerse in agitated bath of solution (2) at room temperature for 1–2 min. Rinse thoroughly in clean cold water, rinse thoroughly in clean hot water at 90–100 °C (190–210 °F), blow dry with clean compressed air. Solutions must be used fresh. (b) First etchant stains $\alpha$ phase; second etchant removes stain.

will be void of $\alpha$ or contain a significantly lower volume fraction of $\alpha$ upon cooling to room temperature, as illustrated in Fig. 115 and 116. These regions in $\beta$ alloys will be harder, will have higher strength and lower ductility, and will have lower low-cycle fatigue strength than the bulk material.

Tree rings (Fig. 36) are another macrostructural anomaly observed in titanium alloy macrosections. This phenomenon represents very minor composition variations that occur during melting. The appearance of tree rings is only a cosmetic nuance, not a cause for concern.

Grain flow of forgings is useful for evaluating the forging process. For high-quality forgings, the grain flow should conform to the general shape of the part. There should be no forging laps, seams, or areas of grain flow that appear as though they could produce forging laps in subsequent operations. In addition, the part should be uniformly recrystallized and sufficiently worked in all areas. Additional information on forging defects and tests conducted to ensure forging quality

can be found in the article "Bulk Workability Testing" in Volume 8 of the 9th Edition of *Metals Handbook*.

## Microexamination

**Alpha Structures.** Equiaxed $\alpha$ grains, such as are shown in Fig. 2 and 50, usually are developed by annealing cold-worked alloys above the recrystallization temperature. Elongated $\alpha$ grains (Fig. 6 and 60) result from unidirectional working of the metal and are commonly found in longitudinal sections of rolled or extruded alloys.

The microstructure of titanium alloys is strongly influenced by the processing history and heat treatment. The effect of cooling rate on Ti-5Al-2.5Sn annealed above the $\beta$ transus can be seen in Fig. 17 to 19. This is also illustrated for Ti-6Al-4V in Fig. 58 and 59. As the cooling rate increases, the lamellar $\alpha$ (or martensite, depending on the alloy and cooling rate) becomes finer. The effect of forging temperature is illustrated for Ti-8Al-

1Mo-1V in Fig. 23 to 25. As the forging temperature increases, the amount of transformed $\beta$ increases until the forging temperature is above the $\beta$ transus, at which point the structure is 100% transformed $\beta$. The effect of the amount of forging deformation is illustrated for Ti-6Al-2Sn-4Zr-2Mo in Fig. 32 and 34. Sufficient working of the cast Widmanstätten structure at a temperature below the $\beta$ transus causes recrystallization of the lamellar structure to a more equiaxed structure. Sufficient working and proper heat treatment can produce a completely equiaxed crystal structure (Fig. 50). The microstructural behavior trends will be similar for all $\alpha$ and $\alpha + \beta$ alloys.

Generally, two types of $\alpha$—primary $\alpha$ and secondary $\alpha$ or transformed $\beta$—are present. The primary $\alpha$ is that present during prior hot working, remnants of which persist through heat treatment. The secondary $\alpha$ is produced by transformation from $\beta$. This may occur upon cooling from above the $\beta$ transus (Fig. 92) or high within the $\alpha + \beta$ phase field (Fig. 90), or by aging of the $\beta$ (Fig. 123). The $\alpha$ in these areas has different appearances and may be acicular or lamellar, platelike, serrated, or Widmanstätten.

Acicular or lamellar $\alpha$ is the most common transformation product formed from $\beta$ during cooling. It is a result of nucleation and growth on crystallographic planes of the prior $\beta$ matrix. Precipitation normally occurs on multiple variants or orientations of this family of habit planes, as illustrated in Fig. 43 and 92. A packet or cluster of acicular $\alpha$ grains aligned in the same orientation is referred to as a "colony." When correlating this type of microstructure with properties such as fatigue or fracture toughness, colony size is often regarded as an important microstructural feature. The multiple orientations of $\alpha$ have a basketweave appearance characteristic of a Widmanstätten structure. Lamellar $\alpha$ forming from small $\beta$ grains may have a singular orientation (Fig. 68).

Under some conditions, the long grains of $\alpha$ produced along preferred planes in the $\beta$ matrix take on a wide, platelike appearance, as shown in Fig. 17. Under other conditions, grains of irregular size and with jagged boundaries, called "serrated $\alpha$," are produced (Fig. 9).

Unless heat treatments are performed in an inert atmosphere, oxygen and nitrogen will be absorbed at the surface, stabilize the $\alpha$, and form a hard, brittle layer referred to as an "$\alpha$ case" (Fig. 42 and 51). This case is normally removed by chemical milling or machining. A part should not be put into service unless this $\alpha$ case has been removed.

The $\alpha$ phase can decompose to $\alpha + \text{Ti}_3\text{Al}$, an ordered phase, at compositions greater than about 6 wt% Al. This ordered phase is submicron in size and can be observed only by electron microscopy (Fig. 13).

**Martensite** is a nonequilibrium supersaturated $\alpha$-type structure produced by diffusionless (martensitic) transformation of the $\beta$.

There are two types of martensite: $\alpha'$, which has a hexagonal crystal structure, and $\alpha''$, which has an orthorhombic crystal structure. Martensite can be produced in titanium alloys by quenching (athermal martensite) or by applying external stress (stress-induced martensite). The $\alpha''$ can be formed athermally or by a stress-assisted transformation (Fig. 113 and 125); however, $\alpha'$ can be formed only by quenching. Examples of $\alpha'$ structures are exhibited in Fig. 40 and 57. Aging of the martensite results in its decomposition to $\alpha + \beta$.

**Beta Structures.** In $\alpha + \beta$ and $\beta$ alloys, some equilibrium $\beta$ is present at room temperature. A nonequilibrium, or metastable, $\beta$ phase can be produced in $\alpha + \beta$ alloys that contain enough $\beta$-stabilizing elements to retain the $\beta$ phase at room temperature on rapid cooling from high in the $\alpha + \beta$ phase field. The composition of the alloy must be such that the temperature for the start of martensite formation is depressed to below room temperature. One hundred percent $\beta$ can be retained by air cooling $\beta$ alloys. The decomposition of this retained $\beta$ (or martensite, if it forms) is the basis for heat treating titanium alloys to higher strengths.

**Aged Structures.** Aging of $\alpha'$ results in the formation of equilibrium $\alpha + \beta$, but most aged martensite structures cannot be distinguished from unaged martensite by optical microscopy. Precipitation of $\alpha$ during aging of $\beta$ results in some darkening of the aged $\beta$ structure. The $\alpha$ that forms upon aging of retained $\beta$ is often too fine to be resolved by optical microscopy, particularly with $\beta$ and near-$\beta$ alloys.

The $\beta$ can decompose by the precipitation of $\alpha$ (Fig. 120 to 123) and/or to eutectoid products; $\omega$ (Fig. 117), which is a transition phase (potentially resulting in severe embrittlement); or phase splitting. Phase splitting or phase separation only occurs in the solute-rich $\beta$ alloys; $\beta \rightarrow \beta_r + \beta_l$, where $\beta_r$ is solute-rich $\beta$ and $\beta_l$ is solute-lean $\beta$. The solute-lean $\beta$ is designated $\beta'$ (Fig. 124). This is not an important decomposition product from a practical standpoint, because it does not occur in commercial alloys with heat treatments that are used. The $\omega$ phase and phase splitting can only be observed using electron microscopy.

## Special Metallographic Techniques

Several metallographic techniques have been developed for specific purposes, including recrystallization studies and microstructure/fracture topography correlations. Decoration aging was developed to study the extent of recrystallization in $\beta$ alloys. After recrystallization annealing, the material is given a partial age at a time and temperature appropriate for the alloy of interest. The incompletely recrystallized grains retain some dislocation substructure (stored energy) that accelerates the aging process, resulting in a more rapidly aged grain. These grains then etch darker than the recrystallized ones, making it easy to identify the extent of recrystallization. This effect is illustrated in Fig. 120 to 123.

Another recently developed technique utilizes deep macroetching and thermal etching. The deformed specimen is polished, then subjected to overetching to produce deep grooves at the deformed grain boundaries. Next, the specimen is subjected to the recrystallization cycle of interest in a hard vacuum ($10^{-6}$ torr), followed by oil quenching. The material recrystallizes and thermal etching occurs, which differentiates between different grains, because surface atoms evaporate or sublimate at different rates on different crystallographic planes. Different grains will have different crystallographic planes at the exposed surface.

The original grain boundaries are observable as ghost boundaries, due to the deep macroetching used previously. Therefore, the recrystallized and original microstructures can be observed simultaneously. This permits studying not only the recrystallized structure but also the recrystallization nucleation sites. The ghost boundaries can be removed by re-polishing and chemically etching. This technique is illustrated in Fig. 118 and 119.

Subgrain boundaries can be revealed using a relatively simple technique. The specimen is electropolished and viewed in the scanning electron microscope in the backscattered electron mode. The contrast and delineation of subgrains are due to differences in crystallographic orientation. Electropolishing occurs at different rates on different crystallographic planes, similar to the thermal etching phenomenon.

Several techniques have been developed to observe fracture topography and microstructure simultaneously in the scanning electron microscope using its large depth of field. A very simple method involves selective polishing and etching of the fracture face. The fracture face and machined surfaces are first masked with a suitable maskant, such as a stop-off lacquer, which can be applied with a small paint brush. Selected areas of the fracture face are left unmasked. The specimen is then electropolished, which will affect only the unmasked areas, and etched. Studying the interface between the polished and etched and the masked area permits a correlation of microstructural features and fractographic details, as illustrated in Fig. 83 and 84. This technique is useful for correlating general microstructural details, but it may be difficult to pinpoint a specific area to study.

Precision sectioning techniques have also been developed. The area of interest on the fracture face, such as crack origin, is first located. The specimen is then cut on a plane perpendicular to the fracture face close to the area of interest. The distance from the cut face to the area of interest is measured. Next, the specimen is placed in a metallurgical mount, then ground and polished the measured distance for metallurgical analysis of the precise area of interest and correlation of microstructure to fractographic features. An example of this technique is illustrated in Fig. 85 and 86. The microstructure and fracture face can be observed simultaneously using the scanning electron microscope by carefully dissolving the mount material.

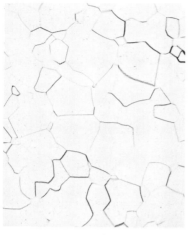

**Fig. 2** High-purity (iodide-process) unalloyed titanium sheet, cold rolled, and annealed 1 h at 700 °C (1290 °F). Equiaxed, recrystallized grains of α. Kroll's reagent (ASTM 192). 250×

**Fig. 3** Commercial-purity unalloyed titanium, hydrogenated to 20 ppm H. Annealed 1 h at 850 °C (1560 °F), air cooled. TiH (black) in equiaxed grains of α. Kroll's reagent (ASTM 192). 250×

**Fig. 4** Same as Fig. 3, except hydrogenated to 80 ppm H, producing a greater amount of TiH (black needles) at grain boundaries and in the α grains. Kroll's reagent (ASTM 192). 250×

**Fig. 5** Same as Fig. 3 and 4, except hydrogenated to 230 ppm H, producing needles of TiH (black) that are larger and more numerous than those shown in Fig. 3. Kroll's reagent (ASTM 192). 250×

**Fig. 6** Commercial-purity (99.0%) unalloyed titanium sheet, as-rolled to 1.0 mm (0.040 in.) thick at 760 °C (1400 °F). Grains of α, which have been elongated by cold working. See also Fig. 7 to 9. Kroll's reagent (ASTM 192). 250×

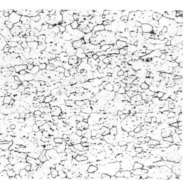

**Fig. 7** Same as Fig. 6, but annealed 2 h at 700 °C (1290 °F) and air cooled. Recrystallized α grains; particles of TiH (black); and particles of β (also black) stabilized by impurities. Kroll's reagent (ASTM 192). 250×

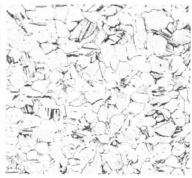

**Fig. 8** Same as Fig. 6, but annealed 1 h at 900 °C (1650 °F)—just below the β transus—and air cooled. Recrystallized grains of "primary" α and transformed β containing acicular α. Kroll's reagent (ASTM 192). 250×

**Fig. 9** Same as Fig. 6, but annealed 2 h at 1000 °C (1830 °F) and air cooled. Colonies of serrated α plates; particles of TiH and retained β (both black) between the plates of α. Kroll's reagent (ASTM 192). 250×

**Fig. 10** Commercial-purity unalloyed titanium bar, annealed for 1 h at 705 °C (1300 °F). The structure consists of equiaxed α grains exhibiting some twin bands (parallel straight lines). 10 mL HF, 5 mL HNO₃, 85 mL H₂O. 250×

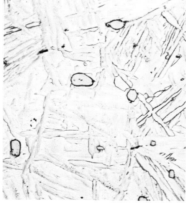

**Fig. 11** Commercial-purity unalloyed titanium containing 0.14% C and 0.12% Fe. Annealed for 1 h at 1095 °C (2000 °F), water quenched. TiC particles (gray and indicated by arrows) in matrix of coarse, acicular α. Kroll's reagent (ASTM 192). 500×

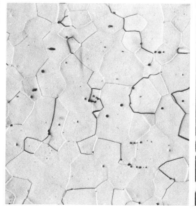

**Fig. 12** Ti-0.2Pd sheet, hot rolled with starting temperature of 760 °C (1400 °F), annealed for 2 h at 705 °C (1300 °F), and slowly cooled. Equiaxed grains of α; iron-stabilized β (black dots). 2 mL HF, 10 mL HNO₃, 88 mL H₂O. 250×

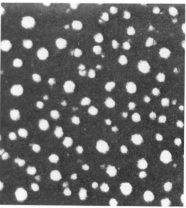

**Fig. 13** Ti-8Al (with 1800 ppm O₂) sheet aged to precipitate the ordered α₂ phase. The dark-field transmission electron micrograph illustrates α₂ precipitates (light) in an α matrix. 105 600×. (J.C. Williams)

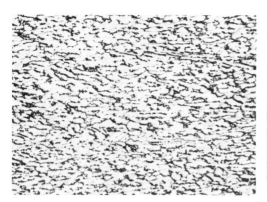

**Fig. 14** Ti-6Al-2Nb-1Ta-0.8Mo plate, hot rolled with starting temperature below the β transus of about 1000 °C (1830 °F), annealed for 30 min at 900 °C (1650 °F) and air cooled. Structure: slightly elongated α grains (light) and intergranular β (dark). 10 mL HF, 5 mL HNO₃, 85 mL H₂O. 100×

**Fig. 15** Ti-6Al-2Nb-1Ta-0.8Mo plate, hot rolled with a starting temperature of 1150 °C (2100 °F), which is above the β transus. Structure: acicular α (light), intergranular β (dark), with boundaries of elongated β grains. 10 mL HF, 5 mL HNO₃, 85 mL H₂O. 100×

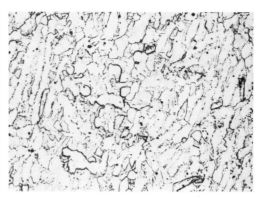

**Fig. 16** Ti-5Al-2.5Sn, forged with starting temperature of 1010 °C (1850 °F), which is below the β-transus temperature, annealed for 1 h at 815 °C (1500 °F), and air cooled. Slightly elongated grains of "primary" α (light) in matrix of acicular α (mottled). Kroll's reagent (ASTM 192). 100×

**Fig. 17** Ti-5Al-2.5Sn, hot worked below the α transus, annealed 30 min at 1175 °C (2150 °F), which is above the β transus, furnace cooled to 790 °C (1450 °F) in 6 h, and furnace cooled to room temperature in 2 h. Coarse, platelike α. See also Fig. 18 and 19. Kroll's reagent (ASTM 192). 100×

**Fig. 18** Same as Fig. 17, but air cooled from the annealing temperature instead of furnace cooled. The faster cooling rate produced acicular α that is finer than the platelike α in Fig. 17. Prior-β grains are outlined by the α that was first to transform. Kroll's reagent (ASTM 192). 100×

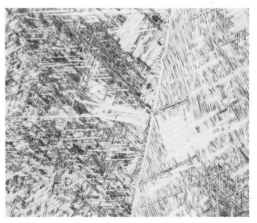

**Fig. 19** Same as Fig. 17, but water quenched from the annealing temperature instead of furnace cooled and shown at a higher magnification. The rapid cooling produced fine acicular α. A prior-β grain boundary can be seen near the center of the micrograph. Kroll's reagent (ASTM 192). 250×

**Fig. 20** Stress-corrosion cracks (black) at the surface of a Ti-5Al-2.5Sn part. These transgranular cracks were caused by exposure to chlorides at 815 °C (1500 °F). Kroll's reagent (ASTM 192). 100×

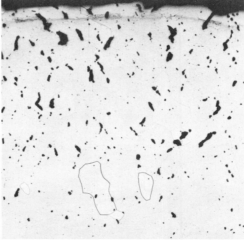

**Fig. 21** Strain-induced porosity near surface of a Ti-5Al-2.5Sn part. Pores (black), caused by severe forming, in equiaxed grains of α (few grain boundaries show). Kroll's reagent (ASTM 192). 100×

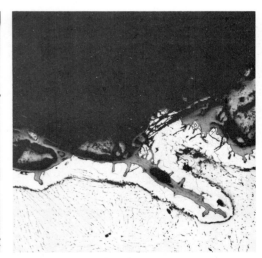

**Fig. 22** Lap, or fold, in the surface of a Ti-5Al-2.5Sn forging. Oxide (gray) on the surface and in the cracks of the white, brittle layer (case) of oxygen-stabilized α. Kroll's reagent (ASTM 192). 100×

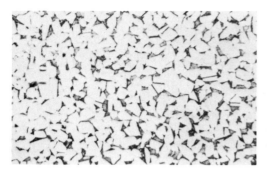

**Fig. 23** Ti-8Al-1Mo-1V, forged with a starting temperature of 900 °C (1650 °F), which is below the normal temperature range for forging this alloy. Structure: equiaxed α grains (light) in a matrix of transformed β (dark). See also Fig. 24 and 25. Kroll's reagent (ASTM 192). 250×

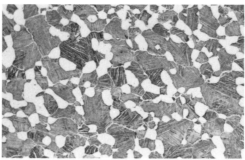

**Fig. 24** Same as Fig. 23, but forged with starting temperature of 1005 °C (1840 °F), which is within the normal range, and air cooled. Equiaxed grains of "primary" α (light) in a matrix of transformed β (dark) containing fine acicular α. See also Fig. 25. Kroll's reagent (ASTM 192). 250×

**Fig. 25** Same as Fig. 23, except the starting temperature for forging was 1095 °C (2000 °F), which is above the β-transus temperature, and the finished forging was rapidly air cooled. The structure consists of transformed β containing coarse and fine acicular α (light). Kroll's reagent (ASTM 192). 250×

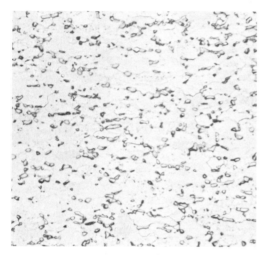

**Fig. 26** Ti-8Al-1Mo-1V sheet, duplex annealed by holding 8 h at 760 °C (1400 °F), furnace cooling to room temperature, holding 20 min at 790 °C (1450 °F), and air cooling. Equiaxed α grains and outlined intergranular β. 2 mL HF, 8 mL HNO₃, 90 mL H₂O. 850×

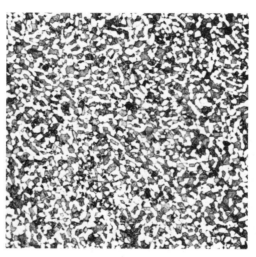

**Fig. 27** Ti-8Al-1Mo-1V forging, solution treated 1 h at 1010 °C (1850 °F), oil quenched, aged 8 h at 595 °C (1100 °F), and air cooled. Structure: same as shown in Fig. 24 (effect of the aging treatment is not resolvable at this magnification). Kroll's reagent (ASTM 192). 100×

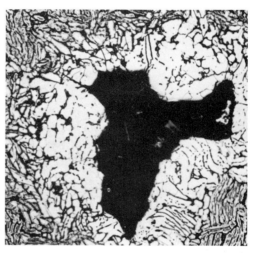

**Fig. 28** Ti-8Al-1Mo-1V, as-forged. Ingot void (black), surrounded by a layer of oxygen-stabilized α (light). The remaining structure consists of elongated α grains in a dark matrix of transformed β. Kroll's reagent (ASTM 192). 25×

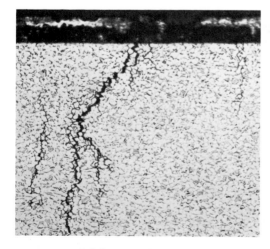

**Fig. 29** Ti-8Al-1Mo-1V sheet, solution treated 10 min at 1010 °C (1850 °F), air cooled, aged 20 min at 745 °C (1375 °F), then exposed to cadmium plate (top) for 1000 h at 260 °C (500 °F) while stressed at 620 MPa (90 ksi). Intergranular stress-corrosion cracks. 2 mL HF, 8 mL HNO₃, 90 mL H₂O. 200×

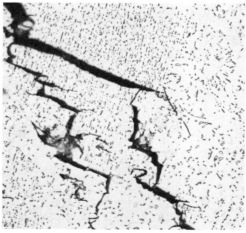

**Fig. 30** Ti-8Al-1Mo-1V sheet, annealed for 8 h at 790 °C (1450 °F) and furnace cooled. Transgranular stress-corrosion cracks, which occurred in a salt-water environment. The microstructure consists of equiaxed grains of α and small, outlined particles of β. Kroll's reagent (ASTM 192). 500×

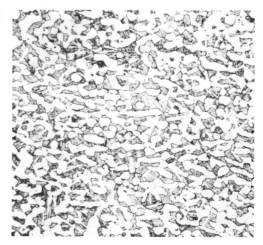

**Fig. 31** Ti-6Al-5Zr-0.5Mo-0.5Si, forged with a starting temperature of 1040 °C (1900 °F), solution treated 1 h at 980 °C (1800 °F), oil quenched, aged 24 h at 495 °C (920 °F), and air cooled. Structure: slightly elongated light α grains in a dark matrix of transformed β. Kroll's reagent (ASTM 192). 100×

**Fig. 32** Ti-6Al-2Sn-4Zr-2Mo forged ingot, held 1 h at 1010 °C (1850 °F), air cooled, heated to 970 °C (1775 °F), and immediately air cooled. Acicular α (transformed β); prior β grain boundaries. See also Fig. 33. Kroll's reagent (ASTM 192). 100×

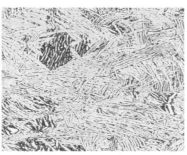

**Fig. 33** Same as Fig. 32, but reduced 15% by upset forging while at 970 °C (1775 °F). The structure consists of slightly deformed acicular α (transformed β); boundaries of elongated prior-β grains. Kroll's reagent (ASTM 192). 100×

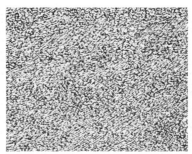

**Fig. 34** Ti-5Al-6Sn-2Zr-1Mo-2.5Si, reduced 75% by upset forging starting at 980 °C (1800 °F), annealed 1 h at 980 °C (1800 °F), air cooled, and stabilized 2 h at 595 °C (1100 °F). Fine α grains (light); intergranular β. See also Fig. 35. HF, HNO₃, HCl, glycerol (ASTM 193). 100×

**Fig. 35** Same as Fig. 34, except upset forged starting at 1150 °C (2100 °F), which is above the β-transus temperature. Distorted acicular α (light constituent); intergranular β; and boundaries of elongated prior-β grains. HF, HNO₃, HCl, glycerol (ASTM 193). 100×

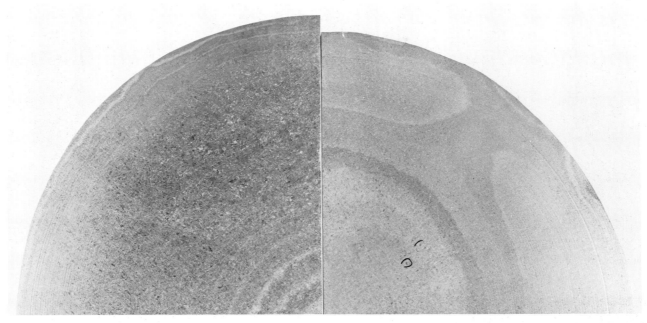

**Fig. 36** Ti-6Al-2Sn-4Zr-2Mo α-β forged billet macroslice illustrating "tree rings," which represent minor compositional fluctuations. The slices are from two ingot locations. Etchant not known. 0.63×. (W. Reinsch)

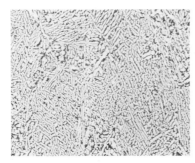

**Fig. 37** Held at 650 °C (1200 °F). A few small, equiaxed "primary" α grains in a matrix of acicular α (transformed β)

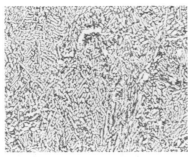

**Fig. 38** Held at 925 °C (1700 °F). A few small, equiaxed "primary" α grains in a matrix of acicular α (transformed β)

**Fig. 39** Held at 980 °C (1800 °F). A few small "primary" α grains (light) in a matrix of α' (martensite)

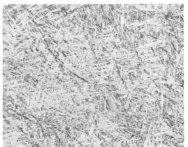

**Fig. 40** Held at 995 °C (1825 °F), the β-transus temperature. The microstructure consists entirely of α'.

**Fig. 37 to 40** Ti-6Al-2Sn-4Zr-2Mo forgings, finish forged starting at 970 °C (1775 °F), air cooled, machined to 13-mm (0.5-in.) diam test bars, reheated to the four temperatures indicated, held for 1 h, and air cooled. All etched with Kroll's reagent (ASTM 192). 100×

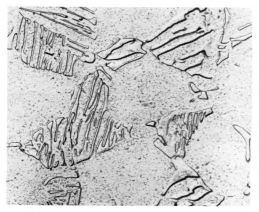

**Fig. 41** Ti-7Al-2Mo-1V plate, solution treated at 995 °C (1825 °F), which is below the β transus. A replica electron micrograph. Structure: equiaxed α, acicular α and β (outlined). 2 mL HF, 8 mL HNO₃, 90 mL H₂O. 3000×

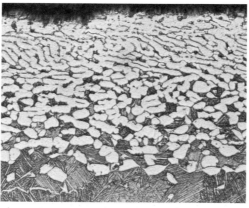

**Fig. 42** Ti-7Al-2Mo-1V plate, heated to 1010 °C (1850 °F), which is above the β transus. Surface layer of white, oxygen-stabilized α (α case); the remainder of the structure is acicular α (transformed β). 2 mL HF, 8 mL HNO₃, 90 mL H₂O. 450×

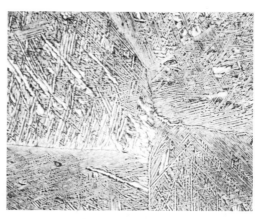

**Fig. 43** Ti-6Al-5Zr-4Mo-1Cu-0.2Si, as-cast. Microstructure: transformed β containing acicular α (light platelets). A thin film of α phase (light) is evident at the prior-β grain boundaries. See Fig. 44 for effects of solution treating. 10 mL HF, 30 mL HNO₃, 50 mL H₂O (ASTM 187). 500×

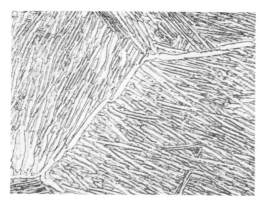

**Fig. 44** Same as Fig. 43, but solution treated 1 h in argon at 845 °C (1550 °F), air cooled, and aged 24 h at 500 °C (930 °F). Acicular α (light) and aged β; α platelets at prior-β grain boundaries. 10 mL HF, 30 mL HNO₃, 50 mL H₂O (ASTM 187). 500×

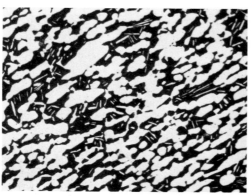

**Fig. 45** Ti-6Al-5Zr-4Mo-1Cu-0.2Si forging, annealed 2 h at 705 °C (1300 °F), and air cooled. The structure consists of slightly elongated grains of α (light) and transformed β (dark) containing some acicular α. 10 mL HF, 30 mL HNO₃, 50 mL H₂O (ASTM 187). 500×

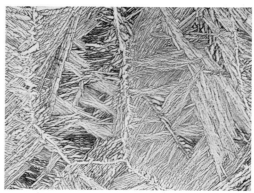

**Fig. 46** Ti-6Al-4V, as-cast. The structure consists of transformed β containing acicular α; α is at prior-β grain boundaries. Keller's reagent. 100×

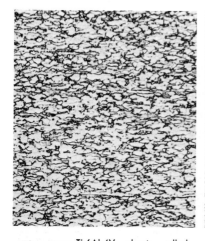

**Fig. 47** Ti-6Al-4V sheet, rolled starting at 925 °C (1700 °F), annealed for 8 h at 730 °C (1350 °F), and furnace cooled. Structure consists of slightly elongated grains of α (light) and intergranular β (gray). See also Fig. 48. 2 mL HF, 10 mL HNO₃, 88 mL H₂O. 250×

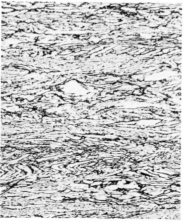

**Fig. 48** Ti-6Al-4V plate, rolled starting at 900 °C (1650 °F), annealed for 1 h at 720 °C (1325 °F), and air cooled. The structure consists of elongated α grains (light) in a matrix of transformed β. See also Fig. 47 and 49. 2 mL HF, 10 mL HNO₃, 88 mL H₂O. 250×

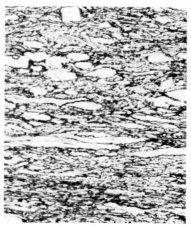

**Fig. 49** Same alloy and processing as in Fig. 48, but a specimen taken from an area of the plate that shows more banding of the structure, which consists of elongated grains of α (light) in a matrix of transformed β. 2 mL HF, 10 mL HNO₃, 88 mL H₂O. 250×

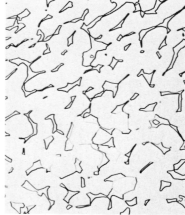

**Fig. 50** Ti-6Al-4V plate, recrystallize-annealed at 925 °C (1700 °F) 1 h, cooled to 760 °C (1400 °F) at 50 to 55 °C/h (90 to 100 °F/h), then air cooled. Equiaxed α with intergranular β. The α-α boundaries are not defined. 50 mL oxalic acid in H₂O, 50 mL 1% HF in H₂O. 500×. (J.C. Chesnutt)

**Fig. 51** Ti-6Al-4V plate diffusion-bonded joint (bonded at 925 °C, or 1700 °F) illustrating bond-line contamination. The white horizontal band is an area of $O_2$ and/or $N_2$ enrichment. An $\alpha$ case is also observable on the exterior surface. 50 mL $H_2O$, 50 mL 10% oxalic acid, 1 mL HF. 58×. (J.C. Chesnutt)

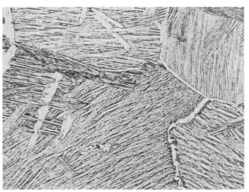

**Fig. 52** Ti-6Al-4V extrusion, heated for 30 min at 1010 °C (1850 °F), air cooled, then heated for 1 h at 675 °C (1250 °F), and air cooled. Structure: acicular $\alpha$ (transformed $\beta$); $\alpha$ at prior-$\beta$ grain boundaries. 2 mL HF, 8 mL $HNO_3$, 90 mL $H_2O$. 200×

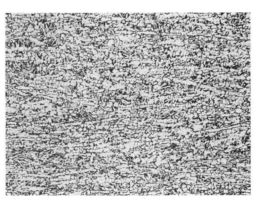

**Fig. 53** Ti-6Al-4V bar, 25 mm (1 in.) diam, annealed 2 h at 705 °C (1300 °F), and air cooled. Elongated grains of $\alpha$ (light) and intergranular $\beta$ (mottled or outlined). See also Fig. 54 to 59. 2 mL HF, 8 mL $HNO_3$, 90 mL $H_2O$. 200×

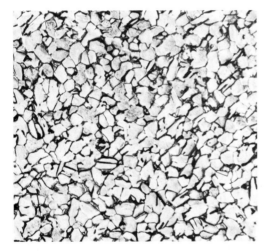

**Fig. 54** Ti-6Al-4V bar, held for 1 h at 955 °C (1750 °F), below the $\beta$ transus, and furnace cooled. Equiaxed $\alpha$ grains (light); intergranular $\beta$ (dark). See also Fig. 55 and 56. 10 mL HF, 5 mL $HNO_3$, 85 mL $H_2O$. 250×

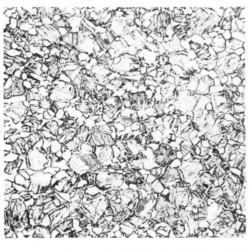

**Fig. 55** Same as Fig. 54, but air cooled instead of furnace cooled. Grains of "primary" $\alpha$ (light) in a matrix of transformed $\beta$ containing acicular $\alpha$. See also Fig. 56. 10 mL HF, 5 mL $HNO_3$, 85 mL $H_2O$. 250×

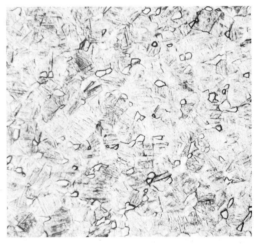

**Fig. 56** Same as Fig. 54, but water quenched instead of furnace cooled. Equiaxed "primary" $\alpha$ grains (light) in a matrix of $\alpha'$ (martensite). See also Fig. 57 to 59. 10 mL HF, 5 mL $HNO_3$, 85 mL $H_2O$. 250×

**Fig. 57** Ti-6Al-4V, thin foil transmission electron micrograph illustrating same microstructure as in Fig. 56, but at higher magnification. The large light grains are primary $\alpha$; the darker region is acicular $\alpha'$ martensite in a $\beta$ matrix. 5880×. (J.C. Williams)

**Fig. 58** Ti-6Al-4V bar, held for 1 h at 1065 °C (1950 °F), above the $\beta$ transus, and furnace cooled. Platelike $\alpha$ (light) and intergranular $\beta$ (dark). See also Fig. 59. 10 mL HF, 5 mL $HNO_3$, 85 mL $H_2O$. 250×

**Fig. 59** Same as Fig. 58, but air cooled instead of furnace cooled. The structure consists of acicular $\alpha$ (transformed $\beta$); prior-$\beta$ grain boundaries. 10 mL HF, 5 mL $HNO_3$, 85 mL $H_2O$. 250×

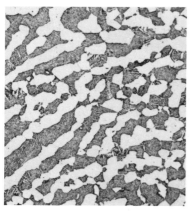

**Fig. 60** Ti-6Al-4V, as-forged at 955 °C (1750 °F), below the $\beta$ transus. Elongated $\alpha$ (light), caused by low reduction (20%) of a billet that had coarse, platelike $\alpha$, in a matrix of transformed $\beta$ containing acicular $\alpha$. Kroll's reagent (ASTM 192). 250×

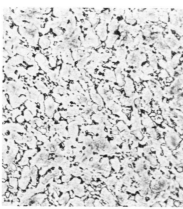

**Fig. 61** Ti-6Al-4V forging, annealed for 2 h at 705 °C (1300 °F), and air cooled. The structure consists of equiaxed grains of $\alpha$ (light) and intergranular $\beta$ (dark or outlined). See also Fig. 62 and 63. Keller's reagent. 250×

**Fig. 62** Ti-6Al-4V, forged at 815 °C (1500 °F), annealed 2 h at 705 °C (1300 °F), and air cooled. Thin-foil transmission electron micrograph. Structure: equiaxed $\alpha$ containing dislocations; some intergranular $\beta$. See also Fig. 63. 23 000×

**Fig. 63** Ti-6Al-4V, forged at 955 °C (1750 °F), annealed 2 h at 705 °C (1300 °F), and air cooled. A thin-foil electron micrograph, showing equiaxed $\alpha$ in matrix of alternate $\beta$ (dark) and acicular $\alpha$ (light). See also Fig. 62. 4500×

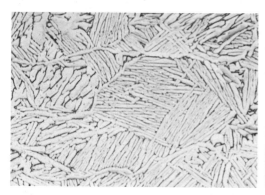

**Fig. 64** Ti-6Al-4V press forging, reduced 50% at 1040 °C (1900 °F), above the $\beta$ transus, then reduced 5% more at 970 °C (1775 °F), below the $\beta$ transus, annealed 2 h at 705 °C (1300 °F), and air cooled. Slightly distorted, coarse, platelike $\alpha$ grains (light) and intergranular $\beta$ phase (dark). See also Fig. 65 and 66. 2 mL HF, 8 mL HNO₃, 90 mL H₂O. 200×

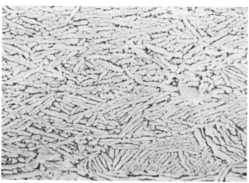

**Fig. 65** Same as Fig. 64, except reduced 21% at 970 °C (1775 °F). The structure is similar to Fig. 64, but the higher reduction below the $\beta$-transus temperature has resulted in some breakup of the coarse, platelike $\alpha$ grains that were still present after forging above the $\beta$ transus. See also Fig. 66. 2 mL HF, 8 mL HNO₃, 90 mL H₂O. 200×

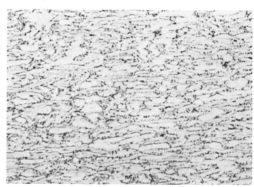

**Fig. 66** Same as Fig. 64 and 65, except reduced 47% at 970 °C (1775 °F). The structure is similar to Fig. 65, but the still higher reduction below the $\beta$-transus temperature has resulted in elongated grains of $\alpha$ (complete breakup of the coarse, platelike $\alpha$ grains that were present after forging above the $\beta$ transus). 2 mL HF, 8 mL HNO₃, 90 mL H₂O. 200×

**Fig. 67** Ti-6Al-4V, forged at 1040 °C (1900 °F), which is above the $\beta$ transus, air cooled, annealed 2 h at 705 °C (1300 °F), and air cooled. Thin-foil transmission electron micrograph illustrates alternate layers of light, platelike $\alpha$ grains and dark intergranular $\beta$. 8500×

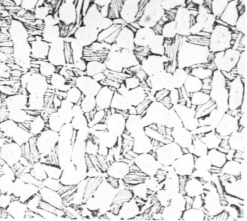

**Fig. 68** Ti-6Al-4V forging solution treated 1 h at 955 °C (1750 °F), air cooled, and annealed 2 h at 705 °C (1300 °F). Equiaxed $\alpha$ grains (light) in transformed $\beta$ matrix (dark) containing coarse, acicular $\alpha$. See also Fig. 69. Kroll's reagent (ASTM 192). 500×

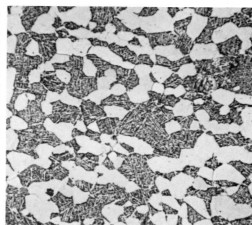

**Fig. 69** Same as Fig. 68, except water quenched from the solution treatment (before the anneal) instead of air cooled. Structure is similar to Fig. 68, but the faster cooling resulted in finer acicular $\alpha$ in the transformed $\beta$. Kroll's reagent (ASTM 192). 500×

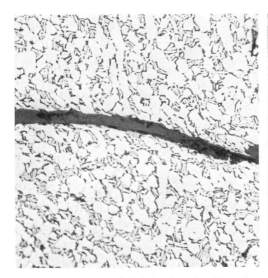

**Fig. 70** Large oxide inclusion (gray band) in a Ti-6Al-4V forging that was annealed 2 h at 705 °C (1300 °F) and air cooled. Structure: grains of α (light) in a matrix of transformed β containing acicular α. Keller's reagent. 500×

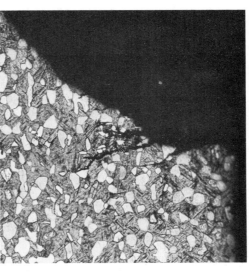

**Fig. 71** Transgranular stress-corrosion cracks in a Ti-6Al-4V forging annealed same as Fig. 70. The cracks resulted from fingerprint contamination followed by bending and stress relieving for 1 h at 540 °C (1000 °F). Keller's reagent. 250×

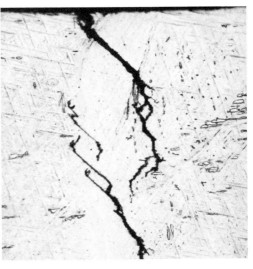

**Fig. 72** Fusion zone of a gas tungsten arc weld in a Ti-6Al-4V forging showing transgranular stress-corrosion cracks caused by contamination with soap before the weld was stress relieved for 1 h at 540 °C (1000 °F). Keller's reagent. 500×

**Fig. 73** Gas tungsten arc butt weld joining Ti-6Al-4V forgings that had been solution treated for 1 h at 955 °C (1750 °F), water quenched, aged 4 h at 540 °C (1000 °F), and air cooled. The forgings were welded using extra-low-interstitial unalloyed titanium filler metal, and the finished weldment was stress relieved for 1 h at 540 °C (1000 °F) and air cooled. See Fig. 74 to 76 for details of the adjacent base metal, the weld bead, and the heat-affected zone. Keller's reagent. 8×

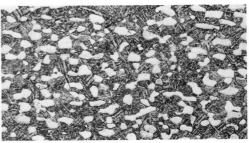

**Fig. 74** Section of the base metal adjacent to the gas tungsten arc butt weld shown in Fig. 73. The structure consists of grains of "primary" α (light) in a matrix of transformed β containing acicular α. Keller's reagent. 250×

**Fig. 75** Bead of the weld shown in Fig. 73. Structure: serrated α (outlined), acicular α (light), and a small amount of β (dark). See also Fig. 74 and 76. Keller's reagent. 250×

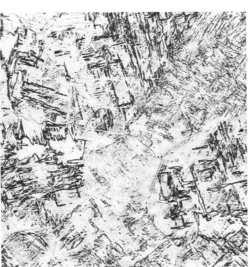

**Fig. 76** Heat-affected zone of the weld shown in Fig. 73. Serrated α (outlined) and transformed β containing acicular α. See also Fig. 74 and 75. Keller's reagent. 250×

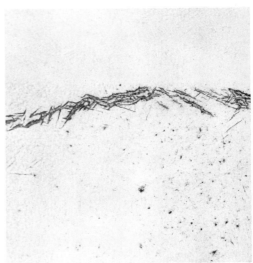

**Fig. 77** Gas tungsten arc weld, which had been stress relieved 1 h at 540 °C (1000 °F), in a Ti-6Al-4V forging, showing needles of titanium hydride at the edge of the fusion zone. 10 mL HF, 30 mL $HNO_3$, 50 mL $H_2O$ (ASTM 187), then light polish. 100×

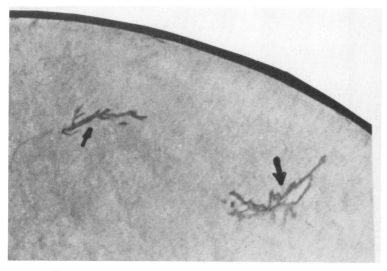

**Fig. 78** Ti-6Al-4V α-β processed billet illustrating macroscopic appearance of a high interstitial defect. See also Fig. 79. Actual size

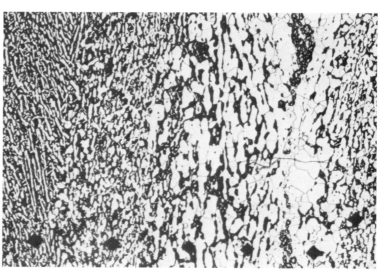

**Fig. 79** Same as Fig. 78. The high oxygen content results in a region of coarser and more brittle oxygen-stabilized α than observed in the bulk material. 100×

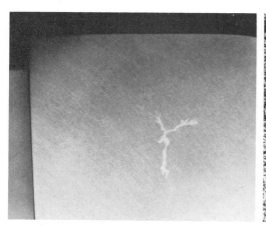

**Fig. 80** Ti-6Al-4V α-β processed billet illustrating the macroscopic appearance of a high aluminum defect. See also Fig. 81. 1.25×. (C. Scholl)

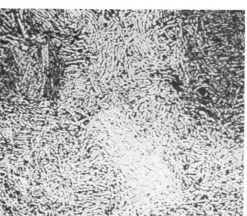

**Fig. 81** Same as Fig. 80. There is a higher volume fraction of more elongated α in the area of high aluminum content. 50×. (C. Scholl)

**Fig. 82** Ti-6Al-4V alloy. A replica electron fractograph. Cleavage facets typical of salt-water stress-corrosion cracking. Cleavage occurs in the α phase. 6500×

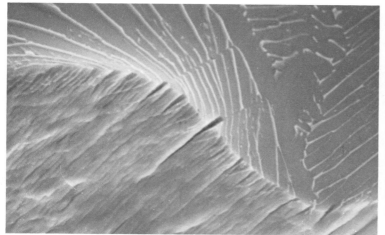

**Fig. 83** Ti-6Al-4V β-annealed fatigued plate specimen. Scanning electron micrograph at the polished and etched/unetched fracture topography interface showing microstructure/fracture topography correlation. Secondary cracks are a result of intense slip bands. Kroll's reagent. 2000×. (R. Boyer)

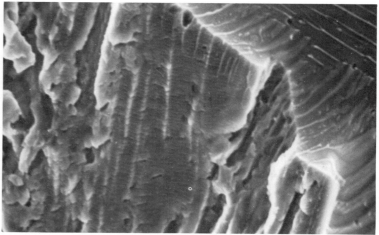

**Fig. 84** Same as Fig. 83. This scanning electron micrograph illustrates that the "furrows" or "troughs" down which the striations propagate are defined by the lamellar α plates. These furrows link up as the crack progresses. Kroll's reagent. 2000×. (R. Boyer)

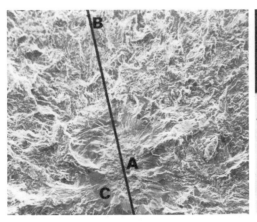

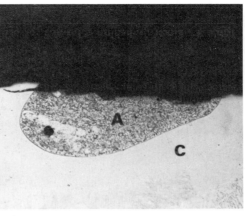

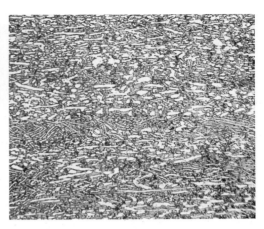

**Fig. 85, 86** Ti-6Al-4V powder metallurgy compact, hot isostatically pressed at 925 °C (1700 °F), 103 MPa (15 ksi), for 2 h. This fatigue specimen had an internal origin at point A, which initiated at an iron inclusion, as determined in Fig. 86 by precision sectioning. The cleavage zone at point C in Fig. 85 is due to the $TiFe_2$ zone seen at point C in Fig. 86. Below the $TiFe_2$, the structure consists of transformed Widmanstätten $\alpha$. The section (Fig. 86) was taken at line B in Fig. 85. Fig. 85: scanning electron micrograph. No etch. 80×. Fig. 86: optical micrograph. Kroll's reagent. 16×. (D. Eylon)

**Fig. 87** Ti-6Al-2Sn-4Zr-6Mo, 100-mm (4-in.) thick forged billet, annealed 2 h at 730 °C (1350 °F). The microstructure consists of a matrix of transformed $\beta$ (dark) containing various sizes of $\alpha$ grains (light), which are elongated in the direction of working. 2 mL HF, 8 mL $HNO_3$, 90 mL $H_2O$. 200×

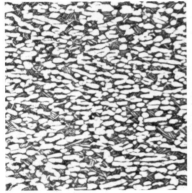

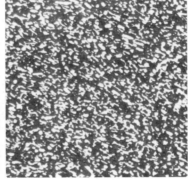

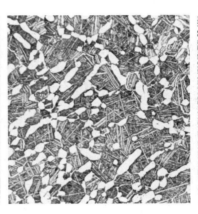

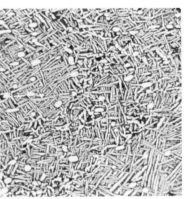

**Fig. 88** Ti-6Al-2Sn-4Zr-6Mo, forged at 870 °C (1600 °F), solution treated 2 h at 870 °C (1600 °F), air cooled, aged 8 h at 595 °C (1100 °F), and air cooled. Elongated "primary" $\alpha$ grains (light) in aged transformed $\beta$ matrix containing acicular $\alpha$. See also Fig. 89 to 92. Kroll's reagent (ASTM 192). 500×

**Fig. 89** Ti-6Al-2Sn-4Zr-6Mo bar, forged at 870 °C (1600 °F), solution treated 1 h at 870 °C (1600 °F), water quenched, and aged 8 h at 595 °C (1100 °F). The structure is similar to that in Fig. 88, except that, as the result of water quenching, no acicular $\alpha$ is visible. 2 mL HF, 10 mL $HNO_3$, 88 mL $H_2O$. 250×

**Fig. 90** Same as Fig. 88, except solution treated at 915 °C (1675 °F) instead of at 870 °C (1600 °F), which reduced the amount of "primary" $\alpha$ grains in the $\alpha + \beta$ matrix. See also Fig. 91 and 92. Kroll's reagent (ASTM 192). 500×

**Fig. 91** Same as Fig. 90, except solution treated at 930 °C (1710 °F) instead of at 915 °C (1675 °F), which reduced the amount of $\alpha$ grains and coarsened the acicular $\alpha$ in the matrix. See also Fig. 92. Kroll's reagent (ASTM 192). 500×

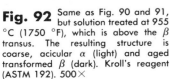

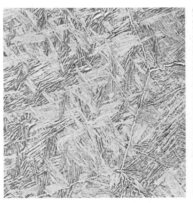

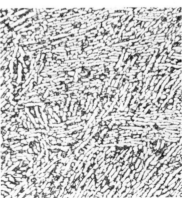

**Fig. 92** Same as Fig. 90 and 91, but solution treated at 955 °C (1750 °F), which is above the $\beta$ transus. The resulting structure is coarse, acicular $\alpha$ (light) and aged transformed $\beta$ (dark). Kroll's reagent (ASTM 192). 500×

**Fig. 93** Ti-6Al-2Sn-4Zr-6Mo forging, solution treated 2 h at 955 °C (1750 °F), above the $\beta$ transus, and quenched in water. The structure consists entirely of $\alpha'$ (martensite). Kroll's reagent (ASTM 192). 500×

**Fig. 94** Ti-6Al-6V-2Sn as-extruded, 8 mm (5/16-in.) thick. The microstructure consists of transformed $\beta$ containing acicular $\alpha$; light $\alpha$ is also evident at the prior-$\beta$ grain boundaries. 2 mL HF, 8 mL $HNO_3$, 90 mL $H_2O$. 200×

**Fig. 95** Ti-6Al-6V-2Sn billet, 100 mm (4 in.) thick, forged below the $\beta$ transus of 945 °C (1730 °F), annealed 2 h at 705 °C (1300 °F), and air cooled. Light $\alpha$ in transformed $\beta$ matrix containing acicular $\alpha$. 2 mL HF, 8 mL $HNO_3$, 90 mL $H_2O$. 200×

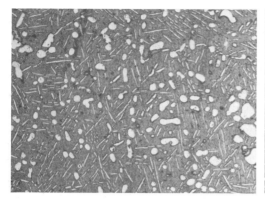

**Fig. 96** Ti-6Al-6V-2Sn hand forging, forged at 925 °C (1700 °F), solution treated for 2 h at 870 °C (1600 °F), water quenched, aged 4 h at 595 °C (1100 °F), and air cooled. Structure: "primary" $\alpha$ grains (light) in a matrix of transformed $\beta$ containing acicular $\alpha$. Kroll's reagent (ASTM 192). 150×

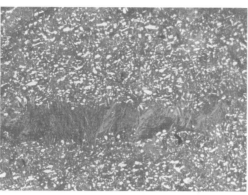

**Fig. 97** Ti-6Al-6V-2Sn forging, solution treated, quenched, and aged same as in Fig. 96. The structure is the same as in Fig. 96, except that alloy segregation has resulted in a dark "$\beta$ fleck" (center of micrograph) that shows no light "primary" $\alpha$. See also Fig. 98 and 102. Kroll's reagent (ASTM 192). 75×

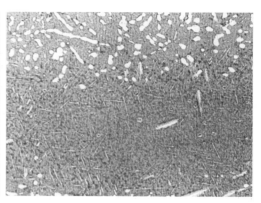

**Fig. 98** Ti-6Al-6V-2Sn forging, solution treated for 1¼ h at 870 °C (1600 °F), water quenched, and aged 4 h at 575 °C (1070 °F). Structure: same as in Fig. 97, but higher magnification shows a small amount of light, acicular $\alpha$ in the dark "$\beta$ fleck." See also Fig. 102. 2 mL HF, 8 mL HNO₃, 90 mL H₂O. 200×

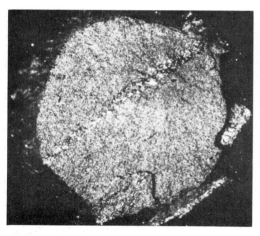

**Fig. 99** Ti-6Al-4V-2Sn alloy; fracture surface of a tension-test bar showing a shiny area of alloy segregation that caused low ductility. See also Fig. 100 and 101. Not polished, Kroll's reagent (ASTM 192). 10×

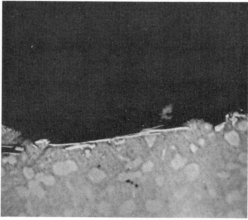

**Fig. 100** Same as Fig 99, except a section normal to the fracture surface, polished down to a stringer of boride compound (light needle) in the area of segregation. See also Fig. 101. Polished, Kroll's reagent (ASTM 192). 400×

**Fig. 101** Same as Fig 99, except a replica transmission electron fractograph of the etched surface, which shows the stringer of boride compound as parallel platelets. Not polished, Kroll's reagent (ASTM 192). 1500×

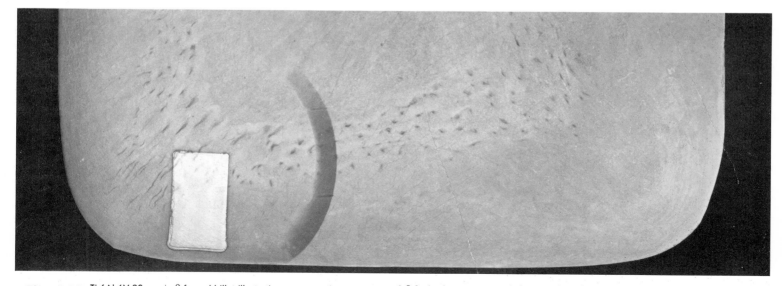

**Fig. 102** Ti-6Al-6V-2Sn $\alpha + \beta$ forged billet illustrating macroscopic appearance of $\beta$ flecks that appear as dark spots. See also Fig. 97 and 98. 8 mL HF, 10 mL HF, 82 mL H₂O, then 18 g/L (2.4 oz/gal) of NH₄HF₂ in H₂O. Less than 1×. (C. Scholl)

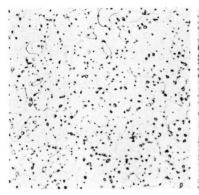

**Fig. 103** Ti-3Al-2.5V tube, vacuum annealed for 2 h at 760 °C (1400 °F). Structure is equiaxed grains of α (light) and small, spheroidal grains of β (outlined). See also Fig. 104. 10 mL HF, 5 mL HNO₃, 85 mL H₂O. 500×

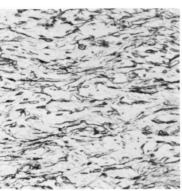

**Fig. 104** Ti-3Al-2.5V tube that was cold drawn, then stress relieved for 1 h at 425 °C (800 °F). Yield strength, 724 MPa (105 ksi); elongation, 15%. Elongated α grains; intergranular β. Kroll's reagent (ASTM 192). 500×

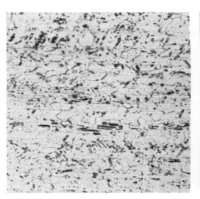

**Fig. 105** Ti-11.5Mo-6Zr-4.5Sn sheet, 2 mm (0.080 in.) thick, solution treated 2 h at 760 °C (1400 °F), and water quenched. Elongated grains of β (light) containing some α (outlined or dark). See also Fig. 106. Kroll's reagent. 150×

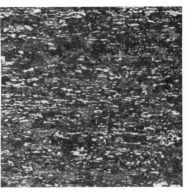

**Fig. 106** Same as Fig. 105, except aged for 8 h at 565 °C (1050 °F) after the water quench following solution treating. Most of the β shown in Fig. 105 has changed to dark α; some β phase (light) has been retained. Kroll's reagent. 150×

**Fig. 107** Ti-5Al-2Sn-2Zr-4Cr-4Mo (Ti-17) β-processed forging with heat treatment at 800 °C (1475 °F), 4 h, water quench, + 620 °C (1150 °F). Consists of lamellar α structure in a β matrix with some grain-boundary α. 95 mL H₂O, 4 mL HNO₃, 1 mL HF. 100×. (T. Redden)

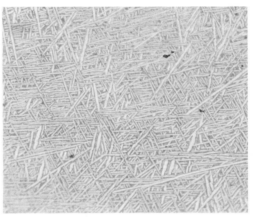

**Fig. 108** Same as Fig. 107, but a higher magnification better illustrating lamellar α structure in an aged β matrix. Acicular secondary α due to aging not resolvable at this magnification. 95 mL H₂O, 4 mL HNO₃, 1 mL HF. 500×. (T. Redden)

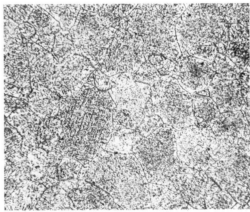

**Fig. 109** Ti-3Al-8V-6Cr-4Zr-4Mo rod, solution treated 15 min at 815 °C (1500 °F), air cooled, and aged 6 h at 565 °C (1050 °F). Precipitated α (dark) in β grains. 30 mL H₂O₂, 3 drops HF. 250×.

**Fig. 110** Ti-3Al-8V-6Cr-4Zr-4Mo rod, cold drawn, solution treated 30 min at 815 °C (1500 °F), and aged 6 h at 675 °C (1250 °F). Precipitated α (dark) in grains of β. Kroll's reagent (ASTM 192). 250×

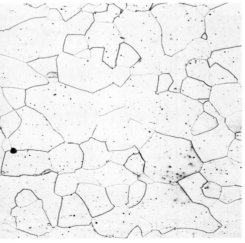

**Fig. 111** Ti-13V-11Cr-3Al sheet, rolled starting at 790 °C (1450 °F), solution treated 10 min at 790 °C (1450 °F), air cooled. Equiaxed grains of metastable β. See also Fig. 112. 2 mL HF, 10 mL HNO₃, 88 mL H₂O. 250×.

**Fig. 112** Same as Fig. 111, except aged for 48 h at 480 °C (900 °F) after solution treating and air cooling. Structure: dark particles of precipitated α in β grains. 2 mL HF, 10 mL HNO₃, 88 mL H₂O. 250×.

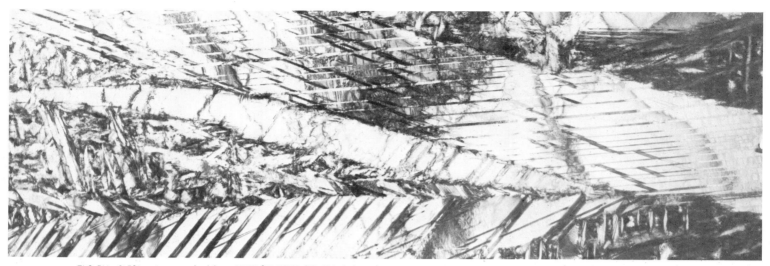

**Fig. 113** Ti-8.5Mo-0.5Si water quenched from 1000 °C (1830 °F). Thin-foil transmission electron micrograph illustrating heavily twinned athermal α" martensite. 5000×. (J.C. Williams)

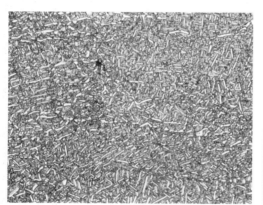

**Fig. 114** Ti-10V-2Fe-3Al pancake forging, β forged about 50% + α-β finish forged about 5%, with heat treatment at 750 °C (1385 °F), 1 h, water quench, + 540 °C (1000 °F), 8 h. Lamellar α with a small amount of equiaxed α in an aged β matrix. 10 s with Kroll's reagent, then 50 mL of 10% oxalic acid, 50 mL of 0.5% HF. 400×. (R. Boyer)

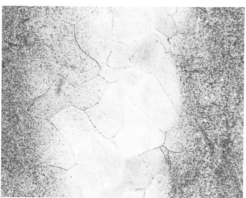

**Fig. 115** Same as Fig. 114, but amount of α + β finish forging is 2%. Micrograph illustrates darkened aged β surrounding a lighter etched β fleck. See also Fig. 116. Same etch as Fig. 114. 50×. (T. Long)

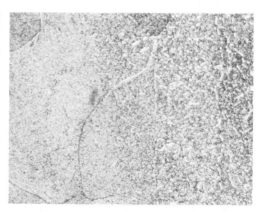

**Fig. 116** Same as Fig. 115, but at higher magnification to demonstrate the reduced amount of α in the β fleck. The α observed (light) is primary α; the α that forms upon aging is too fine to resolve. Same etch as Fig. 114. 200×. (T. Long)

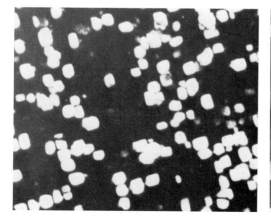

**Fig. 117** A titanium-iron binary alloy, β solution treated, water quenched, and aged to form ω. The ω is the light precipitate in this thin-foil transmission electron micrograph. In alloys where the ω has a high lattice misfit, the ω is cuboidal to minimize elastic strain in the matrix. 320 000×. (J.C. Williams)

**Fig. 118, 119** Ti-10V-2Fe-3Al deformed at 1150 °C (2100 °F). Fig. 118 demonstrates the as-deformed structure that has been heavily etched. The specimen was recrystallized at 925 °C (1700 °F) for 1 h in a vacuum of $10^{-6}$ torr. Recrystallization in vacuum caused thermal etching of the recrystallized grains (Fig. 119 shows recrystallized structure). The prior unrecrystallized structure can still be observed as ghost boundaries remnant from the initial overetching. Fig. 118: 60 mL $H_2O$, 40 mL $HNO_3$, 10 mL HF for 30 min. Fig. 119: 60 mL $H_2O$, 40 mL $HNO_3$, 10 mL HF for 30 min + thermally etched at 925 °C (1700 °F) for 1 h in vacuum ($10^{-6}$ torr). Magnification not known. (D. Eylon)

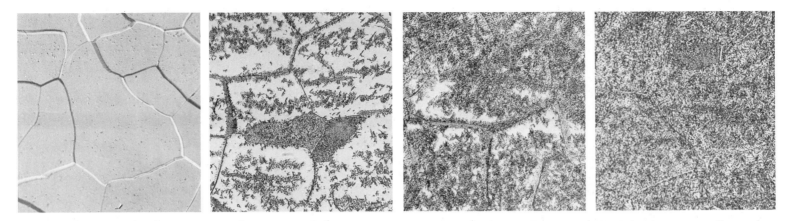

**Fig. 120, 121, 122, 123** Ti-15V-3Cr-3Al-3Sn cold-rolled strip that has been annealed at 790 °C (1450 °F) for 10 min and aged at various times to illustrate the progression of aging and what is termed "decorative aging," a technique used to determine the extent of recrystallization. Equiaxed β grains are observed in Fig. 120, which was not aged. Fig. 121 has been aged 2 h at 540 °C (1000 °F) and shows dark acicular α that forms upon aging. Grains in center are completely aged (uniform α precipitation throughout the grains), which means they were not recrystallized (had more stored energy), resulting in rapid aging. Fig. 122 and 123 carry the progression further with 4- and 8-h aging, respectively. An 8-h age results in a fully aged structure. All etched with Kroll's reagent. All 200×. (P. Bania)

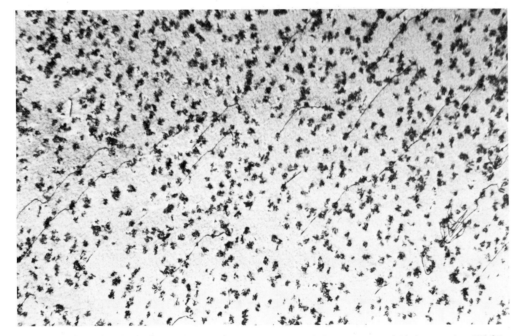

**Fig. 124** Ti-40 at.% Nb, β solution heat treated at 900 °C (1650 °F), water quenched, then aged at 400 °C (750 °F) for 24 h. The dark precipitate is β' (solute-lean β phase) in a solute-enriched β matrix. Thin-foil transmission electron micrograph. 31 000×. (J.C. Williams)

**Fig. 125** Ti-10V-2Fe-3Al, β solution treated, water quenched, and strained 5% at room temperature. This Nomarski interference micrograph illustrates deformation-induced α'' martensite in a β matrix. No etch. 500×. (J.E. Costa)

# Uranium and Uranium Alloys

By Kenneth H. Eckelmeyer
Division Supervisor
Sandia National Laboratories

URANIUM is used in a variety of applications for its high density (19.1 g/cm³, 68% greater than lead) and/or its unique nuclear properties. Uranium and its alloys exhibit typical metallic ductility, can be fabricated by most standard hot and cold working techniques, and can be heat treated to hardnesses ranging from approximately 92 HRB to 55 HRC. Metallography is a useful tool for quality assurance, failure analysis, and understanding the effects of processing on the properties of uranium and its alloys.

Natural uranium consists of two primary isotopes: U235 (0.7%) and U238 (99.3%). Isotopic separation is carried out as one of the steps in converting the ore to metal, resulting in two grades of metallic uranium. Enriched uranium, sometimes termed "oralloy," contains more than 0.7% U235 and is used primarily for its nuclear properties. Depleted uranium, sometimes termed "tuballoy," DU, or D-38, contains only about 0.2% U235 and is used primarily for its high density. Although access to enriched uranium is controlled, depleted uranium is industrially available.

This article will consider the physical metallurgy and metallography of depleted uranium. The metallurgy of enriched uranium is identical to that of depleted uranium, although additional measures are necessary during metallographic preparation to maintain material accountability and to avoid health hazards. Detailed information on uranium alloy metallurgy and microstructures is presented in subsequent sections of this article and in Ref 1 to 8.

## Principles of Uranium Alloy Metallurgy

Uranium ore is processed by mineral beneficiation and chemical procedures to produce enriched or depleted uranium tetrafluoride (UF₄). The UF₄ is then reduced with magnesium or calcium at elevated temperature, resulting in metallic uranium ingots that are known as "derbies." These derbies are vacuum induction remelted and cast into the

shapes required for engineering components or for subsequent mechanical working. Crucibles and molds are usually made of graphite; a zirconia or yttria wash prevents or minimizes carbon pickup by the metal.

Solid elemental uranium exhibits three polymorphic forms: γ phase (body-centered cubic) above 771 °C (1420 °F), β phase (tetragonal) between 665 and 771 °C (1230 and 1420 °F), and α phase (orthorhombic) below 665 °C (1230 °F). Hot working (rolling, forging, extruding) is readily accomplished in the γ (800 to 840 °C, or 1470 to 1545 °F) or high α (600 to 640 °C, or 1110 to 1185 °F) temperature ranges, and cold or warm working (rolling, swaging) can be done from room temperature to about 400 °C (750 °F). Because of its relatively low ductility, deformation in the β-phase is not desirable. Recrystallization of cold-worked material can be performed in the high α region (500 to 640 °C, or 930 to 1185 °F). The material can be machined by most normal cutting and grinding techniques, but special tools and cutting conditions as well as safety precautions are recommended.

Uranium is frequently alloyed to improve its corrosion resistance and/or to modify its mechanical properties. These alloys are produced by vacuum induction or vacuum arc melting and, like unalloyed uranium, can be fabricated hot, warm, or cold. As shown in Fig. 1, the high-temperature γ phase can dissolve substantial amounts of several alloying elements, but these elements are less soluble in the intermediate- and low-temperature β and α phases. Uranium alloys are generally heat treated at approximately 800 °C (1470 °F) to get all the alloying additions into solid solution in the γ phase, then cooled at various rates to room temperature. Slow cooling permits the γ phase to decompose to two-phase structures morphologically similar to pearlite in steels. Rapid quenching suppresses these diffusional decomposition modes, resulting in various metastable phases.

The microstructures and hardnesses produced by quenching are summarized in Fig. 2. Very dilute alloys (Fig. 17) exhibit super-

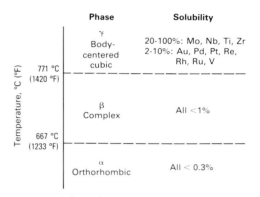

**Fig. 1** Polymorphism and solubilities of alloying elements in uranium. Note that alloying elements are substantially less soluble in lower temperature phases.

saturated α phase with an irregular grain morphology similar to that of unalloyed uranium. Slightly more concentrated alloys exhibit acicular martensitic microstructures (Fig. 21). Both of these microconstituents are orthorhombic variants of α-uranium. Their hardness and yield strength increase with increasing alloy content due to solid-solution effects.

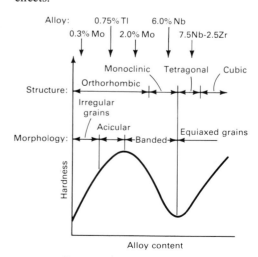

**Fig. 2** Effects of alloy concentration on structure and properties of quenched alloys

The author wishes to thank the following individuals for their assistance: T.N. Simmons, Sandia National Laboratories; A.G. Dobbins, Martin-Marietta; C.E. Polson, NLO, Inc.; A.L. Geary, Nuclear Metals, Inc.; and A.D. Romig, Jr., Sandia National Laboratories.

Further increases in alloy content cause a transition to a thermoelastic, or banded, martensite (Fig. 29 and 38). The hardness and yield strength of the thermoelastic martensites decrease with increasing alloy content, apparently due to increasing mobilities of the boundaries of the many fine twins produced during the transformation. Midway in the thermoelastic martensite composition range, the crystal structure changes to monoclinic, as one lattice angle departs gradually from 90°. This change in crystal structure has little apparent effect on mechanical behavior. These martensitic variants of α-uranium are frequently termed $\alpha'_a$, $\alpha'_b$, and $\alpha''_b$; the subscripts a and b denote the acicular and banded morphologies, respectively, and the prime and double prime superscripts denote the orthorhombic and monoclinic crystal structures, respectively.

Additional increases in alloy content produce a transition to γ°, an ordered tetragonal variant of elevated-temperature γ-uranium (Fig. 40). Further alloy additions cause retention of the cubic γ phase. These variants of the γ phase can be distinguished by x-ray diffraction, but not by metallography.

The phases produced by quenching are metastable and supersaturated; therefore, they are amenable to subsequent heat treatment. As substitutional solid solutions, they are relatively soft (92 HRB to 35 HRC) and ductile (15 to 32% tensile elongation). Subsequent heat treatment increases their hardness and strength. Age hardening occurs at temperatures below approximately 450 °C (840 °F) due to fine-scale microstructural changes observable only by transmission electron microscopy or other very high resolution techniques. Overaging occurs at higher temperatures or longer times by decomposition of the metastable structures. This decomposition, which commonly takes place by cellular or discontinuous precipitation, is revealed by optical metallography (Fig. 24, 30, and 39).

Although heat treatment is the primary method for controlling mechanical properties, ductility is also strongly influenced by the presence of impurities. Carbon, oxygen, and nitrogen are picked up in the melting process from the crucibles and molds (in the case of carbon), from contamination of the surfaces of the materials being melted, or from the furnace atmosphere. These elements cause inclusions to form in the metal. Metal fluorides can also be carried over from the metal reduction process. Other tramp elements, such as silicon and iron, can form intermetallic compound inclusions with uranium. These impurities deleteriously affect ductility when present above various threshold levels.

Perhaps the most insidious impurity, however, is hydrogen, which can be introduced during melting or subsequent processing. (Salt baths for heating metal prior to working are notorious sources of hydrogen.) In some alloys, the presence of less than 1 ppm (by weight) hydrogen causes a 50% decrease in the reduction in area associated with tensile fracture. Hydrogen is commonly removed by vacuum heat treatment at 800 to 900 °C (1470 to 1650 °F).

## Sample Preparation

Methods for preparation of metallographic samples of uranium have been thoroughly reviewed in Ref 1 and 9. This section draws heavily on these references and emphasizes current, successful techniques. Methods for preparation of thin foils for transmission electron microscopy are also described in the literature (Ref 6, 10), but will not be reviewed in this article.

**Health and Safety Considerations.** Handling and metallographic preparation of depleted uranium is similar to that of most metals, although its mild radioactivity, chemical toxicity, and pyrophoricity require additional precautions. Although extreme measures such as shielded glove box handling are not required, a common-sense approach based on a realistic understanding of the hazards involved is essential. This section briefly outlines the principal hazards and necessary precautions associated with the metallographic preparation of depleted uranium. More complete information on the health and safety aspects of working with uranium can be found in Ref 11 to 13. Organizations performing uranium metallography should have their procedures as well as the engineering designs of their cutting and grinding areas approved regularly by an occupational health and safety organization for compliance with the referenced guidelines and state regulations. Personnel and work areas should also be tested and inspected periodically.

The primary radiological hazards associated with depleted uranium are beta and alpha emission. The beta-ray dose rate at the surface of a uranium slug is 0.23 rad/h. This dose rate decreases dramatically with increasing distance from the source, due to absorption in the air and geometric effects. In addition, for specimens mounted in Bakelite or epoxy, virtually none of the beta radiation passes through the mount. Alpha radiation is also emitted, but is almost totally absorbed in 10 mm (0.4 in.) of air or in the 0.07-mm (0.003-in.) thick protective layer of skin and, therefore, presents no external health hazard. The gamma-radiation dose rate measured at a typical working distance of 400 mm (16 in.) from an unmounted 55-g sample is $1 \times 10^{-6}$ R/h, or about one tenth of the natural gamma background rate. (1 R, or roentgen, equals $2.58 \times 10^{-4}$ coulomb per kilogram.) As a result, normal metallographic handling of depleted uranium virtually never causes exposures approaching the federal and state external exposure limits of 3 rem (roentgen equivalent man) per quarter/5 rem per year for whole body exposure or 25 rem per quarter/75 rem per year for extremity (e.g., finger) exposures. Undesirable exposure could result, however, from storing samples in clothes pockets or repeatedly wearing lab coats extensively soiled with fine debris from uranium cutting or grinding operations.

While alpha radiation poses essentially no external health hazard, it does require caution during sectioning and grinding to ensure that finely divided uranium particles do not become airborne, where they could be inhaled and result in alpha irradiation of delicate lung tissue. Methods for ensuring that airborne uranium concentrations remain below the Occupational Safety and Health Administration standard of 0.25 mg/m³ of air are discussed later in this section.

Depleted uranium is about as chemically toxic as other heavy metals, such as lead. Although this does not dictate a need for extreme measures in handling, appropriate housekeeping and personal hygiene practices will minimize the possibility of ingesting uranium, which could damage the kidneys. For example, disposable gloves should be worn during cutting and grinding; hands should be washed thoroughly before eating; smoking, eating or drinking should not be permitted in areas where cutting and grinding are performed; and tabletops and floors should be wet wiped or mopped daily. These measures are particularly important in areas where hot-worked parts are being handled, because the powdery oxide scale accentuates contamination of laboratory furniture and personnel.

Because finely divided uranium is also pyrophoric, sparks are frequently generated during cutting. The ignition temperature for 270-mesh (about 50-μm) powder is only 20 °C (68 °F). Therefore, liberal amounts of cutting fluid should be used in cutting and grinding, and cleaning should be done regularly to avoid accumulation of finely divided waste in saws, cutoff wheels, or grinders. Extinguishers for metal fires should also be available.

**Sectioning.** Samples for metallographic preparation can be cut with a power saw or an abrasive cutoff wheel (see the article "Sectioning" in this Volume for additional information on these methods). Liberal amounts of nonflammable cutting fluid will minimize the generation of airborne material and the danger of fire. In addition, high-speed cutoff wheels that produce finely divided uranium particles should be enclosed and their interiors vented with negative pressure filtered units to prevent airborne material from escaping into the room, where it could be directly inhaled or perhaps eventually ingested after settling on laboratory surfaces. Wearing disposable gloves during cutting as well as washing samples and hands after sectioning will further reduce laboratory contamination and health hazards. Finely divided metal residue should be removed regularly to minimize the danger of fire. Metal scraps, cutting residue, used cutting fluid, worn grinding papers, and so forth should be stored and discarded appropriately.

Excessive heat during sectioning can alter the hardness and microstructures of many uranium alloys. Cutting-induced temperature increases can be minimized with low cutting rates and large amounts of cutting fluid. The care required to avoid heating depends on the material being prepared and on the type of measurements planned. The most temperature-sensitive materials are as-quenched alloys (particularly those containing substantial amounts of alloying elements), such as U-6Nb. In these alloys, changes in hardness and fine microstructural features (sometimes resolvable by transmission electron microscopy and similar techniques, but not by light microscopy) can occur from short-time exposures to temperatures as low as 150 °C (300 °F), and gross microstructural changes (resolvable by light microscopy) can occur below 400 °C (750 °F). As-quenched alloys that contain lesser amounts of alloying elements, such as U-0.75Ti, are more stable, exhibiting fine and gross microstructural changes at approximately 350 °C (660 °F) and 500 °C (930 °F), respectively. Age-hardened materials are stable up to the temperature at which they had been heat treated, while annealed two-phase materials and unalloyed uranium are stable to greater than 600 °C (1110 °F).

Cutting-induced deformation can also result in microstructural artifacts. Sensitivity to deformation generally increases with decreasing hardness and is most acute in unalloyed uranium and as-quenched alloys near the $\alpha''$ to $\gamma°$ transition, such as U-6Nb. Sectioning deformation is best minimized with low cutting rates; when suspected, it can often be removed by careful grinding to below the depth of deformation damage.

**Mounting.** Uranium can be mounted in any of the common metallographic mounting materials, such as Bakelite, phenolic, and epoxy (see the article "Mounting of Specimens" in this Volume for additional information on these materials). Frequently, the metal reacts with epoxy mixtures, resulting in minimal gas evolution during curing. This produces small bubbles in the mount that, during subsequent polishing, can trap abrasives and contaminate polishing cloths. Coating of specimens (nickel plating, spraying with epoxy paint, etc.) prior to mounting can prevent bubble formation. Nickel plating also can be used to avoid edge rounding during polishing—when a fracture profile is to be examined, for example. However, because uranium surfaces oxidize rapidly when exposed to air, the nickel plating may not adhere. This can be overcome by sputter depositing a thin layer of a conductive material, such as a gold-palladium alloy, onto the oxidized surface prior to nickel plating. Sputtering can usually be performed in a scanning electron microscopy laboratory, because nonconductive materials must be coated prior to examination by scanning electron microscopy.

**Grinding.** Uranium samples can be ground by various standard metallographic procedures. Fixed abrasive silicon carbide papers flushed with water work well, as does 600-grit aluminum oxide powder in a kero-sene vehicle on a cast iron lapping wheel. A uniform 600-grit finish is adequate for subsequent polishing.

Sufficient material should be removed in each grinding step to eliminate the deformed material produced by the previous coarser grit. The depth of deformation damage increases with decreasing metal hardness; damage is most severe in soft materials, such as unalloyed uranium and as-quenched U-6Nb. Deformation-induced artifacts in unalloyed uranium are shown in Fig. 10.

The health and safety precautions listed in the previous discussion of uranium sample sectioning also apply to grinding. Dry grinding should always be avoided to minimize the possibility of producing hazardous airborne particulates and to prevent the possibility of excessive specimen heating.

**Polishing.** Uranium can be polished by standard mechanical and electrolytic techniques, as described in the articles "Mechanical Grinding, Abrasion, and Polishing" and "Electrolytic Polishing" in this Volume. Rough polishing is best done on a low-nap cloth, such as nylon. Diamond abrasive with a commercial petroleum-base vehicle works best, but silicon carbide and aluminum oxide ($Al_2O_3$) abrasives with water vehicles are also satisfactory. As a standard technique for rough polishing, the author's laboratory uses 30-$\mu$m diamond paste followed by 6-$\mu$m diamond paste on a nylon lap with a petroleum-base vehicle.

Final polishing can be accomplished mechanically or electrolytically. Mechanical polishing is most frequently used when the samples are to be etched and viewed using bright-field illumination. This is normally the case with multiphase specimens. Chemical differences between the phases cause them to respond differently to etchants, thus producing differential surface relief effects that make the various microstructural features discernible with bright-field illumination. Final mechanical polishing is best done on a high-nap cloth with 0.3-$\mu$m $\alpha$-$Al_2O_3$ abrasive and a deionized water vehicle. In some cases, this can be fol-lowed by a similar step using 0.05-$\mu$m $\gamma$-$Al_2O_3$. These final polishing steps can be carried out on rotating wheels or vibratory polishers. In the author's laboratory, final mechanical polishing is performed by vibratory polishing for 6 to 12 h using a thin paste of 0.3-$\mu$m $Al_2O_3$ in deionized water.

The high chemical reactivity of uranium sometimes results in pitting during these final polishing steps, particularly when long-term vibratory polishing is employed. Often caused by chemical interactions with materials in the polishing system, pitting usually can be overcome by thorough cleaning of the polishing system and use of new polishing cloths and slurry. It can also occur due to galvanic reactions inherent in the sample. This is particularly common with nickel-plated uranium samples and is best avoided by final polishing for a short time on a rotating wheel, although this often compromises the quality of the final polish.

Electrolytic final polishing is frequently used to remove the last vestiges of surface deformation in preparation for polarized light examination. Electrolytic polishing and polarized light examination are usually applied to unalloyed uranium and single-phase alloys, where the primary distinctions between adjacent microstructural features are differences in crystallographic orientation. Electrolytic polishing solutions and the conditions for their use are given in Table 1. Orthophosphoric acid (ortho-$H_3PO_4$) and water (No. 1 in Table 1) works well with many alloys.

An alternative for obtaining deformation-free surfaces for polarized light microscopy is attack polishing, in which chemically active solutions are used as vehicles in final polishing. In addition to producing a deformation-free surface, these solutions often cause a thin epitaxial oxide layer to form on the surface, enhancing the contrast obtained during polarized light examination. Specific solutions for attack polishing are given in Table 4, along with other methods of preparing previously polished samples for polarized light examination.

## Table 1 Electropolishing solutions for uranium and uranium alloys

| Solution | Comments |
|---|---|
| 1. 1 part ortho-$H_3PO_4$ acid<br>1 part $H_2O$ | 30 V open circuit, stainless steel cathode |
| 2. 1 part ortho-$H_3PO_4$ acid<br>1 part ethylene glycol<br>1-2 parts ethyl alcohol | 10-30 A/cm² (65 to 195 A/in.²), must be kept cold and free of water |
| 3. 1 part 118 g $CrO_3$ in 100 mL $H_2O$<br>3-4 parts glacial acetic acid | 40 V open circuit |
| 4. 85 parts ortho-$H_3PO_4$ acid<br>13 parts $H_2O$<br>2 parts $H_2SO_4$ | 0.4 A/cm² (2.5 A/in.²), stainless steel cathode |
| 5. 1-2 parts ortho-$H_3PO_4$ acid<br>2 parts $H_2SO_4$<br>2 parts $H_2O$ | 0.5 A/cm² (3 A/in.²), agitate solution |
| 6. 1 part $HClO_4$ (perchloric acid)(a)<br>20 parts glacial acetic acid | 60 V, 0.6-0.8 A/cm² (4-5 A/in.²), vigorous stirring |

(a) Solutions containing substantial amounts of $HClO_4$ are potentially explosive, especially in contact with oxidizable materials, such as organics. This solution should be prepared by slowly adding $HClO_4$ to acetic acid while stirring. Use of more concentrated solutions is also reported in the literature, but is not recommended because of safety considerations.

# Macroetching and Macroexamination

Macroetching and macroexamination are sometimes used to characterize the grain structures, segregation patterns, and metal flow geometries produced by solidification and mechanical working processes. Macroetching procedures are listed in Table 2. Contrast between regions of different chemical composition may be enhanced by heating the part to the $\gamma$-phase field, quenching, and slightly overaging; because decomposition of the martensite generally begins at lower temperatures in alloy-rich regions, the regions in which alloying elements are concentrated will preferentially overage and etch much darker. Flow lines in forged or extruded parts are often difficult to delineate unless segregation in the original ingot provides bands of varying alloy content. It is sometimes useful to produce deliberately banded vacuum arc melted uranium alloy ingots for studying metal flow during subsequent forming operations.

Macroexamination and photography are carried out with low-magnification optical devices and techniques identical to those used with other alloy systems. Typical macrographs are shown in Fig. 3 and 4.

# Microetching and Microexamination

Inclusions in uranium and uranium alloys are usually visible without etching. Metallographic techniques for inclusion identification include heat tinting, copper plating from a copper cyanide solution, and chemical etching in nitric acid. These methods are detailed in Table 3, along with descriptions of the typical morphologies of inclusions and intermetallic compounds associated with impurities in uranium. Typical micrographs are also shown in Fig. 11 to 14. These indirect metallographic methods were widely used prior to the proliferation of electron beam microanalytical techniques in the 1960s and '70s, and they continue to be useful for rapid analysis of heat-to-heat variations in microcleanliness, etc. More definitive inclusion identification can now be done on as-polished samples with electron probe microanalysis and/or scanning Auger microscopy.

The microstructures of unalloyed uranium and single-phase uranium alloys are most frequently characterized with polarized light microscopy. Although such features as grain and twin boundaries are often difficult to delineate by etching and bright-field examination, the optical anisotropy of the orthorhombic crystal structure of uranium allows adjacent regions of differing crystallographic orientation to be defined by polarized light microscopy. Development of good polarized light contrast requires metallographic surfaces that are free from polishing deforma-

**Table 2  Macroetching procedures for uranium and uranium alloys**

| Procedure | Comments |
|---|---|
| 1. Immerse 30 s to 1 min in HCl<br>Rinse in cold water<br>Rinse in $HNO_3$ 1 to 5 s(a)<br>Rinse in cold water | Macroetches unalloyed uranium |
| 2. Immerse 30 min in:<br>    1 part acetic acid<br>    1 part $HNO_3$(a) | Macroetches unalloyed uranium |
| 3. Electrolytically etch at 0.05<br>    A/cm² (0.3 A/in.²) in:<br>        1 part trichloracetic acid<br>        1 part $H_2O$<br>Remove black film in 50% $HNO_3$(a) | Macroetches unalloyed uranium |
| 4. Electrolytically etch at 0.05<br>    A/cm² (0.3 A/in.²) in:<br>        5 g citric acid<br>        5 mL $H_2SO_4$<br>        450 mL $H_2O$ | Macroetches unalloyed uranium |
| 5. Heat tint at 200 to 400 °C<br>    (390 to 750 °F) for 3 to 5 min | Reveals chemical segregation in alloys. Surface must be clean and free of oxide prior to heat tinting. |
| 6. Water quench from 800 °C (1470 °F)<br>Age to just past peak hardness<br>    (temperature varies depending on alloy)<br>Electroetch with $H_3PO_4$ or oxalic acid (see Table 5) | Reveals chemical segregation in alloys |
| 7. Heat sample to 450 °C (840 °F)<br>Cool<br>Electroetch to 0.01 A/cm²<br>    (0.06 A/in.²) in:<br>        1 part 55 g $CrO_3$ in 50 mL $H_2O$<br>        1 part saturated solution of $Na_2CrO_4$ (sodium chromate) in $H_2O$ | Reveals chemical segregation and flow lines in uranium-niobium alloys |

(a) Solutions containing $HNO_3$ are not recommended for use with uranium-niobium alloys due to the formation of an explosive surface layer.

**Table 3  Metallographic identification of inclusions and intermetallic compounds in uranium and uranium alloys**

| Inclusion/compound | Morphology | Sample condition | Appearance Bright field | Polarized light |
|---|---|---|---|---|
| UC | Small and angular or large and dendritic | As-polished | White/gray | ... |
| | | Heat tinted | Orange/red | ... |
| | | Copper plated 1-2 min | Discontinuous deposit | ... |
| | | $HNO_3$ etched | Black | Black |
| UN | Angular, dendritic, or Chinese script | As-polished | Gray | Dark gray |
| | | Copper plated 3-10 s | Continuous deposit | ... |
| | | $HNO_3$ etched | Gray | Dark gray |
| U(C,N) | Angular, dendritic, or Chinese script | As-polished | Gray | Dark gray |
| | | Heat tinted | Yellow | ... |
| | | Copper plated 20 s | Continuous deposit | ... |
| | | $HNO_3$ etched | Dark gray | Dark gray |
| UO or U(O,C,N) | Spherical, rimmed with second phase, or irregular globules | As-polished | Light gray | Dark gray |
| | | Heat tinted | Dark gray | ... |
| | | Copper plated 1-2 min | No deposit | ... |
| $UO_2$ | Globular or partly elongated | As-polished | Dark gray | Red, rust |
| | | Heat tinted | Dark gray | ... |
| | | Copper plated 1-2 min | No deposit | ... |
| $UH_3$ | Needles or stringers | As-polished | Tan, light brown | Gray |
| | | Heat tinted | Silver halo | ... |
| | | $HNO_3$ etched | No attack | ... |
| $U_3Si_2$ | Globular, frequently rimmed with $U_3Si$ | Attack polished with dilute $HF$-$HNO_3$ | Gray | ... |
| $U_3Si$ | Globular, or rim around globular $U_3Si_2$ | Attack polished with dilute $HF$-$HNO_3$ | Brown | ... |
| $MgF_2$ and $CaF_2$ | Glassy, globular or partly elongated stringers | As-polished | Black | White |
| $UF_3$ | Globular, elongated | As-polished | Black | Violet |
| $U_6Fe$ | Decorates $\gamma$ grain boundaries | Electropolished | Gray | ... |
| | | Copper plated 1 min | Continuous deposit | ... |
| | | $HNO_3$ etched | Gray | ... |
| $Nb_2C$ | Sharp, angular | As-polished | White | ... |
| NbC | Sharp, angular | As-polished | Light gray | ... |

tion; therefore, final polishing is usually done by electropolishing or chemical-attack polishing. Some metallographers perform polarized light microscopy on as-polished samples, but most employ various treatments to form a thin epitaxial oxide film on the polished surface prior to metallographic examination. This thin oxide frequently increases polarized light contrast. Heat tinting, incorporation of chemically active vehicles during final mechanical polishing, and electrolytic anodization are some of the ways epitaxial oxide films can be formed. These preparation treatments for polarized light microscopy are summarized in Table 4. Examples of the microstructures revealed by these techniques are shown in Fig. 5 to 10, 15, 17, 23, 29, 31, 32, 34, and 38.

Uranium alloys with more than one phase are frequently etched and examined by bright-field microscopy. Etching is most often done electrolytically, although some chemical etchants are also used. Preparation treatments for bright-field microscopy are listed in Table 5, and examples of microstructures revealed by this method are shown in Fig. 18 to 22, 24 to 28, 30, 33, 35 to 37, and 39 to 40.

## Microstructures of Uranium and Uranium Alloys

**Unalloyed uranium** is generally vacuum induction melted and cast. Components are sometimes cast to final or near-final dimensions; in other cases, subsequent metalworking operations are employed. Primary metalworking operations such as ingot breakdown by extrusion, forging and rolling are often carried out in the high $\alpha$ range (600 to 640 °C, or 1110 to 1185 °F) if sufficient tonnage equipment is available. Secondary forming operations, including rolling, swaging, and deep drawing, can be done at temperatures as low as 25 °C (75 °F). Cold- and warm-worked parts can be recrystallized at 500 to 650 °C (930 to 1200 °F).

Large uranium castings frequently contain coarse, columnar grain structures that can be revealed by macroetching (Fig. 3). Heating to the $\beta$-phase field and quenching provide significant grain refinement (Fig. 4). The microstructure of as-cast uranium consists of large, irregular grains, each containing slightly misoriented subgrains and a substantial density of thin twins (Fig. 5). The irregular grains and subgrains are produced by the $\gamma$ to $\beta$ and $\beta$ to $\alpha$ phase transformations that occur during cooling. The twins are formed by localized deformation that takes place on cooling to accommodate the extremely anisotropic thermal contraction of the variously oriented $\alpha$-grains. These twins are often bent and deflected as they cross the low-angle subgrain boundaries. Heating into the $\beta$-phase field and quenching produce a finer grain structure, but the grains are still extremely irregular and highly twinned (Fig. 6).

### Table 4  Final preparation of uranium samples for polarized light microexamination

| Solution | Comments |
|---|---|
| **Attack polishing methods** | |
| 1. 5 wt% $CrO_3$ in $H_2O$ | Use as vehicle during final polishing. |
| 2. 1 part HF<br>   1 part $HNO_3$<br>   2 parts $H_2O$ | A few drops on final polishing wheel.<br>*Caution:* Hydrofluoric acid solutions cause severe burns if allowed to contact skin. |
| **Anodizing solutions (electrolytic)(a)** | |
| 3. 1 part $NH_4OH$<br>   30 parts ethylene glycol | 60 V open circuit potential, 30 s to 2 min. Solution must be kept free of water. |
| 4. 1 part $NH_4OH$<br>   4 parts ethanol | |
| **Chemical(a)** | |
| 5. 10% $AgNO_3$ (silver nitrate) in $H_2O$ | Immerse sample in boiling solution. |
| 6. 10% $FeCl_3$ in $H_2O$ | Immerse sample in boiling solution. |
| **Atmospheric oxidation(a)** | |
| 7. Air | Allow sample to oxidize in air at 25 to 300 °C (75 to 570 °F). Temperature and time vary strongly with alloy composition. |

(a) Sample must have deformation-free polished surface prior to treatment; electropolishing is suggested as a means of producing this surface.

### Table 5  Final preparation of uranium samples for bright-field microexamination

| Solution | Comments |
|---|---|
| **Electrolytic etches** | |
| 1. 1 part ortho-$H_3PO_4$ acid<br>   1 part $H_2O$ | 1-5 V open circuit(a), stainless steel cathode |
| 2. 5-10% oxalic acid in $H_2O$ | 1-5 V open circuit(a), stainless steel cathode |
| 3. 1 part 118 g $CrO_3$ in 100 mL $H_2O$<br>   3 parts glacial acetic acid | 5-20 V open circuit(a), stainless steel cathode |
| 4. 1 part ortho-$H_3PO_4$ acid<br>   2 parts $H_2SO_4$<br>   2 parts $H_2O$ | 1-10 V open circuit(a), stainless steel cathode |
| 5. 85 parts ortho-$H_3PO_4$ acid<br>   13 parts $H_2O$<br>   2 parts $H_2SO_4$ | 1-10 V open circuit(a), stainless steel cathode |
| 6. 1 part ortho-$H_3PO_4$ acid<br>   1 part ethylene glycol<br>   1-2 parts ethyl alcohol | 1-5 V open circuit(a), stainless steel cathode |
| 7. 10 g citric acid<br>   215 mL $HNO_3$<br>   490 mL $H_2O$ | 1-10 V open circuit(a), stainless steel cathode |
| 8. 1 part $HClO_4$(b)<br>   20 parts glacial acetic acid | 1-10 V open circuit(a), stainless steel cathode |
| **Chemical etches** | |
| 9. 1 part HF(c)<br>   10 parts $HNO_3$<br>   25 parts ortho-$H_3PO_4$<br>   10 parts $H_2O$ | Immerse. |
| 10. 1 part HF(c)<br>   1 part $HNO_3$<br>   2 parts glycerol | Immerse, can also be used as electrolytic etch. |
| **Attack etches** | |
| 11. 1 part 0.3-$\mu$m $Al_2O_3$<br>   2 parts saturated solution of $Na_2Cr_2O_7 \cdot 2H_2O$ (sodium dichromate)<br>   12 parts $H_2O$ | Use in final polish to sharpen edges of inclusions. |
| **Atmospheric oxidation** | Allow sample to oxidize in air at 25 to 300 °C (75 to 570 °F). Temperature and time vary strongly with alloy composition. |

(a) Voltage varies depending on alloy composition and heat treatment. Best practice is to start with low voltage while watching sample surface and increase voltage until visible etching begins. (b) *Caution:* Solutions containing substantial amounts of $HClO_4$ are potentially explosive, especially when brought into contact with oxidizable material, such as organics. This solution should be prepared by slowly adding $HClO_4$ to acetic acid while stirring. Use of more concentrated solutions are also reported in the literature, but these are not recommended because of safety considerations. (c) *Caution:* Hydrofluoric acid solutions cause severe burns if allowed to contact skin.

Hot working of unalloyed uranium in the high α-phase field (600 to 640 °C, or 1110 to 1185 °F) produces finer and more regularly shaped grains (Fig. 7). Recrystallization occurs during deformation, frequently resulting in a duplex grain structure with some grains substantially larger than others. Despite recrystallization, the grain shapes are usually somewhat elongated in the direction of working, particularly in relatively low-purity materials where grain boundaries are pinned by large numbers of inclusions.

Cold and warm working at temperatures below 350 °C (660 °F) produce an elongated grain structure containing a high density of deformation twins (Fig. 8). The number of twins increases with decreasing deformation temperature. Warm working followed by recrystallization at 500 to 650 °C (930 to 1200 °F) results in the finest and most equiaxed grain structure (Fig. 9). Material in this condition also exhibits the lowest density of twins, apparently because the stresses that develop from anisotropic contraction during cooling are smaller and more easily accommodated in fine-grained material. Examples of inclusions in uranium and artifacts commonly produced during metallographic sample preparation are shown in Fig. 10 to 14.

**U-0.3Mo** is used for applications requiring a higher yield strength than that of unalloyed uranium. The material is usually vacuum induction melted, cast to near final shape, then used in the as-cast condition.

Low-magnification polarized light microscopy of as-cast U-0.3Mo reveals an irregular grain structure similar to that of cast unalloyed uranium, except that the grain size is finer (Fig. 15). High-magnification bright-field microscopy reveals a fine, lamellar two-phase microstructure morphologically similar to pearlite in steels (Fig. 16). Apparently, this microstructure develops when the β phase, which dissolves the 0.3% Mo in solid solution, undergoes eutectoid decomposition to essentially pure α-uranium plus a molybdenum-enriched γ phase. Under some conditions, the γ phase may decompose at a lower temperature to a fine (probably optically unresolvable) mixture of α-uranium and $U_2Mo$.

Quenching of thin sections of U-0.3Mo from the α-phase field suppresses the diffusional transformations that produce two-phase microstructures during slow cooling and results in a microstructure of supersaturated α phase (Fig. 17). The morphological similarities to unalloyed uranium suggest that the quenched material undergoes the γ to β to α transformation sequence of pure metal.

**U-0.75Ti** is used for applications requiring outstanding combinations of strength and ductility. Material is made by vacuum induction melting and casting. It is then mechanically worked in the high α range (600 to 640 °C, or 1110 to 1185 °F) by such processes as extrusion, rolling, and swaging, after which it is vacuum heat treated in the γ-phase field to remove hydrogen, quenched to produce a supersaturated variant of α phase, and age hardened. This alloy is age hardenable to ~50 HRC, but its ductility and toughness are low in the fully aged condition (elongation and reduction in area <3%, $K_{Ic}$ ~ 18 MPa$\sqrt{m}$, or 16 ksi$\sqrt{in.}$). Partial aging to ~44 HRC is more commonly used, resulting in a strong but ductile material with the following properties:

| | |
|---|---|
| Yield strength | 930 MPa (135 ksi) |
| Ultimate tensile strength | 1550 MPa (225 ksi) |
| Elongation | 20% |
| Reduction in area | 32% |
| Plane-strain fracture toughness | 47 MPa$\sqrt{m}$ (43 ksi$\sqrt{in.}$) |

The microstructure of U-0.75Ti varies dramatically with cooling rate from the γ-phase field and subsequent aging treatment. Slow cooling (<2 °C/s, or 3.6 °F/s) permits the equilibrium transformation sequence (γ → β + $U_2Ti$ → α + $U_2Ti$) to occur and produces an optically resolvable two-phase microstructure that etches rapidly (Fig. 18). Faster cooling suppresses formation of the β phase and results in direct decomposition of γ to α + $U_2Ti$. This microconstituent etches a uniform gray, because the individual phases are too fine to be resolved optically (Fig. 19). At cooling rates exceeding 10 °C/s (18 °F/s), the γ → α + $U_2Ti$ reaction begins to be suppressed, resulting in partial transformation of the γ phase by a martensitic (diffusionless) reaction to a supersaturated variant of the α phase (Fig. 20). At cooling rates between 10 and 75 °C/s (18 and 135 °F/s), the α + $U_2Ti$ microconstituent nucleates along the γ-grain boundaries and proceeds inward, beginning to consume the γ phase. Before this reaction is complete, however, martensitic transformation begins and competes with α + $U_2Ti$ formation for the remaining γ phase. The result is a microstructure with α + $U_2Ti$ along the prior γ-grain boundaries and $α'_a$ martensite plus α + $U_2Ti$ in the prior γ-grain interiors (Fig. 20).

The amount of martensite in the microstructure increases with increasing cooling rate. At cooling rates greater than 75 °C/s (135 °F/s), decomposition of γ phase to α + $U_2Ti$ no longer precedes the onset of the martensitic transformation; therefore, no α + $U_2Ti$ is seen along the prior-γ grain boundaries (the martensite start temperature is reached before α + $U_2Ti$ can nucleate). Formation of α + $U_2Ti$, however, continues in the interstices between the martensite plates (nucleation of α + $U_2Ti$ occurs before the martensite finish temperature is reached). This interplate α + $U_2Ti$ forms a background against which the martensite can be revealed by etching and bright-field illumination (Fig. 21). At cooling rates greater than 200 °C/s (360 °F/s), diffusional decomposition is suppressed, and the γ phase transforms to $α'_a$ martensite. Because this is a single-phase microstructure, it is difficult to reveal by etching

and bright-field microscopy (Fig. 22) and can be more easily observed with polarized light microscopy (Fig. 23).

The rapid cooling required to suppress diffusional decomposition of the γ phase limits the section thicknesses in which martensite can be obtained. Water quenching produces fully martensitic microstructures with optimum ductility and age hardenability only in plates thinner than a few millimeters. The amount of martensite decreases with increasing plate thickness, but good mechanical properties can be obtained in plates as thick as at least 25 mm (1 in.). Plates thicker than about 30 mm (1.2 in.) exhibit predominantly nonmartensitic microstructures and substantially lower ductilities, even when quenched in severely agitated cold water. Severe quenching of thick sections (25 mm, or 1 in., or more) may also cause centerbursting in bar stock due to the volume changes associated with phase transformations.

Material with a fully or predominantly martensitic microstructure can be age hardened at 325 to 450 °C (615 to 840 °F). The microstructural changes responsible for age hardening of the martensite are too fine to be resolved by light microscopy, but transmission electron microscopy has shown that strengthening occurs due to the formation of coherent precipitates of $U_2Ti$. Overaging occurs at temperatures above about 450 °C (840 °F) by cellular decomposition of the martensite to the equilibrium α and $U_2Ti$ phases. This decomposition reaction nucleates preferentially along the prior-γ grain boundaries, and its product etches much darker than the $α'_2$ martensite (Fig. 24). The individual α and $U_2Ti$ features are too fine to be resolved optically, except after extensive overaging, when the $U_2Ti$ can be seen to form a semicontinuous, embrittling film along the prior martensite plate boundaries (Fig. 25).

**U-2.0Mo** is used for applications requiring higher strength than unalloyed uranium and where section thickness or other constraints prevent the use of U-0.75Ti. The alloy is made by vacuum induction melting and casting. It is frequently used in the form of castings, but it can also be fabricated in the high α (600 to 640 °C, or 1110 to 1185 °F) or γ (800 to 840 °C, or 1470 to 1545 °F) temperature ranges. Thick components are usually used in the as-cast or annealed (slowly cooled) condition, while thinner parts are sometimes more rapidly cooled, then aged.

The microstructure of a slowly cooled, rapidly etched material consists of a coarse α + Mo-enriched-γ mixture (Fig. 26) similar to that of slowly cooled U-0.75Ti. These phases become more finely divided with increasing cooling rate. At rates from about 2 to 10 °C/s (3.6 to 18 °F/s), the individual phases become difficult to resolve optically, and substantial morphological changes occur (Fig. 27). Although these have not been studied in detail, preliminary indications suggest that these microstructures may be analogous to bainite in steels (that is, fine two-phase microstructures produced by a combination of displacive and diffusional atom movements). Rapid quenching ($>50$ °C/s, or 90 °F/s) suppresses most diffusional transformations and produces a thermoelastic, or banded, martensite. Etching and bright-field examination reveal primarily the prior-$\gamma$ grain boundaries (Fig. 28), but the martensitic structure can be clearly seen by anodizing the sample and using polarized light illumination (Fig. 29).

This martensite and, to a lesser extent, some structures produced by intermediate cooling rates can be age hardened, but the microstructural changes responsible for strengthening have not yet been resolved, even by transmission electron microscopy. Overaging occurs at temperatures above ~400 °C (750 °F) by cellular decomposition of the martensite. Decomposition begins along the prior-$\gamma$ grain boundaries and at inclusions (Fig. 30), eventually consuming the martensite and resulting in what appears metallographically to be a network of fine irregular grains within each prior $\gamma$ grain (Fig. 31). This rapid etching decomposition product consists of a very fine mixture of $\alpha$ phase and molybdenum-enriched $\gamma$ phase that can be resolved only by transmission electron microscopy. Higher temperature or longer aging transforms this decomposition product, through a second discontinuous reaction, into a coarser two-phase mixture of $\alpha$ phase and $U_2Mo$. This reaction nucleates on small persistent vestiges of the original martensite structure, and the crystallographic orientations of the $\alpha$ phase it produces are apparently related to, and perhaps identical to, those of the martensite. As a result, this reaction, when partially complete, gives the appearance that the original banded martensite is reappearing within the irregular grains of the first decomposition product (Fig. 32). When this reaction is complete, the microstructure observable by etching and brightfield microscopy consists of an optically resolvable lamellar mixture of $\alpha$ phase and $U_2Mo$ (Fig. 33). Anodization and polarized light examination, however, reveal that the $\alpha$ phase is crystallographically oriented in parallel bands that span numerous lamellae and are reminiscent of the original martensite morphology (Fig. 34).

**U-6.0Nb** is used for applications requiring excellent corrosion resistance (for a uranium alloy) and outstanding ductility. The material is made by consumable electrode vacuum arc melting. The high amount of alloying element provides relatively high elevated-temperature strength; therefore, equipment tonnage limitations frequently force metalforming operations to be performed in the $\gamma$ region (800 to 840 °C, or 1470 to 1545 °F). The alloy is solution treated in the $\gamma$-phase field and quenched to room temperature, producing a soft and ductile thermoelastic martensite with the following properties:

| | |
|---|---|
| Hardness | 92 HRB |
| Yield strength | 170 MPa (25 ksi) |
| Ultimate tensile strength | 895 MPa (130 ksi) |
| Elongation | 32% |
| Reduction in area | 36% |

This martensite can be aged to hardnesses as high as 54 HRC, but because ductility decreases substantially with increasing strength, age hardening is rarely used. The as-quenched martensite, however, is often given a very low-temperature (~150 °C, or 300 °F) heat treatment to improve dimensional stability. The $\alpha''_b$ to $\gamma°$ reversible martensitic transformation that occurs slightly above room temperature produces a strong mechanical shape memory effect in this alloy. Because arc melting causes significant chemical inhomogeneity and the $\alpha''_b$ to $\gamma°$ transformation temperature is very sensitive to alloy content, the as-quenched material frequently undergoes dimensional instabilities that are related to normal fluctuations in ambient temperature. Very low temperature aging stabilizes the material to these temperature variations without appreciably altering its tensile properties.

U-6.0Nb is markedly less quench-rate sensitive than U-0.75Ti. Only at cooling rates well below 1 °C/s (1.8 °F/s) are rapid-etching two-phase lamellar microstructures produced (Fig. 35). As the cooling rate increases toward 1 °C/s (1.8 °F/s), these regions become confined to the prior-$\gamma$ grain boundaries (Fig. 36); polarized light examination reveals that the remainder of the microstructure consists of martensitic $\alpha''_b$. The martensite produced at cooling rates of 1 to 10 °C/s (1.8 to 18 °F/s), however, contains two features that are not completely understood. Bands parallel to the rolling direction consisting of apparent subgrain boundaries are visible with bright field illumination (Fig. 36). A fine, modulated structure, which can be seen by transmission electron microscopy, substantially increases strength and decreases ductility. At cooling rates greater than 10 °C/s (18 °F/s), the modulated structure disappears, and the $\alpha''_b$ martensite becomes more soft and ductile. The subgrain structure, which has no apparent effect on mechanical properties, becomes more uniformly distributed but less extensive with increasing cooling rate (Fig. 37). Polarized light microscopy reveals the $\alpha''_b$ thermoelastic martensite within the prior-$\gamma$ grains (Fig. 38).

Age hardening produces no microstructural changes resolvable by optical microscopy. A fine, modulated structure, similar to that in higher strength material cooled at about 1 °C/s (1.8 °F/s), can be detected by transmission electron microscopy in agehardened material. Overaging occurs at temperatures in excess of about 400 °C (750 °F) via cellular decomposition of the martensite. As with other alloys, this decomposition nucleates along the prior-$\gamma$ grain boundaries, and the decomposition product etches more rapidly than the martensite (Fig. 39).

**U-7.5Nb-2.5Zr,** sometimes termed "mulberry," is similar to U-6.0Nb. Its high alloy content, however, enables the $\gamma°$ tetragonal distortion of the $\gamma$ phase to be retained after quenching to room temperature. This microstructure appears as simple equiaxed grains with no internal substructure when viewed by optical microscopy (Fig. 40), although transmission electron microscopy has revealed a fine, modulated substructure. The alloy can be age hardened at temperatures between 100 and 400 °C (210 and 750 °F), but is most frequently used in the as-quenched or quenched and thermally stabilized condition. Overaging occurs at temperatures above 400 °C (750 °F) due to grain boundary nucleated cellular decomposition, resulting in microstructures similar to those of U-6.0Nb.

## REFERENCES

1. A.N. Holden, *Physical Metallurgy of Uranium*, Addison-Wesley, 1958
2. W. Lehmann and R.F. Hills, Proposed Nomenclature for Phases in Uranium Alloys, *J. Nucl. Mater.*, Vol 2, 1960, p 261
3. W.D. Wilkinson, *Uranium Metallurgy*, Vol 1 and 2, Interscience, 1962
4. J.J. Burke *et al.*, Ed., *Physical Metallurgy of Uranium Alloys*, Brook Hill, 1976
5. K.H. Eckelmeyer, Microstructural Control in Dilute Uranium Alloys, *Microstruc. Sci.*, Vol 7, 1979, p 133
6. *Metallurgical Technology of Uranium and Uranium Alloys*, Vol 1, 2, and 3, American Society for Metals, 1982
7. J.G. Speer, "A Study of Solid-State Phase Transformations in Uranium Alloys," Ph.D. thesis, Oxford University, 1983
8. K.H. Eckelmeyer, A.D. Romig, and L.J. Weirick, The Effect of Quench Rate on the Microstructure, Mechanical Properties, and Corrosion Behavior of U-6 Wt. Pct. Nb, *Met. Trans. A*, Vol 15, 1984, p 1319
9. R.F. Dickerson, Metallography of Uranium, *Trans. ASM*, Vol 52, 1960, p 748
10. A.D. Romig, Jr. and W.R. Sorenson, Uranium Alloys: Sample Preparation for Transmission Electron Microscopy, *J. Microsc.*, Vol 132, 1983, p 203
11. *Radiological Health Handbook*, U.S. Department of Health, Education, and Welfare, Public Health Service, Food and Drug Administration, Bureau of Radiological Health, Rockville, MD, 1970
12. "Occupational Health Guideline for Uranium and Insoluble Compounds," U.S. Department of Health and Human Services, Washington, DC, 1978
13. "Hygienic Guide Series—Uranium," American Industrial Hygiene Association, Detroit

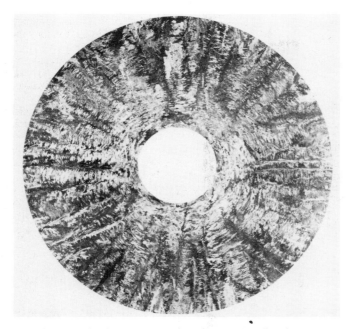

**Fig. 3** Macrograph of cross section through as-cast unalloyed uranium ingot showing coarse columnar grain structure. Etched using procedure 1 in Table 2. One half actual size. (M.H. Cornell and W.N. Wise)

**Fig. 4** Macrograph of cross section through unalloyed uranium ingot showing refined grain structure produced by $\beta$ quenching. Etched using procedure 1 in Table 2. One half actual size. (M.H. Cornell and W.N. Wise)

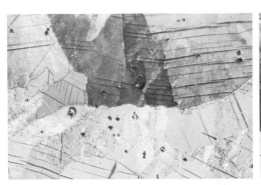

**Fig. 5** Polarized light micrograph of as-cast unalloyed uranium showing large irregular grains, subgrains, and thermal contraction accommodation twins. Attack polished using procedure 1 in Table 4. 100×. (J.W. Koger)

**Fig. 6** Polarized light micrograph of cast and $\beta$-quenched unalloyed uranium showing irregular grains and thermal contraction accommodation twins. Attack polished using procedure 1 in Table 4. 100×. (J.W. Koger)

**Fig. 7** Polarized light micrograph of unalloyed uranium rolled at 630 °C (1165 °F) showing duplex grain structure and few thermal contraction accommodation twins. Attack polished using procedure 1 in Table 4. 100×. (J.W. Koger)

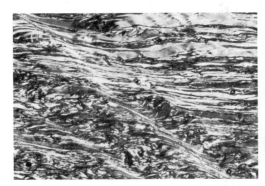

**Fig. 8** Polarized light micrograph of unalloyed uranium hot rolled at 630 °C (1165 °F), then hydroformed at 300 °C (570 °F) showing highly elongated grains. Attack polished using procedure 1 in Table 4. 100×. (J.W. Koger)

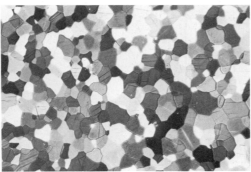

**Fig. 9** Polarized light micrograph of unalloyed uranium hot rolled at 630 °C (1165 °F), then warm rolled at 325 °C (615 °F), and recrystallized at 630 °C (1165 °F) showing fine equiaxed grains with few thermal contraction accommodation twins. Attack polished using procedure 1 in Table 4. 100×. (J.W. Koger)

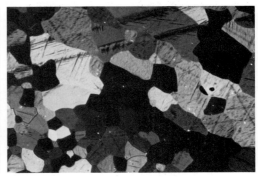

**Fig. 10** Polarized light micrograph showing grinding artifacts in unalloyed uranium. Bands of fine twins are due to deformation from coarse grinding steps that was not removed by subsequent fine grinding and polishing. Electropolished using procedure 1 in Table 1 and anodized using procedure 3 in Table 4. 200×. (M.E. McAllaster)

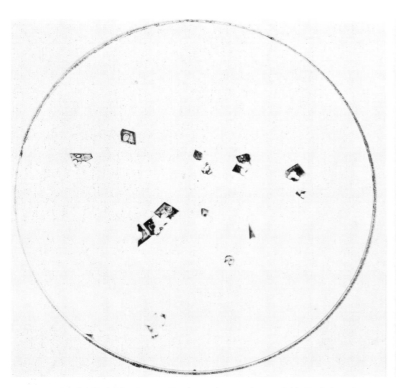

**Fig. 11** Bright-field micrograph of angular uranium carbide inclusions in cast unalloyed uranium. Attack polished using procedure 11 in Table 5. 184×. (W.N. Wise)

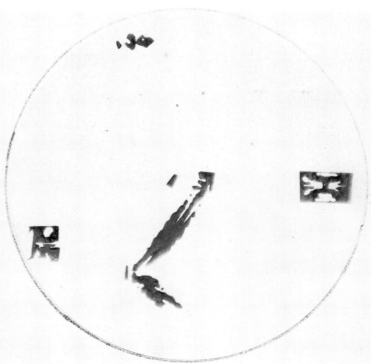

**Fig. 12** Bright-field micrograph of U(CN) inclusions in cast unalloyed uranium. Attack polished using procedure 11 in Table 5. 184×. (W.N. Wise)

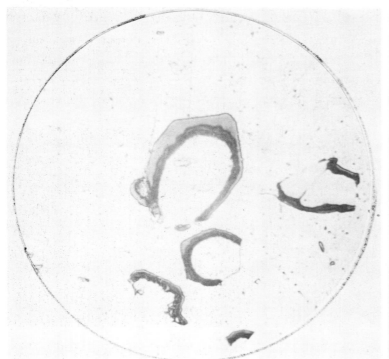

**Fig. 13** Bright-field micrograph of U(CNO) inclusions in cast unalloyed uranium. Attack polished using procedure 11 in Table 5. 184×. (W.N. Wise)

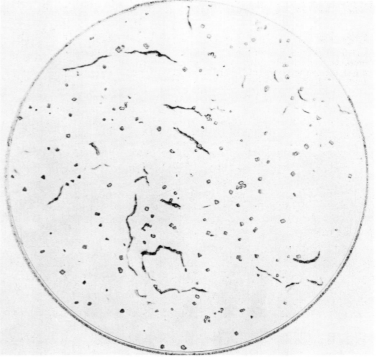

**Fig. 14** Bright-field micrograph of uranium carbide (equiaxed) and $UH_3$ (elongated) in cast unalloyed uranium. Attack polished using procedure 11 in Table 5. 184×. (W.N. Wise)

**Fig. 15** Polarized light micrograph of cast U-0.3Mo showing irregular grain structure similar to that of unalloyed uranium. Electropolished using procedure 1 in Table 1 and anodized using procedure 3 in Table 4. 200×. (M.M. Lappin)

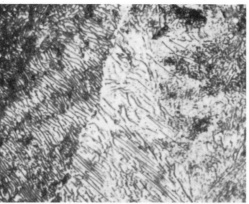

**Fig. 16** Bright-field micrograph of cast U-0.3Mo showing two-phase lamellar structure resulting from eutectoid decomposition of $\beta$ phase. Etched using procedure 1 in Table 5. 1500×. (M.M. Lappin)

**Fig. 17** Polarized light micrograph of U-0.3Mo quenched from 800 °C (1470 °F) showing highly twinned, irregular grains of supersaturated $\alpha$ phase. Electropolished using procedure 1 in Table 1 and anodized using procedure 3 in Table 4. 200×. (M.M. Lappin)

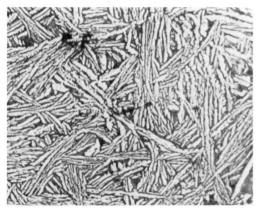

**Fig. 18** Bright-field micrograph of U-0.75Ti cooled from 800 °C (1470 °F) at less than 1 °C/s (1.8 °F/s) showing coarse $\alpha$ + U$_2$Ti microstructure produced by the equilibrium $\gamma \rightarrow \beta$ + U$_2$Ti $\rightarrow \alpha$ + U$_2$Ti transformation sequence. Etched using procedure 1 in Table 5. 400×. (M.E. McAllaster)

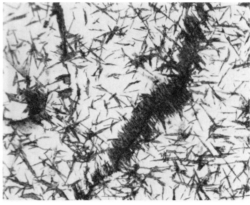

**Fig. 19** Bright-field micrograph of U-0.75Ti cooled from 800 °C (1470 °F) at 5 °C/s (9 °F/s) showing dark-etching $\alpha$ + U$_2$Ti produced by the equilibrium $\gamma \rightarrow \beta$ + U$_2$Ti $\rightarrow \alpha$ + U$_2$Ti transformation sequence and uniform gray $\alpha$ + U$_2$Ti produced by direct transformation of $\gamma \rightarrow \alpha$ + U$_2$Ti. Etched using procedure 1 in Table 5. 200×. (M.E. McAllaster)

**Fig. 20** Bright-field micrograph of U-0.75Ti cooled from 800 °C (1470 °F) at 25 °C/s (45 °F/s) showing light-etching acicular martensite and darker etching $\alpha$ + U$_2$Ti produced by the $\gamma \rightarrow \alpha$ + U$_2$Ti reaction along the prior-$\gamma$ grain boundaries and in the interstices between the martensite plates. Etched using procedure 1 in Table 5. 100×. (M.E. McAllaster)

**Fig. 21** Bright-field micrograph of U-0.75Ti cooled from 800 °C (1470 °F) at 75 °C/s (135 °F/s) showing light-etching acicular martensite and darker etching $\alpha$ + U$_2$Ti produced by the $\gamma \rightarrow \alpha$ + U$_2$Ti reaction in the interstices between the martensite plates. Etched using procedure 1 in Table 5. 100×. (M.E. McAllaster)

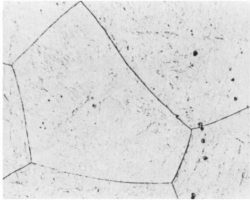

**Fig. 22** Bright-field micrograph of U-0.75Ti cooled from 800 °C (1470 °F) at >200 °C/s (360 °F/s) showing difficulty in revealing fully martensitic structure by etching and bright-field illumination. Etched using procedure 1 in Table 5. 200×. (M.E. McAllaster)

**Fig. 23** Polarized light micrograph of U-0.75Ti cooled from 800 °C (1470 °F) at >200 °C/s (360 °F/s) showing acicular martensite. Electropolished using procedure 1 in Table 1 and anodized using procedure 3 in Table 4. 200×. (M.E. McAllaster)

**Fig. 24** Bright-field micrograph of U-0.75Ti quenched from 800 °C (1470 °F) and partially overaged at 450 °C (840 °F) for 42 h showing cellular decomposition of martensite nucleating along the prior-γ grain boundaries. Etched using procedure 1 in Table 5. 200×. (M.E. McAllaster)

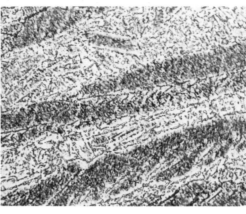

**Fig. 25** Bright-field micrograph of U-0.75Ti quenched from 800 °C (1470 °F) and fully overaged at 600 °C (1110 °F) for 5 h showing decoration of prior martensite plate boundaries with brittle U₂Ti. Etched using procedure 1 in Table 5. 1250×. (M.E. McAllaster)

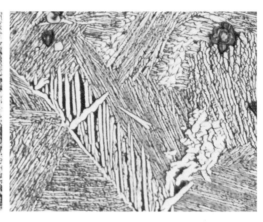

**Fig. 26** Bright-field micrograph of as-cast U-2.0Mo showing coarse $\alpha + \gamma$ microstructure. Etched using procedure 1 in Table 5. 400×. (M.E. McAllaster)

**Fig. 27** Bright-field micrograph of U-2.0Mo cooled from 800 °C (1470 °F) at 4 °C/s (7 °F/s) showing microstructure typical of intermediate cooling rates. Etched using procedure 1 in Table 5. 100×. (M.E. McAllaster)

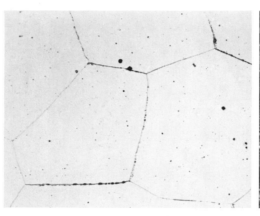

**Fig. 28** Bright-field micrograph of U-2.0Mo cooled from 800 °C (1470 °F) at >100 °C/s (180 °F/s) showing difficulty in revealing thermoelastic martensitic structure by etching and bright-field illumination. Etched using procedure 1 in Table 5. 100×. (M.E. McAllaster)

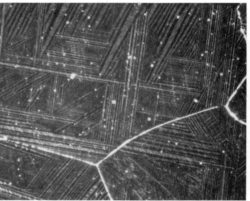

**Fig. 29** Polarized light micrograph of U-2.0Mo cooled from 800 °C (1470 °F) at >100 °C/s (180 °F/s) showing internally twinned thermoelastic martensite, $\alpha'_b$. Electropolished using procedure 1 in Table 1 and anodized using procedure 3 in Table 4. 100×. (M.E. McAllaster)

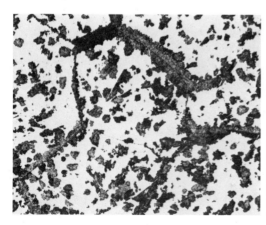

**Fig. 30** Bright-field micrograph of U-2.0Mo quenched from 800 °C (1470 °F) and partially overaged at 400 °C (750 °F) for 5 h showing cellular decomposition of the thermoelastic martensite nucleating at inclusions and along prior-γ grain boundaries. Etched using procedure 1 in Table 5. 100×. (M.E. McAllaster)

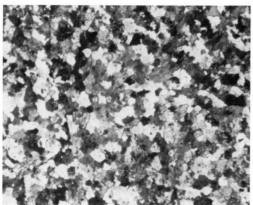

**Fig. 31** Polarized light micrograph of U-2.0Mo quenched from 800 °C (1470 °F) and overaged at 400 °C (750 °F) for 90 h showing colonies of fine (optically unresolvable) $\alpha + \gamma$ produced by cellular decomposition of the thermoelastic martensite. Electropolished using procedure 1 in Table 1 and anodized using procedure 3 in Table 4. 100×. (M.E. McAllaster)

**Fig. 32** Polarized light micrograph of U-2.0Mo quenched from 800 °C (1470 °F) and overaged at 450 °C (840 °F) for 5 h showing beginning of discontinuous transformation of $\alpha + \gamma$ (irregular equiaxed colonies) to $\alpha + U_2Mo$ (long, parallel features). Electropolished using procedure 1 in Table 1 and anodized using procedure 3 in Table 4. 250×. (M.E. McAllaster)

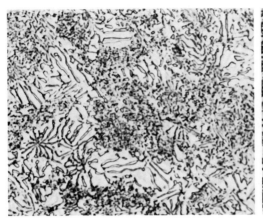

**Fig. 33** Bright-field micrograph of U-2.0Mo quenched from 800 °C (1470 °F) and fully overaged at 500 °C (930 °F) for 90 h showing lamellar $\alpha$ + U$_2$Mo structure. Etched using procedure 1 in Table 5. 1250×. (M.E. McAllaster)

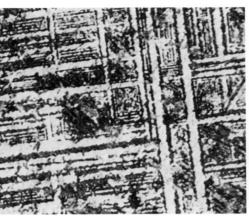

**Fig. 34** Polarized light micrograph of U-2.0Mo quenched from 800 °C (1470 °F) and fully overaged at 500 °C (930 °F) for 90 h showing crystallographic orientation of the $\alpha$ phase in parallel bands reminiscent of the preexisting $\alpha'_b$ martensite. Electropolished using procedure 1 in Table 1 and anodized using procedure 3 in Table 4. 250×. (M.E. McAllaster)

**Fig. 35** Bright-field micrograph of U-6.0Nb cooled from 800 °C (1470 °F) at 0.04 °C/s (0.07 °F/s) showing lamellar two-phase structure. Etched using procedure 1 in Table 5. 1500×. (M.E. McAllaster)

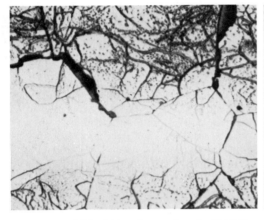

**Fig. 36** Bright-field micrograph of U-6.0Nb cooled from 800 °C (1470 °F) at 0.08 °C/s (1.4 °F/s) showing diffusional decomposition product at some prior-$\gamma$ grain boundaries and bands of subgrain boundaries parallel to the rolling direction. Etched using procedure 1 in Table 5. 500×. (M.E. McAllaster)

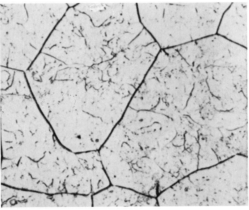

**Fig. 37** Bright-field micrograph of U-6.0Nb cooled from 800 °C (1470 °F) at 20 °C/s (36 °F/s) showing prior-$\gamma$ grain boundaries and more uniformly distributed subgrain structure. Etched using procedure 1 in Table 5. 500×. (M.E. McAllaster)

**Fig. 38** Polarized light micrograph of U-6.0Nb quenched from 800 °C (1470 °F) showing $\alpha''_b$ thermoelastic martensite. Attack polished using procedure 1 in Table 4. 1000×. (J.W. Koger)

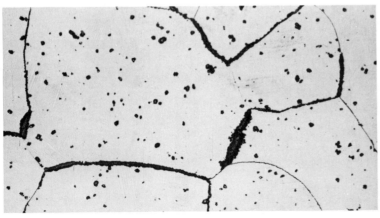

**Fig. 39** Bright-field micrograph of U-6.0Nb quenched from 800 °C (1470 °F) and aged at 400 °C (750 °F) for 6 h showing cellular decomposition of $\alpha'_b$ martensite along prior-$\gamma$ grain boundaries. Etched using procedure 1 in Table 5. 500×. (M.E. McAllaster)

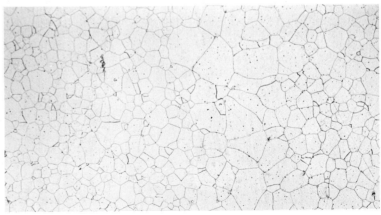

**Fig. 40** Bright-field micrograph of U-7.5Nb-2.5Zr quenched from 800 °C (1470 °F) showing equiaxed grains of $\gamma°$. Etched using procedure 2 in Table 5. 100×. (J.W. Koger)

# Zinc and Zinc Alloys

ZINC AND ZINC ALLOY specimen preparation techniques are discussed in this article. Typical structures observed in these specimens are also covered.

## Specimen Preparation

**Sectioning.** The initial sample can be removed from a larger mass of material by sawing, breaking, or shearing (see the article "Sectioning" in this Volume). Because zinc alloys are comparatively soft, final sectioning of specimens is sometimes performed using an abrasive or diamond wheel. Use of these cutting wheels produces less metal flow than sawing or shearing.

**Mounting.** Specimens of rolled zinc and zinc alloys are usually secured by clamping; plastic mounting materials are rarely used. Several specimens are mounted together in a screw clamp using thin spacers of soft zinc between specimens and heavy strips of zinc between the clamp plates and the outermost specimens. The assembly is tightly clamped to prevent seepage of etchants between specimens. The zinc spacers are of known structure and serve as convenient standards of comparison for determining if the specimens have been prepared correctly. Most specimens, except those of rolled metal, are mounted using conventional plastic molding materials (see the article "Mounting of Specimens" in this Volume).

**Grinding and polishing** of cast zinc can cause distortion to a depth 20 to 100 times as great as the deepest scratch. Therefore, in each stage of grinding and polishing, considerably more metal should be removed than the amount required for eliminating the scratches that remain from the previous stage. It is easier to prepare a distortion-free surface on specimens of fine-grained zinc than on specimens of coarse-grained, soft zinc.

Wet grinding on a belt grinding machine using 60- and 180-grit silicon carbide abrasives is suitable for zinc and zinc alloys. Local heating from grinding must be minimized using water cooling, because heat can cause structural changes too deep to remove by polishing.

Rough polishing is performed using 240-, 320-, 400-, then 600-grit silicon carbide papers. These papers are less susceptible to loading than emery papers. For soft (pure) zinc, polishing can be carried out by hand on papers supported on a flat surface. Zinc alloys are polished on a wheel using the same grades of paper. A low wheel speed (250 rpm maximum) during polishing will minimize overheating of the specimen, as will application of water to the silicon carbide papers and polishing in intervals of a few seconds, allowing the specimen to cool before polishing resumes.

Fine polishing is performed using magnesium oxide (MgO) or alumina ($Al_2O_3$). A method for preparing specially graded wet-polishing abrasives is described in Ref 1. In fine polishing, the first two wheels are covered with smooth canvas; the third wheel with felt or billiard cloth. A soft-nap polishing cloth is used for fine polishing. Hands as well as the specimen must be washed between polishings to prevent carryover of coarser grit from previous steps. Overpolishing and its consequences can be avoided by etching between polishings.

Zinc alloys that have intermetallic phases etch differently than unalloyed zinc. Because the intermetallic phases remain in relief, excessive polishing and etching should be avoided. Some of the steps listed above can often be eliminated for alloys with intermetallic phases.

Polishing through all four wheels is necessary only for specimens with microstructures requiring high magnifications for resolution. Most low-magnification examinations can proceed after polishing on the third wheel. An ethanol powder mixture instead of water should be used when polishing galvanized steel. The specimen is then cleaned ultrasonically with alcohol and blown dry with warm air. Vibratory polishing of zinc and zinc alloys usually does not produce polished surfaces as good as those obtained by mechanical polishing.

**Macroetching.** Use of concentrated hydrochloric acid (HCl) at room temperature followed by rinsing and wiping off the resulting black deposit produces satisfactory grain contrast on copper-free zinc and zinc alloys. Etchant 1 in Table 1 may be used for zinc containing 1% Cu or less, but with this etchant, grain contrast is not well defined. An etchant equal to HCl for producing grain contrast has not been found for the zinc alloys containing copper.

**Microetching.** The most useful etchants for microscopic examination of zinc and zinc alloys are aqueous solutions of chromic acid ($CrO_3$) to which sodium sulfate ($Na_2SO_4$) has been added. The grades of $CrO_3$ used for chromium plating are adequate. The compositions of etchants commonly used are given in Table 1.

Etching should follow soon after final polishing. The specimen should be cleaned in alcohol, then running water, and etched while wet. To avoid staining, the use of etchant 1 or 2 in Table 1 should be followed immediately

**Table 1  Etchants for zinc and zinc alloys**

| Etchant | Composition |
|---|---|
| 1(a) . . . . . . . . | 200 g $CrO_3$, 15 g $Na_2SO_4$, 1000 mL $H_2O$ |
| 2(b) . . . . . . . . | 50 g $CrO_3$, 4 g $Na_2SO_4$, 1000 mL $H_2O$ |
| 3 . . . . . . . . . . . | 200 g $CrO_3$ and 1000 mL $H_2O$ |
| 4 . . . . . . . . . . . | 5 mL $HNO_3$ and 100 mL $H_2O$ |
| 5 . . . . . . . . . . . | 5 g $FeCl_3$, 10 mL $HCl$, 240 mL alcohol |

(a) For rolled zinc-copper alloys, the $Na_2SO_4$ content can be reduced to 7.5 g. If desired, a smoothly etched surface can be obtained by increasing the $Na_2SO_4$ to 30 g. (b) This etchant can be prepared by mixing one part (by volume) etchant 1 and three parts $H_2O$.

Revised by L. Mongeon, Metallographer, Noranda Research Centre, Noranda, Inc., and R.J. Barnhurst, Research Scientist, Noranda Research Centre, Noranda, Inc.

**Table 2 Etchants and etching times for zinc and zinc die-casting alloys**

| Specimen metal | Etchant (from table 1) | Time, s, for examination at | |
|---|---|---|---|
| | | 250X | 1000X |
| Cast or rolled zinc . . . . . . . . . 1 | | 5 | 1 |
| Alloy 3, 5, or 7 . . . . . . . . . . . . 2 | | 1 | 1 |

by a rinse in etchant 3. The specimen is then thoroughly washed in running water, dipped in alcohol, and dried with a stream of warm, clean air.

Table 2 lists recommendations for etchants and etching times for zinc and zinc die-casting alloys. The etching time may be longer or shorter for specific etching conditions; a minor difference in solution temperature may affect etching time. In addition, as indicated in Table 2 for cast or rolled zinc, etching time is often decreased as the magnification to be used is increased. Etchant 4 in Table 1 may also be used for etching zinc pressure die cast and galvanized specimens. Etching should proceed for 4 to 5 s, followed by rinsing in water and drying in warm air.

**Electrolytic etching** has been used to differentiate two intermediate phases of the zinc-copper system ($\gamma$ phase and $\varepsilon$ phase). The electrolyte is a 17% aqueous solution of $CrO_3$. The polished specimen is the anode, and a small coil of platinum wire in the bottom of the dish or beaker holding the electrolyte serves as the cathode. The specimen is connected to the current source before immersion in the electrolyte. At a current density of 0.2 A/cm$^2$ (1.5 A/in.$^2$), $\gamma$ and $\varepsilon$ phases are about equally attacked. At higher current densities, $\gamma$ phase is preferentially attacked; at lower current densities, $\varepsilon$ phase is preferentially attacked.

In a common procedure, the specimen is first etched at 0.78 A/cm$^2$ (5 A/in.$^2$). Gamma, if present, will be attacked; $\varepsilon$ phase will not be attacked. The specimen is then repolished and etched at 0.15 A/cm$^2$ (1 A/in.$^2$), which will reveal any $\varepsilon$ phase present. Further details on electrolytic etching of zinc alloys are available in Ref 2.

## Microstructures of Zinc and Zinc Alloys

The natural impurities, contaminants, and alloying additions present in commercial zinc materials have extremely limited solid solubility. They readily produce alterations in cast or wrought microstructures and changes in one or more properties. Nominal compositions of the alloys depicted in this article are noted in the captions.

The elements commonly found in zinc are lead, cadmium, iron, copper, aluminum, titanium, and tin. Lead, cadmium, tin, and iron are natural impurities in zinc and are also added to zinc to develop desired properties. Zinc casting alloys are primarily zinc-aluminum with small additions of other elements, such as copper and magnesium. Zinc rolling alloys generally contain lead, iron, cadmium, copper, or titanium—alone or in combination

and usually in concentrations under 1%. The effects on microstructure produced by these elements are described below.

**Lead.** The solubility of lead in solid zinc is extremely limited. A monotectic is formed at 418 °C (784 °F) and a lead content of 0.9%, and zinc crystals and liquid exist in equilibrium down to the eutectic temperature of 318 °C (604 °F). As a result, lead appears in cast zinc and zinc alloys at the dendrite boundaries in the form of small, spherical droplets or surface films. Because of their softness, the droplets can be easily pulled out during polishing, leaving holes that appear black in the microstructure. Special care in polishing is required to retain the lead particles.

In rolled zinc, the particles of lead are elongated in the rolling direction and are not located preferentially at the recrystallized grain boundaries. In zinc-aluminum alloys, lead induces intergranular corrosion; concentrations must be maintained below 0.004%.

**The cadmium** present in most commercial zinc products is in solid solution and produces no change in microstructure, except coring in the cast structure. In rolled zinc, the cadmium remains in solid solution, increasing strength, hardness, and creep resistance and raising the recrystallization temperature. In zinc-aluminum alloys, because cadmium lowers resistance to intergranular corrosion, concentrations must remain below 0.003%.

**Iron,** when present in zinc in amounts exceeding approximately 0.001%, appears in the microstructure as an intermetallic compound containing approximately 6% Fe. The particle size is controlled by the amount of iron present and the thermal history of the part. Fine particles in a casting can be coalesced to a coarser form by prolonged heating at 370 °C (700 °F).

The iron-zinc compound, like lead, precipitates at dendrite boundaries. When a zinc casting is rolled, the iron-zinc particles are elongated in the rolling direction along with any lead particles present. The presence of iron particles in the proper concentration and distribution in rolled zinc assists in control of grain size. Iron in zinc-aluminum alloys is present as $FeAl_3$ particles, which can significantly lower ductility.

**Copper,** when present in zinc in amounts to approximately 1%, is in solid solution and results in a cored structure. During hot rolling at approximately 205 °C (400 °F), the copper is retained in supersaturated solid solution. Upon cooling, some of the zinc-copper $\varepsilon$ phase precipitates at the final recrystallized grain boundaries. During long exposures near room temperature, $\varepsilon$ phase will continue to precipitate at grain boundaries and finally in the interior of the grains, ultimately forming T' phase (ternary eutectic). When cold rolled, $\varepsilon$ phase precipitates rapidly and abundantly in the cold-worked structure. In concentrations beyond 1% in zinc-aluminum alloys, $\varepsilon$ phase precipitates as an interdendritic phase.

**Titanium.** The solid solubility of titanium in zinc is very limited. At approximately 0.12% Ti, a lamellar eutectic of zinc and $TiZn_{15}$ (4.66% Ti) forms. The eutectic forms at dendrite boundaries in a casting. The $TiZn_{15}$ compound decreases the cast grain size of zinc and restricts grain growth in hot-rolled zinc. In rolled strip, particles of the compound are elongated in the rolling direction. Zinc grain growth is limited to the spacing between the stringers of compound.

**Aluminum.** A lamellar eutectic forms at 5% Al between aluminum ($\alpha$) and zinc ($\eta$) solid solution at 382 °C (720 °F). The $\alpha$ constituent of the eutectic is stable only above 275 °C (527 °F); at lower temperatures, it transforms eutectoidally into $\alpha$ and $\eta$ phases. Although the solid solubility of aluminum in zinc at the eutectic temperature is approximately 1%, castings containing as little as 0.10% Al display the eutectic structure in interdendritic areas. At the normal aluminum concentration in standard zinc die-casting alloys (4.0% Al), the rate of attack by the melt on iron is sufficiently low to permit die casting in hot-chamber machines in which the operating mechanism is immersed continuously in the molten alloy.

During solidification of hypoeutectic zinc die-casting alloys containing approximately 4% Al, the first material to freeze appears as primary particles of zinc-rich solid solution ($\eta$ phase). Later, the remaining liquid solidifies as eutectic composed of $\eta$ phase and the unstable high-temperature constituent $\alpha$. Aluminum acts as a grain refiner in cast zinc; together with the high solidification rates of the die casting process, this results in a fairly fine equiaxed grain structure, which is primarily responsible for the strength, ductility, and toughness of zinc die castings.

When die castings are aged at room temperature or a slightly elevated temperature, a precipitation reaction occurs in the zinc-rich $\eta$ phase. In a freshly made die casting, $\eta$ phase may contain approximately 0.35% Al in solution. During five weeks at room-temperature, this will decrease to approximately 0.05%, the difference appearing as minute particles of $\alpha$ within the $\eta$-phase structure. Most of the aluminum can be precipitated in much less time by aging at a slightly elevated temperature. Similar aging effects are observed in alloys containing copper, which is added to increase tensile strength and hardness. Copper additions to 1.5% yield die castings with reasonably stable properties and dimensions. Low-temperature stabilization annealing is occasionally used to achieve maximum stability. The zinc-aluminum alloys extend the amount of primary phase; in the ZA-8 and ZA-12 alloys this is $\eta$ phase, but is replaced by $\alpha$ in the ZA-27 alloy.

Wrought alloys based on the eutectoid composition of 78% Zn and 22% Al are of commercial interest because of their superplastic properties. Microstructures developed in this alloy depend on the heat treatment used.

**Magnesium** additions in concentrations of 0.01 to 0.03% to the ZA-8, ZA-12, and ZA-27 alloys increase strength and hardness, but decrease ductility.

**Tin** forms a low-melting eutectic with zinc at 91% Sn at 198 °C (388 °F). The solubility of tin in solid zinc is extremely restricted, and the zinc-tin eutectic appears in alloys containing as little as 0.001% Sn.

The only deliberate use of tin additions to zinc is in certain hot-dip galvanizing operations. In some galvanizing operations, tin additions are widely used to regulate the formation of bright, smooth, large white spangles in the coating. Tin present in hot-rolled zinc can cause hot shortness. In zinc-aluminum alloys, tin induces intergranular corrosion; concentrations must be maintained below 0.002%.

## Microexamination

Grain size is best determined under polarized light illumination, which displays each grain as a different shade depending on orientation. Grain counts can be made with good accuracy. Grain boundaries are poorly defined under bright-field illumination.

Dendrite arm spacing can be measured on photomicrographs of selected areas using the linear intercept procedure in ASTM Standard E 112 (Ref 3). Soundness values (porosity levels) can also be obtained in cast alloys by the use of quantitative analysis on a vol% basis. Specimens to be examined for corrosion should be in the as-polished condition.

### REFERENCES

1. J.L. Rodda, Preparation of Graded Abrasives for Metallographic Polishing, *Trans. AIME*, Vol 99, 1932, p 149-158
2. J.L. Rodda, Notes on Etching and Microscopical Identification of the Phases Present in the Copper-Zinc System, *Trans. AIME*, Vol 124, 1937, p 189-193
3. "Methods for Determining Average Grain Size," E 112, *Annual Book of ASTM Standards*, Vol 03.03, ASTM, Philadelphia, 1984

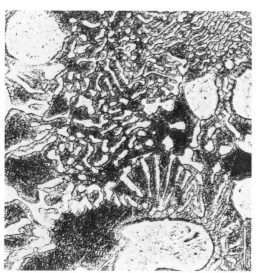
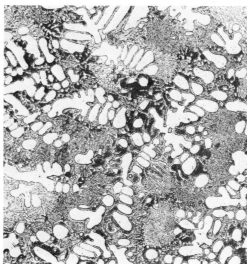
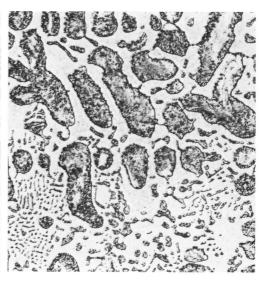

**Fig. 1, 2** ZA-8 alloy (Zn-8Al-1Cu-0.02Mg), as sand cast. Fig. 1: coarse zinc-rich dendrites in a matrix of $\alpha + \eta$ eutectic phase. Fig. 2: same structure at a lower magnification. Both etched in etchant 1, Table 1. Fig. 1: 500×; Fig. 2: 100×

**Fig. 3** Same alloy as Fig. 1, except as-cast in a permanent mold. Same constituents as Fig. 1, but permanent mold casting has resulted in a finer microstructure. Etchant 1, Table 1. 500×

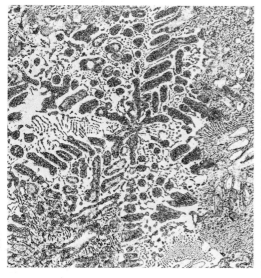
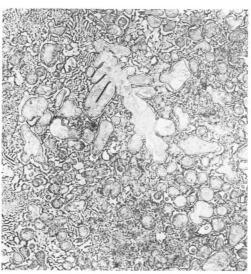
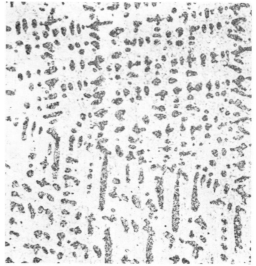

**Fig. 4** Same field of view as Fig. 3, but shown at a lower magnification. Etchant 1, Table 1. 200×

**Fig. 5** Same alloy as Fig. 1, except as pressure die cast. Same constituents as Fig. 1, but pressure die casting has yielded a much finer microstructure. Etchant 2, Table 1. 500×

**Fig. 6** Same alloy as in Fig. 1, except continuously cast in a 50-mm (2-in.) diam ingot. Same constituents as Fig. 1, but continuous casting has resulted in a very fine microstructure. Etchant 1, Table 1. 500×

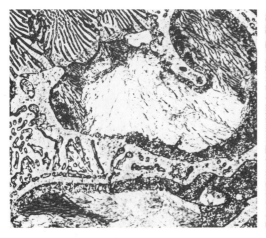

**Fig. 7** ZA-12 alloy (Zn-11Al-0.9Cu-0.02Mg), as sand cast. Coarse zinc-rich dendrites in a matrix of eutectic $\alpha + \eta$ phase. This alloy contains less of the eutectic than ZA-8 (Fig. 1 to 6). Etchant 1, Table 1. 500×

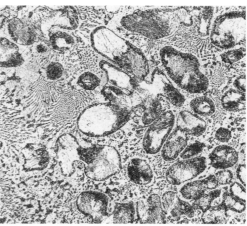

**Fig. 8** Same field of view as Fig. 7, except shown at a lower magnification. Etchant 1, Table 1. 200×

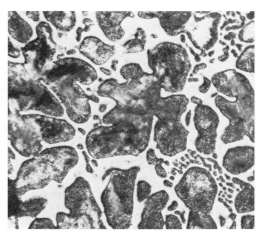

**Fig. 9** Same alloy as Fig. 7, except as-cast in a permanent mold. Same constituents as Fig. 7, but casting in a permanent mold has resulted in a finer microstructure. Etchant 1, Table 1. 500×

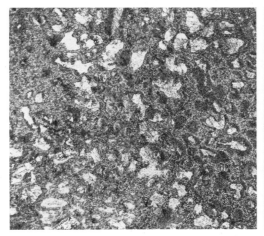

**Fig. 10** Same field of view as Fig. 9, but shown at a lower magnification. Etchant 1, Table 1. 200×

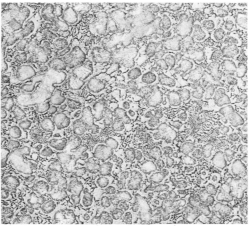

**Fig. 11** Same alloy as Fig. 7, except as pressure die cast. Same constituents as Fig. 7, but pressure die casting results in a much finer microstructure. Etchant 4, Table 1. 500×

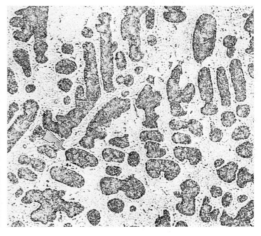

**Fig. 12** Same alloy as Fig. 7, except continuous cast in an 80-mm (3.25-in.) diam ingot. Same constituents as Fig. 7, but a finer structure because of continuous casting. Etchant 1, Table 1. 500×

**Fig. 13** ZA-27 alloy (Zn-11Al-0.9Cu-0.02Mg), as sand cast. Primary, cored aluminum-rich dendrites surrounded by peritectic $\alpha + \eta$. White particles are $\varepsilon$ phase. Less eutectic is apparent than in Fig. 1 to 6 or 7 to 11. Etchant 1, Table 1. 500×

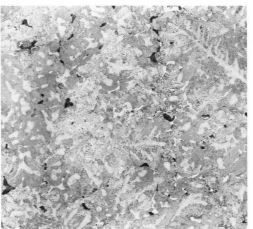

**Fig. 14** Same field of view as Fig. 13, but shown at a lower magnification. See also Fig. 15. Etchant 1, Table 1. 200×

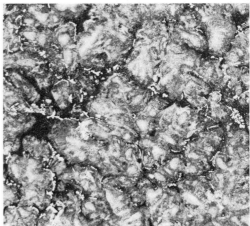

**Fig. 15** Same field of view as Fig. 13 and 14, but shown at a still lower magnification. See also Fig. 14. Etchant 1, Table 1. 100×

**Fig. 16** Same alloy as Fig. 13, except as sand cast, homogenized 3 h at 360 °C (680 °F) and furnace cooled. Structure is fully stabilized $\beta$ phase decomposed into $\alpha + \eta$ lamellar eutectoid. Coarse $\varepsilon$-phase particles are present at old dendritic boundaries. Etchant 1, Table 1. 500×

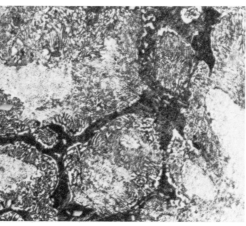

**Fig. 17** Same alloy as Fig. 13, except as sand cast, heat treated 12 h at 250 °C (480 °F), and furnace cooled. Structure consists of coarse eutectoid $\alpha + \eta$ phase and eutectic. The metastable $\varepsilon$ phase has been converted to fine T' (ternary eutectic). Etchant 1, Table 1. 500×

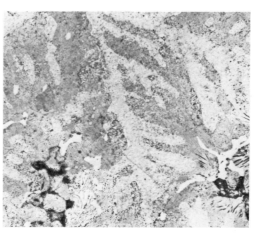

**Fig. 18** Same alloy as Fig. 13, except as-cast in a permanent mold. Constituents are the same as Fig. 13, but permanent mold casting resulted in a much finer microstructure. Compare with Fig. 19. Etchant 1, Table 1. 500×

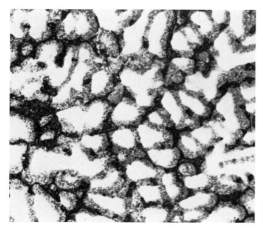

**Fig. 19** Same alloy as Fig. 13, except continuous cast in a 25-mm (1-in.) diam bar. Same constituents as Fig. 13, but a much finer microstructure with more eutectic and no coarse $\varepsilon$-phase particles. Compare with Fig. 21. Etchant 1, Table 1. 500×

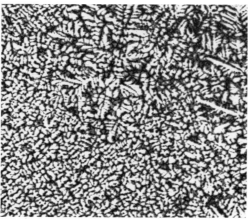

**Fig. 20** Same field as Fig. 19, but at a lower magnification. The fine continuous-cast structure is better resolved at the higher magnification. Etchant 1, Table 1. 100×

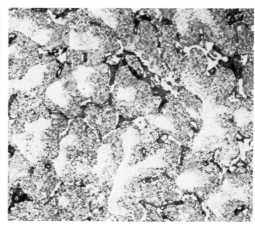

**Fig. 21** Same alloy as Fig. 13, except continuously cast in a 150-mm (6-in.) diam bar. Same constituents as Fig. 13, but a finer structure. Some coarse $\varepsilon$-phase particles (white) are evident. Etchant 1, Table 1. 500×

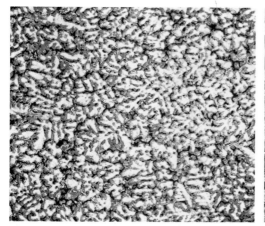

**Fig. 22** Same field as Fig. 21, but at a lower magnification. Compare with Fig. 19 and 20, which show the same alloy cast in a smaller section. Etchant 1, Table 1. 100×

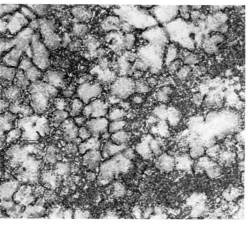

**Fig. 23** Same alloy as Fig. 13, except as-cast in a pressure die. Same constituents as Fig. 13, but much finer microstructure. Note equiaxed dendrites, increased amount of eutectic, and very fine $\varepsilon$-phase particles. Etchant 2, Table 1. 500×

**Fig. 24** ZA-27 alloy, with 0.13% Fe (excess) added, as sand cast. Structure is intermetallic $FeAl_3$ particles (dark gray) in a matrix of $\alpha$ phase and $\varepsilon$ phase. Structure is much coarser than in Fig. 23. As-polished. 100×

**Fig. 25** ZA-27 alloy, with 0.05% Fe, as sand cast. Structure consists of intermetallic $FeAl_3$ particles (dark gray) in a matrix of $\alpha$ particles (light) and $\varepsilon$ particles (light gray). As-polished. 100×

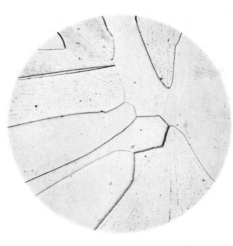

**Fig. 26** Special high grade zinc [99.99% Zn (min), 0.003% Pb (max), 0.003% Fe (max), 0.003% Cd (max)], as-cast. Almost free of microsegregation. Etchant 1, Table 1. 100×

**Fig. 27** Same as Fig. 26, under polarized light illumination to show the extent of grain growth from original etched grain boundaries within large grains. Etchant 1, Table 1. 100×

**Fig. 28** Prime western zinc [98% Zn (min), 1.4% Pb (max), 0.05% Fe (max), 0.20% Cd (max)], as cast. The dark spots are lead particles at the grain boundaries. Etchant 1, Table 1. 100×

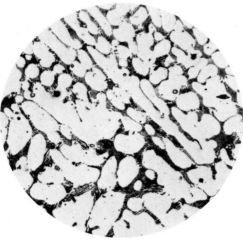

**Fig. 29** Cast zinc with 0.6% Cu and 0.14% Ti. Eutectic (zinc and titanium-zinc phases) at grain boundaries. See also Fig. 30. Etchant 1, Table 1. 100×

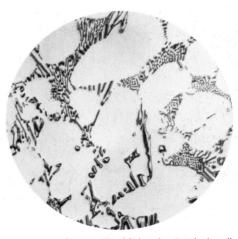

**Fig. 30** Same as Fig. 29, but showing the lamellar eutectic. Coarse needles of titanium-zinc phase are parallel to the polishing plane; fine needles, perpendicular. Etchant 1, Table 1. 250×

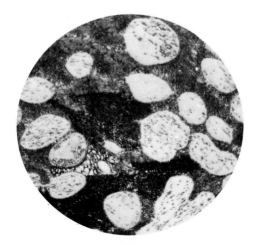

**Fig. 31** Alloy 3 (ASTM AG40A; Zn-4.1Al-0.035Mg), as die cast. Structure is zinc solid solution surrounded by eutectic. See Fig. 32 for the effect of aging. Etchant 2, Table 1. 1000×

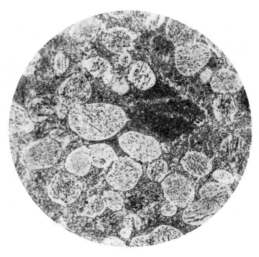

**Fig. 32** Same as Fig. 31, except aged 10 days at 95 °C (205 °F). Aging increased the amount of precipitation in the zinc solid solution. Etchant 2, Table 1. 1000×

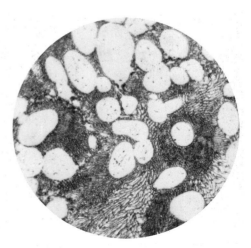

**Fig. 33** Alloy 5 (ASTM AC41A; Zn-4.1Al-0.055Mg-1.0Cu), as die cast. Same constituents as Fig. 31, but has more Cu and Mg, higher strength and hardness. Etchant 2, Table 1. 1000×

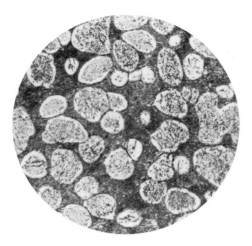

**Fig. 34** Same as Fig. 33, except aged 10 days at 95 °C (205 °F). Aging had the same effect on the die cast structure as for alloy 3 (see Fig. 31 and 32). Etchant 2, Table 1. 1000×

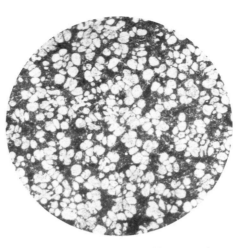

**Fig. 35** Same alloy as Fig. 33, except die cast with rapid freezing. Fine primary crystallites of solid solution in fine lamellar eutectic. The fine structure imparts toughness and high strength to the alloy. Etchant 2, Table 1. 250×

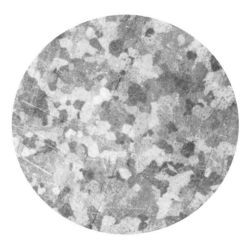

**Fig. 36** Specimen in Fig. 35, unetched. Polarized light illumination shows grain size but not alloy phases. Grains are larger than primary crystallites (see Fig. 35), indicating that the zinc grains extend into the eutectic. As-polished. 250×

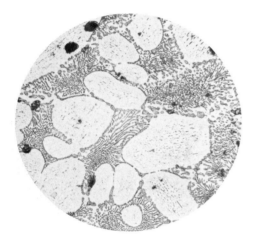

**Fig. 37** Same alloy as Fig. 33, except cast in a permanent mold. This specimen froze more slowly than the die-cast specimen in Fig. 35, resulting in a coarser structure of solid solution and lamellar eutectic. This material has lower strength and toughness than in Fig. 35. Etchant 2, Table 1. 250×

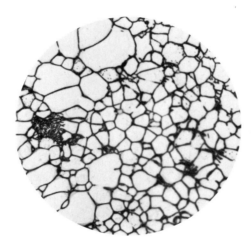

**Fig. 38** Zn-0.55Cu-0.12Ti alloy, as die cast in a cold-chamber machine. Grain boundaries contain a film of zinc-titanium eutectic, which gives this alloy high creep resistance. Etchant 1, Table 1. 250×

**Fig. 39** Zn-12Al-0.75Cu-0.02Mg alloy, as die cast in a cold-chamber machine. Structure is fine primary crystallites consisting of aluminum-rich solid solution and eutectoid in a matrix of eutectic. Compare with Fig. 38. Etchant 2, Table 1. 250×

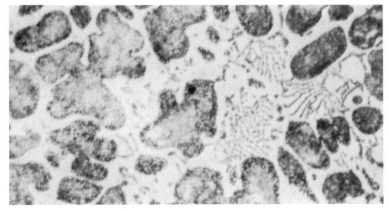

**Fig. 40** Same alloy as Fig. 39, except gravity cast in a permanent mold. With slower freezing than the die-cast specimen in Fig. 39, primary crystals and lamellar matrix are coarser; properties of the alloy are not sensitive to the freezing rate, and the casting has good strength. Compare with Fig. 39. Etchant 2, Table 1. 1000×

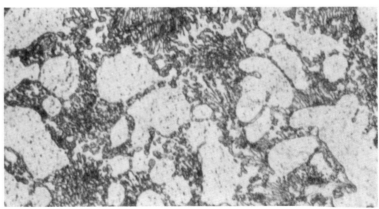

**Fig. 41** Hypoeutectic alloy 3 (ASTM AG40A; 4.1Al-0.35Mg), gravity cast same as Fig. 40. Zinc-rich primary solid solution in a eutectic matrix. This alloy has excellent mechanical properties when die cast with rapid freezing, but properties decrease with slow freezing. Etchant 2, Table 1. 1000×

**Fig. 42** Alloy 3 (ASTM AG40A) within specified composition limits, exposed 10 days to wet steam at 95 °C (205 °F). Specimen shows no intergranular corrosion. Compare with lead-contaminated alloy 3 in Fig. 44. As-polished. 100×

**Fig. 43** Fracture surface of the 10-mm (0.375-in.) diam end of a tension test bar die cast from alloy 3 to which 0.018% Pb was added (0.005% Pb is allowed). Exposed 10 days to wet steam at 95 °C (205 °F). Dark ring is intergranular corrosion. See also Fig. 44. Not polished, not etched. 6×

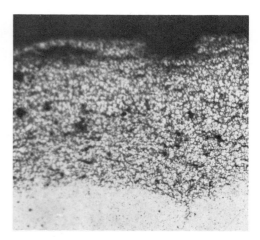

**Fig. 44** Micrograph of edge of fracture surface in Fig. 43. Subsurface intergranular corrosion (top) causes swelling and decrease in mechanical properties. Deliberate addition of 0.018% Pb to the alloy approximates the contamination that might occur from the use of remelted scrap. As-polished. 100×

**Fig. 45** Hot-rolled brass special zinc [99% Zn (min), 0.6% Pb (max), 0.03% Fe (max), 0.50% Cd (max)], under polarized light; grains are clearly defined. Etchant 1, Table 1. 250×

**Fig. 46** Same alloy as Fig. 45, except cold rolled and photographed under polarized light. Note distortion of the grains caused by cold working. Etchant 1, Table 1. 250×

**Fig. 47** Zinc containing 1% Cu, hot rolled. Polarized light illumination clearly defines the zinc-copper ε phase at grain boundaries. Etchant 1, Table 1. 250×

**Fig. 48** Cold-rolled Zn-1Cu alloy, photographed under polarized light. Note the severe distortion of grains caused by cold working (compare with Fig. 47). Etchant 1, Table 1. 250×

**Fig. 49** Hot-rolled Zn-0.6Cu-0.14Ti alloy, photographed under polarized light to define the grains between titanium-zinc stringers (parallel to the direction of rolling). Etchant 1, Table 1. 250×

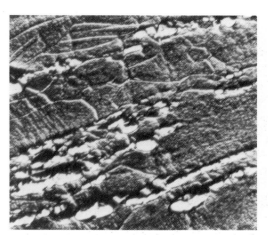

**Fig. 50** Replica electron micrograph of the hot-rolled alloy in Fig. 49, showing the particles (white) that comprise the Ti-Zn stringers in that micrograph. Etchant 2. Table 1. 4400×

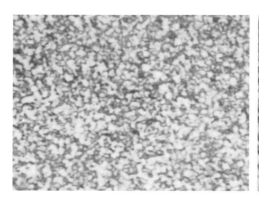

**Fig. 51** Zn-22Al alloy (eutectoid composition), showing superplastic, fine-grained structure obtained by annealing at 350 °C (660 °F) and water quenching. See also Fig. 52. Etchant 2, Table 1. 2500×

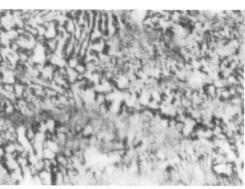

**Fig. 52** Same alloy as Fig. 51, after being held 1 h at 350 °C (660 °F) and air cooled. Structure consists of lamellar and granular $\alpha$ and $\eta$—both products of eutectoid transformation. Etchant 2, Table 1. 2500×

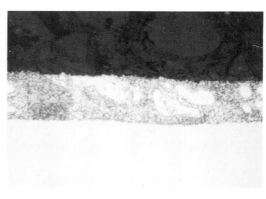

**Fig. 53** Steel coated with Galfan (Zn-5Al-mischmetal) alloy. White zinc-rich phase is surrounded by eutectic phase. Note absence of intermetallic between coating and steel. Etchant 5, Table 1. 500×. (F.E. Goodwin)

# Zirconium and Hafnium and Their Alloys

By Paul E. Danielson
Chief Metallographer
Teledyne Wah Chang Albany

ZIRCONIUM AND HAFNIUM have hexagonal close-packed crystal structures and respond well to polarized light as a result of their strong anisotropy. Zirconium metal is used almost exclusively for cladding uranium fuel elements for nuclear power plants. Alloying additions, such as iron, chromium, tin, hafnium, and niobium, are sometimes incorporated into zirconium for such reasons as improving the corrosion and chemical-attack properties of the metal. These additions may subsequently alter and refine the microstructure. Hafnium is usually produced unalloyed.

Zirconium powder has also been used in photographic flashbulbs, fragmentation devices, and pyrotechnic and special ignition compositions (Ref 1). Hafnium is used in control rods for nuclear reactors. Applications for zirconium carbide, hafnium carbide, and zirconium oxide-base cermets can be found in Ref 1. Additional information on the crystallography, allotropic transformations, and corrosion properties of zirconium and its alloys can be found in Ref 2. This article will examine the metallographic preparation and representative microstructures of zirconium, zirconium alloys, and hafnium.

## Specimen Preparation

Specimens of zirconium and hafnium for metallographic examination should represent the attributes to be studied in a particular product. A longitudinal section is generally used to examine grain size, recrystallization, intermetallics, and second-phase uniformity in wrought products. A transverse section (a full cross section if possible) is used to examine such defects as cracks, voids, porosity, and centerburst in wrought products.

**Sectioning.** Specimens can be sectioned by hacksawing or band sawing. Abrasive cutting may also be used if there is adequate coolant to avoid overheating the material. Some twinning can be expected due to sectioning; however, this is usually removed during subsequent grinding and rough polishing.

Additional information is available in the article "Sectioning" in this Volume.

**Mounting.** Large samples may be polished unmounted if they can be handled easily. Specimens that are too small to be hand held for grinding and polishing or that have a surface that must be preserved may be mounted using hot or cold mounting methods. Cold mounting may be preferred if the material is to be studied for hydrogen content. For hot mounts, thermosetting diallyl phthalate mounting material works well. Bakelite can also be used, but it does not provide the edge retention or resistance to acid corrosion of diallyl phthalate. Because of its ability to absorb light, black-colored mounting material is preferred if polarized light is to be used.

**Grinding.** Wet and dry grinding can be performed using abrasive belts or rotating disks as well as by hand using abrasive papers. Abrasives used include alumina ($Al_2O_3$), silicon carbide, and emery paper. Wet grinding begins with a disk or belt sander using 120-grit $Al_2O_3$ or silicon carbide paper. Water is the preferred coolant. Fine grinding should be performed using dry, 400-grit silicon carbide paper on a disk grinder.

The standard grinding sequence of 240-, 320-, 400-, and 600-grit papers plus water is not necessary because of the fast cutting rate of the subsequent rough polishing, which uses acids and abrasives for metal removal. Hand emery papers with 2, 1, 0, and 00 grits may be substituted for the 400-grit silicon carbide, because heat generated during this dry grinding step can smear or swell the cold mounting materials. Grinding wheel speeds range from 1000 to 1200 rpm.

**Chemical-mechanical polishing,** also known as attack polishing, can be performed in rough or rough and final stages. Specimens to be finished with a chemical swab etching generally require only rough polishing. In both polishings, suspensions of $Al_2O_3$ of different grit sizes with acid solutions are used. The wheel speeds are 550 to 1100 rpm for rough polishing and approximately 550 rpm

for final polishing. The rough polishing wheel consists of a nylon-type cloth on top of a thin cotton cloth, such as Metcloth. Nylon is used for its ability to resist acids.

The polishing suspension contains 10 g 1.0 $\mu$m $\alpha$-$Al_2O_3$ in 150 mL $H_2O$. This suspension is applied to the wheel at approximately 1100 rpm, followed by 5 to 10 mL of an acid solution composed of 250 mL $H_2O$, 22 mL nitric acid ($HNO_3$), and 3 mL hydrofluoric acid (HF). Metal wheels, if used, should be protected from acid attack by placing an acid-resistant material between the cloth and wheel. This also prevents an electrolytic reaction between the specimen and the metallic (brass) wheel. Eye protection and light, acid-proof gloves should also be used while chemical polishing. Rough polishing may require 2 or 3 charges of the acid/slurry combination to remove the grinding and polishing marks. This polishing step usually lasts 2 to 3 min. Hafnium tends to be slightly slower to polish than the zirconium-base materials.

The completed, rough-polished specimen should have only 1.0-$\mu$m scratches. Care should be taken during this rough polishing to ensure that all the embedded silicon carbide and $Al_2O_3$ is removed before proceeding to the next step.

When only the grain size or basic microstructural condition of the material is to be examined, satisfactory results can be obtained with a rough polishing, followed by a swab etching (see Table 1). Anisotropic metals, such as zirconium and hafnium, exhibit their grain structures very well under polarized light. Contrast can be enhanced when viewing with polarized light by depositing a thin 15 to 20 V dc gold bronze anodized layer on the sample after etching. This film layer will also protect the sample from oxidation and staining.

Final polishing is required for a more detailed examination of intermetallics, second phase, or contaminants. The final polishing cloth should be a medium-nap synthetic rayon (Microcloth). A suspension of 2 to 3 g

**Table 1  Selected etchants for macroscopic and microscopic examination of zirconium, hafnium, and their alloys**

| Etchant | Procedure | Characteristics and use |
|---|---|---|
| 1. 4-5% HF (48%), 30-35% HNO$_3$ (70%), and balance H$_2$O | Immerse sample face up; etch 10-15 min; air dry | Shows general macrostructures in zirconium and hafnium |
| 2. 45 mL H$_2$O, 45 mL 70% HNO$_3$, and 10 mL 48% HF | Rough polish, then swab etch 5-10 s; wash in water; air dry | Shows general structure in zirconium and hafnium |
| 3. 20 mL glycerol, 20 mL 70% HNO$_3$, and 2-3 mL 48% HF(a) | Rough polish then swab etch, light pressure 10-15 s; wash in water; air dry | Shows iron-chromium second phase in Zircaloy materials and general structure |
| 4. 25 mL 30% H$_2$O$_2$, 25 mL 70% HNO$_3$, and 8-10 drops 48% HF | Rough and final polish, then swab etch, light pressure 10-20 s; wash in water, air dry | Shows hydrides in zirconium and Zircaloys |
| 5. 45 mL lactic acid, 45 mL HNO$_3$ (conc), and 8 mL 48% HF | Rough polish then swab etch, light pressure 10-20 s; wash in water; air dry | Shows hydrides in zirconium-niobium alloys |

Note: Use fairly large swabs with all swab etching procedures.
(a) Dispose after using because the etchant may become unstable with time and a chemical reaction may result.

0.05-$\mu$m $\alpha$-Al$_2$O$_3$ in 150 mL H$_2$O is used (distilled water is needed only when there are problems with the existing water supply), followed by an acid solution added to the slurry. On zirconium-base materials, approximately 10 mL of a solution consisting of 200 mL H$_2$O, 30 mL HNO$_3$, 20 mL hydrogen peroxide (H$_2$O$_2$), and 8 to 10 drops HF are added to the slurry. Because hafnium tends to be more acid resistant, a stronger HF mixture is used (250 mL H$_2$O, 22 mL HNO$_3$, and 3 mL HF).

The Microcloth is first dampened with water. The wheel is then charged at high speed (approximately 1100 rpm) with the Al$_2$O$_3$ suspension, followed by the desired acid solution. The slower speed (550 rpm) is used to perform the final polishing. Charging at high speed evens out the abrasive suspension and acid solution on the lapping wheel.

The balance of the acid and abrasive ratio can be checked by adding both solutions, then placing the specimen mid-radius on the wheel for 15 to 20 s while applying light pressure. The specimen may exhibit a light yellow discoloration; this indicates that it has been slightly etched. If no etching has occurred, the rotating lap should be washed with water, then recharged with a stronger acid to abrasive ratio until the light discoloration or some light etching occurs. When this happens, more pressure should be applied to the specimen, and it should be moved toward the outside of the wheel until the discoloration and etching lessen due to the faster cutting rate. Acid and slurry should be adjusted to attack and polish at approximately the same rate. When polishing is completed, some faint second-phase structure should be visible using bright-field illumination.

Polarized light also works well for checking the progress during final polishing, especially for scratches and flowed metal. Preparation of the specimen may require 2 to 3 charges of the Al$_2$O$_3$ and acid solutions. The cloth must be washed with water each time before recharging with acid and abrasives to remove any material residue, which can flatten the nap. This final polishing lasts 3 to 5 min.

An additional technique involves using a large, absorbent paper wipe (approximately 375 by 375 mm, or 15 by 15 in.) in the other hand during final polishing. This wipe helps to smooth the solutions on the lap, which lessens the occurrence of scratches. When the specimen shows no scratches or flowed metal under polarized light and the second-phase structure can be seen faintly using bright-field illumination, the specimen is in the desired as-polished condition. Additional techniques can be employed at this time, such as anodization for inclusions, second phase, intermetallics, or slow attacking (sensitive) etchants for hydrogen (hydride) content.

## Macrostructural Examination

Low-magnification examination of macroetched cross sections often reveals considerable structural detail. Cast forms, such as ingot slices, extrusions, forgings, and other large parts, can be examined for grain size variations, weld integrity, porosity, shrinkage cavities, cracks, flow lines, and other macroscopic features.

**Macroetchants** most often used contain HF and HNO$_3$, with water as the carrier. The specimens are usually ground through 180- to 220-grit paper, then immersed for 5 to 10 min in a bath of 4 to 5% HF, 30 to 35% HNO$_3$, and the balance water. Upon removal, the specimens must be rinsed in cold water as quickly as possible to avoid acid staining.

## Microstructural Examination

The etchants and etching times can vary due to alloying and what type structure and phases are to be enhanced. The anodization procedures will also vary, depending on what structures are to be revealed. Tables 1 and 2 list etchants and anodization techniques. Detailed information on anodization procedures can be found in Ref 3.

Polarized light is among the best methods of viewing the basic crystal structure of these hexagonal materials. Etchants 2 or 3 from Table 1 should be used, followed by a 15-V dc anodization layer (see Table 2). Zircon-ium-niobium alloys, following preparation in the as-polished condition, should be anodized at 15 to 20 V dc. When these alloys are etched, the second phase they contain tends to mask their crystal structure when using polarized light.

Anodizing zirconium and its alloys at 110 V dc will show grain structures, cracks, intermetallics, and inclusions when using bright-field illumination. Oxides, nitrides, and hydrides can also be seen. Hydrides in zirconium-niobium alloys tend to be more difficult to reveal; etchant 5 in Table 1 should be used. To bring out the second phase in some Zircaloy alloys, a swab etch (see Table 1) or an as-polishing step can be used, followed by a 180-V dc anodization layer applied with the anodization solution in Table 2.

A specimen that is to be anodized after final polishing should never be air dried with the acid slurry on the surface. If this happens, some acid attack may occur, and an uneven oxide film on the as-polished surface will develop. As a result, an uneven anodized film, staining, or possibly some false microstructure may result when the specimen is anodized. This oxidizing reaction may also occur when swab etching before anodizing. When etching is complete, the specimen should be immediately rinsed in cold running water to help prevent oxidation. The anodization layer can greatly enhance any previous oxide films and stains on the polished and etched surfaces.

A 0- to 180-V dc power supply is required for anodization, as well as a small ampere output (0.25 to 1.0 A). The anode, in the form of a sharpened probe, must be a material that can be anodized, such as zirconium, hafnium, or niobium. Materials such as steels and coppers will not develop an anodized layer and will not allow the specimen to anodize evenly. The mounted specimen should be placed face up in the anodizing solution inside a stainless steel beaker, which acts as the cathode, with approximately 6 mm (0.25 in.) of solution covering the top of the specimen.

The polished surface of the specimen should be touched in an area that will not be conspicuous during examination. The power

**Table 2  Anodization techniques for microscopic examination of zirconium, hafnium, and their alloys**

| Anodization procedure | Characteristics and use |
|---|---|
| 1. 15- to 20-V anodization layer (gold color in zirconium and hafnium) | Improves grain structure contrast under polarized lighting and prevents specimens from staining and oxidizing |
| 2. 110- to 115-V anodization layer (purple-blue color in zirconium) | Reveals intermetallics, inclusions, and lighter element contamination in zirconium (Bright field) |
| 3. 180-V anodization layer (light red color in zirconium) | Enhances second phase in Zircaloys (Bright field) |

Note: Anodization solution consists of 60 mL absolute ethanol, 35 mL H$_2$O, 20 mL glycerine, 10 mL 85% lactic acid, 5 mL 85% H$_3$PO$_4$, and 2 g citric acid.

supply, which is set at 0 V, should be slowly adjusted to the desired voltage to control the color of the anodized layer. Best results are obtained by taking 5 to 10 s to reach the appropriate voltage. Only lower voltage layers ($\leq20$ V) do not need this slower adjustment. Once the appropriate voltage is reached, the specimen should be maintained at that voltage for 10 to 20 s.

The anodizing solution (see Table 2) contains ethanol, which makes it flammable if there is an electrical spark. Moreover, ethanol and water will evaporate if left out for several hours, which can deleteriously affect anodizing. On a final-polished specimen, flowed metal can also be a problem. The purer or softer materials tend to be more difficult to polish flow- or scratch-free. The final polishing cloth should be new or free from abrasive

or metallic residue, and the acid/abrasive slurry ratio should be properly balanced.

As stated previously, these materials are anisotropic, which allows them to be viewed under polarized light. They also exhibit twins and slip lines in their microstructures when plastically deformed (see Fig. 18). Twins and slip lines are most prevalent in the softer, large $\alpha$-type grain structures. These twins can be recognized by their lenticular shape. When they cross from one crystal to another, their direction usually changes.

As-cast zirconium has an acicular (needle-like) microstructure, which varies slightly in appearance depending on the composition and/or cooling rate. Typical examples are shown in Fig. 11 to 13. The transformation from equiaxed $\alpha$ to acicular $\alpha$ takes place at approximately 1015 °C (1860 °F). Moreover,

if a small amount of work (2 to 4%) is induced into the acicular $\alpha$ structure followed by an $\alpha$ anneal (675 to 790 °C, or 1250 to 1450 °F), large $\alpha$ grains can be produced, a condition referred to as "blocky alpha." Hafnium also exhibits an $\alpha$ grain structure.

## REFERENCES

1. *Powder Metallurgy*, Vol 7, 9th ed., *Metals Handbook*, American Society for Metals, 1984
2. *Properties and Selection: Stainless Steels, Tool Materials, and Special-Purpose Metals*, Vol 3, 9th ed., *Metals Handbook*, American Society for Metals, 1980, p 781-791
3. M.L. Picklesimer, Anodizing for Controlled Microstructural Contrast by Color, *The Microscope*, Vol 15, Oct 1967

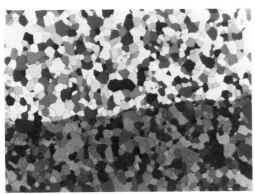

**Fig. 1** Zirconium cold rolled, $\alpha$-annealed 2.5-mm (0.10-in.) thick sheet. A transverse view showing an equiaxed $\alpha$ grain structure. Top part: etched and anodized; bottom part: as-etched. Attack polished, swab etched (etchant 2 in Table 1), and anodized at 15 V (see Table 2). Polarized light. 112×

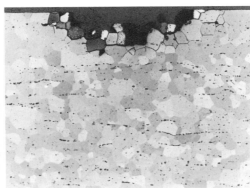

**Fig. 2** Zirconium (Zr702) cold worked and annealed 25-mm (1.0-in.) outside diameter by 1.8-mm (0.07-in.) wall thickness tubing. A longitudinal view showing chemical corrosion intergranular attack. Attack polished and anodized at 115 V (see Table 2). Bright field. 140×

**Fig. 3** Zirconium (Zr702) cold worked and annealed 1.8-mm (0.07-in.) thick sheet. A longitudinal view showing chemical attack on a corrosion coupon. Environment: methyl chloride at elevated temperature. Attack polished and anodized at 115 V (see Table 2). Bright field. 560×

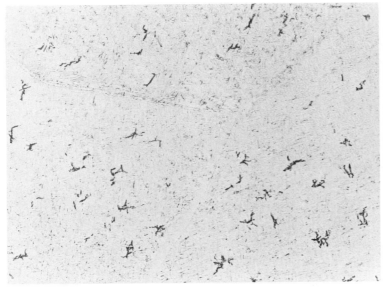

**Fig. 4** ZR705 (Zr-2.5Nb) gas tungsten arc welded 6.2-mm (0.250-in.) thick plate. A transverse view showing hydride platelets in weld metal. Attack polished and swab etched (etchant 5 in Table 1). Bright field. 210×

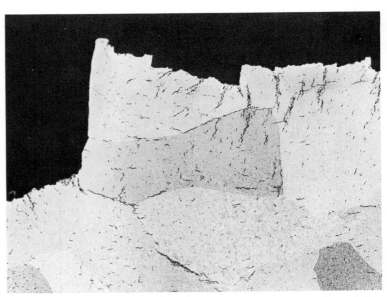

**Fig. 5** Zr705 (Zr-2.5Nb) bolt that was hot headed at about 760 °C (1400 °F). A longitudinal view showing the cracked surface. Failure was caused by fatigue stress, which had an orientation effect on the hydrogen within the material. Micrograph shows hydride platelets aligned below the fractured surface. Attack polished and anodized at 115 V (see Table 2). Bright field. 210×

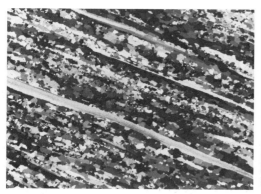

**Fig. 6** Zircaloy 2 200-mm (8-in.) diam rotary forging. A longitudinal view showing a partially recrystallized structure. Attack polished, swab etched (etchant 2 in Table 1), and anodized at 15 V (see Table 2). Polarized light. 56×

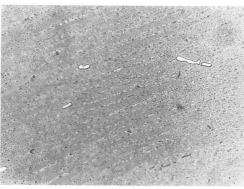

**Fig. 7** Zircaloy 2 (190 ppm Si) 50-mm (2-in.) thick forging. A transverse view showing zirconium phosphide intermetallic particles (white). Attack polished and anodized at 115 V (see Table 2). Bright field. 560×

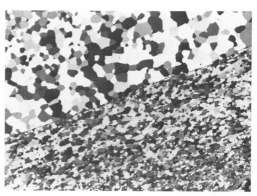

**Fig. 8** Zircaloy 2/zirconium coextruded and annealed tubing. A transverse view showing the interface of the two materials; the zirconium tubing liner has the larger α grains. Attack polished, swab etched (etchant 2 in Table 1) and anodized at 15 V (see Table 2). Polarized light. 56×

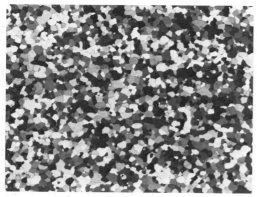

**Fig. 9** Zircaloy 4 hot-rolled and annealed 6.2-mm (0.250-in.) thick plate. A longitudinal view showing equiaxed α grain structure. Attack polished, swab etched (etchant 2 in Table 1), and anodized at 15 V (see Table 2). Polarized light. 58×

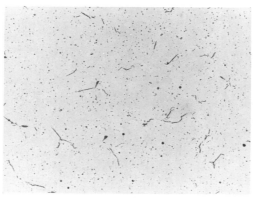

**Fig. 10** Zircaloy 4 cold-rolled and annealed 1-mm (0.040-in.) thick sheet. A transverse view showing hydride platelets and iron-chromium second phase. Attack polished, swab etched (etchant 4 in Table 1). Bright field. 145×

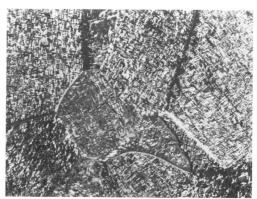

**Fig. 11** Zircaloy 4 as-cast ingot. Micrograph shows acicular α structure. Attack polished, swab etched (etchant 2 in Table 1), and anodized at 15 V (see Table 2). Polarized light. 29×

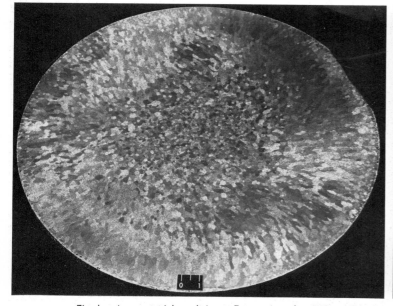

**Fig. 12** Zircaloy 4 as-cast triple melt ingot. Top section of a 575-mm (23-in.) diam ingot slice showing an acicular α crystal structure. Immersed 10 to 15 min in 4 to 5% HF (48%), 30 to 35% HNO₃ (70%), balance H₂O. 0.2×

**Fig. 13** Same as Fig. 12. A longitudinal top section of a 575-mm (23-in.) diam ingot slice showing a shrink cavity and an acicular α crystal structure. Same etchant and magnification as Fig. 12

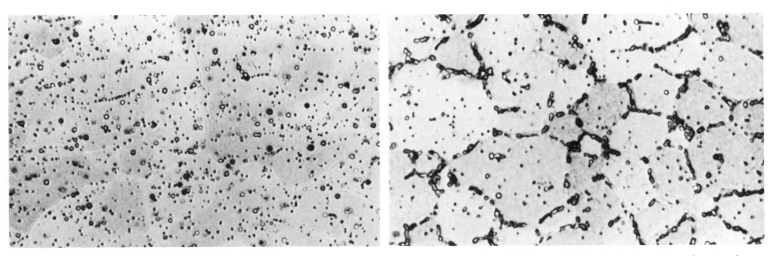

**Fig. 14, 15** Zircaloy 4 cold-rolled and annealed 2.5-mm (0.10-in.) thick sheet. Fig. 14: annealed at 730 °C (1350 °F). Longitudinal view showing the iron-chromium phase precipitated throughout the matrix. Fig. 15: annealed at 900 °C (1650 °F). Longitudinal view showing the iron-chromium phase precipitated into the grain boundaries. Both photographs were taken off a high-contrast monitor for enhanced contrast. Attack polished and anodized at 180 V (see Table 2). Bright field. 1200×

**Fig. 16** Hafnium cold-rolled, annealed, gas tungsten arc welded 1.8-mm (0.070-in.) thick plate. A transverse view showing a full cross section of the weldment. Attack polished, swab etched (etchant 2 in Table 1), and anodized at 15 V (see Table 2). Polarized light. 17×

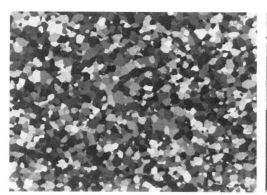

**Fig. 17** Hafnium hot-rolled and annealed 6.2-mm (0.250-in.) thick plate. A longitudinal view showing equiaxed $\alpha$ grain structure. Compare with Fig. 1 and 9. Attack polished, swab etched (etchant 2 in Table 1), and anodized at 15 V (see Table 2). Polarized light. 56×

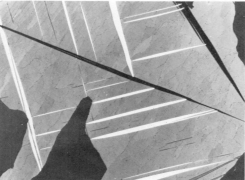

**Fig. 18** As-grown hafnium crystal bar exhibiting twins caused by cold working. Attack polished, swab etched (etchant 2 in Table 1), and anodized at 15 V (see Table 2). Polarized light. 56×

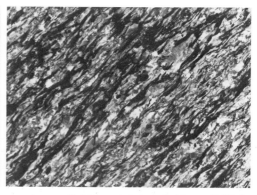

**Fig. 19** Hafnium rotary-forged 18-mm (0.7-in.) diam rod. A longitudinal view showing an as-wrought elongated (not recrystallized) structure. Attack polished, swab etched (etchant 2 in Table 1), and anodized at 15 V (see Table 2). Polarized light. 112×

# Powder Metallurgy Materials

By Leander F. Pease III
President
Powder-Tech Associates, Inc.

POWDER METALLURGY (P/M) MA-TERIALS encompass enough differences to necessitate describing specific specimen preparation procedures in addition to those provided in the Section "Metallographic Techniques" in this Volume. The major difference between parts made of metal powders and those made of wrought metal is the amount of porosity. Sintered materials generally exhibit 0 to 50% porosity, which affects mechanical properties and strongly interferes with metallographic preparation and interpretation of the structure. When examining photomicrographs, it is important to determine how the specimens were prepared. Careful metallographic preparation is significant in the analysis of sintered structures, because the shape of the porosity is as important as the amount in judging sintered strength and degree of sintering.

In metallographic preparation of most sintered specimens, the pores are smeared during grinding and rough polishing. This occurs to some degree even in materials whose pores have been filled with plastic resins. Proper polishing should open the smeared pores, then reveal their true shapes and amounts. Routine metallography of the type used on a medium-carbon, ingot-base steel will not suffice. Showing the proper amount of porosity is necessary to facilitate measuring the density variation from point to point over short distances (0.25 to 6.25 mm, or 0.01 to 0.25 in.), because such measurements cannot be made accurately using ASTM Standard B 328 (Ref 1). When the specimen is properly prepared, the area fraction of porosity will equal the volume fraction of porosity, and these must equal the porosity calculated from the measured and theoretical densities of the part:

$$V_p = \frac{T_\rho - M_\rho}{T_\rho}$$

where $V_p$ is the volume fraction porosity, $T_\rho$ is the theoretical density, and $M_\rho$ is the measured density. Detailed information on density and porosity measurements can be found in Volume 7 of the 9th Edition of *Metals Handbook*.

In a properly prepared specimen that is 80% dense, 20% of the area should appear as porosity if the part is uniformly dense. The surface of cold-pressed and sintered parts will always be somewhat denser than the interior because of pressure losses due to interparticle friction. However, parts that are P/M forged in tools at approximately 370 °C (700 °F) can have a chilled surface lower in density than the hotter, softer interior.

During sintering of cold-pressed compacts, the original particle boundaries disappear and result in a plane of fine pores, then larger pores. In as-pressed parts, particle boundaries appear as thin, gray lines. The progress of sintering can be judged by the disappearance of these boundaries. The original particle boundaries are similar to elongated, disk-shaped pores and have very sharp corners. These are extreme stress raisers. There is virtually no bonding across the original particle boundaries. Proper specimen preparation is required to distinguish residual original particle boundaries from the thin, gray boundaries that often appear at the edges of smeared pores. Therefore, an improperly prepared specimen with smeared porosity is often erroneously judged to be undersintered. If microhardness testing is performed, proper presentation of the porosity will result in fewer diamond indentations falling into hidden pores and thus fewer wasted or incorrect readings. For additional information on microhardness testing of P/M materials, see the article "Inspection and Quality Control" in Volume 7 of the 9th Edition of *Metals Handbook*.

The open porosity in a mounted sintered part can result in trapping of water (moisture). During etching, this water will bleed out, resulting in staining. Water will also corrode some sintered materials and can evaporate, then condense on the objective lens of the microscope, resulting in a foggy image. Etchants cause similar problems. Open porosity can trap abrasives and carry them onto subsequent cloths, which should hold only fine abrasives. The result is an increased tendency toward scratching of specimen surfaces. Filling the pores with epoxy resins alleviates these difficulties, but requires considerable technique.

Many of the interesting structures seen in P/M parts are caused by porosity and by the blends of elemental powders that constitute many alloys. These blends do not always result in homogeneous, well-diffused structures. Such heterogeneity is not necessarily detrimental and, in certain nickel steels and diffusion-alloyed steels, may be advantageous. It is important to recognize when the observed heterogeneity is beneficial. The pores allow carburizing and nitriding gases to penetrate the interior of a sintered steel part, resulting in less well-defined cases on carbon steel and nitriding 300 series stainless steels. The P/M steels are generally low in manganese, and when the alloys are prepared as elemental blends, hardenability is lower than for fully dense, homogeneous low-alloy steels. This is not a problem in the fully dense low-alloyed steels fabricated by forging or injection molding.

## Sample Preparation

**Specimen Selection and Sectioning.** It is usually necessary to examine a section that extends from the surface to the interior of the part and from top to bottom. The surface is susceptible to changes from (1) the sintering atmosphere, such as decarburization in a steel, (2) being sealed over with pure copper, or (3) shallow hardenability in elemental blends of steels. Density can vary from point to point. During sintering, the protected bottom of the part "sees" a different atmosphere than the top, and the internal area can be more protected from the sintering atmosphere than an outer surface. Infiltrated parts have certain artifacts that appear where the infiltrant entered.

Improper tool design or press setup can cause cracks or laminations at different levels in a part, such as between a hub and flange; low-density regions normally occur just below flanges. If a part is overpressed in certain regions or if the tooling does not have the correct exit taper, microcracks can occur upon ejection. These are usually parallel to a punch face (normal to the direction of applied pressure) and are best seen in sections that run parallel to the pressing direction. In a case-carburized gear, a section showing the plan view of the teeth would show the depth of case and whether or not the teeth were through-hardened. Therefore, likely potential defects in a P/M part affect selection of the planes of sectioning.

Because of the difficulty in opening all the smeared pores on a P/M part, the use of smaller sections is recommended. An easily polished specimen will measure less than 12 by 12 mm (½ by ½ in.). A soft abrasive wheel that breaks down easily will control overheating at cutoff and will not glaze easily. Low-speed diamond wheels are very precise and damage free, but require much time. If the conventional abrasive wheel glazes because the workpiece is too large, four small sections (3 cm², or 0.5 in.²) can be removed using pliers at equal positions around the periphery of the wheel. Because this weakens the wheel somewhat, it should always be operated in a well-guarded enclosure. A substantial flow of water that correctly strikes the interface between the wheel and the part is also required. Rust inhibitor should be added to recirculated water.

Sectioning an annularly shaped part with the wheel advancing from the outer diameter toward the inner diameter can result in the wheel being captured when it penetrates the inner diameter. This often occurs in heat-treated parts containing residual stresses and can cause wheel breakage. It can be avoided if the part is sectioned with the wheel moving along the axis of the part so that material on both sides of the inner diameter is cut at the same time. In general, it is preferable to secure in a vise the section of the specimen to be mounted. This section rarely contains burrs and can be mounted without further hand grinding.

**Fluid Removal and Washing.** Entrapped oil from heat treating or machining as well as water and rust inhibitors from the cutoff wheel must be removed from the pores before the specimen is mounted. Other sources of contamination include the sizing lubricants used at repressing and rust inhibitors added during tumbling deburring of the parts. Failure to remove these contaminants will obscure the specimen surface under the microscope. Oils also seem to interfere with

polishing. If the specimen is not heat treated, contains no substantial amount of oil, and can tolerate heating to 260 to 370 °C (500 to 700 °F) for approximately 1 min, then the fluids can be removed on a hot plate under a hood. The specimens are easily heated until straw-colored or light blue. Water or small amounts of oil will evaporate or burn off quickly.

When the specimen cannot be heated, an extractor-condenser of the type shown in Fig. 1 or a Soxhlet apparatus may be used. The extractor-condenser consists of a flask, a siphon cup, and a condensing-coil unit that fits on the top of the flask. A solvent, such as toluene or acetone, is placed in the flask, and the specimens to be cleaned are placed in the siphon cup. Multiple specimens must first be coded for subsequent identification.

A cold-water line is connected to the condensing coil. The flask is heated to the boiling temperatures of the solvent. The solvent evaporates, and when the vapor contacts the cold condensing coil, it drips into the siphon cup and onto the parts. When the siphon cup is filled to the level determined by the upper bend in the exit tube, it empties, returning solvent and dissolved oil to the boiling flask. Recycling allows a subsequent flow of clean solvent over the specimens. The oil and foreign matter removed remain in the flask.

Six cycles, requiring a total of approximately 1 h, will usually ensure removal of the oil. This method is also described in ASTM B 328 (Ref 1) and ISO 2738 (Ref 2). The latter test method includes the technique for removing oil when testing for total carbon. Because laboratory investigations often involve testing for carbon along with metallography, it may be efficient to use the more thorough

ISO method. Following extraction with the solvents, it is necessary to dry the parts for approximately 1 h at 120 °C (250 °F) to remove the solvent.

The ultrasonic cleaner used for washing P/M specimens consists of a power supply and a small tank, which holds a solvent bath. The power source produces high-frequency waves in the bath. The waves force the solvent into the pores of the specimen, removing foreign substances. The specimen is placed in the solvent bath; therefore, most of the washing takes place in contaminated solution. Because the specimens represent a small fraction of the bath volume, the amount of contamination is not significant. The use of 1-1-1 trichloroethane and a hot ultrasonic bath for 1 h has been recommended (Ref 3). The latter procedure should be carried out under a hood. Again, the residual entrapped solvent should be evaporated from the specimens.

**Wax Impregnation.** After removal of fluid from the pores, subsequent abrasives, water, and etchants must be kept out of the pores. Wax impregnation may be used for specimens that are to be hand held or mounted in Bakelite. The specimens are soaked 2 to 4 h in a molten synthetic wax at 175 °C (350 °F). After cooling and removal of the surface wax, the specimens are ready to hand grind or to mount in Bakelite.

Wax impregnation should ideally be carried out in a vacuum oven at the recommended temperature. The vacuum allows the air entrapped in the pores to bubble up through the molten wax. The atmospheric pressure is returned to the system with the specimens immersed in the molten wax. The air pressure then should be allowed to act on the molten wax for 30 min to force it into the pores. Subsequently, the specimens may be cooled, and the excess wax removed.

**Mounting of Compacted Specimens.** Specimens that have been filled with wax may be mounted in thermosetting Bakelite resins, Lucite, or clear-liquid cold-mounting resins. Epoxy resins, rather than wax and Bakelite, are preferred for filling the pores and mounting the specimens, because the pores can be sealed as the multiple specimens are mounted. A convenient container for mounting is a length of 25-mm (1-in.) copper or aluminum tubing with an inner diameter of 32 mm (1¼ in.). This can be placed on a small, flat sheet of glass. The interior of the tube and the glass are coated with a mold-release agent. An alternate two-piece cup can be machined from low-carbon steel (Fig. 2). The steel base may be ground flat in the lab as needed, and excess epoxy may be removed by sintering or heat treating. The bases of the plastic cups commercially available become concave after a few uses.

When more than one specimen is to be inserted in the same mount, each specimen must be identified for future reference. The use of an asymmetric arrangement of specimens or the mounting of a distinctive object,

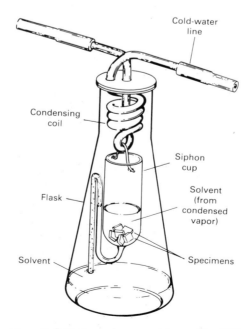

**Fig. 1** Extractor-condenser used for washing P/M specimens to remove contaminants from pores

Labels on figure:
Cold-water line
Condensing coil
Siphon cup
Flask
Solvent (from condensed vapor)
Specimens
Solvent

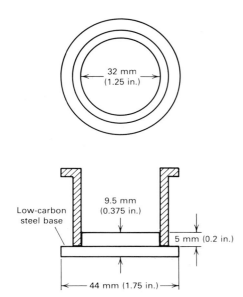

**Fig. 2** Machined two-piece cup for mounting P/M specimens

such as a small, twisted piece of a paper clip, will permit easy, accurate reference.

The epoxy resin should be selected for low vapor pressure of resin and hardener, and any new resin should be tested in the vacuum chamber to note the pressure at which it bubbles. For example, some epoxies should not be used below 75 torr (10 kPa). This limits the amount of air that can be removed and the volume of pores that can be filled. Epoxy resins should be placed in disposable cups for stirring and mixing of resin and hardener. Volumetric measurement of the components with plastic syringes works well. Epoxy resins should be selected for low viscosity. Rapid hardening is convenient, but must not be allowed to interfere with pore filling.

*Epoxy-Resin Impregnation.* In one method, the resin is carefully poured over the specimens in their mounting cups to a depth of approximately 19 mm (3/4 in.). Any bubbles that form during air evacuation can be held in the remaining 6 mm (1/4 in.) of the cup. The cups should be placed in a container that will catch any minor epoxy spills, and the container should be placed in a vacuum chamber. The air is then evacuated to the lowest pressure tolerated by the resin (see example above). The specimens should bubble for approximately 10 min. Air pressure is then restored and allowed to impregnate the specimens for 15 min. The specimens can then be cured overnight (preferred), at an accelerated rate of 1 h at 50 °C (120 °F), or by following manufacturer's directions. Heat often causes cavities to form against the porous specimen. The cavities interfere with polishing and rarely form when the specimen cures slowly at room temperature.

An alternate method for impregnation with epoxy resin involves suspending the specimen above the epoxy bath during air evacuation. This allows the air to exit the pores rapidly and cause no air bubbling in the epoxy. It is

similar to the technique used to fill the pores with oil in a sintered bearing. Yet another method is to hold the specimen above the oil magnetically or with a vacuum feed-through manipulator. After 1 to 2 min at low pressure, no air will remain in the specimen, and it can be lowered into the epoxy bath, at which point the pressure is readmitted into the chamber. This method is limited by the vapor pressure of the epoxy resin and hardener. Commercial equipment with vacuum feed-through evacuates air from the specimens and directs a stream of epoxy from outside the chamber into the specimen cup located in the vacuum. Again, the vapor pressure of the resins determines the lowest usable pressure.

Most mounts show evidence that resin enters the specimen from unmachined surfaces; this is never the surface against the bottom of the specimen cup. Therefore, most mounts show evidence of epoxy resin in the surface pores, but the interior pores are rarely full. This effect is apparent to the unaided eye during initial polishing, because the outer edges will appear more porous (like an orange peel) and the interior more mirrorlike.

*Edge retention,* discussed in the article "Mounting of Specimens" in this Volume, is achieved by adding light or dark alumina ($Al_2O_3$) granules to the epoxy resin (Fig. 3). Some of the ceramic may be blended with resin and poured around the specimens to form a 1.6-mm (1/16-in.) thick layer. The rest of the mount is formed from clear resin poured on top of the mixture.

Alternatively, loose $Al_2O_3$ can be poured into the specimen cup to a depth of 1.6 mm (1/16 in.), surrounding the specimens, and the clear resin carefully poured on top. During vacuum evacuation, the resin flows in among the $Al_2O_3$ particles. This ceramic reinforces the epoxy and results in very little rounding of the specimen edge during polishing. Because the oxide greatly slows the rate of grinding and polishing, the times recommended below must be adjusted. A third

technique involves forming a thin oxide-reinforced layer around the specimen itself by applying a thick, pasty mixture of resin and oxide to the specimen surface. In this way, the entire surface of the mount is not hardened, just a layer approximately 0.5 mm (0.020 in.) adjacent to the specimen. Therefore, the polishing time is not unduly increased.

*Specimen Identification.* The use of epoxy resin, particularly when air cured, produces a surface that is inconvenient for scribing the specimen identification. The back of the specimen mount should be ground through 600 grit, then polished for 1 min using 1-$\mu$m $Al_2O_3$ on a medium-nap cloth. This yields a flat surface that can be scribed for clear identification. If it is necessary to look through the side of the mount to see the specimen inside the epoxy, the round side surfaces must be polished as described above.

**Mounting of uncompacted metal powders** requires special procedures that include the use of epoxy resin and vacuum impregnation. A small amount of properly sampled powder per ASTM Standard B 215 (Ref 4) should be placed in the center of the specimen cup that will hold the epoxy resin. The pile should be approximately 13 mm (1/2 in.) in diameter and approximately 3 mm (1/8 in.) deep at the center. The epoxy should be poured around the pile of powder without disturbing or segregating it. The cup should be filled with resin to a depth of 12 to 18 mm (1/2 to 3/4 in.). The specimen is then evacuated at approximately 75 torr (10 kPa) for 10 min and pressurized at atmospheric pressure. Curing can take place at room temperature; higher temperatures hasten the process, but create problems.

An alternate method is to blend the metal powder with a small amount of epoxy resin, then pour it into the bottom of the cup. This should be a thick, pasty mixture whose consistency will prevent the particles of metal from falling and segregating and will display several close particles in a micrograph at 200×. If segregation is suspected, the specimen can be halved after hardening. The sections can be remounted to note any segregation between top and bottom of the pile. This is important when attempting to measure the particle size distribution from a micrograph of the assembled powder particles.

**Grinding.** Rough grinding of the mount must produce a planar surface for subsequent grinding and polishing. The preferred procedure involves using a water-cooled diamond-plated lap that consists of a perforated metal substrate with 200-mesh diamond particles bonded to the metal surface. The diamond lap is secured to a sheet of magnetic material, which is bonded with adhesive to a revolvable horizontal grinding lap (wheel). The laps are available in various grit sizes; 200 or 100 grit should be used for rough grinding. Diamond laps provide a very flat surface and remove material rapidly. They are invaluable if the epoxy resin has been filled with $Al_2O_3$ for edge retention (Fig. 3). It is important to

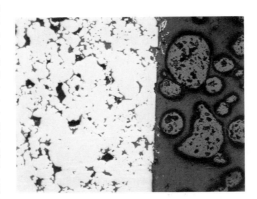

**Fig. 3** Edge-retention technique in which dark $Al_2O_3$ granules (right) are added as a reinforcer to the epoxy resin. Not all of the pores are open, which indicates that $Al_2O_3$ additions necessitate extended polishing times. Fe-0.8C specimen (7.0 g/cm$^3$) pressed at 550 MPa (40 tsi) and sintered 30 min in dissociated ammonia at 1120 °C (2050 °F). 2% nital. 95×

grind a 30° bevel around the specimen periphery; this allows the specimen to pass smoothly over the subsequent polishing laps and prevents the plowing aside of abrasives by a sharp edge. Failure to use a bevel will slow polishing.

Fine grinding should be performed using wet 400- and 600-grit silicon carbide paper. The paper is held by a rotating disk that makes use of the vacuum created by a thin layer of water under the sheet of abrasive paper. The same grinding can be carried out on wet papers placed on top of a sheet of glass. When using grinding wheels, the specimen is held in a fixed position on the wheel so that all scratches are in one direction, which requires even and moderate pressure. When changing papers, the specimen is rotated 90° to note the disappearance of the previous scratches. The use of one single sheet of silicon carbide paper for more than two specimen mounts is not recommended, because this leads to lack of flatness of the specimen surface. Grinding using 400- and 600-grit abrasives and moderate pressure at 125 to 250 rpm on 200-mm (8-in.) laps requires approximately 30 s for each paper.

**Polishing.** Following grinding, the specimen will be flat to the edges, and the pores will be almost completely smeared (Fig. 4). Subsequent polishing will generally round the specimen edges, because the mounting resin is much softer than the metal specimen. This rounding can be prevented by longer polishing, the use of ceramic materials for edge retention, or such conventional techniques as plating of the specimens before mounting. Polishing must open all the pores, show true area fraction of porosity, remove scratches and disturbed metal, and avoid edge rounding. The presence of epoxy resin or wax in the pores facilitates opening the smeared pores, but does not eliminate the problem.

During polishing, the abrasives first open the pores closest to the specimen edges (Ref 5, 6), implying that surfaces are less dense than interiors (Fig. 5 to 7). For ferrous mate-

**Fig. 4** Pressed and sintered Fe-0.8C alloy (6.8 g/cm³), as-ground on 600-grit silicon carbide. Micrograph shows the closure of pores and flatness of specimen (the surface is shown at left). Arrows indicate closed pore edges. 95×

rials, the fastest way to reveal the pores results in slight edge rounding, but is adequate for routine work. These steps should be followed:

1. Etch 2 min in 2% nital by immersion. For materials other than low-alloy steels, use the customary etchants. Etching before polishing initiates pore opening.
2. Rough polish 2 min using 1-$\mu$m $Al_2O_3$ and moderate hand pressure on a long-nap felt cloth (Ref 7). Use 250 rpm on a 200-mm (8-in.) diam wheel, rotating the specimen counter to wheel rotation to prevent comet tails. The long-nap cloth and the fairly coarse $Al_2O_3$ rapidly open the pores (see Ref 8 for an example of another technique that required 300 min).
3. Repeat steps 1 and 2 once or twice. This procedure will generally open all the pores. To the unaided eye, the surface of the specimen should exhibit a uniform orange-peel appearance with no shiny, specular (mirrorlike) regions. If necessary, repeat steps 1 and 2 until the surface is uniformly roughened. Even P/M forgings and injection-molded parts at 98 to 99%

theoretical density will display pores to the unaided eye.
4. This aggressive rough polishing has exaggerated the pore area fraction. That is, the specimen will erroneously appear lower in density. Final polishing must restore the true area fraction of porosity.
5. Polish 2 min using 1-$\mu$m diamond on a short-nap cloth at 250 rpm with moderate hand pressure. This will restore the pores to their true area fraction, eliminate most scratches, but leave the edges of the specimen rounded. A 19-mm (³/₄ in.) long bead of diamond paste, weighing approximately 0.06 g, is recommended for each 2 min of polishing. Use an alcohol-base solvent or thinner for the diamond paste so that it will wash off in water. Oily thinners penetrate the residual pores and bleed out of the specimen.
6. Final polish 30 s using a long-nap cloth and 0.05-$\mu$m deagglomerated $Al_2O_3$. Use light hand pressure or an automatic polisher with 100-g weight on the specimen at 125 rpm. This will remove the fine scratches on most ferrous materials. The true area fraction of porosity of the surface will now be restored. Reference 5 includes information on this method and demonstrates that it is possible to open pores and show the correct porosity area fraction using a method that requires approximately 12 min and does not use diamond. It consists of 10 min of hand polishing using 1-$\mu$m $Al_2O_3$ on a synthetic suede, short-nap cloth at 250 rpm on a 200-mm (8-in.) lap and 2 min of light hand polishing using 0.05-$\mu$m $Al_2O_3$ at 125 rpm on the same type of cloth.

To produce a surface with no edge rounding, it is necessary to eliminate the 1-$\mu$m $Al_2O_3$ and long-nap cloth polishing. Instead, after the 2-min etch in 2% nital, step 5 should be repeated several times. More than five repetitions may be required to open all the pores on a large specimen, particularly if it is soft

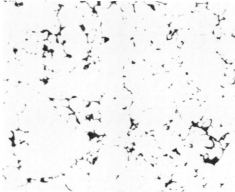

**Fig. 5, 6, 7** Effect of polishing on pore opening in a pressed and sintered Fe-0.8C alloy. Fig. 5: deliberately underpolished specimen. This region, which is adjacent to the specimen edge, shows all the pores open. Compare with Fig. 6 (specimen interior). Fig. 6: center of same specimen. After 2 min of polishing, there are numerous smeared pores. Compare the amount of porosity with Fig. 5. This micrograph shows how the inner part of a specimen polishes more slowly than the edge. Fig. 7: repolished version of Fig. 6 showing more pores in the center of the part (some remain smeared over). The density appears higher than the true density of 6.8 g/cm³. All at 180×

and undersintered. The wheel should be recharged with diamond at each repetition. However, the 2-min etching should not be repeated, because the diamond does not rapidly remove etching effects.

Newly developed P/M materials may require polishing procedures that show the correct area fraction of porosity using standards of known density. Other modern methods of automatic polishing may open all pores, but should first be tested by preparing a specimen, then measuring the area fraction of pores. This should agree with calculations of the known density. A vibratory machine in which the specimens circulate around in the abrasive slurry can also be used. The use of a short-nap chemotextile cloth (Texmet) and 0.3- or 1-$\mu$m Al$_2$O$_3$ will yield a specimen that is virtually free of edge rounding. However, for specimens that have been ground through 600 grit, this procedure requires approximately 3 h because of the slow material removal rate and the need to open all the pores.

The rate of material removal may be measured using a Knoop indenter mark as a reference (Fig. 8). First, a mark approximately 100 $\mu$m long is made in a known location on the specimen. A simple reference point in the interior of the specimen can be made using a Rockwell superficial indenter with the 15-kgf load. The Knoop mark is then placed approximately 0.4 mm (0.015 in.) away from the superficial indenter mark and at a known orientation to it. The Knoop mark is measured from a photograph or with the measuring stage of the microhardness tester. After polishing for a fixed time, such as 1 to 2 min, the Knoop mark is relocated and remeasured. The material removed normal to the specimen surface is the change in length of the Knoop diagonal divided by 30.51 (for a standard indenter). For a 25- by 25-mm (1- by 1-in.) specimen, polishing using a 250-rpm, 200-mm (8-in.) diam lap, 1-$\mu$m Al$_2$O$_3$ on a synthetic suede, short-nap cloth, and moderate hand pressure will remove 0.4 $\mu$m/min. A smaller specimen, such as 12 by 6 mm (0.5 by 0.25 mm) will polish at 1.45 $\mu$m/min. Addi-

tional information on material removal rates can be found in Ref 5.

Soft material, such as pure iron or copper, may still exhibit some fine scratches after the 0.05-$\mu$m Al$_2$O$_3$ polishing described above in step 6. One solution is to use a new long-nap cloth (Microcloth) with adhesive backing attached to a flat glass plate or to a flat bench top. With the deagglomerated 0.05-$\mu$m Al$_2$O$_3$ charged onto the cloth at a ratio of 1 part (by volume) powder to 4 parts distilled water, the specimen should be polished in the abrasive slurry using approximately 50 light hand strokes straight back and forth. This will eliminate the fine scratches from the prior polishing; remaining scratches will be aligned parallel to the direction of polishing, and their source identified. This light final polishing does not cause comet tails or pore beveling.

Titanium alloys require a 4-min rough polishing using 1-$\mu$m Al$_2$O$_3$ on felt cloth at 250 rpm on a 200-mm (8-in.) diam lap with moderate hand pressure. This will open and slightly enlarge the pores. The use of 1-$\mu$m diamond or 0.05-$\mu$m Al$_2$O$_3$ may cause polishing artifacts and is therefore not recommended.

## Metal Powder Particles

The powders, if mounted as noted above, will present a planar surface suitable for fine grinding. It is usually possible to begin using wet 600-grit silicon carbide on revolving wheels or fixed sheets of paper. Approximately 30 s of grinding will expose enough particles to be viewed. The specimen is washed, then polished by hand for 2 min using 1-$\mu$m diamond on a short-nap cloth at 250 rpm on a 200-mm (8-in.) diam lap. The use of an alcohol-base, water-soluble lubricant allows easy specimen cleaning in water.

The powders must not be overpolished, or the epoxy resin will be polished away between them and the particle edges will become rounded. Final polishing should be performed using deagglomerated 0.05-$\mu$m Al$_2$O$_3$ on a long-nap cloth for 30 s with light hand pressure on a 200-mm (8-in.) diam, 125-rpm lap. Prolonged polishing or heavy hand pressure during final polishing will round the particle surfaces.

Because some particles have internal pores that may have been smeared, it is important to examine some of the particles, unetched, at 500 or 1000$\times$ for the thin, gray lines that are the edges of smeared pores (Fig. 9). If such undisclosed pores are noted, the 1-$\mu$m diamond polish must be repeated. Etching the powders will remove enough surface material to lower the particles below the surface of the epoxy resin, which provides an opportunity to repolish them. The repolishing should always be performed using 1-$\mu$m diamond, because 0.05-$\mu$m Al$_2$O$_3$ on a long-nap cloth polishes slowly but rounds particle edges quickly.

**Fig. 9** Intermediate state of polishing showing the edges of smeared pores (see arrows), which have not yet been opened. Low-contrast print focused on smeared pore boundaries of pressed and sintered Fe-0.8C alloy (6.8 g/cm$^3$). 520$\times$

Aluminum powders and alloys must be polished using a 1-$\mu$m or finer magnesia, rather than Al$_2$O$_3$, which reacts with aluminum powders. Hard powders, such as tungsten, may be examined as-polished using 1-$\mu$m diamond. Final polishing of very soft materials, such as pure copper, may be carried out using a fixed, long-nap cloth, as described above for full-size specimens. Pure iron powder may require two or three 30-s fine polishings and light etching in 2% nital to remove fine scratches. The procedure also opens porosity in fine-porosity sponge iron.

## Macroexamination

Macroexamination of sintered materials is not prevalent. In wrought or ingot-base materials, forging flow lines, oxide segregation, and stringers are studied extensively. These features are not usually found in P/M materials, but there are certain other uses for macroexamination.

In sectioning a heat-treated sintered steel, care must be taken not to overheat the specimen and temper or reharden it locally. The etching performed during grinding and polishing to help open the pores will indicate any macroscopic striated or variegated darkening from overheating, as shown in Fig. 10 and 11. By revealing a lighter or darker surface than the interior, this same intermediate etching using 2% nital on steels will show if a specimen ground through 600-grit silicon carbide paper is likely to have a decarburized or carburized surface layer. This effect is apparent to the unaided eye.

During polishing with 1-$\mu$m Al$_2$O$_3$, a porouslike layer similar to orange peel will develop at the outer edges of the specimen adjacent to the mounting medium. This layer will spread inward during subsequent polishing until the entire cross section appears uniformly porous to the unaided eye. If the surface is shiny or specular in certain regions, it almost surely will be found to contain pores that polishing has yet to open (Fig. 5 to 7). The penetration depth of the epoxy resin through the side surfaces of the specimen can

**Fig. 8** Knoop indenter mark (100 gf) used as a reference to note the rate of material removal from the surface by measuring the change in length and depth of the indentation. Surrounding black pores in this unetched, pressed and sintered Fe-0.8C alloy (6.8 g/cm$^3$) are also revealed. 295$\times$

**Fig. 10, 11** Ferrous P/M specimens cut with and without the use of a coolant. Fig. 10: no evidence of overheating when a coolant was used. Fig. 11: evidence of overheating (dark area at right edge of specimen) when coolant was not used. Nital. 12×

be seen during polishing, because the regions where the epoxy is in the pores will display the orange peel appearance more quickly than the unfilled regions. After final polishing, the surface roughness from the pores is much diminished, and variations in density in a part are visible to the unaided eye.

Nital etching of elemental mixtures of nickel steels will reveal the nickel-rich areas as light-reflecting sparkles. Unsintered (green) or sintered unprepared parts may be examined to 25× for cracks or the presence of added copper in iron. The fracture surface of a heat-treated part shows varying degrees of discoloration in bands parallel to the outer surfaces. These dark bands are probably caused by oil impregnation during oil quenching, and the color is caused by *in situ* partial decomposition of the oil. The Metal Powder Industries Federation (MPIF) Test Method 37 for case depth uses the difference in the fracture appearance of the case region and the interior to measure case depth (Ref 9).

## Scanning Electron Microscopy

The scanning electron microscope is a useful tool for examining metal powders, fracture surfaces, as-pressed and sintered surfaces formed by dies and punches, and, potentially, the as-polished sections used for optical microscopy. Scanning electron micrographs of iron, prealloyed steel, and stainless steel powders are shown in Fig. 12 to 24 in the series of representative micrographs in this article. In addition, Fig. 25 and 26 show the smooth outer surfaces of parts that were contacted by punches or dies during consolidation. Figure 26 illustrates the unsintered view of the side of a part that contacted the die. The powders have been pressed into close contact, and the boundaries between particles are readily visible. Sintering, which completes the bonding of adjacent powder particles, is traced in the accompanying optical micrographs (Fig. 27

to 31) that illustrate the disappearance of the particle boundaries and the rounding of pores in a diffusion-alloyed steel.

The development of bonding between metal particles can also be followed by examining their fracture surfaces. As bonds develop, the fracture shows cup and cone or dimpled fracture regions where the bonds have been torn apart. The regions between the ductile cups and cones are the smooth surfaces of the original particles, which were not bonded to the adjacent particles. The progress of sintering can be followed through the increasing area fraction of the ductile torn regions. This is well illustrated in the scanning electron micrographs shown in Fig. 32 to 38.

The energy spectra of the x-rays generated by the electron beam striking the atoms of the specimen can be analyzed to determine which elements are present at the fracture surface. The fracture surface may be scanned for the wavelength characteristic of a particular element and to record the intensity or

concentration of the element as a function of location. This appears on an x-ray dot map that shows if the element is uniformly distributed or somewhat segregated and is useful for monitoring the dissolution of copper or nickel in steel or to check for oxides of manganese or silicon.

## Microexamination

Etchants commonly used for the metallographic examination of sintered metals are listed in Table 1. The first use of the etchant, as noted previously, is to open the smeared porosity during the coarse polishing with 1-$\mu$m $Al_2O_3$. However, it is very important to examine sintered parts in the unetched condition, which displays the number and distribution of original particle boundaries present. Etching reveals grain boundaries, which are easily confused with the particle boundaries that also appear as thin gray or black lines. Cracks, density variation, oxide films or particles, and pore shape or rounding are easier to locate in the absence of distracting features.

**For iron and low-carbon sintered materials,** 2% nital is preferred, because it uncovers the ferrite grain boundaries. It is applied by immersion for 10 to 15 s. The specimen is washed in running water, rinsed in methyl alcohol (optional), then dried in a cool air stream. (If any open porosity is present, the use of warm air will cause subsequent evaporation of entrapped water or alcohol onto the lens of the microscope.) For steels with medium to high carbon content or for heat-treated structures, concentrated picral in methanol works well. It enhances the contrast of carbide platelets in the eutectoid in as-sintered structures.

Picral develops good contrast in the martensite needles and retained austenite of heat-treated materials. The 2% nital also works well for these structures and will not stain hands and clothing. Heat-treated specimens etched in nital should be immersed 6 to 8 s (swabbing causes streaks), rinsed in running

### Table 1 Etchants used for examination of P/M materials

| Etchant | Procedures and applications |
|---|---|
| 2% nital: methyl alcohol plus 2% concentrated $HNO_3$ | For as-sintered irons and steels (best for ferrite and low-carbon steels); immerse for 10–15 s; heat-treated steels: 6–7 s |
| Concentrated picral: picric acid in methyl alcohol; some undissolved crystals remain in the container bottom | For higher carbon-containing materials to develop good contrast with carbides, pearlite, other eutectoid products, martensite, and retained austenite; etch by immersion, 15–20 s |
| Glyceregia: 10 mL $HNO_3$ conc, 15 mL HCl, 35 mL glycerol(a) | Show grain boundaries, twin boundaries, and carbides in austenitic and martensitic stainless steels; immerse for 1–2 min or swab lightly |
| 4% $FeCl_3$ in $H_2O$ | Develops red color in copper-rich regions in bronze; etch by swabbing, 10–20 s |
| 2 g $K_2Cr_2O_7$, 4 mL NaCl, 8 mL $H_2SO_4$, 100 mL $H_2O$ | Develops grain boundaries and small grain clusters in bronze; etch by swabbing, 10–20 s |
| Keller's reagent: 2.5 mL $HNO_3$, 1.5 mL HCl, 1.0 mL HF, 95 mL $H_2O$ | For aluminum and aluminum alloys; immerse 8–15 s, wash in water; do not remove etchant products from surface |
| 5% nital | For as-sintered tool steels; immerse 5 min |
| 5 mL $HNO_3$ conc, 10 mL 48% HF, 85 mL $H_2O$ | For titanium and titanium alloys; immerse 5 s |
| 5 mL $NH_4OH$, 3 drops $H_2O_2$, 5 mL $H_2O$ | For brasses; swab 20 s; make fresh solution every 20 min |

(a) Use hood for fumes and hand and eye protection when mixing this solution.

water, then alcohol, and then blown dry. This will underetch the martensite, but will enhance contrast between the fine pearlite (a dark, unresolved, nodular constituent) and the light-colored martensite—an optimum condition for checking microhardness, because the martensite is light, clearly seen, and forms a good background for measuring the length of the Knoop diamond indentation. The use of picral for 15 to 20 s or 2% nital for slightly longer will enhance the contrast of martensite and retained austenite. For magnifications of $1000\times$, a lightly etched structure affords maximum clarity.

**Sintered stainless steels** are best etched in glyceregia using a protective hood and ventilation. Because this is a strong acid mixture, eye and hand protection is also advised. The glyceregia is applied by immersion with the specimen surface upward; a fraction of a millimeter of the liquid is poured on top of the metal to be etched. When freshly prepared, the action is fairly slow and may require 1 to 2 min. The etchant may also be applied using a very light swabbing action. Glyceregia decomposes with time; it may turn orange and emit nitrous oxide. As the etchant darkens toward orange or brown, it becomes more reactive and less predictable. Shelf life may be extended by cool storage. Nonetheless, glyceregia rarely can be used for more than 2 h before disposal. Additional etching should be preceded by repolishing using 1-$\mu$m diamond and 0.05-$\mu$m $Al_2O_3$ to avoid unwanted etching artifacts.

In well-sintered stainless steel, moderate grain size, annealing twins, and grain boundaries not decorated with precipitated carbides will be visible. When the carbides are present, the grain boundaries will not be clean and straight, but will be ragged, broader, and fast etching. Prolonged etching causes the formation of pits, which can be confused with pores. The stainless steels are judged by freedom from precipitated carbides and original particle boundaries. Some of the new classes of high-temperature sintered stainless steels exhibit very well-rounded pores, which may even be isolated from each other. Such high degrees of sintering are rare in low-alloy steels.

**Copper and bronze materials** are etched in a 4% ferric chloride ($FeCl_3$) solution or the potassium dichromate ($K_2Cr_2O_7$) solution in Table 1. The latter etchant is preferred for bronze. During sintering of bronzes, the elemental tin melts, forming a series of increasingly higher temperature intermetallic compounds, then completely dissolves in the copper at approximately 785 to 845 °C (1450 to 1550 °F). The result of good sintering is $\alpha$-bronze with a moderate grain size and no free tin or blue-gray copper-tin intermetallic compounds. During sintering or in an undersintered condition, intermetallic compounds will be present. As sintering proceeds, the copper recrystallizes and its grains grow as the tin diffuses to form $\alpha$-bronze.

The presence of many reddish copper areas or large area fractions of fine-grained copper-rich or $\alpha$-bronze indicates undersintering. The undersintered materials are the most difficult to etch and to show clear structures. The $K_2Cr_2O_7$ etchant should be applied (always by swabbing) for 15 s. The specimen is then placed under running water, and swabbing is continued for a few seconds. It may be necessary to polish and etch several times to obtain a clear structure free of distortion from grinding.

Bronzes may contain up to 4% free graphite. The epoxy resin helps secure it for polishing and viewing. The use of 1-$\mu$m diamond and light final polishing with 0.05-$\mu$m $Al_2O_3$ on a long-nap cloth will usually preserve the graphite. Brasses and nickel silver are etched using a mixture of ammonium hydroxide ($NH_4OH$) diluted with 50% $H_2O$ and a few drops of 10 to 30% hydrogen peroxide ($H_2O_2$) added at the time of etching. This is carried out by placing approximately 5 cm$^3$ of the diluted ammonia solution in a watch glass and adding 3 to 4 drops $H_2O_2$. The mixture is swabbed on the brass with a cotton-tipped stick for 20 to 40 s (Ref 11). The nickel silver requires 1 to 2 min to etch. The etchant decomposes after 30 min, and a new mixture with the $H_2O_2$ should be prepared as required.

**Aluminum parts** are etched using Keller's reagent, which is applied by swabbing with cotton for 15 to 30 s.

**Titanium parts** are etched by immersion for 15 s using 10 mL concentrated hydrofluoric acid (HF), 5 mL concentrated nitric acid ($HNO_3$), and 85 mL $H_2O$.

**Tool steels** are etched using 5% nital (5% $HNO_3$ concentrate in methyl alcohol). As-sintered materials should be swabbed for 5 min. As-annealed materials may etch within 20 s.

## Microstructures of P/M Materials

Powder metallurgy materials embrace a wide range of alloy systems. A number of these systems will be discussed below, with the main phases and compounds noted. Related information on the production, characterization and testing, consolidation, and applications and properties of these powder systems can be found in Volume 7 of the 9th Edition of *Metals Handbook*.

### Iron-Base P/M Materials

Pure iron or very low-carbon steel is a common structural or bearing material. The microstructure is predominantly ferrite, with modest amounts of pearlite in proportion to the minor amounts of carbon in solution. Several kinds of iron powder are commonly used, including sponge, atomized, electrolytic, and carbonyl powders (Fig. 12 to 22, 39 to 52, and 149 to 152). They have widely differing properties because of differences in surface area, residual alloying, internal poros-

ity, and particle size. For additional information, see the article "Production of Iron Powder" in Volume 7 of the 9th Edition of *Metals Handbook*.

**Sponge irons,** which are produced by the reduction of iron oxide, are very irregularly shaped powders with high surface areas. They are more difficult to compress, but develop good green strength and excellent sintered strength at low densities. The pores inside the particles vary in size according to the temperature and time of reduction from the parent oxides. Low-temperature hydrogen reduction of mill scale leads to a fine sponge, and extended carbon reduction of ore concentrate results in a coarser sponge. These powders are characterized by moderate levels of unreduced oxides inside the particles.

**Atomized iron powders** press easily, but for densities to 6.6 g/cm$^3$, the sponge irons result in higher sintered strength. Therefore, the atomized materials are usually found in materials pressed at 6.6 to 7.2 g/cm$^3$ (theoretical density of iron is 7.87 g/cm$^3$).

**Electrolytic Iron Powder.** The high green strength, high compressibility, irregular particle shape, and high purity of electrolytic iron make it suitable for a number of applications, such as soft magnetic parts and enrichment of food products (see the article "Iron Powders for Food Enrichment" in Volume 7 of the 9th Edition of *Metals Handbook*). Due to its high production costs, however, current usage is limited.

**Carbonyl iron powders** may have a particle size of 2 to 5 $\mu$m and are often used in injection-molded P/M parts (see the article "Injection Molding" in Volume 7 of the 9th Edition of *Metals Handbook*). Their high surface area and fine particle size allow the material to sinter to near full density with large associated shrinkages. The resulting structure will be ferrite, with small rounded and isolated pores.

**Iron-graphite mixtures** result in rapid diffusion of carbon into iron, with resulting steels containing up to 0.8% C. These show increasing amounts of pearlite with increasing carbon content calculated using the lever rule. The combined carbon for these materials is approximately 0.8% times the area of pearlite. That area fraction does not include the area associated with porosity. For materials with hypereutectoid carbon contents (typically >0.8%), iron carbide networks appear in the grain boundaries, and the impact, tensile strength, and elongation are reduced. This carbide network is not to be confused with the divorced eutectoid carbide platelet that will appear occasionally in a grain boundary in the hypoeutectoid steels. This effect, attributed to the low manganese content of sintered iron, is seen at carbon levels as low as 0.25%. Sintered iron bearings are fabricated with graphite in solution and present as free, gray graphite flakes. The combined carbon is judged by the lever rule, which is important in quality control of newly developed iron-graphite bearing materials. Iron-carbon P/M structures are shown in Fig. 53 to 57.

**Iron-Copper Alloys.** Copper is frequently added to iron because it melts and rapidly dissolves, greatly increasing strength. When copper melts, it is drawn by capillary action into the smallest available pores and capillaries. In an atomized iron powder, the copper will flow between the particles that are pressed into close contact. It then dissolves in the iron at these points of contact. The copper activates the sintering of the particles that are in contact, resulting in rapid disappearance of particle boundaries and substantial neck growth.

The copper may separate the iron particles as it flows between them, causing growth of the part in 1 to 2 min, as does the subsequent dissolution of the copper and local lattice expansion at points of contact. In an unsintered part with 2% added Cu, some of the residual copper may occasionally be visible as a thin line between two iron particles. With sponge irons, the copper can flow into the fine pores inside the particles and thus not cause as much separation of particles. The high surface area also contributes to rapid sintering, which is thought to explain why the sponge iron and copper mixtures do not expand as much as the mixes based on atomized iron.

In conventional sintering of iron-copper alloys (20 to 30 min at 1105 to 1120 °C, or 2025 to 2050 °F), at least 2% Cu will disappear into solution in the iron. With 5% or more Cu, some free copper will always be present as a copper-rich solid solution with the iron. Depending on the rate of cooling, copper-rich phases precipitate in the iron, and conversely, the copper-rich phases in the iron darken the ferrite; slow cooling increases darkening. This effect is limited to the outside of the particles, because the copper does not readily penetrate to the centers under conventional sintering conditions. Picral will help to stain the copper-cored areas for easier identification. Iron-copper P/M structures are shown in Fig. 58 to 62.

**Iron-Copper-Carbon Alloys.** The most common of the moderate-strength, as-sintered alloys is iron-copper-carbon with 0.8% C and 2 to 5% Cu (Fig. 63 to 66). It combines the features described above for iron-carbon and iron-copper alloys. The carbon goes rapidly into solution in the iron (perhaps in 5 min at 1040 °C, or 1900 °F) and tends to prevent the expansion prevalent in iron-copper alloys. The combined carbon may be estimated by the lever rule, although the eutectoid may be as low as 0.75% C in this ternary system.

**Copper-Infiltrated Steels.** High-density iron-carbon alloys with 10 or 20% Cu are prepared by infiltrating the copper alloy into the porous steel matrix. Upon sintering and infiltrating, the copper alloy melts and flows into the iron-carbon matrix with which it is in contact. The copper tends to fill the highest density, smallest capillary regions of the matrix first. The lowest density regions are filled last with whatever liquid copper remains. The structure often appears as islands of ferrite and pearlite with a continuous copper-alloy phase. The alloy of copper may include such elements as manganese and cobalt, which alter the alloy content of the steel matrix. Manganese increases the hardenability of the matrix. Elemental nickel contained in the matrix will go into solution in iron and copper, greatly increasing hardenability. Such materials may exhibit regions of martensite, even as furnace cooled. Copper-infiltrated steel structures are shown in Fig. 67 to 72.

**Low-alloy steels** of the 4600 series type are atomized as low-carbon materials with good compressibility. Because of their alloying elements, they display excellent hardenability and are usually used fully hardened. When viewed in the as-sintered condition, such materials exhibit ferrite and a eutectoid product that does not appear similar to the normal iron-carbon materials. The lamellae are more uniformly spread throughout the structure, and the tendency among the constituents to group into ferrite and pearlite is lessened, which complicates estimating the combined carbon content metallographically. However, this should be possible by devising visual standards of reference. The powder may contain up to 5% unalloyed iron as a contaminant. In the as-sintered structure, these free iron particles do not tend to pick up carbon and thus stand out as ferrite. Upon quenching, the unalloyed particles are low in carbon and alloy content, do not harden, and are ferrite or ferrite/pearlite mixtures. Low-alloy steel structures are shown in Fig. 73 to 80.

**Iron-Phosphorus Alloys.** The additions of iron phosphide ($Fe_3P$) to atomized iron results in the dissolution of phosphorus in amounts less than 1%. The phosphorus initiates a transient liquid-phase sintering reaction, then goes partly into solution in the iron, resulting in a material with excellent soft magnetic properties. Some of the phosphorus remains visible as a second phase with the ferrite. For magnetic properties, a low carbon content and freedom from pearlite are required. For optimum toughness and strength characteristics, a mixture of up to 1% P and up to 0.3% C is used. The phosphorus also causes pore rounding by virtue of the transient liquid phase, which gives the alloys their toughness and characteristic well-sintered appearance. Iron-phosphorus alloy structures are shown in Fig. 81 and 82.

**Free-Machining Steels.** The machinability of sintered irons and alloys is improved by adding sulfur. Historically, this has been accomplished by blending fine sulfur powder (-325 mesh) into sponge iron. More recently, sulfur is dissolved in the liquid melt before atomizing (prealloyed sulfur) to form manganese sulfide (MnS) with carefully controlled amounts of manganese. Manganese sulfide has also been blended with iron for a similar benefit. These additions result in particles of MnS in the pores as a gray phase or a MnS phase inside the iron if it was prealloyed. The use of high-hydrogen atmospheres at sintering will desulfurize a material to depths of 0.25 to 0.50 mm (0.01 to 0.02 in.), an effect whose analog in carbon is better known. Structures of P/M steels with additions of manganese and sulfur for enhanced machinability are shown in Fig. 83 to 85.

**Nickel Steels.** The most common high-strength heat-treated materials are the nickel steels. In these mixtures, 2 or 4% elemental nickel is added to iron, along with 0.4 to 0.8% C and up to 2% Cu (optional). The usual nickel is very finely divided and is often prepared by carbonyl decomposition (production of nickel powder by carbonyl vapor metallurgy processing is discussed in the article "Production of Nickel and Nickel Alloy Powders" in Volume 7 of the 9th Edition of *Metals Handbook*). The copper is generally added for size control during sintering, because nickel induces shrinkage and copper causes expansion. The copper activates sintering, as noted above in the section "Iron-Copper Alloys," and promotes the dissolution of nickel in the iron. Nickel-steel structures are shown in Fig. 86 to 98.

Nickel-rich regions comprise 20 to 50% of the area of these structures. The regions are extensive because the nickel content of their interiors has been diluted by inward diffusion of iron to approximately 12%. The nickel-rich regions tend to etch lightly. Their interiors often are unetched austenite, and their peripheries contain martensite or bainite with microhardnesses of 40 to 55 HRC, converted from 100 gf Knoop. The pearlite colonies are usually surrounded by a white band that appears similar to ferrite, but never contains eutectoid products; this is probably a higher alloy diffusion zone. The austenitic cores of the nickel-rich regions increase toughness and strength in these alloys and tend to inhibit ductility. The undiffused nickel-rich regions figure significantly in the overall performances of the alloy. These islands with hard phases in the as-sintered condition contribute wear resistance, which would not normally be expected.

It is difficult to assess the degree of sintering by studying the nickel-rich areas, because copper additions greatly affect their extent and appearance. Sintering is best judged by the disappearance of original particle boundaries and by pore rounding. It is difficult to discern the combined carbon level in the nickel steels because of the presence of the nickel-rich regions, the white diffusion layer, porosity, and the probable lowering of the eutectoid carbon level by the nickel.

**Diffusion-alloyed materials,** such as Distaloy, are powders in which the alloying elements of molybdenum, nickel, and copper are added as finely divided elements or oxides to the iron powder. They are then co-reduced with the iron powders at an annealing step, resulting in the firm attachment and partial diffusion of the elements to the iron. This partial alloying increases hardenability compared to elemental mixtures, and yet these powders exhibit good compressibility. Bonding of the alloying elements also reduces the tendency toward powder segregation.

The sintered structures exhibit ferrite, pearlite, and nickel-rich regions such as those described above for the elemental blends, and the nickel-rich regions have all the benefits noted above. With added copper, additional partial hardening during sintering occurs. In Europe, this is used to advantage by producing medium-carbon alloys that are sold in the pressed, sintered, and sized conditions, but have good strength and impact resistance. This procedure avoids the distortions that can occur during normal heat treating. Diffusion-alloyed structures are shown in Fig. 99 to 101.

**Sintered stainless steels** are available in compositions that approximate AISI designations 303, 304, 316, and 410. The austenitic materials display austenite grains and annealing twins. The most significant disadvantage may be decoration of the grain boundaries with chromium carbides, indicating loss of chromium from solution and reduction in corrosion resistance. The degree of pore rounding is the most important indication of strength and ductility. The materials are virtually always prepared from prealloyed powders; some variants contain added tin or copper for improved corrosion resistance. The 410 materials are often fabricated with 0.15% graphite mixed with prealloyed powders. This results in such high hardenability that the as-sintered structures are essentially all martensite and require tempering after sintering for optimum properties. Stainless steel P/M structures are shown in Fig. 102 to 113.

**P/M tool steels** have long been used for tooling components such as punches and dies. These materials are produced by hot isostatic pressing of water-atomized, tool steel powders, resulting in a fully dense product with fine grain size and very fine, uniform carbide size. The product displays grindability that is superior to ingot-base tool steels. Such alloys as M2 and T15 are also available in molding grade powders. In addition to hot isostatic pressing, P/M tool steels can be fabricated by pressing to approximately 80% density, followed by vacuum sintering to full density.

Tool steel powders of the M2 and T15 compositions can be cold pressed at 550 to 825 MPa (40 to 60 tsi), then liquid phase sintered to full density. For M2, sintering requires 1 h in vacuum at 1240 °C (2260 °F) at 100 to 1000 $\mu$m nitrogen or argon; T15 takes 1 h at 1260 °C (2300 °F) in the same vacuum. Temperature control within 5 °C (9 °F) may be required for product uniformity. The as-sintered T15 structures contain retained austenite, because of the high amount of carbon in solution, as well as primary $M_6C$ and fine MC (vanadium carbide). The M2 structures contain mainly $M_6C$ of varying small sizes against a matrix of retained austenite. The martensite start, $M_s$, temperature for these

materials with the high carbon in solution is below room temperature. Upon annealing, the carbon precipitates out of solution onto the $M_6C$ phase, reducing the carbon in the matrix. This structure may then be heat treated at 1150 to 1205 °C (2100 to 2200 °F), but heating and cooling times must be minimized to avoid putting too much carbon back into solution. Upon furnace cooling or air cooling, the matrix will then form martensite with the proper distribution of fine carbides (Ref 12). Powder metallurgy tool steel structures are shown in Fig. 114 to 116 (see also the article "Tool Steels" in this Volume).

## Nonferrous P/M Materials

As discussed on pages 105 to 175 in Volume 7 of the 9th Edition of *Metals Handbook*, a wide variety of nonferrous metal powders are also produced, including:

- *Copper*: by reduction of oxides, atomization, electrolysis, and hydrometallurgical processing
- *Tin*: by atomization
- *Aluminum*: by atomization
- *Magnesium*: by mechanical comminution and atomization
- *Nickel*: by carbonyl vapormetallurgy, hydrometallurgy, and atomization
- *Cobalt*: by carbonyl vapormetallurgy, hydrometallurgy, reduction of oxides, and atomization
- *Silver*: by chemical precipitation, electrolysis, and reduction of oxides
- *Gold, platinum, and palladium*: by chemical precipitation
- *Tungsten and molybdenum*: by reduction of oxides
- *Metal carbides*: by carburization, Menstruum process, and exothermic thermite reactions
- *Tantalum*: by reduction of potassium tantalum fluoride and a sequence of electron beam melting, hydriding, comminution, and degassing (dehydriding)
- *Niobium*: by aluminothermic reduction of oxides
- *Titanium*: by reduction of oxides and atomization
- *Beryllium*: by reduction of vacuum-melted ingots by comminution
- *Composite powders*: by diffusion (alloy coating)

This section will review copper-base, titanium-base, and aluminum-base P/M materials. Additional microstructures of P/M materials can be found in the articles "Beryllium," "Titanium and Titanium Alloys," "Refractory Metals and Alloys," "Electrical Contact Materials," and "Magnetic and Electrical Materials" in this Volume.

**Copper-base alloys** include pure copper for high-density electrical applications; 90Cu-10Sn bronzes for bearings and structural parts; brasses with 10, 20, and 30% Zn; and nickel silver (Cu-18Zn-18Ni). The brasses and nickel silvers are used for structural parts that require ductility, moderate

strength, corrosion resistance, and decorative value. Copper will exhibit a single-phase structure with some annealing twins. The most significant feature will be the particle boundaries or their absence. There should be virtual freedom from particle boundaries from the surface to the center of the part.

Bronzes should display all $\alpha$-bronze with no gray copper-tin intermetallic compounds. Optimum mechanical properties and machinability dictate a minimum of reddish copper-rich areas and small grain clusters of $\alpha$-bronze. Mixes containing admixed graphite will show the mottled gray flakes in the pores of the part. Bearings exhibit varying degrees of sintering, depending on the final application. In general, however, a well-sintered bearing results in greater ease of oil impregnation. Bronze P/M structures are shown in Fig. 117 to 120.

Brasses and nickel silvers are generally single-phase structures. They should display good pore rounding and almost no original particle boundaries. Some of the materials may contain up to 2% Pb within the particles as an aid to machinability; this will appear as a fine, rounded gray phase (Fig. 121 and 122).

**Titanium and titanium alloys** such as Ti-6Al-4V are variously produced from metal powders. The powders may be prealloyed or may be an elemental blend of titanium and a masteralloy of vanadium and aluminum. The latter can be pressed and vacuum sintered to an impermeable state, which may then be hot isostatically pressed to full density without a can. The prealloyed materials may be vacuum hot-pressed or preformed, canned, and hot isostatically pressed to full density. Titanium alloy P/M structures are shown in Fig. 123 to 125.

**Aluminum P/M alloys** are pressed and sintered to 90 to 95% density. The common alloys are 201AB and 601AB. The alloys are prepared using low-alloy aluminum powder with additions of elemental or master alloy copper, magnesium, and silicon. During sintering, the additions cause a liquid phase to form that fluxes away the surface oxides and allows bonding between the aluminum particles. Sintering in nitrogen or dissociated ammonia is performed at approximately 595 to 620 °C (1100 to 1150 °F) at a dewpoint of $-50$ °C ($-60$ °F) to prevent further oxidation of the aluminum. After sintering, the alloys are often solutionized and quenched, then repressed or coined before aging. The repressing densifies the material and establishes close dimensional tolerances. The materials may also be cold forged or rolled to varying reductions in thickness because of their favorable as-sintered ductility. Aluminum P/M structures are shown in Fig. 126 to 130.

## Representative Micrographs

This section will discuss unusual and defective structures. Also included are examples of heat-treated materials and those subjected to other finishing operations, such as steam blackening. Alternate consolidation processes, such as P/M forging, hot isostatic pressing, injection molding, and liquid-phase sintering, will also be illustrated.

Sintered parts may be undersintered, which is evidenced by the presence of excessive numbers of original particle boundaries. Undersintering is related to the normal pressed and sintered structural materials and their mechanical properties as shown in MPIF Standard 35 or the various ASTM materials standardized by the B-9 Committee in ASTM Volume 02.05. In general, for ferrous materials, a field of view at $200\times$ would not be expected to show more than approximately five small segments of original particle boundaries. The presence of larger quantities of particle boundaries would necessitate verifying the sintering conditions and the strength of the part. Figures 27 to 31 depict an increasing degree of sintering, indicating the disappearance of particle boundaries.

High-temperature (1290 °C, or 2350 °F) sintered austenitic stainless steel does not exhibit particle boundaries, and the degree of rounding of the pores must be examined to compare sintering (Fig. 102 to 111). Injection-molded parts made of fine powders tend to sinter to a closed-pore state with no original particle boundaries (Fig. 131 and 132). Powder metallurgy forgings and hot isostatically pressed parts would not display such boundaries (Fig. 133 and 134).

In the etched condition, sintered steels may exhibit carburization or decarburization (Fig. 135 and 136). If parts of nonuniform section are pressed, density may vary, which may be noted and measured metallographically (Ref 15). If parts are overpressed, the particles will separate, showing microlaminations. Cracks may occur upon ejection at the change in diameter between two sections of a part, such as between a hub and a flange (Fig. 137 and 138). Even in simple shapes, such as flat tensile bars, improper tool design can cause cracks, which then result in reduced mechanical properties (see Fig. 139).

Heat-treated ferrous parts will vary in structure from nearly all martensite at the surface to a mixture of martensite, ferrite, and 10 to 30% fine pearlite in the interior (Fig. 140 to 142). This fine pearlite improves tensile properties (Ref 16). Microhardness testing must be limited to a particular phase when testing with the 100-gf Knoop indenter—for example, martensite. The heat-treated structures can display retained austenite, carbides, and subsurface quench

cracking (Fig. 143 to 145). Most P/M materials do not form a definite shallow case because of penetration of the carburizing gases. At densities above approximately 7.2 g/cm$^3$, a definite case tends to form if the core contains less than 0.2% C, as shown in Fig. 146.

Powder metallurgy parts can be finished by steam blackening. The degree of blackening, which should be controlled, affects tensile properties (Fig. 147 and 148). The gray $Fe_3O_4$ layer penetrates the pores and increases compressive strength and abrasive wear resistance. The thickness of the oxide layer may be measured metallographically.

Most P/M parts that are to be plated are first impregnated with a resin to prevent the corrosive plating solutions from entering and remaining in the pores. This resin is visible using optical metallography. The various plated layers are also visible, but polishing should be limited to 1-$\mu$m diamond on a short-nap cloth to prevent rounding of the plated edge.

Powder metallurgy parts may be joined to others by brazing, welding, or adhesive bonding; special precautions are necessary to prevent penetration of the brazing materials. For additional information on joining P/M parts, see the article "Secondary Operations Performed on P/M Parts and Products" in Volume 7 of the 9th Edition of *Metals Handbook*.

Manufacturers of sintered parts have occasion to examine raw materials (powders) metallographically. This is important, because different production methods may result in powders with the same nominal chemistry, but disparate properties. Typical powder structures are shown in Fig. 12 to 26, 32 to 52, and 149 to 162. These micrographs are intended to simplify the task of examining a sintered part and attempting to deduce which powder was used to prepare it.

Figures 163 to 170 depict various normal, abnormal, or defective structures. Among these are undersintered structures (as shown in Fig. 163 and compared with average sinter in Fig. 164), newly developed wear-resistant steels (Ancorwear 500) with high carbon contents (Fig. 165), gravity-sintered bronze filter powders (Fig. 166 and 167), sintered parts that were blistered during heating to the sintering temperature (Fig. 168), and parts that exhibit varying density due to position in the die (Fig. 169 and 170).

## REFERENCES

1. "Standard Test Method for Density and Interconnected Porosity of Sintered Powder Metal Structural Parts and Oil-Impregnated Bearings," B 328, *Annual Book of ASTM Standards*, Vol 02.05, ASTM, Philadelphia, 1984, p 162-163

2. "Permeable Sintered Metal Materials—Determination of Density, Open Porosity and Oil Content," ISO 2738, International Organization for Standardization, available from American National Standards Institute, New York

3. W. Gambrell, IBM Corp., Lexington, KY, personal communication

4. "Standard Methods of Sampling Finished Lots of Metal Powders," B 215, *Annual Book of ASTM Standards*, Vol 02.05, ASTM, Philadelphia, 1984, p 66-68

5. L.F. Pease, III, in *Powder Metallurgy*, Vol 7, 9th ed., *Metals Handbook*, American Society for Metals, 1984, p 485-486

6. L.F. Pease, III, Metallography and Properties of Sintered Steels, in *Progress in Powder Metallurgy*, Vol 33, Metal Powder Industries Federation, Princeton, NJ, 1977

7. O. Struglics, Höganäs Corp., Höganäs, Sweden, personal communication

8. S. Coleman and D. Tomkins, A Quantitative Assessment of the Mechanical Properties of Sintered Iron Micrographic Specimens, *Powder Metall.*, No. 2, 1976, p 53

9. "Determining the Case Hardness of Powder Metallurgy Parts," MPIF 37, Metal Powder Industries Federation, Princeton, NJ

10. S. Kaufmann, Ford Motor Co., Dearborn, MI, personal communication

11. P. Schmey, United States Bronze Powders, Inc., Flemington, NJ, personal communication

12. M. Svilar, SCM Metal Products, Cleveland, personal communication

13. S. Abkowitz, Dynamet Technology, Burlington, MA, personal communication

14. G.F. Millsaps, Alcoa, Pittsburgh, personal communication

15. L.F. Pease, III, in *Powder Metallurgy*, Vol 7, 9th ed., *Metals Handbook*, American Society for Metals, 1984, p 483

16. L.F. Pease, III, The Mechanical Properties of Sintered Steels and their Derivation for MPIF Standard 35, in *Progress in Powder Metallurgy*, Vol 37, Metal Powder Industries Federation, Princeton, NJ, 1981

17. J. Hurst, C.I. Hayes, Inc., Cranston, RI, personal communication

18. F. Hanejko, Hoeganaes Corp., Riverton, NJ, personal communication

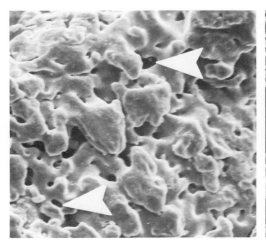

**Fig. 12** Pyron 100, hydrogen-reduced sponge iron. A single particle, arrows indicate pores opening into the spongy interior. Scanning electron micrograph. 1000×

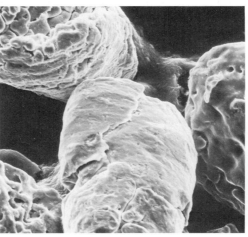

**Fig. 13** Pyron D63, hydrogen-reduced sponge iron, exhibiting high apparent density. Scanning electron micrograph. 750×

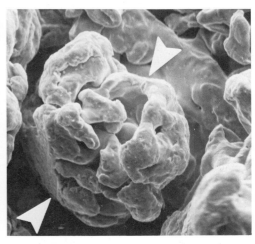

**Fig. 14** MH-100, carbon-reduced iron ore. Arrows indicate one particle with coarse internal porosity. Scanning electron micrograph. 750×

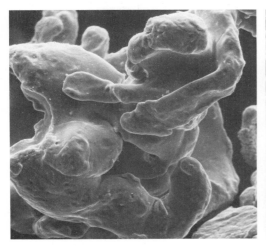

**Fig. 15** Ancormet 101, carbon-reduced iron ore. One individual particle with coarse and extensive internal porosity is shown. Scanning electron micrograph. 750×

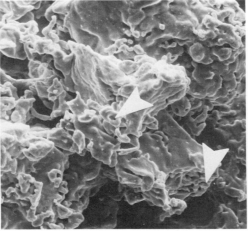

**Fig. 16** Atomet 28 iron powder. Arrows indicate porosity in the spongy regions. Scanning electron micrograph. 750×

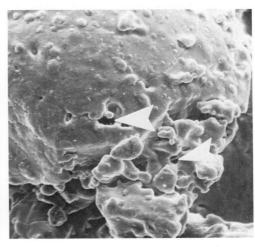

**Fig. 17** MP35HD iron powder. Arrows indicate porosity in spongy regions. Scanning electron micrograph. 750×

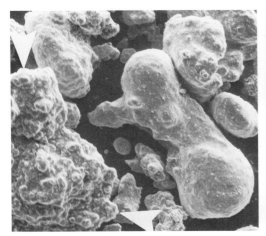

**Fig. 18** Water-atomized iron. Arrows indicate this process can produce iron powder with a fair degree of irregularity or roughness on the surface. Scanning electron micrograph. 190×

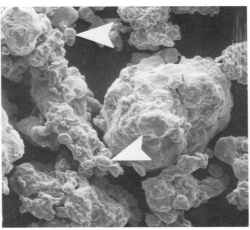

**Fig. 19** Ancorsteel 1000, water-atomized and annealed iron powder. Arrows indicate small fines that were agglomerated onto the larger particles. Scanning electron micrograph. 190×

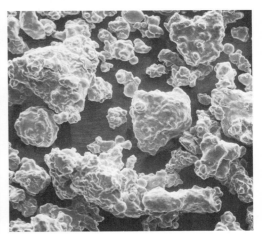

**Fig. 20** Ancorsteel 1000B, water-atomized and double-annealed iron powder. Scanning electron micrograph. 190×

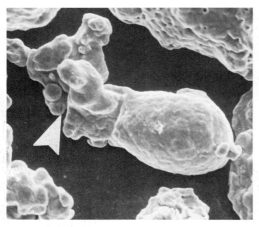

**Fig. 21** Ancorsteel 4600V, water-atomized and annealed prealloyed steel powder. Note that some particles gain surface area and irregularity by agglomeration of fines (see arrow). Scanning electron micrograph. 750×

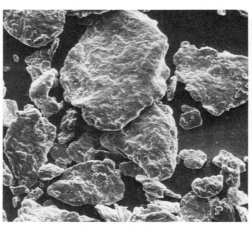

**Fig. 22** SCM A283 electrolytic iron powder. Note the flaky shape characteristic of these powders. Scanning electron micrograph. 190×

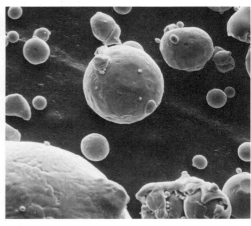

**Fig. 23** Type 316, gas-atomized stainless steel powder. Note attached satellites. Scanning electron micrograph. 750×

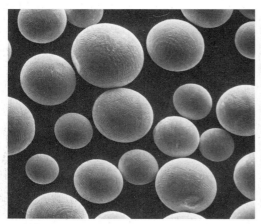

**Fig. 24** Type 316L, rotating electrode processed stainless steel powder. Nearly perfect spheres with absence of satellite formation. Scanning electron micrograph. 190×

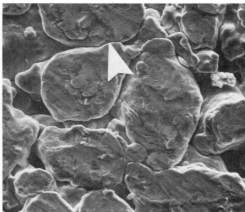

**Fig. 25** Ancorsteel 1000 unsintered iron powder. Surface of part, which had been contacted by the upper punch at 275 MPa (20 tsi). Arrow shows the particle boundaries that will disappear during proper sintering. Scanning electron micrograph. 750×

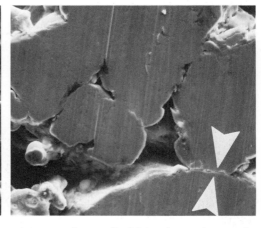

**Fig. 26** Same as Fig. 25, but showing the view of the surface that was in contact with the die wall. Arrows show the boundary between particles that must be eliminated during sintering. Scanning electron micrograph. 750×

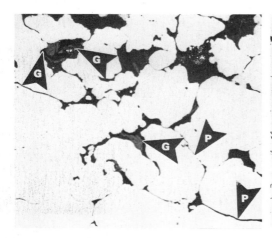

**Fig. 27** Distaloy 4600 A (6.7 g/cm³), pressed at 480 MPa, undersintered 5 min in dissociated ammonia in hot zone at 1120 °C (2050 °F). Arrows P: particle boundaries; arrows G: undiffused, gray flakes of graphite in pores. As-polished. 645×

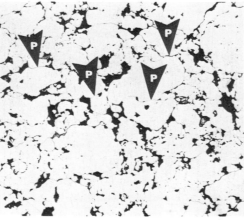

**Fig. 28** Same diffusion-alloyed steel as Fig. 27. Arrows P show the many original particle boundaries. Sintering longer will remove these low-strength boundaries. As-polished. 120×

**Fig. 29** Same as Fig. 27, but sintered 15 min. Arrows P indicate persistence of original particle boundaries; arrows R, rounded pores (compare with Fig. 27). As-polished. 645×

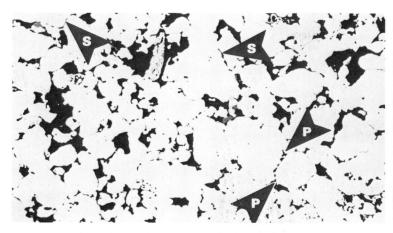

**Fig. 30** Same as Fig. 29. Arrows S show segments of original particle boundaries that are shorter and less numerous than those in Fig. 28. Arrows P indicate a row of pores that show how original particles break down into planes of small voids, which coalesce or disappear from diffusion. As-polished. 180×

**Fig. 31** Same as Fig. 27, but sintered approximately 37 min, which is longer than average. Structure still shows a few segments of original particle boundaries (arrow S). Arrows P indicate a row of pores at which a particle boundary is disappearing. As-polished. 180×

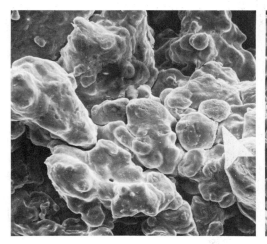

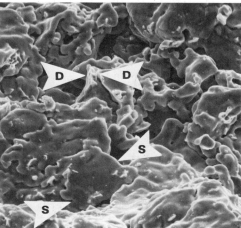

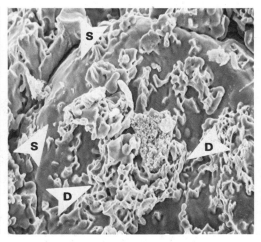

**Fig. 32** Fracture surface of Ancorsteel 1000 iron powder (6.4 g/cm³) pressed without lubricant at 275 MPa (20 tsi). Structure shows no evidence of cold welding or bonding of adjacent particles. Arrow indicates a triple particle boundary that will disappear during sintering. SEM. 750×. (Ref 10)

**Fig. 33** Fracture surface of Atomet 28 iron powder pressed to 6.6 g/cm³ and sintered 3 min in hot zone at 1120 °C (2050 °F) in dissociated ammonia. Arrows D show where a bond has broken. Arrows S outline the smooth, rounded surface of a particle that did not bond to the adjacent particle above it. SEM. 750×. (Ref 10)

**Fig. 34** Same as Fig. 33, but sintered 10 min in hot zone (approximately 1 to 3 min at 1120 °C, or 2050 °F). Arrows D show the ductile cup and cone fractures that occurred when this particle was torn from the adjacent one above it. Arrows S show the smooth surface of the particle that had not sintered to any adjacent particle. SEM. 750×. (Ref 10)

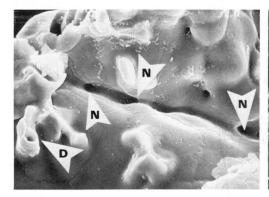

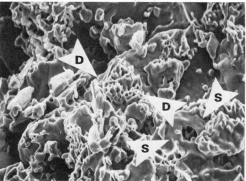

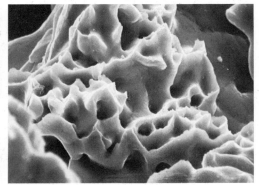

**Fig. 35** Same as Fig. 34, but sintered 10 min in the hot zone at 1120 °C (2050 °F). Arrow D indicates a ductile cup and cone fracture where this particle was joined to the one above it. Arrows N show necks forming between two adjacent particles. These necks (solid regions) replace particle boundaries as sintering progresses. SEM. 2850×. (Ref 10)

**Fig. 36** Same as Fig. 33, but sintered 20 min in the hot zone. Arrows D show the development of ductile cup and cone fracture dimples formed when material was torn away from the adjacent particle. Arrows S indicate smooth surfaces where no adjacent particle bonding has occurred. SEM. 750×. (Ref 10)

**Fig. 37** Same material (Atomet 28) and processing as described in Fig. 36, but shown at higher magnification. Most of the field of view shows the ductile cup and cone fractures that occur when the material is torn apart. SEM. 2850×. (Ref 10)

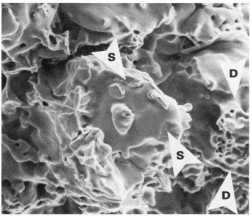

**Fig. 38** Same as Fig. 33, but sintered 40 min in the hot zone. Approximately 50% of the area fraction is occupied by ruptured ductile bonds (arrows D). The remaining area consists of smooth surfaces of particles (arrows S) at which no bonding has occurred. SEM. 750×. (Ref 10)

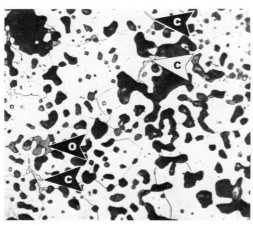

**Fig. 39** Pyron D63 sponge iron (6.2 g/cm³), pressed at 480 MPa (35 tsi) and sintered 30 min at 1120 °C (2050 °F) in dissociated ammonia. Mainly ferrite grain boundaries. Arrow O indicates a small, gray, unreduced oxide particle; arrows C, a few isolated carbide platelets. 2% nital. 645×

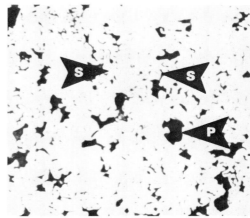

**Fig. 40** Same as Fig. 39, but not etched. Arrows S surround a spongy particle having small, internal pores. Arrow P indicates a much larger pore between powder particles. Very few original particle boundaries are present. As-polished. 180×

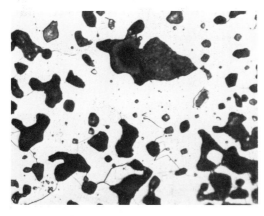

**Fig. 41** Pyron 100 sponge iron (6.2 g/cm³), pressed at 480 MPa (35 tsi) and sintered 30 min at 1120 °C (2050 °F) in dissociated ammonia. Average sinter, no residual particle boundaries. Dark areas are pores. 2% nital. 960×

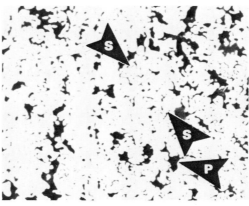

**Fig. 42** Same as Fig. 41, but increased density (6.4 g/cm³). Arrows S surround a spongy particle having small internal pores. Arrow P indicates a larger pore between particles. As-polished. 180×

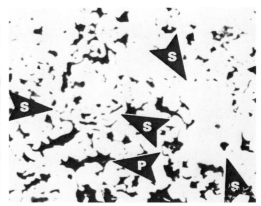

**Fig. 43** MH-100 sponge iron (6.4 g/cm³), pressed at 480 MPa (35 tsi) and sintered 30 min at 1120 °C (2050 °F) in dissociated ammonia. Arrows S indicate the various pore sizes in different particles. The larger pores (arrow P) are between the original particles. As-polished. 180×

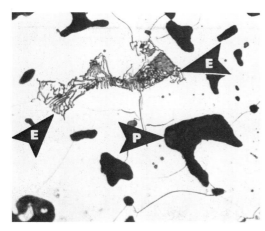

**Fig. 44** Same as Fig. 43, but at higher magnification. Arrows E show eutectoid (pearlite) indicating <0.05% combined carbon. Arrow P indicates a pore. Structure is mainly ferrite. 2% nital. 960×

**Fig. 45** MP35 iron powder (6.6 g/cm³), pressed at 410 to 480 MPa (30 to 35 tsi) and sintered 30 min at 1120 °C (2050 °F) in dissociated ammonia. Arrows S surround a spongy region having pores inside the powder particles. Arrow P shows a pore between particles. As-polished. 180×

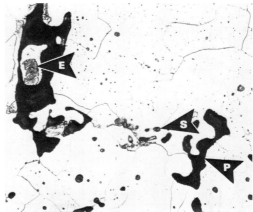

**Fig. 46** Same as Fig. 45. Structure is mainly ferrite. Arrow E shows a colony of eutectoid (pearlite) indicating <0.05% combined carbon. Arrow S indicates pores within a spongy particle; arrow P, a pore between particles. 2% nital, 15 s. 645×

**Fig. 47** Atomet 28 iron powder (6.7 g/cm³), pressed at 410 to 480 MPa (30 to 35 tsi) and sintered 30 min at 1120 °C (2050 °F) in dissociated ammonia. Arrows S surround a spongy region. Arrow P indicates pores between particles. As-polished. 100×

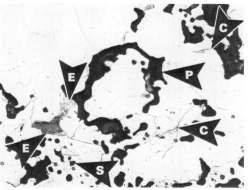

**Fig. 48** Same as Fig. 47, but etched. Structure is mainly ferrite. Arrows E indicate eutectoid (pearlite); arrow C, isolated carbides or divorced eutectoid. Arrow P shows a pore between particles; arrow S, pores within a spongy particle. 2% nital. 545×

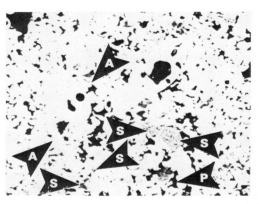

**Fig. 49** Sponge iron blended with atomized low-carbon steel (6.4 g/cm³), pressed at 410 to 480 MPa (30 to 35 tsi) and sintered 30 min at 1120 °C (2050 °F) in dissociated ammonia. Arrows A show an atomized particle with gas porosity. Arrows S indicate particles with interior porosity. Arrow P shows a pore between particles. As-polished. 100×

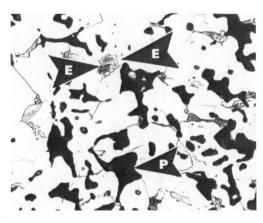

**Fig. 50** Ancormet 100 sponge iron (6.4 g/cm³) with same processing as Fig. 49. Structure is mainly ferrite. Arrows E indicate eutectoid (pearlite). The region shown in this micrograph is less dense than average for the specimen. Arrow P shows a pore between particles. 2% nital. 960×

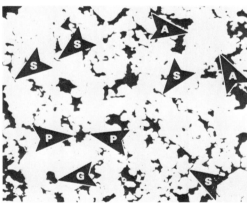

**Fig. 51** Ancorsteel 1000 atomized iron powder (6.7 g/cm³), pressed at 410 to 480 MPa (30 to 35 tsi) and sintered 30 min at 1120 °C (2050 °F) in dissociated ammonia. Arrows S indicate residual particle boundary segments. Dark regions (arrows P) are pores. Arrows A surround a solid atomized particle. Arrow G shows a pore inside a particle formed during atomization. As-polished. 120×

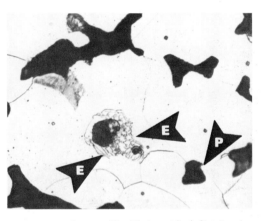

**Fig. 52** Same as Fig. 51, but etched. Structure is mainly α-iron (ferrite). Dark regions (arrow P) are pores. Arrows E surround eutectoid (pearlite). Micrographs above 500× do not always show a representative area fraction of porosity and should not be used to estimate density. Micrographs of unetched structures at 180 to 200× are best suited for this purpose. 2% nital. 960×

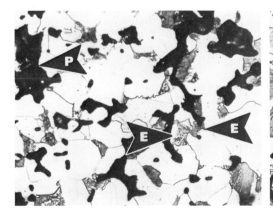

**Fig. 53** Atomized iron powder with 0.3% graphite added to yield 0.1 to 0.2% combined carbon (6.7 g/cm³). Pressed at 410 to 480 MPa (30 to 35 tsi) and sintered 30 min at 1120 °C (2050 °F) in dissociated ammonia. White regions are ferrite. Arrows E surround a colony of eutectoid (pearlite). Arrow P shows a pore. 2% nital. 545×

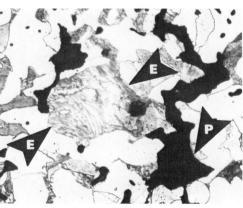

**Fig. 54** Atomized iron with 0.4 to 0.5% C (6.7 g/cm³). See Fig. 53 for processing. P/M steel with 138 MPa (20 ksi) minimum yield strength. Arrows E surround eutectoid (pearlite). White background consists of ferrite grains. Dark areas (arrow P) are pores. 2% nital. 545×

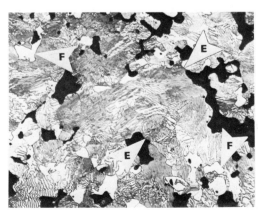

**Fig. 55** Atomized iron with 0.8% C (6.7 g/cm³). See Fig. 53 for processing. P/M steel with 207 MPa (30 ksi) minimum yield strength. Structure is mainly pearlite. Arrows E surround eutectoid (pearlite). Arrows F show a few grains of proeutectoid ferrite. 2% nital. 365×

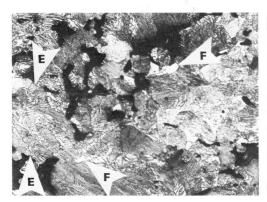

**Fig. 56** Atomized iron with 1.0% combined carbon (6.7 g/cm³). See Fig. 53 for processing. P/M steel with 207 MPa (30 ksi) minimum yield strength. Structure is mainly pearlite. Arrows E surround eutectoid (pearlite). Arrows F show a few grains of proeutectoid ferrite. 2% nital. 310×

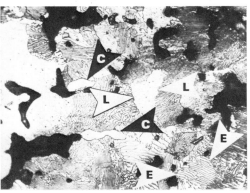

**Fig. 57** Atomized iron with 1.3% graphite added to yield 1.1 to 1.2% combined carbon (6.7 g/cm³). See Fig. 53 for processing. Structure is mainly eutectoid (pearlite), as shown by arrows E. Some pearlite etched very light (arrows L). Arrows C show areas of massive carbide from excessive graphite addition. 2% nital. 310×

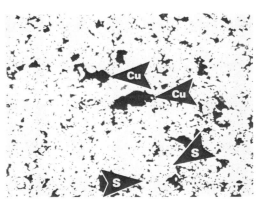

**Fig. 58** Pyron 100 sponge iron with 2% Cu (6.3 g/cm³). See Fig. 53 for processing. P/M copper steel with 124 MPa (18 ksi) minimum yield strength. Arrows Cu indicate pores that were originally occupied by copper particles before their melting and diffusion into the iron. Arrows S surround a spongy region showing pores inside the original iron powder particles. As-polished. 100×

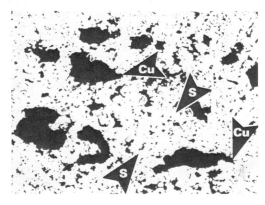

**Fig. 59** Same as Fig. 58, but with 7% Cu added (6.7 g/cm³ with 138 MPa, or 20 ksi, minimum yield strength). Arrows S surround the pores inside the sponge iron. Arrows Cu show pores that were once occupied by copper particles before they melted and filled other, smaller pores and diffused into the iron. As-polished. 310×

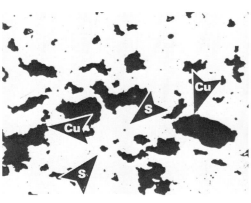

**Fig. 60** Same as Fig. 58, but with 20% Cu added (6.3 g/cm³). Arrows Cu show coarse pores formerly occupied by the copper particles. Arrows S indicate the few pores remaining that may have been present in the original iron particles. The coarse pore size facilitates oil flow in bearings. As-polished. 100×

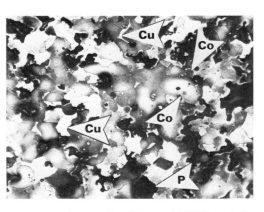

**Fig. 61** Same as Fig. 58, but with 10% Cu added (6.3 g/cm³). White areas (arrows Cu) are melted Cu-rich phase. Arrows Co show coring in iron particles. Darker areas on particle surfaces are where the copper has diffused, then precipitated as a Cu-rich phase upon cooling. The interiors are lighter, indicating no copper diffusion. Arrow P shows a pore previously occupied by a copper particle. 2% nital. 100×

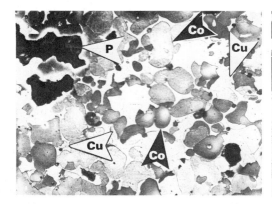

**Fig. 62** Same as Fig. 61, but with 20% Cu added (6.3 g/cm³). The copper is the white phase (arrows Cu). Note coring (arrows Co) as described in Fig. 61. These arrows indicate a string of four iron particles. Arrow P shows a large pore previously occupied by a copper particle. 2% nital. 100×

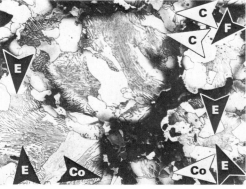

**Fig. 63** Atomet 28 iron powder with 2% Cu and 0.5% C (6.7 g/cm³ with 275 MPa, or 40 ksi, minimum yield strength). See Fig. 53 for processing. Arrows E show eutectoid (pearlite); arrow F, white ferrite grains. Arrows C indicate isolated or divorced eutectoid in the form of separate Fe₃C platelets. Arrows Co show coring from copper dissolving in the outer regions of iron particles. 2% nital. 310×

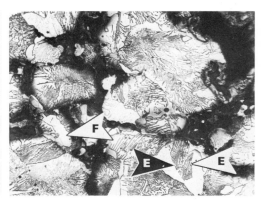

**Fig. 64** Atomet 28 iron powder with 2% Cu and 0.8% C (6.7 g/cm³). See Fig. 53 for processing. Mostly eutectoid (arrows E) with a small amount of white ferrite (arrow F). The shading results from copper coring in the iron. See Fig. 66 and 67 for effects of increased copper content on the resulting properties and structure. 2% nital. 310×

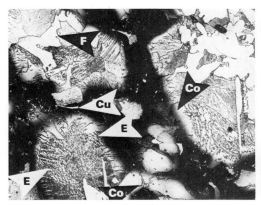

**Fig. 65** Same as Fig. 63, but with 5% Cu and 0.5% C (6.7 g/cm³ with 344 MPa, or 50 ksi, minimum yield strength). At 5% Cu, some residual copper-rich phase is shown as thin, light-colored slivers (arrow Cu). Arrows Co show bands of coring from copper diffusion into the iron. Arrows E indicate eutectoid (pearlite). Arrow F shows ferrite grain. 2% nital. 330×

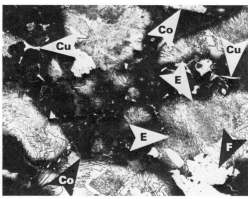

**Fig. 66** Same as Fig. 63, but with 5% Cu and 0.8% C (6.8 g/cm³ with 413 MPa, or 60 ksi, minimum yield strength). Arrows Cu show lenticular regions of melted copper-rich phase; arrows E, eutectoid (pearlite). Arrow F indicates a residual ferrite grain. Arrows Co show coring. 2% nital. 330×

**Fig. 67** Copper-infiltrated steel with 10% Cu and 0.5% C, pressed to 6.65 g/cm³ and infiltrated with copper during 30-min sinter in hot zone at 1120 °C (2050 °F) in endothermic gas. Final density: 7.3 g/cm³. Minimum yield strength: 276 MPa (40 ksi). Arrows Cu show copper phase; arrows E, eutectoid (pearlite); arrow F, white ferrite grain. Picral. 330×

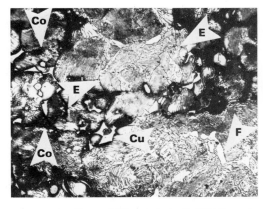

**Fig. 68** Copper-infiltrated steel with 10% Cu and 0.8% C (7.3 g/cm³ final density with 344 MPa, or 50 ksi, minimum yield strength). See Fig. 67 for processing. Arrows E indicate eutectoid (pearlite); arrows Co show coring from partial diffusion of copper in the iron. Arrow Fe shows white ferrite grain. Picral. 330×

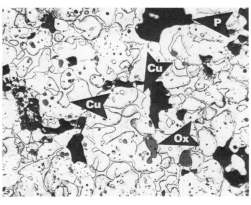

**Fig. 69** Copper-infiltrated, hydrogen-reduced sponge iron with 20% Cu (7.3 g/cm³ final density with 172 MPa, or 25 ksi, minimum yield strength). See Fig. 67 for processing. Arrows Cu show copper phase outlined against the white ferrite matrix. Arrow Ox indicates an unreduced oxide particle, and arrow P a residual pore. 2% nital. 330×

**Fig. 70** Copper-infiltrated steel with 20% Cu and 0.8% C (7.3 g/cm³ final density with 413 MPa, or 60 ksi, minimum yield strength). See Fig. 67 for processing. Arrow Cu shows the light-colored, melted copper-rich phase; arrows E, the eutectoid. Arrow P indicates residual pore. Picral, 30 s. 330×

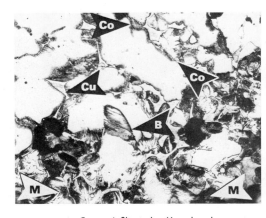

**Fig. 71** Copper-infiltrated, H₂-reduced sponge iron with 10% Cu (7.3 g/cm³ final density). Same processing as Fig. 67, but austenitized 60 min in endothermic gas at 845 °C (1550 °F), oil quenched, and tempered 1 h at 175 °C (350 °F). Arrow Cu shows melted copper-rich phase. Arrows Co indicates a cored region. Arrows M show mixed transformation products present 0.25 mm (0.010 in.) from the surface. Bainite (arrow B) may also be present. Picral. 330×

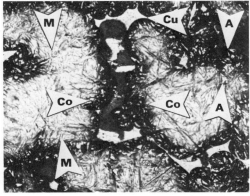

**Fig. 72** Copper-infiltrated steel with 10% Cu and 0.8% C, infiltrated as per Fig. 67 and heat treated as per Fig. 71. Typical structure for interior of 5-mm (0.2-in.) diam tensile bar (minimum ultimate tensile strength of 758 MPa, or 110 ksi). Arrows M show martensite platelets; arrows Co, coring. Arrow C indicates copper-rich region. Arrows A show flecks of retained austenite. Picral. 585×

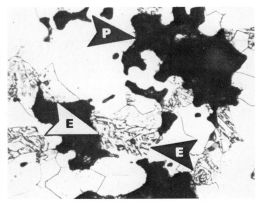

**Fig. 73** Prealloyed low-alloy steel (Fe-0.42Ni-0.62Mo-0.2C, 6.7 g/cm³), pressed at 410 to 480 MPa (30 to 35 tsi) and sintered 30 min at 1120 °C (2050 °F) in dissociated ammonia. Arrows E surround eutectoid region (background is white ferrite). Arrow P shows a pore. See also Fig. 74 and 75 for effects of increasing carbon content. 2% nital. 545×

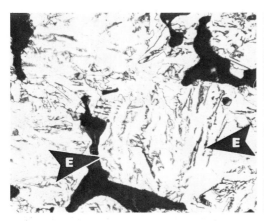

**Fig. 74** Same as Fig. 73, but with 0.5% C. Note that the eutectoid (arrows E) now covers most of the field of view and that the distinction between eutectoid and white proeutectoid ferrite is not clear. 2% nital. 545×

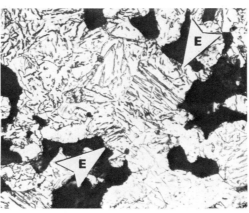

**Fig. 75** Same as Fig. 73, but with 0.8% C. Arrows E show the typical eutectoid product. Dark areas are pores. Note that the density of carbide platelets in the eutectoid is higher than for Fig. 74. 2% nital. 545×

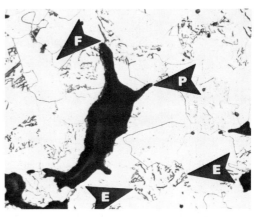

**Fig. 76** Prealloyed, low-alloy steel (Fe-1.85Ni-0.60Mo-0.2C, 6.7 g/cm³), processed as per Fig. 73. Matrix is white ferrite (arrow F). Eutectoid is found in colonies (arrows E). Arrow P shows a pore. Separation of eutectoid and ferrite is distinct, making it possible to estimate carbon content. 2% nital. 545×

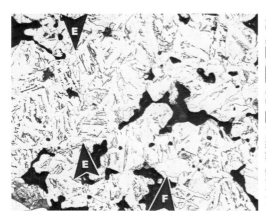

**Fig. 77** Same as Fig. 76, but with 0.5% C. Arrows E outline the eutectoid product, which is so mixed with ferrite that it is difficult to distinguish proeutectoid ferrite. Arrow F shows one small grain that is probably white ferrite. 2% nital. 365×

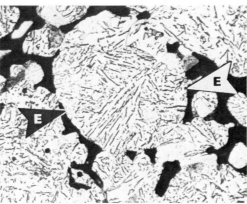

**Fig. 78** Same as Fig. 76, but with 0.8% combined carbon. The increasing carbon content alters the appearance of the eutectoid (compare with Fig. 77). The carbide platelets in the eutectoid colonies (arrows E) are more numerous and more closely spaced than in Fig. 77. 2% nital. 545×

**Fig. 79** Prealloyed steel (Fe-1.85Ni-0.6Mo-0.5C, 6.7 g/cm³), with an impurity particle of unalloyed free ferrite (outlined by arrows FF), which has a carbon content of 0.3 to 0.4%. It is a mixture of proeutectoid ferrite (arrow F) and normal eutectoid (arrows E). Compare this eutectoid with the matrix eutectoid. Arrow P indicates a pore. 2% nital. 365×

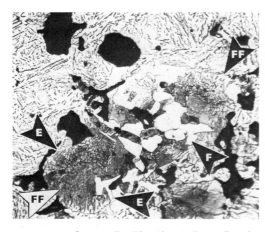

**Fig. 80** Same as Fig. 79, with a similar unalloyed iron particle. Arrows FF outline the free ferrite, which has a carbon content of approximately 0.6%, judging by its pearlite (arrows E) and its white proeutectoid ferrite (arrow F). 2% nital. 365×

**Fig. 81** Iron-phosphorus alloy (atomized iron mixed with Fe₃P to yield 0.45% P) for soft magnetic applications (6.7 g/cm³). Pressed at 410 to 480 MPa (30 to 35 tsi) and sintered 30 min at 1120 °C (2050 °F) in dissociated ammonia. Phosphorus forms a liquid phase that causes pore rounding during sintering. As-polished. 180×

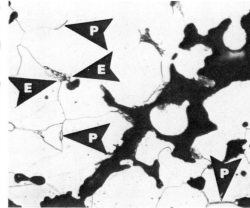

**Fig. 82** Same as Fig. 81, but etched. Arrows E show fine two-phase eutectoid or eutectic of Fe-C-P. Arrows P indicate isolated phosphorus-rich phase in grain boundaries. Matrix is all white ferrite. 2% nital. 545×

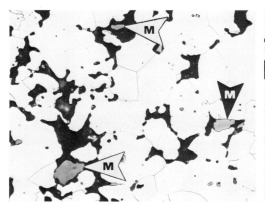

**Fig. 83** Water-atomized iron powder with 0.5% MnS blended for increased machinability. See Fig. 81 for processing (6.7 g/cm³ with 103 MPa, or 15 ksi, minimum yield strength). The MnS is the gray material (see arrows M) inside the darker pores. 2% nital. 330×

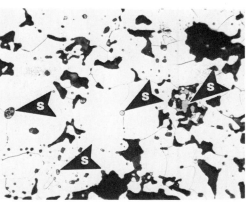

**Fig. 84** Sponge iron powder with 0.27% S and 0.9% Mn added to the melt before particle formation. See Fig. 81 for processing (6.7 g/cm³ with 103 MPa, or 15 ksi, minimum yield strength). Arrows S show gray MnS inclusions within the iron particles and also in the spongy areas. 2% nital. 330×

**Fig. 85** Carbon-reduced sponge iron powder with 0.5% S blended as elemental fines. See Fig. 81 for processing (6.4 g/cm³ with 103 MPa, or 15 ksi, minimum yield strength). Arrows S show two-phase sulfide mixtures of MnS and FeS, which lie within the pores. 2% nital. 330×

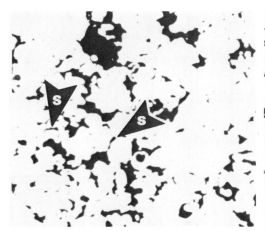

**Fig. 86** Nickel steel (elemental mix of atomized iron, 2% Ni, and 0.8% combined carbon, 6.7 g/cm³), pressed at 410 to 480 MPa (30 to 35 tsi) and sintered 30 min at 1120 °C (2050 °F) in dissociated ammonia. Arrows S indicate short segments of original particle boundaries. See also Fig. 87 to 90. As-polished. 180×

**Fig. 87** Same nickel steel as shown in Fig. 86, but with 1% Cu added. A few short segments of original particle boundaries remain (arrows S). It is difficult to distinguish any microstructural effect of the copper. As-polished. 180×

**Fig. 88** Same nickel steel as shown in Fig. 86, but with 2% Cu added. The additional copper helped to eliminate original particle boundaries, round the pores, and eliminate small pores. As-polished. 180×

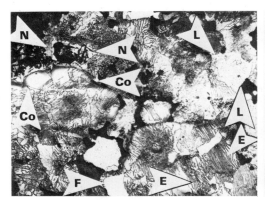

**Fig. 89** Same as Fig. 87, but etched. Arrows N show nickel-rich region, inside which are martensite platelets. The effect of the 1% Cu is indicated by shading or coring of the ferrite (arrows Co). Arrows E show eutectoid; arrows L, an underetched region of eutectoid. Arrow F indicates a white ferrite grain. 2% nital. 310×

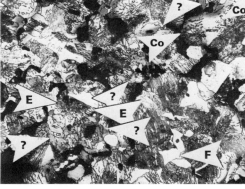

**Fig. 90** Same as Fig. 88, but etched. The 2% Cu causes the nickel to dissolve, eliminating the nickel-rich regions. Arrows ? surround regions where the nickel probably was. These regions are darkened by the coring caused by copper dissolving there and contain carbide platelets. Another cored region is marked Co. Arrows E mark unresolved eutectoid, and arrow F indicates a white ferrite grain. 2% nital. 310×

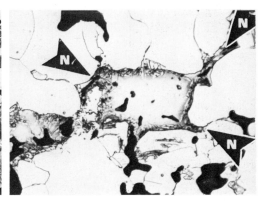

**Fig. 91** Nickel steel (atomized iron mixed with 2% elemental nickel and 0.2% combined carbon). See Fig. 86 for processing (6.7 g/cm³ with 137 MPa, or 20 ksi, minimum yield strength). Arrows N outline a nickel-rich region. The austenitic light-colored center is approximately 12% Ni. The outer edges are lower in nickel and higher in carbon. Dark regions are pores. 2% nital. 545×

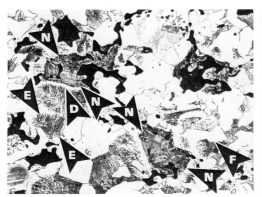

**Fig. 92** Same as Fig. 91, but with 0.5% C. Arrows N outline nickel-rich regions. The fine structure within these regions is martensite and bainite. Arrows E outline a eutectoid region. Arrow F indicates a white ferrite grain. Arrow D shows a white diffusion layer between the eutectoid and the nickel-rich areas. 2% nital. 310×

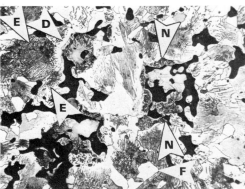

**Fig. 93** Same as Fig. 91, but with 0.8% C. Structure is nearly all eutectoid (arrows E), with some nickel-rich regions (arrows N) and isolated ferrite (arrow F). See also Fig. 94 for higher magnification of this structure. 2% nital. 310×

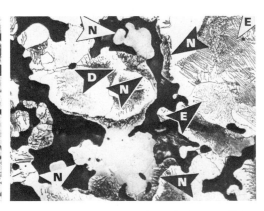

**Fig. 94** Same as Fig. 93, but at higher magnification. Arrows N outline a nickel-rich region running through the structure along the pore surfaces, which probably forms a continuous three-dimensional network within the steel. Martensite needles are visible on the surface of the region. Arrows E show eutectoid; arrow D, white diffusion layer. 2% nital. 550×

**Fig. 95** Nickel steel (4% elemental carbonyl nickel admixed with atomized iron and 0.2% C, 6.7 g/cm³). See Fig. 86 for processing. Arrows E show a small colony of eutectoid, but most of the carbon is tied up in the nickel-rich regions (arrows N). Background is white ferite grains. 2% nital. 330×

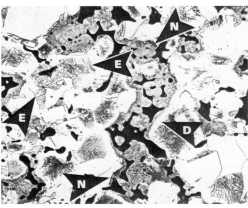

**Fig. 96** Same as Fig. 95, but with 0.5% C. As-sintered part would have a minimum yield strength of 207 MPa (30 ksi) or 723 MPa (105 ksi) if hardened and tempered at 260 °C (500 °F). Arrows N show a nickel-rich region. Arrows E indicate eutectoid, and arrow D shows a white diffusion layer between nickel-rich regions and the eutectoid. 2% nital. 330×

**Fig. 97** Same as Fig. 95, but with 0.8% C. Minimum yield strength: 276 MPa (40 ksi). Arrows N outline nickel-rich regions. Arrows E indicate eutectoid. Very little ferrite is present. 2% nital. 330×

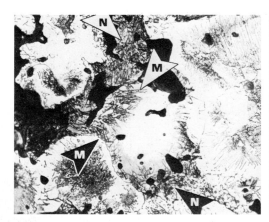

**Fig. 98** Same as Fig. 97, but at higher magnification. A nickel-rich region is bounded by arrows N. Martensite platelets (40 to 50 HRC) are visible on the periphery of this region (arrows M). These convey extra wear resistance in the as-sintered condition. The remaining structure is eutectoid. 2% nital. 585×

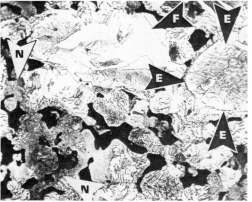

**Fig. 99** Diffusion-alloyed steel (Fe-1.75Ni-0.5Mo-1.5Cu-0.5C, 6.7 g/cm³), pressed at 410 to 480 MPa (60 to 70 ksi) and sintered 30 min at 1120 °C (2050 °F) in dissociated ammonia. Arrows N show nickel-rich regions containing martensite or bainite platelets; arrows E, a eutectoid colony with a white diffusion layer on the periphery. Arrow F indicates ferrite. 2% nital. 330×

**Fig. 100** Same as Fig. 99, but with 0.8% C. Arrows N show nickel-rich areas containing platelets of martensite or bainite. Arrow L indicates a light-etching eutectoid region, and arrow P a pore. Arrows E outline a colony of eutectoid containing thin carbide platelets. 2% nital. 330×

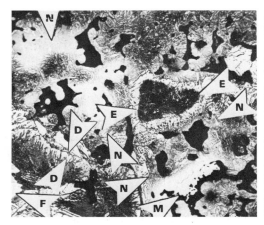

**Fig. 101** Same as Fig. 99, but with 4% Ni. Structure shows extensive nickel-rich areas (arrows N), with light-colored austenite at their interiors and gray martensite at their peripheries. Unresolved eutectoid is shown by arrows E, and a diffusion layer by arrows D. Arrow F indicates white ferrite. Arrows M outline a residual, spongy, undiffused molybdenum particle. 2% nital. 365×

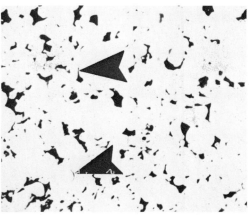

**Fig. 102** Type 316 stainless steel (6.96 g/cm³), pressed at 830 MPa (60 tsi) and sintered 30 min at 1150 °C (2100 °F) in dissociated ammonia. Structure is a tensile bar with tensile strength of 393 MPa (57 ksi) and elongation in 25 mm (1 in.) of 1%. Arrows show original particle boundaries. As-polished. 180×

**Fig. 103** Same as Fig. 102, but sintered 60 min at 1290 °C (2350 °F) in dissociated ammonia (7.15 g/cm³). Many of the small pores have disappeared, and few particle boundary segments remain (see arrows). Specimen from tensile bar with a tensile strength of 432 MPa (62.7 ksi) and elongation in 25 mm (1 in.) of 11%. As-polished. 180×

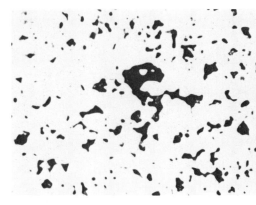

**Fig. 104** Same as Fig. 102, but vacuum sintered at 1290 °C (2350 °F) for 60 min (7.26 g/cm³). Pores are more rounded than the dissociated ammonia sinters in Fig. 102 and 103. Specimen from tensile bar with a tensile strength of 355 MPa (54.4 ksi) and elongation in 25 mm (1 in.) of 25%. As-polished. 180×

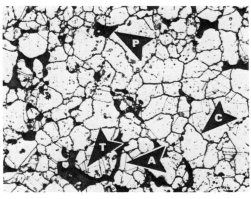

**Fig. 105** Same as Fig 102, but etched, showing the precipitated grain-boundary carbides (arrow C), which cause the irregular grain boundaries. Arrow A shows a normal austenite grain boundary, arrow T a twin boundary, and arrow P a pore. Glyceregia. 365×

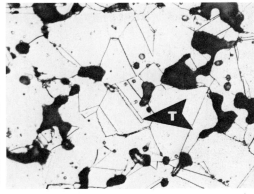

**Fig. 106** Same as Fig. 103, but etched. Note that the austenite grain boundaries and twin boundaries (arrow T) are free of carbides due to the decarburizing effect of the high-temperature dissociated ammonia sinter. Glyceregia. 545×

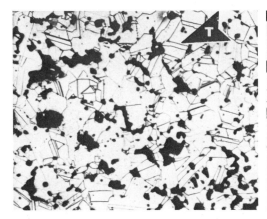

**Fig. 107** Same as Fig. 104, but etched. Structure is free of grain-boundary carbides. Arrow T points to a typical twin boundary. Glyceregia. 180×

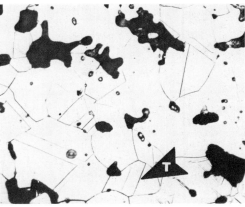

**Fig. 108** Same as Fig. 107, but at higher magnification. Grain boundaries show no carbide precipitates. Arrow T shows an annealing twin. Glyceregia. 545×

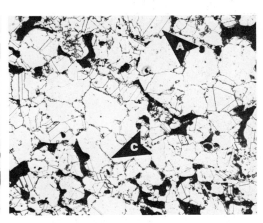

**Fig. 109** Type 303 stainless steel (7.06 g/cm³), pressed at 830 MPa (60 tsi) and sintered 60 min at 1120 °C (2050 °F) in dissociated ammonia. Residual chromium carbides are in the austenite grain boundaries (arrow C). Arrow A shows an austenite grain boundary free of carbides. Glyceregia. 360×

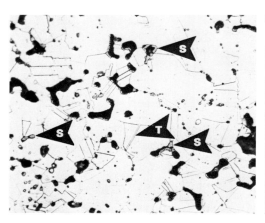

**Fig. 110** Same as Fig. 109, but sintered 60 min at 1190 °C (2350 °F) in dissociated ammonia (7.23 g/cm³). No carbides are present at grain boundaries. Arrows S indicate gray MnS inclusions added for machinability. Arrow T shows a typical annealing twin boundary. Glyceregia. 365×

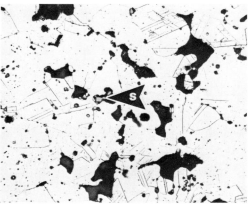

**Fig. 111** Same as Fig. 109, but vacuum sintered at 1290 °C (2350 °F) for 60 min (7.29 g/cm³). Arrow S shows a MnS particle. Glyceregia. 365×

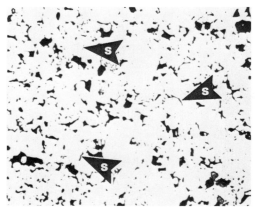

**Fig. 112** Type 410 stainless steel with added 0.15% graphite (6.77 g/cm³), pressed at 830 MPa (60 tsi), sintered 60 min at 1150 °C (2100 °F) in dissociated ammonia, and tempered 1 h at 175 °C (350 °F). Arrows S indicate original particle boundaries. Glyceregia. 120×

**Fig. 113** Same type 410 stainless steel and pressing conditions as described in Fig. 112, but sintered 30 min at 1120 °C (2050 °F) and etched. Structure is all martensite (arrows M). Glyceregia. 545×

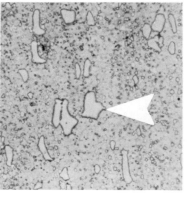

**Fig. 114** Wrought T15 steel. Arrow shows large primary M₆C carbide (compare with P/M tool steels in Fig. 115 and 116). Fine precipitate is vanadium carbide; matrix is martensite. 5% nital. 365×. (Ref 12)

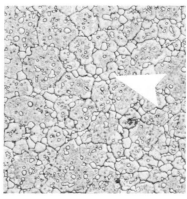

**Fig. 115** P/M T15 tool steel, pressed at 550 MPa (40 tsi), and vacuum sintered 1 h at 1260 °C (2300 °F) to full density (8.25 g/cm³). Arrow indicates primary M₆C carbide (compare with Fig. 114). 5% nital. 500×. (Ref 12)

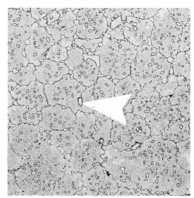

**Fig. 116** P/M M2 tool steel (8.12 g/cm³) pressed at 550 MPa (40 tsi) and vacuum sintered 1 h at 1240 °C (2260 °F). Arrow indicates small M₆C particle. Other small MC precipitates can be seen in the matrix of retained austenite, which also contains martensite. 5% nital. 400×. (Ref 12)

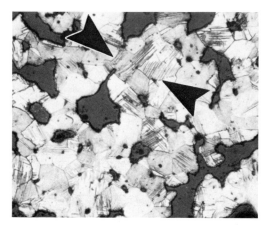

**Fig. 117** Bronze (Cu-10Sn, 6.4 g/cm³) pressed at 140 to 205 MPa (10 to 15 tsi), sintered (conditions not known), and sized for tolerances. Mostly all α-bronze grains. Gray areas are pores. Arrows surround slip line from cold working during sizing. K₂Cr₂O₇. 180×

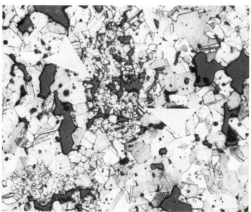

**Fig. 118** Same material and processing as described in Fig. 117. Arrows indicate clusters of small grains that have not grown into larger α grains. Compare with Fig. 119, which shows the effects of a 4% graphite addition on the resulting structure. K₂Cr₂O₇. 180×

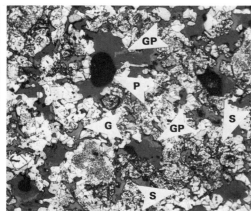

**Fig. 119** Cu-10Sn bronze (6.4 g/cm³) with 4% graphite. Pressed at 165 to 205 MPa (12 to 15 tsi), sintered 15 min at 845 °C (1550 °F), and sized. Arrows GP show graphite in pores surrounded by darker gray epoxy resin; arrow G, graphite flake in the matrix. Arrows S surround a small grain cluster; arrow P indicates a pore. K₂Cr₂O₇. 120×

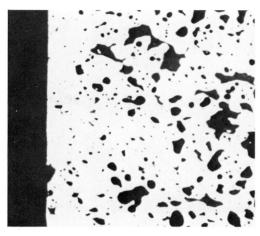

**Fig. 120** Inner diameter (left) of a sized Cu-10Sn bronze bearing (see Fig. 119 for processing). Note that the pores on the ID have been closed by the sizing operation. As a result, oil would not have easy access from the interior to the ID. $K_2Cr_2O_7$. 180×

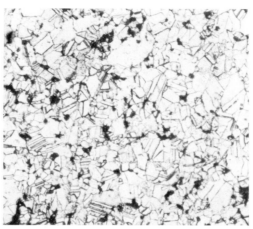

**Fig. 121** Leaded brass (Cu-20Zn-2Pb, 8.1 g/cm³), pressed and sintered 30 min at 870 °C (1600 °F), then re-pressed. Structure is all single-phase α-brass with a few annealing twins. Dark spots are well-rounded pores. 5 mL $NH_4OH$, 5 mL $H_2O$, and 3 drops 30% $H_2O_2$. 180×

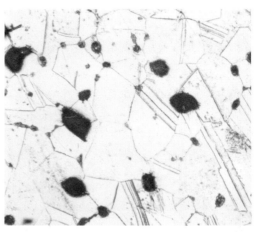

**Fig. 122** Same as Fig. 121, but at higher sintering temperature and/or longer time, which results in much larger grains. The pores (dark areas) are coarser and more rounded than those in Fig. 121. Etchant: same as Fig. 121. 180×

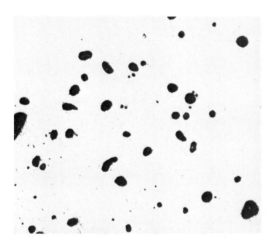

**Fig. 123** Ti-6Al-4V, cold isostatically pressed and vacuum sintered to dissolve the master alloy additions of vanadium and aluminum (94% dense). Rounded pores indicate adequate sintering. As-polished. 180×. (Ref 13)

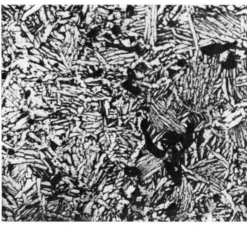

**Fig. 124** Same as Fig. 123, but etched. Dark areas are residual rounded pores. Matrix is transformed β-titanium. 85 mL $H_2O$, 5 mL $HNO_3$, and 10 mL HF. 180×. (Ref 13)

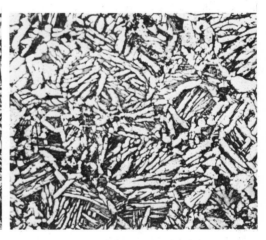

**Fig. 125** Ti-6Al-4V, cold isostatically pressed, vacuum sintered, then hot isostatically pressed to 99.6% density. Structure shows all transformed β. 85 mL $H_2O$, 5 mL $HNO_3$, and 10 mL HF. 180×. (Ref 13)

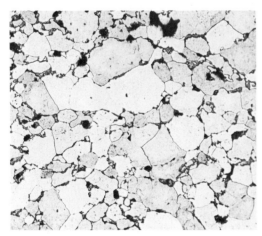

**Fig. 126** Aluminum alloy powder (Al-4.4Cu-0.8Si-0.4Mg), pressed and sintered 30 min at 595 °C (1100 °F) in nitrogen. Typical as-sintered structure. Keller's reagent. 100×. (Ref 14)

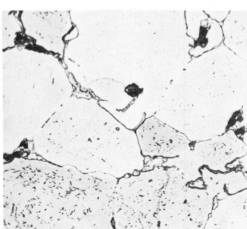

**Fig. 127** Same alloy and processing as Fig. 126, but at higher magnification. Keller's reagent. 500×. (Ref 14)

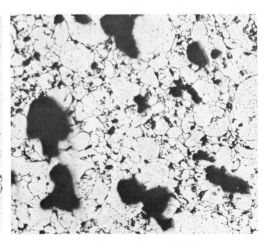

**Fig. 128** Aluminum alloy powder (Al-1.0Mg-0.6Si-0.25Cu), pressed, sintered, and solution heat treated. Typical structure. Dark areas are pores. Keller's reagent. 100×. (Ref 14)

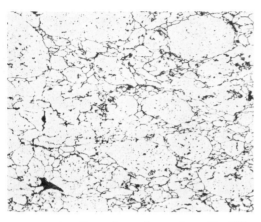

**Fig. 129** Same alloy and processing as Fig. 128, but reduced 25% in thickness by forging, which closed up most of the porosity. Keller's reagent. 100×. (Ref 14)

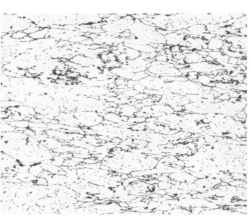

**Fig. 130** Same as Fig. 128, but pressed, sintered at 620 °C (1150 °F), and reduced 50% in thickness by forging or rolling to eliminate porosity. Keller's reagent. 100×. (Ref 14)

**Fig. 131** Nickel steel (carbonyl Fe, 2% carbonyl Ni, and 0.3% C) injection molded and sintered (1120 °C, or 2050 °F) to 97% density. Structure shows fine isolated porosity (gray dots). At surface (bottom left) there is a 0.05-mm (0.002-in.) thick layer that exhibits no apparent porosity. As-polished. 180×

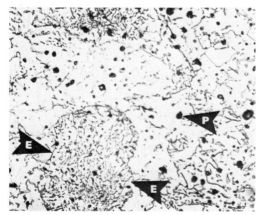

**Fig. 132** Same as Fig. 131, but etched. The nickel has diffused into the iron, resulting in complete homogeneity. The eutectoid (arrows E) is similar to that found in 4600 prealloyed steel (Fig. 78). Arrow P indicates an isolated rounded pore. 2% nital. 365×

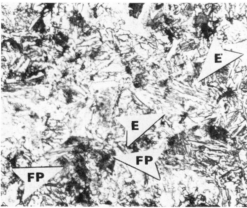

**Fig. 133** Prealloyed steel powder (Fe-2Ni-0.5Mo-0.5C) pressed to 6.6 g/cm³, sintered 30 min at 1120 °C (2050 °F), induction reheated, and hot forged (1095 °C, or 2000 °F) at 830 MPa (60 tsi) to over 99% of theoretical density. Arrows E show typical eutectoid; arrows FP, fine pearlite from rapid cooling of forged part. 2% nital. 545×

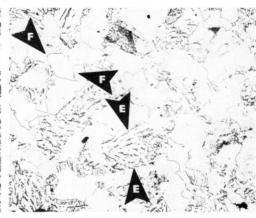

**Fig. 134** Powder-forged gear (Fe-2.0Ni-0.5Mo-0.2C). See Fig. 133 for processing. Arrows E show eutectoid; arrows F, white ferrite grains and grain boundaries. Dark spots are pores. Part is 99% dense. 2% nital. 365×

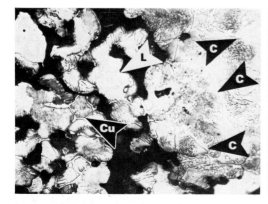

**Fig. 135** Copper steel (Fe-2.0Cu-0.8C, 6.8 g/cm³) that has formed blisters during delubrication and sintering. Arrows C indicate stringer (grain-boundary) carbides resulting from carburization. Some light-colored copper is evident (arrow Cu). Arrow L shows a light-etching eutectoid region. 2% nital. 585×

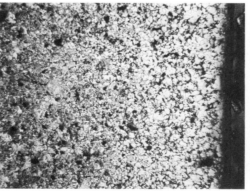

**Fig. 136** Same as Fig. 135, but pressed at 480 MPa (35 tsi), sintered 30 min at 1120 °C (2050 °F) in dissociated ammonia, and decarburized. White ferrite grains near the surface (right) indicate loss of carbon. The interior (left) is a darker eutectoid, containing approximately 0.8% C; the surface is ~1% C. 2% nital. 30×

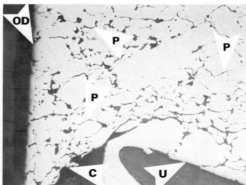

**Fig. 137** Pressed and sintered sprocket gear (composition unknown). Arrow OD shows the outer edge of the tooth, and arrow U the underside. A chamfer has broken off the tooling, resulting in a reverse chamfer (arrow C) on the part. Arrow P indicates original particle boundary resulting from particle separation during part ejection. As-polished. 110×

**Fig. 138** View at the radius between a flange (arrow F) and a hub (arrow H) in a pressed and sintered part (composition unknown). The relative motion between the hub and flange was not adjusted correctly during pressing, resulting in a shear crack (arrows C). As-polished. 120×

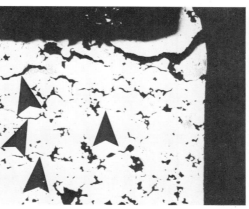

**Fig. 139** A corner of an MPIF tensile bar (Fe-2Ni-0.8C, 6.8 g/cm³) pressed at 550 MPa (40 tsi) and sintered 30 min at 1115 °C (2040 °F) in endothermic gas. Arrows indicate microlaminations that occurred during part ejection. These reduce the tensile strength of the bar by 30 to 40%. As-polished. 120×

**Fig. 140** Fe-0.8C, pressed at 550 MPa (40 tsi) and sintered 30 min at 1120 °C (2050 °F) in dissociated ammonia. Heat-treated structure showing mixture of 50% fine pearlite (dark phase) and 50% martensite (lighter phase). 4% picral. 960×

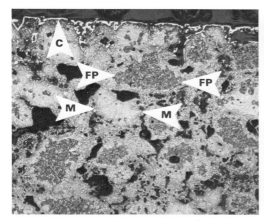

**Fig. 141** Copper steel (Fe-2Cu-0.8C, 6.7 g/cm³) pressed at 480 MPa (35 tsi), sintered 30 min at 1120 °C (2050 °F) in dissociated ammonia, austenitized 1 h at 870 °C (1600 °F), and oil quenched. Surface of part shows a thin, white layer of carbide (arrow C). The structure interior consists of 35% fine pearlite (arrows FP) and balance martensite (arrows M). Picral. 120×

**Fig. 142** Fe-0.37Mn-1.80Ni-0.63Mo alloy powder with added 2% Cu and 0.8% C. Pressed at 480 MPa (35 tsi), sintered 30 min at 1120 °C (2050 °F) in a nitrogen-base atmosphere, and tempered 1 h at 175 °C (350 °F) to 6.85 g/cm³. Structure shows fine pearlite (arrows P) and small amounts of white ferrite (arrow F) in a martensite matrix (arrows M). 2% nital. 365×

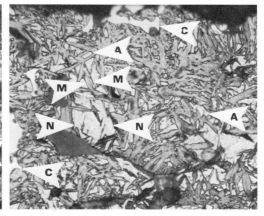

**Fig. 143** Nickel steel (Fe-2Ni-0.8C, 6.7 g/cm³). Pressed and sintered (normal processing) in endothermic gas, austenitized 1 h at 870 °C (1600 °F), oil quenched, and tempered 1 h at 260 °C (500 °F). Arrows C indicate carbide particles. Arrows M show a typical martensite platelet. Arrows N surround a nickel-rich region. Arrows A show light-colored regions of retained austenite. Picral. 645×

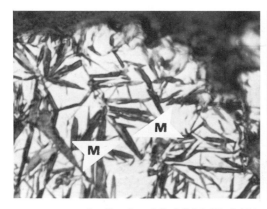

**Fig. 144** Prealloyed steel (Fe-1.8Ni-0.5Mo-0.4C, 6.83 g/cm³), pressed and sintered (normal processing) in dissociated ammonia, austenitized 1 h at 870 °C (1600 °F), oil quenched, and tempered 1 h at 175 °C (350 °F). Matrix (white areas) is retained austenite (excessive, 65 vol%). Arrows M indicate martensite platelets. Picral. 960×

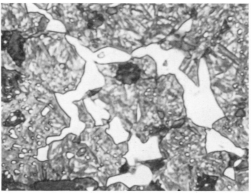

**Fig. 145** Fe-1.5graphite (6.7 g/cm³), pressed and sintered under normal processing conditions and heat treated as described in Fig. 144. Structure shows massive carbides (sharply delineated light phase). Picral. 960×

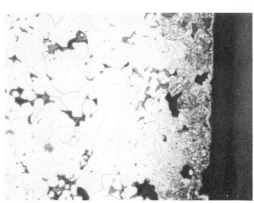

**Fig. 146** Atomized iron powder, pressed to 6.8 g/cm³, sintered in dissociated ammonia, austenitized 30 min in vacuum, gas carburized less than 5 min, and oil quenched. The 0.1-mm (0.004-in.) thick case is the dark martensite on right. Interior is all white ferrite. 2% nital. 180×. (Ref 17)

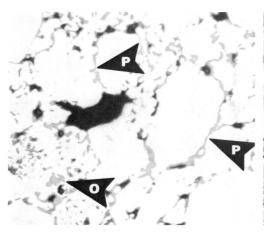

**Fig. 147** Steam-blackened Fe-2Cu-0.8C part that was undersintered. Arrow O shows a spongy pore that has been filled with gray $Fe_3O_4$ during the steam process. Arrows P indicate original particle boundaries, which were filled by the steam process. As-polished. 180×

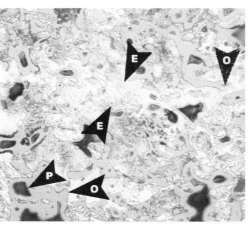

**Fig. 148** Pressed and sintered Fe-0.8C steel (6.4 g/cm³), which was steam blackened. The pores are nearly all filled with gray $Fe_3O_4$ (arrows O). Arrow P shows a pore not filled with oxide. Arrows E surround a eutectoid region. White areas are ferrite. 2% nital. 365×

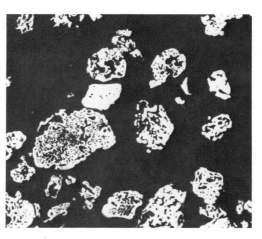

**Fig. 149** Pyron D63, hydrogen-reduced mill scale, sponge iron powder (−100 mesh). Particles contain fine, internal pores and some coarse pores. As-polished. 180×

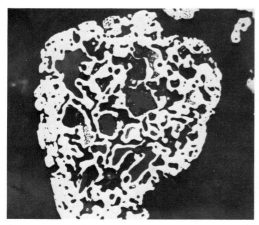

**Fig. 150** Same as Fig. 149, but at higher magnification, showing details of the internal porosity and some unreduced oxides. As-polished. 615×

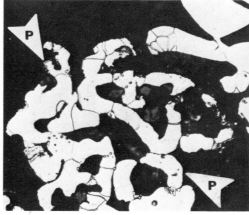

**Fig. 151** MH-100 carbon-reduced sponge iron powder (−100 mesh). A few ferrite grain boundaries are shown, but no iron carbides. Arrows P surround a particle having extensive internal porosity. As-polished. 960×

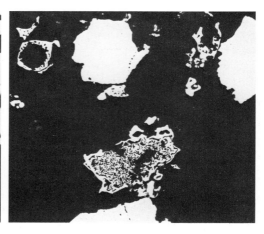

**Fig. 152** Atomet 28 iron powder (granulated and oxidized, hydrogen reduced), showing particles of varying degrees of porosity. As-polished. 645×

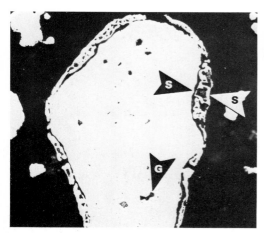

**Fig. 153** Ancorsteel 1000 water-atomized, annealed iron. Solid particle with some gas porosity (arrow G) and some surface porosity (arrows S) caused the reduction of oxides picked up during atomization. As-polished. 645×

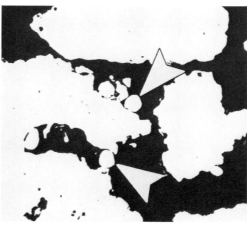

**Fig. 154** Ancorsteel 1000 water-atomized iron (−80 mesh). Arrows indicate fine particles agglomerated to coarser ones during annealing. As-polished. 960×

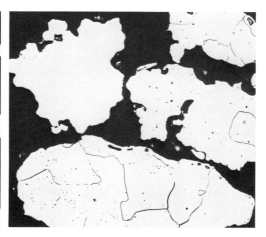

**Fig. 155** Same as Fig. 154, but etched. Grain boundaries are ferrite, indicating low carbon content. Some particles do not etch. Note irregular surface of particle at upper left caused by agglomeration of smaller particles. 2% nital. 615×

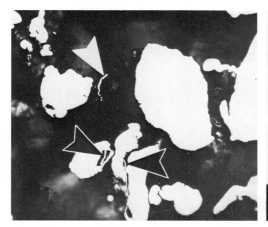

**Fig. 156** 316L stainless steel water-atomized powder (−100 mesh). Irregular particles with attached splatters of material (see arrows). As-polished. 645×

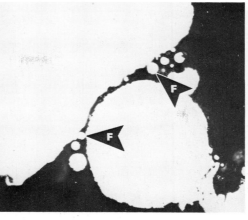

**Fig. 157** 316L stainless steel gas-atomized powder (−100 mesh). The wide range of particle sizes and the agglomeration of several small particles to a larger one (arrows F) during annealing is shown. As-polished. 645×

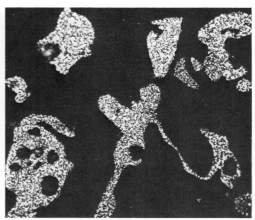

**Fig. 158** M2 tool steel, water-atomized, vacuum-annealed powder. Irregular particles with a fine carbide phase. Equal parts 4% picral and 4% nital. 645×

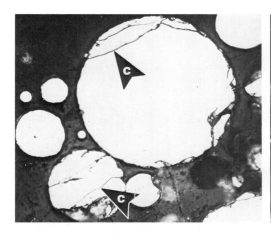

**Fig. 159** Fe-31Si, water-atomized master-alloy powder (−100 mesh). Regular particle shape implies low green strength. Particles cracked (arrows C) during processing. As-polished. 645×

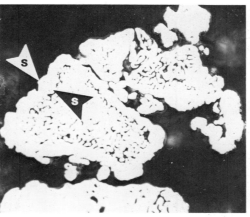

**Fig. 160** 100 RXM copper powder (−100 mesh) subjected to oxidation, grinding, and reduction cycle. Arrows S surround surface pores that have closed during reduction or annealing. As-polished. 645×

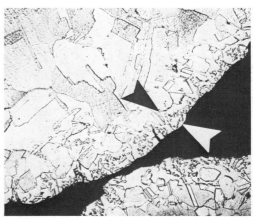

**Fig. 161** 92Cu-8Sn atomized bronze filter powder (−40+60 mesh). Surface of copper is coated with tin, which is partly alloyed, forming intermetallics and some α-bronze. Arrows show depth of tin diffusion. As-polished. 645×

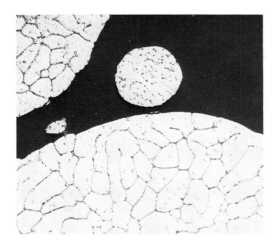

**Fig. 162** 601AC atomized aluminum powder. Very smooth regular particle surfaces with no evidence of the admixed elements. Keller's reagent. 660×

**Fig. 163** Undersintered nickel steel (Fe-2Ni-0.8C, 7.0 g/cm³), pressed at 550 MPa (40 tsi) and sintered 25 min at 1120 °C (2050 °F) in endothermic gas. Arrows indicate numerous original particle boundaries. As-polished. 180×

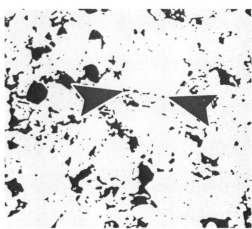

**Fig. 164** Same as Fig. 163, but an average sinter (30 min at 1120 °C, or 2050 °F, in endothermic gas). Arrows show a row of pores at which a particle boundary has broken up during sintering. As-polished. 180×

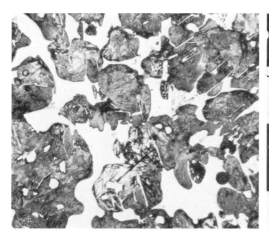

**Fig. 165** Wear-resistant alloy steel (Fe-5Cr-1Mo-2Cu-0.5P-2.5C) pressed at 550 MPa (40 tsi) and liquid phase sintered 30 min at 1110 °C (2030 °F) in dissociated ammonia to 7.6 g/cm³. White areas are primary $M_3C$ for wear resistance. Matrix: martensite and fine pearlite. 2% nital. 545×. (Ref 18)

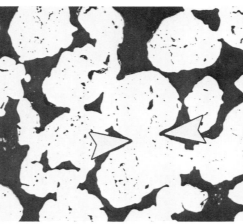

**Fig. 166** Cu-8Sn filter powder, gravity sintered 30 min at 870 °C (1600 °F) in dissociated ammonia. Arrows N show bonding between the particles. Dark areas are pores filled with epoxy resin. As-polished. 65×

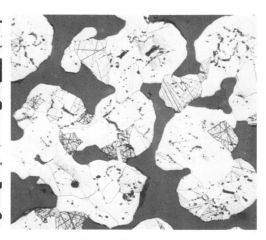

**Fig. 167** Same as Fig. 166, but etched, showing well-sintered α-bronze grains. Cross-hatched grains result from residual scratches and etching. $K_2C_2O_7$. 65×

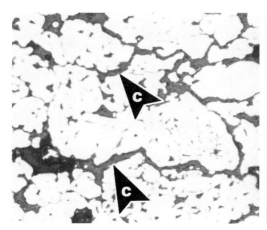

**Fig. 168** Copper steel (Fe-2Cu-0.8C, 6.8 g/cm³), which has blistered during heat up to sintering because of *in situ* formation of soot that expanded the spaces between particles. Arrows C show resulting cracks. As-polished. 180×

**Fig. 169** Pressed and sintered nickel steel. High-density region molded above a shelf in a die that is 7.55 g/cm³, as measured statistically by the area fraction of pores. See also Fig. 170. As-polished. 180×

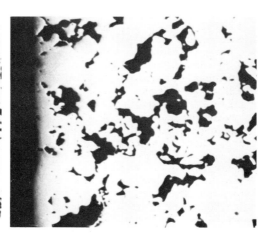

**Fig. 170** Same as Fig. 169, but a low-density region (5.98 g/cm³) molded below the die shelf. As-polished. 180×

# Magnetic and Electrical Materials

By George F. Vander Voort
Supervisor
Applied Physics Research & Development
Carpenter Technology Corporation

MAGNETIC AND ELECTRICAL MATERIAL microstructures are studied using a wide range of metallographic techniques because of the variety of materials in this field. In this article, the metallography and microstructures associated with magnetic materials will be emphasized. Only electrical steels used for laminations in rotors and stators of low-cost electric motors, transformers, and generators are discussed regarding electrical applications. However, these iron-base alloys are also classified as magnetic materials (see discussion below). Information on materials used for other electrical applications can be found in the articles "Beryllium-Copper and Beryllium-Nickel Alloys," "Copper and Copper Alloys," "Refractory Metals and Alloys," and "Electrical Contact Materials" in this Volume.

Magnetic materials are classified as magnetically soft or magnetically hard, that is, permanent magnets. Each class contains various compositions requiring different approaches for preparation. Magnetically soft materials include high-purity irons, low-carbon steels, nonoriented silicon-iron electrical steels, oriented silicon irons, iron-nickel alloys, iron-cobalt alloys, ferritic stainless steels, ferrites, and nickel-iron-cobalt-base amorphous materials. Permanent magnet materials include hard magnetic steel alloys, Alnico alloys (iron-aluminum-nickel-cobalt plus other elements), ferrites, Cunife (copper-iron-nickel), Cunico (copper-cobalt-nickel), Vicalloy alloys, neodymium-iron-boron alloys, cobalt/rare earth alloys, chromium-cobalt-iron alloys, and platinum-cobalt alloys.

Although macrostructural examination is common for only a few of these materials, microstructural examination is used for most, with major emphasis on grain-structure analysis. Much of the microstructural analysis has centered on examination of optical and electron metallographic techniques. General texts on magnetic materials are cited in

Ref 1 to 8. Additional information is available in the articles "Magnetically Soft Materials" and "Materials for Permanent Magnets" in Volume 3 of the 9th Edition of *Metals Handbook*.

## Specimen Preparation

**Electrical Steels.** The general procedures for sectioning, mounting, polishing, and etching electrical steels are basically the same as those described for low-carbon steels in the article "Carbon and Alloy Steels" in this Volume. Silicon-iron electrical steels tend to stain, and the use of water in the final preparation steps and after etching is best avoided. Alcohol is usually an acceptable substitute. Ethanol is preferred, because methanol is a cumulative poison.

Etching is most commonly performed using nital (2 to 3% nitric acid, $HNO_3$, in ethanol), which reveals the ferrite grain boundaries. Because nital is orientation sensitive, a portion of the grain boundaries may not be well delineated. Marshall's reagent (Table 1) fully develops the grain structure in electrical steels. Picral (4% picric acid in ethanol) is preferred when the residual carbide (cementite) is of interest. Unlike nital, picral does not reveal ferrite grain boundaries; therefore, the residual carbide is easier to observe, particularly along grain boundaries.

The degree of grain orientation is often of interest in electrical steels, especially the oriented silicon-iron grades. Several approaches can be used to study the degree and type of crystallographic texture. X-ray procedures are used, as are metallographic approaches, particularly for the large-grain-oriented grades. One common approach involves use of dislocation etch pitting reagents, which require carefully polished specimens. Chemical polishing (Table 2) or electrolytic polishing (Table 3) is normally used as the final preparation step before etching. Solutions that pro-

duce etch pits are listed in Table 4. Many of these reagents pit grains with only certain orientations, usually those with low crystallographic indices. An optical goniometer is used to measure the orientation of the pits within etched grains. Grain-oriented silicon-iron electrical steels often do not require polishing of the sheet surface before etch pitting, because the annealing furnace atmosphere provides a satisfactory surface condition if an insulating coating is not present. Additional information on etch pitting can be found in the article "Etching" in this Volume.

Another approach includes line ("hatch") etching procedures (Ref 9-13). In this technique, an opaque reaction layer is formed on the specimen surface during etching. This layer shrinks and cracks when dried to produce on the surface a lineal pattern that is related to the crystallographic orientation of the underlying grains. Grain-oriented silicon-iron electrical steels exhibit a parallel line pattern in which the lines are parallel to the direction of magnetization. Line etching is also discussed in the article "Etching" in this Volume.

Two reagents have been used for silicon-iron alloys. Klemm's reagent (50 mL cold-saturated aqueous sodium thiosulfate, $Na_2S_2O_3$, plus 1 g potassium metabisulfite, $K_2S_2O_5$) is made fresh before etching for 2 h by immersion. Boiling alkaline sodium picrate (Table 1)—a 20- to 30-min etch—provides more pronounced line patterns. This is followed by a 3- to 5-min etch in 1 to 2% nital to improve contrast. The nital seeps into the cracks in the layer formed by the alkaline sodium picrate and attacks the underlying material to produce lines. The surface layer dissolves, leaving a bright surface with a linear etch pattern.

A parallel line pattern is obtained when the grains deviate only slightly from {110}. As the orientation deviates from {110}, intersecting lines form that are perpendicular for

**Table 1  Etchants for microscopic examination of magnetic alloys**

| No. | Etchant composition | Procedure for use |
|---|---|---|
| 1. | 1-6 mL HNO₃ and 99-94 mL alcohol | Nital. For iron, iron-nickel, iron-cobalt, Alnico 5, and SmCo₅; reveals grain structure; for SmCo₅, a pre-etch with 30% HNO₃ in glycerol may be needed, followed by nital etch for 2-3 min; for iron-cobalt-vanadium (2-3% V) alloys, etch 10-50 s; examination in differential interference contrast shows α₂ in relief and α₁ recessed |
| 2. | 4 g picric acid and 100 mL alcohol | Picral for iron and silicon-iron electrical steels; 0.5-1.0% zephiran chloride may be added; reveals cementite |
| 3. | (a) 10% picral plus zephiran chloride<br>(b) 5% nital | For iron and silicon iron electrical steels; etch using (a) for 4 s, then (b) for 20 s; used to study progress of decarburization |
| 4. | 10 mL HNO₃, 20 mL HF, 30 mL methanol, 40 mL glycerol | For Fe-3Si; swab for 1 min at 20 °C (70 °F); line etches (100) planes completely and exclusively |
| 5. | (a) 5 mL H₂SO₄, 8 g oxalic acid, 10 mL H₂O<br>(b) 30% solution H₂O₂ | Marshall's reagent. For iron and silicon iron electrical steels; mix equal parts (a) and (b); use fresh for 1-3 s; if no reaction occurs, pre-etch with nital for 3 s, then immerse in Marshall's; a post-etch in nital for 20 s increases etch attack; provides uniform grain boundary attack |
| 6. | (a) 2 g picric acid, 25 g NaOH, 100 mL H₂O<br>(b) 1-2% nital | Line-etching technique for grain-oriented silicon iron electrical steels; sample must be well polished; immerse in (a) boiling for 20-30 min, then in (b) for 3-5 min |
| 7. | 5 g FeCl₃, 15 mL HCl, 60 mL alcohol | For nickel-iron alloys; immerse or swab 5-10 s; good for replica work |
| 8. | 50 mL HCl, 2 mL 30% H₂O₂, 50 mL H₂O | For nickel-iron alloys; immerse 10-30 s; do not store |
| 9. | 60 mL HCl, 20 mL HNO₃, 40-60 mL glycerol | Glyceregia. For nickel-iron, iron-cobalt, and iron-cobalt-vanadium (2-3% V) alloys; orientation sensitive etch; use fresh under a hood; do not store; swab up to 1 min; discard when solution turns dark yellow |
| 10. | Saturated aqueous (NH₄)₂S₂O₈ (ammonium persulfate) | For nickel-iron alloys, particularly 50Ni-50Fe; immerse 20-30 s |
| 11. | 100 mL HCl, 2 g CuCl₂ (cupric chloride), 7 g FeCl₃, 200 mL methanol, 100 mL H₂O | For nickel-iron and iron-cobalt alloys; immerse or swab 10-15 s; general purpose etch |
| 12. | 3 parts HCl and 1 part HNO₃; saturate with CuCl₂ | For high nickel alloys, e.g., Moly Permalloy; swab 2-3 s |
| 13. | 50 mL HCl, 10 g CuSO₄ (copper sulfate), 50 mL H₂O | Marble's reagent. For nickel-iron, iron-cobalt, Alnico alloys, and barium ferrite; good for grain structure |
| 14. | 10 mL HNO₃ and 90 mL methanol | 10% nital. For iron-cobalt alloys; immerse up to 30 s |
| 15. | 30 g FeCl₃, 1 g CuCl₂, 0.5 g SnCl₂ (stannous chloride), 100 mL HCl, up to 500 mL H₂O | Double strength Rosenhain's etchant. For iron-nickel-aluminum alloys; darkens iron-rich phases, nickel-rich phases unetched |
| 16. | 10 mL HCl and 90 mL ethanol | For Alnico 5; use by immersion |
| 17. | 5-10 mL HCl and 100 mL H₂O | Electrolytic etch for iron-cobalt alloys; use 2-5 s at 250-500 mA/cm² (1.6-3.2 A/in.²) |
| 18. | 2 g CrO₃ and 100 mL H₂O | Electrolytic etch for Fe-Co alloys; use 2-5 s at 100-200 mA/cm² (0.65-1.3 A/in.²) |
| 19. | 200 mL HCl, 5 mL HNO₃, 65 g FeCl₃ | For Alnico alloys |
| 20. | 1 part HNO₃ and 1 part acetic acid | For Alnico alloys |
| 21. | 50 mL each of ethanol, methanol, HCl and 1 g CuCl₂, 3.5 g FeCl₃, 2.5 mL HNO₃ | Ralph's reagent. For ferritic stainless steels; use by swabbing |
| 22. | 3 parts HNO₃ and 1 part HCl | For cobalt-platinum |
| 23. | 3 parts glycerol, 1 part acetic acid, 1 part HNO₃ | For SmCo₅ |
| 24. | 100 mL H₂O, 1 mL acetic acid, 1 mL HNO₃ | For SmCo₅; immerse a few seconds |
| 25. | 10 g (NH₄)₂S₂O₈ and 100 mL H₂O | For rare earth-cobalt alloys; use boiling, short immersion |
| 26. | 3 parts HCl and 1 part ethanol | For manganese-zinc |
| 27. | 15 mL lactic acid, 15 mL HNO₃, 5 mL HF | For nickel-zinc ferrite and nickel-ferrite; use at 65-80 °C (150-175 °F) for 20 min |
| 28. | 10 mL HF, 10 mL HNO₃, 20 mL H₂O | For ferrites and garnets; use at 60-90 °C (140-195 °F) for a few seconds to 30 min |
| 29. | H₂SO₄ (conc.) | For garnets; immerse up to 30 min at 115 °C (240 °F); use with care; a face shield is recommended |
| 30. | 30 mL lactic acid, 15 mL HNO₃, 5 mL HF | For Y₃Fe₅O₁₂; use at 65 °C (150 °F) for 10 min |

{100} grains. The direction of parallel lines is ⟨100⟩; perpendicular lines, ⟨110⟩. The growth of the surface layer during the alkaline sodium picrate etch has been documented (Ref 10). For best results, the specimen must be carefully polished; electropolishing is recommended (Table 3, etchant 4).

A procedure for detecting undesirably oriented grains in sheets of coarse-grained oriented silicon iron has been developed (Ref 14). This macroscopic approach is suitable for observing the grains on a large sheet surface. The sheet surface is swabbed 1 min at room temperature with an etchant containing 10 mL HNO₃, 20 mL hydrofluoric acid (HF),

30 mL methanol, and 40 mL glycerol (Table 1, etchant 4). This produces a line etching pattern on the (100) planes. The grains are observed using an optical apparatus described in Ref 14.

An additional feature of interest in these steels and many other magnetic materials is grain size. In general, the final annealed or heat-treated grain size is most important, but for some work the penultimate grain size (that prior to the final processing step) must be controlled to obtain the desired properties.

Of the numerous methods for measuring grain size (Ref 15, 16), the intercept procedure is preferred. Grain size measurements in

thin sheet may be complicated by the possibility of the sheet thickness direction restricting growth in that direction compared to that of the rolling direction. Grain size measurement procedures are discussed in "Quantitative Metallography" in this Volume.

The magnetic domain structure of oriented silicon irons has been studied extensively. The various techniques used for magnetic materials are described below. A metallographic approach for revealing the domain structure in ferrite has been developed (Ref 17). Jacquet's electropolishing solution (300 mL acetic acid and 27 mL perchloric acid, HClO₄) is used at 1.5 A/cm² (9.7 A/in.²), 40 V dc, for 5 min with a stainless steel cathode. The electropolishing solution must be used to polish approximately 50 specimens before it will reveal domain structure.

**Iron-nickel and iron-cobalt alloys** require preparation procedures similar to those described for nickel and nickel-copper alloys (see the article "Nickel and Nickel-Copper Alloys" in this Volume). Because they are rather soft, care must be taken during preparation to prevent distortion and smearing. Elimination of fine polishing scratches is most difficult; vibratory final polishing is very useful, as is electropolishing.

Macroetching of iron-nickel alloys is commonly performed by thermal etching. Cold-rolled strip specimens are annealed several hours in dry hydrogen at 1175 °C (2150 °F), followed by furnace cooling. Thermal etching will reveal grain structures, and subsequent etching with Marble's reagent or other solutions will enhance grain contrast. Larger specimens are macroetched during manufacturing using standard hot-acid etching procedures described in the article "Carbon and Alloy Steels" in this Volume.

Sectioning and mounting of iron-nickel and iron-cobalt strip is performed in the same manner as most metals (see the articles "Sectioning" and "Mounting of Specimens" in this Volume). Strip specimens may be bent into self-supporting shapes for mounting, or plastic clamps may be used to support the specimens. Most mounting resins can be used, but thin sheets may fold over during compression mounting. Cold-setting resins can be used to avoid this problem. For edge protection, plating the surface prior to mounting may be beneficial.

Grinding and polishing procedures are basically the same as for low-carbon steel specimens. Wet grinding is recommended to minimize heating problems and abrasive embedment. Silicon carbide of 120, 240, 320, 400, and 600 grit is used with 45 to 90° rotation of the specimen between grinding steps. Rough polishing is performed using 6- or 3-μm diamond abrasive (paste, spray, or slurry) on a napless or low-nap cloth. Selection of the cloth is often a matter of personal preference. Rough polishing may be followed by a 1-μm diamond polish on a medium-nap cloth. Final polishing may involve one or two grades of alumina (Al₂O₃), for example, 0.3-

**Table 2  Chemical polishing solutions**

| Material | Solution | Comments |
|---|---|---|
| Silicon-iron electrical steels | 6 mL HF and 94 mL 30% $H_2O_2$ | Use at room temperature; keep cool; wash in successive baths of $H_2O_2$, $H_2O$, and ethanol. |
| Silicon-iron electrical steels, iron-cobalt, iron-cobalt-vanadium (2-3% V) | 100 mL $H_3PO_4$ and 100 mL 30% $H_2O_2$ | Use at room temperature; keep cool; up to 10-min immersion |

and 0.05-$\mu$m $Al_2O_3$ on a medium-nap cloth. These procedures may be executed manually using a rotating polishing wheel or by automated devices. Final polishing using a vibratory polisher may be preferred for scratch removal. Reference 16 provides additional details on carrying out grinding and polishing.

Electropolishing is an alternative for obtaining high-quality surface finishes on these soft alloys and is especially useful for annealed vacuum-melted alloys. The specimen is usually ground to a 600-grit finish before electropolishing. Through-thickness specimens are difficult to handle; planar surfaces are easier to handle. Table 3 lists commonly used electrolytes and polishing conditions.

Etchants for iron-nickel and iron-cobalt alloys are usually more aggressive than for electrical steels, although nital may be satisfactory for some specimens. Choice of etchants (Table 1) is often a matter of personal preference. Complete delineation of all the grains in iron-nickel alloys, such as stainless steels, can be difficult. The microstructure of these alloys is described below.

**Ferrites and Garnets.** Preparation procedures for ferrites and garnets differ from those for the soft metals previously described because of their brittle nature, chemical inertness, and lack of significant electrical conductivity. Electrolytic techniques cannot be used.

Sectioning is best performed using a low-speed diamond saw. The high quality of the cut surface obviates the need for coarse grinding; that is, grinding can generally begin using 320- or 400-grit silicon carbide paper. Mounting can be performed using most materials, but cold-setting resins offer advantages compared to compression-mounting materials. Because they are made by powder processes, some porosity can be expected. Vacuum impregnation of epoxy into the voids may be quite useful for some specimens.

Grinding is performed up to 600 grit. This should be carried out wet with a high volume of water and somewhat higher pressure than that used for metals. Automatic devices may be desired to reduce operator fatigue. Polishing is executed in the same manner as for metals; 6- and 1-$\mu$m diamond abrasives are frequently used. A 1-$\mu$m diamond finish is generally adequate. Finer abrasives may also be used.

Ferrites and garnets are examined in the as-polished condition to detect porosity and second phases. Etchants (Table 1) are usually mixtures of heated acids. Etch times may be 10 to 30 min.

**Permanent magnet alloys,** such as Alnico alloys, are generally quite hard—to approximately 60 HRC—and their preparation is similar to that of hardened tool steels. Sectioning can be performed using wire saws, diamond saws, or abrasive cutoff saws. For the latter, a soft wheel must be selected. Cutting technique is critical for preventing cracking or burning; light pressure (slow feed) and copious coolant flow are required. Grinding and polishing rates are slow. Therefore, if manual procedures are used, relatively small sections are advisable. Automatic devices easily handle larger specimens. Small sections require mounting to facilitate handling. Most mounting materials can be used (see the article "Mounting of Specimens" in this Volume).

Grinding is performed in the usual manner. If the surface to be polished is cut using a low-speed diamond saw, grinding can begin using 320- or 400-grit silicon carbide. If an abrasive cutoff wheel is used, grinding must commence with a coarser grit, for example, 180- or 240-grit silicon carbide. Grinding should be carried out wet. Kerosene or a lightweight oil is sometimes used for grinding with abrasives finer than 400 grit.

Electropolishing is often used to polish permanent magnet alloys. Polishing is performed after grinding to a 600-grit silicon carbide finish. The primary difficulty in using electropolishing is obtaining electrical contact with the specimen. If the specimen is large enough to grind without mounting, it can be secured with a clamp. If mounting is necessary, a wire can be attached to the back of the specimen by spot welding or by use of a silver paste. The wire must extend through the mount; this is easily accomplished with cold-mounting materials. A suitable electrolyte for polishing is listed in Table 3.

Many of these alloys are routinely examined in the as-polished condition before etching to detect porosity or microshrinkage cavities. Many can be etched using nital; Marble's reagent is also commonly used. Electrolytic etching is sometimes preferred.

The structure of permanent magnet alloys is usually too fine to observe using optical microscopy. Therefore, transmission electron microscopy (TEM) using replicas or thin foils is frequently implemented (see Table 5 for thinning solutions for magnetic materials). More information is provided below and in the article "Transmission Electron Microscopy" in this Volume. Basic texts on specimen preparation for TEM are cited in Ref 18 to 23.

## Microexamination

In a ferromagnetic material, such as iron, each atom has a magnetic moment and can be viewed as an "atomic magnet." The atomic moments will be intercoupled and will be aligned parallel at the lattice sites. In iron, nickel, and cobalt, the magnetic moments are additive, resulting in ferromagnetism. Heating to above the Curie temperature (770 °C, or 1420 °F, for iron; 360 °C, or 680 °F, for nickel) eliminates the preferred alignment; cooling below this temperature restores the coupling forces and permits realignment. Regions of large-scale alignment of the atomic magnets produce domains. Alignment within the domain is produced by the coupling forces; an external field is not required.

Alignment of the magnetic moments varies with the crystal lattice of the element. Body-centered cubic (bcc) iron (at room temperature) has the atomic moments aligned in the direction of the cube edges; for face-centered cubic (fcc) nickel, they are aligned in the direction of the cube diagonals. These preferred alignment directions arise as a result of magnetic anisotropy forces.

**Table 3  Electropolishing solutions for metallographic specimens**

| Material | Solution | Comments |
|---|---|---|
| 1. Iron and iron-nickel | 135 mL glacial acetic acid, 25 g $CrO_3$, 7 mL $H_2O$ | For iron: use at 20 V dc, 0.09-0.22 A/cm² (0.6-1.4 A/in.²), 17-19 °C (63-66 °F), 6 min, stainless steel cathode. For iron-nickel: use at 80 V dc, 0.8-1.6 A/cm² (5-10 A/in.²), 7 °C (45 °F) max. Grind samples to 600-grit surface finish. |
| 2. Fe-3Si nickel alloys | 185 mL $H_3PO_4$, 765 mL acetic anyhdride, 50 mL $H_2O$ | Age solution 24 h before use; use at 50 V dc (external), <30 °C (85 °F), 0.1 A/cm² (0.6 A/in.²), 4-5 min; use large iron or aluminum cathode |
| 3. Iron-nickel and iron-cobalt Alnico alloys | 10 mL $HClO_4$ and 100 mL glacial acetic acid | Use at 45 V dc, 0.2 A/cm² (1.3 A/in.²), 24 °C (75 °F), 3-4 min |
| 4. Silicon iron electrical steels | 80 mL $H_3PO_4$, 13 g $CrO_3$, 7 mL $H_2O$ | Use at 0.6 A/cm² (3.9 A/in.²), 20 °C (68 °F) |
| 5. Permanent magnet alloys | $H_3PO_4$ saturated with $CrO_3$ | Use at approximately 1 A/cm² (6.5 A/in.²) at approximately 75 °C (165 °F), for 30-120 s |

**Table 4  Dislocation etch-pitting solutions**

| Etchant composition(a) | Conditions for use | Purpose |
|---|---|---|
| 1 part HF, 1 part HNO₃, 4 parts H₂O | Immerse 10 s. | Exposes {100} crystallographic faces in (110) [001] (cube-on-edge) oriented 3.25% Si steel |
| 2 parts HF, 1 part HNO₃, 3 parts methanol, 4 parts glycerol | Swab 1 min. | Same as for etchant 1 |
| (A) 6 mL 30% H₂O₂, 0.1 mL HCl, 100 mL H₂O<br>(B) 40 mL FeCl₃, 40 mL ethanol, 20 mL H₂O | Immerse in A for 10 s, rinse and dry; then immerse in B for 3 s, rinse and dry | Develops etch pits in (110) [001] (cube-on-edge) oriented 3.25% Si steel |
| 100 g Fe₂SO₄ (ferric sulfate), 100 mL H₂SO₄, 1000 mL H₂O | Immerse 15 s in solution heated to 80-90 °C (175-195 °F). | Develops etch pits in (100) [001] (cube-on-face) oriented 3.25% Si steel |
| (A) 5 mL HF and 95 mL methanol<br>(B) 100 mL 3% H₂O₂, 100 mL H₂O, 2 drops HCl<br>(C) 5 mL HCl and 95 mL methanol | Polish, etch heavily in nital; repolish, etch in nital to reveal grain boundaries; immerse 10 s in A, rinse, dry; 2 s in B, rinse, dry; 30 s in C, rinse, dry | Exposes {100} crystallographic faces in primary recrystallized 3.25% Si steel and nonoriented silicon steels |

(a) parts are by volume

Boundaries between domains are referred to as domain walls (Bloch walls) and have thicknesses to approximately a thousand atomic distances. The atomic magnet orientations change within the wall from the direction of one domain to that of its neighbor. The walls exhibit fixed angles—90° or 180° between the magnetization directions in each adjacent domain. Each grain in a polycrystalline ferromagnetic metal contains numerous domains and domain walls.

When a ferromagnetic core is placed within a magnetic field, the domain walls begin to move slowly. Wall movement increases with field strength. After a certain field strength, all the atomic moments become aligned preferentially relative to the applied field. This process can be observed using microscopy. If the applied magnetic field is rapidly increased, the domain walls jump from their "rest" position and continue to move until they encounter an obstacle. Such jumps or abrupt changes are referred to as the Barkhausen effect. With the proper equipment, these jumps can be observed and filmed. With certain ferromagnetic materials, the domains can rotate under high applied field strengths to the field direction. When the wall movements, jumps, and domain rotations are complete, the material is "saturated," that is, the maximum level of magnetization is obtained. However, temperature influences the saturation value, with a maximum at absolute zero and essentially none at the Curie temperature. For any given temperature, the magnitude of saturation depends on the composition of the material and its crystal structure.

## Observation of Domains

Numerous techniques are commonly used to observe domain structures; several are used less frequently. The more prevalent methods include the Bitter technique, the magneto-optical Kerr and Faraday methods, Lorentz electron microscopy, scanning electron microscopy (SEM), and x-ray topography. Interferometry and holographic procedures have also been used. These procedures are detailed in Ref 4 and 24 to 30.

**Bitter Patterns.** The oldest and most widely used procedure for studying domains is the powder pattern technique, or Bitter method, developed in 1931 (Ref 31, 32). Magnetite (Fe₃O₄) powder has been used as a colloid (Ref 33). The importance of proper surface preparation and use of electropolishing to produce strain-free surfaces have been established (Ref 34-36). The technique as well as methods for preparing ferromagnetic colloids have been further developed (Ref 4, 37-42). Ferrofluid, a commercially available ferromagnetic colloidal solution, is sometimes used (Ref 43). Optical microscopy procedures for the use of these colloidal suspensions have been documented (Ref 44, 45).

The modified Elmore suspension contains small aggregates of Fe₃O₄ particles (Ref 4, 41). The average diameter of the aggregates has been estimated at 0.1 μm. The individual particles are approximately 0.01 μm in diameter (Ref 46, 47). Ferrofluid contains particles smaller than 0.03 μm and is available as an organic or aqueous suspension. The density is 10¹⁸ particles per cubic centimeter. Additional information on the uses of Ferrofluid is available in the Appendix "Magnetic Etching" to the article "Etching" in this Volume.

To use this method, the specimen must first be carefully polished to minimize residual stresses and artifacts. Final polishing by electropolishing is recommended. A small drop of Ferrofluid, approximately 5 μL, is placed on the surface, and a cover slip is placed over the drop to produce a very thin film. A magnetic coil or yoke around the specimen is desired. Observation is conducted under bright-field or dark-field illumination using a standard metallurgical microscope. Upright and inverted incident-light microscopes have been used with magnifications to several hundred times (see the article "Optical Microscopy" for descriptions and illustrations of standard metallurgical microscopes).

In using the Bitter method, the surface chosen for examination should contain at least one easy axis of magnetization. This facilitates analysis of the domain patterns. When conditions are favorable, the colloid particles will be attracted to the domain walls and produce a well-defined pattern. The

**Table 5  Electropolishing procedures for preparing TEM thin foils**

| Material | Solution | Conditions |
|---|---|---|
| Iron | 5 mL HClO₄ and 100 mL glacial acetic acid | Window method. Use stainless steel cathode, 35-45 V dc, 0.7 A/cm² (4.5 A/in.²), <30 °C (85 °F) |
| Silicon iron electrical steel | 19 mL HNO₃, 1 mL HCl, 80 mL methanol | Jet polish, −50 °C (−60 °F), 30 V dc |
| Silicon iron electrical steels | 135 mL glacial acetic acid | Pointed stainless steel cathode, 25-30 V dc, 0.1-0.2 A/cm² (0.65-1.3 A/in.²), <30 °C (85 °F) |
| 50Fe-50Co | 27 g CrO₃ and 7 mL H₂O | |
| Iron and nickel alloys | 10 mL HClO₄ and 90 mL glacial acetic acid | Jet polish. For iron use 12-13 V dc; for nickel alloys use 30 V dc |
| Nickel alloys | 5 mL HClO₄ and 95 mL ethanol | 18-20 V dc, 0 °C (32 °F) |
| Nickel-iron | 40 mL H₃PO₄, 35 mL H₂SO₄, 24 mL H₂O | Pointed electrode or window method. Use 8-9 V dc, 30 °C (85 °F), stainless steel cathode. |
| Nickel alloys | 320 mL ethanol, 100 mL iso-butanol, 80 mL HClO₄ | Jet polish. Use 150-350 mA/cm² (0.97-2.3 A/in.²). |
| High-nickel alloys | 23 mL HClO₄ and 77 mL acetic acid | Window method. Use stainless steel cathode, 20-30 V dc, 0.7 A/cm² (4.5 A/in.²), 30 °C (85 °F) |
| Alnico 5 | 20 mL HClO₄ and 80 mL ethanol | Use pointed platinum wire cathode, −20 to −50 °C (−5 to −60 °F), 35 V dc, 0.2 A/cm² (1.5 A/in.²). |
| Alnico 5 | 4 mL HClO₄ and 96 mL glacial acetic acid | Use at 80 V dc, 0.6-1.2 A/cm² (4-8 A/in.²). |
| Iron-cobalt-vanadium (2-3% V) | 22 mL HClO₄, 118 mL iso-butanol, 390 mL methanol | Window method. Use at −20 °C (−5 °F), 20 V dc. |
| Cobalt-iron; iron-cobalt-vanadium (2-3% V) | 20 mL HClO₄ and 80 mL methanol | Jet polish −20 to −30 °C (−5 to −20 °F) |
| SmCo₅ | (a) 10 mL HCl and 90 mL H₂O<br>(b) 15 mL HClO₄ and 85 mL glacial acetic acid | Jet polish with (a) at 50 V dc.<br>Electropolish to perforation with (b) at 10 V dc, ion bombardment around perforation |

specimen surface may be coated with a thin layer of collodion before adding the colloidal suspension (Ref 47). The collodion layer thickness produces first-order interference colors and protects the specimen surface from staining by the colloidal suspension.

The $Fe_3O_4$ particles are attracted to the domain walls that intersect the specimen surface and form dark lines. The atomic magnets in the domain wall are not all parallel to the surface as in the adjacent domains. Because the domain wall is a transition zone between the two adjacent domains, poles (north or south) exist that attract the magnetic particle in the suspension.

In addition to domain walls, other irregularities in the magnetic structure can be observed, for example, grain boundaries, impurities, or dislocations. Bitter patterns display a wide variety of detail. One interesting pattern form exhibits a "tree" or chevron pattern, which results when a cube plane is nearly parallel to the surface (Ref 40). Another is the "spike" domain pattern that occurs at inclusions on the surface. Domain walls are attracted to inclusions that exert a pinning force, which becomes more effective as the magnetic anisotropy force of the material increases. The most effective inclusions for pinning are those whose size is on the same order as the domain-wall thickness. Much smaller or larger inclusions have less influence.

Grain and twin boundaries also interrupt the domain structure. As grain size increases and the surface area per unit volume of the grain boundaries decreases, reversal of magnetization becomes easier. However, a fine grain size and a high number of domain walls is sometimes desired. Therefore, depending on application, a certain grain size will be optimum. For example, a fine grain size is desirable for permanent magnets. For soft magnetic materials, a coarse grain size is usually advantageous, as is a low inclusion content.

Polycrystalline ferromagnetic materials may have randomly oriented grains, or may exhibit a well-defined crystallographic texture (see the article "Textured Structures" in this Volume). If the texture is high, the domains in a polycrystalline specimen may exhibit characteristics much like those of a single crystal. In a few such cases, domains have been observed to be continuous over more than one grain. For a randomly oriented material, each grain acts as a single crystal so that the properties are averaged with respect to each grain orientation.

The colloid technique has several limitations and disadvantages. First, only surface domains are observed. Second, the surface should be oriented so that low-index crystal planes are examined. Certain materials, for example, some nickel-iron alloys with low magnetocrystalline anisotropy, cannot be studied using this method, because the domain walls are wide and the low field intensities above the walls do not attract the colloid particles. Other limitations include a limited

temperature range (experiments have been conducted from $-90$ to $380\ °C$, or $-130$ to $715\ °F$), poor pattern quality for high-coercivity materials using high fields, and examination of only static or slowly moving domain structures. The Bitter method cannot be applied to coated, highly oriented silicon-iron electrical steels. An alternate technique (Ref 48) has been developed and refined (Ref 49). Despite these problems, the method remains one of the best procedures for studying domain structures on a wide range of materials.

Improved resolution of Bitter patterns can be obtained with optical or electron microscopy through use of a dry Bitter method procedure (Ref 46, 50, 51). A dry Bitter technique for optical microscopy has also been described (Ref 52).

**Magneto-Optical Faraday Effect.** When plane-polarized light is passed through a ferromagnetic material, the light is rotated by the magnetic component parallel to the direction of light transmittance. The degree of rotation varies with the magnitude of magnetization, and the sense of the rotation is influenced by the magnetization direction.

This effect has been incorporated into study of domains in a thin nickel-iron film (Ref 53). Because the magnetization directions are in the plane of the film, the film was inclined 45° to the light path. A telescope system with a rotatable analyzer adjusted for optimum contrast was used to observe the domains. To obtain transmittance through metal films, the specimen must be thinner than 0.2 $\mu m$. This restriction is a major disadvantage for metals, but it has been used to examine domains in hexagonal ferrites, which will transmit light with thicknesses to approximately 100 $\mu m$ (Ref 54), and in ferrimagnetic garnets (Ref 55) and other transparent oxides (Ref 56).

Preparation of specimens for observation by the Faraday effect is time consuming. The thin metal films discussed in the above study of domains were made by evaporation (Ref 53). Results of observations of such specimens may be of limited value, because the magnetic anisotropy forces of such films are not the same as for bulk samples. Preparation of ferrimagnetic garnets begins by cutting a thin slice from a bulk sample after the crystal orientation is determined by x-ray procedures (Ref 55). Both sides are ground and polished flat and parallel in much the same way as for double-polished mineralogical thin sections. Final polishing is performed by extended lapping with 0.25-$\mu m$ diamond abrasive. A hot stage has been used to observe the ferrimagnetic garnets up to the Curie temperature, at which magnetic contrast was lost (Ref 55).

Use of a high-resolution microscope to examine thin specimens by the Faraday effect and the Kerr effect has been discussed (Ref 57). Modifications to this technique include an electromagnet to study the domains under the influence of strong fields approaching saturations (Ref 54). In addition, a photomultiplier has been incorporated into the sys-

tem to measure intensity variations when the specimen is cycled (Ref 58).

**Magneto-Optical Kerr Effect.** When plane-polarized light is reflected from a metal surface, it is elliptically polarized, except when the incident plane is a symmetry plane, which results in plane-polarized reflected light. However, if the specimen is magnetized, the reflected light is always elliptically polarized, because the magnetic field produces the Kerr component, which removes any influence from crystal symmetry. The net result is a rotation of the plane of polarization of the reflected light rays. However, the degree of rotation is much smaller than that observed using transmitted light by the Faraday effect.

Three forms of the Kerr effect are possible with respect to the incident plane and reflecting surface plane. The polar Kerr effect provides the most rotation of the plane of polarization and arises when magnetization is perpendicular to the reflecting surface. The polar effect, however, is limited to materials with high uniaxial anisotropy. The longitudinal Kerr effect produces approximately one fifth the rotation of the polar effect and arises when magnetization is in the plane of incidence. Rotation of the plane of polarization is zero when the specimen surface is perpendicular to the incident light and maximum when the specimen is 60° to the incident light. In the transverse Kerr effect, magnetization is in the reflecting surface plane but also in a plane perpendicular to the incident light. Rotation of the plane of polarization does not occur, but there are reflectivity differences in the light polarized in the incident plane. Contrast from the longitudinal and transverse Kerr effects is similar.

Of these methods, the polar Kerr effect was the first used to examine domain structures during study of the basal plane of a cobalt single crystal (Ref 59). The polar Kerr effect and the hot stage microscope have been used to examine manganese-bismuth films (Ref 60). The polar Kerr effect has been implemented to inspect domain structures in several orthoferrites (Ref 61). Few studies of domains have been conducted using the transverse Kerr effect. The transverse Kerr effect has been used to study domains in vapor-deposited nickel-iron films using a phase-adjusting arrangement to improve image contrast substantially (Ref 62).

Use of the longitudinal Kerr effect to examine domains first took place in a study of 180° domain walls on a silicon-iron crystal (Ref 63). In this work, the specimen was inclined 60° to the incident light source, which produced a rotation of the plane of polarization of approximately 4' of arc. Therefore, image brightness and contrast between domains was low. In addition, light scattered from surface imperfections was present and obscured detail.

Contrast can be improved to approximately 1° of rotation by vacuum deposition of a quarter-wavelength dielectric coating after specimen preparation (Ref 64). This procedure is similar to the Pepperhoff method for improving contrast differences between phases (see the article "Color Metallography" in this Volume). Zinc sulfide has been chiefly used for this purpose. The layer is deposited until reflectivity is decreased approximately 50% and a deep purple macroscopic color is produced. The influence of zinc sulfide coating thickness on the Kerr effect using nickel-iron films has been studied (Ref 65).

The limitations of the longitudinal Kerr magneto-optical effect have been examined in depth, reaching the conclusion that the major problem is the ellipticity produced by reflection from the metallic surface (Ref 66). It was determined that image contrast could be maximized by compromising between rotation and ellipticity, with maximum contrast occurring with a specimen inclination angle of approximately 20° and a beam divergence of approximately 10°. These ideas were used to design a new Kerr instrument (Ref 67). Further improvements led to a resolution of approximately 1.7 $\mu$m for the Kerr effect (Ref 57). A stroboscopic light source has been used to photograph magnetization reversals (Ref 68, 69).

Specimen preparation is the most critical factor in producing good images by the Kerr effect (Ref 69). The specimen surface must be prepared strain-free, scratch-free, and flat. Strain, if excessive, alters the domain structure, and scratches and surface undulations reduce contrast. A preparation procedure has been outlined for grain-oriented (3% Si) steel (Ref 69). Samples are sheared to size, deburred, and flattened by heating for 2 h at 1150 °C (2100 °F) in dry hydrogen. The specimen is mounted on a flat polishing block and wet ground with light pressure using a series of finer grade papers. Polishing is performed using simultaneous electrolytic and mechanical polishing (electromechanical polishing) or alternate electrolytic and mechanical polishing. Finally, the specimen is stress-relief annealed 2 h at 800 °C (1475 °F) in dry hydrogen, then coated with zinc sulfide. A similar preparation technique has been described for examination by the Kerr effect (Ref 70).

**Lorentz Microscopy.** Thin foils of ferromagnetic materials can be examined in the transmission electron microscope using a technique known as Lorentz microscopy. In such work, the electron beam of the microscope interacts with the magnetic field of the specimen to permit examination of the domain structure at high magnification and high resolution. At the same time, the fine structure of the material can also be examined. The technique was developed using nickel-iron thin films (Ref 71, 72).

Two procedures have been used in Lorentz microscopy. In the first technique, the objective lens is not used, except to produce movement of the domain walls. The condenser lens is overfocused, and the projector lens is adjusted to produce an out-of-focus shadow image of the specimen in the projector focal plane and a screen image at 300 to 400×.

The domain walls appear as alternate light and dark lines. In the second technique, the transmission electron microscope is operated in a more conventional manner that permits higher resolutions and magnifications. However, because of the high magnetic field of the objective lens, lower beam currents are used. The objective lens produces a virtual object plane above the specimen at the projector lens focal plane. Varying the accelerating potential is used to focus the image at the screen. If the microscope is focused on the specimen, magnetic contrast is not observed. A small defocusing distance is required to observe the domains.

The high magnetic field of the objective lens can be controlled in other ways. A specimen holder is available that raises the foil approximately 5 mm (0.2 in.) closer to the electron beam (Ref 73). Again, lower currents are required at the objective lens, but high magnification and resolution can be obtained. An electrostatic transmission electron microscope has been used to avoid the high magnetic field of the objective lens (Ref 74). In this work, a knife edge is inserted from one side at the back focal plane of the intermediate lens or objective lens. This blocks image detail from some of the domains, producing magnetic contrast referred to as Foucault contrast. Difficulty in positioning the knife edge makes the method inconvenient.

Reviews of the Lorentz TEM procedures and examples of its application can be found in Ref 75 and 76. Other techniques, such as differential phase contrast electron microscopy (Ref 77), interference electron microscopy (Ref 78-80), and electron holography (Ref 80, 81), are currently being applied to the study of magnetic materials.

**Scanning Electron Microscopy.** The scanning electron microscope, one of the most useful metallographic instruments, has various operating modes that are useful for studying magnetic materials (see the article "Scanning Electron Microscopy" in this Volume). Domain structures can also be examined by development of magnetic contrast. Although a number of such contrast mechanisms have been discovered, two procedures are most often used. These are referred to as Type I and Type II magnetic contrast. They arise from different effects, and each is useful for certain magnetic materials. Both types of contrast are produced by the Lorentz force experienced by an electron passing through a magnetic field.

*Type I magnetic contrast* arises from the presence of a leakage field above the specimen surface and was first observed in studies of magnetic recording tape, recording heads, and cobalt (Ref 82-84). The leakage field alters the initial direction of secondary electrons emitted from the surface. Depending on the magnetic orientation of the domains, the secondary electrons are deflected toward or away from the collector, producing magnetic contrast. Type I magnetic contrast is ob-

served only in uniaxial materials having strong leakage fields.

Because Type I magnetic contrast is produced above the specimen, contrast is not observed in the specimen current mode. In addition, the high-energy backscattered electrons are not significantly influenced by the leakage field, and contrast is not observed in the backscattered mode. Type I contrast is observed only with secondary electron images, obtaining reasonably good contrast, which can be improved by altering the detector orientation to reduce the collection efficiency of the Everhart-Thornley secondary electron detector. Varying the accelerating potential has little influence on the contrast, but low potentials, which produce a greater yield of secondary electrons, are preferred due to a better signal-to-noise ratio. Placing a diaphragm over the detector also enhances contrast (Ref 85).

Resolution of domain structures using Type I magnetic contrast varies with the material studied from approximately 1 $\mu$m for cobalt to 45 $\mu$m for YFeO$_3$ (Ref 86). The contrast produced, however, is not as sharp as that obtained using the Kerr effect. Despite this limitation, the technique has many advantages (Ref 86), such as simple specimen preparation, good depth of focus, performance of dynamic experiments, observation of surface and internal domain structure, reasonably good resolution for many materials, and ease in interpreting results. The scanning electron microscope can also be used to study general features of the microstructure. Chemical details of features can be obtained by energy-dispersive spectroscopy.

*Type II magnetic contrast* is observed in magnetic uniaxial materials and in magnetic materials with cubic anisotropy, such as silicon-iron electrical steels. Type II contrast was first observed in a study of iron (Ref 87). Details of Type II contrast have been discussed (Ref 88). Type II magnetic contrast arises from interaction of the internal magnetic field with the electrons from the beam that are scattered within the specimen. High beam potentials of 30 keV or greater are used. The specimen must be tilted with respect to the beam (angles of 50 to 64° have been used) and rotated about its surface normal until maximum contrast is obtained (Ref 89-92). Because the contrast is weak, the beam current must exceed 100 nA. The contrast can be observed in the backscattered electron mode or in the specimen current mode; secondary electron images do not detect Type II contrast. Signal processing must be used to enhance the weak contrast to a visible level. Beam probe size limits resolution.

Most of the SEM work with Type II magnetic contrast has concerned domain structures in silicon irons, although other magnetic materials have been examined using high-voltage scanning electron microscopes. Type II magnetic contrast is one of few contrast modes that improve with increasing potential. Although many commercial scanning electron microscopes can be obtained with potentials to 50 keV, a few special instruments have been made with potentials to 200 keV. For example, the domain structures of coated silicon iron can be observed directly and, by changing the accelerating potential, as a function of depth. Examples of high-voltage SEM domain studies are provided in Ref 93 to 96. References 93 and 95 discuss the experimental procedure and optimization of image contast.

## Microstructures of Magnetically Soft Materials

The most commonly used soft magnetic metals are the low-carbon steels (for example, AISI 1006 or 1008), the silicon-iron electrical steels, iron-nickel and iron-cobalt alloys, ferrites (manganese-zinc and nickel-zinc ferrites in particular), and garnets.

**Electrical Steels.** Low-carbon, magnetic-lamination-quality electrical steels have a randomly oriented grain structure, and their microstructures are identical to those of low-carbon sheet steels (see the article "Carbon and Alloy Steels" in this Volume). These alloys are ferritic, containing minor amounts of cementite and inclusions.

Low-carbon ($\leq 0.08\%$) electrical steels contain additions of phosphorus (0.03 to 0.15%) and manganese (0.25 to 0.75%) to increase electrical resistivity, which subsequently reduces eddy current losses. These steels are subjected to a decarburization anneal, which also increases grain size. Oxygen and sulfur increase core loss, but grain size and texture variations have only a small influence on the core loss of magnetic lamination steels (Ref 98).

Silicon-iron electrical steels are flat-rolled sheet with low carbon contents, frequently less then 0.005%. The nonoriented grades have low sulfur levels, often below 0.01%; the oriented grades use sulfides and/or nitrides to improve grain orientation by promoting secondary recrystallization.

Nonoriented silicon iron electrical steels, which are covered in ASTM Standards A 677 (Ref 99) and A 683 (Ref 100), have silicon contents from 0.5 to 3.25%, with up to approximately 0.5% Al added to the highest quality grades. They are available in the semiprocessed (user performs the decarburization/recrystallization/grain growth anneal) or fully processed condition. Semiprocessed steels exhibit improved magnetic properties, because the anneal relieves stresses produced by shearing and punching the laminations.

The magnetic properties of nonoriented steels are improved by reducing the thickness, increasing the silicon and aluminum contents (increases resistivity), obtaining an optimum grain size, and reducing the impurity content. Increasing the grain size reduces core losses up to a critical grain size, but further grain growth produces no further improvement while reducing permeability (Ref 101). The optimum grain size for a 2.89% Si, 0.43% Al nonoriented steel with relatively high impurity (sulfur, oxygen, and nitrogen) levels is approximately 50 $\mu$m (Ref 101).

A study of nonoriented silicon irons with very low impurity contents revealed that the optimum grain size for minimum core loss varies with silicon content (Ref 102). At 1.85% Si, the optimum grain size was approximately 100 $\mu$m; at 3.25% Si, it was approximately 150 $\mu$m. Low residual levels of sulfur ($<$30 ppm), oxygen ($<$20 ppm), and nitrogen ($<$30 ppm) were found to be necessary to obtain minimum core losses. For semiprocessed nonoriented silicon-iron electrical steels, additions of antimony (0.04%) produced strong (100) texture after processing.

In a similar study of high-quality nonoriented silicon-iron electrical steel, zirconium nitrides restricted grain growth, resulting in high core loss (Ref 103). They also encountered high core loss due to oxidation of the subsurface by the annealing atmosphere, which produced aluminum nitride (AlN) and $Al_2O_3$ and restricted grain growth at the surface.

For rotating machinery applications, development of an (001) [$uvw$] texture in low carbon steel (commercial black plate) improves properties. In this texture, the cube plane is parallel to the sheet surface, but the cube edges are randomly oriented in the sheet surface (Ref 104, 105). Therefore, magnetic properties are better than in nonoriented irons.

The magnetocrystalline anistropy of iron is reduced slightly by the addition of silicon, but the [100] direction remains the easy direction of magnetization. Although the benefits of adding silicon to iron have been known since 1900, it was not until 1933 that Goss (U.S. Patent No. 1,965,559) developed a procedure to align preferentially the [100] directions of the grains in the rolling direction (Ref 106). This texture, known as the cube-on-edge (COE) or Goss texture, is a (110) [001] texture that has been widely exploited commercially to produce high-permeability, low-loss silicon-iron electrical steels (Ref 107). Subsequent experimentation demonstrated the technical possibility of developing a texture having the [001] direction parallel to the rolling direction and orienting the (100) plane parallel to the rolling plane (Ref 108). This texture has been referred to as a cube texture, cubex, or four-square texture. Its commercial availability is limited.

The COE silicon-iron electrical steels have been in commercial production since about 1940. These steels include manganese sulfide to inhibit primary grain growth and develop the COE texture by secondary recrystallization (Ref 109). Beginning in the mid-1960s, considerable progress has been made in improving texture, reducing core losses, and raising permeability. The first development was the introduction of the HI-B process by Nippon Steel (U.S. Patent No. 3,287,183) to improve the Goss texture (Ref 110-112). This was achieved by use of AlN for normal grain growth inhibition prior to secondary recrystallization plus a high degree of cold reduction (typically 80 to 90%) in the final step before annealing. Such steels also contain a minor amount of sulfur. Following the last hot-rolling step, the hot band is cooled to approximately 800 °C (1470 °F), then water quenched. This produces a fine dispersion of manganese sulfide (MnS) with sizes of 0.05 to 0.08 $\mu$m (Ref 113). Because of the high final cold reduction, grain growth cannot be inhibited by the MnS alone, but requires a second AlN addition.

The desired fine AlN particle size is also obtained by the final hot-band reduction. Texture is further improved if a hard second phase, such as martensite, is present in small amounts (1 to 10%) before the final cold-reduction step (Ref 114). If the martensite is tempered before the final cold-reduction step, the texture is not favorable. Following the cold-rolling step, the sheet is subjected to a decarburization anneal at approximately 800 °C (1470 °F), then is annealed in a hydrogen atmosphere at approximately 1200 °C (2190 °F) to produce secondary recrystallization, denitriding, and desulfurization (Ref 113). Grain sizes are generally 10 to 20 mm (0.4 to 0.8 in.)

Other improved grain-oriented silicon-iron electrical steels use additions of antimony or boron to inhibit primary recrystallization. These steels also contain MnS (the grain-growth inhibitor in the circa 1940 COE steels), and some also contain manganese selenides. Antimony and boron inhibit primary grain growth due to their segregation to the grain boundaries, which produces a solute drag influence. A wide range of sulfides, carbides, and nitrides have been evaluated for their influence in promoting COE texture during secondary recrystallization (Ref 115).

Streaks of poorly oriented grains in oriented silicon-iron electrical steels containing 3% Si can degrade magnetic properties (Ref 116). These streaks consist of smaller grains that do not have the usual (110) [001] orientation. The percentage of these fine, nonoriented grains increases with average core loss. The fine-grained regions contain approximately three times as many glassy silicate inclusions that were much longer than in the coarse-grained oriented regions. These inclusions prevent the occurrence of recrystallization during the final process anneal, which results in small, poorly oriented grains after secondary recrystallization.

Grain-oriented silicon-iron electrical steels have also been the subject of many studies of domain structures. These studies have led to improved properties. Shilling and Houze have prepared a comprehensive survey of magnetic properties and domain structures in these materials (Ref 29). Core losses are influenced by domain-wall spacing and mobility, which depend on grain size, stress, and defect structure. Tensile stresses in the rolling direction increase losses; stress coatings have been developed to exploit this effect and reduce core losses (Ref 117).

In general, a reduction of the domain size produces lower core losses. This can be accomplished by reducing grain size or by applying a tensile stress in the rolling direction. However, any applied coating must have a smooth surface, because a rough coating surface leads to decreased domain-wall mobility. In commercial COE silicon-iron electrical steels, the grain sizes are much larger than the sheet thickness, and the domains are large. Reduction of the grain size using secondary recrystallization processes, as described above, is difficult. An alternate approach involves use of primary recrystallization to produce the COE texture with grain sizes about the same size as the sheet thickness (Ref 118, 119).

**Nickel-Iron Alloys.** The nickel-iron soft magnetic alloys are the most ductile and most versatile soft magnetic alloys currently in use. Compared to silicon-iron electrical steels, they exhibit much higher permeabilities and lower core losses. Their exceptional ductility permits production of thin foil or wire shapes. Additionally, a large number of elements can enter into solid solution, permitting tailoring of their magnetic and physical properties. Three ranges of nickel content are used as soft magnetic alloys: 36% Ni for maximum resistivity, 50% Ni for maximum saturation magnetization, and 80% Ni for optimum initial and maximum permeabilities. Further iron-nickel alloys containing 6 to 12% Ni have been developed as substitutes for 2V-Permendur (49C-49Fe-2V) for telephone applications. Of the above alloys, the 50% and 80% Ni alloys are most widely used commercially.

Many of these alloys are modified using additions of molybdenum, silicon, manganese, copper, or chromium to produce specific magnetic properties. Alloys in the range of 50 to 65% Ni can be annealed in a magnetic field to produce an easy axis of magnetization and a substantial increase in permeability. Grain-oriented (001) [100] cube-texture 50Ni-50Fe alloys are also produced for applications requiring a square hysteresis loop. As with the silicon-iron electrical steels, high-temperature annealing in dry hydrogen is performed to reduce the carbon, sulfur, and oxygen contents, which greatly improves magnetic properties, especially permeability.

The nickel-iron alloys with 36% or more Ni are austenitic single-phase alloys and exhibit numerous annealing twins due to low stacking-fault energies. Their microstructures are similar to those of austenitic stainless steels. The recently developed iron-nickel alloys containing 6 to 12% Ni are annealed in the two-phase region (650 °C, or 1200 °F, for 6% Ni; 550 °C, or 1020 °F, for 12% Ni) and contain ferrite and martensite and perhaps up to 2% retained austenite.

**Iron-Cobalt Alloys.** The soft magnetic iron-cobalt alloys exhibit high saturation magnetization, a high Curie temperature, and low crystalline anisotropy. Their use, however, has been limited due to the high cost of cobalt and the brittleness of alloys at 35 to 50% Co. These alloys order rapidly upon cooling below 730 °C (1345 °F), which induces extreme brittleness.

**Iron-Cobalt-Vanadium Alloys.** Iron-cobalt alloys containing 2 to 3% V have magnetic properties intermediate to those of the soft iron-cobalt binary alloys and the hard iron-cobalt-vanadium alloys containing 14% V and are more properly classified as semihard magnetic alloys. Iron-cobalt alloys containing 2 to 3% V are much more ductile than the binary Fe-50Co alloy. The embrittlement problems of these alloys have been reviewed (Ref 120, 121).

The physical metallurgy of iron-cobalt alloys containing 2 to 3% V has been studied in depth (Ref 120-127). Heating at 900 to 950 °C (1650 to 1740 °F) produces a two-phase structure, bcc $\alpha_1$ and fcc $\gamma$. Rapid cooling yields $\alpha_1$ and supersaturated bcc $\alpha_2$. Increasing the temperature in this range provides an increased amount of $\gamma$, which results in more $\alpha_2$ upon quenching. Slow cooling from the all-$\gamma$ region produces only $\alpha_2$, which is brittle. The two-phase mixture of $\alpha_1$ and $\alpha_2$ is ductile enough to permit drawing. If the quench rate from the two-phase region is not fast enough, the $\alpha_1$ bcc structure will order, forming $\alpha_1'$, which is very brittle. Heating at 925 °C (1695 °F) produces approximately equal amounts of $\alpha_1$ and $\alpha_2$, which results in optimum magnetic properties after a subsequent precipitation anneal at 600 to 610 °C (1110 to 1130 °F). This anneal produces submicron-size particles of stable cobalt-rich and vanadium-rich fcc $\gamma$ by the decomposition of supersaturated $\alpha_2$ into ordered $\alpha_1'$ and $\gamma$. This increases strength, but results in brittle cleavage fractures rather than ductile fractures that are produced prior to annealing. The favorable magnetic properties result from the fine dispersion of stable $\gamma$ particles that impede domain-wall motion.

**Ferrites** are powder-made products of the cubic spinel crystal structure, the cubic garnet type, or the hexagonal type. The cubic spinel types, also called ferrospinels, have the general formula $MFe_2O_4$, where M is a divalent metal ion with an ionic radius between 0.06 and 0.1 nm (0.6 and 1.0 Å), for example, magnesium, iron, cobalt, nickel, copper, zinc, and cadmium. An exception is lithium ferrite, with the formula $Li_{0.5}Fe_{2.5}O_4$. The two types of ferrites are the "normal" spinel, such as $MgAl_2O_4$ or $ZnFe_2O_4$, and the "inverse" spinel, such as $NiFe_2O_4$. Solid solutions between ferrites also occur and are quite stable, for example, $MnZnFe_4O_8$ and $MnNiFe_4O_8$. The manganese-zinc ferrite is quite important commercially due to its high saturation magnetization, low losses, and relatively high Curie temperature.

The grain structure of ferrites is an important microstructural parameter. Optimum magnetic properties are obtained with very regular grain shapes of nearly equal size and sharply delineated grain boundaries. Therefore, control of the sintering temperature and time is critical. Control of the sintering atmosphere is also important. Silica is the chief impurity in manganese-zinc ferrites. As the amount of silica increases, the magnetic properties are improved, but amounts above approximately 0.04% impair magnetic properties due to discontinuous grain growth (Ref 128).

The cubic ferrites of the garnet type consist of mixed oxides, the most common being $Mn_3Al_2Si_3O_{12}$. Magnetic garnets have the general formula $3M_2O_3 \cdot 5Fe_2O_3$ or $2M_3$, where M is samarium (Sm), europium (Eu), gadolinium (Gd), terbium (Tb), dysprosium (Dy), holmium (Ho), erbium (Er), thulium (Tm), ytterbium (Yb), or yttrium (Y). Because of the nature of the M element, they are often referred to as rare-earth garnets (REG). Specific types are referred to as gadolinium-iron garnet (GdIG) or yttrium-iron garnet (YIG), which have the formulas $Gd_3Fe_5O_{12}$ and $Y_3Fe_5O_{12}$, respectively.

## Microstructures of Permanent Magnets

Permanent magnet materials differ from the soft magnetic materials in that the greatest possible coercivity is developed along with a large hysteresis loop. Coercivity is a structure-sensitive property obtained by controlling composition and processing. Permanent magnet materials can be classified as steels, precipitation alloys, cold deformation hardened alloys, superstructure alloys, dust magnets, ceramic magnets, and materials exhibiting exchange anisotropy (Ref 3). These materials can also be categorized according to structure: magnet steels, precipitation-hardened alloys, order-hardened alloys, and fine-particle magnets (Ref 129). Regarding the origin of their magnetic behavior, only two classes are pertinent: inclusion-hardened alloys and fine-particle magnets.

The earliest permanent magnet alloys were martensitic carbon steels with up to 1.5% C. Later alloys contained additions of manganese, tungsten, or chromium. These were followed by high-cobalt steels containing tungsten and chromium, then by development of iron-cobalt-molybdenum and iron-cobalt-tungsten alloys, such as Remalloy. The iron-cobalt-molybdenum alloys were the first carbon-free alloys, and all subsequent work has centered on carbon-free compositions.

In 1931, iron-nickel-aluminum alloys with high coercive forces were developed. This led to the development of the Alnico alloys, which were improved by additions of cobalt or copper and by advances in heat treatments. Next came the iron-nickel-copper (Cunife) and iron-cobalt-vanadium (Vicalloy) alloys. Further development of the Alnico alloys has produced popular grades such as Alnico 5, 8, and 9, which are still in use.

Research showed that cold work improves magnetic properties of certain alloys. For example, Vicalloy II (Fe-52Co-14V) is nearly nonmagnetic (austenitic) before cold working, but exhibits excellent hard magnetic properties after cold reduction (approximately 95%) and tempering at 600 °C (1110 °F). Permanent magnet properties can also be produced in various austenitic stainless steels by such processing as cold working, which produces ferromagnetic martensite from the paramagnetic austenite.

High coercivity is also obtained in certain binary alloys, for example, platinum-cobalt, platinum-iron, and platinum-nickel. These alloys are precipitation hardened by an ordered tetrahedral precipitate in an unordered matrix. Very high coercivity is obtained in Pt-23.3Co (Platinax II) by oil quenching from 1250 °C (2280 °F), followed by aging at 650 °C (1200 °F).

Development of powder metallurgy magnetic materials began in 1931 with the OP magnets, a mixture of $Fe_3O_4$ and cobalt oxide. This was followed by a "Heusler" alloy containing manganese and bismuth. For manganese-bismuth alloys, the magnetic phase is $Mn_3Bi_2$. The powder is mixed with a small amount of resin and molded under pressure in a magnetic field at approximately 100 °C (212 °F). Coercivity increases as the powder particle size decreases to some critical size.

Intermetallic compounds of rare-earth elements and transition metals, such as iron, nickel, and cobalt are made in the same manner. Typical rare-earth (R)/cobalt intermetallic compounds include $R_2Co_{17}$, $RCo_5$, and $R_2Co_7$. Magnetic properties of $RCo_5$ magnets ($SmCo_5$, $YCo_5$, $LaCo_5$, $CeCo_5$, and $PrCo_5$) have been discussed (Ref 130). Of these, $SmCo_5$ has exceptional properties, with energy densities nearly five times that of the best Alnico magnets. Production of $SmCo_5$ magnets, however, is rather challenging, and they are expensive.

Ceramic magnet materials, ferrites, have become very popular permanent magnet materials. Barium ferrite, $BaO \cdot 6Fe_2O_3$, has considerable commercial value. Ferrites are made by sintering blended powders. Other useful ferrites include lead ferrite and strontium ferrite. Ferrites with a preferred magnetic direction can be produced using powders that will orientate in a magnetic field.

Permanent magnets obtain their useful magnetic properties due to their domain structure, which is controlled by composition, phase distribution, particle size, and crystallographic orientation. Magnetization changes occur by rotation of the magnetization vector, not by domain-wall movements. Permanent magnets must exhibit good remanence and high coercivity with a high maximum energy product. The coercive force is increased if domain-boundary motion can be impeded or if single domain particles are created.

Domain rotation is impeded by four major types of anisotropy forces: crystalline, shape, strain, and exchange anisotropy. The crystalline anisotropy force orients the magnetization vector along a preferred easy crystallographic direction. Shape anisotropy forces cause the magnetization vector to be aligned along the major axis of elongated, single-domain particles. The remaining anisotropy forces are less effective in Alnico alloys.

**Alnico Alloys.** Precipitation-hardenable Alnico alloys in the cast conditions have a coarse-grained macrostructure that appears to be single-phase using optical microscopy. Use of electron microscopy reveals that two phases are present, including fine, rod-shaped $\alpha'$ precipitates of a bcc ferromagnetic phase in an $\alpha$ matrix, which is also bcc but weakly magnetic. The $\alpha'$ precipitates grow in the three $\langle 100 \rangle$ directions. Optimum magnetic properties are obtained by homogenization followed by reprecipitation of the $\alpha'$. For Alnico 5, the heat treatment is performed under a magnetic field aligned in the direction desired for the end use.

Homogenization of Alnico 5 has been conducted in the $\alpha$ solid-solution single-phase region at 930 °C (1705 °F) or 1300 °C (2370 °F). The former temperature must be carefully controlled; the latter is less critical, but oxidation is more of a problem. The cooling rate from the homogenization temperature must be carefully controlled in the magnetic field from either temperature down to approximately 600 °C (1110 °F). This is followed by aging from 550 to 650 °C (1020 to 1200 °F) to develop the magnetic properties. This aligns the $\alpha'$ precipitates in the direction of the applied field, producing a periodic pattern. The precipitation arises from spinodal decomposition (see the article "Spinodal Structures" in this Volume). This transformation process in Alnico alloys has been reviewed (Ref 131).

Aging is usually a two-step process to produce the iron-cobalt rich $\alpha'$ particles in the aluminum-nickel-rich $\alpha$ matrix. To obtain strong shape anisotropy, the aspect ratio of the $\alpha'$ particles must be high. Estimates of the size of the $\alpha'$ precipitates vary from 40 to 150 nm (400 to 1500 Å) in length and 7.5 to 40 nm (75 to 400 Å) in diameter.

Variation of the alloying elements in Alnico 5 can promote formation of an additional fcc $\gamma$ phase at 950 to 1200 °C (1740 to 2190 °F), as described in Ref 132. Upon cooling to room temperature, the $\gamma$ transforms to a nonmagnetic bcc phase called $\alpha_\gamma$, which is detrimental to magnetic properties. Little, if any, of this phase is present in the standard Alnico 5 composition. When present, it can be observed using the optical microscope as feathery needles around or growing from the $\alpha$ grain boundaries.

Addition of titanium, as in Alnico 5E or Alnico 6B, produces an $\varepsilon$ phase that is a modification of $Fe_2Ti$. This is an fcc precipitate ($a = 0.572$ nm, or 5.72 Å) coherent with the $\alpha'$ precipitates that increases the coercivity while decreasing the remanence. The grain size of these alloys is finer due to the presence of titanium nitride. Some manufacturers add niobium rather than titanium, which produces a hexagonal $\varepsilon$ phase, $Fe_2Nb$.

Alnico 8 contains 35% Co and 5% Ti and exhibits increased coercivity due to the $\varepsilon$ phase. Alnico 8 magnets have a finer, elongated precipitate with a higher aspect ratio, sharper delineation between the phases, and less interconnecting growth between the particles than Alnico 5. The particles are rich in iron and cobalt, and the matrix is rich in nickel, aluminum, and titanium. The structure consists of $\alpha'$ precipitates in an $\alpha$ matrix. Both are metastable body-centered tetragonal phases. Processing must be carefully controlled to obtain the optimum $\alpha'$ shape without formation of $\gamma$, which will impair magnetic properties. Columnar grains in as-cast Alnico 8 can be obtained by additions of sulfur, selenium, and tellurium.

## REFERENCES

1. B.D. Cullity, *Introduction to Magnetic Materials*, Addison-Wesley, 1972
2. S. Chikazumi, *Physics of Magnetism*, John Wiley & Sons, 1964
3. C. Heck, *Magnetic Materials and Their Applications*, Crane, Russak and Co., 1974
4. R.M. Bozorth, *Ferromagnetism*, Van Nostrand, 1951
5. J.F. Dillon, Jr., *Magnetism*, Academic Press, 1963
6. R. Boll, Ed., *Soft Magnetic Materials*, Heyden & Son, Ltd., 1978
7. R.S. Tebble and D.J. Craik, *Magnetic Materials*, Wiley-Interscience, 1969
8. C.W. Chen, *Magnetism and Metallurgy of Soft Magnetic Materials*, North-Holland, 1977
9. W. Schatt, Control of Textured Sheet by Means of Line Etching, *Pract. Metallog.*, Vol 4, Dec 1967, p 620-627
10. I. Friede, A Modification of Line Etching According to Šved using Alkaline Sodium Picate on Transformer Sheet, *Pract. Metallog.*, Vol 5, June 1968, p 325-333
11. L. Kosec *et al.*, Production of Etch Figures on Transformer Sheet, *Pract. Metallog.*, Vol 5, June 1968, p 333-337
12. H. Klemm, Uses of Sodium Thiosulphate (Klemm's Reagent) as an Etchant, *Pract. Metallog.*, Vol 5, April 1968, p 163-177
13. W. Schatt, New Investigations on Hatch-Etching, *Radex Runschau*, No. 3/4, 1967, p 657-667
14. L.J. Regitz, Simultaneous Observation of Grain Structure and Orientation in Oriented Silicon Steel, *IEEE Trans. Magnetics*, MAG-6, Sept 1970, p 576-579
15. G.F. Vander Voort, Grain Size Measurement, in *STP 839*, ASTM, Philadelphia, 1984, p 85-131
16. G.F. Vander Voort, *Metallography:*

*Principles and Practice*, McGraw-Hill, 1984

17. A. Scortecci and E. Stagno, New Metallographic Method for Revealing Magnetic Patterns in Ferrite, *Mem. Sci. Rev. Met.*, BISI No. 5569, Vol 62, 1965, p 741-746

18. K.C. Thompson-Russell and J.W. Edington, *Electron Microscope Preparation Techniques in Materials Science*, Macmillan, Philips Technical Library, 1977

19. P.J. Goodhew, *Practical Methods in Electron Microscopy*, Vol 1, *Specimen Preparation in Materials Science*, North-Holland, 1972

20. L.E. Murr, *Electron Optical Applications in Materials Science*, McGraw-Hill, 1970

21. G. Thomas and M.J. Goringe, *Transmission Electron Microscopy of Materials*, John Wiley & Sons, 1979

22. M. Von Heimendahl, *Electron Microscopy of Materials*, Academic Press, 1980

23. G.N. Maniar and A. Szirmae, *Manual on Electron Metallography Techniques*, STP 547, ASTM, Philadelphia, 1973

24. D.J. Craik and R.S. Tebble, *Ferromagnetism and Ferromagnetic Domains*, North-Holland/John Wiley & Sons, 1965

25. R. Carey and E.D. Isaac, *Magnetic Domains and Techniques for Their Observation*, Academic Press, 1966

26. D.J. Craik, Domain Theory and Observation, *J. Appl. Phys.*, Vol 38 (No. 3), 1 March 1967, p 931-938

27. M.J. Bowman and A.D. Booth, A Review of Methods for the Examination of Magnetic Domain Structure, *Metallography*, Vol 4, 1971, p 103-131

28. L.F. Bates, Ferromagnetic Domains, *Endeavour*, Vol 16, July 1957, p 151-160

29. J.W. Shilling and G.L. Houze, Jr., Magnetic Properties and Domain Structure in Grain-Oriented 3% Se-Fe, *IEEE Trans. Magnetics*, MAG-10, No. 2, June 1974, p 195-223

30. K.H. Stewart, *Ferromagnetic Domains*, Cambridge University Press, 1954

31. F. Bitter, On Inhomogeneities in the Magnetization of Ferromagnetic Materials, *Phys. Rev.*, Vol 38, 15 Nov 1931, p 1903-1905

32. F. Bitter, Experiments on the Nature of Ferromagnetism, *Phys. Rev.*, Vol 41, 15 Aug 1932, p 507-515

33. L.W. McKeehan and W.C. Elmore, Surface Magnetization in Ferromagnetic Crystals, *Phys. Rev.*, Vol 46, 1 Aug 1934, p 226-228

34. W.C. Elmore and L.W. McKeehan, Surface Magnetization and Block Structure of Ferrite, *Met. Tech.*, Vol 2, 1935, p 1-15

35. W.C. Elmore, Properties of the Surface Magnetization in Ferromagnetic Crystals, *Phys. Rev.*, Vol 51, 1937, p 982-988

36. W.C. Elmore, Ferromagnetic Colloid for Studying Magnetic Structures, *Phys. Rev.*, Vol 54, 1938, p 309-310

37. E.A.M. Harvey, Metallographic Identification of Ferro-Magnetic Phases, *Metallurgia*, Vol 32, June 1945, p 71-72

38. H.J. Williams, Direction of Domain Magnetization in Powder Patterns, *Phys. Rev.*, Vol 71, 1947, p 646

39. H.J. Williams and W. Shockley, A Simple Domain Structure in an Iron Crystal Showing a Direct Correlation with the Magnetization, *Phys. Rev.*, Vol 75, 1 Jan 1949, p 178-183

40. H.J. Williams et al., Magnetic Domain Patterns on Single Crystals of Silicon Iron, *Phys. Rev.*, Vol 75, 1 Jan 1949, p 155-178

41. C. Kittel and J.K. Galt, Ferromagnetic Domain Theory, in *Solid State Physics*, Vol 3, Academic Press, 1956, p 437-564

42. H. Pfützner, A New Colloid Technique Enabling Domain Observations of Si-Fe Sheets with Coating at Zero Field, *IEEE Trans. Magnetics*, MAG-17, No. 2, March 1981, p 1245-1247

43. Private communication, Ferrofluidics Corp., Nashua, NH

44. R.J. Gray, Magnetics Etching with Ferrofluid, in *Metallographic Specimen Preparation*, Plenum Press, 1974, p 155-177

45. K.J. Kronenberg and D. Feldmann, The Use of Variable, High Magnetic Fields for the Investigation of Magnetic Domain Structures, *Pract. Metallog.*, Vol 11, 1974, p 140-154

46. D.J. Craik, A Study of Bitter Figures Using the Electron Microscope, *Proc. Phys. Soc.*, Vol B69, 1956, p 647-650

47. J.R. Garrood, Methods of Improving the Sensitivity of the Bitter Technique, *Proc. Phys. Soc.*, Vol 79, 1962, p 1252-1262

48. K. Mohri et al., Domain and Grain Observations Using a Colloid Technique for Grain-Oriented Si-Fe with Coatings, *IEEE Trans. Magnetics*, MAG-15, Sept 1979, p 1346-1349

49. G.C. Rauch et al., Enhanced Domain Imaging Techniques, *J. Appl. Phys.*, Vol 55, 15 March 1984, p 2145-2147

50. D.J. Craik and P.M. Griffiths, A New Colloid for Use with the Bitter Figure Technique, *Proc. Phys. Soc.*, Vol B70, 1957, p 1000-1002

51. D.J. Craik and P.M. Griffiths, New Technique for the Study of Bitter Figures, *Br. J. Appl. Phys.*, Vol 9, July 1958, p 279-282, 276-277

52. C. Tanasoiu et al., A Dry Bitter Technique for High Resolution Studies of Magnetic Domains by Optical Microscopy, *Pract. Metallog.*, Vol 10, 1973, p 210-219

53. C.A. Fowler and E.M. Fryer, Magnetic Domains in Thin Films of Nickel-Iron by the Faraday Effect, *Phys. Rev.*, Vol 104 (No. 2), 1956, p 552-553

54. C. Kooy and U. Enz, Experimental and Theoretical Study of the Domain Configuration in Thin Layers of $BaFe_{12}O_{19}$, *Philips Res. Rep.*, Vol 15, 1960, p 7-29

55. J.F. Dillon, Jr., The Observation of Domains in the Ferrimagnetic Garnets by Transmitted Light, *J. Appl. Phys.*, Vol 29, Sept 1958, p 1286-1291

56. R.C. Sherwood et al., Domain Behavior in Some Transparent Oxides, *J. Appl. Phys.*, Vol 30, 1959, p 217-225

57. A. Green et al., A Polarizing Microscope for Observation of Magnetic Domains, *J. Sci. Instr.*, Vol 40 (No. 10), 1963, p 490-493

58. M.A. Jepperson and W.A. Sloan, Optical Observation of Ferrimagnetic Domains, *Am. J. Phys.*, Vol 29, 1961, p 789

59. H.J. Williams et al., Observation of Magnetic Domains by the Kerr Effect, *Phys. Rev.*, Ser. 2, Vol 82, 1 April 1951, p 119-120

60. L. Mayer, Observations on MnBi Films during Heat Treatment, *J. Appl. Phys.*, Vol 31, Feb 1960, p 346-351

61. C.A. Fowler et al., Magnetic Domains in Orthoferrites by the Kerr Effect, *J. Appl. Phys.*, Vol 34, July 1963, p 2064-2067

62. D.B. Dove, Photography of Magnetic Domains Using the Transverse Kerr Effect, *J. Appl. Phys.*, Vol 34, July 1963, p 2067-2070

63. C.A. Fowler and E.M. Fryer, Magnetic Domains on Silicon-Iron by the Longitudinal Kerr Effect, *Phys. Rev.*, Vol 86, 1 May 1952, p 426

64. M. Prutton, The Observation of Domain Structure in Magnetic Thin Films by Means of the Kerr Magneto-Optic Effect, *Philos. Mag.*, Vol 4, Sept 1959, p 1063-1067

65. P.H. Lissberger, Kerr Magneto-Optic Effect in Nickel-Iron Films, *J. Opt. Soc. Am.*, Vol 51, 1961, p 948-966

66. D. Treves, Limitations of the Magneto-Optic Kerr Technique in the Study of Microscopic Magnetic Domain Structures, *J. Appl. Phys.*, Vol 32, March 1961, p 358-364

67. C.A. Fowler et al., Observation of Domains in Iron Whiskers Under High Fields, *J. Appl. Phys.*, Vol 31, Dec 1960, p 2267-2272

68. R.L. Conger and G.H. Moore, Direct Observation of High-Speed Magnetization Reversal in Films, *J. Appl. Phys.*, Vol 34, April 1963, p 1213-1214

69. G.L. Houze, Domain-Wall Motion in Grain-Oriented Silicon Steel in Cyclic Magnetic Fields, *J. Appl. Phys.*, Vol 38, 1 March 1967, p 1089-1096

70. J.A. Salsgiver, Magnetic Domain Observations on 0.014-inch 50-Percent Ni-Fe Strip, *IEEE Trans. Magnetics*, MAG-6, No. 3, Sept. 1970, p 741-744

71. M.E. Hale et al., Magnetic Domain Observations by Electron Microscopy, *J. Appl. Phys.*, Vol 30, May 1959, p 789-791

72. H.W. Fuller and M.E. Hale, Determina-

tion of Magnetization Distribution in Thin Films Using Electron Microscopy, *J. Appl. Phys.*, Vol 31, Feb 1960, p 238-248

73. J. Silcox, Magnetic Domain Walls in Thin Films of Nickel and Cobalt, *Philos. Mag.*, Vol 8 (No. 85), Jan 1963, p 7-28

74. H.W. Fuller and M.E. Hale, Domains in Thin Magnetic Films Observed by Electron Microscopy, *J. Appl. Phys.*, Vol 31, Oct 1960, p 1699-1705

75. D. Wohlleben, Magnetic Phase Contrast, in *Electron Microscopy in Materials Science*, Academic Press, 1971, p 712-757

76. R.H. Wade, Lorentz Microscopy or Electron Phase Microscopy of Magnetic Objects, in *Advances in Optical and Electron Microscopy*, Vol 5, Academic Press, 1973, p 239-296

77. J.N. Chapman *et al.*, The Direct Determination of Magnetic Domain Wall Profiles by Differential Phase Contrast Electron Microscopy, *Ultramicroscopy*, Vol 3, 1978, p 203-214

78. G.F. Missiroli *et al.*, Electron Interferometry and Interference Electron Microscopy, *J. Phys. E., Sci. Instr.*, Vol 14, 1981, p 649-671

79. A. Tonomura, The Electron Interference Method for Magnetization Measurement of Thin Films, *Jap. J. Appl. Phys.*, Vol 11, 1972, p 493-502

80. G. Matteucci *et al.*, Interferometric and Holographic Techniques in Transmission Electron Microscopy for the Observation of Magnetic Domain Structures, *IEEE Trans. Magnetics*, MAG-20, Sept 1984, p 1870-1875

81. T. Matsuda *et al.*, Observation of Microscopic Distribution of Magnetic Fields by Electron Holography, *J. Appl. Phys.*, Vol 53, 1982, p 5444-5446

82. J.R. Banbury and W.C. Nixon, The Direct Observation of Domain Structure and Magnetic Fields in the Scanning Electron Microscope, *J. Sci. Instr.*, Vol 44, Nov 1967, p 889-892

83. D.C. Joy and J.P. Jakubovics, Direct Observation of Magnetic Domains [in Cobalt] by Scanning Electron Microscopy, *Philos. Mag.*, Vol 17, Jan 1968, p 61-69

84. J.R. Dorsey, Scanning Electron Probe Measurement of Magnetic Fields, *Adv. Electronics Electron Phys. Suppl.*, Vol 6, 1969, p 291-312

85. D.C. Joy and J.P. Jakubovics, Direct Observation of Magnetic Domains by Scanning Electron Microscopy, *J. Phys.*, Vol 2, 1969, p 1367-1375

86. G.A. Jones, Magnetic Contrast in the Scanning Electron Microscope: An Appraisal of Techniques and Their Applications, *J. Magnetism Magnetic Mater.*, Vol 8 (No. 4), 1978, p 263-285

87. J. Philibert and R. Tixier, Effects of Crystal Contrast in Scanning Electron Microscopy, *Micron*, Vol 1, 1969, p 174-186

88. D.J. Fathers *et al.*, A New Method of Observing Magnetic Domains by Scanning Electron Microscopy, *Phys. Status Solidi*, Vol 20, 16 Dec 1973, p 535-554; Vol 22, 16 April 1974, p 609-619

89. D.J. Fathers, *et al.*, Magnetic Domain Contrast from Cubic Materials in the Scanning Electron Micoscope, *Philos. Mag.*, Vol 27, March 1973, p 765-768

90. D.E. Newbury and H. Yakowitz, Magnetic Domain Studies in Iron-3¼ Weight Percent Silicon Transformer Sheet Using the Scanning Electron Microscope, in *Magnetism and Magnetic Materials—1973*, AIP Conference Proceedings No. 18, Part 2, American Institute of Physics, New York, 1974, p 1372-1376

91. H. Yakowitz and D.E. Newbury, Magnetic Domains Structures in Fe-3.2 Si Revealed by Scanning Electron Microscopy—A Photo Essay, *J. Test. Eval.*, Vol 3, Jan 1975, p 75-78

92. G. Zwilling, Observation of Magnetic Domains in the Scanning Electron Microscope, *Pract. Metallog.*, Vol 11, 1974, p 716-727

93. T. Yamamoto *et al.*, Observation of Domain Structure in Soft-Magnetic Materials by Means of High Voltage Scanning Electron Microscopy, in *Magnetism and Magnetic Materials—1975*, American Institute of Physics, New York, 1976, p 572-573

94. T. Irie and B. Fukuda, Effect of Insulating Coating on Domain Structure in Grain Oriented 3% Si-Fe Sheet as Observed with a High Voltage Scanning Electron Microscope, in *Magnetism and Magnetic Materials—1975*, American Institute of Physics, New York, 1976, p 514-575

95. T. Yamamoto *et al.*, Magnetic Domain Contrast in Backscattered Electron Images Obtained with a Scanning Electron Microscope, *Philos. Mag.*, Vol 34 (No. 2), 1976, p 311-325

96. J.D. Livingston and W.G. Morris, SEM Studies of Magnetic Domains in Amorphous Ribbons, *IEEE Trans. Magnetics*, MAG-17, No. 6, Nov 1981, p 2624-2626

97. "Standard Specification for Cold-Rolled Carbon Steel Sheet, Magnetic Lamination Quality, Types 1, 2, and 2S," A 726, in *Annual Book of ASTM Standards*, Vol 03.04, ASTM, Philadelphia, 1984, p 204-208

98. E.T. Stephenson and M.R. Amann, Effects of Composition, Grain Size and Texture on the AC Core Loss of Magnetic Lamination Steel, in *Energy Efficient Electrical Steels*, American Institute of Mining, Metallurgical, and Petroleum Engineers, New York, 1981, p 43-60

99. "Standard Specification for Flat Rolled Nonoriented Electrical Steel Fully Processed Types," A 677, in *Annual Book of ASTM Standards*, Vol 03.04, ASTM, Philadelphia, 1984, p 139-144

100. "Standard Specification for Flat-Rolled, Nonoriented Electrical Steel, Semiprocessed Grades," A 683, in *Annual Book of ASTM Standards*, Vol 03.04, ASTM, Philadelphia, 1984, p 151-156

101. R.R. Judd and K.E. Blazek, Effect of High-Temperature Annealing on the Magnetic Properties of Fully Processed Nonoriented Silicon-Steel Sheets, in *Energy Efficient Electrical Steels*, American Institute of Mining, Metallurgical, and Petroleum Engineers, New York, 1981, p 147-155

102. H. Shimanaka *et al.*, Non-Oriented Si-Steels Useful for Energy Efficient Electrical Apparatus, in *Energy Efficient Electrical Steels*, American Institute of Mining, Metallurgical, and Petroleum Engineers, New York, 1981, p 193-204

103. Y. Shimoyama *et al.*, Development of Non-Oriented Silicon Steel Sheet with Very Low Core Loss, *IEEE Trans. Magnetics*, MAG-19, Sept 1983, p 2013-2015

104. R.G. Aspden *et al.*, Anisotropic and Heterogeneous Nucleation During the Gamma to Alpha Transformation in Iron, *Acta Metall.*, Vol 16, Aug 1968, p 1027-1035

105. R.F. Krause and B.A. Popovic, Magnetic Properties of Textured Annealed Commercial Black Plate, *J. Appl. Phys.*, Vol 52, March 1981, p 2419-2421

106. N.P. Goss, New Development in Electrical Strip Steels Characterized by Fine Grain Structure Approaching the Properties of a Single Crystal, *Trans. ASM*, Vol 23, June 1935, p 511-544

107. R.M. Bozorth, The Orientation of Crystals in Silicon Iron, *Trans. ASM*, Vol 23, Dec 1935, p 1107-1111

108. F. Assmus *et al.*, Iron-Silicon Alloy With Cubic Structure, Parts I and II. *Z. Metallk.*, Vol 48, June 1957, p 341-349

109. J.E. May and D. Turnbull, Secondary Recrystallization in Silicon Iron, *Trans. AIME*, Vol 212, Dec 1958, p 769-781

110. S. Taguchi and A. Sakakura, Characteristics of Magnetic Properties of Grain-Oriented Silicon Iron with High Permeability, *J. Appl. Phys.*, Vol 40, 1 March 1969, p 1539-1541

111. A. Sakakura *et al.*, Recent Developments in Magnetic Properties of Grain-Oriented Silicon Steel with High Permeability, in *Magnetism and Magnetic Materials—1974*, AIP Conference Proceedings No. 24, American Institute of Physics, New York, 1975, p 714-715

112. S.M. Pegler, The Magnetic Properties of Japanese HI-B (110) [001] Grain-Oriented Silicon-Iron, in *Magnetism and Magnetic Materials—1974*, AIP Conference Proceedings No. 24, American In-

stitute of Physics, New York, 1975, p 718-720

113. M. Barisoni and M. Candiotti, A New High Permeability Grain Oriented Fe-3% Si Steel, *IEEE Trans. Magnetics*, MAG-14, Sept 1978, p 345-349

114. M. Barisoni *et al.*, Effect of Second Phase on the Primary and Secondary Recrystallization Texture of Grain Oriented Si-Fe Sheets, *IEEE Trans. Magnetics*, MAG-11, 1975, p 1361-1363

115. T. Matsuoka, Effect of Impurities on the Development of (110) [001] Secondary Recrystallization Texture in 3% Silicon Iron, *Trans. ISIJ*, Vol 7 (No. 1), 1967, p 19-28

116. L.J. Regitz, Origins of Streaks of Poorly Oriented Grains in Oriented Silicon Steel, *J. Met.*, Vol 23, Sept 1971, p 17-25

117. D.R.Thornburg and W.M. Swift, The Effect of Coatings on the Stress Dependent Magnetic Properties of Oriented Silicon Steel, *IEEE Trans. Magnetics*, MAG-15, 1979, p 1592-1594

118. G.C. Rauch *et al.*, Development of (110) [001] Texture in Low-Alloy Iron by Primary Recrystallization and Normal Grain Growth, *Met. Trans.*, Vol 8A, Jan 1977, p 210-212, 510, 1835

119. D.R. Thornburg *et al.*, The Effect of Manganese and Sulfur on the Development of Orientation (110) [001]-Oriented Low-Alloy Iron, *J. Appl. Phys.*, Vol 52, March 1981, p 2413-2415

120. C.W. Chen, Soft Magnetic Cobalt-Iron Alloys, *Cobalt*, No. 22, March 1964, p 3-21

121. C.W. Chen, Metallurgy and Magnetic Properties of an Fe-Co-V Alloy, *J. Appl. Phys.*, Vol 32, March 1961, p 348S-355S

122. D.R. Thornburg, High-Strength High-Ductility Cobalt-Iron Alloys, *J. Appl. Phys.*, Vol 40, 1 March 1969, p 1579-1580

123. M.R. Pinnel and J.E. Bennett, The Metallurgy of Remendur: Effects of Processing Variations, *Bell System Tech. J.*, Vol 52, Oct 1973, p 1325-1340

124. J.E. Bennett and M.R. Pinnel, Aspects of Phase Equilibria in Fe/Co/2.5 to 3.0% V. Alloys, *J. Mater. Sci.*, Vol 9, 1974, p 1083-1090

125. S. Mahajan, M.R. Pennel, and J.E. Bennett, Influence of Heat Treatments on Microstructures in an Fe-Co-V Alloy, *Met. Trans.*, Vol 5, June 1974, p 1263-1272

126. M.R. Pinnel and J.E. Bennett, Correlation of Magnetic and Mechanical Properties with Microstructure in Fe/Co/2-3Pct V Alloys, *Met. Trans.*, Vol 5, June 1974, p 1273-1283

127. M.R. Pinnel, S. Mahajan, and J.E. Bennett, Influence of Thermal Treatments on the Mechanical Properties of an Fe-Co-V Alloy (Remendur), *Acta Metall.*, Vol 24, 1976, p 1095-1106

128. G.C. Jain *et al.*, On the Origin of Core Losses in a Manganese Zinc Ferrite With Appreciable Silica Content, *J. Appl. Phys.*, Vol 49, May 1978, p 2894-2897

129. F.E. Luborsky, Permanent Magnets in Use Today, *J. Appl. Phys.*, Vol 37, 1 March 1966, p 1091-1094

130. K.H. Strnat, The Recent Development of Permanent Magnet Materials Containing Rare Earth Metals, *IEEE Trans. Magnetics*, MAG-6, 1970, p 182-190

131. K.J. DeVos, Alnico Permanent Magnet Alloys, in *Magnetism and Metallurgy*, Vol 1, Academic Press, 1969, p 473-512

132. M. Houghton, Controlling the Properties and Structure of Commercial Permanent-Magnet Materials, *J. Aus. Inst. Met.*, Vol 14, Feb 1969, p 42-52

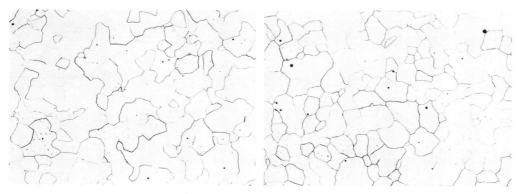

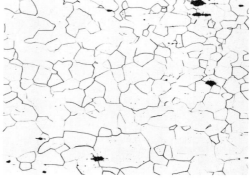

**Fig. 1, 2** Electrical iron (Fe-0.1Mn-0.1Si-0.2Cr-0.08Ni-0.05V-0.03Al) after decarburization annealing 4 h in wet hydrogen at 845 °C (1550 °F) and furnace cooling. Fig. 1: etched using 2% nital. Fig. 2: etched 2 s using 2% nital, 3 s using Marshall's reagent, then 20 s using 2% nital to develop more fully the ferrite grain boundaries. Both 100×

**Fig. 3** 1% silicon iron electrical sheet steel (M-45), cold reduced 70% to approximately 0.6 mm (0.023 in.) thick, annealed 3 min at 815 °C (1500 °F) in a moist decarburizing atmosphere. Structure is ferrite grains (ASTM grain size 6) and silicate inclusions (black). Nital. 100×

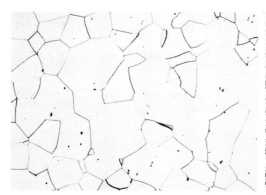

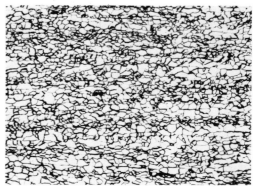

**Fig. 4** Nonoriented (C5) silicon iron (Fe-2.03Si-0.44Al). Longitudinal section shows ferrite grains. 2% nital. 100×

**Fig. 5** 2.5% Si flat-rolled electrical sheet (M-36), as continuously cold rolled to 6 mm (0.25 in.) thick—a 70% reduction. The structure is elongated ferrite grains. See also Fig. 6. 3% nital. 100×

**Fig. 6** Same material, thickness, and cold reduction as Fig. 5, but annealed 2 min at 830 °C (1525 °F). The structure consists of fine recrystallized ferrite grains. Compare with Fig. 5. 3% nital. 100×

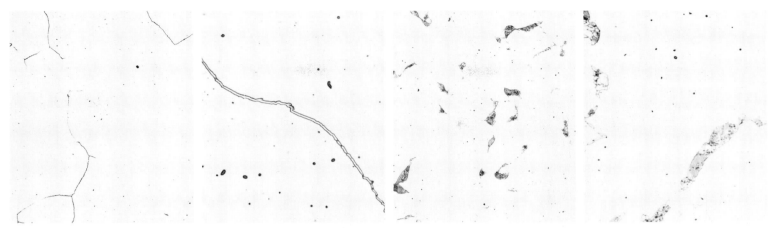

**Fig. 7, 8** Silicon core iron (Fe-0.4Mn-2.5Si-0.1P) bar, 13.5 mm (0.530 in.) in diameter, annealed 4 h in wet hydrogen at 845 °C (1550 °F) and furnace cooled. Specimen from near the surface of the bar shows thin grain-boundary films of cementite. Decarburization was incomplete. Both etched using 4% picral. Fig. 7: 100×. Fig. 8: 1000×

**Fig. 9, 10** Same material and processing as Fig. 7, but a specimen from near the center of the 13.5-mm (0.531-in.) diam bar. Patches of pearlite are typical of the predecarburization microstructure. Both etched using 4% picral. Fig. 9: 400×. Fig 10: 1000×

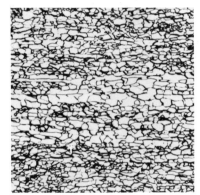

**Fig. 11** 2.5% Si flat-rolled electrical sheet (M-36), cold rolled to 6 mm (0.25 in.) thick (70% reduction), annealed 2 min at 830 °C (1525 °F), then temper rolled (10% additional reduction). Ferrite grains are slightly elongated; some compression of grains is evident at surface. 3% nital. 100×

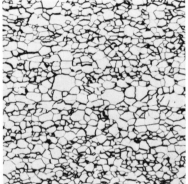

**Fig. 12** Same material, thickness, and cold reduction as Fig. 11, but annealed 2 min at 940 °C (1725 °F). The higher annealing temperature resulted in recrystallized ferrite grains that are coarser than in Fig. 11. 3% nital. 100×

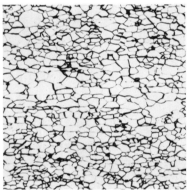

**Fig. 13** Same material, thickness, cold reduction, and annealing as Fig. 12, then temper rolled (10% additional reduction). Ferrite grains are slightly elongated; some compression is evident at the surface. 3% nital. 100×

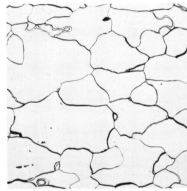

**Fig. 14** Same material, thickness, cold reduction, annealing, and temper-rolling reduction as Fig. 11, but heated to 940 °C (1725 °F) and held 2 min. The recrystallized ferrite grains are very large. 3% nital. 100×

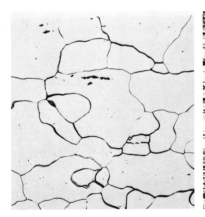

**Fig. 15** Same material, thickness, cold reduction, annealing, and temper-rolling treatment as Fig. 13, but reheated to 940 °C (1725 °F) and held 2 min. Structure: large recrystallized ferrite grains. 3% nital. 100×

**Fig. 16** 3% Si flat-rolled electrical strip (M-22), cold rolled 70% to 0.6 mm (0.025 in.) thick. Structure is ferrite grains elongated in the direction of rolling. See also Fig. 17. 10% nital. 100×

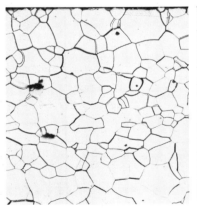

**Fig. 17** Same material, thickness, and cold reduction as Fig. 16, decarburization annealed in moist hydrogen at 815 °C (1500 °F) and annealed for grain growth in dry hydrogen at 870 °C (1600 °F). Compare with Fig. 18. 10% nital. 100×

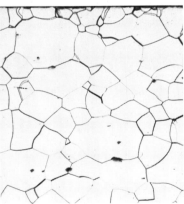

**Fig. 18** 3% Si flat-rolled electrical strip (M-22), cold rolled to ~0.6-mm (0.023 in.) (70% reduction), decarburization annealed in moist hydrogen at 815 °C (1500 °F), and annealed in dry hydrogen at 925 °C (1700 °F) for grain growth. Note large ferrite grain size. 10% nital. 100×

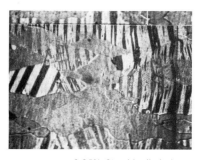

**Fig. 19** 3.25% Si cold-rolled electrical strip, 0.3 mm (0.011 in.) thick, annealed at 1175 °C (2150 °F), showing domain structure of (110) [001] oriented material with no applied field. The specimen was demagnetized at 60 Hz. Domains reveal where the deviation of [001] direction is not more than 3 or 4° from parallel. As-polished. Magnification not reported

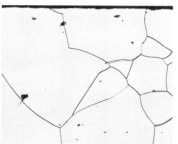

**Fig. 20** 3% Si flat-rolled electrical strip, cold reduced 70% to approximately 0.6 mm (0.025 in.) thick, decarburization annealed in moist hydrogen at 815 °C (1500 °F) and at 1040 °C (1900 °F) in dry hydrogen for grain growth. The ferrite grain size is larger than in Fig. 17 and 18. 10% nital. 100×

**Fig. 21** 3% Si flat-rolled, oriented electrical hot band, as hot rolled. Cross section from near the surface (right) to a depth of approximately 0.5 mm (0.02 in.). Hot finishing temperature was approximately 900 °C (1650 °F). The structure is ferrite grains; note difference in grain shape from near surface to near center. 10% nital. 100×

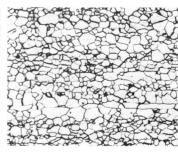

**Fig. 22** 3% Si flat-rolled oriented electrical strip, cold reduced 65% and annealed at 925 °C (1700 °F). Structure: recrystallized ferrite grains. The material is ready for final cold reduction and a grain-coarsening anneal. See also Fig. 23 and 24 for effects of further processing. 10% nital. 100×

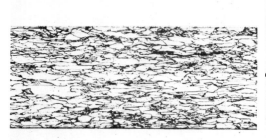

**Fig. 23** Same material as Fig. 22, but given a second cold reduction of 50% to final strip thickness. Ferrite grains are elongated, ready for the grain-coarsening anneal. See also Fig. 24. 10% nital. 100×

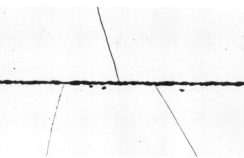

**Fig. 24** Same material and reduction as Fig. 23 after a grain-coarsening box anneal at 1095 to 1205 °C (2000 to 2200 °F) in hydrogen. The upper strip shows portions of two grains; the lower strip, one complete and two partial grains. 10% nital. 100×

**Fig. 25** 3.25% Si flat-rolled, oriented electrical strip, continuously cold rolled to 0.3 mm (0.011 in.) thick, annealed at 1175 °C (2150 °F). Macrograph shows secondary recrystallized ferrite grains with cube-on-edge orientation. 5 mL HCl, 1 mL HF, and 8 mL $H_2O$. Actual size

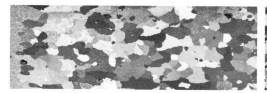

**Fig. 26** 3% Si steel, 0.35 mm (0.014 in.) thick, gradient annealed by heating to 760 °C (1400 °F) in 1 h, then at 65 °C (100 °F) per hour to 1065 °C (1950 °F) at hot end (right) in dry hydrogen and held 3 h. Secondary grain coarsening started at approximately 815 °C (1500 °F). Grain size is typical. 20% $HNO_3$, then 20% HCl (alternated). Actual size

**Fig. 27** 3% Si Steel, hot rolled to 0.35 mm (0.014 in.) thick, annealed 24 h at 1150 °C (2100 °F) in dry hydrogen. Note fine, poorly oriented grains, which are parallel to the rolling direction, in a matrix of normal, well-oriented grains. This can result from stringers of inclusions or from rolled-in scale. 5% HF, then 10% $HNO_3$. Actual size

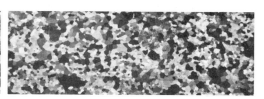

**Fig. 28** 3% Si steel, 0.3 mm (0.012 in.) thick, annealed 7.5 h in dry hydrogen at 1175 °C (2100 °F). Specimen shows abnormally small grain size, which indicates poor orientation. This may be caused by the wrong percentage of cold reduction or by heating too rapidly above 1010 °C (1850 °F). 20% $HNO_3$, then 20% HCl (alternated). Actual size

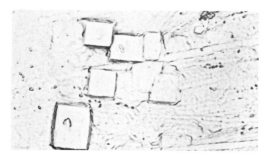

**Fig. 29** Cubic etch pits in cube-on-face grain-oriented 3% Si steel. The area seen is a single ferrite grain, obtained by annealing at 1175 °C (2150 °F) or higher. $Fe_2(SO_4)_3$. 1000×

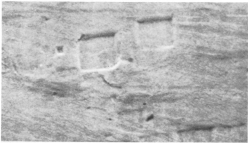

**Fig. 30** Scanning electron micrograph of cubic etch pits in cube-on-face grain-oriented 3% Si steel. The area shown is a single grain of ferrite. See also Fig. 29 and 31. $Fe_2(SO_4)_3$. 1000×

**Fig. 31** Etch pits in a 3% Si steel, showing two orientations. The hexagonal pits have cube-on-corner orientation; the others have cube-on-edge orientations. $Fe_2(SO_4)_3$. 1000×

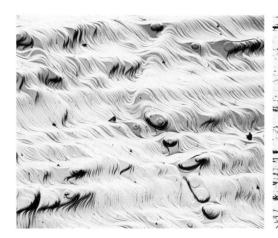

**Fig. 32** Thermal faceting and pitting of (100) planes of ferrite in 3% Si grain-oriented steel, cold rolled from 0.3 to 0.1 mm thick and annealed 3 h in dry hydrogen at 1205 °C (2200 °F). Thermal etch in hydrogen at 1205 °C (2200 °F). 100×

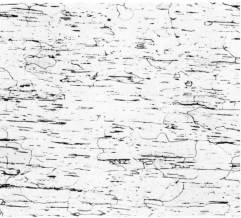

**Fig. 33** Solenoid-quality type 430FR ferritic stainless steel. Note that some of the ferrite grain boundaries were not revealed. Ralph's reagent. 100×

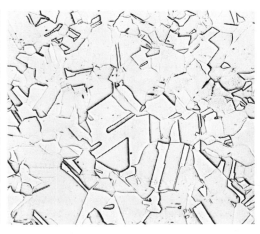

**Fig. 34** Fe-30Ni cold-rolled strip, batch annealed 6 h at 950 °C (1740 °F) and furnace cooled in dry hydrogen. Grains are coarse because carbon content was low. HCl, $CuCl_2$, $FeCl_3$, $HNO_3$, methanol, and $H_2O$. 100×

**Fig. 35, 36** Austenitic Fe-50.5Ni soft magnetic alloy, showing the effects of different etchants. Fig. 35: etched using a flat etchant, glyceregia. Fig. 36: etched using a grain contrast etchant, Marble's reagent. Both 100×. See Fig. 37 to 39 for the effects of deformation (cold rolling) and heat treatment on the structure of a similar Fe-50Ni alloy.

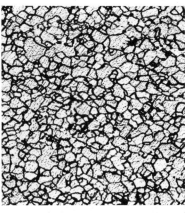

**Fig. 37** Fe-50Ni cold-rolled 0.15-mm strip, annealed 2 h in $H_2$ at 900 °C and furnace cooled. Structure: primary recrystallized grains of austenite. 60 mL ethanol, 15 mL HCl, and 5 g anhydrous $FeCl_3$. 100×

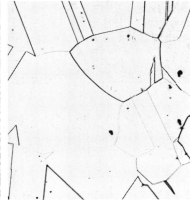

**Fig. 38** Fe-50Ni cold-rolled 0.03-mm strip, annealed 4 h at 1175 °C (2150 °F) in dry $H_2$ and furnace cooled. Structure is nonoriented primary recrystallized grains. See also Fig. 39. Saturated $(NH_4)_2S_2O_8$. 100×

**Fig. 39** Fe-50Ni cold-rolled strip, 0.03 mm (0.014 in.) thick, annealed same as Fig. 38. The structure is comprised of nonoriented secondary recrystallized grains. Thermal etch in hydrogen at 1175 °C (2150 °F). 3×

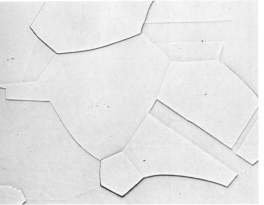

**Fig. 40** 4-79 Moly Permalloy (4Mo-79Ni-17Fe), cold-rolled strip 0.03 mm (0.014 in.) thick, annealed 4 h in dry hydrogen at 1175 °C (2150 °F) and cooled at 320 °C (575 °F) per hour to room temperature. The structure is coarse-grained austenite. HCl, $CuCl_2$, $FeCl_3$, $HNO_3$, methanol, and $H_2O$. 100×

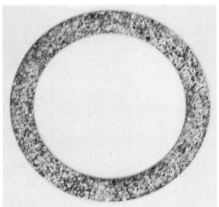

**Fig. 41** 4-79 Moly Permalloy magnetic test-ring specimen taken from 0.3-mm (0.014-in.) thick cold-rolled strip, annealed 4.5 h at 1120 °C (2050 °F) in dry hydrogen. The structure is austenite grains. Marble's reagent. 0.875×

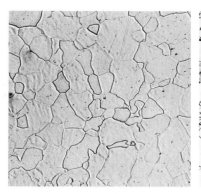

**Fig. 42** Fe-27Co cold-rolled strip, annealed 2 h in dry $H_2$ at 925 °C (1700 °F) and furnace cooled. The microstructure is ferrite solid solution. HCl, $CuCl_2$, $FeCl_3$, methanol, and $H_2O$. 100×

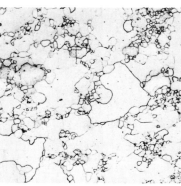

**Fig. 43** Fe-Co-1.9V alloy, annealed 2 h in wet hydrogen at 885 °C (1625 °F). A duplex ferritic grain structure. 2% nital. 50×

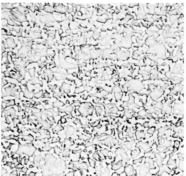

**Fig. 44, 45** Remendur 27 (Fe-Co-2.8V) wire, 0.5 mm (0.021 in.) in diameter. Structure: $\alpha_1$ and $\alpha_2$ phases. Fig. 44: bright-field illumination. Fig. 45: differential interference contrast illumination. 2% nital etches $\alpha_1$, leaving $\alpha_2$ in relief. Both 1000×

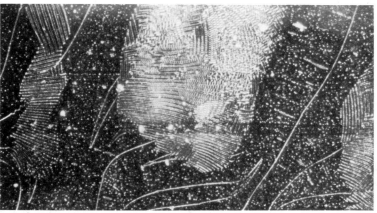

**Fig. 46** $Fe_{80}B_{18.3}P_{1.7}$ amorphous metal ribbon, as-cast. Complex magnetic domain structure resulting from the residual stress pattern produced by rapid solidification (melt spinning). The image was produced using dark-field illumination and the powder pattern technique, which is referred to as the Bitter method (see the section of this article on observation of domains for a description of this technique as well as the Faraday effect, Fig. 47 and 48, and Kerr effect for observing domain structures). 165×. (J.D. Livingston)

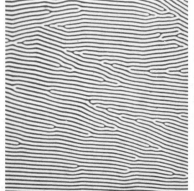

**Fig. 47** $Gd_{0.94}Tb_{0.75}Er_{1.31}Al_{0.5}Fe_{4.5}$-$O_{12}$ garnet, crystal grown in flux containing PbO and $B_2O_3$ at 1300 °C (2370 °F). Magnetic domain structure of 0.05-mm (0.002-in.) platelet cut parallel to the (111) plane. Black and white areas represent domains with opposing magnetic vectors normal to the surface. As-polished. 100×

**Fig. 48** Same garnet as Fig. 47 and produced the same way, but with an applied magnetic field of 150 Oe, which reduced white domains of Fig. 47 to cylinders (seen here as dots) 0.5 $\mu$m in diameter. The observation technique for this figure and Fig. 47 was the Faraday effect (transmitted polarized light). As-polished. 100×

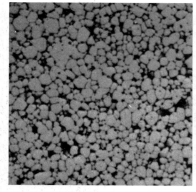

**Fig. 49** Nickel ferrite ($Ni_{0.6}$-$Fe_{2.4}O_4$), prepared from powder precipitated from a solution of $NiSO_4$ and $FeSO_4$, pressed and sintered 4 h at 1250 °C (2280 °F) in $N_2$. The fine grain structure was obtained by adding lithium hydroxide to the solution. 1:1:2 HF, $HNO_3$, and $H_2O$. 1000×

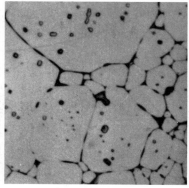

**Fig. 50** Nickel ferrite, same composition as Fig. 49, prepared from powder as described in Fig. 49, but with potassium hydroxide added to the solution instead of lithium hydroxide. As a result, the grains are much coarser than those in Fig. 49. 1:1:2 HF, $HNO_3$, and $H_2O$. 1000×

**Fig. 51** Macrostructure of Chromindur II (Fe-28Cr-10.5Co) cup-shaped telephone receiver magnets that were deep drawn from 1-mm (0.04-in.) thick strip and solution annealed at (left) 980 °C (1795 °F) and (right) 955 °C (1750 °F). Glyceregia. See Fig. 52 for a higher magnification view of a deep-drawn and solution-annealed Chromindur II structure. A transmission electron micrograph of a spark-eroded and electropolished iron-chromium-cobalt specimen is shown in Fig. 53. Approximately 2.5×

**Fig. 52** Chromindur II, deep drawn and solution annealed. A ferritic grain structure. See also Fig. 53. Glyceregia. 200×

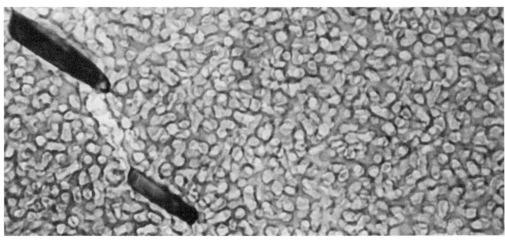

**Fig. 53** Thin-foil transmission electron micrograph of Chromindur II. The specimen was spark eroded, then electropolished by the window method. A very fine, uniform spinodal structure (the large black particles are σ phase). 20% HClO₄ in methanol at −40 °C (−40 °F). 115 000×. (S. Jin)

**Fig. 54** Alnico 5 (Fe-8Al-14Ni-24Co-3Cu), cast with directional grain, annealed 30 min at 925 °C (1700 °F), cooled in a magnetic field of 1000 Oe minimum, and aged 24 h at 550 °C (1020 °F). Note the pattern and boundaries of directional grains. See also Fig. 55 and 56. Marble's reagent. 30×

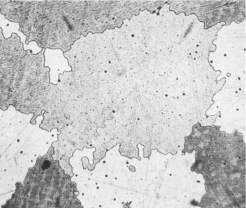

**Fig. 55** Alnico 5, cast with random grains, annealed 30 min at 925 °C (1700 °F) in a magnetic field of 1000 Oe min, and aged 24 h at 550 °C (1020 °F). Note pattern and boundaries of random equiaxed grains of the α-phase matrix. Marble's reagent. 30×

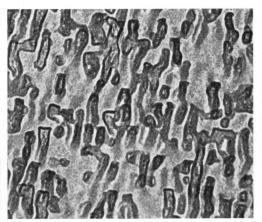

**Fig. 56** Replica electron micrograph of an Alnico 5 casting, solution annealed above the Curie temperature, cooled in a magnetic field, and aged. Particles of α (dark; vertical orientation here is parallel to magnetic field) in an α′ matrix. As-polished. 100 000×

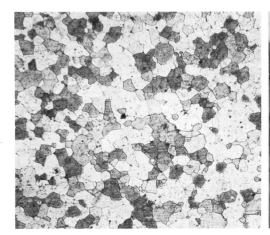

**Fig. 57** Alnico 5, pressed from powder, sintered at 1315 °C (2400 °F), annealed at 1260 °C (2300 °F), cooled in a magnetic field of 1000 Oe min. and aged 24 h at 550 °C (1020 °F). Structure: small equiaxed grains of α phase. Marble's reagent. 30×

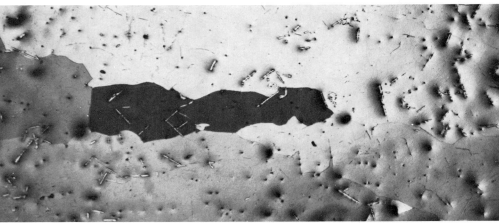

**Fig. 58** Alnico 9 (Fe-35Co-15Ni-4Cu-5Ti-7Al), cast with directional grain, annealed 1 h at 1260 °C (2300 °F), held isothermally 15 min in a magnetic field at 805 °C (1480 °F), then aged by heating to 550 °C (1020 °F) and holding 24 h. Structure is pattern and boundaries of directional grains of the α-phase matrix. The elongated, needlelike particles scattered through the structure are titanium sulfide. Marble's reagent. 100×

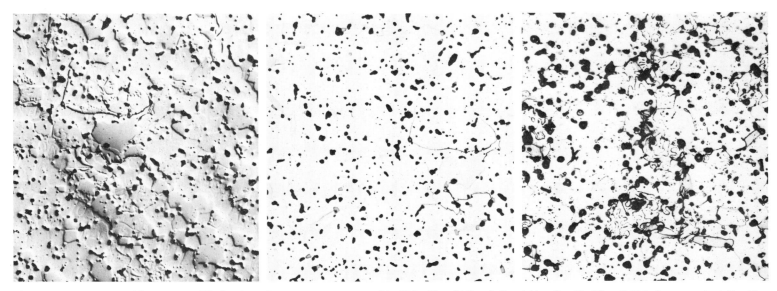

**Fig. 59, 60, 61** Microstructure of SmCo₅ sintered permanent magnet, as-polished (Fig. 59 and 60) and after etching. Fig. 59: differential interference contrast. Fig. 60: bright-field illumination. Fig. 61: bright-field illumination after etching with 3 parts glycerol, 1 part acetic acid, and 1 part HNO₃. All 400×

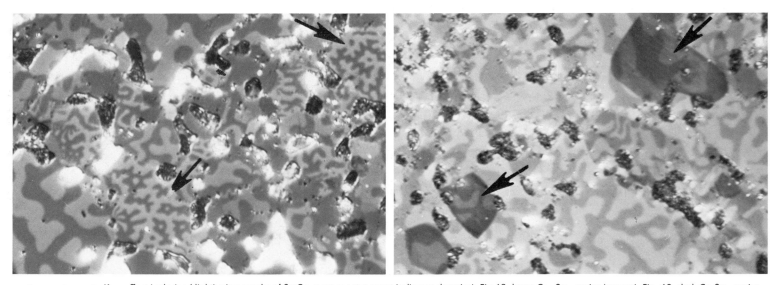

**Fig. 62, 63** Kerr effect (polarized light) micrographs of SmCo₅ permanent magnet (adjacent domains). Fig 62: large Co₁₇Sm₂ grains (arrows). Fig. 63: dark Co₇Sm₂ grains continuous with the surrounding Co₅Sm. As-polished. Both 850×. (J.D. Livingston)

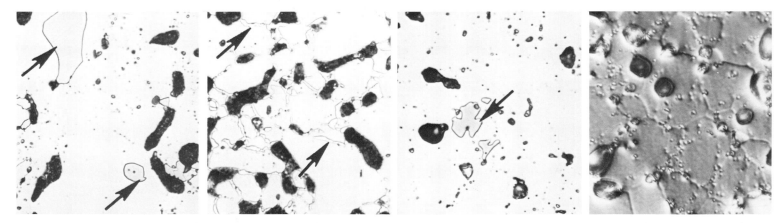

**Fig. 64, 65, 66, 67** Microstructures of SmCo₅ sintered permanent magnets. Fig. 64: a hyperstoichiometric composition containing Co₇Sm₂ (arrows). Fig. 65: hypostoichiometric composition containing Co₁₇Sm₂ (arrows). Fig. 66: a near-stoichiometric composition with a samarium-rich phase. Fig. 67: a near-stoichiometric composition showing Co₅Sm grain boundaries photographed using differential interference contrast. Fig. 64 to 66: as-polished. Fig. 67: 10 mL acetic acid, 10 mL H₂O, 10 mL HNO₃, and 40 mL HCl. All 720×

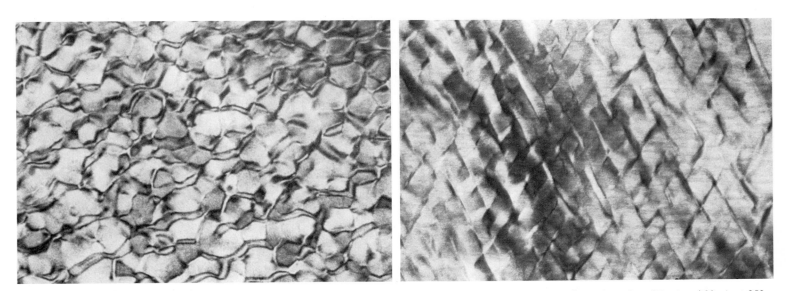

**Fig. 68, 69** Transmission electron micrographs showing the cellular microstructure of Sm(Co,Cu,Fe)$_7$ permanent magnet in the peak aged condition (aged 30 min at 850 °C, or 1560 °F). Fig. 68: a section normal to the magnetic alignment direction (c-axis). Fig. 69: a section including the alignment direction (c-axis vertical). Cell interiors show the 17:2 structure; cell boundaries have the 5:1 structure with the phases fully coherent. As-polished. 160 000×

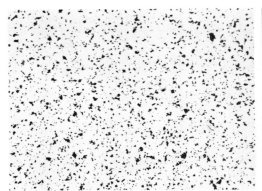

**Fig. 70** Anisotropic barium ferrite (BaO · 6Fe$_2$O$_3$). This hard ferrite was pressed from micron-size barium ferrite powder in a magnetic field and sintered at 1205 °C (2200 °F) to obtain desired magnetic properties. See also Fig. 71. Marble's reagent. 100×

**Fig 71** Replica electron micrograph of a fracture surface of isotropic barium ferrite pressed from micron-size powder and sintered at 1205 °C (2200 °F) to obtain final magnetic properties. Crystals are ∼1 μm in size, which approximates the dimensions of a single domain. As-polished. 10 000×

**Fig. 72** Cunife (Cu-20Ni-20Fe), cold rolled to 80% reduction, then aged 4 h at 565 °C (1050 °F). Specimen is a longitudinal section; grains are elongated in the direction of rolling. Marble's reagent. 50×

# Electrical Contact Materials

ELECTRICAL CONTACT material specimens are prepared in much the same way as those of most other metals. Because electrical contacts are often small, sectioning is more difficult. Some electrical contact materials are made of soft metals, some are composites containing metals that vary widely in hardness, and some are composed partly or completely of noble metals, which are difficult to etch. Therefore, certain problems are likely to be encountered in the preparation of specimens, and some techniques of specimen preparation will differ from those for other materials.

## Specimen Preparation

**Mounting.** Preparation of unmounted specimens is rarely attempted, because electrical contacts are usually small. Bakelite is the mounting material recommended for most applications. Lucite is useful as a mounting material, particularly for contacts to be examined after testing, because its transparency allows visibility of the surface adjacent to the cross section. For fragile specimens, a cold-mounting material should be selected (see the article "Mounting of Specimens" in this Volume). For maximum edge retention, such as for plated specimens, the specimen should be plated with another metal of contrasting color before it is mounted.

**Grinding.** Electrical contact materials are usually wet ground on a series of silicon carbide papers of successively finer grit sizes through 600 mesh. All electrical contact materials are treated the same through this stage of preparation.

**Polishing.** Rough polishing of electrical contact materials is often performed manually using 6- to 9-$\mu$m diamond or 5-$\mu$m alumina ($Al_2O_3$) abrasive on a nylon or silk cloth. Vibratory (automatic) polishing can also be used. Manual polishing with diamond abrasive usually requires the use of lapping oil, kerosene, or a similar vehicle. If $Al_2O_3$ is used, it is mixed with water whether polishing is performed manually or by the vibratory method.

Rapid rough polishing of a hard contact material (for example, tungsten or a refractory-metal composite such as tungsten-silver or tungsten-copper) is handled using a medium-speed wheel covered with cotton cloth of very low nap impregnated with diamond paste without fluid extenders. Depending on the finish obtained from the 600-grit paper in grinding and on the percentage of tungsten in the specimen, rapid rough polishing can begin with 15- or 9-$\mu$m diamond paste and can proceed in steps through 6- and 3-$\mu$m pastes. Cloths containing the different grades of paste can be reused several times if each is kept in a plastic bag to avoid contamination by the others. Specimens must be thoroughly rinsed between polishings to avoid contaminating the subsequent cloth. The use of light to medium pressure on the specimen minimizes pullout of particles.

The most widely used technique for final polishing employs an aqueous slurry of 0.3- or 0.05-$\mu$m $Al_2O_3$ on a soft cloth of medium to long nap. Final polishing is performed manually or by the vibratory method.

The harder contact materials can be final polished manually with 1-$\mu$m diamond on a short-nap cloth. This procedure can also be used for final polishing of the softer metals if a few fine scratches can be tolerated. The procedure is particularly useful for final polishing of the silver-cadmium oxide materials, because it produces no flow of the silver matrix to obscure the cadmium oxide particles. The advantages of this procedure are its speed in polishing and its avoidance of disturbed metal.

A technique for polishing contact materials that contain hard and soft constituents, such as refractory metals with silver or copper, uses vibratory polishing to accomplish rough and final polishing in one operation. Specimens are prepared conventionally through the 600-grit grinding, then are vibratory polished in an aqueous slurry of 0.3-$\mu$m $Al_2O_3$ on nylon cloth for 1 to 6 h. With minimum effort, this procedure produces a distortion-free surface on multiconstituent materials. The procedure is useful also for polishing specimens of pure tungsten and pure molybdenum, because these metals, when prepared by conventional procedures, usually require alternate etching and final polishing to reveal the true structure.

Another procedure for final polishing of tungsten, molybdenum, and tungsten carbide uses an aqueous slurry of 3% potassium ferricyanide ($K_3Fe(CN)_6$), 0.5% sodium hydroxide (NaOH), and 5% 0.05-$\mu$m $Al_2O_3$ on a soft napped cloth.

**As-Polished Examination.** Microscopic examination of electrical contact materials is often accomplished without etching the specimen. In many contact materials, the constituents vary so widely in hardness that one metal will polish in relief, revealing the distribution of one metal in the other. Tungsten compacts infiltrated with silver are often examined without having been etched; other typical examples are copper-tungsten and copper-graphite mixtures as well as silver-graphite, silver-cadmium oxide, and silver-nickel combinations. These materials often are examined in the as-polished (not etched) condition and are subsequently etched for further examination. Numerous examples of as-polished specimens can be found in the series of representative micrographs at the end of this article.

**Chemical Etching.** The solutions used for etching specimens of electrical contact materials are listed in Table 1. Although these etchants have proved successful, all are not used equally. A specific metal or combination of metals often can be etched successfully with two or more different etchants. Similarly, a specific etchant is frequently used for two or more different materials.

**Table 1  Etchants and etching procedures**

| No. | Etchant composition | Procedure for use |
|---|---|---|
| 1 | 20 mL NH$_4$OH, 10-20 mL H$_2$O$_2$ (30%), 10-20 mL H$_2$O | Swab at room temperature, 3-10 s; use fresh; more water, less H$_2$O$_2$ for copper alloys and conversely for silver alloys |
| 2 | 2 g K$_2$Cr$_2$O$_7$, 1.5 g NaCl, 8 mL H$_2$SO$_4$ (conc), 100 mL H$_2$O | Swab at room temperature, 5-10 s; good for etching hard-to-etch copper alloys |
| 3 | 50 mL NH$_4$OH, 10-30 mL H$_2$O$_2$ (30%) | Swab at room temperature for 3-10 s; use fresh |
| 4 | 10 g FeCl$_3$, 90 mL H$_2$O | Swab or immerse |
| 5 | A: 100 mL saturated aqueous solution of K$_2$Cr$_2$O$_7$, 2 mL saturated aqueous solution of NaCl (sodium chloride), 10 mL H$_2$SO$_4$<br>B: 1 part solution A, 10 parts H$_2$O<br>C: 98 mL H$_2$O, 3 g CrO$_3$, 2 mL H$_2$SO$_4$ | Use solutions of A, B, then C; swab at room temperature for 15-20 s with each solution; rinse in water between solutions |
| 6 | 20 g CrO$_3$, 4.5 g NH$_4$Cl (ammonium chloride), 18 mL HNO$_3$ (conc), 15 mL H$_2$SO$_4$ (conc), H$_2$O to make 1/2 L (Waterbury reagent) | Dilute 2:1 with water at time of use; swab at room temperature for 3-10 s |
| 7 | A: 25 mL HNO$_3$, 1 g K$_2$Cr$_2$O$_7$, 100 mL H$_2$O<br>B: 40 g CrO$_3$, 3 g Na$_2$SO$_4$, 200 mL H$_2$O | Mix equal parts of A and B; swab at room temperature for 5-10 s |
| 8 | 20 mL HNO$_3$ (conc), 20 mL acetic acid (glacial), 20 mL glycerol | Swab at 38-42 °C (100-108 °F) for 3-10 s |
| 9 | 0.2% CrO$_3$ and 0.2% H$_2$SO$_4$, in H$_2$O | Swab for 1 min |
| 10 | A: 200 mL HNO$_3$ (50%), 2 g K$_2$Cr$_2$O$_7$<br>B: 20 g CrO$_3$, 1.5 g Na$_2$SO$_4$, 100 mL H$_2$O | Mix 1 part A with 20 parts B at time of use; swab at room temperature, 3-15 s |
| 11 | Murakami's reagent | Swab at room temperature for 5-15 s. Use at half strength for more control |
| 12 | 20 mL HNO$_3$ (conc), 20 mL acetic acid (glacial) | Immerse at room temperature, 10-20 s |
| 13 | 20 mL KCN (10%), 20 mL (NH$_4$)$_2$S$_2$O$_8$ (10%) | Use in a hood; immerse at room temperature for 10-30 s |
| 14 | A: 5% nital etch<br>B: 5% FeCl$_3$ in methanol | Immerse specimen alternately in A and B |
| 15 | 10 mL HNO$_3$, 20 mL HCl, 10 mL glycerol | Swab at room temperature for 3-10 s |
| 16 | 30 mL HCl, 10 mL H$_2$O | Electrolytic; up to 5 V dc; 1.5 A/cm$^2$ (9.7 A/in.$^2$); room temperature, 1-3 min |

The choice of etchant depends largely on the material or the combination of materials to be etched. Although several etchants could be used, the final choice may be arbitrary or may depend on prevailing laboratory conditions.

Etchants composed of ammonium hydroxide (NH$_4$OH) and hydrogen peroxide (H$_2$O$_2$), with and without added water, are frequently used, because they will etch several copper-base and most silver-base alloys (see etchants 1 and 3 in Table 1).

An etchant composed of K$_3$Fe(CN)$_6$, NaOH, and water (Murakami's reagent or a modification) is used extensively for etching electrical contact materials—principally, the copper-tungsten mixtures (Fig. 16 to 20 and 71 to 77).

Two etchants can sometimes be used consecutively, as in preparing the specimen for Fig. 20. This specimen of 70Cu-30W was etched first in a K$_3$Fe(CN)$_6$ + NaOH solution, then in an NH$_4$OH + H$_2$O$_2$ solution. Dual etching often is used for composites of two or more different metals. A typical specimen etched in this way is a 90Ag-10CdO contact clad with silver that was brazed to a brass (Fig. 36). A section of the joint was etched first with a nitric acid plus potassium dichromate (HNO$_3$ + K$_2$Cr$_2$O$_7$) solution, then with a chromic acid plus sodium sulfate (CrO$_3$ + Na$_2$SO$_4$) solution. It is sometimes advantageous to use two etchants alternately through two or more cycles. This practice revealed the structure of a gold-plated nickel-iron alloy (Fig. 93 to 96).

Unalloyed palladium and palladium alloys (50 to 95% Pd) are most often etched in a mixture of potassium cyanide (KCN) and ammonium persulfate [(NH$_4$)$_2$S$_2$O$_8$] (etchant 13 in Table 1). A mixture of nitric acid (HNO$_3$), hydrochloric acid (HCl), and glycerol (etchant 15 in Table 1) has proved useful for distinguishing the rhodium plate from the gold underplate on a cross section of plated nickel-iron alloy (Fig. 111). An etchant composed of HNO$_3$ and acetic acid (etchant 12 in Table 1) is often used for gold-base alloys and sometimes for palladium when welded to nickel silver (Fig. 99 and 104).

**Electrolytic etching** is not necessary or appropriate for etching most electrical contact materials. Exceptions are platinum-base alloys, such as platinum-ruthenium and platinum-iridium alloys. Electrolytic etching is also used for etching contact materials that contain substantial amounts of platinum, such as the 35Pd-10Pt-10Au-30Ag-14Cu-1Zn alloy shown in Fig. 109.

An electrolyte that has proved successful for etching platinum alloys is a mixture of HCl and water (etchant 16 in Table 1). Also suitable is a 5% solution of sodium cyanide (NaCN) in water. A 5 to 7% aqueous solution of KCN has been used for electrolytic etching of gold and silver plates. Cyanide-containing etchants must be used under a hood. Electrolytic etching is usually carried out at room temperature, using up to 5 V dc at a current density of about 1.5 A/cm$^2$ (9.7 A/in.$^2$) for 1 to 3 min.

## Microstructures of Electrical Contact Materials

The electrical contact materials depicted in this article include copper-, silver-, tungsten-, tungsten-carbide-, and molybdenum-base materials, as well as precious metals other than silver. In form, these materials encompass unalloyed metals; bimetals; alloys; mixtures of metals; mixtures of a metal with a metalloid, a metal oxide, or a metal carbide; and electroplated overlays. Among the processes used to produce or prepare these materials are melting and casting, powder metallurgy, cold drawing, mechanical bonding, and electroplating.

The various electrical contact materials are selected for diverse service requirements. For a discussion of the selection criteria and properties, see the article "Electric-Contact Materials" in Volume 3 of the 9th Edition of *Metals Handbook*. Detailed information on electrical contacts produced by powder metallurgy techniques can be found in the article "Electrical and Magnetic Applications" in Volume 7 of the 9th Edition of *Metals Handbook*. The usefulness of an electrical contact material depends on its electrical characteristics and mechanical properties, which are closely related to composition and microstructure.

**Copper-Base Materials.** Unalloyed copper aluminum bronzes, brasses, and other copper-base materials are widely used as contact materials because of their high electrical and thermal conductivities, low cost, and ease of fabrication. Unalloyed copper, bronze, and brass contacts are prepared from wrought products or by powder metallurgy techniques. Graphite or tungsten are added to powder metallurgy contacts to resist sticking or welding; tungsten also contributes to wear resistance. These additions are visible in the microstructures of mixtures containing either element.

Binary age-hardenable alloys of copper-chromium and copper-beryllium are more resistant to thermal softening than unalloyed copper (see the article "Beryllium-Nickel and Beryllium-Copper Alloys" in this Volume). Several ternary and quaternary alloys, including those that contain cobalt and beryllium, or cobalt, cadmium, and silicon, are age hardenable. In these alloys, the precipitate responsible for hardening is usually observable in the microstructure.

**Silver-Base Materials.** Silver, which has the highest electrical and thermal conductivity of all metals, is a widely used contact material; it is also used as a plated, brazed, or mechanically bonded overlay on other contact materials—notably, copper and copper-base materials.

Several binary and ternary alloys provide special properties. Silver-copper alloys combine good electrical characteristics with a higher hardness than that of unalloyed silver; silver-cadmium alloys provide improved arc-quenching characteristics. The ternary alloys silver-copper-nickel and silver-cadmium-nickel offer improved erosion resistance as well as other special properties.

Another class of silver-base compositions contains semirefractory constituents, such as cadmium oxide, magnesium oxide, and graphite, that are made by powder metallurgy techniques. However, additions of cadmium oxide or magnesium oxide can also be made by preparing binary alloys of silver and cadmium or of silver and magnesium, then converting the cadmium or magnesium into an oxide by internal oxidation. In general, the semirefractory constituents promote nonsticking qualities or provide increased resistance to wear. Most of these constituents are observable in the microstructure.

Silver-base contact materials for switchgear contain tungsten or molybdenum, or tungsten carbide. These refractory-metal constituents, which are readily identifiable in the microstructure, do not form solid solutions with silver. Contacts for switchgear are made by powder metallurgy.

**Tungsten-Base and Molybdenum-Base Materials.** Tungsten-base materials are used in contacts for low-current applications that require exceptional resistance to arcing, welding, and sticking. These contacts are made by powder metallurgy techniques and have relatively simple microstructures in which the individual grains of tungsten are clearly defined. In the tungsten-base contact materials that contain silver or copper, these elements appear as a light-etching constituent surrounding tungsten grains. Those materials that contain small amounts of nickel exhibit a nickel precipitate, particularly at grain boundaries.

Unalloyed molybdenum and molybdenum-base materials are also prepared by powder metallurgy techniques. The micrographs included in this section indicate that the microstructure of unalloyed molybdenum is analogous to that of unalloyed tungsten and that the microstructure of a molybdenum-silver material is similar to that of a tungsten-silver material.

**Precious Metals.** Several of the unalloyed precious metals, precious-metal alloys, and electrodeposited overlays of precious metals for which micrographs are shown in this article are high-purity, single-phase materials. Minor insoluble impurities, if present, usually deposit at grain boundaries and, upon etching, will define individual grains.

Microstructures can be enhanced by met- allography employing the differential-interference contrast technique. This technique, using polarized light, is based on the interference of two sets of light waves produced in a birefringent quartz prism above the microscope objective. These beams may be shifted in phase by surface details of the specimen. Surface details not detectable in bright field or dark field assume noticeable contrast as a result of the phase shift. Additional information on differential-interference contrast is available in the articles "Optical Microscopy" and "Color Metallography" in this Volume.

Some of the single-phase alloys and unalloyed precious metals depicted in this article exhibit well-defined grain structures as well as grain deformation and slip planes resulting from cold work (Fig. 101 to 103). Response to recrystallization after cold working can also be shown in the microstructure of a single-phase alloy (Fig. 108). The constituents in two-phase alloys can be well-defined (Fig. 107). Multiple plated coatings can usually be clearly distinguished by differences in color, texture, or both (Fig. 111).

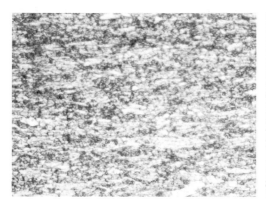

**Fig. 1** Temper: spring (H08). Elongated, cold-worked, fine-grained structure

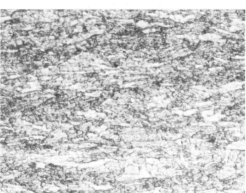

**Fig. 2** Temper: extra hard (H06). Elongated, cold-worked, fine-grained structure

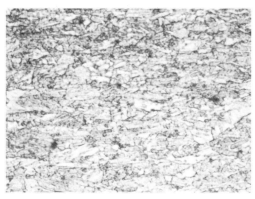

**Fig. 3** Temper: hard (H04). Elongated, cold-worked, fine-grained structure

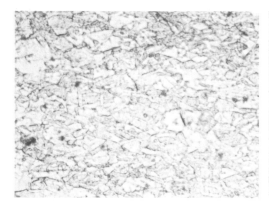

**Fig. 4** Temper: half hard (H02). Moderately cold-worked, fine-grained structure

**Fig. 5** Temper: quarter hard (H01). Slightly cold-worked, fine-grained structure

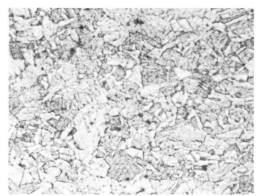

**Fig. 6** Temper: annealed (061). Fine-grained, annealed structure

**Fig. 1 to 6** Longitudinal sections of rolled C69000 alloy (3.3 to 3.5% Al, 21.3 to 24.1% Zn, 0.5 to 0.75% Ni, 0.025% Pb max, 0.05% Fe, rem Cu) electrical contact (outlet) material. Processing history: Fig. 1 to 5, rolled to temper; Fig. 6, annealed to temper. Metallographic technique: diamond polish (0.25 $\mu$m). Etchant: 85% NH$_4$OH + H$_2$O (equal parts), 15% H$_2$O$_2$. 1000$\times$ (P. Basalyk, G. Grosse)

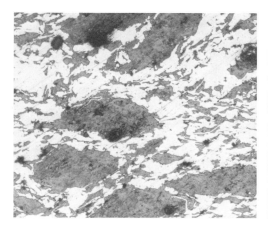

**Fig. 7** 80Cu-20graphite motor brush pressed from powder and sintered. Dark areas are graphite; light areas are copper. As-polished. 100× (W.H. Rowley, Jr.)

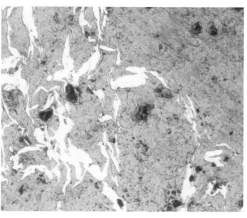

**Fig. 8** 40Cu-60graphite motor brush pressed from powder and sintered. Gray graphite matrix, light areas are copper, black spots are voids. As-polished. 100× (W.H. Rowley, Jr.)

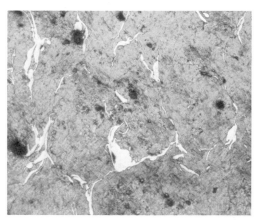

**Fig. 9** 30Cu-70graphite motor brush pressed from powder and sintered. Gray graphite matrix, light areas are copper, black spots are voids. As-polished. 100× (W.H. Rowley, Jr.)

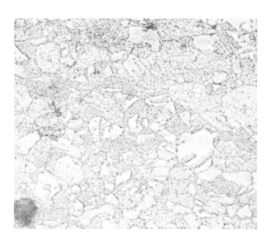

**Fig. 10** Longitudinal section of a brass (68.5 to 71.5% Cu, 0.07% Pb, 0.05% Fe, rem Zn) contact (wall outlet) material that was rolled to temper (extra hard H06) from a fine-grained anneal. Elongated, cold-worked, fine-grained structure shown. 85% $NH_4OH$ + $H_2O$ (equal parts), 15% $H_2O_2$. 1000×. (P. Basalyk, G. Grosse)

**Fig. 11** Chromium copper (Cu-0.8Cr); a transverse section from a 13-mm (0.5-in.) diam rod in the quenched, aged, and cold-drawn condition (85 HRB). Average grain size, 0.015 mm (0.6 mil). Structure is an alloy aggregate. $NH_4OH$ + $H_2O_2$. 75×

**Fig. 12** Cadmium copper (Cu-1Cd). Transverse-section specimen taken from a 13-mm (0.5-in.) diam rod in the cold-drawn condition. The black lines are twinning lines from cold working. The black spheroidal particles are inclusions. $NH_4OH$ + $H_2O_2$. 750×

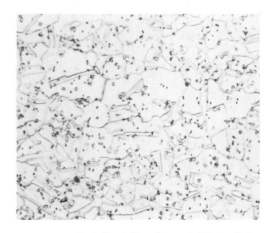

**Fig. 13** Cu-2.5Co-0.5Be alloy rod, 13-mm (0.5-in.) diam, quenched, aged, and cold drawn (102 HRB); transverse section. Small dark particles are free cobalt. $NH_4OH$ + $H_2O_2$. 750×

**Fig. 14** Cu-2.5Co-1.2Cd-0.5Si alloy, as-cast, showing a typical dendritic microstructure. The constituents are not resolved at this magnification; see also Fig. 15. $NH_4OH$ + $H_2O_2$. 22×

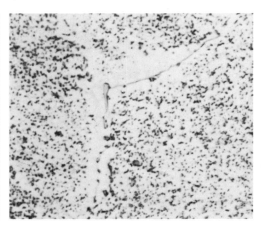

**Fig. 15** Same as Fig. 14, except at higher magnification that reveals a structure consisting of precipitated particles of cobalt silicide (dark) in a copper-cadmium solid solution. $NH_4OH$ + $H_2O_2$. 750×

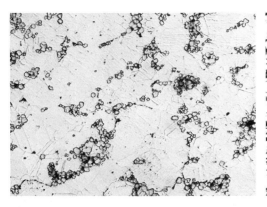

**Fig. 16** 75Cu-25W, pressed, sintered, and coined; annealed at 980 °C (1800 °F). Tungsten particles (gray) in copper matrix; some porosity (black). Compact was polished with Al$_2$O$_3$ slurry in K$_3$Fe(CN)$_6$ + NaOH, then etched in NH$_4$OH + H$_2$O$_2$. 400×

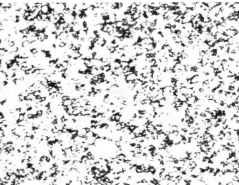

**Fig. 17** 75Cu-25W disk, produced as a tungsten powder compact infiltrated with copper. The microstructure consists of particles of tungsten (dark constituent) in a matrix of copper (light). Compare with Fig. 18. 1:1 30% K$_3$Fe(CN)$_6$ + 10% NaOH. 500×

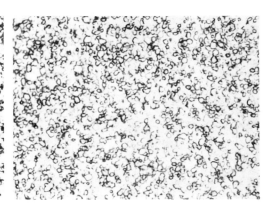

**Fig. 18** 75Cu-25W powder metallurgy disk, pressed and sintered (not infiltrated). The microstructure consists of particles of tungsten (dark-etching constituent) in a matrix of copper (light). Compare with Fig. 17. 1:1 30% K$_3$Fe(CN)$_6$ + 10% NaOH. 1000×

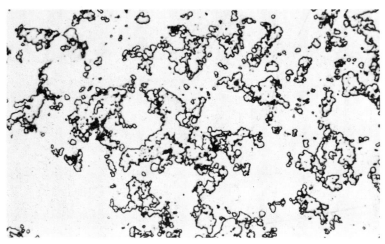

**Fig. 19** 70Cu-30W contact made by pressing and sintering a mixture of copper and tungsten powders. Structure: tungsten phase (gray areas) in a copper matrix. Black spots are voids. See also Fig. 20. As-polished. 250×

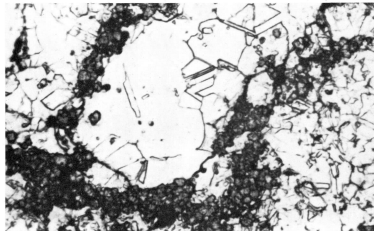

**Fig. 20** Same as Fig. 19, except this specimen was etched and is shown at a higher magnification. Dark areas in the structure are the tungsten phase (with some voids); light areas, the copper matrix. K$_3$Fe(CN)$_6$ + NaOH, then NH$_4$OH + H$_2$O$_2$. 500×

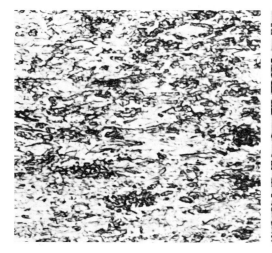

**Fig. 21** Silver (99.9% Ag) sheet, cold rolled. The cold-worked grains are elongated in the rolling direction. See also Fig. 22. NH$_4$OH + H$_2$O$_2$. 500×

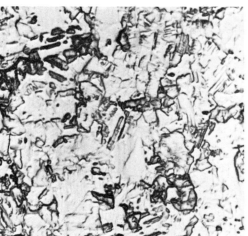

**Fig. 22** Same as Fig. 21, except annealed for 1.5 h at 300 °C (575 °F). Annealing has recrystallized the cold-worked grains. NH$_4$OH + H$_2$O$_2$. 500×

**Fig. 23** Silver (99.9% Ag) rod, 4.8-mm (³/₁₆-in.) diam, cold worked. An unusual structure consisting of large grains with deformation twins. NH$_4$OH + H$_2$O$_2$. 150×

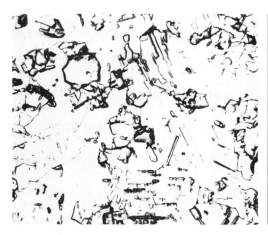

**Fig. 24** Silver (99.9% Ag) ball, cold headed from wire, annealed for 20 min at 650 °C (1200 °F) in a reducing atmosphere. The microstructure consists of recrystallized grains with some evidence of twinning. 25 mL 30% $H_2O_2$, 50 mL $NH_4OH$, 25 mL $H_2O$. 250 ×

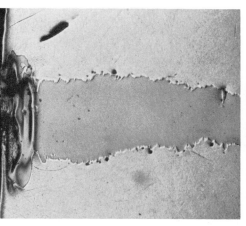

**Fig. 25** Flat, cold-formed silver (99.9% Ag) contact, viewed under oblique illumination, showing an area at which incipient melting occurred, probably caused by electrical overload. Compare with Fig. 26. As-polished. 100×

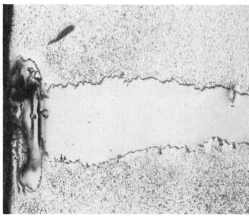

**Fig. 26** Same as Fig. 25, except shown after etching. Note grainy structure of the cold-worked silver that did not melt and smooth surface of the portion that melted incipiently (probably because of electrical overload). $H_2CrO_4$ + $H_2SO_4$. 100×

**Fig. 27** 90Ag-10Cu strip, cold rolled, then annealed at 730 °C (1350 °F). A longitudinal section, in oblique illumination. The structure consists of a copper-rich phase, present as spheroidal particles in bands, in a silver-rich matrix. $HNO_3$ + $K_2Cr_2O_7$ and $CrO_3$ + $Na_2SO_4$. 800×

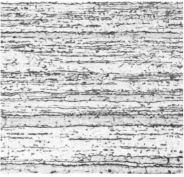

**Fig. 28** 75Ag-24.5Cu-0.5Ni wire, cold drawn, then annealed at 540 °C (1000 °F). A longitudinal section. The microstructure consists of a copper-rich phase, in the form of bands, in a silver-rich matrix. The small particles are nickel. $HNO_3$ + $K_2Cr_2O_7$ and $CrO_3$ + $Na_2SO_4$. 800×

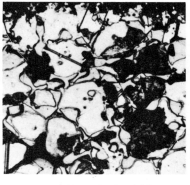

**Fig. 29** 75Ag-19.5Cu-5Cd-0.5Ni cold-headed rivet, annealed 30 min at 760 °C (1400 °F) in air. Grains of silver (white) and copper (gray) in copper matrix. Precipitates in silver grains are nickel and copper; intergranular precipitate is oxidized cadmium. $NH_4OH$ + $H_2O_2$. 250×

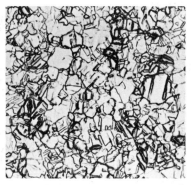

**Fig. 30** 85Ag-15Cd sheet, quarter hard. The microstructure consists of a solid solution of cadmium in silver; structure is characteristic of $\alpha$ phase. The grains show evidence of twinning, which was caused by cold working. $NH_4OH$ + $H_2O_2$. 300×

**Fig. 31** 90Ag-10CdO strip that was internally oxidized, then rolled. The dark particles (which are oriented in the direction of rolling) are cadmium oxide, in a matrix of silver. As-polished. 100×

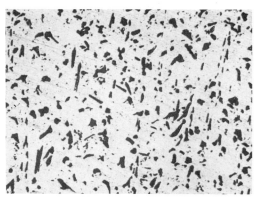

**Fig. 32** 90Ag-10CdO strip after oxidation at 845 °C (1550 °F). The randomly dispersed dark particles are cadmium oxide, in a matrix of silver. As-polished. 400×

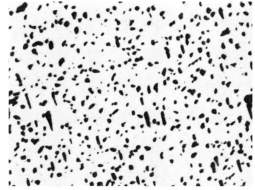

**Fig. 33** 90Ag-10CdO contact stamped from sheet that had been internally oxidized. The randomly dispersed dark particles are cadmium oxide, in a matrix of silver. As-polished. 500×

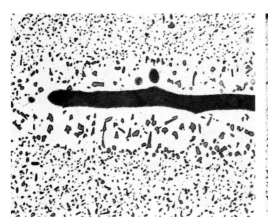

**Fig. 34** Internally oxidized 90Ag-10CdO contact showing an unusually large stringer of cadmium oxide (black) caused by inhomogeneous structure before oxidizing. As-polished. 250×

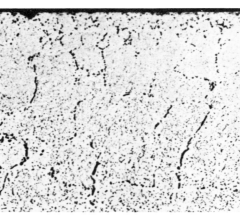

**Fig. 35** Internally oxidized 90Ag-10CdO contact. The microstructure shows undesirable precipitation of cadmium oxide at grain boundaries of the silver matrix. As-polished. 300×

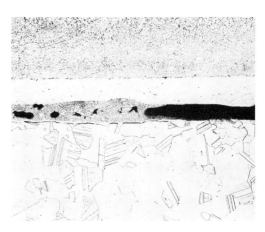

**Fig. 36** 90Ag-10CdO contact (top) clad with silver (light band), brazed to brass (bottom) with BAg-7 (56Ag-22Cu-17Zn-5Sn) filler metal. Voids (black) are trapped gas. $HNO_3$ + $K_2Cr_2O_7$, then $CrO_3$ + $Na_2SO_4$. 50×

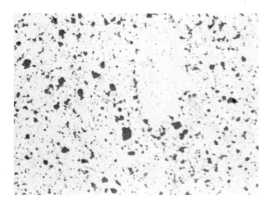

**Fig. 37** 89Ag-11CdO internally oxidized contact. Powder blend pressed and sintered to <95% density, coined to >97% density, and annealed. Structure shows dark cadmium oxide particles in light silver matrix. Note the discrete cadmium oxide particles with fairly large interparticle spacing. As-polished. 400×. (P. Wingert)

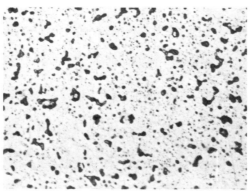

**Fig. 38** 85Ag-15CdO internally oxidized contact. Powder pressed and sintered to >97% density, coined to final part size. Dark cadmium oxide particles in light silver matrix. Larger cadmium oxide particles are those that nucleated on the powder surface during oxidation. Smaller cadmium oxide particles are those that nucleated internally (within the powder) during oxidation. Average cadmium oxide particle size is ~1 $\mu$m. As-polished. 800×. (P. Wingert)

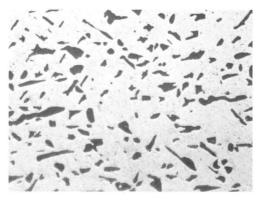

**Fig. 39** 85Ag-15CdO internally oxidized contact. Alloy powder was formed into a contact, then oxidized to yield a silver-cadmium oxide composite. Dark cadmium oxide particles in light silver matrix. Structure is the region between the surface and cadmium-oxide-depleted central region. Note the large crystallographically oriented cadmium oxide particles that are homogeneously distributed in this region. As-polished. 800×. (P. Wingert)

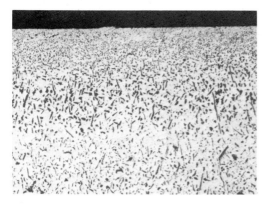

**Fig. 40** 85Ag-15CdO internally oxidized contact. Alloy powder was formed into a contact, then oxidized to yield a silver-cadmium oxide composite. Dark cadmium oxide particles in light silver matrix. Fine oxides at the surface are due to high nucleation rate as alloy was heated. More coarse oxides can be seen moving from the surface. These are aligned in preferred crystallographic orientations. As-polished. 160×. (P. Wingert)

**Fig. 41** 85Ag-15CdO + 50 ppm Li internally oxidized contact. The alloy powder was pressed onto a fine silver backing (bottom), sintered, and coined. Note the fine, uniform dispersion of cadmium oxide particles throughout the cross section and the absence of the silver-rich, cadmium-oxide-depleted zone characteristic of silver-cadmium alloy strip that is oxidized. As-polished. 63×. (J.R. Sims)

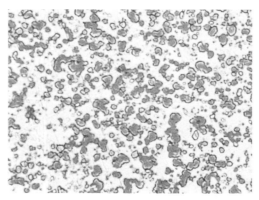

**Fig. 42** 85Ag-15CdO + 50 ppm Li internally oxidized alloy powder contact materials. Same processing as described in Fig. 41, but shown at a higher magnification (silver backing material not shown). Note the equiaxed cadmium oxide particles. As-polished. 1000×. (J.R. Sims)

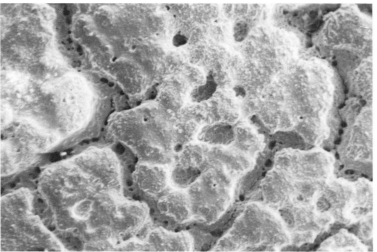

**Fig. 43** 85Ag-15CdO internally oxidized contact. Scanning electron microscope secondary electron image of eroded contact surface after 10 000 cycles that was arced using 50 A rms half-cycle arcs struck across a static gap of initially 1 mm (0.04 in.). Erosion craters and ravines extend down into the contact. Small holes with fine cracks running between them are at the bottom of the ravines. See also Fig. 44. 80×. (P. Wingert)

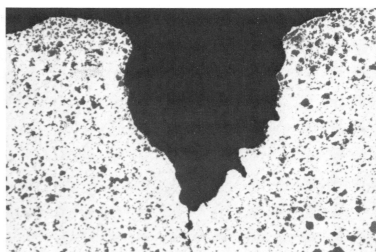

**Fig. 44** Optical micrograph of polished cross section of the 85Ag-15CdO contact in Fig. 43. Erosion ravine extends down into the virgin material structure on either side. Crack extends from the bottom of the open ravine to where the cadmium oxide particles have been preferentially eroded. 350×. (P. Wingert)

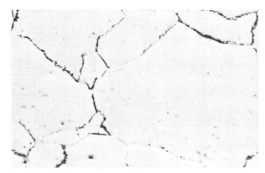

**Fig. 45, 46** 85Ag-15CdO internally oxidized and post-oxidized contact. The majority of cadmium oxidized on the grain boundaries of the large silver grains. Some of the cadmium oxidized as fine particles (<0.1 μm) homogeneously distributed within the silver grains. Some of the grain boundaries parallel to the surface are white because of the total absence of cadmium oxide. As-polished. Fig. 45: 400×. Fig. 46: 800×. (P. Wingert)

**Fig. 47** 85Ag-15CdO internally oxidized contact. Alloy powder was formed into a contact, then oxidized to yield a silver-cadmium oxide composite. Dark cadmium oxide in light silver matrix. Central zone has little cadmium oxide due to cadmium diffusion toward the surface and resulting porosity. As-polished. 80×. (P. Wingert)

**Fig. 48** Brazed contact assembly: 90Ag-10CdO internally oxidized contact, clad with silver, and silver brazed to an OFHC copper strip. Structure consists of oxidized 90Ag-10CdO (A and C), central zone depleted of oxides (B), silver backing (D), silver-based braze layer (E), and copper strip (F). 1:1 NH₄OH + 3% H₂O₂. 80×. (P.K. Lattari)

**Fig. 49** Brazed contact assembly: 85Ag-15CdO contact made by single-sided internal oxidation in 1 atm oxygen, brazed to a 90-10 brass strip. Structure consists of oxide-depleted layer (white area at top of contact assembly indicated by A), eroded 85Ag-15CdO contact material (B), silver-base brazed layer (C), and brass strip (D). 1:1 NH₄OH + 3% H₂O₂. 40×. (P.K. Lattari)

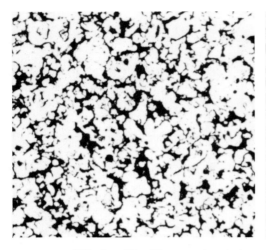

**Fig. 50** 97Ag-3graphite disk, pressed and sintered. The structure consists of a random dispersion of graphite particles (dark areas) in a matrix of silver. 25 mL 30% $H_2O_2$, 50 mL $NH_4OH$, 25 mL $H_2O$. 250×

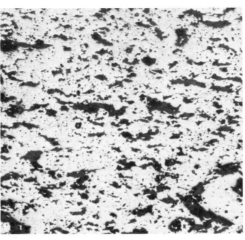

**Fig. 51** 95Ag-5graphite contact, pressed, sintered, re-pressed, and resintered. Structure: random dispersion of graphite particles in a matrix of silver. As-polished. 100×

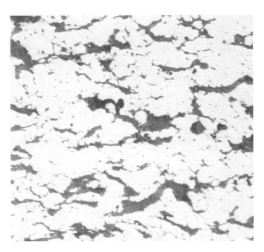

**Fig. 52** 90Ag-10graphite contact, pressed and sintered. Structure: randomly dispersed particles of graphite (dark gray) and a few voids (black dots) in a silver matrix. As-polished. 100×

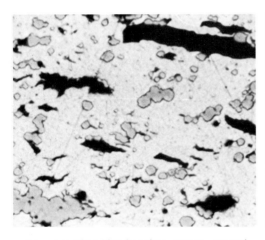

**Fig. 53** 88Ag-10Ni-2graphite contact, pressed, sintered, and re-pressed. Graphite particles (black) and nickel (dark gray) in a matrix of silver (lighter gray). 0.2% chromic acid + 0.2% $H_2SO_4$. 350×

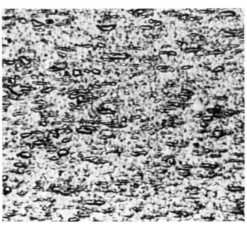

**Fig. 54** 85Ag-15Ni powder metallurgy contact, pressed, sintered, and rolled, showing particles of nickel, elongated in the direction of rolling, in a matrix of silver. As-polished. 100×

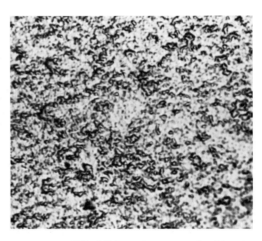

**Fig. 55** 85Ag-15Ni contact, pressed, sintered, and re-pressed. Structure consists of a uniform distribution of nickel particles (randomly oriented) in a matrix of silver. As-polished. 100×

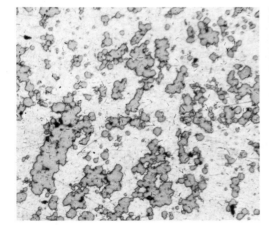

**Fig. 56** 80Ag-20Ni contact, pressed, sintered, and re-pressed. Randomly dispersed particles of nickel (dark gray) and a few voids (black dots) in a matrix of silver. 0.2% chromic acid + 0.2% $H_2SO_4$. 300×

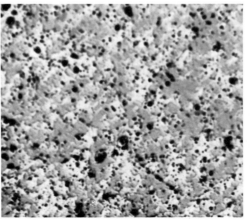

**Fig. 57** 60Ag-40Ni contact, pressed, sintered, re-pressed, and resintered. High degree of porosity (black dots). Gray areas in the structure are nickel; lighter areas are silver. As-polished. 250×

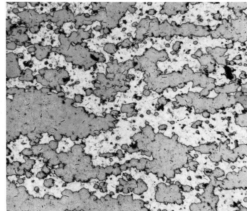

**Fig. 58** 50Ag-50Ni contact, pressed, sintered, re-pressed, and rolled (rolling direction is horizontal here). Dark gray areas are nickel, light areas are silver, black spots are voids. 0.2% chromic acid + 0.2% $H_2SO_4$. 300×

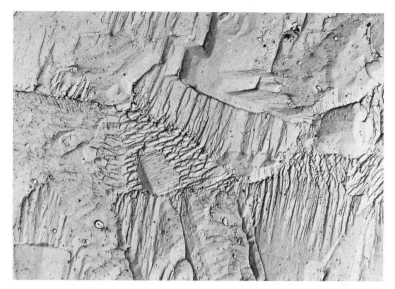

**Fig. 59** 99.58Ag-0.22MgO-0.2Ni contact formed from strip stock, then hardened by internal oxidation. Replica electron micrograph shows the orientation of the grains in the silver solid-solution matrix. See Fig. 60 for a more detailed view. NH₄OH + H₂O₂. 4000×

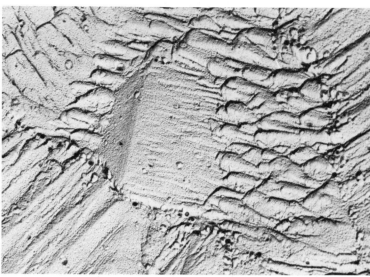

**Fig. 60** Same as Fig. 59, but a replica electron micrograph made at higher magnification to show dispersed magnesium oxide particles formed by internal oxidation of magnesium and that harden the matrix. The 0.2% Ni was added to inhibit grain growth. NH₄OH + H₂O₂. 12 000×

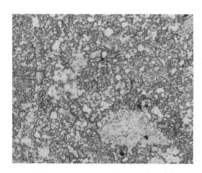

**Fig. 61** 50Ag-50Mo; pressed and sintered compact of molybdenum powder infiltrated with silver. Molybdenum (dark gray); silver (light gray); voids (black dots). As-polished. 200×

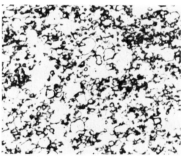

**Fig. 62** 50Ag-50Mo fabricated part that was pressed to shape and sintered. The randomly dispersed particles are molybdenum; the matrix is silver. 30% K₃Fe(CN)₆ + 10% NaOH. 500×

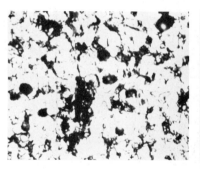

**Fig. 63** 90Ag-10W disk, pressed and sintered. Irregular tungsten particles in silver matrix. Black dots are voids. NH₄OH + H₂O₂, then K₃Fe(CN)₆ + NaOH. 500×

**Fig. 64** 50Ag-50W contact that was fabricated from a pressed and sintered tungsten powder metallurgy compact infiltrated with silver (white constituent). As-polished. 300×

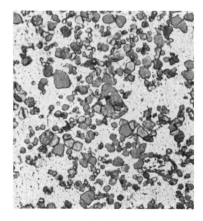

**Fig. 65** 50Ag-50W contact made from a sintered tungsten-powder compact infiltrated with silver at 1205 °C (2200 °F). Tungsten particles (gray) in silver matrix. Compact was polished with Al₂O₃ slurry in K₃Fe(CN)₆ + NaOH, then etched in NH₄OH + H₂O₂. 800×

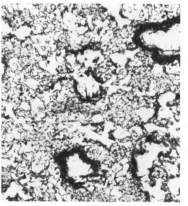

**Fig. 66** 65Ag-35WC disk, pressed from powder, sintered. Dark particles are tungsten carbide; white islands (black rimmed from erosion in polishing) and matrix are silver. As-polished. 250×

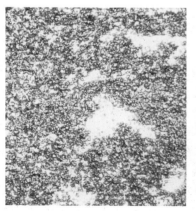

**Fig. 67** 50Ag-50WC; pressed and sintered compact of tungsten carbide powder infiltrated with silver. Large areas of silver (white) in skeleton of tungsten carbide. Murakami's reagent. 500×

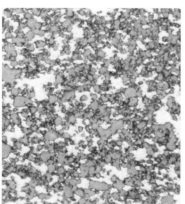

**Fig. 68** 40Ag-60WC contact material, pressed from mixed powder, sintered, and infiltrated with remaining silver. Dark carbide particles in light silver matrix. Murakami's reagent. 800×. (P. Wingert)

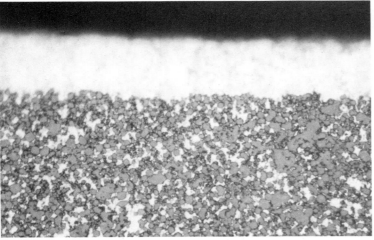

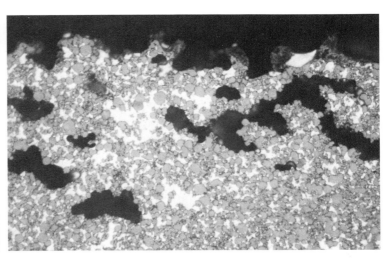

**Fig. 69** 40Ag-60WC contact, pressed from mixed powder, sintered, and infiltrated with remaining silver. Compact then submerged in hot salt bath to etch the carbide from the surface and create a surface layer of pure silver. Bulk of the contact material has dark carbide particles in light silver matrix. Light layer of pure silver is seen at surface. This layer is out of focus, because the softness of silver causes it to be polished away more quickly than the bulk material. Murakami's reagent. 800×. (P. Wingert)

**Fig. 70** 40Ag-60WC contact, pressed from mixed powder, sintered, and infiltrated with remaining silver. Contact surface eroded with 20 two-cycle break arcs at 220 V ac and 1600 A rms with a power factor of 0.7. Dark carbide particles in light silver matrix. Note that no reaction products, such as oxides or molten metal, can be seen at the surface. Particle size and size distribution of virgin material are maintained. Murakami's reagent. 800×. (P. Wingert)

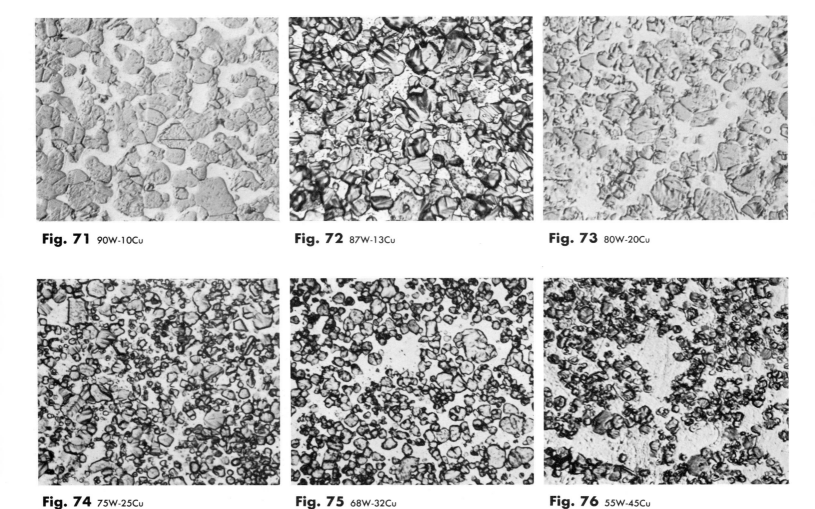

**Fig. 71** 90W-10Cu     **Fig. 72** 87W-13Cu     **Fig. 73** 80W-20Cu

**Fig. 74** 75W-25Cu     **Fig. 75** 68W-32Cu     **Fig. 76** 55W-45Cu

**Fig. 71 to 76** Sintered compacts of tungsten particles (skeletons) infiltrated with copper. Dark areas are tungsten; light areas are copper. Note segregation with high copper content in Fig. 76. Murakami's reagent. 1000×

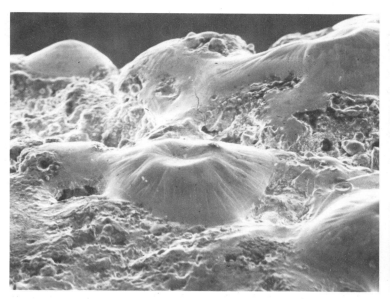

**Fig. 77** 70W-30Cu contact. Scanning electron microscope secondary electron image of eroded contact surface. Resolidified tungsten mounds rise above bulk of copper-tungsten. Long resolidified grain structure is visible on surface of mounds. These mounds are analogous to the tungsten cone in an arced silver-tungsten contact shown in Fig. 79 and 80. 140×. (P. Wingert)

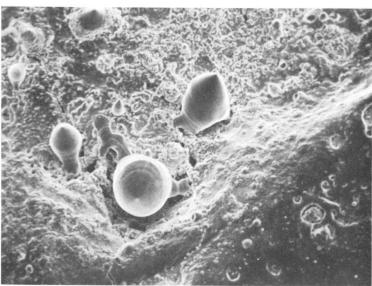

**Fig. 78** 65W-35Ag contact, pressed from mixed powder, sintered, and infiltrated with remaining silver. Scanning electron microscope secondary electron image of eroded contact surface showing protruding cones of pure tungsten. See Fig. 79 and 80 for cross-sectional views of these cones. 305×. (P. Wingert)

**Fig. 79, 80** 65W-35Ag contact, pressed from mixed powder, sintered, and infiltrated with remaining silver. Surface eroded by 20 two-cycle break arcs at 220 V ac, 1600 A rms, with a power factor of 0.7. Fig. 79: Tungsten cone with solidified grains at the surface. Porous, silver-depleted layer beneath. Stress cracks parallel to surface have been filled with silver. Crack at bottom left is still open. 400×. Fig. 80: Higher magnification view of Fig. 79. Virgin contact material shown at bottom. 690×. Both etched in Murakami's reagent. (P. Wingert)

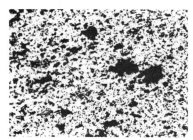

**Fig. 81** 90W-10Ag disk made by pressing and sintering a mixture of tungsten and silver powders. Dark particles are tungsten, in a silver matrix (light). Excessive porosity (black spots). As-polished. 100×

**Fig. 82** 81W-19Ag; a sintered compact of tungsten powder (skeleton) infiltrated with silver. The dark constituent in the microstructure is tungsten; the light areas are silver. Murakami's reagent. 1000×

**Fig. 83** 75W-25Ag sintered compact. Dark gray areas are tungsten; light areas, silver. Oblique illumination shows unwanted particles of tungsten carbide (black). Polished with Al₂O₃ slurry in K₃Fe(CN)₆ + NaOH. 800×

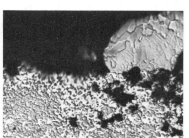

**Fig. 84** Cross section at the surface of a pressed and sintered 75W-25Ag electrical contact, showing melted and resolidified tungsten as well as voids that occurred while the contact was in service. K₃Fe(CN)₆ + NaOH. 500×

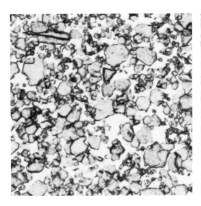

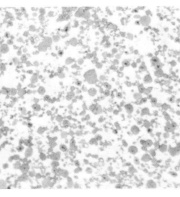

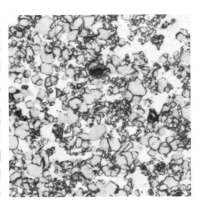

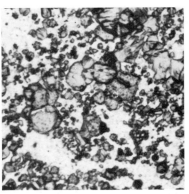

**Fig. 85** 72W-28Ag; a sintered compact of tungsten powder (skeleton) infiltrated with silver. Dark areas in the structure are tungsten; light areas, silver. Murakami's reagent. 500×

**Fig. 86** 65W-35Ag contact material, pressed from mixed powder, sintered, and infiltrated with remaining silver. Gray tungsten particles in light silver matrix. Murakami's reagent. 800×. (P. Wingert)

**Fig. 87** 65W-35Ag; a sintered compact of tungsten powder (skeleton) infiltrated with silver. The dark areas are tungsten; light areas, silver. Murakami's reagent. 500×

**Fig. 88** 51W-49Ag; a sintered compact of tungsten powder (skeleton) that was infiltrated with silver. Dark areas are tungsten; light areas, silver. Murakami's reagent. 500×

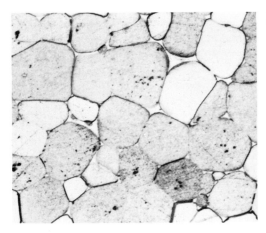

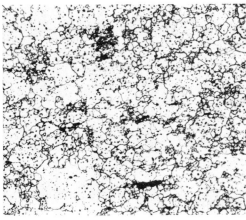

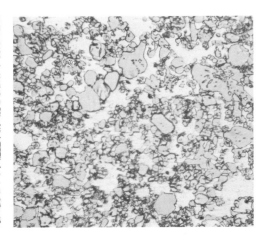

**Fig. 89** 99W-1Ni; sintered compact of tungsten and nickel powders. Tungsten grains in nickel matrix; dispersed and grain-boundary precipitates are tungsten carbides and oxides. 1:1 30% $K_3Fe(CN)_6$ + 10% NaOH. 250×

**Fig. 90** Unalloyed molybdenum; a sintered compact. The aggregate of molybdenum grains shows some evidence of porosity (black areas in the microstructure). 1:1 30% $K_3Fe(CN)_6$ + 10% NaOH. 100×

**Fig. 91** 60Mo-40Ag; a sintered compact of molybdenum powder (skeleton) that was infiltrated with silver. The darker areas are molybdenum; lighter areas, silver. Murakami's reagent. 500×

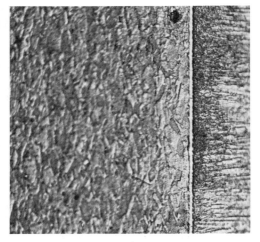

**Fig. 92** 69Au-25Ag-6Pt alloy that was cold worked, then annealed 24 h at 700 °C (1290 °F). This micrograph, made using the differential-interference contrast technique, shows the surface structure or recrystallized grains of the solid solution. 1:1 10% KCN + 10% $(NH_4)_2S_2O_8$. 800×

**Fig. 93** Gold-plated 52Ni-48Fe reed contact annealed at 850 °C (1560 °F). Differential-interference contrast shows diffusion of the plate (light zone) caused by annealing. Dark "hood" is a copper overplate used to retain edge during polishing. See also Fig. 94 and 95. 5% nital, 5% $FeCl_3$ in methanol (alternated). 250×

**Fig. 94** Same as Fig. 93, but showing the gold plate (light vertical band) before diffusion by annealing. Contact is at left of the plate; copper overplate is at right. Differential-interference micrograph. Same etch as Fig. 93. 600×

**Fig. 95** Same as Fig. 94, except showing the gold plate (light gray) after diffusion by annealing (as in Fig. 93). Dark area at right is the copper overplate. Micrograph was made by the differential-interference contrast technique. Same etch as Fig. 93. 600×

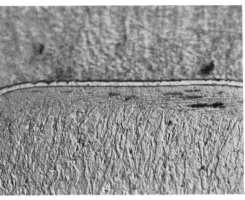

**Fig. 96** Same as Fig. 94, except the gold plate has an underplate of silver. The copper overplate is at top; the 52Ni-48Fe alloy, at bottom. A differential-interference contrast micrograph. See also Fig. 97 and 98. Same etch as Fig. 93. 600×

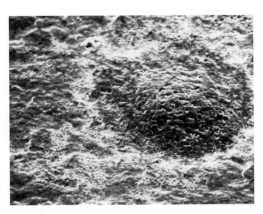

**Fig. 97** Scanning electron micrograph of the surface of a cathode reed contact of same alloy and with same plating as in Fig. 96, but diffused. Buildup of metal was caused by arcing. Mating anode contact shown in Fig. 98. Not polished, not etched. 1000×

**Fig. 98** Scanning electron micrograph of anode reed contact that mated with cathode contact in Fig. 97 (same alloy and plating). Crater is due to arcing, which caused metal transfer from anode to cathode. Not polished, not etched. 1000×

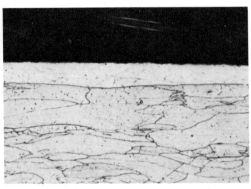

**Fig. 99** Bimetal tape of 91.7Au-8.3Ag cladding (top, below black mount) on unalloyed palladium (bottom); bond is mechanical. Palladium grains are elongated as a result of cold rolling. See also Fig. 100. 1:1 $HNO_3$ + acetic acid. 250×

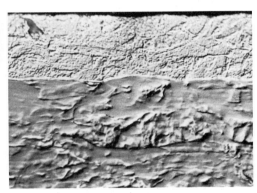

**Fig. 100** Same bimetal tape as in Fig. 99, except this micrograph was made at a higher magnification using the differential-interference contrast technique to delineate the surface structure of the specimen. KCN + $(NH_4)_2S_2O_8$, then $HNO_3$ + acetic acid. 600×

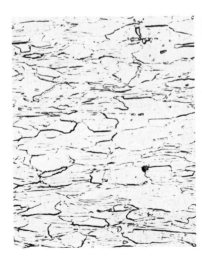

**Fig. 101** 89Pt-11Ru strip, annealed at 1040 °C (1900 °F) and cold rolled (50% reduction). Grains of single-phase solid solution are elongated in direction of rolling. Electrolytic: HCl. 500×

**Fig. 102** 75Pt-25Ir strip, cold rolled. The grains of this single-phase solid solution have been elongated and severely deformed as result of cold rolling. Electrolytic: HCl. 500×

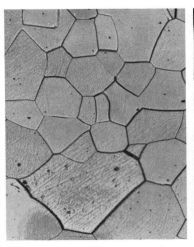

**Fig. 103** Palladium wire, cold drawn and annealed 30 min at 650 to 700 °C (1200 to 1290 °F). Recrystallized grains of single-phase solid solution. Specks are impurities. 10% KCN + 10% $(NH_4)_2S_2O_8$. 75×

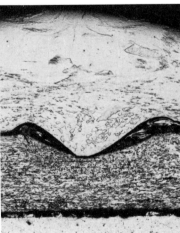

**Fig. 104** Palladium contact welded to nickel silver strip (bottom), then coined, showing some cold work at top of contact and a heat-affected zone at the base. 1:1 $HNO_3$ + acetic acid. 60×

**Fig. 105** Scanning electron micrograph (20 kV, 60° tilt) of a palladium contact used in a telephone relay, with surface erosion due to arcing. Holding screw is at rear. Not polished, not etched. 30×

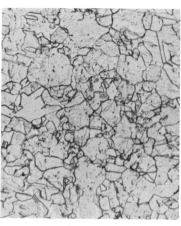

**Fig. 106** 95Pd-5Ru ribbon, annealed for 20 min at 900 °C (1650 °F) to recrystallize the grains. Contact disks are stamped from ribbon and welded to springs. 10% KCN + 10% $(NH_4)_2S_2O_8$. 250×

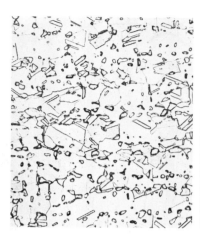

**Fig. 107** 60Pd-40Cu wire, annealed at 955 °C (1750 °F), ordered 2 h at 370 °C (700 °F). Matrix: ordered $\beta$. Disordered grains of $\alpha$ oriented in drawing direction. KCN + $(NH_4)_2S_2O_8$. 500×

**Fig. 108** 50Pd-50Ag, contact, cold worked and annealed 30 min at 1100 °C (2010 °F). Note severely cold-worked grains at outer edges and recrystallized grains within. 10% KCN + 10% $(NH_4)_2S_2O_8$. 75×

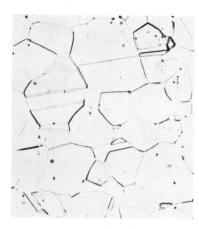

**Fig. 109** 35Pd-10Pt-10Au-30Ag-14Cu-1Zn contact tape, solution annealed at 900 °C (1650 °F), water quenched. Recrystallized grains of solid solution. See also Fig. 110. Electrolytic: HCl. 500×

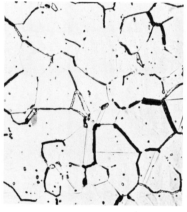

**Fig. 110** Same as Fig. 109, but aged 30 min at 525 °C (980 °F) after annealing. Structure shows coarse grain boundaries because of preferential attack by the etchant. Electrolytic: HCl. 500×

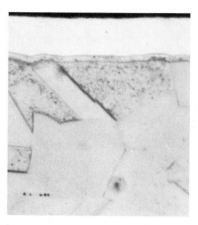

**Fig. 111** Rhodium plate (white) and a gold underplate (gray band) on a 52Ni-48Fe alloy (single-phase fcc solid solution); a reed-switch contact. See also Fig. 112. $HNO_3$ + HCl + glycerol. 2000×

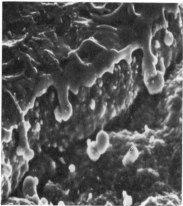

**Fig. 112** Scanning electron micrograph (20 kV, 45° tilt) of surface of a rhodium-plated reed switch showing melting of plate at contact point due to arcing. Not polished, not etched. 3500×

# Sleeve Bearing Materials

By Milton W. Toaz
Senior Scientist
Imperial Clevite

SLEEVE BEARINGS usually consist of one or more layers of a comparatively soft bearing alloy(s), or liner, bonded to a relatively thick steel backing. Therefore, they require metallographic preparation techniques that differ somewhat from those used for singular metals and alloys.

## Specimen Preparation

**Sectioning.** Small specimens for metallographic preparation reduce polishing time. A recommended length is 19 mm ($^3/_4$ in.); the width should be equal to the thickness of the bearing alloy wall for thin-wall liners or a maximum of 6.4 mm ($^1/_4$ in.) for heavy-wall liners.

When sampling a piece of bearing material to produce a specimen, the thickness of the steel backing should be minimized in proportion to that of the bearing alloy. A thick steel layer increases the probability that a relief will be produced during polishing, because the softer bearing liner will be polished away more rapidly. As a result, the bearing alloy and the steel will not be viewed in the same plane, and part of the structure shown will appear out of focus.

Initial cutting can be performed with a handsaw, power saw, or cutoff wheel. Cutting should begin at the bearing alloy and proceed through the steel, or it should begin with the bearing alloy/steel interface parallel to the plane of cutting and proceed through the sleeve bearing. Cutting should never take place from the steel into the bearing alloy. If the initial cutting severely distorts the bearing alloy, the disturbed metal should be removed by wet abrasive belt grinding. The finishing cut should also proceed from the bearing alloy into the steel backing.

**Mounting.** Specimens of sleeve bearing materials are mounted in much the same way as specimens of other metals. For additional information, see the article "Mounting of Specimens" in this Volume. It is often conve-

nient to mount several small specimens together. Each specimen should then be positioned so that the bearing liner faces the same direction.

Thermosetting polymers are frequently used as mounting materials. They are unsuitable, however, for examining a bearing alloy for internal voids, which would likely be collapsed by the time-temperature-pressure combination used. Such examinations require a cold-mounting material, such as a self-curing acrylic or an epoxy liquid. A short vacuum treatment applied immediately after pouring the mounting liquid over the specimen will eliminate as much of the trapped air as possible and will improve penetration of the cold-mounting liquid.

**Grinding** is performed first on an abrasive belt flooded with water or on a low-speed disk grinder (approximately 500 rpm) using water-cooled 180-grit silicon carbide abrasive. The mount is ground next with 240-, 320-, 400-, then 600-grit silicon carbide papers placed on a flat marble pedestal, a plate-glass surface, or a rotating wheel. The grinding is preferably performed wet, with thorough washings of the mount between abrasives. As an alternative, grinding may be performed successively with grades 1, 0, 00, and 000 alumina ($Al_2O_3$) paper using frequent applications of kerosene as a lubricant; the mount should be thoroughly rinsed with kerosene between grindings.

Grinding should begin at the bearing alloy and proceed toward the steel backing, or it should begin with the bearing alloy/steel interface parallel to the direction of grinding and proceed along the specimen. Frequent washings of the abrasive paper with water or kerosene minimize contamination of the bearing alloy by abrasive particles or other debris.

**Polishing** usually begins on a 500- to 600-rpm wheel covered with nylon, to which a coating of 6- to 10-$\mu$m diamond paste has been applied. Polishing should continue with

**Table 1  Etchants for microscopic examination of sleeve bearing materials**

| Etchant | Bearing material |
|---|---|
| $NH_4OH$ and $H_2O_2$(a) | Commercial bronze liner |
| | Copper-lead alloy liner |
| | Copper-lead-tin alloy liner |
| | High-leaded tin bronze liner |
| | Leaded tin bronze liner |
| | Lead-tin-copper overlay on copper-lead alloy liner |
| | Nickel bronze infiltrated with lead-base babbitt |
| | Nickel-tin bronze infiltrated with lead-base babbitt |
| | Silver electroplate on steel |
| | Silver-lead alloy electroplate on steel |
| | Tin-base babbitt overlay on copper-lead-tin alloy liner |
| | Tin bronze infiltrated with lead-base babbitt |
| | Tin bronze infiltrated with Teflon |
| | Trimetal bearing: lead-tin-copper electroplated overlay, brass electroplated barrier, copper-lead alloy |
| 0.5% HF | Aluminum alloy clad to steel |
| | Aluminum-silicon alloy clad to steel |
| | High-tin aluminum alloy clad with unalloyed aluminum |
| | Lead-tin-copper overlay on aluminum alloy liner |
| | Low-tin aluminum alloy clad to steel |
| | Trimetal bearing: lead-tin-copper electroplated overlay, copper electroplated barrier, aluminum-silicon-cadmium alloy |
| 5% nital | High-tin aluminum alloy clad to nickel-plated steel |
| | Lead-base babbitt liner |
| | Tin-base babbitt liner |
| | Steel backing of any bearing alloy |
| Keller's reagent | Lead-tin-copper overlay on aluminum-cadmium alloy |

(a) Equal parts of concentrated $NH_4OH$ and water with 2-4 drops of $H_2O_2$ (30%) per 10 mL of solution.

The author wishes to thank the following individuals for their assistance: K. Summerton, Plant Metallurgist, Imperial Clevite; J. Rigler, Senior Metallographer, Imperial Clevite Technology Center; W.A. Yahraus, Manager, Product Analysis and Field Engineering, Imperial Clevite; and A. Blazy, Retired Senior Metallographer, Imperial Clevite.

**Table 2  Chemical compositions of sleeve bearing alloys**

### Tin base

| Fig. | Alloy designation | Composition, %(a) | | | | | | | | | |
|---|---|---|---|---|---|---|---|---|---|---|---|
| | | Sn | Sb | Pb | Cu | Fe | As | Bi | Zn | Al | Others (total) |
| 1, 2, 47 .........SAE 12 | | 88.0 | 7.0–8.0 | 0.50 | 3.0–4.0 | 0.10 | 0.10 | 0.08 | 0.005 | 0.005 | 0.02 |

### Lead base

| Fig. | Alloy designation | Composition, %(a) | | | | | | | | | |
|---|---|---|---|---|---|---|---|---|---|---|---|
| | | Pb | Sn | Sb | Cu | As | Bi | Zn | Al | Cd | Others (total) |
| 6–8 .............SAE 13 | | rem | 5.0–7.0 | 9.0–11.0 | 0.7 | 0.25 | 0.10 | 0.005 | 0.005 | 0.05 | 0.02 |
| 3–5 .............SAE 14 | | rem | 9.0–11.0 | 14.0–16.0 | 0.7 | 0.6 | 0.10 | 0.005 | 0.005 | 0.05 | 0.02 |
| 9–11 .............SAE 15 | | rem | 0.9–1.7 | 13.5–15.5 | 0.7 | 0.8–1.2 | 0.10 | 0.005 | 0.005 | 0.02 | 0.02 |
| 40 .............SAE 16(b) | | rem | 3.5–4.7 | 3.0–4.0 | 0.10 | 0.05 | 0.10 | 0.005 | 0.005 | 0.005 | 0.40 |

### Plated overlay

| Fig. | Alloy designation | Composition, %(a) | | | | |
|---|---|---|---|---|---|---|
| | | Pb | Sn | Cu | In | Others (total) |
| 36, 37 ........................ | SAE 191 | rem | 8.0–12.0 | ... | ... | 0.5 |
| 42–46, 51–57 ................ | SAE 192 | rem | 8.0–12.0 | 1.0–3.0 | ... | 0.5 |
| 38, 39 ........................ | SAE 193 | rem | 16.0–20.0 | 2.0–3.0 | ... | 0.5 |
| 83, 84 ........................ | SAE 194 | rem | ... | ... | 5.0–10.0 | 0.5 |

### Copper-lead(c)

| Fig. | Alloy designation | Composition, %(a) | | | | | | | | |
|---|---|---|---|---|---|---|---|---|---|---|
| | | Cu | Pb | Sn | Ag | Zn | P | Fe | Others (total) | Others (each) |
| 15, 16 ....................SAE 48 | | 67.0–74.0 | 26.0–33.0 | 0.5 | 1.5 | 0.10 | 0.02 | 0.7 | 0.15 | ... |
| 12–14, 33 ..................SAE 49 | | 73.0–79.0 | 21.0–27.0 | 0.6–2.0 | ... | ... | ... | 0.7 | 0.45 | ... |
| 34, 35 ....................SAE 485 | | rem | 44.0–58.0 | 1.0–5.0 | ... | ... | ... | 0.35 | 0.45 | 0.15 |

### Aluminum base

| Fig. | Alloy designation | Composition, %(a) | | | | | | | | | | |
|---|---|---|---|---|---|---|---|---|---|---|---|---|
| | | Al | Sn | Cd | Si | Cu | Fe | Ni | Pb | Zn | Others (total) | Others (each) |
| 59 ...................SAE 770 | | rem | 5.5–7.0 | ... | 0.7 | 0.7–1.3 | 0.7 | 0.7–1.3 | ... | ... | 0.30 | 0.10 |
| 82, 85–87 .............SAE 780 | | rem | 5.5–7.0 | ... | 1.0–2.0 | 0.7–1.3 | 0.7 | 0.2–0.7 | ... | ... | 0.15 | 0.10 |
| 60, 61, 78, 79 .........SAE 781(d) | | rem | ... | 0.8–1.4 | 3.5–4.5 | 0.05–0.15 | 0.35 | ... | ... | ... | 0.25(e) | 0.10 |
| 80, 81 ...............SAE 782 | | rem | ... | 2.7–3.5 | 0.30 | 0.7–1.3 | 0.30 | 0.7–1.3 | ... | ... | 0.15 | 0.10 |
| 64–67 ...............SAE 783 | | rem | 17.5–22.5 | ... | 0.50 | 0.7–1.3 | 0.50 | 0.10 | ... | ... | 0.15 | 0.10 |
| 68, 69 ...............SAE 784 | | rem | 0.2 | ... | 10.0–12.0 | 0.7–1.3 | 0.30 | 0.10 | ... | ... | 0.03 | 0.10 |
| 70, 71 ...............SAE 785 | | rem | 0.2 | ... | 0.7–1.3 | 0.7–1.3 | 0.30 | ... | ... | 4.5–5.5 | 0.30 | 0.10 |
| 72, 73 ...............SAE 786 | | rem | 37.5–42.5 | ... | ... | ... | 0.30 | ... | ... | ... | 0.30 | 0.10 |
| 74, 75 ...............SAE 787 | | rem | 0.5–2.0 | ... | 3.5–4.5 | 0.5–1.0(f) | 0.30 | ... | 4.0–9.0 | ... | 0.30 | 0.10 |

### Copper base (bronze)

| Fig. | Alloy designation | Composition, %(a) | | | | | | | |
|---|---|---|---|---|---|---|---|---|---|
| | | Cu | Pb | Sn | Zn | Sb | Ni | Fe | Others (total) |
| 21 ........................ | SAE 791(g) | rem | 3.5–4.5 | 3.5–4.5 | 1.5–4.0 | ... | ... | 0.10 | 0.20 |
| 19, 20, 30, 31 ............ | SAE 792 | 77.0 min | 9.0–11.0 | 9.0–11.0 | 0.7 | 0.50 | 0.50 | 0.7 | 0.40 |
| 17, 18 .................... | SAE 793 | 83.0 min | 7.0–9.0 | 3.5–4.5 | 0.5(h) | 0.50 | 0.50 | 0.7 | 0.30 |
| 23 ........................ | ... | 72.0–76.0 | 14.0–18.0 | 9.0–11.0 | 0.5 | 0.50 | 0.50 | 0.7 | 0.30 |
| 24–28, 32 ................ | SAE 794 | 68.5–75.5 | 21.0–25.0 | 3.0–4.0 | 0.5(h) | 0.50 | 0.50 | 0.7 | 0.40 |
| 22 ........................ | SAE 795 | 88.0–92.0(j) | ... | 0.25–0.7 | rem | ... | ... | 0.10 | 0.20 |
| 41 ........................ | ... | 88.0–92.0(j) | ... | 9.5–10.5 | ... | ... | ... | 0.10 | 0.20 |
| 40 ........................ | ... | 83.0–87.0 | ... | ... | ... | ... | 14.0–16.0 | 0.10 | 0.30 |

### Silver base

| Fig. | Alloy designation | Composition, %(a) | | |
|---|---|---|---|---|
| | | Ag | Pb | Others (total) |
| 88, 89 ........................................ | AMS 4815 | Unalloyed | ... | ... |
| 90, 91 ........................................ | ... | 99.3–99.7 | 0.3–0.7 | 0.30 |
| 92, 93 ........................................ | ... | 97.5–98.5 | 1.7–2.3 | 0.30 |

(a) All values not given as ranges are maximum except as shown otherwise. (b) SAE 16 is cast into and on a porous sintered matrix (usually copper-nickel bonded to steel). The surface layer is 0.025 to 0.13-mm (0.001 to 0.005-in.) thick. (c) A corrosion-resistant overlay, such as SAE alloys 191 to 194, may be used with SAE alloys 48, 480, and 481 and is recommended for SAE 49. (d) SAE 781 contains a magnesium content specified at 0.05–0.15%. (e) A 0.15% maximum zinc content is permissible within this range. (f) A modification of this alloy contains 0.05–0.15% Cu, 0.2–0.4% Mn, and 0.05–0.15% Mg (see Fig. 83 and 84). (g) SAE 791 is similar to SAE CA544. (h) The maximum zinc content may be raised to 3.0% upon agreement between purchaser and supplier. (j) Compositions listed are those of a sintered grid prior to infiltration with babbitt or Teflon.

firm pressure for approximately 5 min or until the scratches and disturbed metal from grinding have been removed. The mount should then be thoroughly washed to remove all the diamond abrasive.

Intermediate polishing is performed on a 300-rpm wheel using 0.3-$\mu$m $Al_2O_3$ abrasive and a medium-nap cloth. The abrasive is mixed with distilled water before polishing to form a suspension that should be applied frequently to the cloth during polishing. The mount should be polished for 1 min using light pressure. Additional distilled water is then added to remove most of the $Al_2O_3$ abrasive. After the mount is removed from the wheel, the polished surface should be thoroughly and alternately rinsed in cold and hot water. Excess water should be wiped away with a damp cotton square while the surface is exposed to a dry air blast.

The intermediate polish often yields a surface that is suitable for routine examination. However, a final step using a 300-rpm wheel with a medium-nap cloth will produce a perfect polish. The cloth is moistened with distilled water, then dusted with magnesium oxide abrasive, which is worked into a paste. The mount should be polished for several minutes using heavy pressure. The wheel is then flooded with distilled water, and the pressure is reduced to complete the polish. The mount should be thoroughly rinsed with cold, then hot, water and wiped with a moist cotton square while the surface is exposed to a dry air blast.

Certain polishing techniques that are standard for most singular materials are not always suited to bimetal or trimetal sleeve bearing structures. For sleeve bearing materials, a circular rotation of the mount should be avoided. Instead, the mount should be moved laterally across the wheel with the specimen oriented such that polishing proceeds from the steel toward the bearing alloy (the opposite of the orientation used in grinding). This procedure lessens the tendency of the bearing alloy to polish away at a faster rate than the steel, producing a relief or step at the interface between the two layers.

A relief, if produced, is visible under low magnification as a dark line at the interface between the steel backing and the bearing alloy. This line could easily be misinterpreted as a bond defect. However, examination at high magnification will reveal the true nature of the bond line. Minimizing the ratio of steel backing to bearing alloy, keeping the specimen size small, and following the instructions on mount orientation during polishing will help minimize bond-line relief.

**Etching** of sleeve bearing materials for metallographic examination is usually performed by immersion, although it is sometimes desirable to swab the surface with a cotton square saturated with the etchant just before the rinse. Immediately following removal from the etching reagent, the mount should be thoroughly rinsed in cold, then hot, water, and excess moisture should be removed with a damp cotton square while the surface is exposed to a dry air blast. Rinsing or wiping the surface of a mount with alcohol will promote staining, especially on aluminum bearing alloys. The most common etchants and some of the sleeve bearing alloys to which they best apply are listed in Table 1.

## Microstructures of Sleeve Bearing Materials

Sleeve bearing materials depicted in micrographs in this article are identified and nominal compositions of the materials are given in Table 2. The properties of these materials in bearings are described in the article "Materials for Sliding Bearings" in Volume 3 of the 9th Edition of *Metals Handbook*.

Materials used as solid bearings (no backing) include wrought bronzes and aluminum alloys, microstructures of which are shown in this article. These and other bearing materials are usually used in thinner sections as bearing liners, as described below.

**Bimetal Bearings.** Bearing materials are often bonded to a backing of stronger material such as steel to form a bimetal bearing with increased load-carrying capacity. The bonded layer of the bearing material can be thinner than 0.13 mm (0.005 in.). Babbitts, copper-lead alloys, and leaded tin bronzes are often bonded to steel backing by such processes as continuous gravity casting onto a steel strip as well as static gravity and centrifugal casting against the inside surface of a cylindrical shell.

Aluminum alloys are generally clad to a steel backing by warm rolling. To facilitate bonding, the steel is roughened by belt sanding or grit blasting and is sometimes electroplated with a thin layer of nickel before being clad with the aluminum alloy (the resulting bearing is still referred to as "bimetal").

Other aluminum bearing alloy liners are bonded using an unalloyed aluminum layer. This layer may be formed as part of the bearing alloy fabrication process (as is the case with the powder rolled Al-8Pb-4Si-1Sn-1Cu alloy), or it may be established during fabrication of the bearing alloy strip prior to its cladding to steel (as is often true for SAE 783 alloy).

Silver and silver alloy liners can also be deposited onto a steel backing. A layer of unalloyed silver is deposited by electroplating, followed by a layer of alloyed silver.

**Sintered liners** for sleeve bearings are made from prealloyed powders of copper-lead alloys or high-leaded tin bronzes by spreading the powder uniformly on a continuously moving steel strip that passes through a sintering furnace with a reducing atmosphere. The particles of powder become sintered together, forming an open grid bonded to the steel strip. This bimetal is then rolled to compact the liner and resintered to improve the bond strength. However, aluminum alloy powder for liners is usually roll compacted and sintered before being roll clad to the steel backing strip.

Liners are also made by infiltration of a lower melting material into a layer of sintered copper or copper alloy powder. The powder layer, usually a copper alloy, is not compacted after sintering; the open grid of the sintered powder layer is infiltrated with molten material having a lower melting temperature than that of the grid alloy. This infiltrant is often lead or a lead alloy, but it may be a nonmetallic material such as Teflon. Detailed information on sintering, infiltration, and roll compaction of metal powders can be found in Volume 7 of the 9th Edition of *Metals Handbook*.

**Trimetal Bearings.** The fatigue strength of babbitt or lead-tin alloy can be increased significantly by reducing the thickness of the material to 0.013 to 0.05 mm (0.0005 to 0.0020 in.). Such layers are typically produced by electrodeposition. Under severe operating conditions, these layers may easily wear through; if the backing is steel, seizure can result. To avoid seizure, an interlayer of strong bearing material is placed between the steel backing and the babbitt surface layer.

During the operation of some trimetal bearings, the temperature may rise enough to cause the diffusion of tin from overlays of lead-tin alloys into the intermediate liners of copper alloy, with resulting deterioration of the bearings. To prevent this diffusion, the liner material of such bearings is first electroplated with a thin barrier layer of brass or nickel (the resulting bearing is still referred to as "trimetal"). Aluminum alloy liners are given a zinc immersion coating (zincate), then a thin electroplated layer of copper or nickel in preparation for electrodeposition of the overlay. Thin overlays can also be cast in place by using an excess amount of the lower melting material when infiltrating sintered liners as described above.

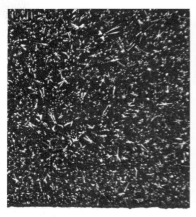

**Fig. 1** Tin-base babbitt liner (SAE 12), continuously cast on steel backing strip (bottom). White second-phase particles (see Fig. 2); matrix of tin saturated with copper and antimony. Nital. 100×

**Fig. 2** Same as Fig. 1, except at higher magnification, which reveals starlike arrays of needles of copper-rich constituent and small, round particles of precipitated antimony-tin. Nital. 500×

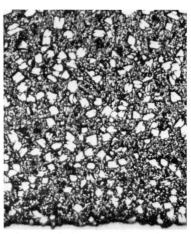

**Fig. 3** Lead-base babbitt liner (SAE 14), continuously cast on steel backing strip (bottom). White particles of antimony-tin in a dark matrix of lead-rich solid solution. See also Fig. 4. Nital. 100×

**Fig. 4** Same as Fig. 3, except at higher magnification, which reveals that the white antimony-tin compound is in the form of cuboid-shaped primary crystals and small eutectic particles. See also Fig. 5. Nital. 500×

**Fig. 5** Same as Fig. 3, but centrifugally cast against inside wall of cylindrical steel shell (bottom). Primary crystals of antimony-tin segregated away from bond between babbitt and steel backing. Nital. 50×

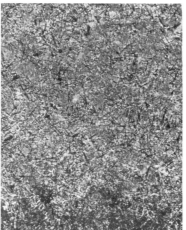

**Fig. 6** Lead-base babbitt liner (SAE 13), continuously cast on steel backing strip (bottom). Dark primary crystals of lead in a light matrix of antimony-tin and lead. See also Fig. 7. Nital. 100×

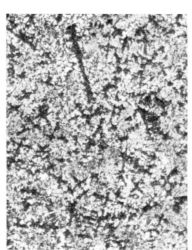

**Fig. 7** Same as Fig. 6, except at higher magnification, which reveals that the configuration of the lead dendrites and the structure of the eutectic-like matrix of antimony-tin and lead. Compare with Fig. 8. Nital. 500×

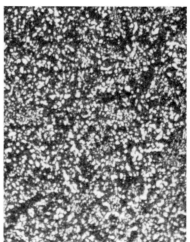

**Fig. 8** Same as Fig. 7, except annealed to increase formability, which changed the microstructure to white crystals of eutectic antimony-tin in a dark matrix of lead-rich solid solution. Nital. 500×

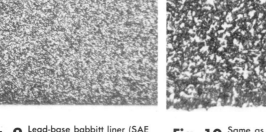

**Fig. 9** Lead-base babbitt liner (SAE 15), continuously cast on steel backing strip (bottom). Antimony-arsenic phase (white) in dark matrix of lead-rich solid solution. See also Fig. 10. Nital. 100×

**Fig. 10** Same as Fig. 9, except at higher magnification showing the white particles of antimony-arsenic phase to be of two types: small eutectic particles and large primary crystals. Compare with Fig. 11. Nital. 500×

**Fig. 11** Same as Fig. 10, except that improper casting conditions have caused the primary antimony-arsenic crystals to form undesirable starlike patterns of needles, causing a decrease in formability. Nital. 500×

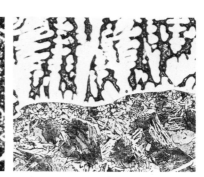

**Fig. 12** Copper-lead alloy liner (SAE 49), gravity cast against inside wall of cylindrical steel shell (bottom). Copper dendrites (light) in a lead matrix (dark). 4% picral, 2% nital. 200×

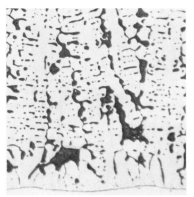

**Fig. 13** Copper-lead alloy liner (SAE 49), gravity cast against inside wall of cylindrical steel shell (bottom). Coarse copper dendrites (light) in a matrix of lead (dark). Compare with Fig. 14. NH₄OH + H₂O₂. 100×

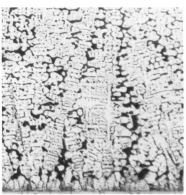

**Fig. 14** Same as Fig. 13, except the copper-lead alloy was continuously cast on a steel backing strip (bottom), which resulted in faster cooling and thus produced finer dendrites of copper. NH₄OH + H₂O₂. 100×

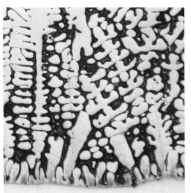

**Fig. 15** Copper-lead alloy liner (SAE 48), gravity cast against inner wall of cylindrical steel shell (bottom). Coarse copper dendrites, blunted by addition of silver, in a continuous matrix of lead. Compare with Fig. 16. NH₄OH + H₂O₂. 100×

**Fig. 16** Same as Fig. 15, except the copper-lead alloy liner was continuously cast on a steel backing strip (bottom of micrograph), which resulted in a faster cooling rate and thus produced finer dendrites of copper. NH₄OH + H₂O₂. 100×

**Fig. 17** Leaded tin bronze liner (SAE 793), continuously cast on steel backing strip (bottom). Cored, fine dendrites of copper solid solution; particles of lead. Compare with Fig. 18. NH₄OH + H₂O₂. 100×

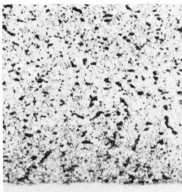

**Fig. 18** Same as Fig. 17, except the strip casting was cold rolled and annealed, which produced globular particles of lead (black) and small equiaxed grains of solid solution of tin and zinc in copper. NH₄OH + H₂O₂. 100×

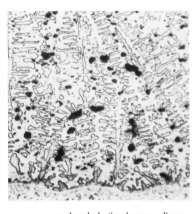

**Fig. 19** Leaded tin bronze liner (SAE 792), gravity cast against inner wall of cylindrical steel shell (bottom). Coarse dendrites of copper solid solution; particles of lead. Compare with Fig. 20. NH₄OH + H₂O₂. 100×

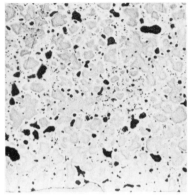

**Fig. 20** Same as Fig. 19, except the liner was centrifugally cast instead of gravity cast. Globular particles of lead (black); cored, fragmented dendrites of solid solution of tin in copper. NH₄OH + H₂O₂. 100×

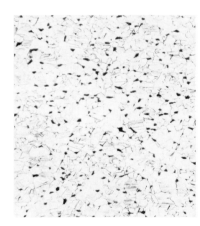

**Fig. 21** Leaded tin bronze (SAE 791) strip, cold rolled and annealed. Globular particles of lead (black) and small, equiaxed, recrystallized grains of solid solution of tin and zinc in copper. See also Fig. 22. NH₄OH + H₂O₂. 100×

**Fig. 22** Commercial bronze (SAE 795) strip, hot rolled. Grains are larger than those in Fig. 21. Absence of lead increases fatigue resistance, but also increases surface sensitivity (susceptibility to seizure). NH₄OH + H₂O₂. 100×

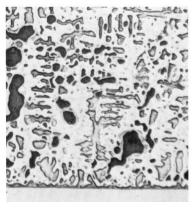

**Fig. 23** High-leaded tin bronze liner (AMS 4825, 74Cu-16Pb-10Sn), gravity cast against inside surface of cylindrical steel shell (bottom). Cored, coarse dendrites of solid solution of tin in copper; interdendritic particles of lead (black). NH₄OH + H₂O₂. 100×

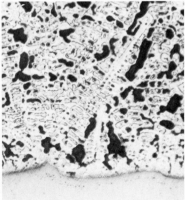

**Fig. 24** High-leaded tin bronze liner (SAE 794), gravity cast against inside wall of cylindrical steel shell (bottom). Same structure as in Fig. 23, except for more interdendritic particles of lead. See also Fig. 25. NH₄OH + H₂O₂. 100×

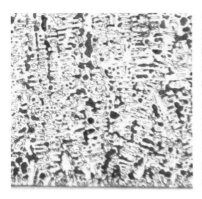

**Fig. 25** Same as Fig. 24, except the liner was continuously cast on steel backing strip (bottom), resulting in faster cooling, which reduced the coarseness of the cored, columnar dendrites of copper solid solution. See also Fig. 26. NH$_4$OH + H$_2$O$_2$. 100×

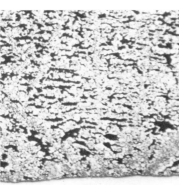

**Fig. 26** Same as Fig. 25, except the strip casting was subsequently cold rolled and annealed, producing a structure consisting of small, equiaxed grains of copper solid solution and an irregular dispersion of lead particles. NH$_4$OH + H$_2$O$_2$. 100×

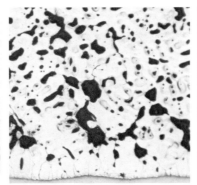

**Fig. 27** High leaded tin bronze liner (SAE 49), gravity cast against inside surface of cylindrical steel shell (bottom). Cored dendrites of solid solution of tin in copper; interdendritic particles of lead. Compare with Fig. 28. NH$_4$OH + H$_2$O$_2$. 100×

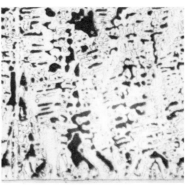

**Fig. 28** Same as Fig. 27, except the liner was continuously cast on the steel backing strip (bottom), resulting in more rapid cooling, which reduced the coarseness of the cored, columnar dendrites of copper solid solution. NH$_4$OH + H$_2$O$_2$. 100×

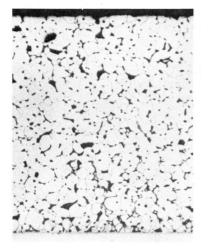

**Fig. 29** Leaded tin bronze liner (SAE 793); prealloyed powder, sintered on a steel backing strip (bottom), cold rolled, and resintered. Copper solid solution; intergranular lead (black). NH$_4$OH + H$_2$O$_2$. 100×

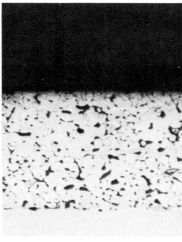

**Fig. 30** Leaded tin bronze liner (SAE 792); prealloyed powder, processed same as Fig. 29, resulting in the same structure, but with more intergranular lead (black). See also Fig. 31. NH$_4$OH + H$_2$O$_2$. 100×

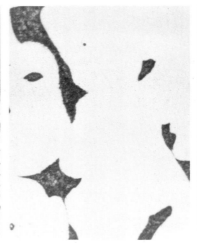

**Fig. 31** Same as Fig. 30, except at higher magnification, which reveals the details of the structure of the bonded particles of copper powder and the intergranular particles of lead. NH$_4$OH + H$_2$O$_2$. 500×

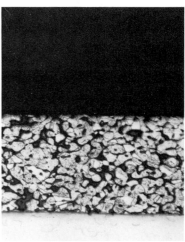

**Fig. 32** High-leaded tin bronze liner (SAE 794); prealloyed powder, processed same as Fig. 29 and 30, resulting in the same structure but with still more intergranular lead (black). NH$_4$OH + H$_2$O$_2$. 100×

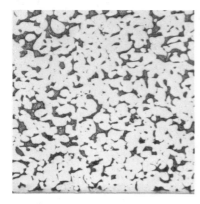

**Fig. 33** Copper-lead alloy liner (SAE 49); prealloyed powder, sintered on a steel backing strip (bottom), cold rolled, and resintered. Unalloyed copper and intergranular lead (black). NH$_4$OH + H$_2$O$_2$. 100×

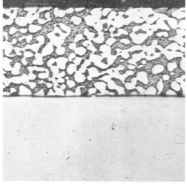

**Fig. 34** High-leaded tin bronze liner (SAE 485); prealloyed powder, sintered on a steel backing strip (bottom), cold rolled, resintered. Copper grains; intergranular lead (black). See also Fig. 35. NH$_4$OH + H$_2$O$_2$. 100×

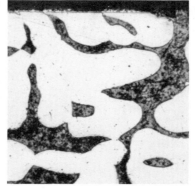

**Fig. 35** Same as Fig. 34, but higher magnification reveals the details of the structure, which is similar to that shown in Fig. 31, except the dark intergranular matrix of lead is almost continuous. NH$_4$OH + H$_2$O$_2$. 500×

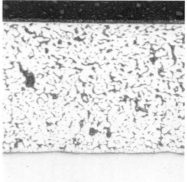

**Fig. 36** From top: electroplated 0.013-mm (0.0005-in.) overlay of lead-tin alloy (SAE 191), sintered copper-lead alloy (SAE 49) liner, and steel backing. See also Fig. 37. NH$_4$OH + H$_2$O$_2$. 100×

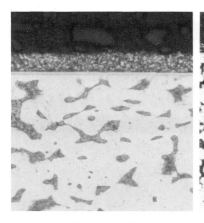

**Fig. 37** Higher magnification view of Fig. 36 showing SAE 191 overlay at top of micrograph separated from sintered SAE 49 bearing liner by flashed 0.001-mm (0.00004-in.) nickel diffusion barrier (gray band below overlay). Light areas in overlay are tin-rich phase; dark areas, lead-rich phase. NH₄OH + H₂O₂. 500×

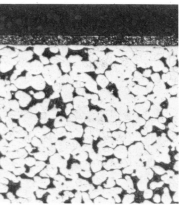

**Fig. 38** From top: electroplated 0.02-mm (0.0008-in.) overlay of lead-tin-copper alloy (SAE 193) and sintered copper-lead alloy (SAE 49) liner. See also Fig. 39, which shows both tin and nickel diffusion barriers not resolvable at lower magnifications. NH₄OH + H₂O₂. 100×

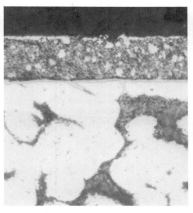

**Fig. 39** Higher magnification view of Fig. 38 showing from top: tin flash (thin white band along upper edge of overlay), SAE 193 overlay, 0.001-mm (0.00004-in.) nickel flash (gray band below overlay) to prevent diffusion of tin into the liner alloy, and SAE 49 liner. Light areas in overlay are tin-rich phase; dark areas, lead-rich phase. NH₄OH + H₂O₂. 500×

**Fig. 40** Liner that was made by infiltrating an open grid of tin bronze (98Cu-2Sn) with molten lead-base babbitt (SAE 16). The grid was made by sintering a mixture of copper and copper-tin alloy powders on a steel backing strip. The excess babbitt formed an overlay. NH₄OH + H₂O₂. 100×

**Fig. 41** Liner made by infiltrating an open grid of tin bronze (90Cu-10Sn) with Teflon paste. The grid was made by sintering prealloyed copper-tin powder (spherical granules) on a steel backing strip (bottom). The excess Teflon formed a thin overlay. NH₄OH + H₂O₂. 100×

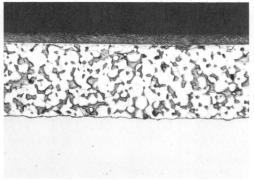

**Fig. 42** From top: electroplated overlay of lead-tin-copper alloy (SAE 192), electroplated brass barrier layer (see Fig. 43 for better detail), sintered copper-lead alloy liner (SAE 49), and steel backing strip (bottom). NH₄OH + H₂O₂. 100×

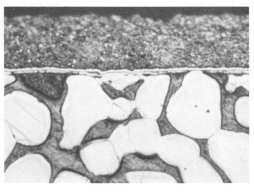

**Fig. 43** Upper part of Fig. 42 at higher magnification. Light bands are the brass plated between overlay (top) and liner (bottom) to prevent diffusion of tin from overlay into liner during operation. Duplex brass layer resulted when tin diffused into upper part of the brass. NH₄OH + H₂O₂. 500×

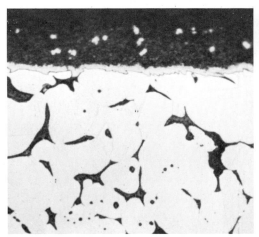

**Fig. 44** Same as Fig. 43, except electroplated diffusion barrier (light gray band) was nickel instead of brass. Note the absence of tin diffusion into the nickel plate. NH₄OH + H₂O₂. 500×

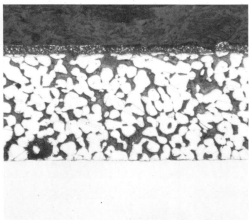

**Fig. 45** Same as Fig. 42, except no barrier layer was placed between the sintered liner and the electroplated lead-tin-copper overlay. See Fig. 46 for details of the overlay. NH₄OH + H₂O₂. 100×

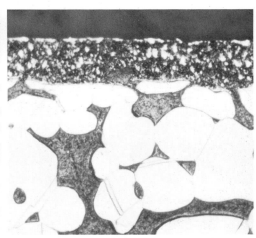

**Fig. 46** Higher magnification view of Fig. 45 (without steel backing), showing the tin (small white areas) in the overlay. The tin inhibits corrosion of the lead. NH₄OH + H₂O₂. 500×

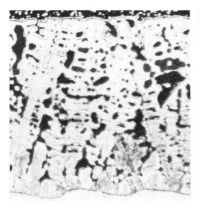

**Fig. 47** Overlay of tin-base babbitt (SAE 12), centrifugally cast on the cast 75Cu-24Pb-1Sn liner shown in Fig. 12; steel backing at bottom. See also Fig. 48. $NH_4OH + H_2O_2$. 100×

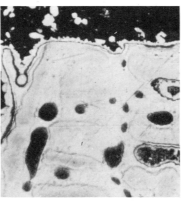

**Fig. 48** Higher magnification view of Fig. 47 (without steel), showing details of structure at interface between liner (light matrix and overlay (dark matrix). $NH_4OH + H_2O_2$. 500×

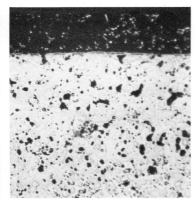

**Fig. 49** Overlay of tin-base babbitt (SAE 12) centrifugally cast on the cast leaded tin bronze liner (SAE 792) shown in Fig. 20. See also Fig. 50. $NH_4OH + H_2O_2$. 100×

**Fig. 50** Same as Fig. 49, except higher magnification shows details of the structure at the interface between liner (light matrix) and overlay (dark matrix). $NH_4OH + H_2O_2$. 500×

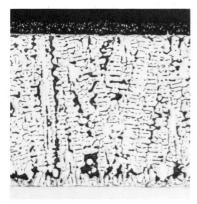

**Fig. 51** Electroplated overlay of SAE 192 on the cast 75Cu-25Pb alloy liner shown in Fig. 14, which first had been nickel plated; steel backing strip is at bottom. See also Fig. 52. $NH_4OH + H_2O_2$. 100×

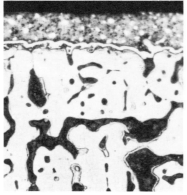

**Fig. 52** Higher magnification view of Fig. 51 (without steel), showing the nickel (light band) plated on the liner to prevent diffusion of tin from the overlay into the copper-lead alloy liner. See also Fig. 53. $NH_4OH + H_2O_2$. 500×

**Fig. 53** Same as Fig. 51, except the copper-lead alloy liner was continuously cast on a thick steel backing slab (not shown) instead of on a thin steel strip. See Fig. 54 for details of the nickel barrier. $NH_4OH + H_2O_2$. 100×

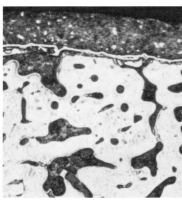

**Fig. 54** Same as Fig. 53, except higher magnification shows nickel barrier (light band) placed between liner and overlay (top) to prevent diffusion of tin into the copper-lead alloy. See also Fig. 55 to 58. $NH_4OH + H_2O_2$. 500×

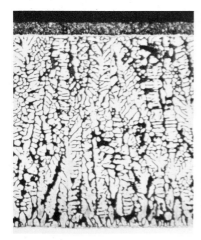

**Fig. 55** Same as Fig. 51, except the lead-tin-copper alloy overlay was electroplated on the copper-lead alloy liner (SAE 48) shown in Fig. 16, which first had been nickel electroplated. $NH_4OH + H_2O_2$. 100×

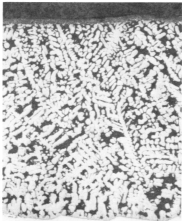

**Fig. 56** Same as Fig. 51, except the lead-tin-copper alloy overlay was electroplated on a Cu-40Pb-5.5Ag alloy liner that first had been nickel electroplated. $NH_4OH + H_2O_2$. 100×

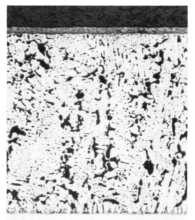

**Fig. 57** Same as Fig. 51, except the lead-tin-copper overlay was electroplated on high-leaded tin bronze liner (SAE 49) shown in Fig. 28 (except cast on thick slab instead of strip). See also Fig. 58. $NH_4OH + H_2O_2$. 100×

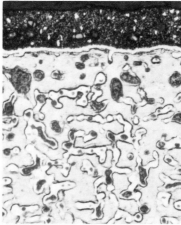

**Fig. 58** Same as Fig. 57 (without steel); higher magnification shows nickel plate (light band) deposited between liner and overlay to prevent diffusion of tin into the lead in the bronze liner. $NH_4OH + H_2O_2$. 500×

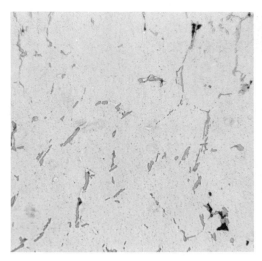

**Fig. 59** Low-tin aluminum alloy (SAE 770), solid cast (no backing was used) in a permanent mold. Interdendritic tin (pale gray particles) and NiAl$_3$ (darker gray particles) in aluminum solid solution. 0.5% HF. 200×

**Fig. 60** Aluminum-silicon alloy strip (SAE 781) clad to a steel backing strip (bottom) by warm rolling. See Fig. 61 for details of the structure of the aluminum alloy liner and bond between liner and steel. 0.5% HF. 100×

**Fig. 61** Higher magnification view of Fig. 60. Aluminum alloy structure; fragmented particles of silicon (gray, outlined) and small particles of cadmium and other insoluble phases in an aluminum matrix. 0.5% HF. 500×

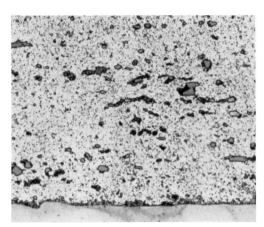

**Fig. 62** Low-tin aluminum alloy strip (SAE 780) clad to steel backing strip (bottom) by warm rolling. Particles of tin (elongated), silicon (equiaxed), and other insoluble phases (dots) in aluminum. 0.5% HF. 500×

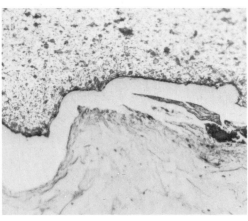

**Fig. 63** Same as Fig. 62, except that the steel was roughened by grit blasting, then electroplated with a layer of nickel (light band) to facilitate bonding of the aluminum alloy to the steel backing strip (bottom). 0.5% HF. 500×

**Fig. 64** High-tin aluminum alloy strip (SAE 783), clad to nickel-electroplated steel backing strip (bottom) by warm rolling. See Fig. 65 for details of the aluminum alloy layer and its bond with the steel. Nital. 100×

**Fig. 65** Same as Fig. 64, except higher magnification shows the structure of the aluminum alloy containing large particles of tin (light, outlined), elongated in the rolling direction in a matrix of aluminum solid solution. Nital. 500×

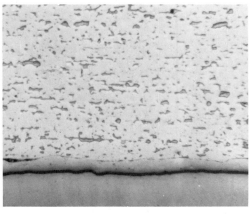

**Fig. 66** High-tin aluminum alloy strip (SAE 783), clad (by rolling) with a layer of unalloyed aluminum, then clad (by rolling) to steel backing strip (layer of unalloyed aluminum faces steel). See also Fig. 67. As-polished. 100×

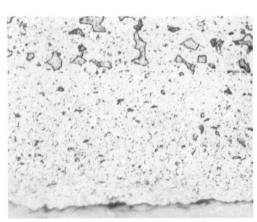

**Fig. 67** Same as Fig. 66, but higher magnification shows details of the bond area. Large particles of tin (outlined) are present only in aluminum alloy liner, not in layer of unalloyed aluminum between liner and steel. 0.5% HF. 500×

**Fig. 68** Aluminum-silicon alloy strip (SAE 784) clad to a low-carbon steel backing strip (bottom) by warm rolling. See Fig. 69 for an enlarged view of the alloy structure. 0.5% HF. 200×

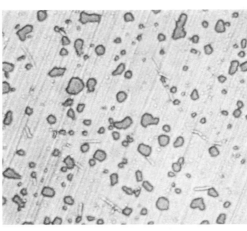

**Fig. 69** Higher magnification view of Fig. 68 (steel not shown). The aluminum alloy structure consists of blocky silicon particles in an aluminum solid-solution matrix. 0.5% HF. 1000×

**Fig. 70** Aluminum alloy strip (SAE 785) clad to a low-carbon steel backing strip (bottom) by warm rolling. See Fig. 71 for an enlarged view of the alloy structure. 0.5% HF. 100×

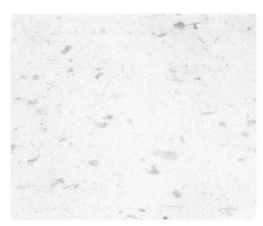

**Fig. 71** Higher magnification view of Fig. 70 (steel not shown). Blade-like particles are aluminum-silicon compound; darker gray rounded particles are silicon; lighter gray particles are copper-rich phase. Matrix is aluminum-zinc solid solution. 0.5% HF. 500×

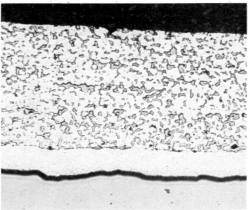

**Fig. 72** Aluminum-tin alloy strip (SAE 786) clad to an unalloyed aluminum bonding layer (center) by warm rolling. The composite strip was subsequently clad to a steel backing strip (bottom) by warm rolling. See Fig. 73 for an enlarged view of the alloy structure. 0.5% HF. 100×

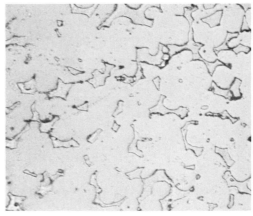

**Fig. 73** Higher magnification view of Fig. 72 (unalloyed aluminum bonding layer and steel not shown). The aluminum alloy structure consists of tin particles (outlined) that are uniformly distributed and somewhat elongated in the rolling direction in an aluminum solid-solution matrix. 0.5% HF. 500×

**Fig. 74** Aluminum-lead alloy strip (SAE 787) clad to a low-carbon steel backing strip (bottom) by warm rolling. See Fig. 75 for an enlarged view of the alloy structure. 0.5% HF. 100×

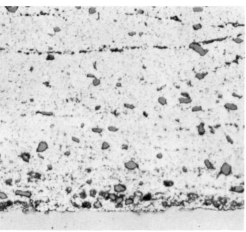

**Fig. 75** Higher magnification view of Fig. 74. The aluminum alloy structure consists of stringers of lead (dark) and equiaxed particles of silicon (gray) in an aluminum solid-solution matrix. 0.5% HF. 500×

**Fig. 76** Aluminum alloy liner SAE 787 clad to steel backing strip (bottom) by warm rolling. Liner was made from prealloyed powder, roll compacted and sintered. See Fig 77 for an enlarged view of the alloy structure. 0.5% HF. 100×

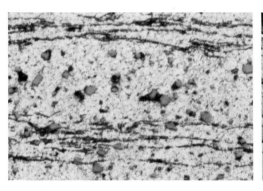

**Fig. 77** Higher magnification view of Fig. 76 (steel not shown). The aluminum alloy structure consists of stringers of lead-tin constituent and equiaxed particles of silicon (gray) in an aluminum solid-solution matrix. 0.5% HF. 500×

**Fig. 78** From top: electroplated overlay of lead-tin-copper alloy (SAE 192), electroplated copper (white band), rolled aluminum-silicon-cadmium alloy (SAE 781) liner, and steel backing. See Fig. 79 for details of copper layer. 0.5% HF. 100×

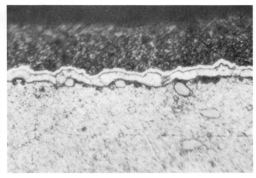

**Fig. 79** Upper part of Fig. 78, shown at higher magnification. Copper (light bands) was plated on a zinc immersion coating (invisible here) prior to plating overlay. Duplex copper layer is result of tin diffusion into upper part of copper. NH₄OH + H₂O₂. 1000×

**Fig. 80** Same as Fig. 78, except overlay (top) was electroplated onto aluminum-cadmium alloy (SAE 782) strip that had been clad to a steel backing strip (bottom) by warm rolling. See Fig. 81 for details of bond. Keller's reagent. 100×

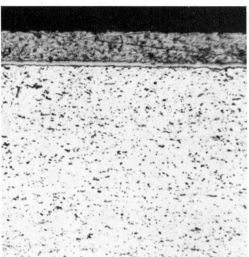

**Fig. 81** Higher magnification view of Fig. 80 (steel not shown). Copper (band below overlay) was electroplated on a zinc immersion coating (invisible here) on the aluminum alloy liner, prior to electroplating the overlay. Keller's reagent. 500×

**Fig. 82** Overlay (dark, at top) of lead-tin-copper alloy (SAE 192) electroplated on a low-tin aluminum alloy liner (SAE 780) clad to a steel backing strip (bottom). See also Fig. 85. 0.5% HF. 250×

**Fig. 83** From top: electroplated 0.02-mm (0.0008-in.) overlay of lead-indium alloy (SAE 194), cast copper-lead alloy (SAE 49) liner, and steel backing. See also Fig. 84. NH₄OH + H₂O₂. 105×

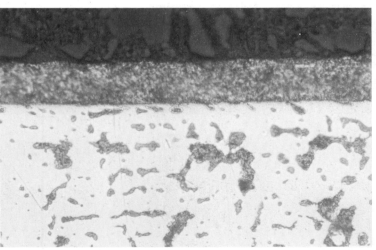

**Fig. 84** Higher magnification view of Fig. 83 (steel not shown). Light areas in the overlay are indium-rich phase; dark areas, lead-rich phase. NH₄OH + H₂O₂. 525×

**Fig. 85** Same as Fig. 82, except that the steel was roughened by grit blasting, then electroplated with nickel to increase bond strength between the aluminum alloy liner and the steel backing strip (bottom). See also Fig. 86 and 87. 0.5% HF. 100×

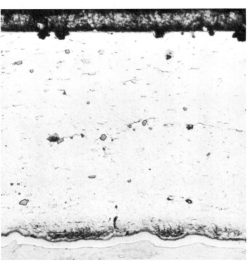

**Fig. 86** Same as Fig. 85, except at higher magnification, which shows structural details of the aluminum alloy liner and more clearly shows the layer of nickel plate (light band) at the bond between the liner and the steel backing strip (bottom). See also Fig. 87. 0.5% HF. 250×

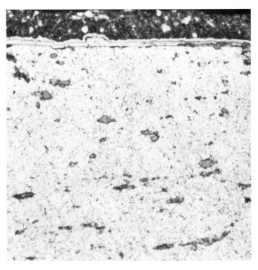

**Fig. 87** Upper part of Fig. 86 at higher magnification. Copper (light bands) was electroplated on a zinc immersion coating (invisible here) on the liner, prior to plating the overlay. A duplex copper layer resulted from diffusion of tin from overlay into upper part of copper. 0.5% HF. 500×

**Fig. 88** Unalloyed silver (AMS 4815) electroplated on a steel backing strip (bottom); as-plated. This type of bearing is subsequently electroplated with an overlay of lead, then of indium. See also Fig. 89. NH₄OH + H₂O₂. 100×

**Fig. 89** Same as Fig. 88, except annealed to set the bond and recrystallize the silver. The bearing is usually reannealed, after the lead and indium electroplated overlays have been added, to diffuse indium into the lead. NH₄OH + H₂O₂. 100×

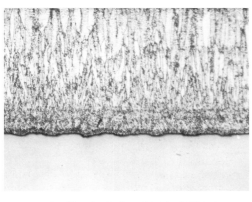

**Fig. 90** Silver-lead alloy (99.5Ag-0.5Pb) electroplated on a steel backing strip (bottom), which first had been electroplated with unalloyed silver. As-plated. See Fig. 91 for effects of annealing. NH₄OH + H₂O₂. 100×

**Fig. 91** Same as Fig. 90, except annealed to set the bonds and recrystallize the unalloyed silver (dark band). Columnar grains of the silver-lead alloy were not noticeably affected. NH₄OH + H₂O₂. 100×

**Fig. 92** Silver-lead alloy (98Ag-2Pb) electroplated on a steel backing strip (bottom) that had been electroplated with unalloyed silver (dark band); as-plated. See also Fig. 93. NH₄OH + H₂O₂. 100×

**Fig. 93** Same as Fig. 92, except annealed to set the bonds, homogenize the silver-lead alloy, and recrystallize the silver-lead alloy and the unalloyed silver on the steel strip (bottom). NH₄OH + H₂O₂. 100×

# Weldments

By Glenn S. Huppi
Research Engineer
Center for Welding Research
Colorado School of Mines

Brian K. Damkroger
Research Engineer
Center for Welding Research
Colorado School of Mines

and

Craig B. Dallam
Research Engineer
Center for Welding Research
Colorado School of Mines

FUSION WELDING is the joining of two or more pieces of material by melting a portion of each and allowing the liquefied portions to solidify together. This can be accomplished with or without filler metal, and one or more passes can be made.

The term "weld" denotes the area of coalescence produced by welding (Ref 1). A welded joint is a composite of three regions: the fusion zone, heat-affected zone, and unaffected base metal. These zones are shown in Fig. 1, 5, and 6. The fusion zone is the material that was melted during welding. It is bordered by the fusion line. The fusion zone material usually has a chemical composition similar to that of the base metal(s). In the heat-affected zone, which is the area adjacent to the fusion zone, the material has undergone a thermal cycle that observably alters the microstructure of the base material. The base metal is the material that is not observably altered by welding. In multiple-pass welds, successive passes produce changes in the fusion and heat-affected zones of earlier passes. These regions, shown in Fig. 6, are called reheat zones. Additional terms used to refer to specific portions of welded joints are illustrated in Fig. 1.

This article will consider joints produced by arc welding. The metallography and structure of welded joints and the problems and techniques associated with their study will be discussed. When standard sample preparation and analytical techniques for a given material are used, they will be covered briefly

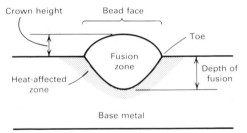

**Fig. 1** Schematic diagram of a fusion weld bead defining terminology used in this article

here, and the reader will be referred to the article on that topic in this Volume. Similarly, the metallurgical aspects of welding and specific materials will be discussed only to the extent necessary to explain the microstructures observed. Chemical compositions of base metal, filler metal (weld wires), and fusion zones for which micrographs are shown in this article are given in Table 1.

The remainder of this article consists of six sections. The first describes the techniques used in the sectioning and sample preparation of welded joints. The next four sections each deal with a particular metallurgical aspect of welded joints: the overall bead morphology, the solidification structure, the solid-state transformation structure, and metallurgical defects produced by the welding process. The techniques required to study each particular metallurgical aspect in several common alloy systems are discussed. The last

section is an overview of characteristics specific to several different welding processes.

## Sample Preparation

The transverse section, which is most often used to observe and document welded joint macrostructure and microstructure, may be supplemented by additional viewing and sectioning techniques, including the top-view photograph, the longitudinal section, and the normal section. For studies of solidification effects, a section normal to the solidification direction may be useful. These sections are illustrated in Fig. 2. Applications for sectioning techniques are summarized in Table 2.

Preparation of weld metal sections requires the same precautions as those for wrought and cast material. Sufficient material must be removed during grinding to eliminate the thermal and mechanical effects of rough cutting or sawing. Care must then be taken to maintain the proper plane of section, particularly when the section is used for such measurements as bead area, depth of fusion, or grain aspect ratio. Clear or translucent mounting materials are therefore recommended for small pieces when the joint is subject to quantitative measurement. Preservation of the proper plane of section may become a problem when materials of significantly different hardness are joined or when the weld deposit differs greatly in hardness from the substrate. In these cases, extra care and/or automatic grinding equipment are

The authors wish to thank the following individuals for their assistance: P.F. Slebodnik, GEO Centers; J. Dyck, Colorado School of Mines; and P. Dunn, Colorado School of Mines.

**Table 1  Chemical composition of base metals, weld wires, and fusion zones**

| Fig. | Alloy | Composition, % | | | | | | | | | | | |
|---|---|---|---|---|---|---|---|---|---|---|---|---|---|
| | | C | Mn | S | P | Si | Cr | Ni | Mo | Nb | Al | Cu | Other |
| **Low-alloy steels** | | | | | | | | | | | | | |
| 5 ............... A-710 | | | | | | | | | | | | | ... |
| | Base metal | 0.05 | 0.54 | 0.006 | 0.01 | 0.26 | 0.72 | 0.91 | 0.20 | 0.05 | 0.03 | 1.20 | 0.005 Ti |
| | Fusion zone | 0.06 | 0.85 | 0.005 | 0.01 | 0.22 | 0.53 | 0.62 | 0.24 | 0.03 | 0.025 | 0.90 | 0.001 B |
| 6 ............... A-710 | | | | | | | | | | | | | |
| | Base metal | 0.05 | 0.54 | 0.006 | 0.01 | 0.26 | 0.72 | 0.91 | 0.20 | 0.05 | 0.03 | ... | ... |
| | Weld wire | 0.06 | 1.40 | ... | ... | 0.35 | 0.10 | 1.75 | 0.35 | ... | ... | ... | ... |
| 7, 28 ........... A-170 (a) | | 0.04 | 0.55 | 0.01 | 0.01 | 0.25 | 0.70 | 0.90 | ... | 0.05 | 0.03 | 1.20 | ... |
| 8 ............... 2.25Cr-1 Mo | | | | | | | | | | | | | |
| | Base metal | 0.11 | 0.51 | 0.004 | 0.003 | 0.13 | 2.23 | 0.01 | 0.93 | 0.05 | 0.026 | 0.01 | ... |
| 9, 21 ........... Lukens Frostline (b) | | | | | | | | | | | | | |
| | Fusion zone | 0.14 | 1.4 | ... | ... | 0.4 | ... | 0.14 | 0.05 | ... | ... | 0.18 | |
| 14, 27 .......... AISI 4340 | | | | | | | | | | | | | |
| | Base metal | 0.41 | 0.65 | 0.04 | 0.01 | 0.20 | 0.76 | 1.65 | 0.21 | ... | ... | ... | ... |
| | Weld wire | 0.31 | 0.55 | 0.01 | 0.01 | 0.65 | 1.25 | ... | 0.50 | ... | ... | ... | ... |
| 17, 20, 22 ........ A-36 (c) | | | | | | | | | | | | | 0.027 O |
| | Fusion zone | 0.05 | 1.07 | 0.016 | 0.019 | 0.42 | 0.01 | 0.05 | 0.01 | ... | ... | ... | 0.009 N |
| 19 .............. A-710 | | | | | | | | | | | | | |
| | Fusion zone | 0.06 | 1.4 | 0.01 | 0.01 | 0.31 | 0.15 | 1.8 | 0.35 | ... | ... | 0.15 | |
| 26 .............. HY 80 | | | | | | | | | | | | | |
| | Base metal | 0.08 | 0.75 | ... | ... | 0.35 | 1.10 | 2.30 | 0.4 | ... | ... | ... | ... |
| | Weld wire | 0.04 | 1.0 | ... | ... | 0.60 | ... | 1.50 | 0.5 | ... | ... | ... | ... |

| Fig. | Alloy | Composition, % | | | | | | | | | |
|---|---|---|---|---|---|---|---|---|---|---|---|
| | | Al | V | Nb | Ta | Mo | C | N | Fe | O | H |
| **Titanium alloys** | | | | | | | | | | | |
| 12, 16, 24, 25 ................. Ti-6Al-2Nb-1Ta-1Mo | | | | | | | | | | | |
| | Base metal | 6.0 | ... | 1.9 | 0.9 | 0.81 | 0.02 | 0.009 | 0.09 | 0.071 | 0.005 |
| | Weld wire (d) | 5.7 | ... | 2.1 | 1.0 | 0.68 | 0.03 | 0.01 | 0.04 | 0.07 | 0.004 |
| 13, 23 ...................... Ti-6Al-4V | | | | | | | | | | | |
| | Base metal | 6.59 | 4.11 | ... | ... | ... | 0.14 | 0.01 | 0.13 | 0.07 | 0.007 |
| | Fusion zone (e) | | | | | | | | | | |

(a) Nominal composition. (b) Welded using AWS E70S-3 wire. (c) Welded using AWS E7018 wire. (d) Weld wire chemistry for Fig. 16 and 25 only. (e) Same as base metal for Fig. 13, except for addition of 0.01 wt% yttrium

recommended. Final grinding and polishing should be performed as recommended for the alloy system(s) present in the joint.

Special precautions apply to welds made with a backing plate. The gap between the base and backup plates should be filled with epoxy or a similar material to prevent buildup of grinding debris. Heavy oxides on surfaces between the base and backup plates should be removed by pickling before the epoxy is applied to prevent dragout during polishing (Fig. 7).

## Weld Bead Morphology

The weld bead morphology for fusion welding can be described by the appearance of the bead face and the weld bead cross section. A top-view photograph will depict the general appearance of the weld, illustrating surface irregularities, spatter, or macroscopic defects such as hot cracking or porosity. The weld bead cross section can be described by measurement of toe-to-toe width, bead penetration or depth of fusion, crown height, and total area of the weld bead. All of these parameters are best determined from a transverse section. Incorrect sectioning will cause errors in depth of penetration and bead area measurement. These errors are summarized in Fig. 3. Except in the most severe cases, the sectioning error introduced on bead area and

depth of fusion measurements will likely be lower than the sampling error due to variability along the length of the weld. The welding process, parameters, consumables, and base material are equally important in determining the final weld bead morphology. Various bead morphologies may be observed in Fig. 5, 6, 8, and 9.

## Solidification Structures in Welded Joints

Fusion metal in a welded joint solidifies by epitaxial growth from partially melted grains in the heat-affected zone. Cells or dendrites grow in packets from each heat-affected zone

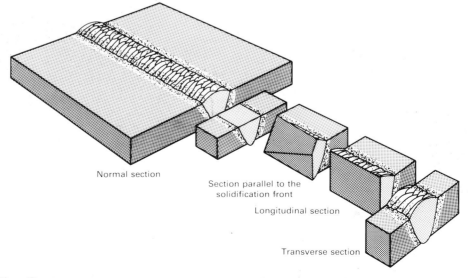

**Fig. 2** Sections used in the metallographic examination of welded joints. See also Table 2.

Normal section

Section parallel to the solidification front

Longitudinal section

Transverse section

grain into the weld pool in a preferential crystallographic direction (Ref 2). A dendritic structure in a type 304 stainless steel weldment is shown in Fig. 10. One consequence of epitaxial growth is that a single, favorably oriented grain (packet) can traverse many successive beads in a multiple-pass weld (Fig.

**Table 2   A summary of welded joint sections and their uses**

See also Fig. 2.

| Section | Uses |
|---|---|
| Transverse .......... | Bead geometry |
| | Joint characterization |
| | Microstructural characterization |
| | Solidification structure |
| | Defect documentation |
| |    Solidification shrinkage cracks |
| |    Underbead cracks |
| |    Toe cracks |
| |    Hydrogen cracks |
| |    Weld metal longitudinal cracks |
| |    Weld metal root cracks |
| |    Slag entrapment |
| |    Incomplete fusion |
| |    Inadequate joint penetration |
| |    Pile-up |
| |    Undercut |
| |    Porosity |
| Longitudinal ........ | Solidification structure |
| | Defect documentation |
| |    Transverse heat-affected zone base metal cracks |
| |    Transverse weld metal cracks |
| Normal to solidification direction .......... | Solidification cell or dendrite characterization |
| Normal ............. | Solidification structure |
| | Defect documentation |
| |    Solidification shrinkage cracks |
| |    Hydrogen cracks |
| Top surface (a) ...... | Appearance of joint |
| | Defect documentation |
| |    Arc strike |
| |    Spatter |
| |    Porosity (blow holes) |
| |    Weld metal crater cracks |
| |    Transverse heat-affected zone base metal cracks |
| |    Transverse weld metal cracks |
| |    Weld metal longitudinal cracks |
| |    Toe cracks |

(a) Not truly a section; does not require destructive sampling

11). As solidification progresses, grains bend to follow the maximum thermal gradient (Fig. 12). This phenomenon can be employed to map solidification isotherms through the use of longitudinal, transverse, and normal sections.

During solidification, alloying elements may be rejected by the solid into the liquid regions between the dendrites, cells, and/or neighboring grains. With sufficient segregation, the solidification mode (cellular or dendritic) can be determined using appropriate etches. The pattern of oxides entrapped between cells or dendrites (Fig. 13) may also reveal how the weld metal solidified.

It is often difficult to observe the as-solidified structure, because the microstructure is altered by one or more solid-state phase transformations during cooling. However, in some materials the solidification grain or packet boundaries act as preferential sites for the nucleation of solid-state transformation products. In these cases, the solidification grain structure is marked by discontinuities in the transformation structure.

**Ferrous Alloys.** In low-alloy steels, the solidification packet or austenite grain size may be marked by continuous veins of proeutectoid ferrite (Fig. 14). The solidification mode is often difficult to determine because of solid-state phase transformations that mask the solidification structure. However, in some low-alloy steels segregation is sufficient to allow observation. This is usually the case with alloys that contain slightly higher concentrations of chromium and nickel, such as AISI 4340. In these alloys, the solidification structure can be inferred from the distribution of the solid-state transformation products and is best shown by using a picral or nital etch (Fig. 14).

Many austenitic steels are welded with filler metals that have a stable duplex δ-ferrite/austenite structure at room temperature. These filler metals solidify by epitaxial

growth of the phase present (austenite) in the heat-affected zone (Ref 3, 4). In many commercial stainless steel alloys, this results in primary austenite dendrites with some δ-ferrite in the interdendritic regions. In these alloys, the solidification structure is observable due to segregation (Fig. 10). Delta-ferrite is highlighted by the use of Murakami's etch, allowing the volume fraction of δ-ferrite, an important parameter in the welding of these alloys, to be determined by point counting (Ref 5). However, the volume fraction of δ-ferrite retained at room temperature is usually indicated by the magnetic properties of the material rather than by point counting.

**Aluminum Alloys.** Commercial alloys of aluminum are usually based on eutectic systems with limited solid solubility. Weld metal in these alloys solidifies by epitaxial growth of proeutectic, aluminum-rich dendrites. Solute rejection during solidification results in a final structure of divorced eutectic between aluminum-rich dendrites (Fig. 15).

**Titanium Alloys.** Metastable β-titanium alloys retain their solidification structure to room temperature. Evidence of the solidification type in β and heavily stabilized α-β alloys can be seen due to microsegregation. Solidification structures have been studied using a hydrofluoric acid plus nitric acid (HF + HNO$_3$) etch and oblique illumination or dendrite decoration techniques (Ref 6). The solidification grain structure of α alloys and "lean" α-β alloys, which contain much more α than β, remains observable (Fig. 16), although these alloys undergo extensive solid-state phase transformations. The large, columnar, prior-β grains in the fusion and grain growth zones can be easily seen. Another aspect of welded joints in these alloys is the extensive epitaxial growth and the similarity of structures in the fusion and grain growth zones, which causes difficulty in locating the fusion line (Fig. 16). Observation of solidification structures in titanium alloys may be

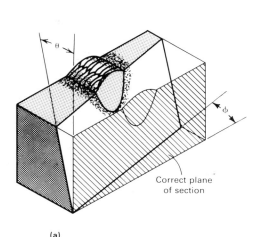

(a)

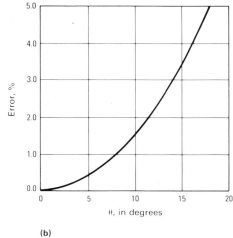

(b)

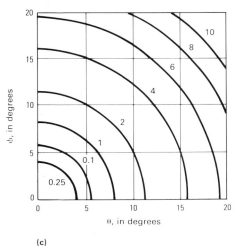

(c)

**Fig. 3**  Measurement errors introduced in the determination of joint penetration (or depth of fusion) and weld bead area as a function of θ and φ as shown in (a). (b) Joint penetration error. (c) Weld bead area error

accomplished with the use of a HF + HNO₃-based etchant. A detailed guide to the metallography of titanium alloys can be found in Ref 7.

**Other Alloy Systems.** Weld metal solidification structures in copper alloys based on eutectic systems are similar to commercial aluminum alloys with divorced eutectic outlining copper-rich dendrites. The dendritic solidification structures in the peritectic systems (brasses, beryllium coppers, and silicon bronzes) and continuous solid-solution systems, such as nickel-copper alloys, are frequently discernible due to microsegregation (Ref 8, 9). Etch-polish and electropolishing techniques are recommended to prevent smearing or embedding particles in the specimen surface. Etchants used for copper-base alloy weldments are similar to those used for wrought plate material of the same composition. For additional information, see the articles "Copper and Copper Alloys" and "Beryllium-Nickel and Beryllium-Copper Alloys" in this Volume.

Solidification structures in the welds of highly alloyed nickel-, cobalt-, and iron-base superalloys are usually discernible due to the segregation of one or more solute elements during solidification. For example, in the iron-base A286 and JBK75 alloys, titanium, phosphorus, and sulfur strongly segregate to the interdendritic regions, allowing the solidification structure to be revealed by a phoschromic electroetch (Ref 5, 10). In aged welds, the solidification structure may be inferred from the inhomogeneous distribution of γ' precipitates. Nickel-base superalloys with low aluminum and titanium contents are considered to be readily weldable (Ref 11). In these alloys, the solidification structure can be revealed by electroetching with phoschromic or a solution of 10 mL phosphoric acid (H₃PO₄) plus 50 mL sulfuric acid (H₂SO₄) plus 40 mL HNO₃. A technique of etch-polishing with a 1:1 solution of acetic acid and HNO₃ followed by etching with glyceregia also produces good results with many nickel-base superalloys (Ref 5). As in copper systems, special care must be taken to avoid smearing the sample.

In most alloy systems, the solidification type or grain structure can be observed. Etchants appropriate for the base plate often will be suitable for weld metal of the same composition. Etches used for several alloy systems are listed in Table 3. For further information, see Ref 5 and the Section "Metallographic Techniques and Microstructures: Specific Metals and Alloys" in this Volume.

# Solid-State Transformation Structures in Welded Joints

The room-temperature microstructure of the fusion zone can consist of a combination

**Table 3  Room-temperature macroetches used for the characterization of welded joints**

The steel etches are normally used only for welded joints.

| Etching solution | Surface preparation (a) | Comments |
| --- | --- | --- |
| **Carbon and low-alloy steels** | | |
| 10 g (NH₃)₂S₂O₈ (ammonium persulfate) + 100 mL H₂O | B | Swab; macroetch brings out fusion line, heat-affected zone, reheated zones, columnar zones |
| 15 mL HNO₃ + 85 mL H₂O + 5 mL methanol or ethanol | A, B | Swab; macroetch brings out fusion line, heat-affected zone, reheated zones, columnar zones; scrub gently under running water to remove any black residue |
| 8 mL HNO₃ + 2 g picric acid + 10 g (NH₃)₂S₂O₈ + 10 g citric acid + 10 drops (0.5 mL) benzalkonium chloride + 1500 mL H₂O | B | Immerse; highlights partially transformed regions in reheat and heat-affected zones (Ref 13) |
| **Aluminum alloys** | | |
| Tucker's reagent, 45 mL HCl + 15 mL HNO₃ + 15 mL HF (48%) + 25 mL H₂O | A, B | Immerse or swab; use freshly mixed; general macroetch, all alloys |
| Poulton's reagent, 60 mL HCl + 30 mL HNO₃ + 5 mL HF (48%) + 5 mL H₂O | A, B | Immerse or swab; general macroetch, all alloys |
| **Copper and copper alloys** | | |
| 50 mL HNO₃ + 0.5 g AgNO₃ (silver nitrate) + 50 mL H₂O | A, B | Immerse; general macroetch, all alloys |
| **Titanium alloys** | | |
| Kroll's reagent, 10–30 mL HNO₃ + 5–15 mL HF + 50 mL H₂O | B | Immerse; general macro- and microetch; increase HNO₃ and reduce HF to bring out the fine structures in weldments |

(a) Surface preparation: A, finish grind; B, polish

of both solidification structures and the products of one or more solid-state transformations. For example, low-alloy steel weld metal solidifies as austenite, then upon cooling transforms to a mixture of ferrite and M₃C carbide (Fig. 17). The prior austenite grain size and the resulting ferrite plus carbide transformation structure are easily observed.

Solid-state phase transformations often create nonequilibrium phases or structures, which are usually characterized by continuous cooling transformation (CCT) diagrams (Fig. 4). If a welding process or parameter change can be described in terms of cooling rates, the resulting microstructural effects can be predicted by superimposing a particular cooling rate onto an applicable CCT diagram (Ref 12). However, any predictions based on a CCT diagram are only approximate, because factors other than the bulk composition of a material affect solid-state transformations. Solid-state transformation structures in welded joints are usually examined using a transverse section, although other views can be used.

**Ferrous Alloys.** Most ferrous weld metal deposits consist of plain carbon and low-alloy plate as well as structural steel weldments. The microstructural classifications and weld zones specific to weldments in these materials are considered in this section. The fusion zone, heat-affected zone, and, in the case of multiple-pass welds, the reheated zones can be further classified.

The transformation behavior of the reheated zones and heat-affected zone are iden-

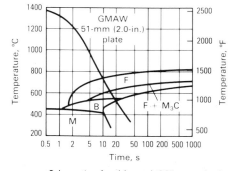

**Fig. 4** Schematic of weld metal CCT curve for low carbon-manganese steel plate. Weld process: gas metal arc welding (GMAW). Heat input: 1.6 MJ/m. M, martensite; F, ferrite; B, bainite. (Ref 12)

tical, resulting in microstructures that can be divided into four regions, traversing from the fusion zone outward: the grain growth zone, the fine grain zone, the partially transformed zone, and the tempered zone. Examples of these zones in a carbon steel welded joint are shown in Fig. 18. The reaustenitized region, consisting of coarse and fine grain regions, is often referred to as the recrystallized zone. The unaffected weld metal as well as the partially transformed and tempered zones in the fusion zone are often collectively referred to as columnar zones. Etches that assist the delineation of the fusion line, reheated zone, or heat-affected zone in steel weldments are presented in Table 3 (Ref 5, 13).

The following microstructure constituent classifications for the fusion zone in ferritic weldments have been adopted by the International Institute for Welding (Ref 14-16). Proeutectoid ferrite that nucleates at austenite grain boundaries and often results in a grain boundary film is classified as grain boundary ferrite (Fig. 19). Proeutectoid ferrite that nucleates intragranularly is classified as polygonal ferrite (Fig. 20). Upper bainite and Widmanstätten ferrite are classified as ferrite with aligned second phase (Fig. 21 and 22). Pearlite and nonaligned ferrite-carbide eutectoid decomposition products are classified as ferrite carbide aggregate (Fig. 22). An interlocking aggregate of fine, randomly oriented, intragranular laths of ferrite with an aspect ratio of approximately 4:1 is classified as acicular ferrite (Fig. 19 and 20). Martensite may also be present as a constituent in fusion zone microstructures.

Aluminum alloys may undergo solid-state transformations that alter their microstructures. However, these transformations do not usually occur during welding processes due to the rapid thermal cycles in welding. Thus, the microstructures observed in aluminum weldments will usually be the solidification structure.

**Titanium alloys** are classified as $\alpha$, $\alpha$-$\beta$, or metastable $\beta$ alloys based on the structure present at room temperature. Metastable $\beta$ alloys, which are not significantly altered by solid-state transformations during welding, will not be discussed here. The structures observed in $\alpha$ and $\alpha$-$\beta$ alloys are composed of retained $\beta$ and one or more $\beta$ decomposition products, including grain boundary and Widmanstätten $\alpha$, massive $\alpha$, and $\alpha'$ or $\alpha''$ martensites (Ref 17-19). These structures, essentially identical to those that occur in plate material exposed to similar cooling rates, are observed using standard sample preparation techniques and a 1:1 solution of Kroll's reagent in distilled water. Resolving the fine transformation products usually seen in weldments often requires reducing the HF and increasing the $HNO_3$ in the etching solution. This is especially true for low-energy welding processes and/or higher alloy contents. For additional information on the metallography and physical metallurgy of titanium, see Ref 6, 7, and 17 to 20 as well as the article "Titanium and Titanium Alloys" in this Volume.

The most common microstructural constituent in the fusion and grain growth zones of $\alpha$ alloy welded joints is acicular $\alpha$ (Ref 17). At high cooling rates, $\alpha'$ hexagonal martensite may also be formed, but this constituent is difficult to distinguish from acicular $\alpha$. In $\alpha$-$\beta$ titanium alloys, the structure most often observed in the fusion and grain growth zones is a combination of grain boundary $\alpha$, massive $\alpha$, Widmanstätten $\alpha + \beta$, and $\alpha'$, as shown in Fig. 23 and 24 and discussed in Ref 19. In more heavily $\beta$-stabilized alloys, $\alpha''$ orthorhombic martensite may be formed rather than $\alpha'$, but the two martensites are similar in appearance.

Reheat zones in $\alpha$-$\beta$ alloys consist of two regions. The grain growth zone next to the weld appears identical to the grain growth zone in the heat-affected zone. The partially transformed zone, rarely observed in the heat-affected zones, is easily detected in the reheat zones. This region contains equiaxed primary $\alpha$ as well as $\beta$ and $\beta$ decomposition products and retains a slightly larger amount of $\beta$ at room temperature (Fig. 25). The area etches more heavily than the surrounding material with a HF + $HNO_3$-based etchant.

**Other alloy systems** that undergo solid-state transformations during welding include cobalt, tin, uranium, and zirconium. Etchants appropriate for wrought and cast material of similar composition are usually adequate for examining weld metal microstructures. Etching techniques and appropriate etchants can be found in the articles on these specific alloy systems in this Volume.

## Defects in Welded Joints

Visual inspection, with or without the aid of some other nondestructive testing technique, usually is used to evaluate production weldments (Ref 1). However, metallography is a valuable tool in the evaluation of weld quality if destructive sectioning techniques can be tolerated. The sectioning technique used must ensure that the type of defect expected is in the plane of section. Typical defects and the sections used for their documentation are listed in Table 2. A discussion of the defects commonly seen in the welding of most alloy systems is available in Ref 1.

A macrosection can be used for detecting large defects, such as porosity and slag entrapment (Fig. 26). Macrosections also allow the integrity of the welded joint to be evaluated, allowing detection of such defects as inadequate fusion or insufficient penetration. Small defects, such as micropores and inclusions, may be observed in as-polished sections. Locating cracks, porosity, or slag entrapment is sometimes further aided by etching, because residual etchant "bleeds out" of the defect and stains adjacent areas (Fig. 27).

## Additional Welding Processes

Although arc welding is the most commonly used technique, many other processes are also employed. This section will briefly discuss the metallographic considerations particular to three areas: laser and electron beam welding, resistance and spot welding, and dissimilar-metal welding. For additional information about specific welding processes, see Volume 6 of the 9th Edition of *Metals Handbook* and Volume 3 of the *AWS Welding Handbook* (Ref 1). Microstructures of electron beam welded, flash welded, and explosive welded materials, including dissimilar-metal combinations, can also be found in the article "Color Metallography" in this Volume.

**Laser and Electron Beam Welding.** Many alloy systems can be welded using laser and electron beam processes, including materials that cannot be easily welded by other methods, such as refractory or highly reactive metals. The high energy densities of these processes allow welds to be made with low heat inputs. This results in a welded joint with a high depth-to-width ratio, a small heat-affected zone, and nonequilibrium microstructural components reflecting the high cooling rates (Fig. 8 and 29). Metallography is often used to evaluate weld bead integrity and workpiece alignment, which are critical because of the narrow width of the welded joint. If the high cooling rate of these welding processes can create deleterious phases in a particular system, the metallography of the welded joint should be directed toward the detection of these phases. Porosity can also be a problem in some systems due to the metal vaporization inherent in these processes. In most cases, metallographic techniques suitable for rapidly cooled plate material of the same composition will produce good results in laser and electron beam welded joints.

**Resistance Spot and Seam Welding.** Metal sheets and thin section shapes are often joined by resistance spot or seam welding. These processes result in a fusion zone, referred to as the "nugget," between the overlapping sheets (Fig. 28). Although the surface appearance of the welded joint is important for aesthetic reasons in the manufacture of consumer goods, it provides no indication of the size and soundness of spot welds. The soundness of spot welds may be estimated by measurements of penetration and nugget diameter (Ref 1, 20). In resistance spot welds, these measurements may be made with sections through the center of the nugget. The plane of section cannot deviate from the true plane of section by more than 16% of the nugget diameter if measurement errors of more than 5% are to be avoided. Clear mounting materials are recommended. The sectioning considerations for arc welds apply to seam welds, which are best characterized with transverse sections.

Dissimilar-metal sheets or coated sheet steels are often resistance spot or seam welded and may require the special preparation techniques described below and in the article "Coated Sheet Steel" in this Volume.

**Dissimilar-metal welded joints** are often made between materials of widely differing structures and properties, both with and without the addition of filler metal. Not only can this create microstructures uncommon to either base material and severe microstructural variations, but the welded joint and base material can have very different hardnesses. As a result, two specific considerations are involved in the metallography of dissimilar-metal joints: first, the preparation of a suitable specimen for metallographic examination and, second, the selection of the proper etching technique to allow identification of the phases present in the welded joint.

The hardness variations of many dissimilar-metal welded joints require that special care be taken during sample preparation to avoid preferential material removal of any part of the sample. Automatic grinding and polishing equipment is recommended for maximum flatness retention. Best polishing results are obtained with diamond polishing compounds and napless polishing cloths.

Different etchants are often required for different portions of the welded joint. If the sample geometry permits, parts of the specimen may be masked with glyptal or a similar product, and each portion of the sample etched individually. In joints with similar base metals, the sample can be mounted in copper-filled Bakelite to minimize the relative electrochemical difference between regions of the sample, then electroetched (Ref 6).

In most cases, the microstructures produced by dissimilar-metal welding cannot be accurately predicted, and metallography must be used to evaluate the weld structures to ensure that no deleterious phases are present. However, in welded joints of carbon or alloy steels and stainless steels, predictions can be made using a Schaeffler diagram (Ref 21) or one of its modified forms (Ref 22, 23). Examples of Schaeffler diagrams can be found on pages 322 and 808 of Volume 6 of the 9th Edition of *Metals Handbook*. Dissimilar-metal welding of several important alloy systems is discussed in Volume 4 of Ref 1.

## REFERENCES

1. W.H. Kearns, Ed., *Welding Handbook*, American Welding Society, Miami, 1978-1984
2. W.F. Savage and A. Aaronson, Preferred Orientation in the Weld Fusion Zone, *Weld. J.*, Vol 45 (No. 2), Feb 1966, p 855s-895s
3. K. Easterling, *Introduction to the Physical Metallurgy of Welding*, Butterworths, 1983
4. V.P. Kujanpaa, Weld Discontinuities in Austenitic Stainless Steel Sheets—Effects of Impurities and Solidification Mode, *Weld. J.*, Vol 63 (No. 12), Dec 1984, p 369s-375s
5. C.A. Johnson, "Metallography Principles and Procedures," Leco Corp., St. Joseph, MI, 1977
6. J.E. Gould and J.C. Williams, Solidification Structures and Phase Transformations in Welded Ti Alloys, in *Titanium '80 Science and Technology*, Proceedings of the Fourth International Conference on Titanium, H. Kimura and O. Izumi, Ed., TMS-AIME, Warrendale, PA, 1980, p 2337-2346
7. "Facts About the Metallography of Titanium," RMI Co., Niles, OH, 1970
8. R.W. Heckel, J.H. Ricketts, Jr., and J. Buchwald, Measurement of the Degree of Segregation in Monel 404 Weld Metal by X-Ray Line Broadening, *Weld. J.*, Vol 44 (No. 7), July 1965, p 332s-340s
9. W.F. Savage, E.F. Nippes, and T.W. Miller, Microsegregation in 70Cu-30Ni Weld Metal, *Weld. J.*, Vol 55 (No. 7), July 1976, p 165s-173s
10. M.J. Strum, L.T. Summers, and J.W. Morris, Jr., The Aging Response of a Welded Iron-Base Superalloy, *Weld. J.*, Vol 62 (No. 9), Sept 1983, p 235s-242s
11. B. Jahnke, High-Temperature Electron Beam Welding of the Nickel-Base Superalloy IN-738 LC, *Weld. J.*, Vol 61 (No. 11), Nov 1982, p 343s-347s
12. J.E. Lyttle, K.E. Dorschu, and W.A. Fraagetta, Some Metallurgical Characteristics of Tough High Strength Welds, *Weld. J.*, Vol 48 (No. 11), Nov 1969, p 493s-498s
13. S.S. Strunk and R.D. Stout, Heat Treatment Effects in Multipass Weldments of a High Strength Steel, *Weld. J.*, Vol 51 (No. 10), Oct 1972, p 508s-520s
14. D.J. Abson and R.E. Dolby, A Scheme for the Quantitative Description of Weld Metal Microstructures, *Weld. Inst. Res. Bull.*, Vol 21 (No. 4), 1980, p 100-103
15. "Classification of Microstructure in Low C Low Alloy Steel Weld Metal and Terminology," IIW Report 1X-1282-83, Committee on Welding Metallurgy, Japan Welding Society, Tokyo, Japan, 1983
16. R.W. Pargeter, "Quantification of Weld Metal Microstructure," IIW Document No. 1XJ-78-83, International Institute of Welding, London, England, 1983
17. D.W. Becker, R.W. Messler, and W.A. Baeslack, Titanium Welding—A Critical Review, in *Titanium '80 Science and Technology*, Proceedings of the Fourth International Conference on Titanium, H. Kimura and O. Izumi, Ed., TMS-AIME, Warrendale, PA, 1980, p 255-276
18. J.C. Williams, Critical Review Kinetics and Phase Transformations, in *Titanium Science and Technology*, Proceedings of the Second International Conference on Titanium, R.I. Jaffee and J.M. Burte, Ed., Plenum Press, 1973, p 1433-1487
19. R.E. Lewis, W.C. Koons, J.C. Williams, and G.K. Scarr, Continuous Cooling Transformation in Ti-6Al-2Cb-1Ta-0.8Mo, in *Solid-Solid Phase Transformations*, Proceedings of an International Conference, H.I. Aaronson, D.E. Laughlin, R.F. Sekerka, and C.M. Wayman, Ed., TMS-AIME, Warrendale, PA, 1982, p 1499-1503
20. M. Kimchi, "Resistance Spot Welding," paper presented at the Colorado School of Mines, Golden, CO, April 19, 1984
21. A.L. Schaeffler, Constitutional Diagram for Stainless Steel Weld Metal, *Met. Prog.*, Vol 56, 1949, p 680-687
22. C.J. Long and W.T. DeLong, The Ferrite Content of Austenitic Stainless Steel Weld Metal, *Weld. J.*, Vol 52 (No. 7), July 1973, p 281s-297s
23. J.A. Self, D.K. Matlock, and D.L. Olson, An Evaluation of Austenitic Fe-Mn-Ni Weld Metal for Dissimilar Metal Welding, *Weld. J.*, Vol 63 (No. 9), Sept 1984, p 282s-288s

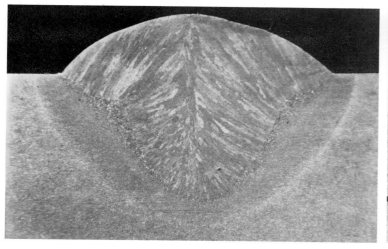

**Fig. 5** 19-mm (0.75-in.) A-710 steel plate, submerged arc weld. Heat input: 3.0 MJ/m. Macrostructure shows the fusion zone, heat-affected zone, and base metal in a single-pass, bead-on-plate weld. 85 mL $H_2O$ + 15 mL $HNO_3$ + 5 mL methanol. 3.5×

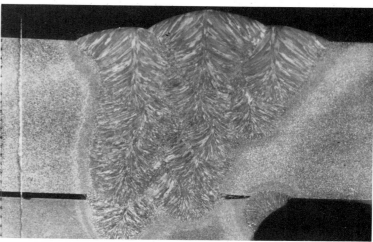

**Fig. 6** Same as Fig. 5. Weld wire: 2.4 mm (3/32 in.). Mil Spec 100S-1, OP121TT flux. Heat input: 1.0 MJ/m. Macrostructure shows the fusion zone, heat-affected zone, reheat zones, and base metal in a multiple-pass butt weld. 85 mL $H_2O$ + 15 mL $HNO_3$ + 5 mL methanol. 2×

**Fig. 7** 19-mm (0.75-in.) A-710 steel plate, submerged arc weld. Microstructure shows dragout of base metal scale between the base metal and the epoxy filler used in the gap between the base plate and backup plate in a multiple-pass butt weld. As-polished. 280×

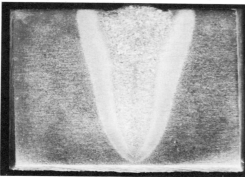

**Fig. 8** 2.25Cr-1Mo steel plate, single-pass electron beam weld. Heat input: 0.5 MJ/m. Macrostructure shows high depth-to-width ratio of the fusion zone, which is typical of high energy density welding processes. 85 mL $H_2O$ + 15 mL $HNO_3$ + 5 mL methanol. 2.8×

**Fig. 9** 13-mm (0.5-in.) Lukens Frostline steel plate, submerged arc weld. Heat input: 2.0 MJ/m. Weld wire: AWS E70S-3. Macrostructure shows unusual bead shape due to surface tension and viscosity abnormalities in a calcium-fluoride-base experimental fused flux. 85 mL $H_2O$ + 15 mL $HNO_3$ + 5 mL methanol. 1.5×

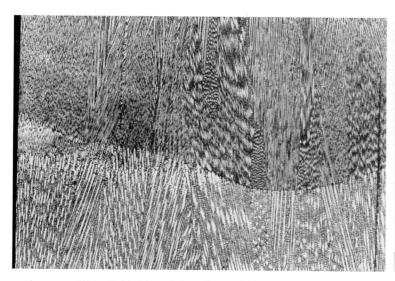

**Fig. 10** 25-mm (1.0-in.) type 304 stainless steel plate, shielded metal arc weld. Heat input: 1.0 MJ/m. Micrograph shows austenite-dendrite structure retained across successive weld passes in the fusion zone. 10% oxalic acid electroetch. 40×

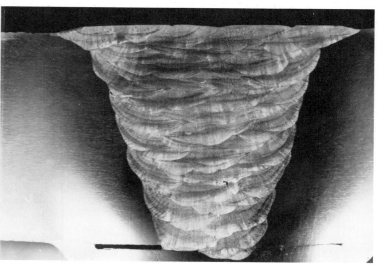

**Fig. 11** 25-mm (1.0-in.) type 304 stainless steel plate, shielded metal arc weld. Heat input: 1.0 MJ/m. Macrograph shows epitaxial grain growth resulting in continuous columnar grains occurring through successive passes in a multiple-pass weld. 10% oxalic acid electroetch. 2×

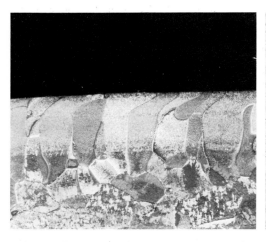

**Fig. 12** 13-mm (0.5-in.) Ti-6Al-2Nb-1Ta-1Mo alloy plate, autogenous single-pass gas tungsten arc weld. Heat input: 2.0 MJ/m. Longitudinal section showing curvature of the prior-$\beta$ grains, which follow the maximum thermal gradient in the weld pool. 1:1 solution, Kroll's etch and distilled water. 3×

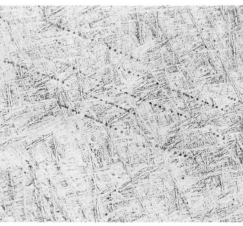

**Fig. 13** 13-mm (0.5-in.) Ti-6Al-4V alloy plate, autogenous two-pass gas tungsten arc weld. Heat input: 2.0 MJ/m. Weld was made over a groove in the base plate into which metallic yttrium had been pressed. Microstructure shows aligned yttrium oxide particles, indicating the segregation that occurred during solidification. 1:1 solution, Kroll's etch and distilled water. 100×

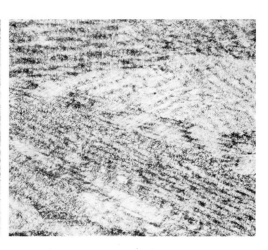

**Fig. 14** 13-mm (0.5-in.) AISI 4340 steel plate, submerged arc weld. Heat input: 1.9 MJ/m. Fusion zone microstructure in which the dendrite solidification structure is revealed by the distribution of tempered martensite and upper bainite. 2% nital. 50×

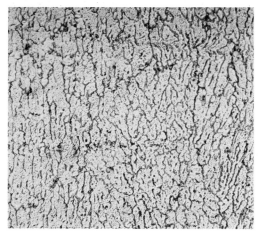

**Fig. 15** 2219 aluminum alloy, gas metal arc weld (parameters unknown). Fusion zone microstructure in which the cellular solidification structure is revealed by the distribution of the divorced eutectic microconstituent between the cells. Kroll's etch. 200×

**Fig. 16** 13-mm (0.5-in.) Ti-6Al-2Nb-1Ta-1Mo alloy plate, single-pass gas metal arc weld. Heat input: 0.8 MJ/m. Macrograph showing the columnar prior-$\beta$ grains resulting from epitaxial growth. 1:1 solution, Kroll's etch and distilled water. 4×

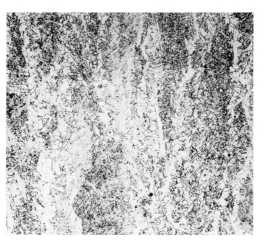

**Fig. 17** 16-mm (⁵⁄₈-in.) A-36 steel plate, single-V butt multiple-pass shielded metal arc weld. Heat input: 1.3 MJ/m. Weld wire: AWS E7018. Low-carbon fusion zone microstructure showing veins of grain boundary ferrite on prior austenite grain boundaries. 2% nital. 50×

**Fig. 18** 16-mm (⁵⁄₈-in.) A-36 steel plate, multiple-pass shielded metal arc weld. Heat input: 1.3 MJ/m. Composite micrograph of the heat-affected zone showing (from left to right) base plate, tempered zone, partially transformed zone, fine grain zone, coarse grain zone, fusion line, and fusion zone. 2% nital. 36×

END

END

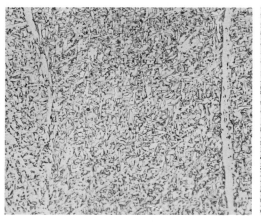

**Fig. 19** 19-mm (0.75-in.) A-710 steel plate, last pass (12th) of a submerged arc single-V butt weld. Heat input: 1.3 MJ/m. Grain boundary ferrite on prior austenite grain boundaries in a microstructure of fine acicular ferrite. 2% nital. 500×

**Fig. 20** 16-mm (⅝-in.) A-36 steel plate, multiple-pass shielded metal arc single-V butt weld. Heat input: 1.3 MJ/m. Weld wire: AWS E7018. Fusion zone microstructure containing polygonal ferrite in coarse acicular ferrite. 2% nital. 500×

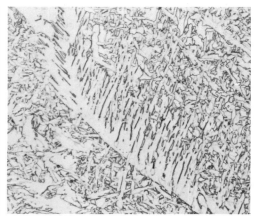

**Fig. 21** 13-mm (0.5-in.) Lukens Frostline steel plate, submerged arc bead-on-plate weld. Heat input: 1.9 MJ/m. Weld wire: AWS E70S-3. Fusion zone microstructure with Widmanstätten ferrite growth from grain boundary ferrite with coarse acicular ferrite. 2% nital. 500×

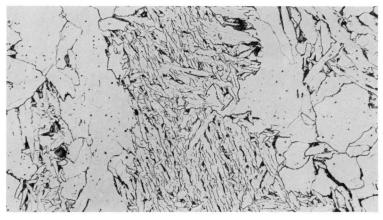
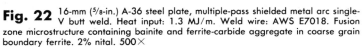

**Fig. 22** 16-mm (⅝-in.) A-36 steel plate, multiple-pass shielded metal arc single-V butt weld. Heat input: 1.3 MJ/m. Weld wire: AWS E7018. Fusion zone microstructure containing bainite and ferrite-carbide aggregate in coarse grain boundary ferrite. 2% nital. 500×

**Fig. 23** 13-mm (0.5-in.) Ti-6Al-4V alloy plate, autogenous single-pass gas tungsten arc weld. Heat input: 2.0 MJ/m. Fusion zone microstructure consisting of fine Widmanstätten $\alpha + \beta$ and grain boundary $\alpha$. 1:1 solution, Kroll's etch and distilled water. 100×

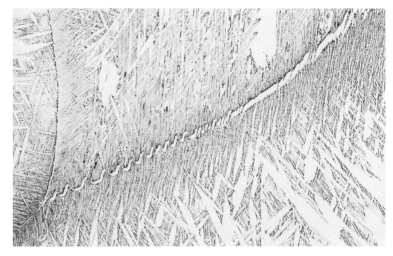

**Fig. 24** 13-mm (0.5-in.) Ti-6Al-2Nb-1Ta-1Mo alloy plate, autogenous single-pass gas tungsten arc weld. Heat input: 2.0 MJ/m. Fusion zone microstructure containing grain boundary $\alpha$, $\alpha'$, massive $\alpha$, and Widmanstätten $\alpha + \beta$. 1:1 solution, Kroll's etch and distilled water. 400×

**Fig. 25** 13-mm (0.5-in.) Ti-6Al-2Nb-1Ta-1Mo alloy plate, three-pass gas metal arc weld. Heat input: 0.8 MJ/m. Reheat zone of the third pass showing $\alpha'$, Widmanstätten $\alpha + \beta$, equiaxed $\alpha$, and slightly higher amount of retained $\beta$ than the areas surrounding the reheat zone. 1:1 solution, Kroll's etch and distilled water. 250×

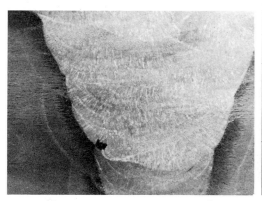

**Fig. 26** 38-mm (1.5-in.) HY 80 steel plate, gas shielded flux core weld. Heat input: 2.0 MJ/m. Macrosection revealing slag entrapment in a double-V butt weld. Use of etchants is helpful in locating such defects because residual etchant "bleeds out" of defect and stains adjacent areas. 2% nital. 3×

**Fig. 27** 13-mm (0.5-in.) AISI 4340 steel plate, submerged arc weld. Heat input: 1.9 MJ/m. Macrograph shows solidification (centerline) cracking. Crack position is highlighted by etchant "bleed-out." 85 mL $H_2O$ + 15 mL $HNO_3$ + 5 mL methanol. 1.5×

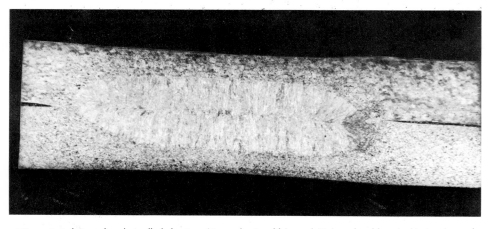

**Fig. 28** Low-carbon hot-rolled sheet, resistance spot weld (composition and weld parameters unknown). Macrostructure shows 60% penetration of the weld and columnar growth pattern in the fusion zone. 85 mL $H_2O$ + 15 mL $HNO_3$ + 5 mL methanol. 10×

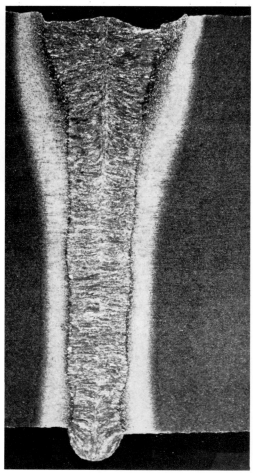

**Fig. 29** 14-mm (9/16-in.) A-710 steel plate, autogenous single-pass laser butt weld. Heat input: 0.014 MJ/m. Macrograph shows the high depth-to-width ratio of the weld bead and the limited size of the heat-affected zone. 2% nital. 8×

# Fiber Composite Materials

By Linda L. Clements
Professor
Materials Engineering Department
San Jose State University

CONTINUOUS-FILAMENT FIBER COMPOSITES are examined using optical microscopy for such purposes as inspection, quality assurance, process development, material or component selection, proof testing analysis, research on failure mechanisms, and failure analysis. Features that may be studied include:

- Fiber and ply orientation, number of plies, and filament size and distribution
- Size and distribution of flaws, such as voids, inclusions, fiber bundle misalignment, improper laps, and distorted layers
- Damage, such as delamination, microcracks, and through cracks

Many of the techniques used and problems encountered with fiber composites are the same as those of the matrix alone. Therefore, a composite specimen must be prepared at least as carefully as a specimen of the fiberless matrix material; this precaution alone is sometimes sufficient. However, in most examinations of composites, special problems exist that require extra care or special preparation techniques.

Most precautions in preparing composite specimens involve two problems: first, fibers tearing away from the matrix during cutting, grinding, or polishing and, second, difficulties caused by the mismatch—often substantial—in the properties of fiber and matrix. In most composites, the fibers are harder than the matrix and often more abrasion resistant. This mismatch can cause differential topography between fiber and matrix (protruding and rounded or recessed and dished fibers), damage to fibers during preparation (cracking, tearing, edge damage), and/or damage to the material at the fiber-matrix interface. Special techniques are often required to overcome these obstacles, and in a few cases, their effects can only be minimized, but not eliminated.

Most composite matrices are moderately to very heat sensitive. Therefore, a coolant should be used for all cutting and grinding steps, and the specimen should be lifted fre-

quently to avoid heat buildup. The coolant used, as well as any polishing lubricant or cleaning medium, should not damage the composite. This is a problem particularly with resin-matrix composites, for which water is generally the preferred coolant, lubricant, and cleaning agent.

Metal-matrix composites, especially those containing carbon/graphite fibers, are susceptible to galvanic corrosion during preparation. This can be controlled by (1) using distilled rather than tap water, (2) avoiding grinding and polishing wheels that will be cathodic to the composite matrix (such as a brass polishing wheel used with an aluminum-matrix composite) or by lacquering such wheels, and (3) minimizing preparation times.

The most difficult composites to prepare well are those with a large mismatch in fiber and matrix properties and those containing prior damage. Many of the special techniques suggested in this article will be aimed at these composites. One approach not discussed, however, is the temporary altering of fiber or matrix properties. As an example, for very soft matrices, the specimen may be chilled or frozen prior to or during preparation. Successfully applied techniques minimize the amount of damage produced at each preparation step, which lessens the subsequent preparation required.

All the techniques described will produce high-quality composite specimens for optical microscopy. Producing an ideal specimen requires that (Ref 1):

- There should be minimal damage to the specimen during cutting.
- The mounting medium should have hardness and abrasion resistance characteristics that closely match those of the composite matrix material.
- The procedure chosen should be designed to reduce progressively the mechanical damage induced in the composite from cutting and subsequent grinding.
- Grinding and polishing must not damage the filaments by chipping or bending and

must not induce or propagate existing cracks in the filaments.
- Topographic variations should be held to a minimum (5 $\mu$m or less) to obtain a metallographically acceptable specimen that can be easily examined at high magnification.

These goals may not always be achievable and may not even be necessary for quick or quality-control examinations. However, they should be the aim of any high-quality, detailed metallographic examination of composites.

## Specimen Preparation

**Sectioning.** Except in the unusual situation when a specimen is to be sectioned in a plane parallel to the filament direction or when only gross features are to be examined, it is generally best to section the sample using a low-speed saw with a thin diamond-impregnated blade or using a diamond-impregnated wire saw. In most cases, an appropriate coolant should be used. Cutting across fibers and/or layers must be performed carefully to avoid fiber splitting and layer delamination. For ductile composite matrices, significant matrix distortion can be produced by all but the gentlest cutting techniques.

If more damaging cutting techniques are used, more material will have to be removed during grinding and polishing, which, for some composites—particularly those with a large mismatch in fiber and matrix properties or those with damage from service or testing—may produce additional damage that will compromise the quality of the resulting micrograph. If fiber tearing is a serious problem, the specimen surface can be coated with a thick layer of epoxy or other plastic resin prior to cutting.

**Mounting.** Even fairly large composite sections generally should be mounted or at least coated before metallographic preparation to avoid the tearing out of fibers at the specimen edges. These torn filaments damage the specimen surface and may embed in the polishing cloth, where they may seriously scratch the specimen. Because composite materials tend to be light, it may be necessary to weight the specimen to keep it from floating in the mounting medium. This can be accomplished by bonding the specimen to or between metal. The specimen can also be held down using electrical alligator clips, wire, or other similar means.

Selecting the correct mounting medium is important to the overall successful preparation of the specimen. For resin-matrix composites, the elevated temperature required to cure Bakelite and other similar mounting materials may be high enough to alter or damage the composite. For soft matrices, the pressures required may also produce damage. Therefore, cold-mounting materials are often used for composites. However, they are not to be chosen indiscriminately, but should be carefully tailored to the composite specimen.

As an example, for epoxy-matrix composites, an epoxy mounting material with properties similar to those of the matrix is best. For this reason, a moderate-temperature cure (for example, 60 °C, or 140 °F) will often produce improved properties and thus superior results if the specimen can tolerate the cure. Reinforcing filler particles, such as alumina ($Al_2O_3$), may also be added to improve the mount properties. For metal-matrix composites, polyvinyl formal resin (Formvar) backed with acrylic resin filled with chopped glass fibers has been used with success (Ref 2). The resin is very tough and abrasion resistant and results in a flat surface with minimum relief between mount and specimen. Acrylic cold-mounting materials are usually unsuitable, because they are too soft, provide poor edge retention, and may even produce smearing during grinding and polishing.

Composites often have rough surfaces, and mounting materials may not easily wet the surface of a resin-matrix composite. This problem may be overcome by vacuum outgassing and impregnation and/or a moderate-temperature cure, which reduces initial viscosity. Such techniques can also be used to minimize or eliminate fiber tearout at cracks, delamination, and large voids if the mounting material can reach and fill these defects. Vacuum impregnation with moderate-temperature curable epoxy is particularly important with carbon-carbon composites, because these composites have pores and cracks (Ref 3). For cold or moderate-temperature mounts, flexible molds are commonly used. However, another suitable mold is a flat-bottomed plastic medicine bottle, which then can be ground off or, more commonly, can become part of the mount (Ref 4).

The mounting medium should be carefully selected or modified to provide distinct contrast with the composite matrix. For example, when a plastic mounting material, such as epoxy, is chosen for use with a resin-matrix composite, added filler or coloring particles may be used to produce appropriate contrast. Such contrast is particularly important when

cracks, voids, or delaminations are to be filled. This can also be accomplished by adding a fluorescent dye to the mounting material so that an ultraviolet light can be used to detect filled defects (Ref 5).

A problem arises if bare or resin-impregnated composite "strands" (fiber bundles containing many filaments) are to be examined. One way to mount such specimens is to wet them with epoxy and thread them through drilled holes in an aluminum block. Vacuum impregnation or moderate heat—from a heat gun, for example—can be used to produce adequate flow and impregnation of the mounting epoxy into the holes and the strands prior to curing (Ref 6).

**Cleaning.** Many composite specimens require only standard washing between grinding and/or polishing steps. For most resin-matrix composites, it is best to use nothing harsher than mild soap and water. This may involve, for example, washing with running water (perhaps with light swabbing), flooding with methanol, and blow drying with freon. However, if the composite contains unfilled voids, cracks, or delaminations, thorough cleaning may be necessary to remove trapped abrasive or fibers. Ultrasonic cleaning using water containing mild phosphate-free soap is generally successful. The specimen should be placed on its side in this solution for approximately 2 min. If the flaws are small, wheel cleaning on a soft cloth with a soap and water solution may be useful. In all these cases, microscopic examination should be used to verify that the cleaning has removed trapped abrasive and fibers.

**Grinding.** For many composites, standard grinding techniques are suitable. In many resin-matrix composites, however, it is necessary to lift and cool the specimen frequently to avoid heat buildup and matrix damage. For most resin matrices, water is the preferred coolant. Distilled water should be used for metal-matrix composites. Dry grinding should usually be avoided. Coolants other than water should be used only if they are known not to damage the matrix.

For metals, standard practice is to continue grinding for twice the time required to remove the scratches from the previous operation. For fiber composites, however, this practice may produce damage, particularly if fiber and matrix properties differ greatly or if the composite shows broken fibers, unfilled matrix cracks, or other prior damage. Therefore, in most cases, grinding should remove only as much material as necessary to eliminate prior damage. For materials with prior damage, it is best to avoid grinding if possible. For example, excellent results have been obtained on titanium-matrix composites containing boron or silicon carbide fibers when cutting and mounting was followed by polishing (Ref 7).

Grinding by lapping with an abrasive charge or, if available, automatic vibratory grinding is sometimes preferred. However, disk grinding on silicon carbide paper has

produced excellent results. Also suitable is hand grinding on silicon carbide paper using a figure-8 motion and frequent changes of paper. Some of these recommendations are based on individual preference, and some are due to different materials and problems. Usually, the best grinding method for a specific application must be determined by trial and error. Grinding procedures for the micrographs presented in this article are listed in Table 1.

If the fiber and matrix do not have extremely different properties, as with most carbon- or graphite-epoxy composites, a common grinding sequence begins with removal of 1 to 2 mm (0.04 to 0.08 in.) of material by disk grinding at medium to high speeds using 240-grit silicon carbide paper and abundant running water. Subsequent grinding proceeds through 400- and 600-grit papers (Ref 4). A grinding sequence of 80-, 120-, 180-, 240-, 320-, 400-, and 600-grit silicon carbide or $Al_2O_3$ can also be used (Ref 8). For carbon-carbon composites, the recommended grinding procedure uses 240-, 320-, 400-, then 600-grit silicon carbide papers (Ref 3).

For resin-matrix graphite- or carbon-fiber composites with a large mismatch in fiber and matrix properties, the following procedure has been successful when prior damage or excess mounting materials necessitate grinding prior to polishing (Ref 9). Such materials require a light touch and careful technique. Grinding should begin with 600-grit paper using a high speed and a heavy flow of water. Larger grit sizes tend to chip the graphite filaments, causing severe damage. Moderate to light pressure should be used during grinding so that scratches extend from corner to corner across the specimen. Grinding should proceed at 5-s intervals to avoid heat buildup; after the specimen has been lifted and allowed to cool, grinding can begin again at a slightly different corner-to-corner angle. Two or three papers may be required. If necessary, pressure can be increased to remove damage. Once this step is completed, polishing should immediately follow. The best technique can be determined only by trying and comparing different preparations of similar specimens.

For metal-matrix composites, galvanic corrosion must be minimized. When conventional techniques are applied to metal-matrix fiber composites, the most prevalent problem is the large degree of topographical relief between matrix and fibers. This occurs because of the mismatch in friction and wear characteristics between the two. Specimens containing fibers that display prior damage are also very difficult to prepare without further damaging the fibers.

For metal-matrix composites, diamond disk grinding and polishing, using water sparingly, produce satisfactory results (Ref 2). Because these disks tend to load up with the plastic mounting materials, the plastic mount may be first differentially ground toward its outside using a small electric deburring tool.

The diamond disks recommended are 100-mesh, 45-$\mu$m, and 30-$\mu$m (all metal bond), followed by 30-$\mu$m, 15-$\mu$m, 9-$\mu$m, and 6-$\mu$m (all resin bond).

Boron-aluminum composites, particularly those with prior damage, may be hand ground on 600-grit silicon carbide paper using a figure-8 pattern, heavy pressure, and a substantial flow of water (Ref 1). The paper should be rotated frequently and changed often. Polishing should immediately follow.

**Polishing.** Because polishing techniques for composites vary more than grinding and other techniques, this section will summarize many of the different approaches used, although experience, common sense, and trial and error should determine the best approach for a specific application.

Because the properties of the fiber and matrix frequently do not match, special care is required to avoid damaging the components during polishing. Snagging and damaging of fibers should be avoided, and polishing times should be as brief as possible to avoid damage. Topographical variations—such as protruding, rounded fibers or recessed, dished fibers—are common problems that must be dealt with. Most of the steps involved in polishing fiber composites will cause some problem, even while remedying another. For this reason, the steps taken in polishing a composite involve tradeoffs, and often a complex sequence of steps is recommended to overcome the problems caused by any one approach.

Diamond, $Al_2O_3$, or other polishing compounds, such as cerium oxide ($CeO_2$) or magnesium oxide ($MgO$), may be used, although synthetic diamond may produce the best overall results. Natural diamond compound has needlelike particles, which are more efficient in polishing, but will embed in a soft matrix, causing excessive damage. Synthetic diamond particles are more spherical. Although $Al_2O_3$ provides superior scratch removal, it tends to produce protruding, rounded fibers. Therefore, diamond polishing with a quick, final $Al_2O_3$ polish or other combinations of steps to remove scratches and topographical variations are usually used. For example, diamond polishing followed by final polish with a $CeO_2$ slurry results in excellent scratch removal with minimum topographic variations (Ref 6).

Distilled water is the preferred lubricant for most polishing, particularly with resin-matrix composites, although oil-base polishing lubricants are often recommended. For metal-matrix composites, kerosene is sometimes used. The polishing compound selected must be compatible with the lubricant chosen; for example, water-soluble diamond compound should not be used with kerosene.

Automatic vibratory lapping produces good results. However, excellent results can be obtained with wheel lapping, and wheel-mounted diamond disks can be used for polishing.

**Table 1  Grinding and polishing procedures for fiber composites**

| Procedure | Grinding sequence, polishing compounds, lubricants, and polishing cloths | Suitable materials | Ref | Fig. |
|---|---|---|---|---|
| 1 | Grind 240-, 400-, 600-grit<br>3-, 0.25-$\mu$m diamond polish in oil-base fluid on short-nap synthetic rayon cloth | Graphite or carbon-epoxy resin matrix | 4 | 3 |
| 2 | Grind 180-, 240-, 320-, 400-, 600-grit<br>15-, 6-, 3-$\mu$m diamond polish in lapping oil on silk<br>1-$\mu$m diamond (optional)<br>0.05-$\mu$m $Al_2O_3$ final polish (optional) in water on short-nap synthetic rayon cloth | Graphite or carbon-epoxy matrix | 8 | 6, 7 |
| 3 | Grind 600-grit<br>9-$\mu$m diamond polish in soapy water on silk<br>1-$\mu$m diamond polish in soapy water on boiled short-nap synthetic rayon cloth<br>0.25-$\mu$m diamond polish (optional) | Resin matrix with large fiber-resin mismatch | 9 | . . . |
| 4 | Automatic grind<br>1-, 0.25-$\mu$m diamond polish in lapping oil on automatic polisher<br>0.05-$\mu$m $Al_2O_3$ polish (optional) in water | Glass-epoxy, aramid-epoxy resin matrix | 10 | 1 |
| 5 | Grind 600-grit<br>3-, 1-$\mu$m diamond polish in grinding fluid on optical glass plate<br>0.3-$\mu$m $Al_2O_3$ polish on silk in water on automatic polisher<br>0.25-$\mu$m diamond polish in water on boiled short-nap synthetic rayon cloth | Boron-aluminum matrix | 1 | . . . |
| 6 | Grind 600-grit<br>9-$\mu$m diamond polish in water on silk<br>1-$\mu$m diamond polish in water on short-nap synthetic rayon cloth | Graphite or carbon-aluminum matrix<br>Graphite or carbon-magnesium matrix<br>Carbon-carbon | 11 | 9, 11–14, 19–21, 23<br>19–21, 23 |
| 7 | Procedure 5 plus 0.25-$\mu$m diamond polish in water on boiled short-nap synthetic rayon cloth | Graphite-aluminum matrix | 1 | . . . |
| 8 | Procedure 5, except on chemotextile cloth<br>0.25-$\mu$m diamond polish in water on short-nap synthetic rayon cloth | Alumina-aluminum matrix | 11 | . . . |
| 9 | Grind 400-, 600-grit<br>1-$\mu$m $Al_2O_3$ polish in water on short-nap synthetic rayon cloth<br>0.05-$\mu$m $Al_2O_3$ polish in water on short-nap synthetic rayon cloth | Graphite-aluminum matrix | 7 | . . . |
| 10 | Grind 600-grit<br>1-$\mu$m $Al_2O_3$ polish in water on short-pile wool broadcloth<br>0.3-$\mu$m $Al_2O_3$ polish in water on boiled short-nap synthetic rayon cloth<br>0.05-$\mu$m $Al_2O_3$ polish in water on boiled short-nap synthetic rayon cloth | Carbon-aluminum matrix | 1 | . . . |
| 11 | Diamond disk grind<br>Diamond disk polish 100-mesh through 6-$\mu$m in water<br>3-$\mu$m diamond polish in kerosene on silk<br>0.25-$\mu$m diamond polish in kerosene on hard-bond paper<br>0.3-$\mu$m $Al_2O_3$ polish in water on short-nap synthetic rayon cloth on automatic polisher | Boron-aluminum matrix<br>Boron-titanium matrix<br>Silicon carbide-nickel matrix<br>Silicon carbide-titanium matrix<br>Molybdenum-nickel matrix | 2 | 15 |
| 12 | No grinding<br>9-, 6-, 0.25-$\mu$m diamond in lapping oil on chemotextile cloth on glass on automatic polisher | Boron-titanium matrix<br>Silicon carbide-titanium matrix | 7 | . . . |
| 13 | Grind through 600-grit 0.05-$\mu$m $Al_2O_3$ polish in water on automatic polisher | Glassy carbon or ceramic matrix | 12 | 25 |
| 14 | Grind 240-, 320-, 400-, 600-grit 1-$\mu$m $Al_2O_3$ polish in water on silk<br>0.05-$\mu$m $CeO_2$ polish in water on short-nap synthetic rayon cloth | Carbon-carbon | 3 | 17, 18, 22 |
| 15 | Grind 180-, 240-, 320-, 400-, 600-grit<br>1-, 0.3-, 0.05-$\mu$m $Al_2O_3$ polish in water on short-nap synthetic rayon cloth | Resin matrix | . . . | 5 |
| 16 | Grind 180-, 240-, 320-, 400-, 600-grit<br>6- or 3-, 1-$\mu$m diamond polish in kerosene or lapping oil on silk cloth | Resin matrix | . . . | 2, 3, 8, 24 |
| 17 | Grind 240-, 320-, 400-, 600-grit<br>0.3-, 0.05-$\mu$m $Al_2O_3$ polish in water. Cloth unreported | Metal matrix | . . . | 10 |

Note: See text for detailed descriptions of all procedures for which references are given.

Nylon polishing cloths tend to leave scratches; silk cloths, even more. Scratches are not a problem if they can be removed in subsequent polishings and/or etchings. A soft, napped cloth is often preferred for one or more polishing steps for the most difficult materials.

Before polishing, any wheels to be used should be carefully cleaned and, if necessary, lacquered prior to fitting with a polishing cloth. It is preferred, and required for the most difficult materials, that this cloth be new at the beginning of the polishing operation.

Specific polishing approaches that have yielded good results will be summarized. The goal of each of these procedures is to produce a high-quality, scratch-free specimen with minimum topographical variation. All accomplish this with good to excellent success, but the approaches vary widely, depending on the material, the needs of the microscopic examination, the time and resources that can be expended, and the style and philosophy of the microscopist. Polishing procedures for the micrographs presented in this article are given in Table 1.

*Resin-matrix composites.* For graphite- or carbon-epoxy, one recommended procedure (Ref 4) is to polish first on a soft, short-nap synthetic rayon cloth (Microcloth), beginning with 3-$\mu$m diamond in a standard oil-base polishing fluid. Water may be a preferable lubricant, depending on the susceptibility of the matrix. The wheel should be well but not excessively lubricated. Slow to medium wheel speed and heavy pressure are required. After initial polishing, the diamond paste should be renewed, the wheel speed increased, and the specimen pressure decreased. After 10 min of polishing, the diamond paste should be renewed again. Polishing should then continue at medium to high wheel speed using light specimen pressure for another 10 to 15 min or until microscopic examination shows that all grinding scratches have been removed. The final polish should be performed using 0.25-$\mu$m diamond, following the same procedure.

An alternative for carbon- or graphite-epoxy is to proceed with 15-, 6-, 3-, and 1-$\mu$m diamond (optional) compounds using high wheel speeds, moderate to heavy pressure, and an oil-base lubricating fluid. A brief final polish with 0.05-$\mu$m $Al_2O_3$ on short-nap synthetic rayon cloth using light pressure may be implemented to remove any remaining scratches (Ref 8).

For resin-matrix composites with a substantial fiber-matrix mismatch, particularly when the resin is extremely soft, good results can be achieved with the following procedure (Ref 9). After grinding on 600-grit abrasive, polishing should begin with 9-$\mu$m water-soluble diamond paste on silk cloth. The lubricant is a 5:1 to 10:1 solution of distilled water and phosphate-free liquid soap. With moderate to fast wheel speed, the specimen should be polished using moderate pressure and a "modified daisy" pattern, which consists of

looping movements into, out from, and around the center of the wheel. A very visible polishing should be apparent in 1 to 2 min. Polishing should then continue for a few minutes using 1-$\mu$m diamond in soapy water on a soft, boiled, short-nap synthetic rayon cloth with very high speed and very light pressure. The purpose of boiling the polishing cloth is to soften the stiff fibers, which have a tendency to scratch soft matrix materials. If extremely fine results are required, a final 0.25-$\mu$m diamond polish can be used.

Glass-epoxy, aramid-epoxy, and other resin-matrix composites can be polished using 1-$\mu$m, then 0.25-$\mu$m diamond in lapping oil in an automatic polisher. A quick 0.05-$\mu$m $Al_2O_3$ polish may be used if necessary for final scratch removal (Ref 6).

*Boron-aluminum composites.* Topological variations in boron-aluminum composites can be removed by figure-8 lapping using diamond compound placed on an index card. This technique benefits undamaged composites, but will produce further damage in composites showing prior fiber damage (Ref 1). For such composites, a successful technique continues from the 600-grit grinding described in the previous section. After grinding, the specimen will have filaments that protrude approximately 0.2 mm (0.008 in.) above the surrounding matrix (Ref 1). Next, the specimen should be cleaned ultrasonically, then ground using a thin suspension of 3-$\mu$m diamond paste in grinding fluid on an optically ground glass plate.

Hand lapping should then begin using firm pressure and a figure-8 pattern; it should proceed until the fibers are ground to the same level as the matrix material, as determined by microscopic examination. After ultrasonic cleaning, lapping should be repeated using a 1-$\mu$m diamond suspension. In this case, polishing on a glass plate will eliminate the topological differences as well as the likelihood that the protruding filaments will snag on a polishing cloth and be damaged. After ultrasonic cleaning, the specimen will be ready for final polishing.

An automatic vibratory polisher with a tightly stretched silk polishing cloth and 0.3-$\mu$m $Al_2O_3$ in distilled water should be used. At least 2 h of polishing are required. This step will produce well-polished fibers, but will still leave a mechanically worked aluminum matrix. The specimen should then be final polished using 0.25-$\mu$m diamond paste on a boiled, soft, short-nap synthetic rayon cloth to remove this artifact. Light pressure is required.

*For graphite fibers in an aluminum matrix,* in which the property mismatch is less severe than for boron-aluminum but the fibers are very abrasion resistant, grinding should be followed by wheel polishing with 9-$\mu$m diamond paste on a silk polishing cloth (Ref 1). Small amounts of distilled water are used as a lubricant. With a wheel speed of approximately 200 rpm, the specimen is counter-rotated approximately once per second. Fairly

heavy pressure is necessary for 1 min to achieve a rapid removal of grinding scratches. Once prior scratches have been removed, as verified microscopically, the specimen should be cleaned, then polished with 1-$\mu$m diamond on a boiled, soft, short-nap synthetic rayon cloth. The wheel should be rotated at approximately 150 rpm while the specimen is counter-rotated, using light pressure, approximately once per second. A small amount of distilled water is used as a lubricant.

Polishing should continue until microscopic examination verifies that all scratches from the previous 9-$\mu$m operation have been removed. Finally, to remove the last scratches and any topological variations, the specimen should be polished on a soft, boiled, short-nap synthetic rayon cloth that has been heavily impregnated with 0.25-$\mu$m diamond. Wheel speed should be approximately 200 rpm. The specimen should be counter-rotated once per second using extremely light pressure. Distilled water is used as the lubricant. This operation should last only approximately 1 min. Following microscopic examination, the final polish should be repeated if necessary.

This procedure can also be used without the 0.25-$\mu$m diamond final polish (600-grit grind, 9-$\mu$m diamond on silk, and 1-$\mu$m diamond on a short-nap synthetic rayon cloth) to achieve excellent results on carbon or graphite fibers in aluminum and magnesium matrices and on carbon-carbon composites (Ref 11). A modification of this procedure has been used with excellent results on $Al_2O_3$ fibers in an aluminum matrix (Ref 11). In this case, the 9- and 1-$\mu$m polishes are performed using a chemotextile (Texmet) cloth, then are followed by the 0.25-$\mu$m final polish on a short-nap synthetic rayon cloth.

An alternate approach for graphite-aluminum (Ref 7) involves wet-disk grinding on 400- and 600-grit papers, followed by wheel polishing with 1-$\mu$m $Al_2O_3$ on a short-nap synthetic rayon cloth for 30 s to 3 min using abundant distilled water as a lubricant. Very light pressure is used, and polishing times should be as brief as possible. A similar polishing using 0.05-$\mu$m $Al_2O_3$ should follow. This technique, however, produces some topographical variation between fiber and matrix.

*For carbon-fibers in an aluminum matrix,* the property mismatch is not severe. The following procedure has been recommended (Ref 1). Grinding should be followed by polishing with 1-$\mu$m $Al_2O_3$ in distilled water on a short-pile wool broadcloth (kitten-ear). The specimen should be counter-rotated once per second using light pressure on a 150-rpm wheel. Scratches are removed quickly, as verified microscopically. Polishing then continues on a boiled, soft, short-nap synthetic rayon cloth using generous amounts of 0.3-$\mu$m $Al_2O_3$ in distilled water. With a wheel speed of 200 rpm, the specimen should be slowly rotated using very light pressure for approximately 1 min. This removes scratches caused by the 1-$\mu$m $Al_2O_3$. An additional polishing using 0.05-$\mu$m $Al_2O_3$ and extremely light pressure is required. Frequent microscopic examination will determine when all scratches are removed. However, this technique may produce fibers with a slightly rounded edge.

*Additional metal-matrix composites.* Diamond-disk grinding and polishing for metal-matrix composites was mentioned above. Such polishing has been used with success on boron fibers in aluminum or titanium matrices, silicon-carbide fibers in nickel or titanium, and molybdenum wire in nickel-base superalloys (Ref 2). Polishing should proceed for 10 to 45 min for each grit size down through 6 $\mu$m grit using very light pressure. Water is used sparingly as a lubricant. Disk polishing should be followed by a 3-$\mu$m diamond polish in kerosene on a silk cloth using a wheel rotating at approximately 150 rpm.

Polishing then proceeds using 0.25-$\mu$m diamond and kerosene lubricant on a wheel covered with hard bond paper. Light but firm pressure and slow wheel speed are used for approximately 10 to 15 min. Final polishing takes place on a vibratory polisher covered with short-nap synthetic rayon cloth and 0.3-$\mu$m $Al_2O_3$ in distilled water for approximately 3 h. If topological differences are produced by this step, abbreviated versions of the silk-cloth and paper polishing steps can be repeated, followed by abbreviated vibratory polishing. Etch-polishing can also be used to remove topographical variations and damage.

The following preparation technique has been reported for titanium-matrix composites containing boron or silicon carbide fibers (Ref 7). Grinding is omitted. After sectioning and mounting, automatic polishing begins using natural diamond paste in lapping oil on a chemotextile cloth mounted on a glass platen. The first polish uses 9-$\mu$m diamond and requires 3 to 7 days, depending on the fiber. During this step, pressure should be reduced from fairly heavy to moderate. Sufficient lubricant should be used to maintain a thin visible film and keep the surface continuously lubricated for 24 h; this is critical, because too little will cause topographical relief, and too much can cause fiber damage. After cleaning, polishing should be repeated using 6-$\mu$m diamond paste for 1 to 2 days, reducing the pressure from moderate to light during the process. Final polishing requires 0.25-$\mu$m diamond paste, very light pressure, and 1 to 3 days.

*Ceramic and glassy carbon matrix composites* can be polished successfully using standard grinding to 600 grit, followed by slow automatic polishing with 0.05 $\mu$m $Al_2O_3$ (Ref 12).

*For carbon-carbon composites,* the following procedure has been used with success (Ref 3). Polishing begins with 1-$\mu$m $Al_2O_3$ on silk cloth for 1 to 2 min. After ultrasonic cleaning, the specimen is final polished using 0.05-$\mu$m $CeO_2$ on a soft short-nap synthetic rayon cloth for approximately 30 s. As noted in the discussion of graphite-aluminum composites, a 600-grit grind followed by 9-$\mu$m diamond on silk, then 1-$\mu$m diamond on a short-nap synthetic rayon cloth also produces excellent results (Ref 11).

**Etching.** For most resin-matrix fiber composite specimens, no etchant is used, because the contrast between fibers and matrix is already great, and the matrix itself shows virtually no substructure. However, for metal-matrix composites, the common etchants are the same as those used for the matrix alone if they are compatible with the fiber.

Etchants can be valuable for glass-epoxy composites. Quality control inspection of glass-epoxy composites can be slowed, because glass fibers show low to moderate contrast with epoxy matrices. Hydrofluoric acid (HF) (0.5%) used for a few seconds will etch the epoxy matrix and highlight the fibers in these composites (Ref 5). Such an etchant could be used, but is generally unnecessary for epoxy-matrix composites with other fibers.

If polishing techniques have left damage or topological variations in a composite specimen, ion bombardment etching (cathodic sputtering by a gas discharge under vacuum) may remedy the situation. Argon, xenon, and other gases may be used; xenon produces the fastest etch. Such a technique can be used to remove carefully the damage produced by previous operations and can be helpful on a very soft matrix containing very hard fibers.

Carbon-carbon composites must be etched to discern the structure of the carbon matrix. Xenon ion etchant has also been used successfully for this purpose (Ref 3, 13). Chromic acid ($H_2CrO_4$), which is formed when chromium trioxide ($CrO_3$) is dissolved in water, or oxygen-plasma chemical etching has also been used successfully for carbon-carbon composites (Ref 3).

## Macroexamination

The features of interest for macro- or microexamination of a composite specimen vary with the materials (fibers and resins) and the fabrication process involved. Resin-matrix fiber composite materials are most commonly prepared by filament winding or by lay-up.

In filament winding, a fiber bundle or ribbon is impregnated with resin and wound on a mandrel to produce a shape that may be comparable to a spool of thread or a ball of yarn. The wound shape is then cured or consolidated using elevated temperature and/or pressure. After curing, the mandrel may be removed or may be part of the finished composite part. Pressure vessels and piping are commonly prepared by filament winding.

Lay-up may use prepreg tape, which is a ribbon, typically 305 mm (12 in.) wide, consisting of many unidirectional fiber bundles and preimpregnated with a resin. The tape is cut and "laid up" layer by layer to produce a laminate of the desired thickness and ply (layer) orientation. A similar lay-up may be produced, for example, using fabric and "wet" (uncured) resin. In either case, the laminate is then cured or consolidated using elevated temperature and/or pressure in an autoclave, a press, or a mold. Another fabrication technique is pultrusion, which is a continuous production process using a heated dye.

In most types of resin-matrix fabrication, the finished composite consists of layers (plies) or, for some filament-wound parts, bands, in which all fibers in a single layer lie at the same angle, but adjacent layers may be composed of fibers at a different angle. The composite should therefore have a known number of plies at specific angles and in a specific order (lamination sequence). If tape is used, joints within a layer are inevitable, and these usually "butt" rather than "overlap" or "gap." Flaws that can be reduced but not eliminated include voids and matrix-rich regions. Inclusions may also be present. Cracks and delaminations may already exist or may be produced during later fabrication steps or proof testing. Fiber volume fraction may vary considerably by design and because of the fabrication and curing.

The common fabrication processes for continuous-filament metal-matrix composites are powder metallurgy techniques, liquid metal infiltration followed by diffusion bonding, and, for large fibers such as boron, fiber on foil or plasma spraying of fibers followed by diffusion bonding (Ref 14). Therefore, the structures or features of interest in metal-matrix composites include those resulting from the metal matrix and its specific fabrication process. A major concern for the fabrication techniques involving diffusion bonding is possible incomplete bonding between layers.

Carbon-carbon composites are produced by pyrolysis and consolidation of a pitch- or petroleum-matrix carbon-fiber composite. Because of the high-temperature pyrolysis and processing, pores and shrinkage microcracks are a serious problem.

In fiber composites, macroscopic examination commonly includes visual or low-power optical examination as well as such techniques as ultrasonic scanning, dye penetrant inspection, and x-ray radiography. All these techniques provide information on the identity, quality, damage state, and failure mode of composite materials. For quality assurance purposes, nondestructive ultrasonic and radiographic techniques are used extensively to obtain a "picture" of composite internal quality and integrity. Dye penetrant inspection is routinely used to detect incompletely bonded areas in many metal-matrix composites. Visual and low-power optical examination are used for such purposes as identifying grossly defective parts, detecting parts or specimens with delaminations or torn fibers during machining, and classifying gross failure surface appearance.

## Microexamination

Microscopic examination of composite materials may involve such extremes as fairly low-magnification optical examination for quality control purposes and high-magnification electron microscope examination for studies of the fiber-matrix interface. Features that may be revealed by low-magnification examination include the number of plies, possible incomplete or warped layers, variations in ply thickness, nature of tape joins within plies, ply character (unidirectional tape or fabric), and major defects. Examination at low to intermediate magnifications will determine ply orientation as well as the number and distribution of voids, inclusions, matrix-rich regions, cracks, and delaminations. Identifying fiber and matrix, however, may require high-magnification optical or electron microscopy and x-ray or chemical analyses. Fractography generally involves scanning electron microscopy. Studies of the fiber-matrix interface may involve optical techniques, scanning electron microscopy, transmission electron microscopy, and other procedures, such as Auger analysis.

**Optical microscopy** is most commonly performed on polished sections or on fracture surfaces for limited low-magnification ($\sim 25\times$) examination. The type of preparation for optical microscopy will vary, depending on the purpose of the examination. Therefore, although mounting, grinding, polishing, and perhaps etching may be required for a study of detailed composite structures, a cursory grinding and quick polish may be sufficient preparation for a quality assurance verification of the number of plies. As shown, for example, in Fig. 4, careful specimen preparation reveals a wealth of information even at low magnification in graphite-epoxy composites. Here ply orientation, voids, epoxy-rich regions, and unusual oversize and hollow fibers are all obvious.

On the other hand, Fig. 5 shows a warped layer in a unidirectional graphite-epoxy specimen. The darkened areas in this micrograph are caused by fibers that were damaged intentionally during specimen preparation. These darkened fibers were useful, because they revealed areas where the epoxy matrix was incompletely cured and provided the contrast that readily revealed layer defects. Figure 6 shows a detail of such a region, in which fibers were damaged during preparation. Therefore, specimen preparation that may be unacceptable in some circumstances may be adequate or even desirable in others.

**Scanning electron microscopy** is prevalent for the examination of polished sections; the greater depth of field allows good results from specimens showing topological variations or unfilled voids or delaminations (Fig. 20). Scanning electron microscopy is also used for fracture studies, for which the large depth of field is often critical (see Fig. 26 to 31), and it is useful in studies of delamination as a function of testing conditions. In this case, replicas of the edge of the composite specimen may be taken while the specimen is under load, and progressive edge delamination or cracking may be readily studied. X-ray radiography has also been used while the composite is under load to reveal the progress of internal delamination and cracking.

Scanning electron microscopy is also used for studies of interfacial properties, such as fiber wetting, and for studies of the failure modes of fibers. In carbon-carbon composites that have been properly etched, scanning electron microscopy can reveal the details of the graphitic layer structure of the carbon matrix (Fig. 23).

**Transmission electron microscopy** has only limited application for composite materials. In general, magnifications obtained by scanning electron microscopy are sufficient. Exceptions are situations requiring details of fiber, matrix, or interfacial structures.

**Optical microscopy using polarized light** has been implemented with success in some applications. For example, polarized light can minimize the effects of topological variations (Fig. 1). In a more specialized application, the birefringent (optically anisotropic) nature of the graphitic matrix of carbon-carbon composites can be used under cross-polarized light to identify and determine the structure of each microconstituent (Fig. 22). Polarized light can reveal the structure of the matrix, pore morphology, microcrack morphology, degree of densification, and fiber volume fraction. In bidirectional composites, ply orientation and spacing as well as the extent of any anomalies can also be determined (Ref 3).

**Thin-section polarized light microscopy** has also been used with considerable success to view the matrix spherulite (grain) size in semicrystalline, thermoplastic-matrix composites (Ref 14). The end of a thin composite specimen is mounted and polished, from which a thin slice is removed. This is bonded to a 6.4-mm ($\frac{1}{4}$-in.) thick glass plate with room-temperature curable adhesive having the same refractive index as the glass. The laminate surface is then polished to a thickness of 2 to 3 $\mu$m and examined with transmitted-plane polarized light. The spherulites, which are birefringent, will be readily observable.

Ply orientation and stacking sequence can be determined by optical examination of appropriate sections at approximately 50 to 100$\times$. If the 0° axis orientation of the laminate (the direction of the fibers in at least one of the plies) is known, the first section is taken perpendicular to this direction. After preparation, the section is examined, and the 0° layers are noted; in these layers, the fibers should be circular in cross section. The orientation of any nonzero plies can then be verified by cutting another section at an angle that should be perpendicular to one such layer; if the ply angle is as supposed, the fibers in that layer will then display a circular cross section. This can be continued, by trial and error if necessary, until the ply angles of all layers are identified (Ref 8).

## Microstructures of Fiber Composites

The most common "high-performance" composites* are carbon/graphite, aramid, or glass fibers in epoxy matrices. Fiberglass in a polyester matrix is even more extensively used, but is not strictly a "high-performance" composite. Boron fibers in aluminum (alloy) are also used. Boron fibers are made by chemical vapor deposition of boron on a precursor tungsten or carbon filament. Figures 15 and 16 show tungsten cores in boron fibers. Carbon or graphite fibers in aluminum and boron-epoxy have limited aerospace applications, and carbon or graphite fibers in a carbon matrix are used in very high-temperature applications. Also in limited use are graphite-polyimide composites and glass, aramid, and graphite fibers in high-temperature thermoplastic matrices. Many other composites are in research and development, including graphite-magnesium and graphite-copper composites, those containing silicon carbide and $Al_2O_3$ fibers, and ceramic- and glass-matrix composites. For special applications, "hybrid" composites composed of different types of fibers, usually in the same matrix, are used.

The following microstructures are taken from various composites and illustrate many of the observable features and flaws described in the section on microexamination as well as many of the preparation techniques described elsewhere in this article. In polished specimens, differences among the various composites are more pronounced when the matrices are disparate (for example, metal rather than resin) than when the fibers are dissimilar, although variations in reflectivity are also seen for the latter. Generally, polished sections of resin matrices reveal little substructure, with voids, resin-rich regions, and other flaws being their most interesting features. Metal and carbon matrices, on the other hand, show considerable microstructure. The fracture surfaces vary considerably between composites; the exact matrix formulation, the fiber, and the fiber-resin interface, as well as the testing conditions, environmental exposure, the laminate, and the existence of flaws contribute significantly to the resulting structure.

## REFERENCES

1. T.J. Bertone, The Metallographic Sample Preparation of Fiber-Reinforced Composites, in *Metallographic Specimen Preparation, Optical and Electron Microscopy*,

*"High-performance" composites exhibit a higher strength-to-weight or stiffness-to-weight ratio than competing metallic materials.

J.L. McCall and W.M. Mueller, Ed., Plenum Press, 1974, p 251-273

2. Personnel of the Metallographic Laboratory, Materials and Process Engineering, General Dynamics Convair, San Diego, private communication, Feb 1985

3. J.E. Zimmer, Acurex Aerotherm, Mountain View, CA, private communication, Feb 1985

4. G. Shaw, Midwest Research Institute, Kansas City, private communication, Feb 1985

5. D.L. Dozer, Lockheed Missiles and Space Co., Sunnyvale, CA, private communication, Jan 1985

6. P. Ambalal, Lawrence Livermore National Laboratory, Livermore, CA, private communication, Jan 1985

7. T.K. Towns and R.A. Breazeale, Preparation of Metal Matrix Continuous Fiber Composite for Optical Metallography, in *Proceedings of the 1982 ASM Metals Congress*, American Society for Metals, Oct 1982

8. P.F. Dolan and G.B. Wadsworth, Boeing Vertol Co., Philadelphia, private communication, Feb 1985

9. T.J. Bertone, The Aerospace Corp., El Segundo, CA, private communication, Nov 1979

10. E. Snell, Lawrence Livermore National Laboratory, Livermore, CA, private communication, Feb 1979

11. Ca Ngoc Su, The Aerospace Corp., El Segundo, CA, private communication, March 1985

12. F.I. Hurwitz, NASA Lewis Research Center, Cleveland, private communication, April 1985

13. W. Stuckey, The Aerospace Corp., El Segundo, CA, private communication, Jan 1985

14. W.C. Harrigan, DWA Composite Specialties, Inc., Chatsworth, CA, private communication, April 1985

15. S. Christensen, Boeing Military Airplane Co., Seattle, private communication, Jan 1985

**Fig. 1** Aramid-epoxy composite (Kevlar 49 fibers in bisphernol F epoxy resin), unidirectional. Filament-wound hoop, standard moderate-temperature (60 to 80 °C, or 140 to 175 °F) cure. Unidirectional aramid fibers are weak in the transverse direction. The transverse damage to the fibers circles the numerous small (unfilled) voids (see arrows). Damage probably caused during specimen preparation. Void content in filament-wound composites is approximately ten times as high (5% vs. 0.5%) as in prepregged composites. Polarized light. As-polished (procedure 4 in Table 1). 500×. (E. Snell and L. Clements)

**Fig. 2** Graphite-epoxy composite (Thornel 300 graphite fibers in 5208 epoxy resin), (±45)₂ₛ. Standard autoclave cure of lay-up made from prepreg tape. Two glass tracer-fiber bundles are shown. These are x-ray opaque, permitting use of x-ray radiography to confirm ply orientation and lamination sequence. Note the difference in reflectivity between graphite and glass fibers. As-polished (procedure 16 in Table 1). 100×. (H.M. Shih)

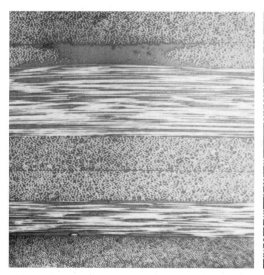

**Fig. 3** Graphite-epoxy composite, 96-ply, quasi-isotropic. Lay-up made from prepreg tape. The large resin-rich area results from a gap join within a ply; 90° layers show horizontal graphite fibers. As-polished (procedure 1 in Table 1). 54×. (L. Penn and G. Shaw)

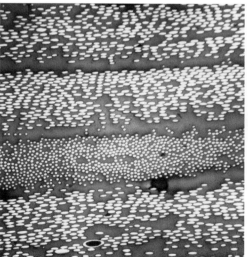

**Fig. 4** Graphite-epoxy composite (AS graphite fibers in 3501 epoxy matrix), quasi-isotropic, (0, ±60)₂ₛ. Lay-up made from prepreg tape. The oversize and hollow filaments resulted from oversize filaments in the organic textile precursor. Resin-rich areas and large voids may result from inadequate resin bleedout during cure. As-polished (procedure 16 in Table 1). 50×. (S.V. Ramani)

**Fig. 5** Graphite-epoxy composite (Thornel 300 graphite fibers in Narmco 5208 epoxy resin), unidirectional, section at 90° to fiber axis. Lay-up from prepreg tape. The distorted layers may result from butt joins. Dark areas result from intentional fiber damage during preparation. See also Fig. 6. As-polished (procedure 15 in Table 1). 50×. (M. Lee and L. Clements)

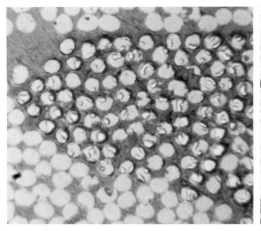

**Fig. 6** Graphite-epoxy composite (Thornel 300 graphite fibers in 5208 epoxy resin), unidirectional. Lay-up from prepreg tape. Detail of dark area in Fig. 5. Matrix around and within fiber bundle shown is incompletely cured. As-polished (procedure 2 in Table 1). 540×. (P.R. Lee and L. Clements)

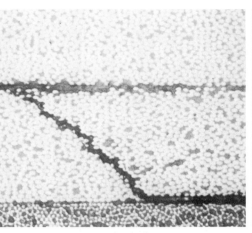

**Fig. 7** Graphite-epoxy composite (IM6 graphite fibers in 3501 epoxy resin), $(0_4/\pm45/0_6)$. Lay-up from prepreg tape. A delamination/crack runs from the left between the two 45° layers, across one 45° layer, then between the 45° and 0° layers. As-polished (procedure 2 in Table 1). 200×. (V.L. Shultes and G.B. Wadsworth)

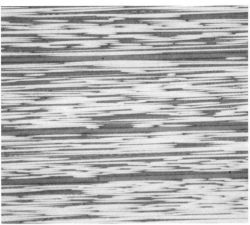

**Fig. 8** Graphite-epoxy composite (interlayered graphite/epoxy), unidirectional. Standard autoclave cure of lay-up from prepreg tape and interlayer material. The thin interlayer between plies toughens the interply region. As-polished (procedure 16 in Table 1). 100×. (J. Masters)

**Fig. 9** Graphite-aluminum composite, unidirectional. Liquid-metal infiltration of fiber bundles followed by diffusion bonding. Intermetallic aluminum carbide ($Al_4C_3$) crystals form at the uncoated fiber/matrix interface. Keller's reagent (procedure 6 in Table 1). 1000×. (C.N. Su)

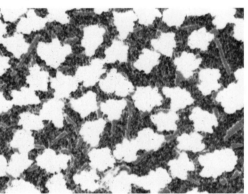

**Fig. 10** Graphite-aluminum composite (Thornel 50 graphite fibers in Al-13Si alloy), unidirectional. Old version (~1973) of Thornel 50 fiber was noncircular in cross section. Matrix shows gray needles of silicon, a structural feature that led to abandonment of this alloy. As-polished (procedure 17 in Table 1). 1000×. (L.W. Davis)

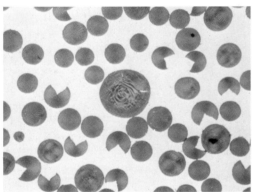

**Fig. 11** Graphite-aluminum composite (pitch precursor fibers in aluminum 201 alloy matrix). Liquid-metal infiltration of fiber bundles followed by diffusion bonding. Carbon fiber prepared by spinning of mesophase pitch results in a radial structure and open-wedge shape for many of the smaller fibers. As-polished (procedure 6 in Table 1). 500×. (C.N. Su)

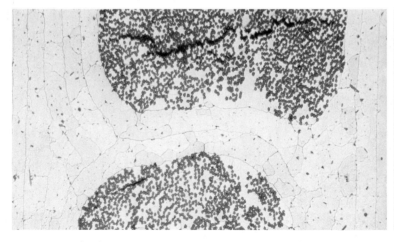

**Fig. 12** Graphite-aluminum composite (Thornel 50 graphite fibers, ~1976 version, in 6061 Al matrix in ~0.25% Ti and 0.025% B), unidirectional. Fibers precoated by vapor deposition of Ti and B. Fiber bundles impregnated by liquid-metal infiltration with 6061. Composite consolidation by diffusion bonding at 600 °C (1110 °F) with internal 6061 foil. The upper fiber bundle has a through crack. Keller's reagent (procedure 6 in Table 1). 100×. (C.N. Su)

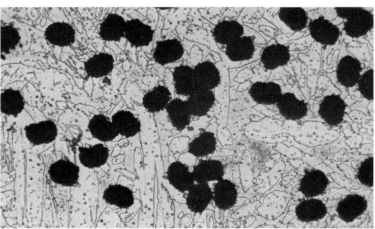

**Fig. 13** Graphite-aluminum bronze composite (Thornel 300 fibers in 89Cu-10Al-1Fe alloy matrix). Liquid-metal infiltration of fiber bundles followed by diffusion bonding. Carbide particles forming near the interface account for apparent fiber crenelling. These older (~1977) graphite fibers were partly elongated in cross section. Polished (procedure 6 in Table 1) and swab etched using 20 mL distilled $H_2O$, 10 mL $NH_4OH$, and 7 to 10 drops $H_2O_2$. 1000×. (W.C. Harrigan and C.N. Su)

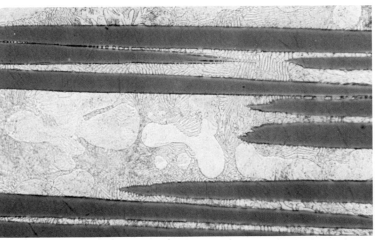

**Fig. 14** Graphite-silver copper composite (Thornel 300 fibers in 70Ag-30Cu matrix), unidirectional. Liquid-metal infiltration of fiber bundles followed by diffusion bonding. The 90° fibers (~1977 version) and eutectic morphology of matrix are evident. Same polish and etchant as Fig. 13. 1000×. (W.C. Harrigan and C.N. Su)

**Fig. 15** Boron-aluminum composite (boron fibers in 6061 aluminum matrix) diffusion bonded to Ti-6Al-4V. Plasma spray followed by diffusion bonding. The boron fibers are quite large (approximately 125 μm). In some locations, the tungsten core of the fibers can be seen. The fibers exhibit numerous transverse cracks. As-polished (procedure 11 in Table 1). 75×. (General Dynamics Convair)

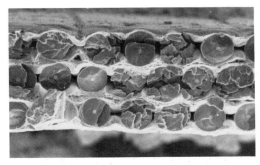

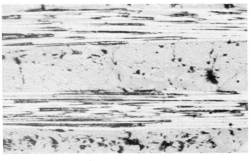

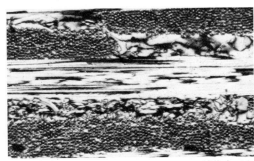

**Fig. 16** Boron-aluminum composite (boron fibers in 6061 Al matrix), unidirectional. Fiber on foil consolidated by diffusion bonding. SEM of tensile failure surface. Due to incomplete bonding of the foil layers, the failure has progressed in places through the boron fibers. The tungsten cores of the fibers can be clearly seen. 50×. (L.W. Davis)

**Fig. 17** Carbon-carbon composite (polyacrylonitrile-precursor graphite fibers in carbonaceous mesophase matrix produced by pyrolysis of coal-tar pitch). This tape-wound composite has 13% porosity consisting of voids and shrinkage cracks. As-polished (procedure 14 in Table 1). Bright field. 100×. (J.E. Zimmer)

**Fig. 18** Same composite as shown in Fig. 17, except specimen is viewed under cross-polarized light. Note that the individual graphite fibers are now much more apparent, as is the structure of the carbon matrix. As-polished (procedure 14 in Table 1). 100×. (J.E. Zimmer)

**Fig. 19** Chemical vapor deposited pyrolytic graphite used to redensify the matrix of carbon-carbon composites. This material fills shrinkage cracks and voids. See also Fig. 20 and 21. As-polished (procedure 6 in Table 1). Cross-polarized light. 440×. (C.N. Su)

**Fig. 20** Carbon-carbon composite (graphite fibers in carbonaceous mesophase matrix), bidirectional. Pores and shrinkage cracks redensified by chemical vapor deposition of pyrolytic graphite (see Fig. 19). The 0° layer at the top of the SEM shows pyrolytic graphite deposited around fibers. As-polished (procedure 6 in Table 1). 1000×. (C.N. Su)

**Fig. 21** Carbon-carbon composite (graphite fibers in a carbonaceous mesophase matrix). Matrix produced by pyrolysis of precursor resin matrix, then redensified by chemical vapor deposition of pyrolytic graphite (see Fig. 19), followed by filling of cracks and pores with an organic resin. Two graphite fibers surrounded by cones of pyrolytic graphite, which are surrounded by the organic resin. As-polished (procedure 6 in Table 1). Cross-polarized light. 1000×. (C.N. Su)

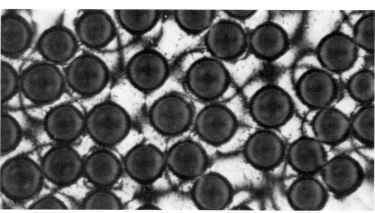

**Fig. 22** Carbon-carbon composite (graphite fibers in a carbonaceous mesophase matrix). Carbon matrix produced by pyrolysis of pitch precursor matrix. Dark lines are extinction contours in cross-polarized light that map out graphite layers perpendicular to the polarizers. Nodes and crosses in extinction contours denote disclinations in layer structure about the filaments. As-polished (procedure 14 in Table 1). 1600×. (J.E. Zimmer)

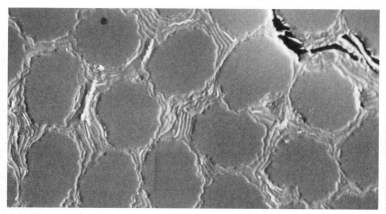

**Fig. 23** Carbon-carbon composite (graphite fibers in carbonaceous mesophase matrix), unidirectional. Matrix produced by pyrolysis of precursor resin matrix. SEM showing the graphite layers that develop in the matrix during pyrolysis. A shrinkage crack developing between mesophase layers is seen in the upper right. Polished (procedure 6 in Table 1) and xenon ion etched. 3000×. (C.N. Su)

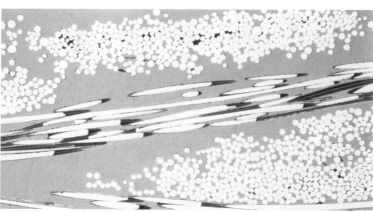

**Fig. 24** Silicon carbide-glass ceramic composite (woven silicon carbide fibers in a glass ceramic matrix). Matrix infiltration of fabric using a slurry of glass frit to produce a prepreg. Prepreg lay-up then placed in a mold and hot pressed. The woven cloth produces matrix-rich regions. Some porosity is seen within the fiber bundles. As-polished (procedure 16 in Table 1). 100×. (K.M. Prewo)

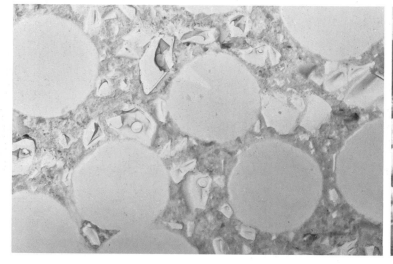

**Fig. 25** Graphite-glassy carbon ceramic composite (Celion 6000 graphite fibers in experimental resin precursor pyrolyzed at 600 °C, or 1110 °F, to yield a glassy carbon; particulate filler is α-silicon carbide), unidirectional. The excellent interfacial wetting and absence of voids is apparent. The filler particles are somewhat larger than optimum. As-polished (procedure 13 in Table 1). Replica electron micrograph. 3990×. (B.C. Buzek and F.I. Hurwitz)

**Fig. 26** Graphite-epoxy composite (Thornel 300 graphite fibers in 5208 epoxy matrix), unidirectional. Standard autoclave cure of lay-up made from prepreg tape. Scanning electron micrograph of a failed tensile surface, which is tiered, as is typical of this particular graphite epoxy. Considerable resin adheres to the fibers, indicating good interfacial bond strength. 500×. (P.R. Lee)

**Fig. 27** Graphite-PPS composite (AS4 graphite fibers in thermoplastic polyphenylene-sulfide matrix), film stacked and hot pressed. Scanning electron micrograph of a failed tensile surface. The high ductility of the thermoplastic matrix results in the ''tails'' of drawn matrix materials shown. 500×. (A.C. Lou)

**Fig. 28** Graphite-Al composite (Thornel 50 fibers in 6061 Al matrix), unidirectional. Liquid-metal infiltration and consolidation in a liquid-phase press. SEM of a failed surface. The older version (~1973) of this graphite fiber, with its crenelated cross section, has debonded and pulled out of the Al matrix. Pull-out holes are also seen. 1000×. (L.W. Davis)

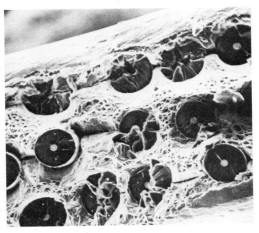

**Fig. 29** B-Al composite (25% B fibers in 6061 Al matrix), unidirectional. Fiber on foil and diffusion bonded. SEM of a fairly flat, failed tensile surface, characteristic of this material. Little matrix adheres to the fiber surface, indicating fairly low interfacial bond strength. The Al matrix shows good ductility. The tungsten cores of the vapor-deposited fibers are evident. 105×. (R. Moss)

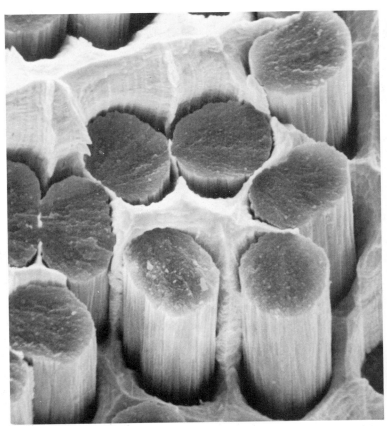

**Fig. 30** Graphite-silver copper composite (Thornel 300 fiber in 70Ag-30Cu eutectic matrix), unidirectional. Liquid-metal infiltration of fiber bundles followed by diffusion bonding. Scanning electron micrograph of a failed tensile surface. The matrix shows good ductility, but the lack of matrix adhering to the fibers (~1977 version) indicates low interfacial bond strength. 3000×. (W.C. Harrigan)

**Fig. 31** Silicon carbide-glass ceramic composite (unidirectional silicon carbide fibers in glass ceramic matrix). Ply lay-up and hot press densification. Scanning electron micrograph of a failed tensile surface. Although the ceramic matrix has failed in a brittle manner, the long pull-out length of the fibers indicates high composite toughness. 20×. (K.M. Prewo)

# Structures

# Introduction

By Michael B. Bever*
Professor of Materials Science
and Engineering, Emeritus
Massachusetts Institute of Technology

FOR MORE THAN A CENTURY, dating back to the pioneering contributions of Henry Clifton Sorby, metallurgists have not been satisfied merely to describe their metallographic observations, but have striven to explain them and to understand their implications (Ref 1-4). In addition, new techniques of structural investigation have yielded new observations and posed new problems. The quest for meaningful and precise explanations of metallurgical structures has been the primary driving force in the development of the science of physical metallurgy (Ref 5-8). Physical metallurgy now comprises a very broad spectrum. That portion of the spectrum dealing with the structure of metals is the subject of the articles in this Section.

This article will develop the sequence in which the articles in this Section are presented and establish some connections among them, provide background for the subject matter explored more fully in the specialized articles, and furnish general references. It will also treat important topics, such as grain structure and substructure, that are not covered systematically and comprehensively in the other articles. Finally, it will describe the scale of structural features and introduce the concept of hierarchical relations among them.

The term structure, as used here, refers primarily to the study of those microstructural features that can be investigated using optical (light) and electron microscopy (Ref 9-16). The results of investigations using other techniques, such as x-ray diffraction, are included when pertinent (Ref 17, 18). Macrostructural features, which can be observed with little or no magnification, will also be considered.

The purpose of the articles in this Section is to assist in the interpretation of microstructure. Such interpretation requires an understanding of the processes by which various structures are formed; therefore, the articles are organized according to the major processes that produce characteristic structures.

A special article describes textures that can result from several of these processes.

The principles applicable to various types of structures are illustrated by micrographs in the respective articles; references are also made to micrographs that appear in the Sections "Metallographic Techniques" and "Metallographic Techniques and Microstructures: Specific Metals and Alloys" in this Volume. Several works that treat the interpretation of microstructures systematically are cited in Ref 9 to 12.

## General Features of Structure

The structure of metals comprises features of various magnitudes. Major structural features, listed generally in increasing size, are:

- *Atomic structure:* nuclei, atoms
- *Electronic structure*
- *Crystal structure:* perfect crystals, crystal imperfections
- *Substructure:* subgrains, other cellular structures
- *Microstructure:* grains of single-phase metals and alloys, shapes and sizes of microconstituents and their configurational arrangements in multiphase systems
- *Textures*
- *Structural features* related to composition
- *Structural gradients*
- *Porosity and voids*
- *Macrostructure*

The structure of nuclei and atoms and the electronic structure are beyond the scope of this Volume, but are covered in texts on general physics and in specialized presentations (Ref 19-21). Some texts apply the fundamentals of crystallography to metals (Ref 22, 23). Crystal structures often found in metallic phases are listed and described in the article "Crystal Structure of Metals" in this Section.

**Crystal imperfections** include point defects, such as impurity atoms, vacancies and vacancy aggregates, and interstitial atoms; line defects (dislocations); and area defects, for example, stacking faults, twin interfaces, subboundaries, and grain boundaries. They are described in specialized texts on the theory of dislocations and other crystal imperfections (Ref 24-26).

Examples of various crystal defects are presented throughout this Volume. In the article "Transmission Electron Microscopy," dislocations (Fig. 21 to 24 and 26 to 29), dislocation dipoles (Fig. 30), dislocation networks (Fig. 31 to 33), and dislocation loops (Fig. 34 to 36) are shown. Dislocations are also shown in Fig. 3 to 6, 11, and 12 in the article "Solidification Structures of Pure Metals" in this Section. Stacking faults are shown in Fig. 44 to 47 in the article "Transmission Electron Microscopy."

**Subgrains** and cellular structures are formed by subboundaries (low-angle boundaries). The simplest of these boundaries consists of periodically spaced dislocations. In more complex instances, particularly in structures resulting from deformation, dislocation tangles can form cellular structures. Crystal imperfections of all kinds, including subboundaries, may occur in single crystals and within the grains of polycrystalline metals.

**Grain structure** of single-phase polycrystalline metals, which is the most characteristic feature of their microstructure, will be discussed below.

**Twins,** which occur within grains, are special imperfections that may originate during growth processes, for example, the annealing of cold-worked metal, or during deformation.

**Antiphase domain boundaries** occur in solid solutions with long-range order, reducing the perfection of the order.

**Ferromagnetic domains** are characteristic of ferromagnetic materials, as described in the article "Magnetic and Electrical Materials" in this Volume. Unlike typical metallurgical processes, a change in ferromagnetic domain structure requires a variation in

*The author gratefully acknowledges contributions by several of his colleagues to this article, particularly Professor Samuel M. Allen.

magnetic field. Antiferromagnets also have domain structures.

**Multiphase Structures.** As discussed below, the shapes, sizes, and configurational arrangements of two or more microconstituents in a multiphase system produce a variety of typical microstructures.

**Textures** combine the crystallographic feature of lattice orientation with the microstructural feature of grain structure. In a metal having a texture, or preferred orientation, the crystal lattices of the grain are arranged in a correlated and organized manner.

**Chemical composition** affects structure through its influence on phase relations. Composition is also involved in such structural features as microsegregation in solidified metals and solute-enriched regions at grain boundaries and other crystal imperfections (Ref 27).

**Structural gradients** reflect changes of structural features with position. For example, a plate can have a grain-size gradient from the surface toward the interior. Composition gradients can cause structural gradients, as in case-hardened metals. Composites present special opportunities for establishing structural gradients by controlling the spatial arrangements of the reinforcing phase—for example, fibers (Ref 28). Additional information is provided in the article "Fiber Composite Materials" in this Volume.

**Porosity and voids** are structural features that are characterized by a large range of sizes.

**Macrostructure** is discussed below and is also considered in the articles "Solidification Structures of Steel," "Solidification Structures of Aluminum Alloy Ingots," "Solidification Structures of Copper Alloy Ingots," and "Plastic Deformation Structures" in this Section.

## Origins of Structures

The characteristic structures of metals and alloys are produced by (1) transformations in which one or more parent phases are converted into one or more new phases, (2) deformation processes, (3) thermal processes, (4) thermomechanical processes, or (5) diffusion processes that do not result in a transformation, such as sintering. A typical deformation process is cold working. Examples of thermal processes are the annealing of a cold-worked metal and the homogenization of an alloy with microsegregation. The principles underlying and governing these processes are the province of physical metallurgy (see Ref 5-8, 29-31).

The transformations and processes that result in the production of typical structures involve characteristic basic mechanisms. The transformations that produce solidification structures and solid-state transformation structures involve several such mechanisms. The most important of these are diffusion, nucleation, and growth; more complex mechanisms operate in martensitic and bainitic transformations.

Basic deformation mechanisms include slip, twinning, and grain-boundary sliding. Annealing processes leading to recovery, recrystallization, and grain growth proceed by the mechanisms of polygonization, nucleation and growth, and grain-boundary migration, respectively.

Processes developed in recent years, such as rapid solidification, mechanical alloying, ion implantation, deformation of superplastic alloys, and laser annealing, have introduced new structural morphologies. For example, a structure without dendritic or cellular microsegregation was produced in an Ag-5Cu alloy that was electron beam melted and rapidly resolidified at 600 mm/s (see Fig. 21 and 22 in the article "Solidification Structures of Solid Solutions" in this Section). In addition, rapid solidification techniques, such as melt spinning and splat cooling, can produce metallic glasses, that is, amorphous (noncrystalline) metals, as described in the articles "Ultrarapid Solidification Processes" and "Amorphous Metal Powders" in Volume 7 of the 9th Edition of *Metals Handbook*.

## Single-Phase Microstructures

The major types of microstructures—solidification structures, solid-state transformation structures, and deformation and annealing structures—are shown in Fig. 1 to 3. The characteristic structural features of single-phase metals and alloys, such as grain structure and substructure, are discussed below. Some of the features of single-phase metals are also found in multiphase structures (Ref 32, 33).

**Grain Structure.** Grains are small crystals (crystallites) that form a three-dimensional aggregate; they are normally viewed in sections, which by their nature are limited to two dimensions. The main characteristics of a grain structure are grain size, grain shape, and grain-shape anisotropy.

**Types of Grain Structure.** Typical grain structures include impingement structure, columnar structure, equiaxed grain structure, mature grain structure, deformed grain structure, inhibited recrystallization structure, and duplex grain structure.

*Impingement structure* forms when grains grow until they meet or impinge, producing characteristic ragged interfaces. This type of

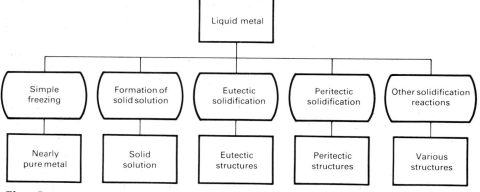

**Fig. 1** An outline of solidification structures

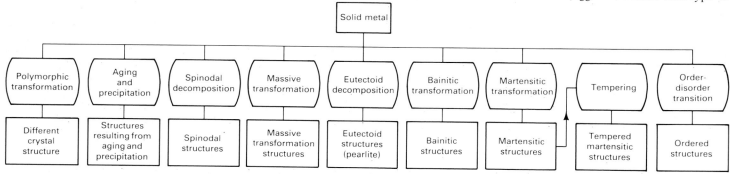

**Fig. 2** An outline of solid-state transformation structures

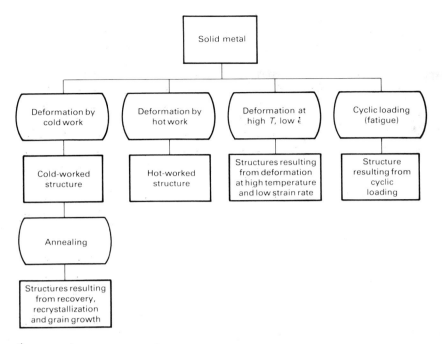

**Fig. 3** An outline of deformation and annealing structures

structure is rarely observed, because the interfaces usually are smoothed while the specimen remains at elevated temperature. Impingement grains have been observed after secondary recrystallization (Ref 34).

*Columnar structure* forms by unidirectional growth processes, especially during solidification, and by a growth process involving diffusion accompanied by a solid-state transformation. A columnar structure is shown in Fig. 2 in the article "Solidification Structures of Steel" in this Section.

*Equiaxed grain structure* may form by several processes, such as solidification (see Fig. 2 in the article "Solidification Structures of Steel") and recrystallization (see Fig. 80 to 87 in the article "Copper and Copper Alloys" and Fig. 1, 9, and 17 in the article "Zirconium and Hafnium and Their Alloys" in this Volume as well as Fig. 1 in the article "Textured Structures" in this Section).

*Mature grain structure* forms when the interfaces—for example, those resulting from impingement—adjust themselves under capillarity driving forces.

*Deformed grain structure* is the product of cold working. In such a structure, the grain shapes are anisotropic (see Fig. 60 to 68 in the article "Carbon and Alloy Steels" in this Volume and Fig. 1 in "Textured Structures" in this Section).

*Inhibited recrystallization structure* forms when second-phase particles arranged in a nonrandom pattern inhibit the motion of grain boundaries and impose their nonrandom pattern on the resulting recrystallized structure (see Fig. 29 and 30 in the article "Refractory Metals and Alloys" in this Volume).

*Duplex grain structure* (see Fig. 47 in the article "Carbon and Alloy Steels" in this Vol-

ume) consists of discrete regions of larger and smaller grain sizes, that is, a bimodal distribution of grain sizes. This structure is not related to microduplex alloys, which have characteristic duplex structures involving composition of two coexisting microconstituents rather than grain size (see the section "Multiphase Microstructures" below).

**Three-Dimensional Grain Structure.** Grain structures exist in three dimensions. In a typical structure, two grains are separated by an interface; three interfaces join along a line or edge, and four edges join at a point or junction. Six interfaces and four grains join at a junction in addition to the four edges. Junctions of four grain edges are the basic units of a mature grain structure; these junctions can be connected in innumerable ways without structural symmetry or exact repetition of detail (Ref 34, 35).

The major factors controlling grain structure are the requirement of space filling and the tendency toward minimum interfacial energy. Space filling implies that adjoining grains interact to determine each other's shapes. The problem of filling space with regular geometrical bodies has been studied over the past 100 years, beginning with Lord Kelvin in 1887 (Ref 34, 35). These studies have contributed to the understanding of grain structure, although actual grains may have irregular shapes.

The tendency toward minimum interfacial energy operates by reducing the grain-boundary area as much as possible or, when applicable, by rotating the grain boundary into low-energy orientations. The reduced grain-boundary area is an essential characteristic of mature grain structures.

Topological relations for three-dimensional grain structures, such as the average

number of sides of a grain face, have been analyzed. The relations applicable to metal grains resemble those for certain nonmetallic materials, such as biological cell structures and foam structures (Ref 34-36).

**Crystallography of Grain Boundaries.** Various models have been proposed for the grain-boundary region, ranging from simple models for low-angle tilt boundaries to complicated transition regions in high-angle boundaries (Ref 37). Coincidence and twin boundaries are discussed in the article "Solidification Structures of Pure Metals" in this Section.

**Two-Dimensional Grain Structure.** Sectioning of a three-dimensional grain structure presents the grain structure in only two dimensions for observation. In a typical grain structure, the following simple relations between the three-dimensional and the two-dimensional structures can be established:

- A volume—three-dimensional cell or spatial grain—becomes an area, that is, a two-dimensional cell or planar grain.
- An interface in a three-dimensional structure becomes a line or a grain boundary in a two dimensional structure.
- An edge becomes a point.
- A corner or junction (zero-dimensional cell) has an infinitesimal probability of being intersected by the plane of observation.
- The true dihedral angle becomes an apparent dihedral angle, as discussed below.

In the transition from a three- to a two-dimensional grain structure, another basic relation is that a structure consisting of uniformly sized three-dimensional, or spatial, grains becomes a two-dimensional structure in which the planar grains are not of uniform size. This is because a random plane cuts grains at random positions, ranging from a corner to the largest cross section. However, the resulting two-dimensional distribution of a grain structure of uniform three-dimensional grain size has definite statistical regularity. In general, the true three-dimensional grain size is more nearly uniform than the apparent two-dimensional grain size. The problems of grain-size measurement and grain-size statistics are covered in the article "Quantitative Metallography" in this Volume and in Ref 38 to 40.

The topological relations of grains in two dimensions (planar grains) have been observed, demonstrating that the average planar grain in a mature structure is a hexagon. Consequently, a seven-sided grain in a microsection must be balanced by a five-sided grain, a nine-sided grain by a three-sided grain, or by three five-sided grains, and so on. In addition, correct sampling for polygon distribution ensures better sampling for size (see Ref 34-36).

**Grain Shape.** In three dimensions, the average shape of equiaxed grains may, for some purposes, be approximated by a sphere. Similarly, nonequiaxed grains may be represented by ellipsoids. When viewed in two dimensions, nonequiaxed grains have extended shapes, as shown in Fig. 1 in the article "Textured Structures" in this Section. The quantitative determination of grain shape has been discussed (Ref 41).

**Dihedral Angles.** In three dimensions, the true dihedral angle is the angle between two faces of a grain measured in a plane normal to the edge at which the faces intersect. In any actual section, the faces are intersected by planes oriented randomly at all angles. Therefore, the apparent angle in two dimensions generally differs from the true angle in three dimensions. Stated differently, the apparent or observed angle is the angle between the traces of grain faces in the plane of a random section. The angles in a two-dimensional section are statistically random in the absence of any orientation effect or preselection.

Quantitative relations exist between the true angle in three dimensions and the apparent angle observed in two dimensions. If the true angle is 120°, as in a mature grain structure, the probability of finding an angle within 5° of the true angle is greater than the probability of finding an angle in any other 10° range (Ref 42). In fact, four angles out of five are expected to be within 25° of the true angle. However, in actual grain structures, the true angles and, to a greater extent, the observed angles will have a distribution range.

In two-phase structures, the true dihedral angles may differ from 120° even if the structure is equilibrated. The extent to which the true angles differ depends on the relative interfacial tensions between grains of the two phases present. It has been suggested that the true angle can be found by matching calculated and observed frequency plots. The most probable angle is in every instance the true dihedral angle (Ref 43).

A simpler procedure for finding the true angle uses a cumulative distribution curve. The median angle differs only slightly, and correctably, from the true angle. In addition, fewer measurements—perhaps 25 instead of several hundred—are sufficient (Ref 44). Errors in measurement have been systematically analyzed, and dihedral angles with nonunique values have been considered (Ref 45).

## Substructure

In the broadest sense, substructure comprises all imperfections within the grains of a polycrystalline metal or a single crystal. In the conventional sense, substructure refers to the subgrains formed by subboundaries (low-angle boundaries). This structure is revealed at intermediate magnifications; crystal imperfections, such as dislocations and stacking faults, can be revealed individually only at much higher magnifications.

Examples of special kinds of substructure are:

- *Lineage structure,* mosaics originating by solidification
- *Veining* originating by transformation of face-centered cubic (fcc) iron to body-centered cubic (bcc) iron
- *The cellular structure* resulting from cold work
- *Impurity substructure* involving solute atmospheres associated with dislocations
- *Dislocation networks* originating by solidification, cold work, or fatigue (cyclic loading)
- *Polygonized structure* resulting from cold work followed by annealing
- *Imperfections* resulting from quenching or radiation damage

The subgrains that constitute substructure in the conventional sense have a large range of possible sizes. The angular misorientations resulting from subboundaries range from a fraction of 1° to well over 1°.

## Multiphase Microstructures

Although many industrial alloys are single-phase materials—for example, cartridge brass, silicon steel, and austenitic stainless steels—multiphase alloys are more often encountered. Most ferrous metals as well as many nonferrous alloys, especially the age-hardening and precipitation-hardening alloys, consist of more than one phase.

The characteristic multiphase structures can be related to their modes of origin (see Fig. 1 and 2). The major types of multiphase structures are discussed below.

**Structures in which both phases form entirely distinct grains** have been called aggregated two-phase structures or random duplex aggregates. They develop most clearly in alloys in which both phases are present in approximately equal volume fractions (Ref 46). In microduplex alloys, the two phases are distributed uniformly such that the boundaries are predominantly interphase interfaces. This structure is usually fine scale and resistant to microstructural coarsening.

**Structures in which each phase is closely interconnected** can result from spinodal decomposition (see the article "Spinodal Structures" in this Volume). The scale of these spinodal structures is very small. They are characterized principally by their high degree of connectivity and often by crystallographic alignment of the phases (Ref 47).

**Structures consisting of one continuous phase and isolated particles of a second phase (the matrix-plus-dispersed-phase structure)** are the most varied of the multiphase structures. Among their characteristic variables are the relative volumes of the two phases, the size of the particles of the dispersed phase, the interparticle distance, the shape of the dispersed particles, and any special orientation of the dispersed particles with respect to each other and the matrix. Some of these variables are interdependent; all of them can be measured. Examples of the ma-

trix-plus-dispersed-phase structure are rod-shaped particles embedded in a matrix and cellular precipitates. The development of high-strength steels has introduced the dual-phase microstructure in which a ferrite matrix contains small islands (approximately 20 vol%) of dispersed martensite. A dual-phase steel microstructure is shown in Fig. 1 and 2 in the article "Carbon and Alloy Steels" in this Volume.

**Structures in which the two phases are arranged in alternate layers or lamellae** form as eutectics, as pearlites in steels, and as pearlites in nonferrous eutectoid alloys. Their characteristic variable is the interlamellar spacing or thickness of the lamellae.

**A second phase** can be distributed along the grain boundaries of a matrix phase, as in copper that is contaminated by bismuth. Particles of a dispersed phase can also be located at other preferential sites, such as at slip planes after cold work followed by a precipitation process.

**Crystallography of Interphase Interfaces.** The two phases that meet at an interface may differ in lattice constants, lattice type, and orientation. These differences result in a mismatch or disregistry at the interface.

This mismatch can be accommodated in one of the following three ways (Ref 37, 48): (1) A coherent interface exists when, in two adjoining structures, corresponding rows and planes of lattice points are continuous across the interface. However, the rows and planes may change direction, resembling a coherent twin boundary. Fully coherent interfaces between crystals of appreciable size are rare. However, in limited areas, elastic straining can make it possible for coherency to exist. The particles of transformation products with such coherency generally are too small to be observed using optical microscopy. (2) At a semicoherent interface, the two lattices are elastically strained into coherence over limited areas; they accumulate misfit that is corrected periodically by discontinuities (dislocations). In other words, regions of forced elastic coherence alternate with regions of misfit. (3) At an incoherent interface, the two lattices are discontinuous. It was thought that such an interface could be explained in terms of dislocations compensating for the mismatch; however, such explanations have no physical significance, and the dislocation model of incoherent interfaces retains little interest.

## Macrostructure

The macrostructure of metals and alloys consists of inhomogeneities on a fairly large scale. For example, gradients in a macrostructure exist on a much larger scale than that of the constituents of the microstructure. A macrostructure may also comprise other inhomogeneities, such as blowholes or porosity in cast or weld metal (see Fig. 54 in the article "Magnesium Alloys" in this Volume), which originate during solidification, and flow lines in forgings (see Fig. 82 in the article "Aluminum Alloys" in this Volume and Fig. 11 in the article "Plastic Deformation Structures" in this Section), which originate during deformation. Flow lines in forgings may be caused by elongated inclusions or by inhomogeneities in grain-shape alignment. Other examples of macrostructures are presented in the articles in this Volume dealing with metallographic procedures and representative microstructures of specific metals and alloys.

**Size Scales and Hierarchical Structures.** The size scales of structural features of metals extend from the atomic level, ~0.1 nm (1 Å) to the size of entire metallic objects, ~1 m (3¼ ft). This range spans 10 orders of magnitude. The techniques for observing structural features at different levels within this range

must have adequate resolving powers. Figure 4 shows the sizes of some common structural features of metals and various techniques for their observation with limits of resolution.

Frequently, several structural features on different levels in a given metallic system are of interest. For example, a polycrystalline single-phase metal has a grain structure, and within each grain a substructure may be present; or, in a polycrystalline long-range ordered binary alloy, a substructure of antiphase boundaries may exist within each grain. In a forging, the macroscopic flow lines may coexist with a structure of matrix grains in which precipitates are dispersed. These examples of structural features that coexist at different levels are typical hierarchical structures.

## REFERENCES

1. R.F. Mehl, *A Brief History of the Science of Metals*, American Institute of Mining and Metallurgical Engineers, Warrendale, PA, 1948
2. C.S. Smith, *A History of Metallography*, University of Chicago Press, 1960
3. C.S. Smith, Ed., *Sorby Centennial Symposium on the History of Metallurgy*, Gordon and Breach, 1965
4. R.F. Mehl and R.W. Cahn, The Historical Development of Physical Metallurgy, in *Physical Metallurgy*, Part I, 3rd ed., R.W. Cahn and R. Haasen, Ed., North-Holland, 1983, p 1-35
5. R.W. Cahn and P. Haasen, Ed., *Physical Metallurgy*, Parts I and II, 3rd ed., North-Holland, 1983
6. A.G. Guy and J.J. Hren, *Elements of Physical Metallurgy*, 3rd ed., Addison-Wesley, 1974
7. W.F. Smith, *Structures and Properties of Engineering Alloys*, McGraw-Hill, 1981
8. R.E. Smallman, *Modern Physical Metallurgy*, 4th ed., Butterworths, 1985
9. R.H. Greaves and H. Wrighton, *Practical Microscopical Metallography*, 4th ed., Chapman & Hall, 1957
10. H. Gleiter, Microstructure, in *Physical Metallurgy*, Part I, 3rd ed., R.W. Cahn and P. Haasen, Ed., North-Holland, 1983, p 650-712
11. G.F. Vander Voort, *Metallography: Principles and Practice*, McGraw-Hill Book Co., 1984
12. W. Rostoker and J.R. Dvorak, *Interpretation of Metallographic Structures*, 2nd ed., Academic Press, 1977
13. J.W. Edington, *Practical Electron Microscopy in Materials Science*, Van Nostrand Reinhold, 1976
14. P.J. Goodhew, *Electron Microscopy and Analysis*, Wykeham Publications, 1975
15. M.H. Loretto and R.E. Smallman, *Defect Analysis in Electron Microscopy*, Chapman & Hall—Halsted/Wiley, 1975
16. G. Thomas and M.J. Goringe, *Transmission Electron Microscopy of Materials*, John Wiley & Sons, 1979
17. C.S. Barrett and T.B. Massalski, *Structure of Metals*, 3rd ed., Pergamon Press, 1980
18. B.D. Cullity, *Elements of X-ray Diffraction*, 2nd ed., Addison-Wesley, 1978
19. H.W. King, Structure of the Pure Metals, in *Physical Metallurgy*, Part I, 3rd ed., R.W. Cahn and P. Haasen, Ed., North-Holland, 1983, p 37-79
20. D.G. Pettifor, Electron Theory of Metals, in *Physical Metallurgy*, Part I, 3rd ed., R.W. Cahn and P. Haasen, Ed., North-Holland, 1983, p 73-152
21. W.A. Harrison, *Electronic Structure and the Properties of Solids*, Freeman, 1980
22. A. Kelly and G.W. Groves, *Crystallography and Crystal Defects*, Addison-Wesley, 1970

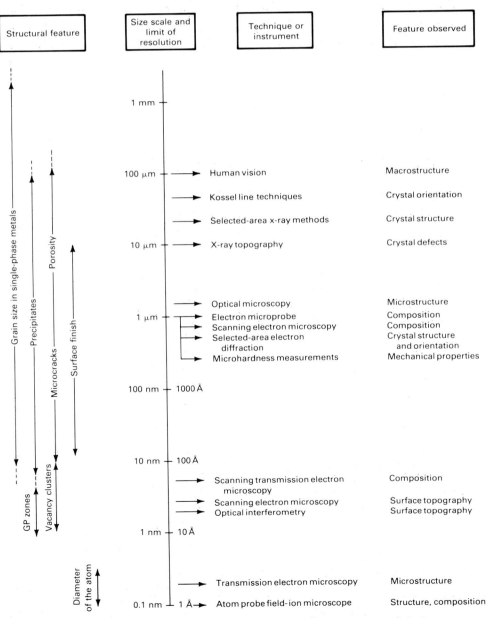

**Fig. 4** Size scale relating structural features of metals to techniques of observation (after Ref 49)

23. E. Prince, *Mathematical Techniques in Crystallography and Materials Science*, Springer-Verlag, 1982

24. H.G. van Bueren, *Imperfections in Crystals*, North-Holland, 1960

25. J.P. Hirth and J. Lothe, *Theory of Dislocations*, 2nd ed., John Wiley & Sons, 1982

26. D. Hull, *Introduction to Dislocations*, 3rd ed., Pergamon Press, 1975

27. R.W. Balluffi, Grain Boundary Structure and Segregation, in *Interfacial Segregation*, W.C. Johnson and J.M. Blakely, Ed., American Society for Metals, 1979, p 193-236

28. M.B. Bever and P.E. Duwez, Gradients in Composite Materials, *Mater. Sci. Eng.*, Vol 10, 1972, p 1-8

29. J.W. Christian, *The Theory of Transformations in Metals and Alloys*, Pergamon Press, 1965; 2nd ed., Part I, Pergamon Press, 1975

30. D.A. Porter and K.E. Easterling, *Phase Transformations in Metals and Alloys*, Van Nostrand Reinhold, 1981

31. R.W.K. Honeycombe, *The Plastic Deformation of Metals*, 2nd ed., St. Martin's Press, 1982

32. R.D. Doherty, Stability of Grain Structure in Metals, *J. Mater. Educ.*, Vol 6, 1984, p 845

33. A.P. Sutton, Grain Boundary Structure, *Int. Met. Rev.*, Vol 29, 1984, p 377

34. C.S. Smith, Some Elementary Principles of Polycrystalline Microstructure, *Met. Rev.*, Vol 9, 1964, p 1-62

35. C.S. Smith, Grain Shapes and Other Metallurgical Applications of Topology, in *Metal Interfaces*, American Society for Metals, 1952, p 65-133

36. C.S. Smith, Microstructure, *Trans. ASM*, Vol 45, 1953, p 533-575

37. R.W. Balluffi, Ed., *Grain Boundary Structure and Kinetics*, American Society for Metals, 1979

38. F. Schückher, Grain Size, in *Quantitative Microscopy*, R.T. DeHoff and F.N. Rhines, Ed., McGraw-Hill, 1968

39. E.E. Underwood, in *Quantitative Stereology*, Addison-Wesley, 1970, Chapters 4 and 5

40. H.E. Exner, Analysis of Grain- and Particle-Size Distributions in Metallic Materials, *Int. Met. Rev.*, Vol 17, March 1972, p 24-52

41. E.E. Underwood, in *Quantitative Stereology*, Addison-Wesley, 1970, p 228

42. D. Harker and E.R. Parker, Grain Shape and Grain Growth, *Trans. ASM*, Vol 34, 1945, p 156-195

43. C.S. Smith, Grains, Phases and Interfaces: An Interpretation of Microstructure, *Trans. AIME*, Vol 175, 1948, p 15

44. O.K. Riegger and L.H. Van Vlack, Dihedral Angle Measurement, *Trans. Met. Soc. AIME*, Vol 218, 1960, p 933-935

45. C.A. Stickels and E.E. Hucke, Measurement of Dihedral Angles, *Trans. Met. Soc. AIME*, Vol 230, 1964, p 795-801

46. R.W. Cahn, Metal Systems, in *Composite Materials*, L. Holliday, Ed., Elsevier, 1966, p 65-90

47. J.W. Cahn, A Model for Connectivity in Multiphase Structures, *Acta Metall.*, Vol 14, 1966, p 477-480

48. G.B. Olson and M. Cohen, Interphase Boundaries and the Concept of Coherency, *Acta Metall.*, Vol 27, 1979, p 1907-1918

49. S.M. Allen and M.B. Bever, Structure of Materials, in *Encyclopedia of Materials Science and Engineering*, to be published

# Solidification Structures of Pure Metals

By K.A. Jackson
Head, Optical Materials Research Department
AT&T Bell Laboratories

PURE METALS normally solidify into polycrystalline masses, but it is relatively easy to produce single crystals by directional solidification from the melt. The three common ways of growing single crystals are the Bridgman method, in which a mold is lowered out of a vertical tubular furnace; the Chalmers method, in which a boat is passed through a horizontal tubular furnace; and the Czochralski method, in which a crystal is pulled from a crucible containing the melt. Much effort has been directed toward obtaining high-purity starting materials (often by zone refining) and toward maintaining purity during crystal growth. Metal single crystals have been prepared with very low dislocation densities, but because pure metal crystals are

very soft, this requires great care to reduce thermal and mechanical stresses during growth and subsequent handling. Most metal single crystals have dislocation densities of about $10^6$ to $10^7$ per square centimeter. These dislocations result from stresses induced during growth by thermal, mechanical, and composition gradients, as well as from entrapped particles. In addition, vacancies can condense to form small dislocation loops subsequent to growth.

Dislocations present in a metal crystal often polygonize into subboundaries during growth. These subboundaries, which frequently intersect the growth front, are propagated by the growth process and result in subgrains that are elongated in the direction

of the growth. Subboundaries originating in this way are irregular (Fig. 1) if the material is pure, but are regular and straight (Fig. 2) in a very dilute alloy in which cellular growth has occurred. Subboundaries also are formed where the liquid between two slightly misoriented dendrite arms freezes.

Dislocations in subboundaries can be resolved by careful metallography; an example is shown in Fig. 3. A specimen etched to reveal the subboundaries and dislocations is depicted in Fig. 4. The number of dislocations in the subboundaries often approximately equals the number of isolated dislocations in the subgrains.

Dislocations produced by thermal or mechanical stresses at low temperature often

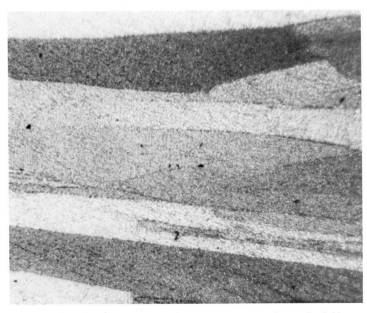

**Fig. 1** Irregular subboundaries in high-purity tin grown without cells. Subboundaries similar to these form in many high-purity metals during solidification. Compare with the structure shown in Fig. 2. 10% $FeCl_3$ + 2% HCl, in $H_2O$. 40×

**Fig. 2** Regular subboundaries in tin of lower purity than that in Fig. 1, grown with cells. Cellular growth, resulting from the presence of minute amounts of impurity, makes the subboundaries straight during solidification. 10% $FeCl_3$ + 2% HCl, in $H_2O$. 35×

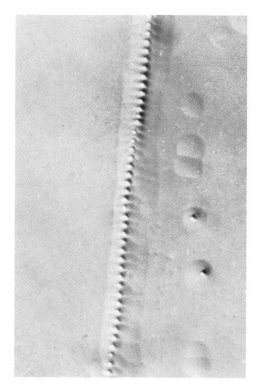

**Fig. 3** Individual dislocations (revealed by careful etching) that comprise a subboundary in germanium. $HNO_3$-acetic-HF-bromine. 1500×. (W.G. Pfann)

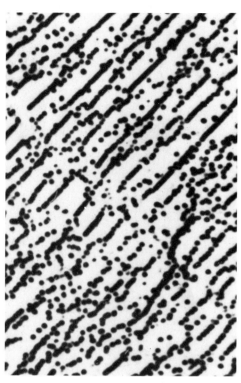

**Fig. 4** Dislocations and subboundaries produced by polygonization in germanium annealed after deformation. $HNO_3$-acetic-HF-bromine. 250×. (J.R. Patel)

line up on the traces of slip planes, as shown in Fig. 5. Dislocations produced by precipitation and condensation of vacancies during cooling usually are in the form of small loops (Fig. 6). These vacancies can also form other clusters, such as stacking-fault tetrahedra.

## Polycrystalline Metals

The shape and size of the grains in a polycrystalline specimen of a pure metal are determined initially by nucleation and growth during solidification and ultimately by grain growth after solidification. Castings are usually made by pouring hot liquid into a cold mold. The solidification process depends on the degree of superheat—that is, the degree to which the pouring temperature exceeds the melting point—and on the shape and properties of the mold. For a small superheat, crystals will nucleate on the cold mold wall, and solidification will proceed inward from the mold wall. For a large superheat, the surface of the mold may be heated above the melting point during pouring so that nucleation occurs in the bulk of the liquid.

Nucleating agents added to the melt will promote nucleation at many sites to produce a fine grain structure. If the mold shape is intricate, it may be necessary to pour the liquid metal at a high temperature to prevent blockage of some of the channels by freezing before the mold has been filled. Proper filling of the mold also depends on its design and material. Mold design affords control of the size and shape of grains in various parts of a casting.

The initial grain structure of a casting is determined by the distribution of nucleation

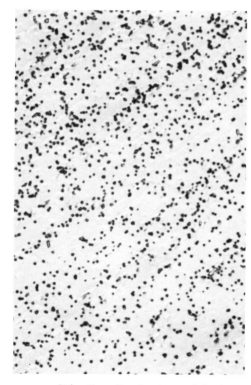

**Fig. 5** Dislocations aligned on traces of slip planes in germanium deformed at low temperature. $HNO_3$-acetic-HF-bromine. 200×. (J.R. Patel)

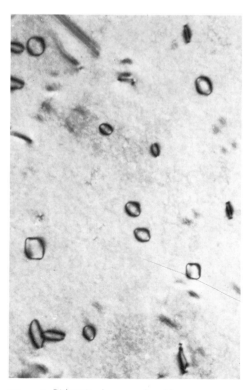

**Fig. 6** Dislocation loops produced by vacancy precipitation in germanium. Thin-foil electron micrograph. 60 000×. (D.M. Maher)

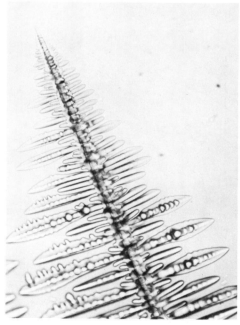

**Fig. 7** Dendrites in cyclohexanol, an organic compound that crystallizes like a metal. 45×

sites and by the subsequent growth that proceeds from these sites. If nucleation occurs in the bulk of the melt, then it must have been supercooled (that is, at a temperature below its melting point); therefore, the initial growth is likely to be dendritic. The dendrites from one nucleus grow out until they impinge upon dendrites growing from adjacent nuclei (Fig. 7). This process defines the initial shape of the grains, as illustrated in Fig. 8. The den-

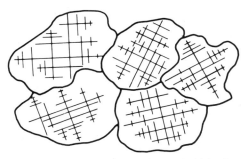

**Fig. 8** Coarse, equiaxed grains produced by dendritic growth in an undercooled melt of pure metal

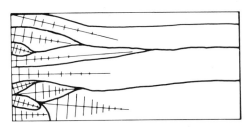

**Fig. 9** Elongated grains and preferred orientation produced by directional solidification

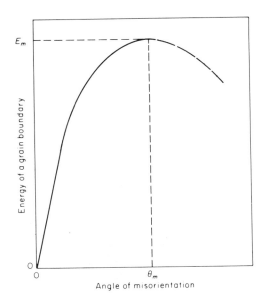

**Fig. 10** Calculated energy of the boundary between two grains as a function of the angle of misorientation between the crystal lattices of the grains. The energy becomes maximum ($E_m$) at angle $\theta_m$.

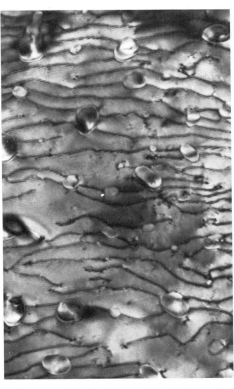

**Fig. 11** Dislocations in a small-angle tilt boundary in gold. Thin-foil transmission electron micrograph. See also Fig. 10. 24 000×. (R.W. Balluffi)

**Fig. 12** Dislocations in a small-angle twist boundary in gold. Thin-foil transmission electron micrograph. See also Fig. 10. 24 000×. (R.W. Balluffi)

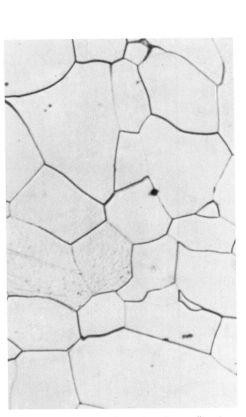

**Fig. 13** Grain boundaries in polycrystalline iron. Most of the triple junctions of the grain boundaries form 120° angles. 5% nital. 250×

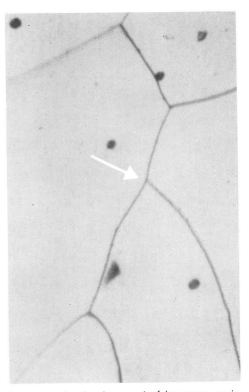

**Fig. 14** Junction (at arrow) of low-energy grain boundary with high-energy grain boundary in polycrystalline iron. 5% nital. 800×

drites continue to grow and thicken until the temperature is raised to the melting point by the heat of fusion, which is released by the freezing process. The interdendritic liquid, not frozen at this point, can freeze only as heat is extracted from the sample.

Nucleation can occur on the cold walls of the mold without most of the liquid being undercooled. In this case, there may be a short zone of dendritic growth, but only in a layer near the cold mold wall where the melt is undercooled. Depending on the thermal conditions, the melting point isotherm will be established somewhere between the hot melt and the cold wall. The solidification of the casting will then proceed inward, with a more or less uniform isothermal front. The grains that nucleated on the mold wall will elongate in the direction of heat flow, as illustrated in Fig. 9, resulting in a columnar grain structure. As growth proceeds, some crystal orientations will tend to persist at the expense of others, resulting in a preferred orientation texture.

Dendritic growth occurs in a pure material only if the melt is undercooled. This is because dendritic growth results from instability of the solid-liquid interface due to a diffusion process, which for a pure material can only be thermal diffusion. In an alloy, interface instabilities from chemical diffusion often result in dendritic growth.

Although the grain boundaries in high-purity metals are very mobile, they may be slowed down or pinned by small concentrations of impurities. If the initial grain size was large, grain growth is less likely, but there will usually be some adjustment of the grain boundaries to lower energy configurations.

## Grain Boundaries

The energy of a single grain boundary as a function of the angle of misorientation is shown in Fig. 10. Small-angle boundaries, consisting of dislocation arrays, have much lower energies than large-angle boundaries. The dislocation arrays in tilt and twist boundaries are illustrated in Fig. 11 and 12, respectively.

Large-angle boundaries contain regions of good fit and of bad fit. Low-energy, small-angle boundaries usually represent less than 10° to 15° of misorientation. This range is a small fraction of the total range of possible misorientations. Therefore, most random boundaries, formed by the growing together of two grains will be large-angle boundaries—that is, will have more than 10° misorientation. All large-angle boundaries except twin or coincidence boundaries have roughly the same energy and so form 120° angles with each other when equilibrated at the junction of three grains, as illustrated in Fig. 13 (coincidence boundaries have some lattice sites common to both crystals). In Fig. 14, the junction of a small-angle boundary with two large-angle boundaries is shown. The ratios of the boundary energies can be calculated from the angles.

Coincidence boundaries usually have lower energies than those of large-angle grain boundaries. A boundary that separates twins (two crystals oriented in a special crystallographic arrangement in which they are related by mirror symmetry) has low energy if it is coherent; that is, if it lies in the mirror plane. Twin boundaries can be produced during crystal growth or annealing. Small-angle boundaries and individual dislocations are usually present within the grains of a polycrystal, just as in a single crystal.

## SELECTED REFERENCES

- H.D. Brody and D. Apelian, Ed., *Modeling of Casting and Welding Processes*, symposium proceedings, Solidification Committee, Metallurgical Society of AIME, Warrendale, PA, 1981
- B. Chalmers, *Principles of Solidification*, John Wiley & Sons, 1964
- G.J. Davies, *Solidification and Casting*, John Wiley & Sons, 1973
- R. Elliot, *Eutectic Solidification Processing: Glassy and Crystalline Alloys*, Butterworths, 1983
- J. Friedel, *Dislocations*, Pergamon Press, 1964
- A.G. Guy, *Introduction to Materials Science*, McGraw-Hill, 1972
- *Interfaces Conference*, R.C. Gifkins, Ed., Butterworths, 1969
- "Solidification," 1969 seminar, American Society for Metals, 1971

# Solidification Structures of Solid Solutions

By William J. Boettinger
Metallurgist
Metallurgy Division
National Bureau of Standards

SOLIDIFICATION is one of the most common steps in the materials processing cycle of metals and alloys. Whether the material is used in service as a casting, a heat-treated casting, or a wrought product, the cast microstructure is important in determining properties and service life. The microstructure of an as-solidified alloy can be described on three different size scales of magnification. At the largest scale are grain size and gross casting defects such as macroporosity or long-range segregation of alloying additions (macrosegregation). At an intermediate scale, usually found within individual grains, are microscopic nonuniformities of composition termed microsegregation (coring) and associated second-phase segregates, inclusions, and microporosity. At the finest scale are modifications of the cast structure by solid-state transformations, such as precipitation, which occur during solid-state cooling.

This article discusses only microsegregation. For castings solidified slowly, the length scale of microsegregation may be as large as 1 mm (0.04 in.); in rapidly solidified alloys, the scale of microsegregation may be as small as 0.1 $\mu$m.

## Phase Diagrams and Solute Segregation

Alloys consist of a base metal, such as iron, aluminum, copper, or nickel, to which other elements (solutes) are added to yield desired properties. These alloying elements are normally soluble in the liquid metal and the solid metal, but usually in different concentrations. This difference is shown in Fig. 1, which is part of a binary phase diagram. The top curve is called the liquidus. At temperatures above this curve, the base metal and the alloying element are completely soluble as a liquid phase. The bottom curve is called the solidus. At temperatures below this curve, the

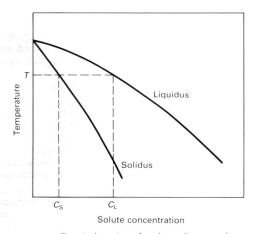

**Fig. 1** Terminal portion of a phase diagram, showing the solute concentration of liquid ($C_L$) and solid ($C_S$) that are in equilibrium at temperature $T$. Solute segregation occurs when, during freezing, solute is rejected into the remaining liquid.

two components are completely soluble as a single solid crystalline phase called a solid solution. The ratio, $k$, between the solidus composition and liquidus composition at a fixed temperature is called the equilibrium partition (or distribution) coefficient.

In Fig. 1, at the temperature $T$ shown, $k = C_S/C_L$. Figure 1 shows a case where the liquidus and solidus temperatures fall with increasing alloying addition. In this case, $k$ is less than 1. For the type of partial phase diagram shown, $k$ is near unity when the gap between the liquidus and solidus is narrow. When the gap is large, $k$ is small. If the liquidus and solidus are straight lines, the equilibrium partition coefficient is a constant independent of temperature.

The existence of a gap between the liquidus and solidus leads to segregation of the alloying elements during the solidification process. Consider the case shown in Fig. 1, where $k$ is less than 1. If a liquid alloy of composition

$C_L$ is cooled to the liquidus temperature, the first solid to form has a composition, $C_S$, that is equal to $kC_L$. Further cooling, especially when diffusion is slow, continues the formation of solid with a composition less than that of the liquid and causes a solute-rich layer of liquid to form near the liquid-solid interface. The presence of this solute-rich layer promotes further segregation.

Many alloys have phase diagrams containing regions of composition where the liquidus and solidus are separated. Figure 2 shows three schematic binary phase diagrams that exhibit complete solid solubility (Fig. 2a), a eutectic reaction (Fig. 2b), and a peritectic reaction (Fig. 2c). The primary (or first) product of solidification will be a solid solution, except for the eutectic composition in Fig. 2(b). For the cases shown in Fig. 2(b) and (c), solidification may be completed by some other process, such as a eutectic or peritectic reaction. However, the details of the solidification of the solid solution remain important in determining the final microstructure.

## Constitutional Supercooling

Practical metallurgical alloys rarely solidify with a flat liquid-solid interface. The interface usually is bumpy or treelike, and as a result the solidified alloy will be nonuniform in composition. The reason for these shapes can be seen by examining a flat liquid-solid interface growing at a constant speed, $V$, with heat flowing from the liquid into the solid under the influence of a temperature gradient in the liquid of $G$. In this case the composition in the liquid ahead of the freezing solid is not uniform and contains a layer enriched in solute (for $k < 1$), as shown in Fig. 3. Because of this enrichment, the liquidus temperature at some positions ahead of the interface may actually lie below the real temperature, as shown in Fig. 3. In this case, the liquid ahead of the interface is said to be constitutionally

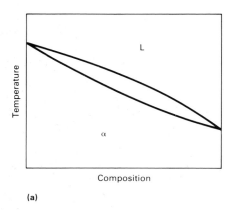
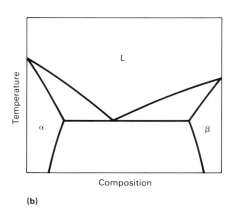
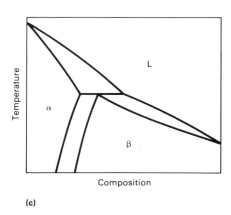

(a)     (b)     (c)

**Fig. 2** Schematic binary phase diagrams that exhibit (a) complete solid solubility, (b) partial solid solubility with a eutectic reaction, and (c) partial solid solubility with a peritectic reaction: L, liquid; $\alpha$ and $\beta$, solid solutions

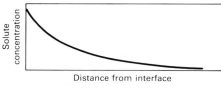

(a)

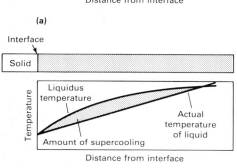

(b)

**Fig. 3** Constitutional supercooling. Formation of solute-rich layer in the liquid adjacent to the solid-liquid interface (a) lowers the local liquidus temperature (b). In the region of liquid near interface, the actual temperature may be below the local liquidus, causing the interface to become nonplanar.

supercooled. Consequently, the liquid-solid interface usually cannot remain flat, and the interface will develop bumps or cells, resulting in microsegregation.

The conditions necessary to obtain a flat liquid-solid interface can be estimated from the following inequality:

$$\frac{G}{V} > \frac{\Delta T}{D}$$

where $G$ is the liquid temperature gradient in K/cm, $V$ is the interface speed in cm/s, $\Delta T$ is the equilibrium freezing range of the alloy in K (temperature difference between liquidus and solidus for the original alloy composition), and $D$ is the liquid diffusion coefficient. In most cases, $D \approx 10^{-5}$ cm²/s for liquid metals. Planar growth of alloys can usually be achieved only in crystal growth furnaces with high temperature gradients and low solidification speeds. For example, for planar solidification of an alloy with $\Delta T = 5$ K and $G = 200$ K/cm, the solidification speed must be less than 4 $\mu$m/s (14 mm/h, or 0.6 in./h). Figure 4 shows a dilute tin-cadmium alloy solidified at high temperature gradient and low so-

lidification speed to achieve planar growth (Ref 1). Note the absence of any microsegregation due to solidification. Planar growth of doped semiconductors, where $\Delta T$ is very small due to the low concentration of solute, constitutes the basis of an entire industry. However, most metallurgical alloys solidify with nonplanar interfaces.

## Cellular and Dendritic Structures

When constitutional supercooling is present, the interface between the liquid and solid takes on a cellular or dendritic morphology. Figures 5 and 6 show the solidification of a transparent organic "alloy" that freezes like a metallic alloy (Ref 2). For conditions of growth where the ratio $G/V$ is only slightly smaller than the ratio $\Delta T/D$, the interface is cellular, as shown in Fig. 5. For conditions of growth where the ratio $G/V$ is much smaller than the ratio $\Delta T/D$, the interface becomes treelike or dendritic, as shown in Fig. 6. The regions between the cells and dendrites, which are still liquid in the micrographs, are greatly enriched in solute and produce micro-

**Fig. 4** Directionally solidified Sn-0.6Cd alloy. Section parallel to the growth direction shows a quenched planar liquid-solid interface, indicating the absence of constitutional supercooling. $G = 320$ K/cm, $V = 0.85$ $\mu$m/s, $\Delta T = 5.7$ K. 5 mL HNO₃, 95 mL lactic acid. 80×. (C. Brady)

**Fig. 5** Directionally solidified transparent organic "alloy," succinonitrile-5.5 mole% acetone. *In situ* observation of a growing cellular liquid-solid interface. Growth direction is shown horizontal. $G = 67$ K/cm, $V = 0.58$ $\mu$m/s, $\Delta T = 103$ K, $D \approx 10^{-5}$ cm²/s. 32×. (Ref 2)

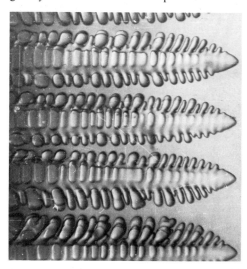

**Fig. 6** Same organic compound as in Fig. 5. $V$ was increased to 1.17 $\mu$m/s to produce a dendritic liquid-solid interface. 36×. (Ref 2)

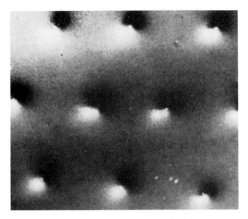 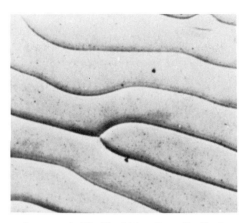 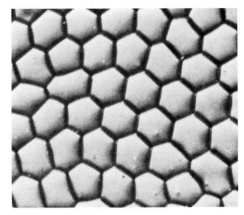

**Fig. 7, 8, 9** Sn-0.05Pb alloy; liquid decanted to reveal structures of liquid-solid interfaces. Fig. 7: photographed under oblique illumination, showing nodes in the interface. Fig. 8: elongated cells in the interface under bright-field illumination. Fig. 9: under bright-field illumination, revealing fully developed hexagonal cells in the interface. Not polished, not etched. 150×

segregation when freezing is complete. It should be noted that the cells or dendrites in each micrograph share a common crystallographic orientation and thus belong to the same grain.

**Cells.** Cellular structures are most often observed in dilute alloys where $\Delta T$ is small. Cellular structures can take on three characteristic morphologies when viewed in a metallographic section transverse to the growth direction: nodes (Fig. 7), elongated cells (Fig. 8), and hexagonal cells (Fig. 9). In each case, a physical depression in the liquid-solid interface leads to an increased concentration of solute in the material solidified near the depression. The hexagonal cellular structure is observed much more frequently than the node or elongated cell structures.

When cellular structures are observed by optical microscopy, contrast is usually developed by the preferential attack of the etchant on the regions of the structure enriched in solute, that is, the cell walls. An example of an optical micrograph of an etched transverse section through a cellular structure is shown in Fig. 10. When hexagonal cellular structures are observed in a plane of section that is not transverse to the growth direction, the

hexagonal structure may appear elongated in one direction. In the limiting case of a plane of section parallel to the growth direction, the hexagonal appearance is completely lost and the structure will appear more as the elongated cells in Fig. 8.

**Dendrites.** The most commonly observed solidification structure is dendritic. These treelike shapes of solid solution are observed when the degree of constitutional supercooling is large, or when the alloy solidifies from a liquid that is cooled to a temperature below the liquidus prior to the start of solidification. Dendritic structures exist within single grains, and their main trunks and branches usually follow specific crystallographic directions within the grains.

Depending on the type of phase diagram, dendritic structures may differ. If the phase diagram shows complete solid solubility (Fig. 2a), the structure will be single phase, containing only dendritic composition variations (Fig. 11). If the phase diagram contains a eutectic (Fig. 2b), the interdendritic regions will be composed of the two-phase eutectic. In some cases, especially when the volume fraction of the interdendritic regions is small, the interdendritic region may be composed of a

layer or discrete particles of a single second phase. This situation is referred to as a divorced eutectic structure. Figure 12 shows a dendritic structure with a large volume fraction of interdendritic eutectic. For alloys where primary solidification is followed by a peritectic reaction, the microstructure depends strongly on solid diffusion rates. When this diffusion is slow, the dendrites are coated by the peritectic phase.

Because dendrites are complex, three-dimensional structures, plane-section micrographs must be interpreted carefully. Figure 13 shows the structure of dendrites when the material surrounding the dendrites has been removed by selective deep etching. Figure 14 shows the same structure observed in a plane section. Parts of a single dendrite often appear disconnected when viewed in a plane section. The high degree of segregation pres-

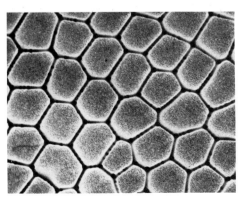 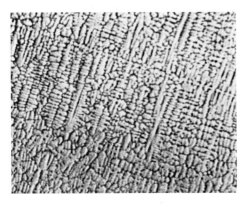 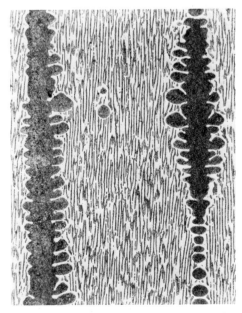

**Fig. 10** Pb-0.26Sb alloy casting. Section shows a cellular solidification structure. Etched at 1 V in a mixture of 10 mL 70% HClO₄ and 50 mL methanol. 50×. (L.R. Morris)

**Fig. 11** Ni-25Cu (at.%) alloy. Section shows dendritic solidification structure. 70 mL HNO₃ and 30 mL H₂O. 10×

**Fig. 12** Ni-25Cu (at.%) alloy. Section shows dendritic solidification structure. 70 mL HNO₃ and 30 mL H₂O. 175×. (C. Brady)

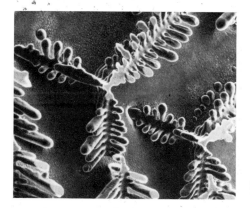

**Fig. 13** Scanning electron micrograph of Cu-10Co (at.%) alloy casting. Matrix has been selectively etched to reveal structure of individual cobalt solid solution dendrites. Etchant not reported. 150×

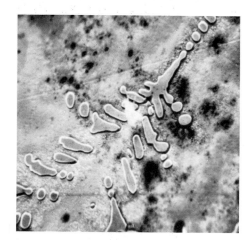

**Fig. 14** Scanning electron micrograph of Cu-10Co (at.%) alloy casting. Section through cast specimen shows a cobalt dendrite (smooth, gray). Image was formed using secondary electrons emitted by the specimen. As-polished. 400×

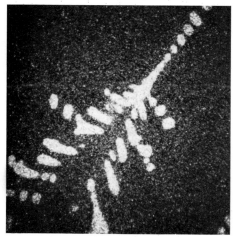

**Fig. 15, 16** Scanning electron micrographs of Cu-10Co (at.%) casting. Fig. 15: Image was formed using x-rays of Co-Kα wavelength emitted from the specimen under electron bombardment; the cobalt-rich dendrite appears light. Fig. 16: Image was formed using x-rays of Cu-Kα wavelength emitted from the specimen under electron bombardment. The copper-rich matrix appears light. As-polished. 400×

ent in this structure is revealed in Fig. 15 and 16.

**Solute Redistribution in Dendritic Solidification.** There is a simple method of estimating the compositional nonuniformity that can exist in a dendritic structure. A small volume element of the dendritic or "mushy" zone of a casting that contains several dendrite arms can be characterized at any instant by a volume fraction of solid $f_s$. The volume fraction ranges from 0 to 1 as solidification proceeds from start to finish. Assuming (1) no solid diffusion, (2) complete composition uniformity of the liquid remaining at any instant, (3) fluid flow adequate only to feed shrinkage, and (4) a constant $k$, the composition of the solid that forms as a function of the fraction solid is given by the Scheil, or normal freeze, equation:

$$C_S = kC_o(1 - f_s)^{k-1}$$

where $C_S$ is the solid composition formed, $k$ is the equilibrium partition coefficient as de-

fined earlier, $C_o$ is the initial alloy composition, and $f_s$ is the volume fraction solidified.

Figure 17 shows an example of the use of this equation for an Al-4.5Cu alloy for which $C_o$ is 4.5% Cu and $k$ is 0.17. Figure 17(a) shows part of the aluminum-copper phase diagram. The equation is used only for values of $f_s$ from zero up to a value at which $C_S$ reaches the maximum solubility of copper in

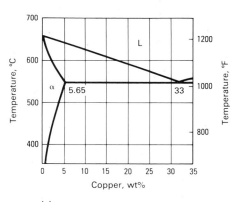

**(a)**

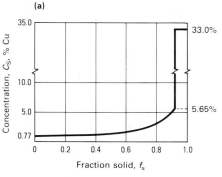

**(b)**

**Fig. 17** (a) The aluminum-rich end of the aluminum-copper phase diagram. (b) Solid composition ($C_S$) versus fraction solid ($f_s$) for Al-4.5Cu. L, liquid; α, aluminum solid solution. (Ref 3)

solid aluminum (5.65% Cu). From Fig. 17, the Scheil equation predicts that the first solid to form (the centers of dendrites) will have a composition of 0.77% Cu and that the composition will increase to 5.65% Cu when $f_s = 0.91$ (near the edge of the dendrites). The remaining fraction of the alloy (0.91 to 1.00) freezes as an interdendritic eutectic with an average composition of 33% Cu. Another simple equation follows from the Scheil equation to predict the volume fraction of eutectic, $f_E$, in a cast structure:

$$f_E = \left(\frac{C_E}{C_o}\right)^{\frac{1}{k-1}}$$

where $C_E$ is the eutectic composition ($C_E = 33\%$ Cu and $f_E = 0.09$ for the example above). If multicomponent phase diagram data are available, this method can be extended to more complex alloys.

The predictions of the Scheil equation should be used carefully. Generally, the equation tends to underestimate slightly the composition at the center of a dendrite and to overestimate the volume fraction of eutectic (for $k < 1$). These errors can be simply traced to deviations of real alloys from the assumptions stated above. The presence of significant rates of solid diffusion (important for interstitial solutes, such as carbon in iron, or for very slow cooling) or of significant composition gradients in the liquid phase (important in chill casting and rapid solidification) is an effect that generally lessens microsegregation. Also, if extensive fluid flow exists through the dendritic or "mushy" zone, the average composition of the solidified castings may be significantly altered in regions that are large compared to the dendrite scale. This is called macrosegregation. Details regarding this subject and the field of solidification can be found in Ref 4 and 5.

## Rapid Solidification

The microstructural scale of solidified alloys generally decreases as the rate of heat extraction (cooling rate) increases. The term rapid solidification is normally applied to casting processes in which the liquid cooling rate exceeds $10^3$ K/s. This definition is rather vague, because different alloys respond very differently to high rates of cooling. Also, some microstructures observed in rapidly solidified alloys can be achieved by slow cooling when large liquid supercoolings are achieved prior to nucleation (Ref 6).

Techniques usually used to produce rapidly solidified alloys are melt spinning, planar flow casting, or melt extraction, which produce thin ($\sim$25- to 100-$\mu$m) ribbon, tape, sheet, or fiber; atomization, which produces powder ($\sim$10 to 200 $\mu$m); and surface melting and resolidification, which produce thin surface layers. These methods may be considered casting techniques where at least one physical dimension of the final product is small. Consolidation is used to yield large products from rapidly solidified alloys. This consolidation often alters the solidification microstructure in final products; however, as with ordinary castings, many features of the solidification structure can remain in the final product. For more information on rapid solidification processes and properties and applications of rapidly solidified metals, refer to Volume 7 of the 9th Edition of *Metals Handbook: Powder Metallurgy*.

Many rapidly solidified structures differ little from those solidified at slow rates except for scale. However, the details of the microsegregation (composition) profile within cells or dendrites, the volume fraction of intercellular or interdendritic material, and/or the actual identity of phases found in intercellular or interdendritic regions may differ from those found in more slowly solidified alloys. Figure 18 shows a transverse section of a fine cellular structure of the silver-rich

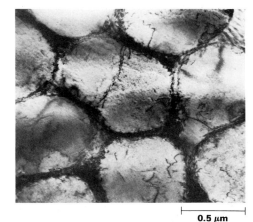

**Fig. 18** Cellular microsegregation pattern observed in Ag-15Cu alloy, electron beam melted and resolidified at approximately 25 mm/s (1 in./s). Thin foil transmission electron micrograph prepared by ion milling. 32 000×. (Ref 7)

1.0 $\mu$m

**Fig. 19** Thin foil transmission electron micrograph of cellular structure of $\alpha$-aluminum seen in a melt-spun Al-12Mn alloy. Small particles of another phase decorate the cell walls. Electropolished at $-30$ °C ($-20$ °F) in 950 mL methanol, 50 mL HClO$_4$, and 15 mL HNO$_3$. 16 000×. (Ref 8)

phase in Ag-15Cu alloy (Ref 7). In this figure, most of the intercellular regions are filled with the copper-rich phase, not the eutectic of silver and copper.

A common occurrence in some rapidly solidified alloys is a change in the identity of the primary solidification phase from that observed for slow solidification. Many excellent examples are found in hypereutectic aluminum alloys containing transition elements such as iron, manganese, or chromium. If the alloy is hypereutectic, slowly cooled castings will contain intermetallics such as Al$_3$Fe or Al$_6$Mn as the primary (or first) phase to solidify. However, under rapid solidification conditions the primary phase in these alloys is the aluminum solid solution usually found in a cellular structure with an intermetallic in the intercellular regions. Figures 19 and 20 show cellular structures of the $\alpha$-aluminum solid solution in hypereutectic aluminum-manganese alloys (Ref 8). This transition from an intermetallic to an aluminum solid solution as the primary phase can be understood by a careful examination of the kinetics of the competitive nucleation and growth of the intermetallic and $\alpha$-aluminum solid solution (Ref 9).

In some cases, an intermetallic that is not on the equilibrium phase diagram may compete with $\alpha$-aluminum. In aluminum-iron alloys, a metastable phase, Al$_6$Fe, rather than the stable phase, Al$_3$Fe, can form under some rapid solidification conditions. This situation is analogous to the appearance of cementite rather than graphite in some cast irons. The

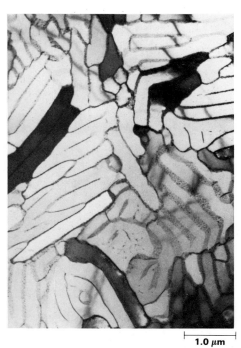

1.0 $\mu$m

**Fig. 20** Thin foil transmission electron micrograph of elongated cellular structure in a melt-spun Al-15Mn alloy. The contrast between some cells indicates crystallographic misorientation (subgrains). Electropolished at $-30$ °C ($-20$ °F) in 950 mL methanol, 50 mL HClO$_4$, and 15 mL HNO$_3$. 13 000×. (Ref 8)

0.5 $\mu$m

**Fig. 21** Cellular microsegregation pattern in Ag-5Cu alloy revealed by dislocation networks along cell walls. Specimen was electron beam melted and resolidified at approximately 300 mm/s (12 in./s). Thin foil transmission electron micrograph prepared by ion milling. 18 000×. (Ref 7)

use of metastable phase diagrams to assist in the interpretation of rapidly solidified microstructures is described in Ref 10.

**Microsegregation-Free Structures.** A particularly dramatic microstructural change that occurs in some rapidly solidified crystalline alloys is the complete absence of dendritic or cellular microsegregation. Figures 21 and 22 show Ag-5Cu alloys solidified using

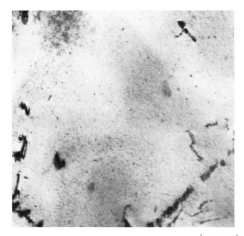

**Fig. 22** Same as Fig. 21, except resolidified at approximately 600 mm/s (24 in./s). The cellular structure is absent, and the solid produced is uniform in composition except for fine copper precipitates formed during solid-state cooling. 87 000×. (Ref 7)

electron beam surface melting and resolidification at speeds of 300 and 600 mm/s (12 and 24 in./s), respectively. Figure 21 shows a longitudinal view of a cellular solidification structure. In Fig. 22, the alloy has solidified with a planar interface to produce a microsegregation-free alloy. The fine particles are the result of a solid-state precipitation. This type of microstructure can be understood by a theory that incorporates the effects of liquid-solid interfacial energy in the constitutional supercooling analysis described earlier (Ref 11).

Other rapidly solidified alloys have microsegregation-free structures formed by a liquid-solid transformation similar to a massive solid-solid transformation. Solidification by this mechanism is called partitionless (diffusionless) solidification, whereby the liquid transforms to solid without a change in composition. In other words, the ratio of the solid composition at the interface to the liquid composition is 1, rather than the equilibrium partition coefficient. Velocities required to produce partitionless solidification range from 1 to 10 m/s (40 to 400 in./s). The liquidus and solidus of the phase diagrams obviously do not apply in this situation. For more information on massive transformation, see the article "Massive Transformation Structures" in this Volume.

Figures 23 and 24 show optical and transmission electron micrographs, respectively, of a single-phase microsegregation-free solid solution of a silver-copper alloy of eutectic composition (28% Cu) that formed by partitionless solidification. The alloy is not only free of microsegregation, but also has a solid solubility of copper in silver far in excess of the equilibrium solubility limit (~9% Cu). Solubility extension is commonly seen in many aluminum alloys (Ref 13).

**Structure of Atomized Powders.** Rapidly solidified alloy powders exhibit a broad spectrum of solidification structures, depending on alloy composition and solidification conditions. Figure 25 shows a single powder particle of Al-4.5Cu in which dendritic structure radiates from a point on the surface where nucleation has occurred. The scale of the structure is relatively uniform across the powder particle.

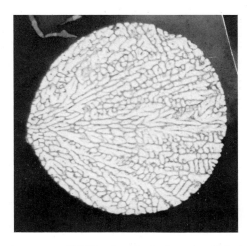

**Fig. 25** Al-4.5Cu alloy atomized powder. Optical microscopy shows dendritic structure in rapidly solidified powder particle. Keller's reagent. 390×. (S. Wright)

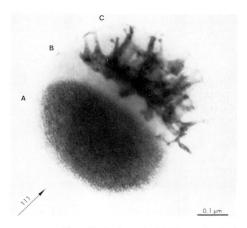

**Fig. 26** Electrohydrodynamic (EHD) atomized Al-6Si powder. Transmission electron micrograph of unthinned particle mounted on TEM replication tape, carbon coated and tape dissolved. Rapid solidification has produced (A) a supersaturated zone, (B) a transition zone where solute has built up in front of the interface, and (C) cells formed after the droplet has recalesced. Thin foil preparation of the specimen was not necessary because of the small diameter of the particle and the low atomic number of aluminum. 80 000×. (Ref 14)

Other rapidly solidified powders often show significant microstructural variations across individual powder particles. Figure 26 shows an entire submicron Al-6Si powder particle with three microstructural zones. On the lower left is a zone containing only fine precipitates formed by solid-state transformation of an initially uniform supersaturated solid solution. On the upper right is a zone with a cellular solidification structure. An intermediate region in the center of the particle is a transition zone. All of the aluminum solid solution in the particle has the same crystallographic orientation; therefore, the particle is a single grain. This particle is estimated to have been supercooled by approximately 200 K while in liquid form before nucleation oc-

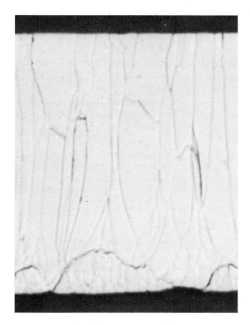

**Fig. 23** Columnar grains of single-phase solid solution of melt-spun Ag-28Cu alloy (eutectic composition). Section of full ribbon cross section. Chill (wheel) side is at bottom. 20 mL NH₄OH, 10 mL 3% H₂O₂, 10 mL H₂O (used fresh). 2000×. (Ref 12)

**Fig. 24** Same alloy as Fig. 23. Transmission electron micrograph of thin foil parallel to the chill surface prepared by ion milling. Three grains are shown. The fine mottled structure is the result of solid-state decomposition. 100 000×. (D. Shechtman)

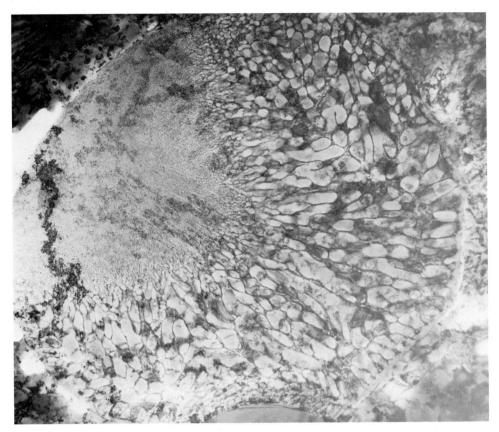

**Fig. 27** Thin foil transmission electron micrograph of vacuum-atomized Al-8Fe powder. A single nucleation site of the supercooled particle (left) initiated solidification at a high interface rate to produce a fine cellular structure. Recalescence slowed the interface rate to produce the coarser cellular structure at the right. The green powder compact was electropolished at −30 °C (−20 °F) in 950 mL methanol, 50 mL HClO₄, and 15 mL HNO₃. 6300×. (Ref 15)

curred on the surface at the lower left. Initial growth of the solid occurred very rapidly in a partitionless manner. The interface speed is reduced as the liquid-solid interface crosses the particle due to the release of latent heat of fusion and warming of the powder particle. Because of this reduction in interface speed, the solidification front becomes cellular.

Figure 27 shows a two-zone microstructure observed in a larger diameter (~10 μm) hypereutectic Al-8Fe powder particle (Ref 15). A thin foil was prepared by electropolishing a 3-mm (0.12-in.) diam green powder compact (Ref 16). In this alloy, however, the zone to the left where nucleation occurs contains a very fine cellular structure, and the zone to

the right contains a coarse cellular structure of α-aluminum with Al₆Fe between the cells. Larger powder particles of the alloy frequently do not supercool significantly before the start of solidification and contain Al₃Fe as the primary phase.

## REFERENCES

1. W.J. Boettinger, The Structure of Directionally Solidified Two-Phase Sn-Cd Peritectic Alloys, *Met. Trans.*, Vol 5, 1974, p 2026
2. R. Trivedi, Interdendritic Spacing: Part II. A Comparison of Theory and Experiment, *Met. Trans. A*, Vol 15, 1984, p 977
3. M.C. Flemings and R. Mehrabian, Segregation in Castings and Ingots, in *Solidification*, American Society for Metals, 1971
4. M.C. Flemings, *Solidification Processing*, McGraw-Hill, 1974
5. W. Kurz and D.J. Fisher, *Fundamentals of Solidification*, Trans. Tech., 1984
6. J.H. Perepezko and J.J. Paike, Undercooling Behavior of Liquid Metals, in *Rapidly Solidified Amorphous and Crystalline Alloys*, B.H. Kear, B.C. Giessen, and M. Cohen, Ed., North Holland, 1982, p 49
7. W.J. Boettinger, D. Shechtman, R.J. Schaefer, and F.S. Biancaniello, The Effect of Rapid Solidification Velocity on the Microstructure of Ag-Cu Alloys, *Met. Trans. A*, Vol 15, 1984, p 55
8. D. Shechtman, R.J. Schaefer, and F.S. Biancaniello, Precipitation in Rapidly Solidified Al-Mn Alloys, *Met. Trans. A*, Vol 15, 1984, p 1987
9. I.R. Hughes and H. Jones, Coupled Eutectic Growth in Al-Fe Alloys: Part I. Effects of High Growth Velocity, *J. Mater. Sci.*, Vol 11, 1976, p 1781
10. J.H. Perepezko and W.J. Boettinger, Use of Metastable Phase Diagrams in Rapid Solidification, *Mat. Res. Soc. Symp. Proc.*, Vol 19, 1983, p 223
11. W.W. Mullins and R.F. Sekerka, Stability of a Planar Interface During Solidification of a Dilute Binary Alloy, *J. Appl. Phys.*, Vol 35, 1964, p 444
12. W.J. Boettinger, Growth Kinetic Limitations in Rapid Solidification, in *Rapidly Solidified Amorphous and Crystalline Alloys*, B.H. Kear, B.C. Giessen, and M. Cohen, Ed., North Holland, 1982, p 15
13. H. Jones, *Rapid Solidification of Metals and Alloys*, Institute of Metallurgists, London, 1984
14. C. Levi and R. Mehrabian, Microstructure of Rapidly Solidified Aluminum Alloy Submicron Powders, *Met. Trans. A*, Vol 13, 1982, p 13
15. W.J. Boettinger, L. Bendersky, and J.G. Early, An Analysis of the Microstructure of Rapidly Solidified Al-8 wt% Iron Powder, *Met. Trans. A*, submitted for publication
16. D. Shechtman and E. Gutmanas, Transmission Electron Microscopy of Metallic Powder, *Prakt. Metallogr.*, Vol 18, 1981, p 587

# Solidification Structures of Eutectic Alloys

By Franklin D. Lemkey
Senior Consulting Scientist
United Technologies Research Center
Adjunct Professor of Engineering
Dartmouth College

and

R. Wayne Kraft
Professor of Metallurgy and Materials Science
Lehigh University

EUTECTIC STRUCTURES can form beautiful and regular arrays of lamellae or rods, depending on the nature and amounts of the phases and the conditions of solidification. As many as four phases have been observed to grow simultaneously from the melt; however, most technologically useful eutectic alloys consist of two phases. In general, eutectic microstructures have certain similar characteristics that allow arbitrary classification by structure. When interpreting eutectic structures, it is necessary to consider (1) the types of phases, dictated by their amounts and growth kinetics, (2) the scale, or size range, of the phases, which is determined by solid/liquid interface shape and solidification velocity, (3) the operating compositional range, and (4) the sectioning techniques.

## Solidification and Size of Eutectic Structures

The schematic phase diagram in Fig. 1 shows a binary eutectic invariant point at temperature, $T_e$, and composition, $C_e$. At this point, solid phases $\alpha$ and $\beta$ simultaneously solidify from the liquid, L. For most eutectic systems, if the solidification occurs directionally, an aligned two-phase solid can be produced. At least three conditions must be simultaneously satisfied, however, to produce parallel duplex microstructure: (1) the heat must be removed from the melt unidirectionally, (2) a sufficiently positive temperature gradient must be maintained ahead of the solidifying interface to prevent unwanted nucleation and preserve solid/liquid interface planarity, and (3) cooperative nucleation and

growth processes must occur between the phases.

Examining this process reveals that the major solidification parameters—for example, the thermal gradient, $G$, at the liquid/solid interface and the growth rate, $R$, or the velocity at which the liquid/solid interface advances—are keys to the control and size of the structure. If both phases occur with approximately equal volume fractions, a situation encouraged by a symmetrical phase diagram, a preference for the formation of lamellar structures is found (for example, Al-$CuAl_2$, lead-tin, and $Ni_3Al$-$Ni_3Nb$). On the other hand, if one phase is present in a small

volume fraction, there is a tendency to the formation of fibers of that phase (for example, chromium in copper-chromium, molybdenum in $Ni_3Al$-Mo). When the volume fraction of one phase is less than 0.3, the eutectic will probably be fibrous. If the volume fraction of one phase is between 0.3 and 0.5, the eutectic will tend to be lamellar. Because eutectic structures are often more complex than this simplified model implies, it is useful to consider three of their features individually: particle structure, colony structure, and grain structure. Their nominal size ranges are shown in Fig. 2; the extremes of the ranges overlap somewhat.

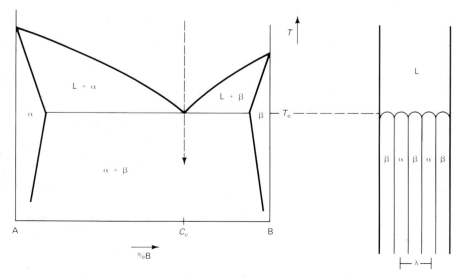

**Fig. 1** Phase diagram for a eutectic system showing the eutectic invariant point at temperature ($T_e$) and composition ($C_e$)

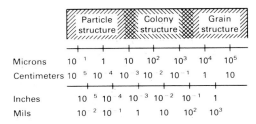

**Fig. 2** Size ranges of eutectic structures

**Particle Structure.** Individual phase particles typically have micron dimensions. Their size and shape strongly affect the mechanical and physical properties of the eutectic aggregate. Size and shape are affected by solidification rate, thermal gradients, atomic bonding, relative amounts, crystallographic factors, interfacial energies, impurity content, and alloy composition.

One condition that affects the size of phase particles, which has been explained theoretically and confirmed experimentally, is illustrated in Fig. 3. The interparticle spacing, $\lambda$, and the solidification rate, $R$, for an alloy system are related by the equation $\lambda^2 R = $ constant. Because the volume percentage of the phases in a particular alloy is fixed, the equation permits determination of effect of solidification rate on particle size from size measurements made on only one specimen solidified at a known rate.

The shape of a particle can be defined by the three principal dimensions: $x$, $y$, and $z$. Describing the phase particles as fibrous ($x \gg y \approx z$), lamellar ($x \approx y \gg z$), or equiaxed ($x \approx y \approx z$) is useful. Illustrated in Fig. 4 to 7 are the lamellar and fibrous forms. Each casting was unidirectionally solidified to produce specimens in which the nominal size and shape could be established by examining the microstructures of sections parallel to and normal to the direction of solidification.

**Colony Structure.** Eutectic colonies are aggregates of phase particles with a characteristic arrangement. Colonies are not present in all eutectic structures. They are frequently confused with eutectic grains, particularly in specimens cut from material that was not solidified unidirectionally. Eutectic colonies are formed when the alloy solidifies with a cellular, rather than an essentially planar, freezing interface (Fig. 8). The cellular freezing face

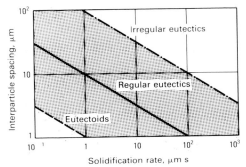

**Fig. 3** Eutectic spacings as a function of growth rate. (Ref 1)

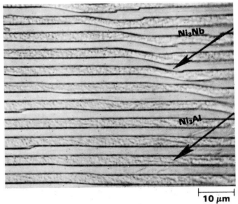

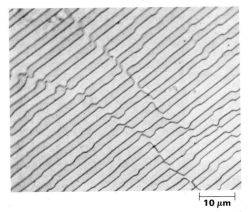

**Fig. 4, 5** Lamellar eutectic structures. Fig. 4: Casting of Ni$_3$Al-Ni$_3$Nb solidified unidirectionally (left to right). Fig. 5: Same casting as Fig. 4, but a section taken normal to the direction of solidification, showing alternate lamellae of Ni$_3$Al and Ni$_3$Nb. Both etched in 5 parts HCl, 1 part HNO$_3$, 6 parts glycerol. 1000×

is caused by constitutional undercooling brought about by rejection of an impurity from the solidifying eutectic phases into the liquid (see the article "Solidification Structures of Solid Solutions" in this Volume).

The arrangement of phase particles in a eutectic colony is typically fanlike on a section cut parallel to the direction of solidification (Fig. 8); a section cut normal to the direction

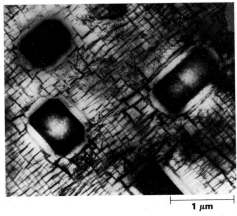

**Fig. 6** Fibrous eutectic in section taken normal to growth. Faceted dark phase is molybdenum in a solid-solution ($\gamma$) matrix of nickel containing cuboidal precipitates of Ni$_3$Al ($\gamma'$). Electrolytic etch: 10 parts H$_3$PO$_4$, 50 parts H$_2$SO$_4$, 40 parts HNO$_3$. 15 000×

**Fig. 7** Scanning electron micrograph of fibrous eutectic unidirectionally solidified vertically. Section shows exposed tantalum carbide particles in a superalloy nickel matrix. Etchant not identified. 40 000×. (M. Henry)

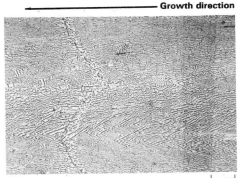

**Fig. 8** Colony structure of rod eutectic that was solidified unidirectionally (right to left). Section parallel to direction of growth shows fanlike arrangement of niobium carbide rods (dark) in nickel matrix (light) resulting from curved liquid-solid interface. Murakami's reagent. 30×

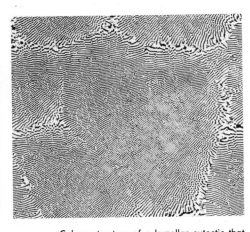

**Fig. 9** Colony structure of a lamellar eutectic that was solidified unidirectionally. Section taken normal to the direction of solidification showing the honeycomb pattern of the colonies, which were formed when constitutional undercooling caused the freezing face to be cellular in shape, rather than essentially planar. Dark and light layers in each colony are Mg$_2$Al$_3$ phase and aluminum, respectively. Etchant not identified. 200×

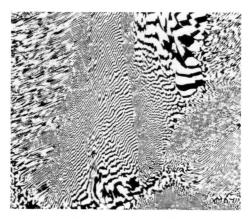

**Fig. 10** Colony structure of a CuAl$_2$-Al lamellar eutectic in a casting that was not unidirectionally solidified. Section shows the honeycomb pattern (where section is normal to direction of solidification) and the fanlike arrangement (where section is parallel to direction of solidification). As-polished. 250×

of solidification displays a honeycomb pattern (Fig. 9). In castings not unidirectionally solidified, the honeycomb and the fanlike features identify eutectic colonies (Fig. 10).

**Grain Structure.** Eutectic grains are structural features visible on a polished or fractured surface at magnifications close to unity. Eutectic grains can be more difficult to define and identify than are grains of a single-phase metal. For example, the right side of Fig. 11 has the appearance of a specimen containing two grains: the lamellae in one grain are at an angle of about 40° to the lamellae in the other grain. At the left of the micrograph, however, the two grains merge into one. In other eutectics, particularly those in which the volume fraction of one phase is $f \cong 0.01$ to 0.02, grains of the predominant phase will be visible. Under these circumstances, a eutectic grain can properly be identified with grains of the phase that is present in major proportions; the minor phase will then appear as a dispersoid in the major phase.

Despite the difficulty in defining eutectic grains and distinguishing them from eutectic colonies, the concept is useful. One definition of a eutectic grain in a specimen of eutectic is "the portion that nucleated at a certain site and/or in which the phase particles have definite crystallographic and metallographic relationships to one another."

**Sectioning and Sampling.** The true shapes of phase particles, colonies, and grains in a eutectic can be determined by serial sectioning, phase extraction, or projection onto different planes, in radiography or microradiography. Unfortunately, most of these techniques are laborious. To simplify investigating the factors governing eutectic structures, unidirectional solidification, such as in the Bridgman or Czochralski crystal-growing techniques, is widely used in laboratory studies instead of the more laborious procedures listed above. Examination of sections parallel and normal to the solidification direction of unidirectionally solidified specimens affords reasonably reliable interpretation of structures (Fig. 4 and 5).

**Particle Connection.** Serial sectioning, phase-extraction techniques, and examination of two sections meeting at a common edge have revealed that the microstructures of most eutectics cannot be considered aggregates of many simply shaped, discrete particles of one phase embedded in a matrix of the other phase or phases. Rather, if the three-dimensional forms of all phases are examined, the apparently individual particles of each phase ordinarily are found to be interconnected in a topologically complex arrangement. For example, most of the silicon particles in an aluminum-silicon eutectic are connected and continuous (Fig. 12). The same is true of some graphite flakes in gray iron (Fig. 13), but it would not be true of graphite nodules (spherulites) in ductile iron (see also the article "Cast Irons" in this Volume).

In fibrous eutectics, branching of fibers has been observed. Similarly, serial sectioning has

**Fig. 13** Section of a gray iron casting showing the iron-carbon eutectic, which consists of dark flakes of carbon (graphite), some of which are connected, in a matrix of eutectoid decomposed austenite (pearlite). As-polished. 100×. (J.J. Manganello)

shown that the lamellae of both phases in many lamellar eutectics are branched and interconnected, resulting in a topologically complex arrangement of phase particles. The complexity arises because of the formation, during solidification, of defects called "terminations" or "lamellar faults." These defects are depicted in micrographs (see Fig. 4 and 5) by the appearance of an imperfectly parallel arrangement of lamellae. Detailed analysis has shown that in many eutectics, both phases are continuous. Therefore, either phase can properly be called the matrix phase, because each forms a matrix in which the other is embedded.

**Sampling factors** that must be considered when interpreting eutectic structures are the orientation of the section with respect to the direction of heat flow and the orientation of the structural features with respect to the sectioning plane. Phase particles in eutectics usually grow with a long dimension parallel to the direction of heat flow during solidification. For this reason, and because the shape of a structural feature as seen on a two-dimensional section is only a section, when interpreting eutectic structures it is necessary to (1) constantly keep sound statistical sampling procedures in mind, (2) realize that the appearance of a structure can vary markedly, depending on the angle at which a specimen has been cut from an ingot or casting, (3) interpret eutectic structures using solidification history, and (4) become familiar with the phases present in a given eutectic system.

## Operating Compositional Range

When an alloy deviates from the binary eutectic composition (Fig. 1), it may still be possible to maintain a eutectic-like microstructure if solidification is carried out in a sufficiently steep gradient or at a sufficiently slow rate. Coupled two-phase eutectic structures also can be produced whose amounts

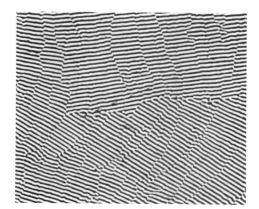

**Fig. 11** Lower magnification view of a CuAl$_2$-Al lamellar eutectic in a casting that was solidified unidirectionally showing difficulty of identifying the grain structure of this eutectic. The two "grains" at right (lamellae at about 40° to one another) merge into one "grain" at left. As-polished. 180×

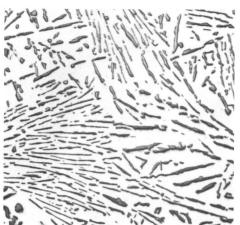

**Fig. 12** Section of a casting showing the aluminum-silicon eutectic, which consists of short particles of silicon (dark) in an aluminum matrix. Some particles are connected in the plane shown; others are connected in other planes. As-polished. 200×. (Ref 2)

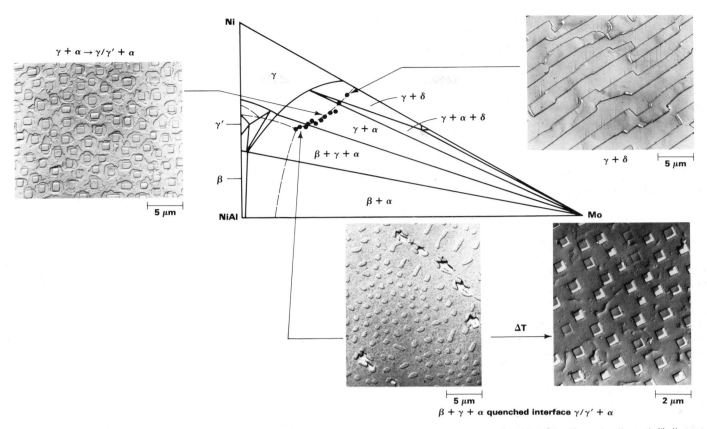

$\gamma + \alpha \rightarrow \gamma/\gamma' + \alpha$

$5\ \mu m$

$\gamma + \delta$    $5\ \mu m$

$\Delta T$

$5\ \mu m$    $2\ \mu m$

$\beta + \gamma + \alpha$ quenched interface $\gamma/\gamma' + \alpha$

**Fig. 14** Monovariant liquidus troughs (dashed lines) on a nickel-aluminum-molybdenum isothermal section at 1300 °C (2370 °F) with varying "eutectic-like" structure produced by compositional adjustment. (Ref 3)

and individual phase chemistries can be varied by solidification of compositions that lay on or near eutectic troughs in the liquidus surface of ternary alloys (see Fig. 14). The solidification considerations to promote planar coupled growth are given by the simplified constitutional supercooling equation

$$\frac{G}{R} \geq \frac{\Delta T}{D}$$

where $G$ is the temperature gradient in the liquid, $D$ is the diffusion coefficient, and $\Delta T$ is the temperature range between start and completion of solidification. (Note that in the simple binary system of Fig. 1, $\Delta T$ is zero and increases monotonically as the composition departs from $C_e$.)

The ability to depart from the precise eutectic composition is extremely important from a technological point of view, because it permits the addition of various alloying elements to modify the chemistry of the phases and their volume fractions. This "alloyability" in multicomponent systems is important in the development of complex eutectic superalloys.

## Classification of Eutectic Morphologies

Many attempts have been made to classify the various types of microstructures. The early schemes were based simply on appearance, using such descriptive terms as "divorced," "degenerate," "regular," "complex-regular," "normal," "faceted," and so on. A more useful approach (Ref 4) relates the eutectic structure to how the individual phases of the eutectic grow. Although a correlation exists between solidification morphology and the entropy of fusion of the phases, this criterion does not account for all the features of the structure having the size ranges discussed earlier and shown in Fig. 2.

**Fig. 15** "Chinese script" modification of lamellar eutectic in a casting. The eutectic consists of sharply angular Mg$_2$Sn phase (dark) in magnesium matrix (light). Glycol etchant (ASTM E407, No. 118). 250×

For the practicing metallurgist, perhaps the best method of classification is based on the distinction between regular (rod or lamellar) and irregular eutectics. Between the extremes of regular and irregular eutectics, a range of structure type occurs, sometimes in the same alloy system, depending on solidification conditions. In addition, variations such as a sharply angular "Chinese script" lamellar microstructure produced by unusual crystallographic factors in an otherwise "regular" eutectic sometimes occur (Fig. 15).

**Regular Eutectics.** Broadly speaking, a regular eutectic is formed when solidification is diffusion controlled. The solid-liquid interface is sharp, and the two solid phases alternate periodically to form a single, continuous freezing face (see Fig. 16). In this case, the eutectic phases are said to be solidifying under "coupled" solidification conditions.

The two phases often freeze simultaneously so that a preferred crystallographic-orientation relationship develops between the phases. The microstructure exhibits a high degree of regularity, particularly in unidirectionally solidified specimens. Lamellar and fibrous shapes are characteristic of regular eutectics. Regular eutectics are typical of systems whose phases are "metallic."

**Irregular Eutectics.** An irregular eutectic forms when one solid phase of the eutectic projects into the liquid far in advance of the other solid phase, frequently with a faceted dendritic morphology. Under these condi-

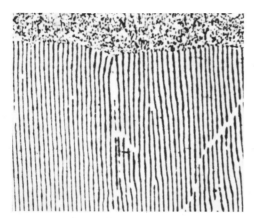

**Fig. 16** Regular eutectic in a casting solidified unidirectionally (bottom to top), then rapidly cooled to preserve shape of freezing face. Section parallel to solidification direction shows a smooth face between cadmium-tin eutectic (bottom) and quenched metal. Aqueous solution of FeCl₃. 210×

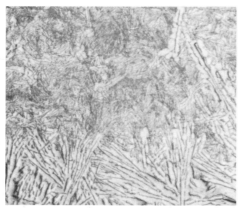

**Fig. 17** Irregular eutectic in a casting solidified unidirectionally (bottom to top), then rapidly cooled to preserve shape of freezing face. Section taken parallel to solidification direction shows aluminum-silicon eutectic (bottom) projecting into quenched metal. As-polished. 100×. (Ref 6)

tions of solidification, the freezing interface is very irregular (see Fig. 17), no crystallographic-orientation relationship exists between the phases, and no marked metallographic periodicity is observed. Perhaps the most marked feature of irregular eutectics is that nothing that could be called a eutectic grain boundary is observed. Irregular eutectics are most likely to occur in alloys in which one phase has strong covalent bonding; examples are aluminum-silicon, iron-graphite and Al-Al₃Fe.

## REFERENCES

1. J.D. Livingston, H.E. Cline, E.F. Koch, and R.R. Russell, *Acta Metall.,* Vol 18, 1970, p 399-405
2. W. Kurz and D.J. Fisher, *Fundamentals of Solidification*, Trans. Tech. Publications, 1984, p 110
3. M.G. Day and A. Hellawell, The Microstructure and Crystallography of Aluminum-Silicon Alloys, *Proc. Roy. Soc.,* Vol A305, 1968, p 479-491
4. D.D. Pearson and F.D. Lemkey, *Solidification and Casting of Metals*, The Metals Society, 1977
5. J.D. Hunt and K.A. Jackson, *Trans. Met. Soc. AIME*, Vol 236, 1966, p 843
6. J.E. Gruzleski and W.C. Winegard, The Cellular Structure in the Sn-Cd Eutectic, *Trans. Met. Soc. AIME*, Vol 242, 1968, p 1785
7. G.A. Chadwick, Eutectic Solidification, in *Liquids: Structure, Properties, Solid Interactions*, T.J. Hughel, Ed., Elsevier, 1965, p 326-352

## SELECTED REFERENCES

- F.D. Lemkey, H.E. Cline, and M. McLean, Ed., *In Situ Composites—IV*, Vol 12, North-Holland, 1982
- F.D. Lemkey, Advanced In-Situ Composites, in *Industrial Materials Science and Engineering*, L.E. Murr, Ed., Marcel Dekker, 1984
- M. McLean, *Directionally Solidified Materials for High Temperature Service*, The Metals Society, 1983
- E. Thompson and F.D. Lemkey, *Composite Materials*, Vol 4, Academic Press, 1974

# Solidification Structures of Steel

By B.L. Bramfitt
Senior Scientist
Homer Research Laboratories
Bethlehem Steel Corporation

PLAIN CARBON and low-alloy steels solidify with a typical dendritic growth morphology regardless of casting conditions and deoxidation practice. The type of dendritic morphology found in the center of a steel ingot is shown in Fig. 1.

## Macrostructure

The macrostructure of a solidified steel ingot, casting, or strand-cast slab or bloom consists of columnar or equiaxed grains or a mixture of both, depending on solidification conditions. A diagram of a cross section through a typical steel ingot, showing an outer chill zone, a columnar zone, and a central equiaxed zone, is illustrated in Fig. 2. Small equiaxed crystals nucleate at the mold surface and form the chill zone. Some of these crystals grow dendritically into the liquid, but only those that are oriented favorably regarding the direction of heat flow grow an appreciable distance and produce the columnar zone.

The equiaxed zone at the center forms by nucleation and growth of dendritic crystals in the liquid or by the growth of dendritic branches that have been detached from dendrites in the columnar zone by convection currents in the liquid. Although most ingots have these three zones, some have only two: the chill zone surrounding a columnar or an equiaxed zone. The macrostructure depends primarily on the degree to which the steel is deoxidized. Rimmed, capped, semikilled, and killed steels require different steelmaking and deoxidation practices.

## Microstructure

Plain carbon and low-alloy steels have similar macrostructural features, but develop appreciably dissimilar microstructures, depending on composition and cooling rate. A typical solidification microstructure of an ingot of a plain carbon steel (1010, with 0.10% C and 0.61% Mn), shown in Fig. 3, consists of pearlite surrounded by ferrite, some of which has a Widmanstätten pattern. Other types of ferrite may also appear in these steels; for example, rapid cooling may produce massive ferrite, and slow cooling may produce equiaxed or polygonal ferrite.

Figure 4 shows a low-alloy steel (1524, with 0.24% C, 1.34% Mn, 0.24% Si, and 0.05% V) that was produced by strand casting, a continuous casting process with faster cooling than that of the conventional static casting process used for ingots. In this microstructure, the predominant constituent is pearlite, and the two other constituents are acicular bainite and grain-boundary ferrite. However, depending on cooling rate and composition, low-alloy steels can have various microstructures consisting of different forms and combinations of pearlite, bainite, martensite, cementite, and ferrite.

As shown by the absence in Fig. 3 and 4 of the dendritic structure formed during solidification, the cooling period following solidification produces phase transformations that almost entirely conceal the original as-cast structure. Because a more precise knowledge about what happens during solidification is important in improving casting practice, metallographic methods have been developed for revealing features of the original as-cast structure.

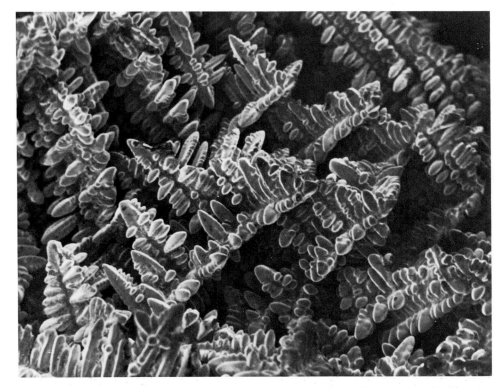

**Fig. 1** Scanning electron micrograph of the center of an as-cast low-carbon steel ingot showing dendrite spikes (primary arms) and secondary arms. Unetched. 10×. (B.L. Bramfitt, J.R. Kilpatrick)

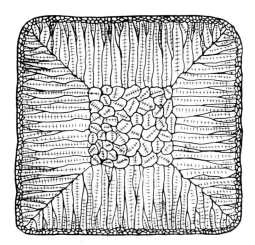

**Fig. 2** Schematic cross section of a steel ingot showing typical macrostructure: an outer chill zone, a columnar zone, and a central equiaxed zone

## Revealing As-Cast Structure

During solidification of plain carbon and low-alloy steels, solute elements are rejected by the solidifying iron-rich phase into the surrounding liquid, causing regions of high alloy or carbon concentration to accumulate around the iron-rich dendrites. With this pattern of segregation, various metallographic techniques can be used to reveal more clearly the original as-cast dendritic structure.

**Macroetching** is the most common method used to reveal the dendritic structure of an ingot or casting. Results are illustrated in Fig. 5, which shows an area of a strand-cast slab. The macroetchant has attacked the regions of high carbon concentration in the solidified structure, revealing the outlines of the original dendrites. A disadvantage of macroetching is the required severity of the etching, which destroys the fine details of the structure. Techniques for macroetching are described in the article "Carbon and Alloy Steels" in this Volume.

**Sulfur printing,** another common technique, brings out the sulfur-rich areas in a solidified steel, uncovering the outlines of the original dendrites. A typical sulfur print is shown in Fig. 6. As with macroetching, the fine details of the structure are not revealed. Details of the procedure are given in the article "Carbon and Alloy Steels" in this Volume.

**Short-time annealing** at temperatures high enough to austenitize a specimen produces a microstructure free of nonequilibrium constituents (in particular, bainite, martensite, and the massive and Widmanstätten ferrites) that obscure the original dendritic structure. As shown in Fig. 7 and 8, this treatment reveals the outlines of the dendrites that would be only faintly discernible in the as-cast condition.

**Microradiography.** Specimens of solidified steel less than 0.05-mm (0.002-in.) thick are x-rayed. Differences in x-ray absorption, caused by variations in composition, produce a radiograph, which can be magnified for examination. This technique can be extended to stereomicroradiography, which yields a three-dimensional view of a solidified structure.

**Autoradiography.** A radioactive isotope (for example, $P^{32}$) is added to the molten steel before solidification. Because the isotope segregates into the interdendritic regions, an image of the dendritic structure can be obtained by exposing a fine-grained x-ray film against a specimen from the steel casting. This technique can also be used to investigate the contours of the solid-liquid interface at different stages of solidification.

## Dendrite Arm Spacing

Once the dendritic structure is revealed in a specimen from a steel casting, ingot, or strand-cast shape, quantitative determinations, such as measurements of primary and secondary dendrite arm spacing, can be made. More attention has been directed in current literature to measuring secondary dendrite arm spacing, which is the distance between adjacent branches growing from the main dendritic spike or primary branch. Several investigators have maintained that secondary arm spacing is a good index of solidification conditions in a steel ingot or casting (Ref 1, 2). Figure 9 shows the variation in secondary arm spacing with distance from the chilled surface of a directionally solidified 4340 steel casting.

Other investigators favor measuring primary arm spacing, that is, the spacing between the main dendritic spikes (Ref 3). Figure 10 presents data on primary and secondary arm spacing for 4340 steel obtained in several investigations. Although measurements of primary or secondary arm spacing quantitatively reflect the solidification history of an ingot or casting, Fig. 10 shows that primary arm spacing is somewhat more responsive to differences in growth conditions than is secondary arm spacing. However, secondary arm spacing is more closely related to the degree of homogenization that occurs during further processing of cast structures.

The dendritic spacing parameters indicate solidification history and how that history can affect the results of postsolidification processing. For example, examination was made of the manganese and nickel distributions in columnar dendrites of cast 4340 steel (Ref 6). Using an idealized model of dendritic morphology, the diffusion of these two solute atoms that would take place during a 1-h anneal was calculated for different annealing temperatures. The resulting diffusion was then compared to the amount required to achieve complete homogenization in dendrites having secondary arms with very fine spacing (50 μm) and with fairly coarse spacing (400 μm). As shown in Fig. 11, the structure with the very fine spacing, as found within approximately 6 mm (0.25 in.) from a chill, would be completely homogenized after 1 h at 1400 °C (2550 °F), but with the same annealing treatment, homogenization would just be beginning in the structure with the coarser dendritic spacings and the larger diffusion distances, as found in material 100 to 125 mm (4 to 5 in.) from a chill. Calculations for carbon atoms show that this element would be completely homogenized in both structures after 1 h at temperatures below 900 °C (1650 °F).

**Fig. 3** 1010 steel ingot, as static cast. Microstructure, which resulted from slow cooling, shows pearlite (dark) surrounded by ferrite (light), some of which has a Widmanstätten pattern. Nital. 50×. (J.R. Kilpatrick)

**Fig. 4** 1524 steel, as strand cast. The microstructure, which resulted from rapid cooling, shows pearlite (variegated gray constituent), acicular bainite (light), and grain-boundary ferrite (also light). Nital. 100×. (J.R. Kilpatrick)

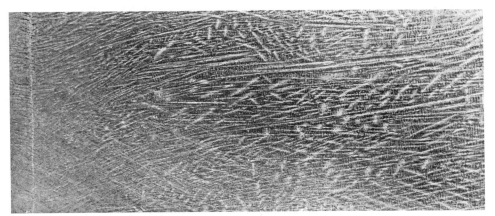

**Fig. 5** 1017 steel, as strand cast. Macrostructure shows the outlines of the original columnar dendrites (light), which are oriented normal to the chill surface (left edge of macrograph). The vertical white line near the chill surface resulted from a disruption in solidification. Compare with Fig. 6. 10% $HNO_3$ in $H_2O$. 4.75×. (J.R. Kilpatrick)

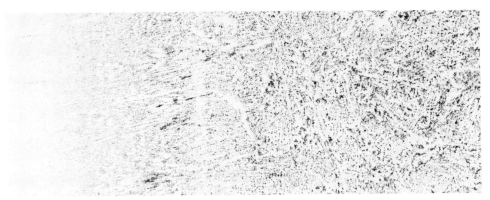

**Fig. 6** Sulfur print of 1017 steel, as strand cast, showing the outlines of the original columnar dendrites (light), which are oriented normal to the chill surface (left edge). Compare with Fig. 5. As-polished. 1.25×. (J.R. Kilpatrick)

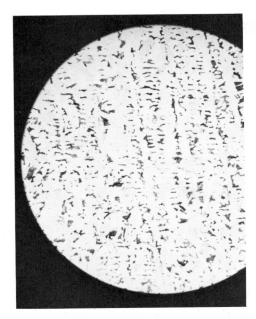

**Fig. 7** 1017 steel, as strand cast. Original columnar dendrites (light) are partially obscured by the presence of nonequilibrium constituents. Compare with Fig. 8. Picral. 25×. (J.R. Kilpatrick)

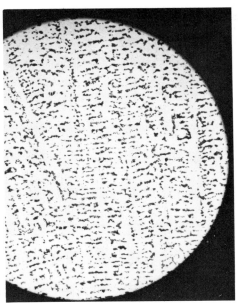

**Fig. 8** Same as Fig. 7, except the casting was given a short austenitizing anneal that eliminated the nonequilibrium constituents and made the outlines of the original dendrites more visible. Picral. 25×. (J.R. Kilpatrick)

## Segregation

Segregation occurs during the dendritic growth of plain carbon and low-alloy steels, because alloying elements are rejected into the liquid and form regions of high carbon or alloy concentration on subsequent solidification. Microsegregation characterizes concentrations of elements in interdendritic regions that range in size from a few to several hundred microns. By contrast, macrosegregation is the gradient difference, measurable on a macroscale, in alloying elements from the surface to the center of an ingot or casting. Macrosegregation becomes more pronounced with increasing section size. Microsegregation, particularly within secondary arm branches, can be eliminated by homogenization. However, macrosegregation is harder to eliminate, because complete homogenization would require longer times than are economically acceptable under production conditions. Therefore, in very large sections, gross differences in alloy concentration sometimes persist and are carried into the final product.

## Nonmetallic Inclusions

Nonmetallic inclusions can segregate with the alloying elements as a result of microsegregation and macrosegregation. Nonmetallic inclusions, except for manganese sulfides, generally are not affected by homogenization and therefore remain unchanged during phase transformations, thus retaining their original position and shape in the solidified ingot.

Some nonmetallic inclusions form in the liquid before solidification; others, during solidification. Aluminates and silicates generally form before solidification, but sulfides form during solidification. Manganese sulfide inclusions frequently form in interdendritic regions and primary grain boundaries, where the last of the liquid freezes. An example of manganese sulfide inclusions distributed along the boundaries of the solidified grains

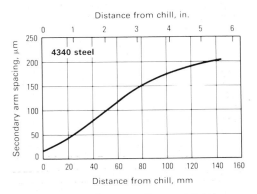

**Fig. 9** Spacing between adjacent secondary arms in dendrites of a directionally solidified 4340 steel casting as a function of the distance of the secondary arms from the surface that was cast against a chill. (Ref 2)

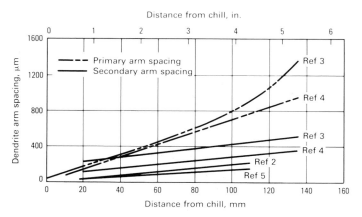

**Fig. 10** Spacing between adjacent primary arms (main spikes) and between adjacent secondary arms of dendrites in 4340 steel castings as a function of the distance of the arms from a surface that was cast against a chill. (Ref 2-5)

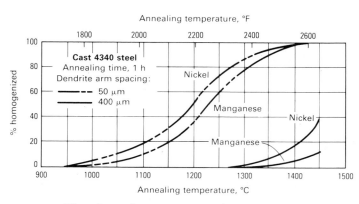

**Fig. 11** Effect of annealing temperature on the amount of homogenization in cast 4340 steel as calculated for diffusion of nickel and manganese solute atoms in dendrites with secondary arm spacings of 50 and 400 μm. (Ref 6)

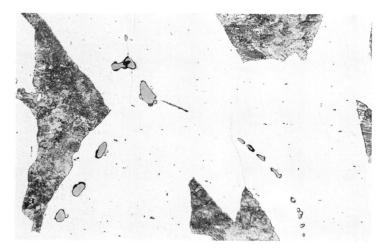

**Fig. 12** Manganese sulfide inclusions (rounded gray particles) at dendrite boundaries of strand-cast 1017 steel that contains pearlite (mottled gray) in a matrix of ferrite (light). Picral. 500×. (J.R. Kilpatrick)

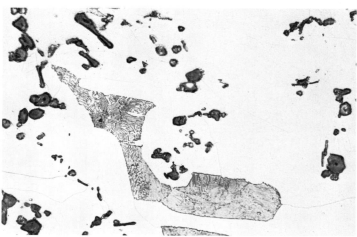

**Fig. 13** Silicate inclusions (dark gray particles) randomly distributed in the ferrite matrix (light) of strand-cast 1017 steel that also contains pearlite (medium gray). Picral. 500×. (J.R. Kilpatrick)

is shown in Fig. 12. These inclusions represent type II sulfides, which are commonly found in aluminum-killed steel ingots and castings (Ref 7). By contrast, Fig. 13 illustrates how the inclusions formed from a higher melting-point compound—in this instance, a silicate—are distributed as clusters in isolated regions in the cast product.

## Effect of Hot Rolling on Structure

Depending on the kind and degree of segregation that develops during solidification, hot rolling induces or intensifies undesirable physical characteristics in the rolled product. Banding can be caused in a hot-rolled steel by severe segregation of carbon and alloying elements, particularly manganese, during solidification and during decomposition of the austenite on cooling.

In a hot-rolled low-alloy steel such as the 1041 steel shown in Fig. 14, banding may exist as a carbon-rich centerline condition. Fig-

**Fig. 14** Longitudinal section through a hot-rolled 1041 steel bar showing a carbon-rich centerline (dark horizontal bands) that resulted from segregation in the ingot. Picral. 3×. (J.R. Kilpatrick)

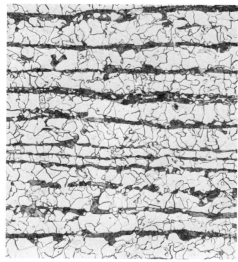

**Fig. 15** Hot-rolled 1022 steel showing severe banding. Bands of pearlite (dark) and ferrite were caused by segregation of carbon and other elements during solidification and later decomposition of austenite. Nital. 250×. (J.R. Kilpatrick)

**Fig. 16** 45% reduction

**Fig. 17** 63% reduction

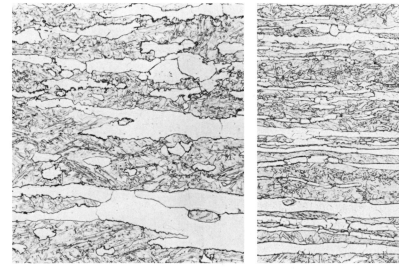

**Fig. 18** 81% reduction

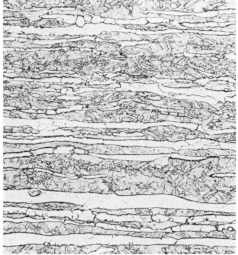

**Fig. 19** 94% reduction

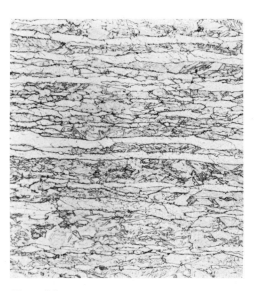

**Fig. 20** 97% reduction

**Fig. 16 to 20** Type 430 stainless steel hot rolled to various percentages of reduction showing development of a banded structure consisting of alternate layers of ferrite (light) and martensite (dark) as the amount of hot work is increased. 55 mL 35% HCl, 1 to 2 g potassium metabisulfite, 275 mL $H_2O$ (Beraha's tint reagent No. 2). 500×. (Ref 8)

ure 15 shows an extreme example of banding in a hot-rolled plain carbon steel (1022) in which alternate layers of ferrite and pearlite have formed along the rolling direction. The relationship between increasing percentages of reduction by hot rolling and the intensity of banding in type 430 stainless steel is demonstrated in Fig. 16 to 20.

**Dendritic Pattern.** During severe hot deformation, the dendritic structure is completely destroyed. Figures 21 to 23 show how the original dendritic pattern in a directionally solidified steel ingot is obscured, then finally almost completely eliminated by hot rolling as the percentage of reduction increases.

**Inclusions.** Nonmetallic inclusions are not eliminated by homogenization and so are present in the final product. Ductile inclusions, such as manganese sulfide, elongate along the rolling direction and form stringers (Ref 9).

An example of manganese sulfide stringers (and of banding) is shown in Fig. 24. On the other hand, inclusions such as aluminates remain unchanged during rolling. However, silicates, which are brittle during cold rolling, can elongate considerably during hot rolling.

Rare earths are added to liquid steel before solidification to change sulfide inclusion morphology and composition (Ref 10). The rare earth sulfides are less ductile during hot rolling than manganese sulfide and remain globular in the final product. Globular sulfides provide more isotropic properties. Recent technology involves injecting calcium into liquid steel to reduce sulfur levels and change inclusion morphology and composition. Figure 25 shows a typical calcium-containing inclusion, where calcium sulfide forms a shell around a core of calcium aluminate.

## REFERENCES

1. M.C. Flemings, Application of Solidification Theory to Large Castings and Ingots, in *Solidification of Metals*, ISI 110, The Iron and Steel Institute, London, 1968, p 277-288

2. R.F. Polich and M.C. Flemings, Mechanical Properties of Unidirectional Steel Castings, *Trans. Am. Foundrymen's Soc.*, Vol 73, 1965, p 28-33

3. F. Weinberg and R.K. Buhr, Solidification Studies of Steel Castings, in *Solidification of Metals*, ISI 110, The Iron and Steel Institute, London, 1968, p 294-304

4. M.C. Flemings, R.V. Barone, S.Z. Uram, and H.F. Taylor, Solidification of Steel Castings and Ingots, *Trans. Am. Foundrymen's Soc.*, Vol 69, 1961, p 422-435

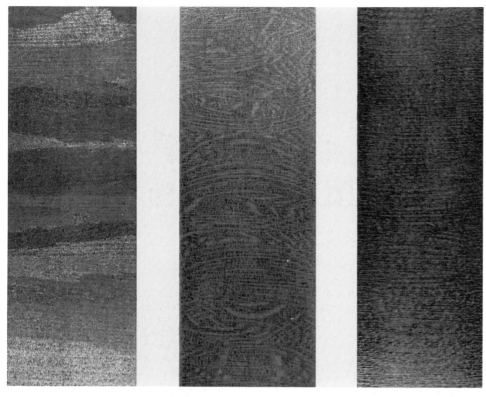

**Fig. 21, 22, 23** Effect of severe hot deformation on the dendritic pattern in directionally solidified 4340 steel. Fig. 21: Dendrites in the as-cast ingot. Fig. 22: Dendrites obscured by a 50% reduction. Fig. 23: Dendrites almost entirely eliminated by an 83% reduction. 10% $HNO_3$ in $H_2O$. 1.3×

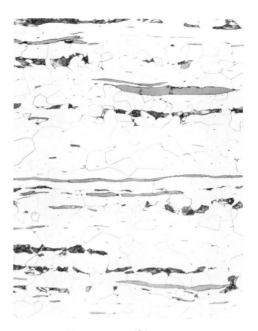

**Fig. 24** Manganese sulfide stringers (medium gray), formed from inclusions in the ingot, in a hot-rolled bar of resulfurized 1213 steel showing a banded structure of ferrite (light) and pearlite (dark). Nital. 200×. (J.R. Kilpatrick)

5. P.J. Ahearn and F.C. Quigley, Dendrite Morphology of High-Strength Steel Castings, *J. Iron Steel Inst.*, Vol 204, 1966, p 16-22

6. T.Z. Kattamis and M.C. Flemings, Dendrite Morphology, Microsegregation, and Homogenization of Low-Alloy Steel, *Trans. Met. Soc. AIME*, Vol 233, 1965, p 992-999

7. C.E. Sims, The Nonmetallic Constituents of Steel, *Trans. Met. Soc. AIME*, Vol 215, 1959, p 367-393

8. B.L. Bramfitt, Effect of Hot Rolling on the Dendritic Texture of Directionally Solidified Steel Ingots, *Met. Trans.*, Vol 1, 1970, p 2495-2505

9. R. Kiessling, The Behaviour of Non-Metallic Inclusions in Wrought Steel, in *Nonmetallic Inclusions in Steel*, ISI 115, Part III, The Iron and Steel Institute, London, 1968, p 51-73

10. W.G. Wilson and A. McLean, *Desulfurization of Iron and Steel and Sulfide Shape Control*, Iron and Steel Society of AIME, Warrendale, PA, 1980

## SELECTED REFERENCES

- G. Lambert, Ed., *Typical Microstructures of Cast Metals*, Institute of British Foundrymen, London, 1966
- A. Pokorny and J. Pokorny, *Metallographic Atlas of Iron, Steels and Cast Irons*, Vol III of *De Ferri Metallographia*, 1966 (in English, French, and German)

**Fig. 25** Low-carbon steel showing inclusions of calcium sulfide outer rim (light gray) and calcium aluminate core (dark gray). The matrix is pearlite and ferrite. As-polished. 500×. (B.L. Bramfitt, J.R. Kilpatrick)

# Solidification Structures of Aluminum Alloy Ingots

By Douglas A. Granger
Fellow
Aluminum Company of America

ALUMINUM ALLOY INGOTS intended for subsequent rolling, extruding, or forging are considered in this article. Ingots intended for remelting and shaped castings produced in foundries are not discussed, although their solidification structures are similar to those of ingots for working.

## Dendrites

Dendritic solidification macrostructure is characteristic of all aluminum alloy castings. A variety of such structures in sand, permanent mold, investment, and die castings are shown in Fig. 103 to 179 in the article "Aluminum Alloys" in this Volume. Dendrites in aluminum alloy welds and brazed joints are shown in Fig. 180 to 229 in the same article.

The first systematic attempt to relate dendritic solidification to casting conditions for a number of aluminum alloys was reported in 1950 (Ref 1). It was established that the spacing between adjacent arms in dendrites decreases as solidification time decreases. Subsequent investigations have confirmed this result (Ref 2); data from a selection of published papers are shown in Fig. 1. The relationship between dendrite arm spacing and solidification time is given by the equation:

$$d = 7.5\theta^{0.39} \qquad \text{(Eq 1)}$$

where dendrite arm spacing ($d$) is in microns and solidification time ($\theta$) is in seconds. Constants depend on the alloy in question, but equations of this form have been shown to fit extensive data from the aluminum-copper system.

The influence of solute content is less well defined. In general, up to eutectic compositions, the effect of increasing solute content at a constant freezing rate is to decrease dendrite arm spacing (Fig. 2). The relationship between solute content and dendrite arm spacing has been well documented also for steel and for copper alloys, as described in the articles "Solidification Structures of Steel" and "Solidification Structures of Copper Alloy Ingots" in this Volume.

Fine and coarse dendritic structures typical of aluminum alloy ingots are illustrated in Fig. 3 and 4, respectively. Fine dendrite arm spacing is usually associated with a uniform distribution of small constituent particles and generally is preferred. However, fine spacing is not always compatible with the desired grain structure. In general, dendrite arm spacing is most important in ingots of heat-treatable alloys and in ingots that are cast close to final part size and shape and thus subjected to a minimum of deformation during subsequent fabrication.

## Grain Structure

Grain size is an important, readily observed feature of aluminum alloy ingots. A uniform, fine grain size is sought in most instances to obtain optimum properties in the wrought product. Grain refinement also increases resistance to hot cracking during casting.

The columnar grain structure shown in Fig. 5 is characteristic of a low-solute alloy that has solidified in a steep temperature gradient with little turbulence in the melt to effect grain refinement by detachment of dendrite arms. In the presence of turbulent directed metal flow, the structure of such an alloy would consist of columnar and equiaxed grains, as illustrated in Fig. 6.

**Grain Refining.** The addition of a grain refiner resulted in the nearly equiaxed struc-

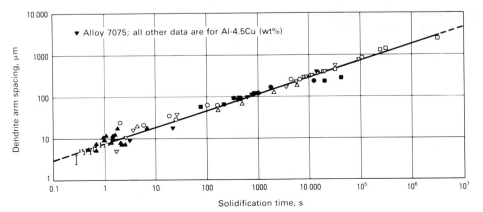

**Fig. 1** Effect of solidification rate, as measured by solidification time, on secondary dendrite arm spacing of castings of aluminum alloys 7075 and Al-4.5Cu (wt%). The log-log plot includes data from nine investigations indicated by nine symbols.

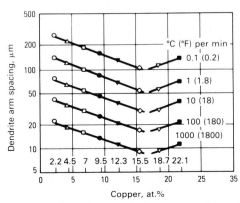

**Fig. 2** Effect of copper solute content (internal scale) on secondary dendrite arm spacing in eight aluminum alloys, as plotted for five cooling rates. (Ref 3)

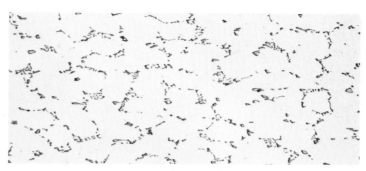

**Fig. 3** Direct-chill semicontinuous cast alloy 3003 ingot. Solidification time of approximately 1 s produced fine dendrite arm spacing, as shown by the interdendritic network of manganese-bearing constituents (dark). See also Fig. 4. Keller's reagent. 500×

**Fig. 4** Same as Fig. 3, except that solidification was approximately 10 s, which produced coarser dendrite arm spacing than in Fig. 3. Note that the manganese-bearing constituents are also coarser. Keller's reagent. 500×

**Fig. 5** Transverse section through an ingot of alloy 1100 that was cast by the Properzi (wheel-and-belt) method. Note the consistency with which columnar grains have grown perpendicularly to each face of the mold. Tucker's reagent. 1½×

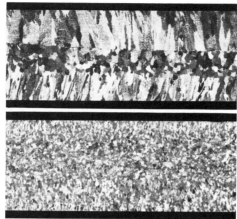

**Fig. 6, 7** Longitudinal sections through 25-mm (1-in.) thick slabs of alloy 1100 cast by the Hazelett (two-belt) method. Upper slab (Fig. 6) was cast without a grain refiner; lower slab (Fig. 7), with a grain refiner. Tucker's reagent. Actual size

ture shown in Fig. 7. The grain-refining inoculants commonly used in the aluminum industry are master alloys containing titanium or titanium plus boron (Ref 4-7). It is common practice to add grain-refining master alloy in the form of a 9.55-mm (0.38-in.) diam rod continuously to the molten metal as it flows from the holding furnace to the casting unit. Grain-refining additions are used to obtain a fine, uniform grain structure and to reduce the formation of center cracks. The coarse, nonuniform structure obtained in alloy 6063, which was cast without a grain refiner added to the melt, is shown in Fig. 8. The dramatic reduction in grain size and improvement in structure uniformity as a result of adding a grain refiner is shown in Fig. 9.

The conflict that may exist between obtaining a fine dendritic structure and a uniform, small grain size is illustrated in Fig. 10 and 11. Cast without a grain refiner, an ingot exhibits fine dendrite spacing but wide, columnar grains (Fig. 10). By contrast, a somewhat coarser dendritic structure with much smaller, equiaxed grains is illustrated in Fig. 11, which shows a section from an ingot cast with a grain refiner.

Grain size may be controlled by such methods as vibration, stirring, and control of metal flow, which provide nuclei by detachment of dendrite arms. A successful application of the latter method has been reported in Ref 8. The fully columnar structure produced when the metal feed is located at the center of the mold cavity is illustrated in Fig. 12. When the stream is directed across the solidifying shell of the casting, the largely equiaxed structure shown in Fig. 13 is obtained.

**Twinned Columnar Growth (Feather Crystals).** Aluminum alloy ingots cast without a grain refiner often exhibit a fan-shaped columnar structure, referred to as "feather crystals." This structure, illustrated in Fig. 14 (see also Fig. 8), may be found in low- and high-solute alloys. It is most likely to develop when there is a steep thermal gradient ahead of the solidifying interface (Ref 8) or an inadequate addition of grain refiner (Ref 9). At higher magnification, the feather crystals consist of twinned columnar grains (Fig. 15).

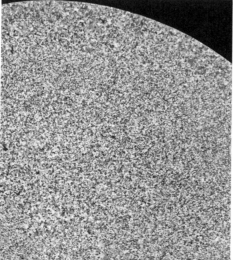

**Fig. 8, 9** Portions of transverse sections through two 150-mm (6-in.) diam ingots of alloy 6063 that were direct-chill semicontinuous cast. Fig. 8: Ingot was cast without a grain refiner, note columnar grains and colonies of featherlike crystals near the center of the section. Fig. 9: Ingot, which shows a fine, equiaxed grain structure, was cast with a grain refiner. Tucker's reagent. Actual size

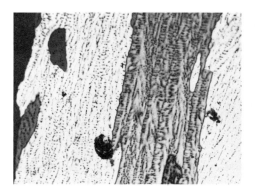

**Fig. 10** Wide, columnar grains and fine dendrite arm spacing in alloy 6063 ingot cast without a grain refiner. Polarized light. Compare with Fig. 11. Barker's reagent. 40×

**Fig. 11** Same as Fig. 10, except cast with a grain refiner. Note small, equiaxed grains and increased dendrite arm spacing compared with Fig. 10. Polarized light. Barker's reagent. 40×

## Microsegregation

Most of the major alloying additions made to aluminum are less soluble in the solid phase than in the liquid phase; that is, the equilibrium distribution coefficient ($k_o$) is less than 1 (see the article "Solidification Structures of Solid Solutions" in this Volume). Moreover, for most solutes, aluminum exhibits a relatively low terminal solid solubility; therefore, second-phase constituents are invariably present in ingot structures. For these reasons, the dendrites, which are the first portions of a cast structure to solidify, are low in solute content and are surrounded by interdendritic networks of one or more second-phase constituents. The size and distribution of the constituents depend on such factors as solute concentration, dendrite arm spacing, and grain size. The solute distribution characteristic of cast alloys, referred to as "coring," may be described (Ref 10) with reasonable accuracy by the Scheil equation:

$$C_s = C_o k_o (1 - f_s)^{k-1} \qquad \text{(Eq 2)}$$

where $C_o$ is the concentration of a solute in the alloy, $k_o$ is the equilibrium distribution coefficient, and $C_s$ is the composition at weight fraction solid $f_s$.

Copper and magnesium microsegregation in a 2124 direct-chill cast ingot, observed using electron probe microanalysis, is shown in Fig. 16. The path traversed by the electron

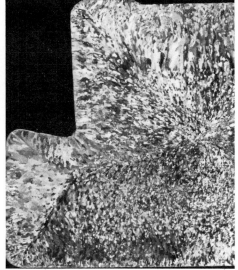

**Fig. 12, 13** Transverse slices through portions of two continuously cast 75 × 100-mm (3 × 4-in.) T-section ingots of alloy 1100 illustrating the effect of metal-feed location on structure. Fig. 12: the liquid metal entered at the center of the section. Fig. 13: the metal-feed location caused a flow of hot metal across the solidifying shell. Modified aqua regia (50 mL HNO₃, 50 mL HCl). Actual size. (Ref 8)

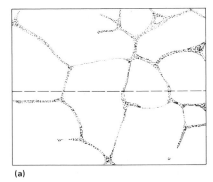

(a)

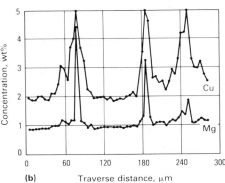

(b)

**Fig. 16** Copper and magnesium microsegregation in a direct-chill semicontinuous cast (610 × 1372 mm, or 24 × 54 in.) 2124 alloy ingot. (a) Dendrite cells at midthickness location in ingot and enrichment of copper and magnesium at the cell boundaries. When observed in conjunction with the electron probe microanalysis, the gradual increase in solute concentration across the dendrite cell is readily apparent. (b) Microprobe traverse across dendrites

**Fig. 14** Portion of a longitudinal section through a 75-mm (3-in.) diam alloy 1100 ingot, direct-chill cast without a grain refiner. Center of section contains fan-shape zones of feather crystals. Tucker's reagent. Actual size

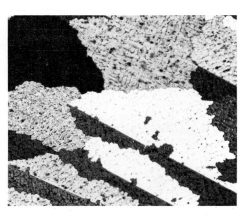

**Fig. 15** Feather crystals in an alloy 3003 ingot that was cast by the direct-chill semicontinuous process. Growth twins in the crystals have been revealed by photographing the specimen with polarized light. Barker's reagent. 50×

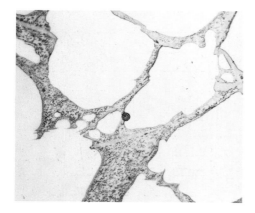

**Fig. 17** Alloy 2011 ingot, as-cast. Structure: network of CuAl$_2$ (mottled) at boundaries of aluminum grains, needles and other large particles of Cu$_2$FeAl$_7$, and dark globules of lead and bismuth. See also Fig. 18 and Fig. 19. Keller's reagent. 500×

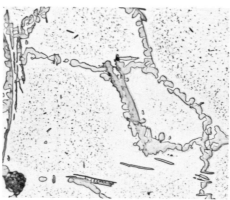

**Fig. 18** Same as Fig. 17, but homogenized at 525 °C (975 °F) for 2 h. Note that the CuAl$_2$ has coagulated into a clear constituent and has partly dissolved. Fine precipitate of CuAl$_2$ within the aluminum grains. See also Fig. 19. Keller's reagent. 500×

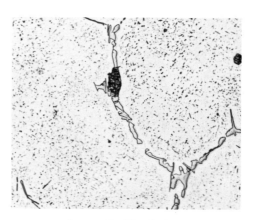

**Fig. 19** Same as Fig. 17 and 18, except the ingot was homogenized at 525 °C (975 °F) for 12 h. The CuAl$_2$ at the grain boundaries has almost completely dissolved, and there is much fine precipitate of CuAl$_2$ within the aluminum grains. Keller's reagent. 500×

**Fig. 20** Transverse section through a portion of an alloy 5657 ingot that was cast by the direct-chill continuous process, then homogenized at 600 °C (1110 °F) for 48 h. Residual stresses and a high temperature (above the alloy solvus temperature) have caused development of a coarse grain structure at the surface of the ingot (right). Modified Tucker's reagent: 10 mL HCl, 10 mL HNO$_3$, 5 mL HF (48%), 75 mL H$_2$O. Actual size

**Fig. 21** Alloy 5052 ingot, as-cast. Angular interdendritic shrinkage porosity resulting from excessively high hydrogen content in the melt. Compare with Fig. 22. As-polished. 50×

**Fig. 22** Same as Fig. 21, but after homogenization at 565 °C (1050 °F) for 12 h. Note that large pores are now rounded and that small spheroidal pores have formed. As-polished. 50×

beam to determine the solute enrichment at the dendrite boundaries is indicated in Fig. 16(a). Therefore, ingots of most aluminum alloys must be heated for an extended period close to the solidus temperature to homogenize the structure (obtain a more uniform distribution of solute).

## Homogenization

Homogenization reduces microsegregation, a primary benefit that improves the response of the ingot to subsequent thermomechanical treatments. This reduction is illustrated in Fig. 17 to 19, which show the dissolution and reprecipitation of a more dispersed coarse CuAl$_2$ constituent in a 2011 alloy ingot. Homogenization is also important for some 3XXX series alloy ingots to produce a controlled precipitation of manganese-containing constituents from supersaturated solid solutions in forms that will not disturb the grain structure resulting from recrystallization, and therefore, the ultimate forming characteristics of the mill product.

Another benefit of homogenization is the reduction of residual internal stresses that result from the presence of steep temperature gradients during solidification. However, if these internal stresses are at or above the critical level for grain growth, large grains will form during a high-temperature heat treatment such as homogenization. This abnormal grain growth is illustrated in Fig. 20, which shows the grain structure of an alloy 5657 ingot. The surfaces of high-purity alloy ingots such as 5657 are especially susceptible to abnormal grain growth.

Assuming that other casting conditions are satisfactory, angular interdendritic cavities such as those shown in Fig. 21 are typical of aluminum alloy ingots cast from a melt with an excessively high hydrogen content. Such an ingot structure is not improved by conventional homogenization, which only rounds off the large cavities and promotes the growth of smaller pores (Fig. 22).

## Macrosegregation

The chemical composition of large, commercial-size ingots can vary significantly from point to point through the ingot thickness, which is usually greater than 406 mm (16 in.) (Fig. 23). This type of segregation, referred to as "macrosegregation," is only slightly affected by homogenization. In general, macrosegregation can be reduced in direct-chill ingot casting by decreasing ingot thickness, lowering the casting speed, and maximizing molten metal superheat. The origin of macrosegregation and its magnitude are discussed in Ref 11.

## Hydrogen Porosity

Hydrogen porosity in aluminum alloy ingots appears as angular interdendritic cavities or as comparatively small spheroidal pores (Fig. 24 and 25). The former type of porosity is associated with higher gas contents than the latter, but the division between the two depends also on solidification rate and freezing range. These relationships are shown in Fig. 26. Macroscopic interdendritic

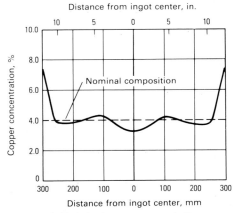

Fig. 23 Variation in copper concentration across a 600-mm (24-in.) thick direct-chill semicontinuous cast ingot of 2124 alloy

Fig. 24 Portion of a transverse section through a 150-mm (6-in.) diam ingot of alloy 6063 showing hydrogen porosity. See also Fig. 25. Fluorescent penetrant. Actual size

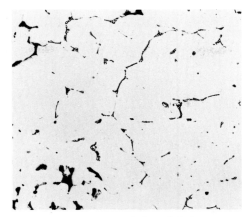

Fig. 25 As-cast ingot of alloy 6063 that contains a heavy concentration of coarse, angular porosity at interdendritic locations. See also Fig. 24. Hot 20% $H_2SO_4$. 100×

porosity results from the rejection of hydrogen from the solid to the liquid metal until the solution pressure of the hydrogen in the liquid exceeds 1 atm. Small spheroidal porosity forms from a portion of the hydrogen that remained in the solid metal. The gas in these small pores is at high pressure (Ref 13). During a high-temperature heat treatment, macroscopic interdendritic porosity may become rounded, and small spheroidal porosity may appear (Fig. 24). Ingot density or gas content, however, is not significantly decreased. By contrast, redistribution of gas enlarges the small spheroidal pores and significantly decreases density without an appreciable reduction in gas content (Fig. 27).

## Surface Defects

A surface layer containing an undesirable concentration of alloying elements and associated coarse constituent particles is often found in direct-chill semicontinuous cast aluminum alloy ingots. A typical example in an

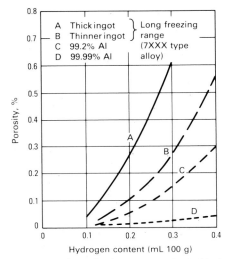

Fig. 26 Relationship between porosity and hydrogen content in semicontinuous direct-chill cast ingot. (Ref 12)

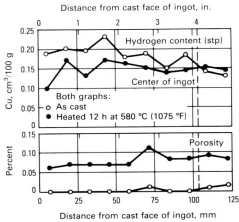

Fig. 27 Distribution of hydrogen content and amount of porosity across a 200-mm (8-in.) thick ingot of alloy 1100 in the as-cast condition, and after having been held for 12 h at 580 °C (1075 °F) (Ref 13)

alloy 7075 ingot is shown in Fig. 28. When this condition is present in alloys with a wide freezing range (such as alloy 7075), exudations may occur on the surface. A similar surface defect, associated with dilute alloys, is the presence of bleed bands (see Fig. 29). Both defects are caused by reheating the solidified shell of the casting when it separates from the mold wall, briefly ceasing heat removal. Bleed bands exhibit coarse constituents that often extend well below the surface as shown in Fig. 30.

The surfaces of aluminum alloy ingots are often "scalped" to remove segregated or nonuniform surface layers, which vary in thickness and may extend 20 mm (0.75 in.) below the chilled surface (Ref 15). The contrast between the coarse structure of the surface layer and the fine subsurface structure of an alloy 2024 ingot is shown in Fig. 31. Illustrated in Fig. 32 is the increased dendrite arm spacing 50 mm (2 in.) below the ingot surface; Fig. 33 depicts the mixed dendrite structure sometimes found at the center of direct-chill semicontinuous cast ingots. The coarse dendrites in Fig. 33 have grown under conditions of

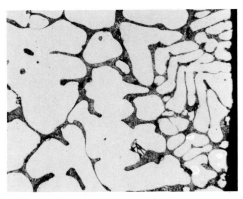

Fig. 28 Section through the edge (right) of an alloy 7075 ingot, direct-chill semicontinuous cast. The constituents that have segregated near the surface are mainly Al-MgZn₂, iron-containing phases, and $Mg_2Si$. Dilute Keller's reagent. 250×

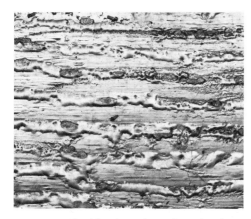

**Fig. 29** Bleed bands on the surface of a direct-chill semicontinuous cast ingot of alloy 3003. The bands are normal to the casting direction. See Fig. 30 for a view through one of these bands. Not polished. One fourth actual size. (Ref 14)

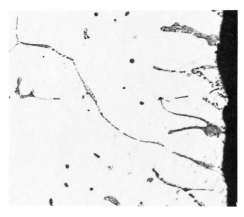

**Fig. 30** Section taken parallel to the casting direction, through one of the bleed bands shown in Fig. 29. Note the numerous coarse constituents well below the surface of the ingot. Keller's reagent. 200×. (Ref 14)

different types of aluminum alloys is shown in Fig. 36. More recently, however, it has been demonstrated that the casting speed threshold, above which center cracking occurs, may be raised by providing a controlled secondary cooling system (Ref 22).

## Effects in Fabrication

To ensure a high-quality product, molten alloys are often treated to reduce the hydrogen content and alkali element concentration as well as to remove nonmetallic inclusions. This treatment is usually performed in-line, that is, as the molten metal flows from the holding furnace to the casting unit. Several metal treatment units have been developed for this purpose, many of which are discussed in Ref 23. Despite these methods of producing high-quality metal, problems sometimes

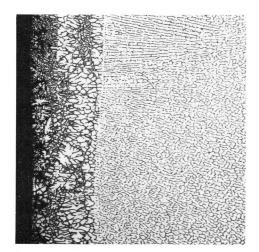

**Fig. 31** Section from outer edge of 305-mm (12-in.) diam alloy 2024 ingot, direct-chill semicontinuous cast. Surface layer has coarse dendrites and concentration of constituents containing copper and magnesium. See also Fig. 32 and 33. As-polished. 25×

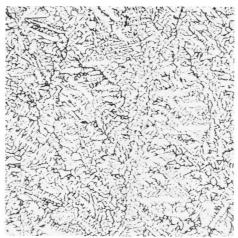

**Fig. 32** Same as Fig. 31, except area shown is 50 mm (2 in.) below the ingot surface. At this location, dendrite arm spacing is greater than that nearer the surface, although similar to that in the surface layer. See also Fig. 33. As-polished. 25×

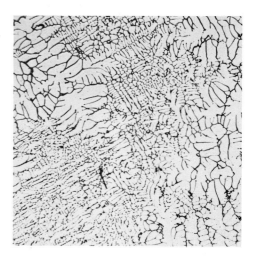

**Fig. 33** Same as Fig. 31 and 32, but a section taken from the center of the 305-mm (12-in.) diam ingot. The structure consists of a mixture of fine and coarse dendrites. Coarse dendrites originate from presolidified metal, which grew isothermally. As-polished. 25×

heat removal that are slower than those for the fine dendrites, which are comparable in dimension with the finest dendrites close to the chill surface.

Efforts have been made to eliminate surface defects and avoid the need for "scalping" prior to fabrication. The processes developed to achieve this are (in order of increasing effectiveness) low-head direct-chill casting (Ref 16), the Showa Denko process (Ref 17), and electromagnetic casting (Ref 18). The electromagnetic method is in commercial use for producing 1*xxx*, 3*xxx*, and 5*xxx* series alloy ingots that may be rolled with an as-cast surface. An example of an electromagnetic cast 3004 alloy ingot is shown in Fig. 34. Variations in cooling rate close to the ingot surface sometimes cause nonequilibrium constituents, which can respond differently to surface finishing treatments and can result in streaking or discoloration of the wrought product (Ref 19).

## Center Cracking

Center cracking often results from attempts to improve the surface condition by increasing casting speed. Center cracks, sometimes referred to as "spider cracks," are caused by a buildup of internal tension stresses during final freezing (Ref 20). Because the absence of liquid metal to feed the center enhances this type of cracking, this defect is most prevalent in dilute alloys. An example of center cracking in an alloy 1100 ingot is shown in Fig. 35.

Cracking caused by internal tension stresses alone takes place after final freezing. This problem is inherent in direct-chill semicontinuous casting. Results reported in 1954 showed that each aluminum alloy ingot has a practical upper limit on casting speed for the conventional direct-chill semicontinuous process (Ref 21). The relationship between permissible casting speed and ingot diameter for

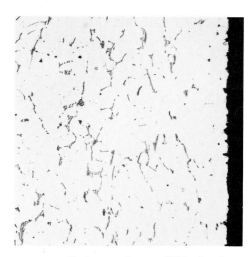

**Fig. 34** Electromagnetic cast 3004 alloy ingot. Note the freedom from liquation and the uniformity of the constituent particle distribution. Keller's reagent. 200×

**Fig. 35** Transverse section through a 75-mm (3-in.) diam alloy 1100 ingot, direct-chill cast. Center cracks (at arrow) resulted from excessively steep temperature gradients. Tucker's reagent. Actual size

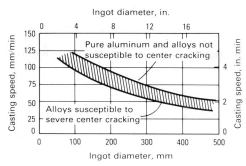

**Fig. 36** Relation between permissible speed of conventional direct-chill semicontinuous casting and ingot diameter for aluminum alloys with and without susceptibility to center cracking. (Ref 21)

arise, particularly because there are no methods available for continuously monitoring metal quality.

Excessive gas contents are most serious when present in ingots that contain oxide inclusions of the type shown in Fig. 37. The oxide clumps and films become oxide stringers in rolled products, such as those shown in Fig. 38, and provide sites for the agglomeration of gas, which then forms blisters in sheet during subsequent annealing (Ref 24).

A coarse primary constituent in alloy 7075 that homogenization will probably not remove is shown in Fig. 39. During subsequent working of this ingot material, the constituent will break up, producing a stringer defect of the type shown in Fig. 40, which results in a reduction of fatigue resistance.

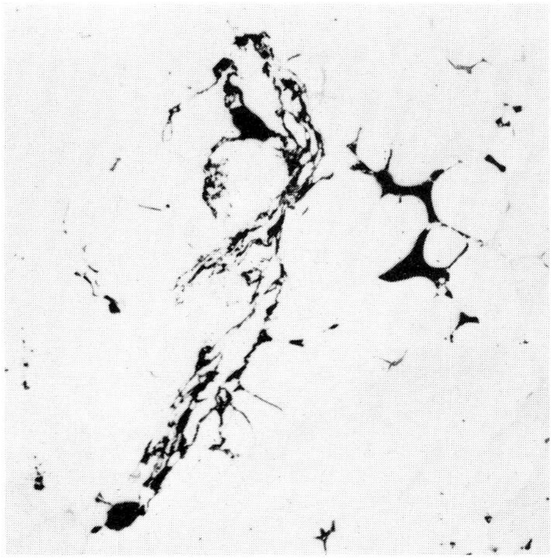

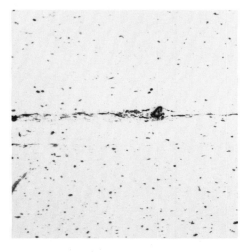

**Fig. 37** Oxide inclusion in direct-chill semicontinuous cast ingot of alloy 2024. See also Fig. 38. As-polished. 250×

**Fig. 38** Stringer produced in alloy 1100 sheet during rolling of an oxide inclusion of the type shown in Fig. 37. As-polished. 250×

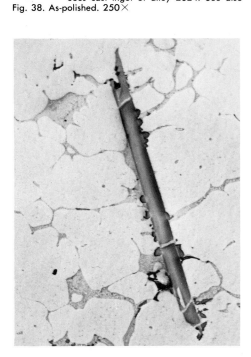

**Fig. 39** Coarse primary crystal of CrAl₇ in an alloy 7075 ingot. See Fig. 40 for a view after rolling. As-polished. 100×

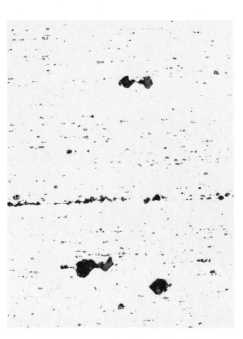

**Fig. 40** Stringer of CrAl₇ crystals in sheet rolled from the alloy 7075 ingot shown in Fig. 39. 0.5% HF, 10 s. 100×

## REFERENCES

1. B.H. Alexander and F.N. Rhines, Dendritic Crystallization of Alloys, *Trans. AIME*, Vol 188, 1950, p 1267-1273
2. B.P. Bardes and M.C. Flemings, Dendrite Arm Spacing and Solidification Time in a Cast Aluminum-Copper Alloy, *Trans. Am. Foundrymen's Soc.*, Vol 74, 1966, p 406-412
3. J.A. Horwath and L.F. Mondolfo, Dendritic Growth, *Acta. Metall.*, Vol 10, 1962, p 1037-1042
4. A. Cibula, The Grain Refinement of Aluminum Alloy Castings by Additions of Titanium and Boron, *J. Inst. Metals*, Vol 80, 1951, p 1-16
5. L. Bäckerud, On the Grain Refining Mechanism in Al-Ti-B Alloys, *Jernkontorets Ann.*, Vol 155, 1971, p 422-424
6. L. Bäckerud, How Does a Good Grain Refiner Work?, *Light Met. Age*, Oct 1983, p 6-12
7. L.F. Mondolfo, Grain Refinement in Aluminum Alloys, in *Light Metals 1972*, Metallurgical Society of AIME, Warrendale, PA, p 405-426
8. R.E. Spear, R.T. Craig, and C.R. Howle, The Influence of Metal Flow on the Grain Morphology in Continuously Cast Aluminum, *J. Met.*, Vol 23 (No. 10), 1971, p 42-45
9. D.A. Granger and J. Liu, The Occurrence, Effect and Control of Twinned Columnar Growth in Aluminum Alloys, *J. Met.*, Vol 35 (No. 6), 1983, p 54-59
10. M.C. Flemings, *Solidification Processing*, McGraw-Hill, 1974
11. H. Yu and D.A. Granger, Macrosegregation in Aluminum Alloy Ingot Cast by Semicontinuous Direct-Chill Method in symposium proceedings, NASA-Lewis Research Center, Cleveland, Sept 1984, p 157-168
12. D.A. Granger, Use of Telegas Instrument in Quality Control in *Proceedings of the Third International Aluminum Extrusion Technology Seminar*, Atlanta, April 1984, p 269-272

13. D.E.J. Talbot and D.A. Granger, Secondary Hydrogen Porosity in Aluminum, *J. Inst. Met.*, Vol 92, May 1964, p 290-297

14. D.L.W. Collins, A New Explanation of the Surface Structures of Direct Chill Ingots, *Metallurgia*, Vol 76, Oct 1967, p 137-144

15. G. Siebel, D. Altenpohl, and M.H. Cohen, Periodic Segregation in Continuously Cast Aluminum (in German), *Z. Metallk.*, Vol 44, 1953, p 173-183

16. D. Altenpohl, New or Fundamentally Improved Casting Methods for Aluminum Materials in *Proceedings, Fifth International Light Metals Conference*, Leoben, Austria, 1968, p 367-373

17. R. Mitamara, T. Ito, Y. Takahashi, and T. Hiraoka, New Hot-Top Continuous Casting Method Featuring Application of Air Pressure to Mold in *Light Metals 1978*, Metallurgical Society of AIME, Warrendale, PA, p 281-291

18. H.A. Meier, G.B. Leconte, and A.M. Odok, Alusuisse Experience with Electromagnetic Moulds, in *Light Metals 1977*, Metallurgical Society of AIME, Warrendale, PA, p 223-233

19. D.A. Granger and C.L. Jensen, Role of Ingot Structure in Structural Streaking, in *Light Metals 1984*, Metallurgical Society of AIME, Warrendale, PA, p 1249-1263

20. D.M. Lewis and J. Savage, The Principles of Continuous Casting of Metals, *Met. Rev.*, Vol 1, 1956, p 65-116

21. G. Porro and P. Lombardi, Continuous Casting and Empirical Calculation of Descent Speed in Casting of Light Alloy Ingots, *Aluminio*, Vol 23, 1954, p 23 (in Italian)

22. N.B. Bryson, Increasing the Productivity of Aluminum DC Casting, in *Light Metals 1972*, Metallurgical Society of AIME, Warrendale, PA, p 429-435

23. E.F. Emley, Cleaning and Degassing of Light Metals, *Met. Technol.*, Vol 3, March 1976, p 118-127

24. C.E. Ransley and D.E.J. Talbot, Hydrogen Porosity in Metals, With Special Reference to Aluminum and Its Alloys, *Z. Metallk.*, Vol 46, 1955, p 328-337 (in German)

# Solidification Structures of Copper Alloy Ingots

By T.F. Bower
Director of Metallurgical
  Process Development
Chase Brass & Copper Company

and

M.R. Randlett
Manager, Process Development
Chase Brass & Copper Company

SOLIDIFICATION STRUCTURES OF COPPER ALLOY INGOTS intended for subsequent working are primarily discussed in this article. Ingots intended for remelting and shaped castings produced in foundries are not specifically discussed, although they have solidification structures that in many respects are similar to those of ingots intended for subsequent working. Also discussed briefly are cast structures produced by novel technologies.

## Dendrites

Dendritic structure is an almost universal feature of copper alloy ingots. A variety of dendritic structures are pictured in micrographs in this article.

Figure 1(a) shows the effect, during solidification, of cooling rate on the spacing between adjacent arms in dendrites in two bronze alloys (Ref 1). Increasing the cooling rate (decreasing the solidification time) leads to finer dendrite arm spacing. Solidification time generally is more useful than cooling rate in interpreting dendritic structure of copper alloys, regardless of solute content. Cooling rate has little meaning for pure or nearly pure metals, which have near zero change in temperature during solidification.

Figure 1(b) provides data on the spacing of dendrite arms for various solidification times in slowly cast laboratory specimens of alloy 12200 (DHP copper). The small amount of solute in alloy 12200 (0.015 to 0.040% P) does not result in thermal behavior different from that of unalloyed copper, but does cause dendritic growth. Figure 1(b) also presents data on the spacing of dendrite arms in cast alloy 71500 (copper nickel, 30%) (Ref 2).

The phase diagram for the copper-nickel system shows that, although only one phase forms in the solid, solute redistribution occurs during solidification. Dendrite arm spacings in the alloy 71500 ingot were smaller than those in the alloy 12200 ingot, because the dendrite arms in the alloy 71500 ingot were branched into secondary arms. Secondary dendrite arm spacing is also called cell size. Branched dendrite arms are typical of highly alloyed ingots.

As shown in Fig. 2(a), dendrite arm spacing varies greatly across this ingot. If these data are compared to those in Fig. 1(b) for the same alloy, the microstructure may be interpreted regarding solidification time; solidification time was shortest—cooling rate was highest—at the center of the ingot.

Figure 2(b) presents a curve of dendrite arm spacing versus position in a 229-mm (9-in.) diam semicontinuous-cast ingot of alloy 71500 (Ref 2). These data and those in Fig. 1(b) for the same alloy indicate that the finest dendrite arm spacing is at the surface, which solidified in the shortest time, or cooled at the highest rate. These results contrast with those for the smaller ingot of continuous-cast DHP copper, which was solidified under conditions of high heat transfer in the secondary cooling zone.

**Factors affecting dendritic structure** of copper alloy ingots include composition, cooling rate, and agitation during solidification (Ref 3-6). Increasing the cooling rate produces finer secondary dendrite arm spacing. For many alloy systems, increasing the

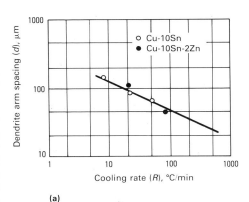

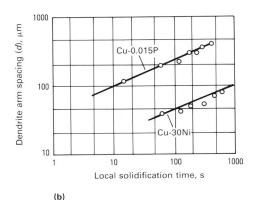

(a)

(b)

**Fig. 1** Dendrite arm spacing as affected by solidification conditions in specimens of four cast copper alloys. (a) Effect of cooling rate on two bronze alloys (Ref 1). (b) Effect of local solidification time on alloy 71500 (copper nickel, 30%) (Ref 2) and on alloy 12200 (DHP copper)

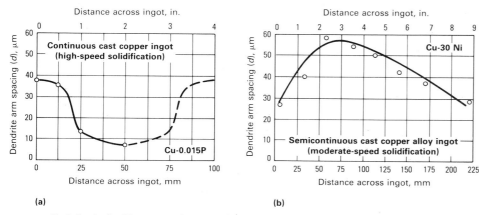

**Fig. 2** Variation in dendrite arm spacing across (a) a continuous-cast ingot of alloy 12200 (DHP copper, see Fig. 16 and 17) and (b) a semicontinuous-cast ingot of alloy 71500 (copper nickel, 30%). (Ref 2)

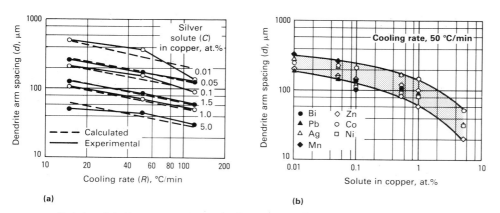

**Fig. 3** Variation of dendrite arm spacing in cast copper alloy specimens with (a) cooling rate during solidification for various amounts of silver solute and (b) amount of solute for various alloying elements (specimens solidified at the same rate). (Ref 4)

solute content also produces finer spacing. As shown in Fig. 3(a), the relationship between composition and dendrite arm spacing for copper-silver alloys is approximated by Eq 1, which was determined by curve-fitting techniques:

$$d = 306 \times R^{-0.39} \times C^{-0.31} \qquad \text{(Eq 1)}$$

where $d$ is dendrite arm spacing in microns, $R$ is the cooling rate in degrees centigrade per minute, and $C$ is silver content in atomic percent. Equations of this form, with different constants, have been shown to fit extensive data in other binary systems.

Dendritic structure also depends on the equilibrium distribution coefficient, $k_0$. Figure 3(b) illustrates that with the same cooling rate, a finer dendritic structure usually is achieved at lower solute levels in alloy systems having a low $k_0$ value, such as the copper-lead system, than in those having a higher $k_0$ value, such as the copper-cobalt system (Ref 4).

Data on dendrite arm spacing in various commercial alloys are presented in Fig. 4. Although freezing range and other solidification characteristics in these nine commercial alloys vary considerably, the data fall between two curves:

$$d = 290R^{-0.42} \qquad \text{(Eq 2)}$$

$$d = 180R^{-0.43} \qquad \text{(Eq 3)}$$

Thus, dependence of dendrite arm spacing on cooling rate is similar over a wide range of commercial alloys, despite wide variations in other characteristics of the alloy systems.

**Interpretation of Dendrite Patterns.** The dendritic structure in the columnar region of an ingot of alloy 71500, shown in Fig. 5, is typical of many copper-base and other alloy systems. Etching reveals a relatively consistent pattern of coring, or variation in local solute content within each grain. This basic pattern is produced by the intersection of the plane of polish with the randomly oriented platelike regions of equal solute concentration within the three-dimensional dendritic structure (Ref 7). The platelike regions in Fig. 5 are high in solute content, because $k_0 > 1$ for copper-rich copper-nickel alloys. Such platelike regions have low solute content in

alloys for which $k_0 < 1$, such as copper-zinc alloys. The wide variation in the angle of intersection of the plane of polish with these relatively planar regions of equal solute content leads to considerable variation in the observed dendritic pattern.

Within one cast grain, there is one crystallographic orientation, to which the dendrite structure has a definite relationship (Ref 8). In copper alloys, dendrites grow in (100) crystallographic directions and tend to develop low solute ($k_0 < 1$) concentration contours in (100) planes (Ref 9). Because grains have various orientations, their dendritic structures are intersected by the plane of polish as determined by the crystallographic orientation of the grain.

At a free, or outside surface, various orientations are apparent (Ref 10). In addition, dendrites can be bent and broken, that is, remelted at branching points. Similar effects are visible in the interiors of cast structures. These effects result in structures in which the "dendrites" no longer have one orientation; in crystal multiplication (Ref 5, 6), where new grains form from the detached dendrite arms of other grains; and in nondendritic solidification, where the dendritic structure is disrupted to the point that dendrite fragments produce a grain size equivalent to the dendrite arm spacing (Ref 11).

Disruption of dendrite structure is caused by liquid metal movement in the less extreme case of crystal multiplication. Strong agitation is required to produce the unusual structures in nondendritic solidification. A copper-base cast structure produced by semisolid processing is illustrated in Fig. 6 (Ref 12).

At the opposite end of the spectrum of disrupted dendritic growth are structures solidified in zero gravity (Ref 13) or in other environments that tend to preserve growth of specific dendritic orientations. In electromagnetic casting of copper alloys (Ref 14), casting takes place in an electromagnetic field rather than a mold. Mold contact can lead to some undesirable effects, but also tends to be the source of grains of varying orientation. Dendrites tend to grow along a free surface in the direction of heat flow. In the case of electromagnetic casting, this results in surface dendrites (and grains) that align parallel to the casting direction (Fig. 7).

The preceding discussion of dendrite structures has shown the relationship between dendritic structures and grain structure in ingots. Grains form by a dendritic growth process (with the exceptions noted below). Dendritic fragmentation or disruption changes grain size, columnar/equiaxed relationship, semisolid flow properties, and so on. Thus, factors that influence dendritic structure are significant for grain structure as well. Because dendritic structure is the result of solute redistribution (coring) during solidification, second-phase structures and homogenization are also influenced by dendrite structure, especially the characteristic dimension of solute variations (dendrite arm spacing).

**Second Phase.** Many commercially produced copper alloy ingots are basically of the single-phase solid-solution type. However, even alloys that should be single phase, such as alloy 26000 (cartridge brass, 70%), can contain nonequilibrium $\beta$ phase in interdendritic locations. A nonequilibrium second phase also occurs in ingots of alloy 52400 (phosphor bronze D), which contains 10% Sn (Ref 15).

High-zinc brasses generally contain some equilibrium $\beta$ phase. Figure 8 shows an ingot of alloy 36000 (free-cutting brass) in which $\alpha$-dendrite arms are separated by regions of $\beta$ phase. This type of microstructure is caused by cooling conditions and by the resulting grain structure in the region of equiaxed grains at the center of the ingot. In the columnar region near the surface of the same ingot (Fig. 9), the $\alpha$ dendrites are more uniformly distributed in the structure. In addition, the $\beta$ phase is not concentrated, but has formed in close association with the $\alpha$ dendrites.

Gross macrosegregation is observed in certain alloys, especially those with long freezing ranges. The result can be solute enrichment, or depletion, which produces compositions having unusual second phases. An example is direct-chill cast alloy 19400, shown in Fig. 10; compare this to the electromagnetic-cast ingot surface shown in Fig 7.

Segregation between grains is a form of macrosegregation that occurs in late stages of freezing as solute-rich liquid fills stressed low-integrity grain boundaries. This problem is most apparent in alloys with a long freezing range, such as alloys with substantial tin, phosphorus, or lead. One recent approach to solving this problem is application of electromagnetic stirring to refine grain size (Ref 16) in copper-base alloys. Similar successful application of electromagnetic stirring has solved problems in steel ingot "hot tear" segregation (Ref 17).

**Homogenization** variously affects different copper alloys. Coring in brass often is eliminated unintentionally during high-tem-

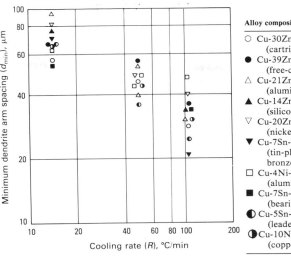

| Alloy composition | Minimum dendrite arm spacing, um, for cooling rates, °C/min (°F/min) of: | | |
|---|---|---|---|
| | 15 (27) | 50 (90) | 120 (216) |
| ○ Cu-30Zn (cartridge brass) ......58 | | 46 | 29.5 |
| ● Cu-39Zn-3Pb (free-cutting brass) ....64 | | 57 | 36 |
| △ Cu-21Zn-2Al (aluminum brass) .....94 | | 56 | 32 |
| ▲ Cu-14Zn-4Si (silicon brass).........79 | | 40 | 35 |
| ▽ Cu-20Zn-18Ni (nickel silver)........82 | | 53 | 40 |
| ▼ Cu-7Sn-0.3P (tin-phosphorus bronze) ..............73 | | 44 | 23 |
| □ Cu-4Ni-10Al-4Fe (aluminum bronze) ....62 | | 53 | 50 |
| ■ Cu-7Sn-5Pb (bearing alloy) ........57 | | 45 | 35 |
| ◑ Cu-5Sn-5Zn-5Pb (leaded red brass) .....64 | | 37 | 26.5 |
| ◐ Cu-10Ni-1.3Fe-0.7Mn (copper nickel) .......63 | | 45 | 32 |

**Fig. 4** Minimum dendrite arm spacing as a function of cooling rate for 10 commercial alloys. Higher cooling rates result in smaller dendrite arm spacing.

**Fig. 5** Alloy 71500 (copper nickel, 30%) ingot. Dendritic structure in the columnar region of the ingot shows coring (variation in solute concentration). The light areas are nickel-rich; the dark areas are low in nickel. Waterbury reagent. 20×

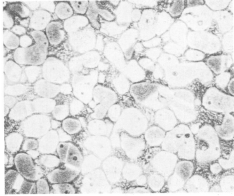

**Fig. 6** Alloy 36000 (free-cutting brass), semisolid formed. Large grains originate from solid material present before casting; the remainder of the structure was solidified more rapidly to produce the structure shown. NH₄OH, H₂O₂, and H₂O. 155×. (K.P. Young)

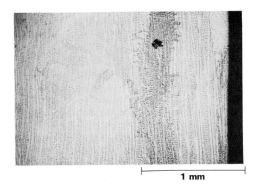

1 mm

**Fig. 7** Alloy 19400 produced by mold-free electromagnetic casting. Surface dendrites are aligned parallel to the casting direction. Compare with Fig. 10. Equal parts saturated NH₄OH, H₂O₂, and H₂O. 25×. (D. Tyler)

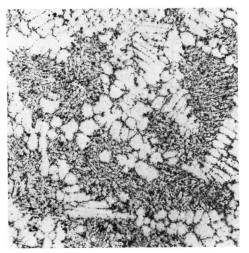

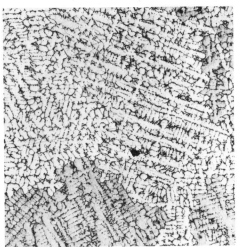

**Fig. 8, 9** Alloy 36000 (free-cutting brass), semicontinuous cast. Dendritic structure in specimens from two locations in the ingot. Fig. 8: mixed structure of $\alpha$ dendrites (light) and $\beta$ phase (dark) at the center of the ingot. Fig. 9: uniform distribution of $\alpha$ dendrites (light) with interdendritic $\beta$ phase (dark) near the surface of the ingot. NH₄OH + H₂O₂. 30×

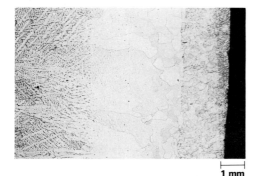

**Fig. 10** Alloy 19400, direct-chill cast. Inverse segregation (a high level of solute at the surface of the ingot) has produced a nondendritic structure at the surface (right). Compare with Fig. 7. Same etchant as Fig. 7. 5×. (D. Tyler)

perature fabrication or even slow cooling of a large ingot after casting (Ref 18). However, coring persists in most cast ingots of copper-nickel alloys. Figure 11 shows segregation in the equiaxed zone at the center of an alloy 71500 direct-chill semicontinuous-cast ingot (Ref 2). Also shown are the results of a microprobe traverse across the section. The dark-etching copper-rich areas illustrated in this micrograph reach copper concentrations of 80%; in the less heavily cored regions near the surface of the ingot (not shown in the micrograph), the maximum copper content was 75%.

High rates of solidification produce fine dendrite arm spacing; such a structure homogenizes more quickly than a coarse dendritic structure. Rapid cooling after solidification reduces the time available for homogenization. Rapid solidification followed by slow cooling can result in a degree of coring very different from that resulting from slow solidification followed by rapid cooling. This accounts for the wide variation in degree of homogenization found in the structure of as-cast ingots of the same alloy.

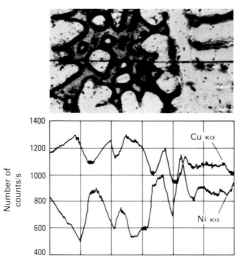

**Fig. 11** Alloy 71500 (copper nickel, 30%) ingot, direct-chill semicontinuous cast. Microprobe record of solute distribution in the equiaxed zone of the ingot. 8 mL $HNO_3$, 15 mL $H_2SO_4$, 5 mL HCl, 5 g $FeCl_3$, and 145 mL $H_2O$, then Waterbury reagent. 85×

Some solutes, such as nickel, diffuse more slowly in copper at casting and working temperatures than other solutes, such as zinc (Ref 2).

**Rapid solidification technology** is evolving from a subject of considerable academic interest to a technology with great promise in some applications. Figure 12 shows the range of cooling rates under consideration, which may be compared to cooling rates in Fig. 1. At rapid cooling rates, alloys can be produced with microcrystalline or even glassy structures. For example, Cu-50Zr has a glass transition temperature of 480 °C (895 °F) (Ref 19). Very fine grain structure can be produced from a glass.

Other advantages of rapid solidification include reduced chemical segregation, fine grain microstructure, uniform distribution of very fine precipitates, increased tolerance for

residual elements, and extended solid solubilities for solutes as compared to expectations based on equilibrium phase diagrams (Ref 20). An example of a rapidly solidified Cu-Zn-Al alloy is presented in Fig. 13. Possible applications for various alloy systems produced by rapid solidification are listed in Table 1. Although opportunities for applying this technology are numerous, processing technology will require dedicated effort. It is likely that applications will be unrelated to most products made from more conventional copper ingot processing.

## Grains

Typical grain structures that occur in continuous-cast ingots, static-cast ingots, and continuous-cast wirebars of various copper alloys are discussed in the following paragraphs. Proper procedures for the investigation of these grain structures are indicated.

**Grain Structure in Continuous-Cast Ingots.** Figures 14 and 15 show a transverse section and a longitudinal section of a continuous-cast ingot of alloy 12200 (DHP copper). The sections illustrated in Fig. 16 and 17 are from this same ingot. In the transverse section, the grains are essentially radial from the surface to the center. Care was taken to cut the longitudinal section exactly through the center of the ingot. The black line at the middle of the longitudinal section is a columnar grain oriented along the axis of the ingot; this grain is barely discernible in the transverse section. As is typical of relatively pure copper, the grain boundaries are sharply defined.

Figure 18 is a schematic approximation of the freezing front in the continuous process used for casting the ingot in Fig. 14 and 15. At the surface of the ingot, the interface advances approximately at right angles to the mold wall; at the center of the ingot, the interface advances along the axis of the ingot. Columnar grains usually develop with a pre-

**Table 1 Advantages of rapidly solidified copper alloys**

| Alloy system | Comments |
|---|---|
| Cu-Al | Enhanced mechanical properties; superplasticity |
| Cu-Zr | Amorphous; enhanced mechanical properties |
| Cu-Fe | Enhanced mechanical properties; (low-cost additive) |
| Cu-Be | Enhanced mechanical properties |
| Cu-Be + (Zr, Cr, Mg, Ni, Ti) | Combination of high strength and high thermal conductivity |
| Cu-Pb | Enhanced lubrication |
| Cu-Cr | Hot hardness; high strength and electrical conductivity |
| Cu-Ga, Cu-Si, Cu-Ge, Cu-Sn | Enhanced mechanical properties; strength and ductility |
| Cu-Ti, Cu-Zr, Cu-40Zr-10Fe | Very low (~0) magnetoresistance |
| Cu-Zr-P | Amorphous; enhanced corrosion resistance |

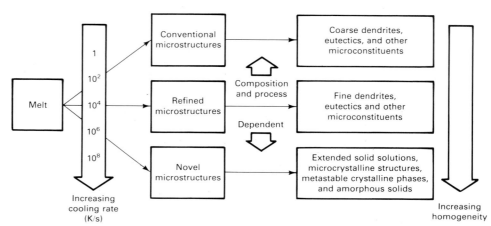

**Fig. 12** The effect of cooling rate on microstructure. Rapid solidification increases homogeneity and results in microcrystalline or glassy structures. Classifications are approximate and depend on composition and processing as well as cooling rate. (R. Carbonara)

ferred crystal orientation in the direction of heat flow and with the grain boundaries parallel to this direction (Ref 8).

In the structure shown in Fig. 15, the grain boundaries near the center of the ingot do not follow the isotherms during growth, but continue parallel to the crystal direction established near the surface, that is, at the start of growth. The longitudinal center grain is an exception. At the very center of the ingot, a grain can grow continuously and still maintain a constant orientation of its direction of growth.

As noted earlier in discussing electromagnetic casting, dendrites at the surface can also

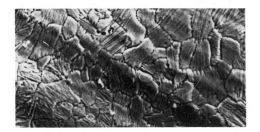

**Fig. 13** Scanning electron micrograph of Cu-24.3Zn-9Al (at. %) alloy, rapidly solidified by melt spinning. Beta-phase grain size is very fine, and the structure shows no evidence of segregation. As-polished. 950×. (J. Perkins)

**Fig. 14, 15** Alloy 12200 (DHP copper), continuous cast in a 102-mm (4-in.) diam ingot. Fig. 14: transverse section. Fig. 15: longitudinal section. Columnar grains are oriented along the axis. See also Fig. 25 and 26. Waterbury reagent. 0.6×

grow parallel to the casting direction along the ingot surface. Because the start of freezing is a discontinuity in the freezing front, there are two preferred growth directions—one in the casting direction and one approximately perpendicular to the freezing front. This is true at all mold and chill surfaces and explains the appearance of branched dendrites at chill surfaces as well as their absence in the interior of lightly alloyed castings (Ref 21).

A notable feature of DHP copper ingots is the relationship between grain structure and dendritic structure. The unbranched dendrites characteristic of this alloy are not effective sources of detached arms, which would form new equiaxed grains (Ref 22). As a result, the internal structure of DHP copper ingots is completely columnar. However, the chill surface structure is branched dendritic. Therefore, grain refinement at the chill surface is possible, for example, by stirring at the start-of-freezing position (Ref 23).

The influence of dendrite structure on grain structure is demonstrated by the differing effects of different solute element additions on the change from columnar to equiaxed solidification. A higher concentration of elements produces a result similar to a low partition coefficient. This follows the same trend as reported in aluminum (Ref 24), which is explained by the influence of alloying elements on dendritic branching and therefore crystal multiplication. Table 2 summarizes the possibilities for crystal multiplication at the surface and interior of ingots, depending on the dendritic structure.

**Grain Structure in Static-Cast Ingots.** Figures 19 and 20 show transverse and longitudinal sections of a static-cast ingot of alloy 36000 (free-cutting brass). In the transverse section, the structure appears completely equiaxed, with finer grains at the edge and coarser grains at the center. In the longitudinal section, columnar grains are visible that extend for almost half the radius toward the center of the ingot. This demonstrates the importance of orientation of the macrosection in providing an accurate representation of grain structure; the transverse section is clearly misleading. In the transverse section

**Table 2** The effect of dendrite structure on crystal multiplication

| | "Low" solute | "High" solute |
|---|---|---|
| Surface of ingot ... | Branched dendrites Crystal multiplication possible | Branched dendrites Crystal multiplication possible |
| Interior of ingot ... | Unbranched dendrites No crystal multiplication | Branched dendrites Crystal multiplication possible |

and the longitudinal section, close examination shows concentric rings of relatively fine, equiaxed grains within the zone of columnar grains. These fine grains are formed from dendrite arms that are detached by convection during solidification, such as the convection caused by afterpouring to prevent top-pipe formation. Marked variation in local grain size is a typical condition in alloys in which the dendrite arms are branched. Branched dendrites are an effective source of detached arms for the formation of new equiaxed grains (Ref 6).

**Grain Structure in Wirebars.** Figure 21 shows a transverse section through a wirebar of tough-pitch (level-set) copper, which contains approximately 0.04% O. Measurements of dendrite arm spacing indicate the minimal correlation between grain size and dendrite spacing (Ref 25). Interpretation of complex structures of this kind must consider heat loss from the open (top) surface and to the mold as well as the movement of partially formed (dendritic) grains during ingot solidification. Structures rather different from that shown in Fig. 21 are seen in "wirebar" produced by continuous casting processes such as the wheel-and-belt or Hazelett twin-belt methods. Figures 22 and 23 illustrate the grain structure produced in a continuous-cast wirebar (Ref 26). In this copper alloy having only

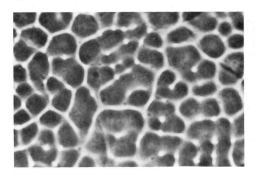 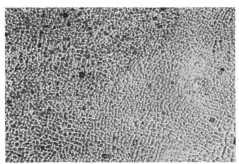

**Fig. 16, 17** Same alloy and processing as Fig. 14 and 15. Fig. 16: section normal to the direction of columnar growth taken from near the surface of the ingot. The structure is coarse, unbranched dendrites. Fig. 17: longitudinal section taken from near the center of the ingot. Dendrite spacing is much finer than in Fig. 16. Waterbury reagent. 150×

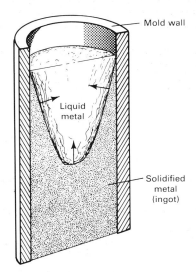

**Fig. 18** The freezing front during continuous casting of a copper alloy ingot. Arrows are normal to the liquid-solid interface and show the freezing direction.

**Fig. 19, 20** Alloy 36000 (free-cutting brass), static-cast 203-mm (8-in.) diam ingot. Fig. 19: transverse section. Fig. 20: longitudinal section. Columnar grains extend nearly halfway to the center of the ingot. Boiling 20% $HNO_3$ + 20% acetic acid. $0.3 \times$

**Fig. 21** Alloy 11000 (ETP copper) wirebar. Transverse section shows a pattern of coarse and fine grains. 50% $HNO_3$ + 50% $H_2O$. $0.6 \times$

**Fig. 22, 23** The effect of casting temperature on continuous-cast copper wirebar. Fig. 22: cast at 1150 °C (2100 °F). Fig. 23: cast at 1120 °C (2050 °F). The higher casting temperature produced a coarser grain structure in the ingot. Etchant not reported. $0.4 \times$. (Metallurgie Hoboken-Overpelt and Hazelett Strip-Casting Corp.)

150 to 200 ppm oxygen, grain size can be varied greatly primarily by changing the casting temperature. Lower casting temperature allows the solid fragments produced by crystal multiplication to survive as the nuclei of new grains. Although grain structure is more uniform, the main improvement in the cast structure of continuous-cast processes for wire rod is control of oxygen content. In static-cast wire bar, the set surface absorbs oxygen from the air. By contrast, continuous-cast wire bar has oxides distributed evenly throughout the cross section. In addition, because feeding of shrinkage in continuous casting differs from static casting, good results are obtained at lower oxygen contents.

## Ingot Defects

Defects in ingots are regarded as those nonuniform features of the structure that usually are the direct cause of rejections during subsequent working. Examples of ingot defects are macrosegregation, inclusions, unsoundness, and cracks originating from thermal stresses or frictional forces.

**Thermal-Stress Cracking.** Longitudinal surface cracks are common in ingots fabricated with poor control conditions (leaving a hot spot). This type of crack is illustrated in Fig. 24. Center cracks, which are also called spider cracks, may form in an ingot that has excessive cooling at the end of solidification combined with intergranular segregation that weakens the grain boundaries.

Dye-penetrant indications of center cracks in such an ingot of alloy 12200 (DHP copper) are shown in transverse and longitudinal sections in Fig. 25 and 26. Etched sections through the same continuous-cast 102-mm (4-in.) diam ingot are shown in Fig. 14 and 15. The cracks, which were not readily visible in the etched cast structure, are easily discernible by dye-penetrant inspection of the transverse section (Fig. 25); the severity of the cracks is further revealed by inspection of the longitudinal section (Fig. 26). Even more

sensitive is a freon leak test of a wafer or a fracture test of suspect material, followed by scanning electron microscopy (SEM) of the fracture surface. Separation during fracture of solids is easily differentiated from solidification cracks.

Fine, intergranular cracking may occur in the center of ingots having equiaxed grains in the center region. This type of cracking is illustrated in Fig. 27, which shows an ingot of alloy 36000 (free-cutting brass). The cracking discussed to this point results from the thermal stresses of solidification.

**Transverse Defects.** Transverse cracking is common in continuous-cast ingots. The mechanism of formation of these cracks, called witness marks, has been explained (Ref 27). Surface cold shuts, another transverse

defect, are illustrated in Fig. 28 and 29. Cold shuts and similar surface defects often result from low casting speed (Ref 28). Figure 30 shows hot tears at the grain boundaries and between dendrite cells in an ingot of low-oxygen, high-purity copper. Even in high-purity material, some segregation of solute can occur during solidification, weakening the grain boundaries and leading to hot tears (Ref 1). Solutes at a level of 1 ppm can segregate to very high levels at grain boundaries (Ref 29). This is a result of solute redistribution during solidification combined with favorable energetics for solute buildup at grain boundaries at the atomic level and is best determined by Auger analysis of fracture surfaces.

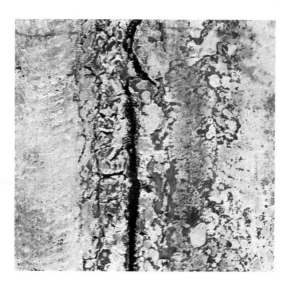

**Fig. 24** Alloy 36000 (free-cutting brass) semicontinuous cast in a 254-mm (10-in.) diam ingot. A longitudinal crack in the surface of the ingot. Severe macrosegregation can accompany cracks of this type. See also Fig. 39. Not polished, not etched. Actual size

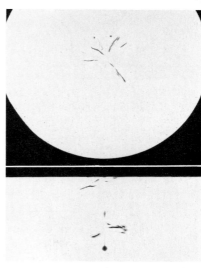

**Fig. 25, 26** Spider cracks in the center of the ingot in Fig. 14 and 15. Fig. 25: transverse section. Fig. 26: longitudinal section. Dye penetrant. Approximately $0.5 \times$

**Fig. 27** Same alloy and processing as Fig. 24, showing fine intergranular cracks in the region of equiaxed grains at the center of the ingot. $HNO_3 + H_2O$ at 60 °C (140 °F). 4×

**Fig. 28** Alloy 36000 (free-cutting brass), slowly poured semicontinuous-cast ingot showing cold shuts on the surface of the ingot. Cold shuts often result from low casting speeds. See also Fig. 29. Not polished, not etched. 0.25×. (Ref 28)

**Unsoundness.** Gas that evolved during solidification can result in diverse structural features, including those that clearly constitute defects. The gas is evolved because of its lower solubility in the solid metal than in the liquid phase.

Unsoundness in semicontinuous-cast ingots is usually nonuniform (Ref 2). Shrinkage cavities near the surface of an ingot of alloy 71500 (copper nickel, 30%) are revealed by microradiography (Fig. 31), but not by optical microscopy (Fig. 32). The gross unsoundness at the center of the ingot, which is the result of microshrinkage and gas evolution, is shown in Fig. 33. Usually, gas evolution and microshrinkage result in a higher percentage of porosity in the more slowly cooled central region of the ingot than in the rapidly frozen outer regions (Ref 30).

**Macrosegregation.** A common type of segregation is macrosegregation, which results from the interdendritic flow of solute-enriched liquid (Ref 31). The variation in tin concentration in a cast slab of tin bronze (8% Sn) is illustrated in Fig. 34. A higher level of solute at the surface is often observed and is termed inverse segregation.

Figure 35 shows a high percentage of an intermetallic tin-rich phase near the bottom surface of an ingot of tin bronze having 5% Sn (Ref 1). The surface layer of tin-rich phase that is nearly pure tin presumably was formed by exudation. The exudation results from the flow of solute-enriched, interdendritic liquid out of the surface region of the casting during the late stages of solidification.

An example of extreme segregation in alloy 36000 (free-cutting brass) is presented in Fig. 36. The segregate is greatly enriched in zinc. Replacing the cover of carbon powder formerly used in casting brass (Fig. 36) with a light glass cover (supplied as proprietary formulations) prevents vaporization of zinc.

Severe macrosegregation can accompany ingot cracks caused by thermal stresses. Figure 37 shows the region adjacent to the longitudinal surface crack in an ingot of alloy 36000 (free-cutting brass) shown in Fig. 24.

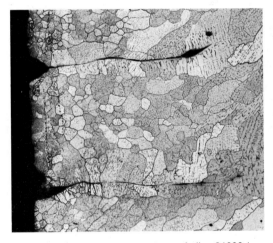

**Fig. 29** Semicontinuous-cast ingot of alloy 26000 (cartridge brass). Longitudinal section through cold shuts on the surface of the ingot (left). See also Fig. 28. Etchant not reported. 6×. (Ref 28)

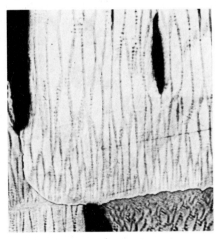

**Fig. 30** Low-oxygen, high-purity copper ingot, with hot tears (black) at grain boundaries and between dendrite cells. Some segregation of solute occurs even in high-purity materials and can weaken grain boundaries and hot tears. Alcoholic $FeCl_3$. 60×. (Ref 1)

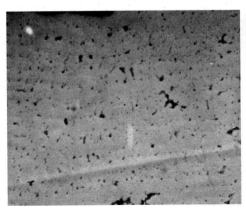
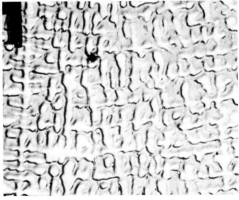
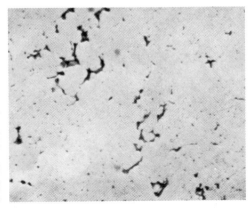

**Fig. 31, 32, 33** Alloy 71500 (copper nickel, 30%), semicontinuous cast in a 229-mm (9-in.) diam ingot. Fig. 31: shrinkage porosity in the ingot is revealed by microradiography. Fig. 32: the same section, but optical microscopy does not reveal the interdendritic shrinkage cavities. Fig. 33: specimen from near the center of the ingot. The pores are larger than in Fig. 31. Fig. 31 and 33: as-polished. Fig. 32: Waterbury reagent. All 50×. (Ref 1)

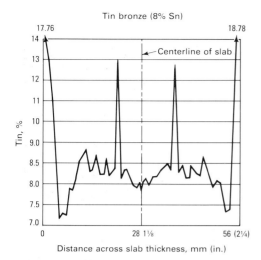

Tin bronze (8% Sn)

**Fig. 34** Variation in tin content across a 56-mm (2.25-in.) thick slab of tin bronze (8% Sn). See also Fig. 35 and Fig. 10. (Ref 32)

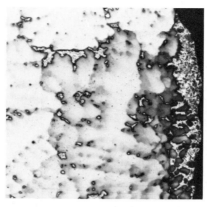

**Fig. 35** Horizontal cast strip of tin bronze (5% Sn), showing inverse segregation at the bottom surface of the casting (right). The surface layer is nearly pure tin. 40 mL HNO₃, 25 g CrO₃, and 35 mL H₂O. 100×. (Ref 1)

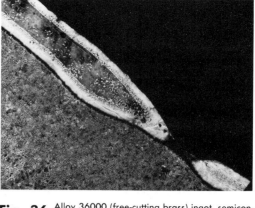

**Fig. 36** Alloy 36000 (free-cutting brass) ingot, semicontinuous cast. Zinc-rich "smudges" on the surface (top left to bottom right) are the result of condensation, on the mold wall, of zinc vapor trapped by the layer of carbon powder covering the melt. This problem has been solved by the use of proprietary glass covers that prevent zinc evaporation and recondensation. NH₄OH + H₂O₂. 10×

The light areas have a high coefficient of x-ray absorption and have been identified as lead rich.

Macrosegregation can also result from other mechanisms, such as the reaction of two elements to form an undesirable stable solid constituent in the melt; the constituent agglomerates during melting and often is nonuniformly distributed in the casting. Such constituents having high melting points are usually hard and brittle and thus undesirable. Figure 38 illustrates inclusions in a brass alloy of high tensile strength; this alloy contained 2% Fe (Ref 33). The inclusions formed when 0.01% Si was added to the melt.

**Effects of Defects on Fabrication.** In some instances, relationships between ingot structure and success of fabrication are clearly established. For example, segregation caused by exudation will persist into the fabricated structure, as shown in Fig. 39. Another example is the extrusion defect of the type presented in Fig. 40 and 41; this defect can result when longitudinal surface cracks in the ingot flow inward during extrusion.

Advantages claimed for electromagnetic casting include better surface after hot rolling in material free of inverse segregation (Ref 12). Similarly, edge condition after hot or cold reduction is better when the casting is free of surface defects, which induce edge cracking in hot and cold rolling. Figures 42 and 43 illustrate the edges of alloy 63800 ingots after hot rolling to a total of 80% reduction. The edge rolled from an ingot without surface defects (Fig. 42) is in much better condition than the edge rolled from an ingot with surface defects (Fig. 43).

## REFERENCES

1. A. Cibula, Review of Metallurgical Factors Influencing the Quality of Copper and Copper Alloy Castings, BNFMRA International Conference on the Control of the Composition and Quality of Copper and Copper Alloy Castings for Fabrication, Düsseldorf, Oct 1967
2. D.A. Granger and T.F. Bower, Techniques for the Interpretation of Cast Structures in Two Semi-Continuous Cast Copper Alloys, *J. Inst. Met.*, Vol 98, 1970, p 353
3. L. Backerud and L.M. Liljenvall, *Copper and Its Alloys*, Monograph and Report Series No. 34, Institute of Metals, London, 1970, p 65
4. L. Backerud and L.M. Liljenvall, "The Solidification Characteristics of 7 Constitutionally Different Types of Binary Copper Alloys," INCRA Project 165, Swedish Institute for Metals Research, Stockholm, 1971
5. M.C. Flemings, *Solidification Processing*, McGraw-Hill, 1974
6. W. Kurtz and D.J. Fisher, *Fundamentals of Solidification*, Trans Tech Publications, 1984
7. L. Backerud and L.M. Liljenvall, "The Solidification Characteristics of 12 Commercial Copper-Base Alloys," INCRA Report 165A, Swedish Institute for Metals Research, Stockholm, 1973
8. B. Chalmers, *Principles of Solidification*, John Wiley & Sons, 1964

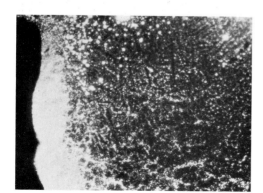

**Fig. 37** Alloy 36000 (free-cutting brass) ingot. A microradiograph of a thin section taken from an area near the longitudinal crack in the specimen shown in Fig. 24. Light areas are lead rich. As-polished. 50×

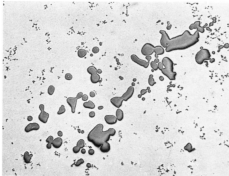

**Fig. 38** Cu-37Zn-2Al-2Fe alloy, showing globular inclusions of a hard, iron-rich constituent that precipitated after the addition of 0.01% Si to the melt. The specimen is from a sample quenched from the top of the melt. As-polished. 40×. (Ref 33)

**Fig. 39** Phosphor bronze strip rolled from a static-cast ingot, showing gross tin sweat on the surface (top). Illustrates how segregation caused by exudation persists in the fabricated structure. Etchant not reported. 300×. (Ref 34)

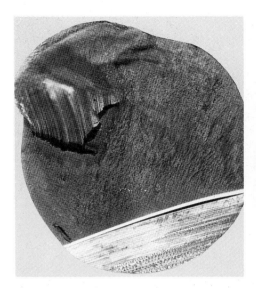

**Fig. 40** Alloy 36000 (free-cutting brass) extrusion. Transverse fracture shows internal cracks, which are associated with a pipe, or extrusion, defect. See also Fig. 41. Not polished, not etched. 1.4×. (P. Yaffe and J. Dibee)

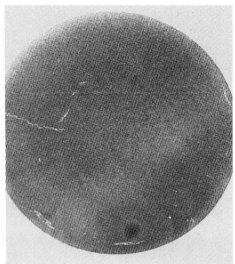

**Fig. 41** Same specimen as Fig. 40. Polished and etched transverse section shows internal cracks, which result when longitudinal surface cracks in the ingot flow inward during extrusion. 50 mL HNO₃ + 50 mL acetic acid. 1.4×. (P. Yaffe and J. Dibee)

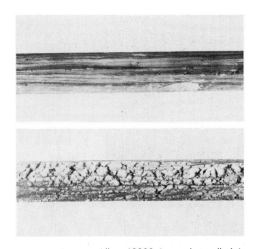

**Fig. 42, 43** Alloy 63800 ingot, hot rolled in several passes to 80% total reduction. Fig. 42: the edge was rolled from an ingot without inverse segregation. Fig 43: the edge was rolled from an ingot with inverse segregation. (D. Tyler)

9. L. Northcott, *J. Inst. Met.*, Vol 73, 1946, p 283-291
10. T.F. Bower and M.C. Flemings, Structure of Dendrites at Chill Surfaces, *Trans. AIME*, Vol 239, 1967, p 1620
11. M.C. Flemings, R.C. Rick, and K.P. Young, Rheocasting, *Mater. Sci. Eng.*, Vol 25, 1976, p 103-117
12. K.P. Young, private communication, ITT Engineered Metals Process Co., St. Louis, 1985
13. V.S. Zemskov, I.H. Belokurova, A.A. Babareko, V.V. Savytchev, and N.F. Boskanova, *J. Cryst. Growth*, Vol 60, Nov 1982, p 89-90
14. D.E. Tyler, Electromagnetic Casting of Copper Alloys, Paper 22, Copper '83, The Metals Society and Copper Development Association, London, Nov 1983
15. A. Butts, Ed., *Copper*, Hafner, 1970 (facsimile of the 1959 edition), p 879
16. D.S. Calvert, private communication, BNF Metals Technology Center, Wantage, U.K., 1985
17. J.J. Moore, The Application of Electromagnetic Stirring (EMS) in the Continuous Casting of Steel, in *Continuous Casting*, Vol 3, Iron and Steel Society of AIME, Warrendale, PA, 1984
18. H.D. Brody and M.C. Flemings, Solute Redistribution in Dendritic Solidification, *Trans. AIME*, Vol 236, 1966, p 615
19. H. Jones, *Rapid Solidification of Metals and Alloys*, The Institution of Metallurgists, London, 1984
20. R.J. Carbonara, private communication, 1985; see also INCRA Planning Study PR10, Battelle Columbus Laboratories, Columbus, OH, 1985
21. T.F. Bower, Dendrite Structure in Unidirectional Solidification, master's thesis, Massachusetts Institute of Technology, 1962
22. R.T. Southin, *Trans. AIME*, Vol 242, 1968, p 2240
23. T.F. Bower and M.C. Flemings, Formation of the Chill Zone in Ingot Solidification, *Trans. AIME*, Vol 239, 1967, p 216
24. L.A. Tarshis, J.L. Walker, and J.W. Rutter, Experiments in the Solidification Structure of Alloy Castings, *Met. Trans.*, Vol 2, 1971, p 2589
25. J. McCloskey and H. Popps, Solidification of Electrolytic Tough Pitch Copper, *Wire J. Int.*, Oct 1970
26. J.M.A. Dompas, J.G. Smets, and J.R. Schoofs, Continuous Casting and Rolling of Copper Rod at the M.H. Olin Copper Refinery, *Wire J. Int.*, Sept 1974; C.J. Petry, Use of the Hazelett Twin-Belt Mold for Continuous Casting of Copper, Paper No. 78-19, TMS Paper Selection
27. *Continuous Casting of Steel*, Proceedings of the 2nd Process Technology Conference, Vol 2, American Institute of Mining, Metallurgical, and Petroleum Engineers, Warrendale, PA, Feb 1981
28. H. Beissner, The Need for Non-Destructive Testing of Cast Slabs and Billets, BNFMRA International Conference on the Control of the Composition and Quality of Copper and Copper Alloy Castings for Fabrication, Düsseldorf, Germany, Oct 1967
29. R.W. Bulluffi, Grain Boundary Structures and Segregation, in *Interfacial Segregation*, American Society for Metals, 1979
30. C.E. Ransley and D.E.J. Talbot, Hydrogen Porosity in Metals, With Special Reference to Aluminum and Its Alloys, *Z. Metallk.*, Vol 46, 1955, p 328
31. M.C. Flemings and R. Mehrabian, Segregation in Castings and Ingots, in *Solidification*, 1969 Seminar, American Society for Metals, 1970
32. A. Krell, H. Vosskühler, and K. Walter, The Continuous Casting of Copper and Its Alloys, *Met. Rev.*, Vol 5, 1950, p 413
33. D.A. Hudson, Iron-Rich Spots Formed by Silicon and Boron in Brasses, *J. Inst. Met.*, Vol 92, 1963-64, p 280
34. G.L. Bailey and W.A. Baker, *Melting and Casting of Non-Ferrous Metals*, Monograph and Report Series No. 6, Institute of Metals, London, 1949

# Structures Resulting From Precipitation From Solid Solution

By William A. Soffa
Professor of Metallurgical
and Materials Engineering
University of Pittsburgh

PRECIPITATION REACTIONS that occur in the solid state and the resulting microstructures are discussed in this article. This transformation generally produces a phase mixture from an initial supersaturated phase during aging. The resultant phases consist of a matrix whose crystal structure is similar to that of the parent phase, but has a different composition and usually a different lattice parameter as well as a precipitate that may differ in crystal structure, composition, and/ or degree of long-range order. The physical, chemical, and mechanical properties of the two-phase alloy can vary markedly with the nature, size, shape, and distribution of the precipitate phase in the microstructure. This is the fundamental basis for the age hardening treatment of commercial alloys in which controlled precipitation from solid solution is used to enhance engineering properties for various applications.

Phase diagram configurations that give rise to precipitation reactions are illustrated in Fig. 1. The heat treatment of an age-hardening alloy often consists of (1) solution treatment (solutionizing) to produce a homogeneous solid solution, (2) quenching to room temperature to retain a supersaturated solid solution, and (3) reheating to an intermediate temperature to precipitate the second phase within the matrix. Thermomechanical processing, which involves cold working the as-quenched alloy before aging, is sometimes used. The deformation can affect the subsequent precipitation reaction kinetics and modify the resultant properties through the influence of the strain hardening of the matrix. Quenching directly to the aging temperature also can influence the kinetics and reaction path controlling decomposition of the supersaturated parent phase.

The distribution of phases and precipitate morphologies that evolve during a precipitation reaction is controlled by the processes of nucleation, growth, and coarsening and by the competition among them. Nucleation produces the first aggregates of the new phase that grow spontaneously and begin to relieve the supersaturation of the parent matrix. Nucleation is fundamentally a fluctuation phenomenon whose rate is controlled by the density of sites at which nuclei can develop, the work required to form a critical nucleus, and the rate of atomic migration.

The nucleation barrier controlling the formation of a second phase depends on the interfacial energy and strain energy of the "critical nucleus." The nucleus shape essentially establishes a compromise between these factors. Precipitates often nucleate with a special crystallographic relationship with respect to the parent phase primarily to allow low-energy interfaces to develop at least at some orientations of the interphase boundary (see Table 1).

Nucleation can occur uniformly through-

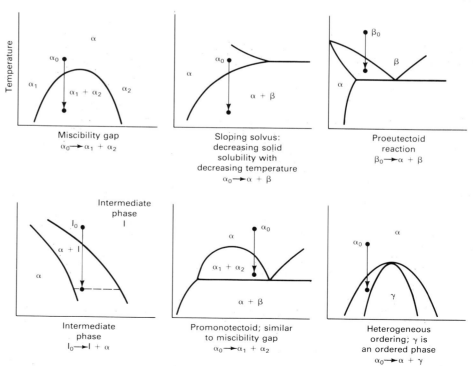

**Fig. 1** Phase diagrams giving rise to precipitation reactions

out the supersaturated matrix (homogeneous nucleation) or preferentially at specific sites (heterogeneous nucleation), such as grain boundaries or dislocations. Preferential nucleation occurs at structural irregularities that catalyze nucleation by decreasing the work required to create a critical nucleus; however, the rate of heterogeneous nucleation is limited by the density of these irregularities.

The subsequent growth of the precipitate requires diffusion of solute toward or away from the precipitate/matrix interface. The rate of diffusion-controlled growth may be determined by mass transport within the matrix (volume diffusion) or by transport along short-circuit paths, such as grain boundaries or interphase interfaces. Despite the requirement for solute diffusion in the matrix, the rate of advance of the interface may be controlled by mechanisms operating within the interface—ledge formation or migration, for example. This latter aspect of precipitate growth can help determine the kinetics and the morphology of the evolving second-phase particles. This is important, because various types of interfaces with different migration characteristics can develop between the precipitate and matrix, depending on their "mismatch."

The types of interphase boundaries are depicted in Fig. 2. A coherent interface (Fig. 2a and 2b) is characterized by atomic matching at the boundary and a continuity of lattice planes, although a small mismatch between the crystal lattices can lead to coherency strains (Fig. 2c). Coherent interfaces have a relatively low interfacial energy that typically ranges from 50 to 200 ergs/cm² (0.05 to 0.2 J/m²). An incoherent interface (Fig. 2e and 2f) is an interphase boundary that results when the matrix and precipitate have very different crystal structures and little or no atomic matching can occur across the interface. The boundary is essentially a high-angle grain boundary characterized by a relatively high energy ($\simeq$500 to 1000 ergs/cm², or 0.5 to 1.0 J/m²). Semicoherent interfaces (Fig. 2d) represent an intermediate case in which it becomes energetically favorable to relax partially the coherency strains, which would develop if perfect matching occurred across the boundary by introducing an array of misfit dislocations. These interfaces, which are characterized by regions of good fit punctuated by dislocations that accommodate some of the disregistry, have energies from 200 to 500 ergs/cm² (0.2 to 0.5 J/m²). During aging, an initially coherent precipitate will tend to lose coherency as it grows beyond a critical size by nucleating misfit dislocations at the interface or by attracting matrix dislocations.

Coarsening, or Ostwald ripening, is an interfacial energy or capillarity-driven process in which larger and more stable particles grow at the expense of the smaller ones. The driving force is the decrease in the interphase interfacial energy per unit volume of the phase mixture. The solute concentration in the matrix in local equilibrium with a particle

is less for large particles; therefore, solute flows from the vicinity of the smaller particles to the larger particles. This difference in solubility generally causes particles to grow and smaller particles to shrink. During this stage of the precipitate reaction, the average particle size increases and the particle density decreases. The volume fraction, however, remains essentially constant.

## Modes of Precipitation

**General Precipitation.** The terms "continuous" and "general" precipitation have been used to describe the generally uniform appearance of second-phase particles throughout the grains of the matrix (the use of the term "continuous" here is not to be confused with the concept of a continuous transformation, such as spinodal decomposition or homogeneous ordering). This fairly uniform precipitation contrasts with the preferential or localized formation of the precipitate at certain sites, such as grain boundaries. Figures 3 and 4 show general and grain-boundary precipitation. In Fig. 5, preferential grain-boundary nucleation predominates. Preferential precipitation along slip bands (heterogeneous nucleation at dislocations) and along the grain boundaries is revealed in

the microstructure of a plastically deformed alloy in Fig. 6. The distribution of phases clearly is governed by the nucleation kinetics discussed above.

**Widmanstätten Structures.** The energetics of nucleation and the structures of migrating interphase interfaces can lead to the development of characteristic platelike or lathlike precipitates, referred to as Widmanstätten structures. Typical Widmanstätten morphologies are shown in Fig. 7 and 8. This structure almost certainly derives from the crystallographic relationship between precipitate and matrix along the habit plane of the plates. The low-energy, broad faces of the plates form during nucleation, but migration of these coherent or semicoherent boundaries during growth requires lateral motion of ledges achieved by diffusion to or from the ledge edges. These edges, or "disordered" steps, are highly mobile, and this mechanism allows the plates to thicken normal to the broad faces, thereby maintaining coherency along the habit plane. This process is illustrated in Fig. 9.

**Cellular Precipitation.** Precipitation of a second phase from a supersaturated solid solution also may occur through a reaction involving the formation of colonies, consisting

**Table 1  Crystallographic relations between precipitate and parent phases in selected alloy systems**

| Alloy system | Parent phase and lattice (a) | Precipitate phase and lattice (a) | Crystallographic relations (precipitate phase described first) |
|---|---|---|---|
| Ag-Al | Al solid solution; fcc | γ (Ag₂Al); hcp | (0001) ∥ (111), [11$\bar{2}$0] ∥ [1$\bar{1}$0] |
| | Al solid solution; fcc | γ' (transitional); hcp | (0001) ∥ (111), [11$\bar{2}$0] ∥ [1$\bar{1}$0] |
| Ag-Cu | Ag solid solution; fcc | Cu solid solution; fcc | Plates ∥ {100}; all directions ∥ |
| | Cu solid solution; fcc | Ag solid solution; fcc | Plates ∥ {111} or {100}; all directions ∥ |
| Ag-Zn | β (βAgZn); bcc | Ag solid solution; fcc | (111) ∥ (110), [1$\bar{1}$0] ∥ [1$\bar{1}$1] |
| | β (βAgZn); bcc | γ (γAg₅Zn₈); bcc | (100) ∥ (100), [010] ∥ [010] |
| Al-Cu | Al solid solution; fcc | θ (CuAl₂); bct | Plates ∥ (100); (100) ∥ (100), [011] ∥ [120] |
| | Al solid solution; fcc | θ' (transitional); tet | (001) ∥ (100), [010] ∥ [011] |
| Al-Mg | Al solid solution; fcc | β (β-Al₃Mg₂); fcc | Plates first ∥ {110}; later probably ∥ {120} |
| Al-Mg-Si | Al solid solution; fcc | Mg₂Si; fcc | Plates ∥ {100} |
| Al-Zn | Al solid solution; fcc | Nearly pure Zn; hcp | Plates ∥ {111}; (0001) ∥ {111}, [11$\bar{2}$0] ∥ <110> |
| Au-Cu (b) | Au-Cu solid solution; fcc | α''₁ (AuCu I); ord fct | (100) ∥ (100), [010] ∥ [010] |
| Be-Cu | Cu solid solution; fcc | γ₂ (γ-BeCu); ord bcc | G-P zones ∥ {100}; later γ₂ with [100] ∥ [100], [010] ∥ [011] |
| 0.4C-Fe | Austenite (γ-Fe); fcc | Ferrite (α-Fe) (proeutectoid); bcc | (110) ∥ (111), [1$\bar{1}$1] ∥ [1$\bar{1}$0] |
| 0.8C-Fe | Austenite (γ-Fe); fcc | Ferrite in pearlite; bcc | (011) ∥ (001), [1$\bar{0}$0] ∥ [100], [0$\bar{1}$1] ∥ [010] |
| | Austenite (γ-Fe); fcc | Ferrite in upper bainite; bcc | (110) ∥ (111), [1$\bar{1}$0] ∥ [$\bar{2}$11] |
| | | Ferrite in lower bainite; bcc | (110) ∥ (111), [1$\bar{1}$1] ∥ [1$\bar{1}$0] |
| 1.3C-Fe | Austenite (γ-Fe); fcc | Cementite (Fe₃C); ortho | Plates not ∥ (111); (001) Fe₃C ∥ to plane of plate |
| Co-Cu | Cu solid solution; fcc | α-Co solid solution; fcc | Plates ∥ {100}; lattice orientation same as parent matrix |
| Co-Pt (b) | Pt-Co solid solution; fcc | α'' (CoPt); ord fct | Plates ∥ {100}; all directions ∥ |
| Cu-Fe | Cu solid solution; fcc | γ-Fe (transitional); fcc | Cubes {100}; lattice orientation same as parent matrix |
| | | α-Fe; bcc | Plates ∥ {111}; lattice orientation random |
| Cu-Si | Cu solid solution; fcc | β (ζ Cu-Si); hcp | Plates ∥ {111}; (0001) ∥ (111), [11$\bar{2}$0] ∥ [1$\bar{1}$0] |
| Cu-Sn | β phase; bcc | Cu solid solution; fcc | (111) ∥ (110), [1$\bar{1}$0] ∥ [$\bar{1}$11] |
| Cu-Zn | β (CuZn); bcc | Cu solid solution; fcc | (111) ∥ (110), [1$\bar{1}$0] ∥ [$\bar{1}$11]; variable habit; plates or needles ∥ [556] |
| | β (CuZn); bcc | γ (γ-Cu₅Zn₈); ord bcc | (100) ∥ (100), [010] ∥ [010] |
| | ε (εCu-Zn); hcp | Zn solid solution; hcp | (10$\bar{1}$4) ∥ (10$\bar{1}$4), [11$\bar{2}$0] ∥ [11$\bar{2}$0] |
| Fe-N | Ferrite (α-Fe); bcc | γ₁ (Fe₄N); fcc | (112) ∥ (210) |
| Fe-P | Ferrite (α-Fe); bcc | δ (Fe₃P); bct | Plates ∥ (21,1,4) |
| Pb-Sb | Pb solid solution; fcc | Sb solid solution; rhom | (001) ∥ (111), [100] ∥ [1$\bar{1}$0] |

(a) bcc, body-centered cubic; bct, body-centered tetragonal; fcc, face-centered cubic; hcp, hexagonal close-packed; ord bcc, ordered body-centered cubic; ord fct, ordered face-centered tetragonal; ortho, orthorhombic; rhom, rhombohedral; tet, tetragonal. (b) Ordering transformation

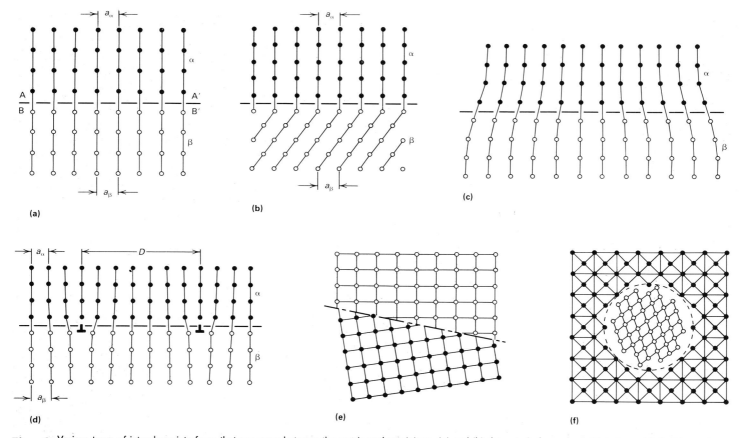

**Fig. 2** Various types of interphase interfaces that can occur between the matrix and precipitate. (a) and (b) show strain-free coherent interfaces; (c) depicts a coherent interface with a slight mismatch leading to coherency strains. (d) shows a semicoherent interface with regions of good fit and an array of misfit dislocations of spacing *D*. (e) and (f) depict incoherent interphase boundaries. (Ref 1)

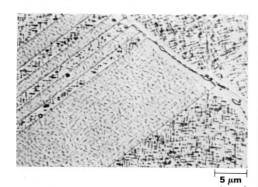

**Fig. 3** General and grain-boundary precipitation of Co₃Ti (γ' phase) precipitation in a Co-12Fe-6Ti alloy aged 3 × 10³ min at 800 °C (1470 °F). A slightly denuded or precipitate-free zone is noticeable in the vicinity of the grain boundary. The straight line segments in the micrograph are annealing twin boundaries. Etchant not reported. 1260×. (J.W. Shilling)

**Fig. 4** General precipitation (intragranular Widmanstätten) and localized grain-boundary precipitation in Al-18Ag alloy aged 90 h at 375 °C (710 °F). A distinct precipitate-free zone is evident near the grain boundaries. These regions arise from solute or vacancy depletion adjacent to the boundaries. 0.5% HF. 500×. (J.B. Clark)

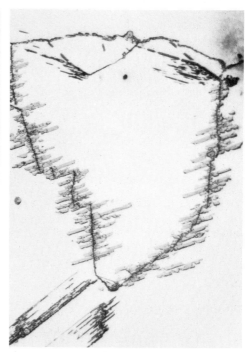

**Fig. 5** Preferential or localized precipitation along the grain boundaries in Nimonic 80A (Ni-20Cr-1Al). 35 mL HCl, 65 mL ethanol, and 7 drops 30% H₂O₂. 500×. (J.H. Wood)

of a two-phase mixture, that grow and consume the matrix. The morphology most often consists of alternating lamellae of the precipitate phase and compositionally depleted matrix. These duplex cells are generally, but not always, surrounded by a high-angle grain boundary that acts as a reaction front and

advances into the matrix, depositing the cellular product in its wake. This cellular precipitation reaction is similar to the cooperative growth of two-phase aggregates that occurs during eutectoid decomposition (austenite → pearlite reaction). The cellular colonies most often originate at the matrix grain

**Fig. 6** Preferential or localized precipitation along grain boundaries and slip planes (dislocations) in plastically deformed Cu-2.1Be-0.4Ni alloy aged 75 min at 390 °C (735 °F) after being subjected to 7100 MPa (1030 ksi). Etch not reported. 500×. (V.A. Phillips)

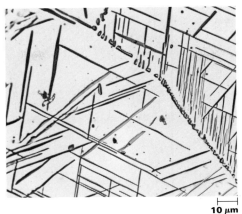

**Fig. 7** Widmanstätten precipitation in a Cu-3Ti alloy aged 10 h at 730 °C (1345 °F). Plates lie along {111} planes of the fcc matrix. Etchant not reported. 420×. (R. Gronsky and D. Metzler)

**Fig. 8** Transmission electron micrograph revealing Widmanstätten plates along the {111} matrix planes in an Al-20Ag alloy aged 144 h at 180 °C (355 °F). 20 000×. (M.S. Hunter)

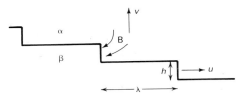

**Fig. 9** The thickening of a platelike precipitate by a ledge mechanism. The ledges of height $h$ and spacing $\lambda$ move laterally with a velocity $u$ by diffusion to the ledge edges, for example, at B. The broad face of the plate advances along the normal to the interface with a velocity $v$ governed by the ledge migration. (Ref 1)

boundaries, and the grain boundary—at which nucleation of the precipitate occurs—moves and becomes the growth front.

The migration of the boundaries can be driven by chemical and strain-energy gradients across the reaction front and can be catalyzed by cold working the matrix before aging. This reaction is propagated by a front that advances into the supersaturated matrix and spatially partitions the structure into transformed and untransformed regions; it is termed discontinuous precipitation. Figures 10 and 11 depict the cellular reaction propagating into the supersaturated matrix from the grain boundaries. The lamellar morphology of the transformation product is clearly revealed. The cellular reaction often moves into a matrix in which a less stable transition precipitate has already precipitated. The residual chemical-free energy drives the reaction front, and the duplex colonies consume the initial precipitate and produce a matrix of modified composition, as shown in Fig. 12 and 13.

## Precipitation Sequence

In many precipitation systems and in virtually all effective commercial age-hardening alloys, the supersaturated matrix transforms along a multistage reaction path, producing one or more metastable transition precipitates before the appearance of the equilib-

**Fig. 10** Cellular or discontinuous precipitation growing out uniformly from the grain boundaries in an Fe-24.8Zn alloy aged 6 min at 600 °C (1110 °F). 2% nital. 1000×. (W.C. Leslie)

rium phase. The approach to equilibrium is controlled by the activation (nucleation) barriers separating the initial state from the states of lower free energy. The transition precipitate is generally crystallographically similar to the matrix, allowing the formation of a low energy coherent interface during the nucleation process. Classical nucleation theory shows that the nucleation barrier $\Delta G^*$ is proportional to $\sigma_{M-P}^3/(\Delta G_V + G_S)^2$, where $\sigma_{M-P}$ is the interfacial energy of the matrix-precipitate interphase interface, $\Delta G_V$ is the

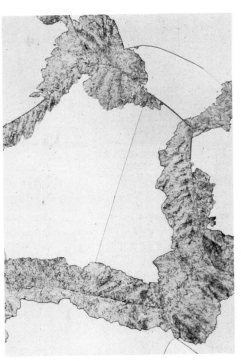

**Fig. 11** Cellular colonies growing out from grain boundaries in Au-30Ni alloy aged 50 min at 425 °C (795 °F). 50 mL 5% ammonium persulfate and 50 mL 5% potassium cyanide. 100×. (R.D. Buchheit)

thermodynamic driving force per unit volume of the nucleus (which is proportional to the undercooling), and $G_S$ is the strain energy per unit volume associated with the coherency strains. Because the nucleation rate is proportional to $\exp -\Delta G^*/kT$ ($k$ is Boltzmann's constant, and $T$ is the absolute temperature), the transition phase nucleates more rapidly despite the smaller driving force ($\Delta G_V$) for its formation compared to the equilibrium precipitate. Transmission electron microscopy reveals coherent transition precipitates

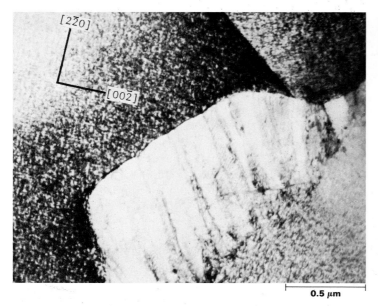

**Fig. 12** Transmission electron micrograph showing early stages of cellular reaction in a Cu-3Ti alloy aged $10^4$ min at 375 °C (710 °F). The cellular product consumes the fine, coherent precipitates, which are revealed by strain contrast in the matrix. $57\,400\times$. (J. Cornie)

**Fig. 13** Cellular reaction in a Cu-4Ti alloy aged $10^3$ min at 600 °C (1110 °F). The cellular reaction produces the lamellar equilibrium phase and leads to overaging and loss of ductility. Diagonal band is an annealing twin in the matrix phase. $1245\times$. (A. Datta)

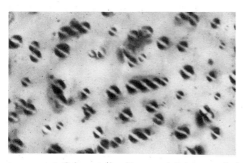

**Fig. 14** Coherent transition precipitates revealed by strain contrast (dark-field) in transmission electron microscopy. The specimen is a Cu-3.1Co alloy aged 24 h at 650 °C (1200 °F). The precipitate is a metastable fcc phase of virtually pure cobalt in the fcc matrix. The particles are essentially spherical, and the "lobe" contrast is characteristic of an embedded "misfitting sphere." This strain contrast reveals the particles indirectly through their coherency strain fields. $70\,000\times$. (V.A. Phillips)

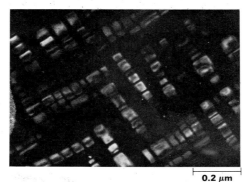

**Fig. 15** Coherent $(Co,Fe)_3Ti$ metastable precipitates in a Co-12Fe-6Ti alloy aged $10^4$ min at 700 °C (1290 °F). The ordered particles are imaged in dark-field transmission electron microscopy using an $L1_2$ superlattice reflection. This imaging mode reveals the actual size of the particle, because the superlattice reflection stems only from the precipitate. The precipitates are aligned along the $\langle 100 \rangle$ directions of the matrix. The foil normal is near [100]. $60\,000\times$. (J.W. Shilling)

formed during aging before the formation of the equilibrium phase (Fig. 14 and 15).

The decomposition of a supersaturated solid solution typically occurs by a sequence of reactions:

$$\alpha_o \rightarrow \alpha'' + \text{Guinier-Preston zones}$$
$$\text{(Metastable)}$$
$$\rightarrow \alpha' + \beta' \rightarrow \alpha_{eq} + \beta_{eq} \quad\quad \text{(Eq 1)}$$
$$\text{(Metastable)} \quad \text{(Stable equilibrium)}$$

where $\alpha_o$ is the supersaturated parent phase. Each step in the precipitation sequence leads to a decrease in the free energy and represents a state of metastable or stable equilibrium. The $(n + 1)$ transition phase tends to (but not exclusively) nucleate heterogeneously at the interphase boundaries of the $n^{th}$ transition phase. This is due to the role of the interfaces in catalyzing the nucleation process and to the reduction of the available driving force resulting from the prior precipitation of the $n^{th}$ transition phase. The precipitation scheme can be depicted in a free-energy composition diagram, as shown in Fig. 16. The metastable phases have corresponding solvus curves determined by the common tangent construction at each temperature. The metastable solvi are included in the hypothetical phase diagram of Fig. 17, which shows that the solubility is less the more thermodynamically stable the phase.

Guinier-Preston (GP) zones are coherent, solute-rich clusters resulting from phase separation or precipitation within a metastable miscibility gap in the alloy system. They may form by homogeneous nucleation and grow at small undercoolings or by spinodal decomposition at large undercoolings or supersaturations (see the article "Spinodal Structures" in this Volume). After GP zone formation,

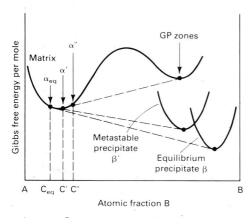

**Fig. 16** Free-energy composition diagram showing the metastable and stable equilibria in the precipitation sequence. The points of common tangency at compositions $C''$, $C'$, and $C_{eq}$ are points on the metastable and stable solvi at this temperature.

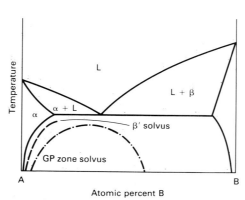

**Fig. 17** Hypothetical simple phase diagram showing the locus of metastable and stable solvus curves. L, liquid

**Fig. 18** GP zones (dark spots) in matrix of an Al-15Ag alloy dissolving near plates of the more stable γ′ precipitates (dark lines). Transmission electron micrograph of a specimen aged 1200 h at 160 °C (320 °F). 22 500×. (J.B. Clark)

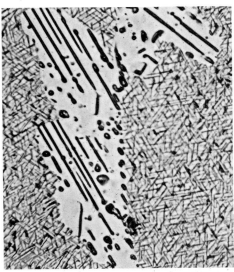

**Fig. 19** Colonies of cellular precipitation reaction growing out and consuming a metastable Widmanstätten precipitate in an Al-18Ag alloy aged 4 h at 300 °C (570 °F). 0.5% HF. 1000×. (J.B. Clark)

the appearance of a more stable phase (for example, $\beta'$ in Eq 1) leads to the dissolution of the zones, as revealed in Fig. 18. Each successive step replaces the less stable phase by a more stable one, lowering the free energy. In Fig. 19, the equilibrium phase is shown growing by a cellular reaction into a metastable Widmanstätten structure.

## Microstructural Features

The microstructures that evolve during the aging of a supersaturated solid solution are governed by the complex interplay of thermodynamic, kinetic, and structural factors controlling the basic processes of nucleation, growth, and coarsening. The precipitation system maximizes the rate of free energy release and not the overall free energy change as it decomposes toward the state of stable equilibrium. Thus, coherent transition precipitates often appear in preference to the equilibrium phase, because of more favorable nucleation kinetics. Precipitation of these metastable phases generally produces uni-

form, fine-scale microstructures that can enhance the physical and mechanical properties of commercial alloys. The location of metastable solvus curves is essential to understanding and controlling the precipitation sequences of age-hardening systems.

The distribution and morphology of the precipitate phase depend on the nature of the active nucleation sites, the compromise between surface and strain energies, and the type of interphase interface that develops between the precipitate and matrix. A two-phase mixture can also evolve during precipitation through a cooperative growth mechanism similar to the cellular phase separation in eutectic and eutectoid transformations. This cellular precipitation reaction often leads to the formation of the equilibrium precipitate and subsequent degradation of such properties as strength and ductility. Therefore, control of this reaction can be critical to optimizing properties in age-hardenable alloys. Trace element additions have been used effectively to suppress the nucleation and growth of this microconstituent.

## REFERENCE

1. D.A. Porter and K.E. Easterling, *Phase Transformation in Metals and Alloys*, Van Nostrand Reinhold Co., 1981

## SELECTED REFERENCES

- H.I. Aaronson, H.B. Aaron, and K.R. Kinsman, Origins of Microstructure Resulting from Precipitation, *Metallography*, Vol 4, 1971, p 1
- A. Kelly and R.B. Nicholson, Precipitation Hardening, *Prog. Mater. Sci.*, Vol 10, 1963, p 149
- K.C. Russell and H.I. Aaronson, Ed., *Precipitation Processes in Solids*, American Institute of Mining, Metallurgical, and Petroleum Engineers, Warrendale, PA, 1978
- K.C. Russell and H.I. Aaronson, Sequences of Precipitate Nucleation, *J. Mater. Sci.*, Vol 10, 1975, p 1991
- D.B. Williams and E.P. Butler, Grain Boundary Discontinous Reactions, *Int. Met. Rev.*, No. 3, 1981, p 153

# Spinodal Structures

By David E. Laughlin
Professor of Metallurgical
   Engineering and Materials Science
Carnegie-Mellon University

and

William A. Soffa
Professor of Metallurgical
   and Materials Engineering
University of Pittsburgh

SPINODAL STRUCTURES are fine-scale, homogenous two-phase mixtures resulting from a phase separation that takes place under certain conditions of temperature and composition. The conjugate phases produced by the spinodal decomposition of a supersaturated solid solution differ in composition from the parent phase, but have essentially the same crystal structure. Precipitation by spinodal decomposition may occur in conjunction with an ordering reaction, as discussed below.

The simplest phase transformation that can produce a spinodal reaction product is decomposition within a stable or metastable miscibility gap, as shown in Fig. 1. If a solid solution of composition $C_0$ is solution treated in the single-phase field at a temperature $T_0$, then aged at an intermediate temperature $T_A$ (or $T_{A'}$), the single-phase alloy tends to separate into a two-phase mixture. At the temperature $T_A$, the compositions of the conjugate phases $\alpha_1$ and $\alpha_2$ under equilibrium conditions are $C_1$ and $C_2$, respectively. However,

the supersaturated solid solution may decompose into two phases along two different reaction paths.

At small undercoolings or low supersaturations ($T_{A'}$), the solution is metastable; appearance of a second phase requires relatively large localized composition fluctuations. This is the classical nucleation process, giving rise to "critical nuclei," which can grow spontaneously. As the particles of the new phase grow by diffusion, the matrix composition adjusts toward equilibrium. At large supersaturations ($T_A$), the solution is unstable, and the two-phase mixture gradually emerges by the continuous growth of initially small amplitude fluctuations (see Fig. 2). The rate of reaction is controlled by the rate of atomic migration and the diffusion distances involved, which depend on the scale of decomposition (undercooling). Therefore, spinodal structures refer to phase mixtures that derive from a particular kinetic process governing the initial stages of phase separation. The "spinodal line" shown in Fig. 1 is not a phase boundary but a demarcation indicating a difference in thermodynamic stability.

## Theory of Spinodal Reactions

The spinodal reaction is a spontaneous unmixing or diffusional clustering distinct from classical nucleation and growth in metastable solutions. This different kinetic behavior, which does not require a nucleation step, was first described by Gibbs in his treatment of the thermodynamic stability of undercooled or supersaturated phases. The spinodal line in Fig. 1 indicates a limit of metastability with respect to the response of the system to compositional fluctuations. The locus, called the "chemical spinodal," is defined by the in-

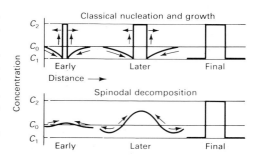

Fig. 2 Schematic illustrating two sequences for the formation of a two-phase mixture by diffusion processes: nucleation and growth and spinodal decomposition. (Ref 1)

flexion points of the isothermal free energy ($G$) composition curves ($\partial^2 G/\partial C^2 = 0$). Within the spinodes where $\partial^2 G/\partial C^2 < 0$, the supersaturated solution is unstable and spinodal decomposition can occur. Spinodal decomposition or continuous phase separation involves the selective amplification of long wavelength concentration waves within the supersaturated state resulting from random fluctuations. The transformation occurs homogenously throughout the alloy via the gradual buildup of regions enriched in solute, resulting in a two-phase modulated structure. The continuous amplification of a quasi-sinusoidal fluctuation depicted in Fig. 2 is rather general, because this sinusoidal composition wave may be viewed as a Fourier component of an arbitrary composition variation that grows preferentially.

The essential features of the spinodal process can be understood by considering this diffusional clustering as the inverse of the homogenization of a nonuniform solid solution exhibiting a sinusoidal variation of composition with distance. In metastable solutions, the small deviations from the average concentration, $C_0$, will decay with time according to the equation $\Delta C = \Delta C_0 \exp(-t/\tau)$, where

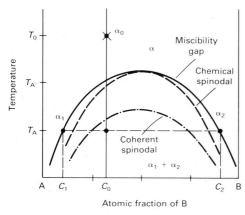

Fig. 1 Schematic showing miscibility gap in the solid state and spinodal lines (chemical and coherent)

the relaxation time $\tau \approx \lambda^2/\tilde{D}$; $\lambda$ is the wavelength of the fluctuation and $\tilde{D}$ is the appropriate diffusion coefficient. In a binary system $\tilde{D} \propto \partial^2 G/\partial C^2$, and within the spinodes $\partial^2 G/\partial C^2 < 0$; that is, the curvature of the free energy-composition curve is negative. Therefore, in an unstable solid solution $\tilde{D}$ is negative, and "uphill" diffusion occurs. The amplitude of the concentration wave grows with time, that is, $\Delta C = \Delta C_0 \exp(+R(\beta)t)$, where the amplification factor $R(\beta)$ is a function of the wave number $\beta = 2\pi/\lambda$. The factor $R(\beta)$ is a maximum for intermediate wavelengths. Long wavelength fluctuations grow sluggishly because of the large diffusion distances; short wavelength fluctuations are suppressed by the so-called gradient or surface energy of the diffuse or incipient interfaces that evolve during phase separation. Therefore, the microstructure that develops during spinodal decomposition has a characteristic periodicity that is typically 2.5 to 10 nm (25 to 100 Å) in metallic systems.

The factors controlling the spinodal reaction and resultant structures are clarified by examining the energetics of small-amplitude fluctuations in solid solutions. The free energy of an inhomogenous solution expressed as an integral over the volume, $V$, of the crystal can be written as:

$$G = \int \{f(C) + \mathrm{K}\nabla C^2 + E_s\}dV$$

where $f(C)$ is the free energy per unit volume of a uniform solution of composition $C$, K is the gradient energy parameter, and $E_s$ is a strain energy term that depends on the elastic constants and misfit (difference in lattice parameter) between the solute-enriched and solute-depleted regions. For a sinusoidal composition fluctuation $C - C_0 = A \sin \beta x$ (where $A$ is the amplitude of the sine wave), the gradient or surface energy term varies as $\mathrm{K}\beta^2$ and prohibits decomposition on a fine scale. The wavelength of the dominant concentration wave that essentially determines the scale of decomposition varies as

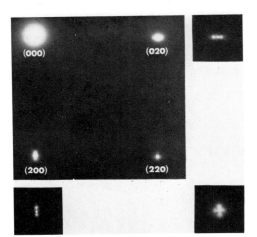

**Fig. 3** [001] electron diffraction pattern from spinodally decomposed Cu-4Ti (wt%) alloy aged 100 min at 400 °C (750 °F) showing satellites flanking the matrix reflections. (A. Datta)

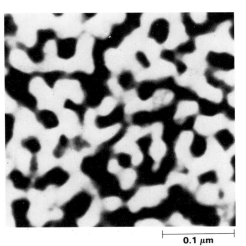

**Fig. 4** Transmission electron micrograph of isotropic spinodal structure developed in Fe-28.5Cr-10.6Co (wt%) alloy aged 4 h at 600 °C (1110 °F). Contrast derives mainly from structure-factor differences. 225 000×. (A. Zeltser)

$\mathrm{K}^{1/2}(\Delta T)^{-1/2}$, where $\Delta T = T_S - T_A$, in which $T_S$ is the spinodal temperature. The coherency strain energy term is independent of wavelength, but can vary markedly with crystallographic direction in elastically anisotropic crystals. Therefore, the dominant concentration waves will develop along elastically "soft" directions in anisotropic systems. For most cubic materials, the $\langle 100 \rangle$ directions are preferred, although $\langle 111 \rangle$ waves are predicted in certain alloys, depending on the so-called anisotropy factor. The strain energy can also stabilize the system against decomposition and effectively displace the spinodal curve (and the solvus), thus defining a "coherent spinodal" (Fig. 1).

Periodic composition fluctuations in the decomposing solid solution cause diffraction effects known as "satellites" or "sidebands." The fundamental reflections in reciprocal space are flanked by satellites or secondary maxima, and the distance of the satellites from the fundamental varies inversely with the wavelength of the growing concentration wave. This diffuse scattering arises from the periodic variation of the lattice parameter and/or scattering factor. The strain effects are negligible around the origin of reciprocal space. Small-angle x-ray and neutron scattering can be used to study quantitatively the kinetics of the reaction by monitoring the changes in the intensity distribution around the direct beam due to changes in the structure factor modulations. The electron diffraction pattern of a spinodally decomposed copper-titanium alloy shown in Fig. 3 reveals the dominant $\langle 100 \rangle$ concentration waves that develop during the early stages of phase separation.

## Microstructure

If the strain energy term in the free energy expression is negligible (small misfit) or if the elastic modulus is isotropic, the resultant mi-

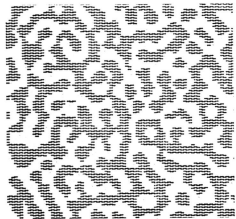

**Fig. 5** Computer simulation of an isotropically decomposed microstructure. (J.W. Cahn and M.K. Miller)

crostructure will be isotropic, similar to the morphologies evolving in phase-separated glasses. In Fig. 4, an isotropic spinodal structure developed in a phase-separated iron-chromium-cobalt permanent magnet alloy is clearly revealed by transmission electron microscopy. The two-phase mixture is interconnected in three dimensions and exhibits no directionality. The microstructure is comparable to the computer simulation of an isotropically decomposed alloy shown in Fig. 5 (Ref 1). In Fig. 6, the dominant composition waves have developed preferentially along the $\langle 100 \rangle$ matrix directions to produce an aligned modulated structure in a copper-nickel-iron alloy. Because the homogenous phase separation process is relatively structure-insensitive, the spinodal product is generally uniform within the grains up to the grain boundaries, as revealed in the copper-nickel-chromium spinodal alloy shown in Fig. 7.

Atomic ordering and spinodal clustering can occur concomitantly in a precipitation system (see Ref 2 for a review of ordering and spinodal decomposition). In these systems, a

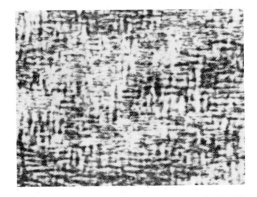

**Fig. 6** Spinodal microstructure in a 51.5Cu-33.5Ni-15Fe (at.%) alloy aged 15 min at 775 °C (1425 °F) revealed by transmission electron microscopy. Foil normal is approximately [001], and the alignment along the $\langle 100 \rangle$ matrix directions is apparent. The wavelength of the modulated structure is approximately 25 nm (250 Å). 70 000×. (G. Thomas)

**Fig. 7** Transmission electron micrograph of spinodal microstructure developed in a 66.3Cu-30Ni-2.8Cr (wt%) alloy during slow cooling from 950 °C (1740 °F). The microstructure is homogenous up to the grain boundary indicated by the arrow. 35 000×. (F.A. Badia)

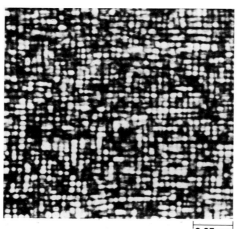

0.05 μm

**Fig. 8** Spinodal structure aligned along ⟨100⟩ directions of decomposed Fe-25Be (at.%) alloy aged 2 h at 400 °C (750 °F). The bright phase is the Be-enriched ordered B2 structure revealed by dark-field imaging using a superlattice reflection; the dark phase is the Fe-rich disordered (or weakly ordered) transformation product. The TEM foil normal is approximately [001]. 200 000×. (M.G. Burke)

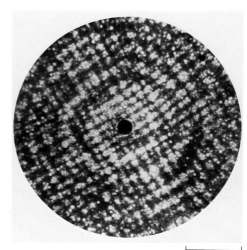

0.04 μm

**Fig. 9** Field-ion micrograph of spinodally decomposed Fe-25Be (at.%) alloy aged 20 min at 400 °C (750 °F). The axis of the needle-like specimen is [001]. The iron-rich phase images brightly because of the different contrast mechanism operating in the field-ion microscope. 375 000×. (M.K. Miller)

supersaturated phase spinodally decomposes into two phases, one or both of which are ordered. A transmission electron micrograph of a spinodally decomposed iron-beryllium alloy is shown in Fig. 8, and a corresponding field-ion micrograph is shown in Fig. 9. The brightly imaged phase in the electron micrograph (Fig. 8) is the ordered phase (B2 superstructure), whereas the brightly imaged phase in the field-ion micrograph (Fig. 9) is the iron-rich disordered phase. The microstructure is periodic and aligned along the "soft" ⟨100⟩ directions.

The spinodal mechanism provides an important mode of transformation, producing uniform, fine-scale, two-phase mixtures that can enhance the physical and mechanical

properties of commercial alloys. Spinodal decomposition has been particularly useful in the production of permanent magnet materials, because the morphologies favor high coercivities. The structure can be optimized by thermomechanical processing, step aging, and magnetic aging. Continuous phase separation or spinodal decomposition appears to be important in the classic Alnicos and copper-nickel-iron alloys, as well as in the newly developed iron-chromium-cobalt materials.

## REFERENCES

1. J.W. Cahn, *Trans. Met. Soc. AIME*, Vol 242, 1968, p 166

2. W.A. Soffa and D.E. Laughlin, in *Solid-Solid Phase Transformations, Proceedings of an International Conference*, H.I. Aaronson, D.E. Laughlin, R.F. Sekerka, and C.M. Wayman, Ed., AIME, Warrendale, PA, 1982, p 159

## SELECTED REFERENCES

• D. DeFontaine, in *Ultrafine Grain Metals*, J. Burke, and V. Weiss, Ed., Syracuse University Press, 1970, p 93
• J.E. Hilliard, in *Phase Transformations*, H.I. Aaronson, Ed., American Society for Metals, 1970

# Massive Transformation Structures

By T.B. Massalski
Professor of Metallurgical Engineering,
Materials Science and Physics
Carnegie-Mellon University

MASSIVE TRANSFORMATION may change crystal structure during heating or cooling if no change of composition occurs and if the rate of heating or cooling is rapid enough to allow only a limited amount of diffusion. Massive transformation appears to proceed primarily by a noncooperative (random) transfer of atoms across the interfaces between the parent and product phases. The details of the atomic movements at a transformation interface are not well understood, but the process does not appear to involve shearlike movements.

Massive transformations are thermally activated and exhibit nucleation and growth characteristics. The kinetics of these transformations are controlled primarily by interface diffusion and other interface features such as lack of coherence between the parent and product phases. Growth of the product phase during massive transformations thus occurs mainly by displacement of incoherent (high-energy) boundaries, often at speeds up to 10 to 20 mm/s (0.39 to 0.79 in./s). In these transformations, no simple orientation relationships are known to exist between the parent and product phases.

The microstructure in a specimen that has undergone a massive transformation often exhibits massive patches of grains that have irregular boundaries. These patches are surrounded by a mixture of planar and curving boundaries.

The phase relations that are necessary for massive transformation to occur are illustrated in Fig. 1. For alloys (Fig. 1b to d), the two different crystal structures must be simple and stable or metastable at the same composition, but at different temperatures. These conditions are also satisfied during allotropic transformations in pure metals (see Fig. 1), which may occur by massive transformation. Details of typical massive transformations for pure metals and binary systems are given in Table 1.

**Allotropy and Congruent Points.** The compositions in Fig. 1(a) and (b) correspond, respectively, to a pure metal that can exist in more than one allotropic form and an alloy in which the two phase fields touch at a congruent point (such as the bcc and hcp phases in aluminum-silver at 24.5 at.% Ag). In these instances, the critical composition line does not cross a two-phase field, and thus a possible massive transformation is not interfered with by another transformation that might require long-range diffusion and solute partitioning. Therefore, in such alloys, or in others for which the two-phase field is suitably narrow, a massive transformation is likely.

The resulting microstructure is characteristic of a process of random and rapid growth (Fig. 2). Microstructures of this type have been observed in iron, low-carbon steels, and low-nickel steels.

**Two-Phase Fields.** Massive transformations that correspond to the compositions in Fig. 1(c) and (d) usually occur in brass alloys of the β type as a result of decomposition of the high-temperature bcc phase. Three competing transformations that may occur in alloys of this type upon cooling through the two-phase fields are (1) growth of Widmanstätten precipitates of the equilibrium phases adjoining the β phase, (2) equilibrium decomposition into two phases, and (3) a bainitic transformation. At lower temperatures, the formation of martensite also may occur. Therefore, the products of these other transformations frequently may be present to-

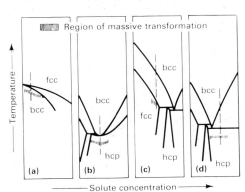

**Fig. 1** Schematic phase diagrams for (a) a pure metal and (b to d) three types of alloys that may undergo massive transformations. Critical compositions are indicated by the dashed vertical lines.

**Table 1  Typical massive transformations**

| Alloy system or metal | Amount of solute at which transformation occurs(a), at.% | Temperature during quenching at which transformation occurs(a) °C | °F | Change in crystal structure(b) |
|---|---|---|---|---|
| Silver-aluminum | 23–28 | 600 | 1110 | bcc → hcp |
| Silver-cadmium | 41–42 | 300–450 | 570–840 | bcc → fcc |
| | 50 | 300 | 570 | bcc → hcp |
| Silver-zinc | 37–40 | 250–350 | 480–660 | bcc → fcc |
| Copper-aluminum | 19 | 550 | 1020 | bcc → fcc |
| Copper-zinc | 37–38 | 400–500 | 750–930 | bcc ⇌ hcp |
| Copper-gallium | 21–27 | 580 | 1075 | bcc → fcc |
| | 20 | 600 | 1110 | bcc → fcc |
| Iron | ... | 700 | 1290 | fcc → bcc |
| Iron-cobalt | 0–25 | 650–800 | 1200–1470 | fcc → bcc |
| Iron-chromium | 0–10 | 600–800 | 1110–1470 | fcc → bcc |
| Iron-nickel | 0–6 | 500–700 | 930–1290 | fcc → bcc |
| Plutonium-zirconium | 5–45 | 450 | 840 | bcc → fcc |

(a) Values listed are approximate. (b) bcc, body-centered cubic; fcc, face-centered cubic; hcp, hexagonal close-packed

gether with the massive phase in the resulting microstructure.

An example of a partial massive transformation of the bcc $\beta$ phase in a specimen of Cu-19.3Al (at.%) that had initially consisted of an equilibrium two-phase mixture of $\alpha$ and $\beta$ phases is shown in Fig. 3. The massive

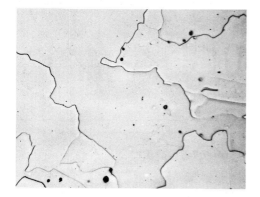

**Fig. 2** Fe-0.002C alloy quenched in iced brine from 1000 °C (1830 °F). Microstructure, which resulted from a massive transformation, shows ferrite grains with irregular boundaries. Etchant: 2% nital. 350×

transformation of $\beta$ during cooling was arrested by the formation of martensite. The irregular boundaries of the massive patches reveal the pattern of random growth (Ref 1).

When only a partial massive transformation has occurred on cooling, the remaining parent matrix is sometimes retained in a metastable state. In Fig. 4, growth of the massive $\alpha$ phase has occurred at the boundaries of and inside the parent (bcc) grains. Patches of the massive phase extend on both sides of a prior parent grain boundary, indicating that the growth of massive phase was unaffected by orientation relationships between the parent and product phases. The lack of any simple orientation relationship across interfaces between massive and parent phases was confirmed further by electron diffraction studies (Ref 3). In a similar manner, the massive hcp phase grains in a copper-gallium-germanium alloy (Fig. 5) cross the prior $\beta$ (bcc) boundaries (Ref 4).

**Feathery structures,** a common transformation product in copper-gallium and silver-cadmium alloys, result from the formation of duplex fcc-hcp massive grains, each associated with a twin on the hcp (10$\bar{1}$1) plane. A

characteristic feature of the feathery growth is that layers of fcc $\alpha$ terminal solid solution and hcp intermediate phase form alternately and share a common close-packed plane as the plane of contact (Ref 5). Figure 6 shows that the feathery grains are again able to cross prior-$\beta$ grain boundaries. The duplex growth occurs through a two-dimensional nucleation and growth of close-packed planes (Ref 6). Figure 7, which shows a tip of an advancing duplex massive grain, reveals that the lamellae of alpha and the hcp phase originate at dislocations on the twin plane.

**Growth Without Conventional Nucleation.** Figure 8 illustrates the result of massive transformation in the $\beta$ phase of an initially two-phase hcp-bcc alloy. The transformation of bcc beta to the hcp phase is accomplished by the growth of the original hcp phase into bcc $\beta$ without formation of new incoherent nuclei. The massive hcp phase has the orientation of the equilibrium hcp phase, but with a different composition (Ref 7).

**Growth of Single Crystals.** Because a large driving force is required to nucleate incoherent grains, a single massive grain, once it is nucleated, may consume all prior parent

**Fig. 3** Cu-19.3Al (at.%) alloy quenched in ice water from 900 °C (1650 °F). Irregularly shaped patches (light), resulting from $\beta$-to-$\alpha$ massive transformation, are visible in a background of equilibrium $\alpha$ grains in martensite. 5 g FeCl$_3$, 15 mL HCl, 60 mL ethanol. 135×. (Ref 1)

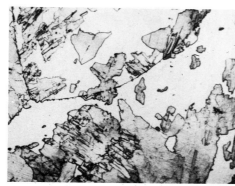

**Fig. 4** Cu-37.8Zn (at.%) alloy after a partial massive transformation. Massive $\alpha$ phase (dark, mottled) has formed at the boundaries of and inside the parent grains of $\beta$ phase. Etchant: Same as Fig. 3. 40×. (Ref 2)

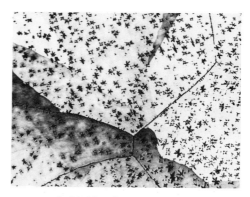

**Fig. 5** Cu-18.4Ga-5Ge (at.%) alloy, quenched. Massive hcp phase grains containing $\gamma$ precipitation (rosettes) that formed in the prior-$\beta$ phase before the massive transformation occurred. 5 g FeCl$_3$, 15 mL HCl, 60 mL ethanol. 60×. (Ref 4)

**Fig. 6** Cu-21.5Ga (at.%) alloy quenched from $\beta$ structure (temperature above 775 °C (1425 °F). Twinned feathery grains formed by massive transformation, cross prior grain boundaries (arrows) revealed by $\alpha$ precipitation. Etchant: Same as Fig. 5. 250×

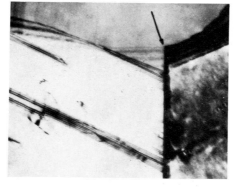

**Fig. 7** Thin-foil transmission electron micrograph of Cu-21.5Ga (at.%) alloy. Tip of a feather unit shows fine lamellae of $\alpha$ and hcp phases that originated at dislocations on twin plane (arrow). 66 000×

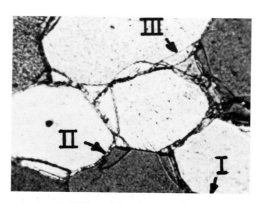

**Fig. 8** Cu-21Ga-1.5Ge alloy, quenched from a two-phase structure at 650 °C (1200 °F). During quenching, bcc $\beta$ phase at the grain boundaries transformed to massive hcp phase. One hcp-bcc boundary was active at I, two were active at II, and three were active at III. 1 g FeCl$_3$, 10 mL HCl, 100 mL H$_2$O. 250×

**Fig. 9** Ag-24.5Al (at.%) alloy, consisting of a single crystal of hcp phase. The crystal was formed from a polycrystalline specimen of bcc phase by massive transformation during controlled cooling. Etchant: Same as Fig. 8. 6×. (J.H. Perepezko)

grains if a temperature gradient is moved through the specimen in a controlled manner as the boundary of the massive grain advances. Figure 9 illustrates a single crystal that was produced by massive transformation of the $\beta$ phase in a silver-aluminum alloy of congruent composition.

**Recent Developments.** Detailed crystallographic orientation relationship studies and theoretical considerations (Ref 8) suggest that in almost all cases of nucleation during massive transformations some form of a rational, or nearly rational, orientation relationship appears necessary at the nucleation stage to reduce the activation energy for nucleation of the massive phase. The concept of crystallographic relationships remains somewhat unsettled and has been reviewed recently at an AIME symposium on massive transformations. At this symposium, the feasibility of the occurrence of a metastable, compositionally invariant massive transformation in two-phase fields in phase diagrams was reexamined, and the current status of various distinguishing features of the massive transformation mode was also reviewed.

## REFERENCES

1. T.B. Massalski, A.J. Perkins, and J. Jaklovsky, Extension of Solid Solubility During Massive Transformations, *Met. Trans.*, Vol 3, 1972, p 687
2. T.B. Massalski, Massive Transformations, in *Phase Transformations*, American Society for Metals, 1970
3. E.B. Hawbolt and T.B. Massalski, Observations Concerning the $\beta \rightarrow \alpha_m$ Massive Transformation in Cu-Zn Alloys, *Met. Trans.*, Vol 1, 1970, p 2315
4. T.B. Massalski, The Mode and Morphology of Massive Transformations in Cu-Ga, Cu-Zn, Cu-Zn-Ga and Cu-Ga-Ge Alloys, *Acta Metall.*, Vol 6, 1958, p 243
5. G.A. Sargent, L. Delaey, and T.B. Massalski, Formation of "Feathery" Structures During Massive Transformation in Cu-Ga Alloys, *Acta Metall.*, Vol 16, 1968, p 723
6. H. Gleiter and T.B. Massalski, Atomistic Model for the Growth of Feathery Structures in Duplex Massive Transformations, *Acta Metall.*, Vol 18, 1970, p 649
7. A.J. Perkins and T.B. Massalski, Observations on the $\beta \rightarrow \zeta_m$ Massive Transformation in Two-Phase ($\beta + \zeta$) Alloys of the Cu-Ga-Ge System, *Met. Trans.*, Vol 2, 1971, p 2701
8. "The Massive Transformation," American Society of Metallurgical, Mining, and Petroleum Engineers Symposium, published in *Met. Trans. A*, Vol 15, 1984, p 410

# Eutectoid Structures

By A.R. Marder
Senior Scientist
Technology Department
Bethlehem Steel Corporation

and

J.A. Kowalik
Graduate Student
Department of Metallurgy
and Materials Engineering
Lehigh University

EUTECTOID REACTIONS are defined as the transformation of a metastable solid phase to a mixture of two other solid phases. This transformation involves long-range diffusion due to the compositional invariance between the two products and the parent phase. The most common microstructure resulting from eutectoid transformation is a lamellar structure, for example, pearlite (Fig. 1) in the Fe-Fe$_3$C system (Fig. 2). In this system, the austenite phase, which is face-centered cubic (fcc), decomposes at 727 °C (1341 °F) and 0.77% C to the ferrite phase, which is body-centered cubic (bcc), and the cementite phase, which is orthorhombic. Eutectoid reactions producing pearlitic structures are not limited only to ferrous alloys; Table 1 lists some ferrous and nonferrous alloy systems that contain eutectoid transformations that produce lamellar structures as well as other morphologies. Figure 3 shows a typical example of nonlamellar eutectoid decomposition in the Cu-Sn system. This article, however, will review the Fe-Fe$_3$C pearlite eutectoid structure because of its commercial importance and the extensive body of knowledge available (Ref 2).

## Pearlite Microstructures

Figure 4 depicts the individual constituents of pearlite. A nodule nucleates at a grain boundary, triple point, grain corner, or surface and grows radially until impingement occurs with surrounding nodules (Ref 4). Individual colonies are present inside the nodule, each nodule having an orientation relationship with the parent austenite grain. Inside the colonies a complex microstructure forms, consisting of alternating parallel lamellae of the two product phases (ferrite and cementite). Figure 5 illustrates the typical mi-

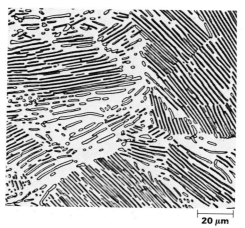

**Fig. 1** Typical pearlite structure of alternate layers of ferrite and cementite in an Fe-0.8C alloy. Picral. 500×

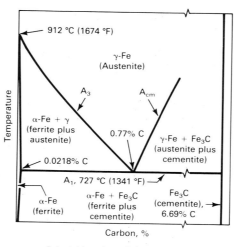

**Fig. 2** Eutectoid region of the Fe-Fe$_3$C phase diagram

crostructure of a partially transformed eutectoid steel in which the morphology of the nodules is apparent.

Figure 6 shows the colonies of pearlite with faults and imperfections present in the lamellar structure. Changes in orientation are observed at the boundaries between the colonies. These changes occur because of faults in the structure. Figure 7, a transmission electron micrograph, shows the cementite lamellae (dark rods) stopping at a cell boundary. Also noted is the occasional bending of the lamellae achieved by a series of growth steps. The growth of the cementite-ferrite interface, which is very sensitive to crystallographic relationships, occurs by a ledge-type mechanism (Ref 5). Figure 8 illustrates the ledges in cementite lamellae.

## Crystal Orientation

Pearlite colonies grow as if they were two interpenetrating single crystals. Measurements of the orientation relationships of the phases of ferrous pearlite colonies have been determined through transmission electron microscopy:

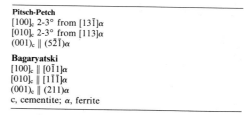

**Pitsch-Petch**
[100]$_c$ 2-3° from [13$\bar{1}$]$\alpha$
[010]$_c$ 2-3° from [113]$\alpha$
(001)$_c$ ∥ (5$\bar{2}$$\bar{1}$)$\alpha$

**Bagaryatski**
[100]$_c$ ∥ [0$\bar{1}$1]$\alpha$
[010]$_c$ ∥ [1$\bar{1}$$\bar{1}$]$\alpha$
(001)$_c$ ∥ (211)$\alpha$

c, cementite; $\alpha$, ferrite

In ferrous alloys, the Pitsch-Petch relationship is dominant at eutectoid compositions. However, the Bagaryatski relationship is increasingly apparent in hyper- and hypoeutectoid compositions, in which the nucleation of

**Table 1    Eutectoid transformations in nonferrous and ferrous alloys**

| Alloy | Eutectoid composition, wt% | Eutectoid temperature °C | °F | High-temperature phase and crystal structure | Low-temperature phases and crystal structures | Reactions observed |
|---|---|---|---|---|---|---|
| Cu-Al | 11.8 Al | 565 | 1049 | $\beta$-bcc | $\alpha$-fcc<br>$\gamma_2$ (gamma brass) | Lamellar pearlite; granular pearlite |
| Cu-Be | 6 Be | 605 | 1121 | $\beta$-bcc | $\alpha$-fcc<br>$\beta'$-bcc (CsCl) | Lamellar pearlite |
| Cu-In | 31.4 In | 574 | 1065 | $\beta$-bcc | $\alpha$-fcc<br>$\delta$ (deformed gamma brass) | Lamellar pearlite; granular pearlite |
| Cu-Si | 5.2 Si | 555 | 1031 | $\kappa$-hcp | $\alpha$-fcc<br>$\gamma$-cubic ($\beta$-Mn) | Granular pearlite |
| Cu-Sn | 27.0 Sn | 520 | 968 | $\gamma$-bcc | $\alpha$-fcc<br>$\delta$ (gamma brass) | Lamellar pearlite; needles of $\alpha$ about which $\delta$ precipitates |
| Cu-Sn | 32.5 Sn | 350 | 662 | $\delta$ (gamma brass) | $\alpha$-fcc<br>$\varepsilon$-orthorhombic | Lamellar pearlite |
| Fe-C | 0.80 C | 723 | 1333 | $\gamma$-fcc (interstitial C) | $\alpha$-bcc<br>$Fe_3C$-orthorhombic | Lamellar pearlite |
| Fe-N | 2.35 N | 590 | 1094 | $\gamma$-fcc (interstitial N) | $\alpha$-bcc<br>$\gamma'$-fcc (interstitial N) | Lamellar pearlite; granular pearlite |
| Fe-O | 23.3 O | 560 | 1040 | Wüstite cubic (NaCl) | $\alpha$-bcc<br>$Fe_3O_4$ cubic (spinel) | Lamellar pearlite; granular pearlite |
| Ni-Zn | 56 Zn | 675 | 1247 | $\beta$-cubic (CsCl) | $\beta_1$-tetragonal (CuAu)<br>$\gamma$ (gamma brass) | Lamellar pearlite |
| Ti-Cr | 15 Cr | 680 | 1256 | $\beta$-bcc | $\alpha$-hcp<br>$TiCr_2$-fcc ($MgCu_2$) | Lamellar pearlite; granular pearlite |

Source: Ref 1

**Fig. 5** Cross-sectional views of the microstructure of pearlite nodules in partially transformed hot-stage Fe-0.8C specimens showing nodule formation. Picral. 220×. (Ref 3)

a colony forms not on a prior-austenite grain, but on the proeutectoid ferrite or cementite.

## Pearlite Nucleation

Pearlite nucleation is heterogeneous and is generally restricted to the austenite grain boundaries and surface sites. Saturation of these sites generally occurs within 20 to 25% of the total transformation time, followed by growth of the nodules until impingement. Pearlite nucleates in a eutectoid alloy by the cementite or the ferrite nucleating on the austenite grain boundary (Fig. 9a). This nucleus will form an orientation relationship with the prior-austenite grain ($\gamma_1$) to lower the energy barrier. If the first nucleus to form is cementite, the area surrounding this nucleus will be depleted of carbon, which enhances the formation of ferrite. As the ferrite forms, the carbon is rejected into the surrounding matrix, further encouraging cementite to form.

Hyper- and hypoeutectoid alloys decompose similarly. The hyper- or hypoeutectoid composition causes proeutectoid ferrite (in a hypoeutectoid composition) or cementite (in a hypereutectoid composition) to form before the pearlite transformation. In a hypereutectoid steel, for example, ferrite nucleates on the proeutectoid cementite (Fig. 9b) and forms an orientation relationship with the cementite. A similar growth process occurs for the hypoeutectoid steel, with proeutectoid ferrite forming initially at prior-austenite grain boundaries.

## Pearlite Growth

The growth rate of pearlite changes as a function of the time, transformation temperature, and prior-austenite grain size. For a

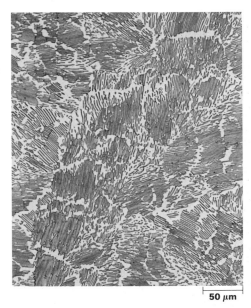

**Fig. 6** Faults found in the colonies of pearlite in an Fe-0.8C specimen. Picral. 200×

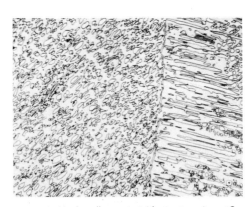

**Fig. 3** Nonlamellar eutectoid structure in a Cu-27Sn alloy. Electrolytic etchant: 1% $CrO_3$. 150×

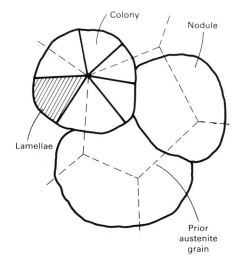

Colony

Nodule

Lamellae

Prior austenite grain

**Fig. 4** Microstructural features of the pearlite eutectoid transformation. (Ref 3)

**Fig. 7** A transmission electron micrograph of a ferrite cell interrupting the growth or bending the cementite in a thin-foil Fe-0.8C specimen. 17 250×. (Ref 6)

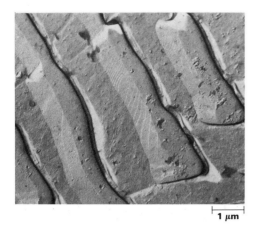

**Fig. 8** A surface replica transmission electron micrograph showing growth steps on the cementite lamellae in an Fe-0.8C specimen. Picral. 8000×. (Ref 6)

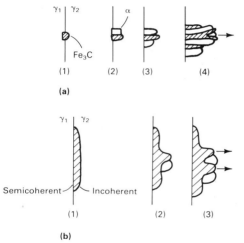

**Fig. 9** Nucleation and growth of pearlite. (a) On a "clean" austenite grain boundary. (1) Cementite nucleates on grain boundary with coherent interface and orientation relationship with $\gamma_2$. (2) $\alpha$ nucleates adjacent to cementite with a coherent interface and orientation relationship with $\gamma_1$. In addition, this produces an orientation relationship between the cementite and ferrite. (3) The nucleation process repeats sideways while incoherent interfaces grow into $\gamma_2$. (4) New plates can also form by a branching mechanism. (b) When a proeutectoid phase (cementite or ferrite) already exists on an austenite boundary, pearlite will nucleate and grow on the incoherent side, resulting in a different orientation relationship between the cementite and ferrite. (Ref 7)

given temperature and austenite grain size, the transformation rate occurs in three stages. As shown in Fig. 10, at any given temperature the volume fraction of pearlite at any given time, $f(t)$, fits an S-shaped or sigmoidal curve. Initially, the transformation rate is quite low and depends on site saturation. As more nodules develop, the rate of transformation increases. Finally, the nodules impinge, and the rate of transformation again slows as the microstructure gradually approaches complete transformation.

The temperature at which the austenite is transformed also affects the pearlite growth

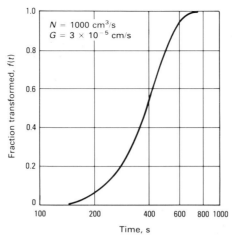

**Fig. 10** Calculated fraction austenite transformed to pearlite as a function of time for the parameters shown $f(t) = 1 - \exp\left[-\pi NG^3 t^4/3\right]$, where $f(t)$ is the volume fraction pearlite formed at any given time, $t$, at a given temperature, $N$ is the nucleation rate of the pearlite colonies, and $G$ is the rate at which the colonies grow into the austenite. (Ref 8)

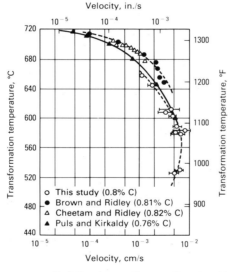

**Fig. 11** Variation in pearlite growth rate with transformation temperature. (Ref 9)

rate. Lowering the temperature increases the driving force for nucleation, which increases the transformation rate. Figure 11 illustrates a C-curve relationship between transformation temperature and growth rate. Finally, decreasing the austenite grain size will increase the number of nucleation sites. More nuclei growing into the austenite decrease the time for transformation and increase the transformation rate.

## Interlamellar Spacing

Interlamellar spacing is a strong function of the transformation temperature. Lower temperatures will result in a finer lamellar structure. Figure 12 illustrates the relationship between the reciprocal of the interlamellar spacing and transformation temperature.

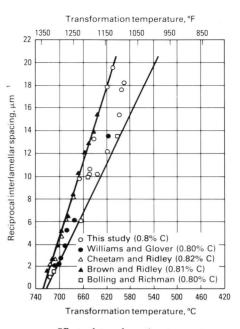

**Fig. 12** Effect of transformation temperature on the reciprocal of interlamellar spacing. (Ref 9)

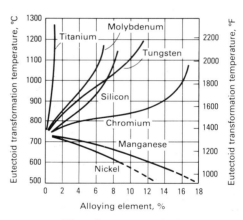

**Fig. 13** Effect of percentage of substitutional alloying elements on the temperature of the eutectoid transformation point in steel. See also Fig. 14. (Ref 10)

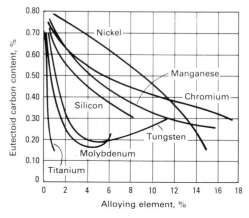

**Fig. 14** Effect of percentage of substitutional alloying elements on the carbon content of the eutectoid transformation point in steel. See also Fig. 13. (Ref 10)

# Alloying Effects

Substitutional alloying elements added to the Fe-C system affect all the transformation parameters. The transformation temperature (Fig. 13) and the eutectoid carbon content (Fig. 14) are significantly altered. Furthermore, alloying additions can significantly decrease the pearlite growth rate because of the partitioning of these elements between the ferrite and cementite (Fig. 15).

In an equilibrium alloy Fe-C-X, in which X is a substitutional element, decomposition of austenite to pearlite will occur in two ways. First, substitutional elements will diffuse more slowly than carbon, which decreases the transformation rate. This type of reaction partitions the substitutional element X between the two phases. The carbide-forming elements, such as chromium and molybdenum, will concentrate in the carbide. Ferrite-stabilizing elements—silicon, for example—will concentrate in the ferrite. Figure 16 depicts the concentration of chromium, manganese, and silicon in the ferrite and cementite. The second type of decomposition in an Fe-C-X alloy occurs when the X alloy does not undergo any long-range diffusion. The rate of the reaction, therefore, is controlled solely by the diffusion of carbon. For example, nickel additions will stabilize the austenite to lower temperatures, causing high undercoolings and preventing partitioning.

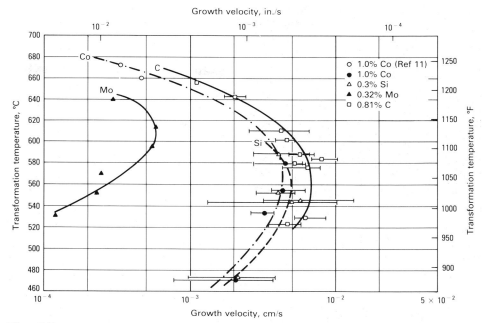

**Fig. 15** Pearlite growth rate of Fe-C-X alloys. (Ref 11)

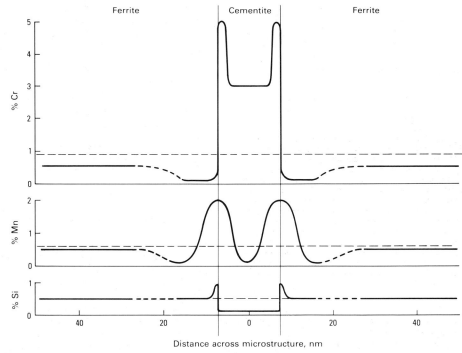

**Fig. 16** Schematic distribution of the alloy elements across the microstructure. (Ref 12)

## REFERENCES

1. C.W. Spencer and D.J. Mack, *Decomposition of Austenite by Diffusional Processes*, V.F. Zackay and H.I. Aaronson, Ed., Interscience—John Wiley & Sons, 1962, p 549-606
2. N. Ridley, in *Phase Transformations in Ferrous Alloys*, A.R. Marder and J.I. Goldstein, Ed., TMS/AIME, Warrendale, PA, 1984, p 201-236
3. A.R. Marder, in *Phase Transformations in Ferrous Alloys*, A.R. Marder and J.I. Goldstein, Ed., TMS/AIME, Warrendale, PA, 1984, p 201-236
4. B.L. Bramfitt and A.R. Marder, *Met. Trans.*, Vol 4, 1973, p 2291-2301
5. S.A. Hackney and G.J. Shiflet, in *Phase Transformations in Ferrous Alloys*, A.R. Marder and J.I. Goldstein, Ed., TMS/AIME, Warrendale, PA, 1984, p 237-242
6. B.L. Bramfitt and A.R. Marder, *Metallography*, Vol 6, 1974, p 483-495
7. D.A. Porter and K.E. Easterling, *Phase Transformations in Metals and Alloys*, Van Nostrand Reinhold, 1981, p 331
8. G. Krauss, *Principles of Heat Treatment of Steel*, American Society for Metals, 1980
9. A.R. Marder and B.L. Bramfitt, *Met. Trans. A*, Vol 6, 1975, p 2009-2014
10. E.C. Bain and H.W. Paxton, *Alloying Elements in Steel*, American Society for Metals, 1962, p 112
11. A.R. Marder and B.L. Bramfitt, *Met. Trans. A*, Vol 7, 1976, p 902-906
12. P.R. Williams, M.K. Miller, P.A. Beavan, and G.D.W. Smith, in *Phase Transformations*, Vol 2, The Institution of Metallurgists, London, 1979, p 11.98-11.100

# Bainitic Structures

By D.V. Edmonds
Lecturer
Department of Metallurgy and
    Science of Materials
University of Oxford

BAINITE refers to the microstructure resulting from the decomposition of austenite in steels at temperatures above the martensitic transformation and below the pearlite reaction. In plain-carbon steels, however, the bainitic temperature range overlaps the pearlite reaction range considerably. The transformation can occur isothermally, or during continuous cooling.

In many alloy steels, the bainitic temperature range is separate from the pearlite range, and a bay occurs in the isothermal time-temperature transformation (TTT) diagram between the two reactions. Below the $B_f$ (bainite finish) temperature, fully bainitic structures can be achieved, but at higher temperatures isothermal bainitic transformation may stop before complete decomposition of the austenite—a phenomenon known as incomplete reaction. The extent of decomposition is a function of steel composition and reaction temperature and decreases as the isothermal reaction temperature is increased to the point at which zero percentage transformation defines the $B_s$ (bainitic start) temperature, above which bainite does not form (Fig. 1). The $B_s$ temperature corresponds approximately to the temperature of the bay in the TTT curve.

Classical ferrous bainite consists of a nonlamellar aggregate of lath- or plate-shaped ferrite grains with carbide precipitation within the ferrite grains or in the interlath regions. However, in some steels (for example, steels containing significant silicon content), carbide precipitation can be suppressed completely, although a lathlike ferritic product forms in a manner identical in morphology and kinetics to the formation of classical upper bainitic ferrite. Such special carbide-free structures are also generally referred to as bainitic.

Several nonferrous alloys also produce microstructures similar to bainite in steels, either as nonlamellar aggregates of two phases or, frequently, with only one lathlike phase precipitating from the parent matrix, similar to the silicon steels mentioned above. These nonferrous structures frequently are described as bainitic, although the implication that their formation occurs by a mechanism similar to that in steels is often disputed.

Another important characteristic of bainite in ferrous and nonferrous alloys is that the formation of the bainitic ferrite plates results in surface relief that is indicative of a shape change accompanied by a significant shear component similar to that found in martensite plates (Fig. 2 and 3).

Numerous terms have been adopted to describe the more recognizable microstructures that frequently result from steels that are transformed in the bainitic temperature range. Well-documented differences in the distribution of carbides formed in the upper and lower portions of the temperature range, as well as evidence of different reaction kinetics, have led to the distinct classifications of upper and lower bainite. These terms are generally adopted to describe the classical forms of steel microstructures.

**Fig. 1** Total dilation (proportional to the degree of completion of reaction) versus transformation temperature during isothermal formation of bainite in 4340 steel. (Ref 1)

**Fig. 2** Hot-stage micrograph of surface relief from formation of upper bainite in nickel steel (0.15% C, 9.0% Ni), austenitized, transformed at 400 °C (750 °F). Prepolished, not etched. 360×. (Ref 1)

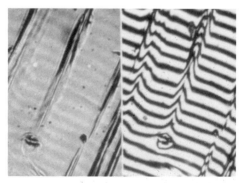

**Fig. 3** Optical micrograph (left) and matching interferogram (right) of surface relief from formation of bainitic plates in Cu-44.1Zn alloy, solution treated at 830 °C (1525 °F) for 2 min, quenched into 10% aqueous sodium hydroxide at 0 °C (32 °F), heat treated at 520 °C (970 °F) for 6 min. Electropolished in ortho-$H_3PO_4$, not etched. 3000×. (Ref 2)

**Fig. 4** Upper bainite in a 4360 steel specimen that was austenitized, isothermally transformed at 495 °C (925 °F), and quenched. Picral. 750×

In hypereutectoid steels, the carbide phase can apparently precipitate first, and the resulting initial microstructural unit has been termed "inverse" bainite. The bainite terminology also has been extended further to describe the more complex structures that are formed in alloy steels or that are formed under special experimental conditions.

## Classical Forms of Ferrous Bainite

**Upper bainite** in hypoeutectoid steels comprises an aggregate of ferrite laths that usually are formed in parallel groups to yield plate-shaped regions, often described as sheaves (Fig. 4 and 5). Nucleation occurs predominantly at prior austenite grain boundaries. The individual laths, or ferrite subunits, have similar orientations within a sheaf and usually are separated by low-angle grain boundaries (Ref 3, 4). These laths generally adopt an orientation relationship with the parent austenite (Ref 5-7), as given by Kurdjumov-Sachs and Nishiyama-Wassermann (Table 1).

A common habit plane has not been identified, and $\{111\}_\gamma$, $\{\bar{2}23\}_\gamma$, $\{569\}_\gamma$, and $\{0.37, 0.66, 0.65\}_\gamma$ have been reported (Ref 5-7, 15, 16), although there is greater agreement that the long direction of the laths follows $\langle 111 \rangle_\alpha$. The orientation relationship and habit plane may thus be irrational. Decreasing the trans-

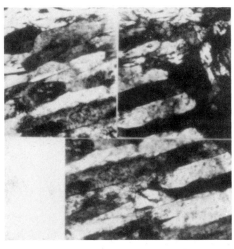

**Fig. 5** Thin-foil transmission electron micrograph illustrating substructure of upper bainite plates in a 2340 steel, austenitized at 1095 °C (2000 °F) and isothermally transformed at 540 °C (1000 °F) for 15 h. 6000×. (Ref 3)

formation temperature or increasing the carbon content decreases the widths of the individual laths and increases the amount of carbide precipitation. The laths also have a high dislocation density, which increases with decreasing transformation temperature.

Cementite ($Fe_3C$ $\theta$-phase) usually is precipitated in the interlath regions and, at higher carbon contents, often forms nearly complete carbide films between the parallel ferrite laths to give the microstructure an almost lamellar appearance (Fig. 6). The cementite spacing is generally larger than that in pearlite formed at the same temperature and results in different etching characteristics, thus enabling the two structures to be distinguished by optical (light) microscopy.

Silicon-containing steels are unique in that carbides do not form and the separately nucleated ferrite subunits are then divided by films of carbon-enriched retained austenite (Fig. 7) (Ref 3, 17). The retained austenite can then be observed to contain a distribution of planar faults (Fig. 8), analyzed to be

**Table 1 Orientation relationships for bainitic structures**

**Kurdjumov-Sachs (Ref 8)**

$(011)_\alpha \| (111)_\gamma$
$[11\bar{1}]_\alpha \| [10\bar{1}]_\gamma$

**Nishiyama-Wassermann (Ref 9, 10)**

$(011)_\alpha \| (111)_\gamma$
$[0\bar{1}1]_\alpha \| [\bar{1}\,\bar{1}2]_\gamma$

**Bagaryatski (Ref 11)**

$(001)_\theta \| (211)_\alpha$
$[100]_\theta \| [0\bar{1}1]_\alpha$

**Isaichev (Ref 12)**

$(010)_\theta \| (\bar{1}11)_\alpha$
$[103]_\theta \| [101]_\alpha$

**Pitsch (Ref 13)**

$(010)_\theta \| (110)_\gamma$
$[001]_\theta \| [\bar{2}25]_\gamma$

**Jack (Ref 14)**

$(0001)_\epsilon \| (011)_\alpha$
$[10\bar{1}1]_\epsilon \| [101]_\alpha$

deformation twins, probably produced to accommodate the transformation stresses. The density of the twins increases upon subsequent deformation of the structure (Fig. 9).

The stability of the retained austenite allows examination of the bainitic ferrite/austenite interface, and high-resolution images using weak-beam techniques indicate the presence of a closely spaced distribution of linear defects in the interface (Fig. 10). Tempering these silicon steels at elevated temperatures leads to decomposition of the retained austenite and the precipitation of carbides, thus yielding structures more equivalent to classical upper bainite (Fig. 11).

The orientation relationships found between cementite and the bainitic ferrite are

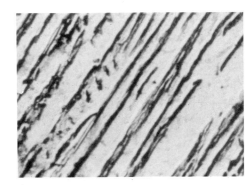

**Fig. 6** Replica electron micrograph of upper bainitic microstructure in a high-carbon hypoeutectoid steel (Fe-0.61C-0.53Mn-0.36Si-0.53Mo-0.0023B), austenitized and isothermally transformed at 500 °C (930 °F). 12 500×. (Ref 4)

0.5 μm

**Fig. 7** Thin-foil transmission electron micrograph of upper bainitic ferrite with interwoven laths of retained austenite (gray phase) in a high-silicon steel (Fe-0.43C-3.0Mn-2.12Si), austenitized at 1200 °C (2190 °F) for 5 min and isothermally transformed at 350 °C (660 °F) for 205 min. 22 000×. (Ref 17)

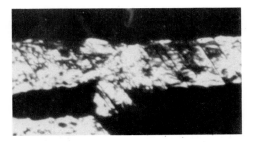

0.5 μm

**Fig. 8** Thin-foil transmission electron micrograph (dark-field image) of upper bainitic, retained austenite illustrating faulted structure in a high-silicon steel (Fe-0.43C-3.0Mn-2.12Si) austenitized at 1200 °C (2190 °F) for 5 min and isothermally transformed at 350 °C (660 °F) for 205 min. 20 000×. (Ref 17)

**Fig. 9** Thin-foil transmission electron micrograph illustrating deformation twinning in retained austenite of upper bainite microstructure in a high-silicon steel (Fe-0.4C-4.15Ni-2.01Si), austenitized at 950 °C (2120 °F) for 15 min and isothermally transformed at 400 °C (750 °F) for 1 h. Specimen deformed to fracture. 45 000×. (Ref 18)

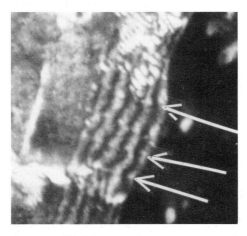

**Fig. 10** Thin-foil transmission electron micrograph (weak beam image) showing evidence of a distribution of linear defects (see arrows) spaced 10 to 15 nm (100 to 150 Å) in the bainite/ferrite interface of a high-silicon steel (Fe-0.4C-4.15Ni-2.01Si), austenitized at 1100 °C (2010 °F) for 30 min and isothermally transformed at 370 °C (700 °F) for 8 h. 580 000×. (Ref 19)

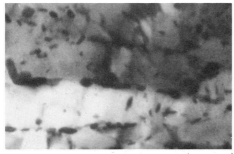

**Fig. 11** Thin-foil transmission electron micrograph of a tempered upper bainite microstructure in a high-silicon steel (Fe-0.43C-3.0Mn-2.12Si) that was austenitized at 1200 °C (2190 °F) for 5 min, isothermally transformed 350 °C (660 °F) for 205 min, and tempered at 500 °C (930 °F) for 120 min. 37 000×. (Ref 17)

commonly those of Bagaryatski or Isaichev (see Table 1) and are consistent with carbide precipitation from the parent austenite. The habit plane and long direction reported are $(101)_\theta$ and $[010]_\theta$, respectively (Ref 20, 21). The orientation relationship between cementite and austenite is generally assumed to be that given by Pitsch (see Table 1).

**Lower bainite.** The transition between upper and lower bainite usually is reported to vary from approximately 550 °C (1020 °F) at low carbon contents to approximately 350 °C (660 °F) at 0.8% C. As shown in Fig. 12, it is paralleled by similar variations in the $B_s$ and $M_s$ (martensite start) temperatures (Ref 4, 22, 23).

Lower bainite consists of heavily dislocated ferritic plates, rather than laths (Ref 24), and although the evidence is less substantial, the plates are probably comprised of a cluster of smaller ferrite subunits (Fig. 13) as in upper bainite (Ref 3, 17). Nucleation of the plates occurs from prior austenite grain boundaries or from previously formed plates (Fig. 14).

The orientation relationship between lower bainite plates and parent austenite is close to Kurdjumov-Sachs or Nishiyama-Wassermann (see Table 1) (Ref 17, 20, 24). Different habit planes of $\{496\}_\gamma$ and $\{254\}_\gamma$ have been reported (Ref 15, 24), from which it may be concluded that the orientation relationship and habit plane, as in the case of upper bainite, are likely to be irrational.

Refinement of the plate structure at low temperature makes it difficult to differentiate between lower bainite and either upper bainite or tempered martensite using optical microscopy. However, the most characteristic metallographic difference between classical upper and lower bainite is the distribution of carbides, which is readily apparent using electron microscopy. In the lower bainitic microstructure, carbide precipitates are located within the ferrite plates (Fig. 15), rather than between plates.

The lathlike carbides typically adopt a unique habit plane variant in the ferrite, usually oriented at a characteristic angle of approximately 60° to the long axis of the bainitic plate. This feature is in contrast to tempered martensitic structures, in which more than one variant is always observed.

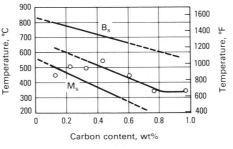

**Fig. 12** Lower bainite start temperature (data from Ref 4) in relation to the $B_s$ and $M_s$ temperatures. (Ref 23)

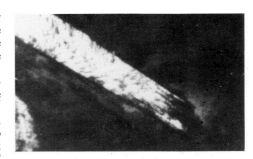

**Fig. 13** Thin-foil transmission electron micrograph showing the morphology at the tip of a lower bainitic ferrite plate in a high-silicon steel (Fe-0.43C-3.0Mn-2.12Si), austenitized 1200 °C (2190 °F) for 5 min and isothermally transformed at 255 °C (495 °F) for 10 min. 19 000×. (Ref 17)

Furthermore, lower bainitic ferrite does not contain transformation twins that are characteristic of martensite in medium- and high-carbon steels. Lower bainitic carbides are identified as cementite or ε-carbide (Fe$_{2.4}$C). Generally, ε-carbide forms first and is then succeeded by cementite, as in the tempering of martensitic steels, provided that the carbon concentration is sufficiently high to overcome the energetically more favorable conditions for carbon atom segregation to dislocations (estimated to be ~0.55% C for bainitic structures) (Ref 23).

It has been shown (Ref 25) that ε-carbide occurs in lower bainite with an orientation relationship to the ferrite close to that proposed by Jack (see Table 1). Cementite has been reported (Ref 4, 15, 20, 25) to adopt the Bagaryatski or Isaichev orientation relationships, with a habit plane of $(201)_\theta$ or $(213)_\alpha$ suggested in the case of the Isaichev relationship. Jack and Bagaryatski orientation relationships are found for ε-carbide and cementite precipitates, respectively, in tempered martensite, in which the carbides have formed directly from supersaturated ferrite. However, both relationships can be interpreted in terms of precipitation from austenite. Moreover, the observation of a unique variant of the orientation relationship and a linear dispersion of the carbides within the plates (Fig. 16) has been interpreted as evidence for precipitation in contact with parent austenite at the bainitic plate interface (Ref 14). However, a rational orientation relationship of:

$$(011)_\theta \parallel \{011\}_\alpha$$
$$[1\bar{2}2]_\theta \parallel \langle 100 \rangle_\alpha$$

with up to four different variants of the cementite $\{011\}_\alpha$ habit plane (Fig. 17) has been found in a silicon-manganese steel (Ref 17). Because this unique orientation relationship cannot be combined with the Kurdjumov-Sachs relation to yield the anticipated three-phase α-γ-θ relationship, it is consistent only with direct precipitation from supersaturated ferrite.

## Extensions of Bainite Terminology

**Inverse Bainite.** Bainitic structures are also produced in hypereutectoid steels. In these materials, however, the carbide phase can nucleate first, thus leading to differences in the overall appearance of the microstructure compared to typical ferrous bainite (Ref 4, 26, 27). The initial cementite precipitates as a lath or plate, which then becomes engulfed by a sheath of ferrite. This formation (Fig. 18), also known as inverse bainite, then acts as the nucleus for adjacent austenite decomposition to produce larger ferrite laths and smaller cementite particles by a more classical bainitic reaction (Fig. 19).

The initial structural unit of inverse bainite may also change to normal bainite during lengthening. The limited ability of the inverse bainite unit to reproduce itself, due to the greater volume fraction and higher growth velocity of the ferrite regions, ensures that it generally occupies only a relatively small fraction of the total microstructure. A significant proportion of the normal bainite fraction of the microstructure nucleates independently of the inverse bainite structure.

**Granular bainite** refers to granular structures comprising classical bainite mixed with relatively coarse grains of polygonal and massive ferrite and regions of martensite and retained austenite (Fig. 20). These granular structures are observed only in low- or medium-alloy steels and are most often produced by continuous cooling rather than isothermal treatment (Ref 28).

**Columnar bainite** refers to nonacicular ferritic grains containing cementite precipitates observed in medium-carbon steels partially transformed in the bainitic temperature range under very high pressures (Fig. 21). However, similar structures have also been reported to occur in higher carbon steels (Ref 29).

**Nonferrous Bainite.** Some nonferrous alloys transform in a temperature range between a higher temperature discontinuous reaction and a lower temperature martensitic reaction to reveal structures morphologically similar to classical bainite in steel. However, this similarity in microstructural appearance with steels does not imply a common transformation mechanism.

For example, macroscopic plates of $\alpha$ phase formed isothermally from $\gamma$ phase in a U-0.75Ti alloy can be composed of a sheaf of narrower plates (Fig. 22) and can have precipitates between them (Fig. 23), analogous in overall appearance to the classical form of upper bainite in steels (Ref 30).

Many titanium-base alloys also show bainitic-like microstructures (Ref 31), perhaps the most typical being Ti-4Ni, which produces nonlamellar plates of $\alpha$ phase with retained $\beta$

**Fig. 14** Lower bainite in a 4360 steel specimen, austenitized, isothermally transformed at 300 °C (570 °F), and quenched. The matrix is untempered martensite. Picral. 500×. (Ref 1)

**Fig. 15** Thin-foil transmission electron micrograph of lower bainite in 4360 steel that was austenitized, isothermally transformed at 300 °C (570 °F), and quenched. The dark bands in the bainite are cementite. 15 000×. (Ref 1)

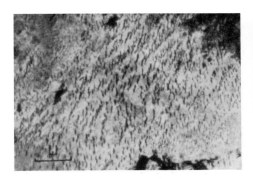

**Fig. 16** Thin-foil transmission electron micrograph of cementite distribution within a lower bainite plate in a plain-carbon steel (0.69% C), austenitized at 1200 °C (2190 °F) for 3 min and isothermally transformed at 300 °C (570 °F). The habit plane of the bainite plate is nearly parallel to the foil surface. 9500×. (Ref 22)

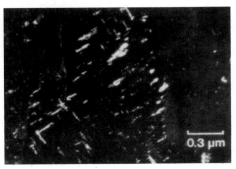

**Fig. 17** Thin-foil transmission electron micrograph (dark-field image) illuminating several cementite variants precipitated intragranularly within a single plate of lower bainite in a high-silicon steel (Fe-0.43C-3.0Mn-2.12Si), austenitized at 1200 °C (2190 °F) for 5 min and isothermally transformed at 300 °C (570 °F) for 2 min. 32 000×. (Ref 17)

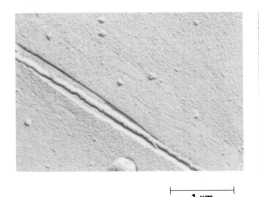

**Fig. 18** Replica electron micrograph showing the microstructural unit of inverse bainite comprising a single cementite plate sheathed with ferrite in an Fe-1.34C alloy, austenitized at 1200 °C (2190 °F) for 15 min and isothermally transformed at 600 °C (1110 °F) for 2 s. 17 000×. (Ref 27)

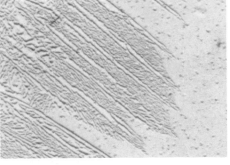

**Fig. 19** Replica electron micrograph showing the evolution of a normal bainitic structure from initially formed units of inverse bainite in an Fe-1.34C alloy, austenitized 1200 °C (2190 °F) for 15 min and isothermally transformed at 550 °C (1020 °F) for 7 s. 7000×. (Ref 27)

**Fig. 20** Replica electron micrograph of mixed microstructure with the original austenite grain boundaries delineated by irregularly shaped particles, identified as two-phase austenite-martensite, but occasionally also containing ferrite and carbide. Specimen was low-alloy steel (Fe-0.2C-1Cr-0.5Mo), austenitized and transformed during continuous cooling at 185 °C (335 °F) per minute. No magnification given. (Ref 28)

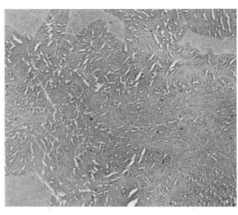

**Fig. 21** Replica electron micrograph of blocky, or columnar-shaped, regions generally nucleated at grain boundaries that contain a coarse dispersion of carbides (sometimes in a fanlike distribution) in a steel, austenitized and isothermally transformed at 290 °C (550 °F) under a pressure of 24 kbar (2400 MPa). 2800×. (Ref 29)

0.5 μm

**Fig. 22** Thin-foil transmission electron micrograph showing a sheaf of narrow α-phase plates in a U-0.75Ti alloy, solution treated at 800 °C (1470 °F) for 30 min and isothermally transformed at 630 °C (1165 °F) for 5 s. Use of an optical microscope resulted in the appearance of a single plate. 23 000×. (Ref 30)

0.3 μm

**Fig. 23** Thin-foil transmission electron micrograph of neighboring α-phase plates with precipitation visible between the plates in a U-0.75Ti alloy, solution treated at 800 °C (1470 °F) for 30 min and isothermally transformed at 610 °C (1130 °F) for 20 s. 37 000×. (Ref 30)

phase and precipitates of $Ti_2Ni$ between (Fig. 24).

Some copper-base alloys form plate structures at temperatures below that at which pearlitic structures form. Copper-aluminum and copper-tin exhibit structures similar to the Cu-27Sn alloy in Fig. 25, which shows grain-boundary-nucleated α-phase plates projecting into the parent matrix with precipitation between the plates (Ref 32).

The nonferrous system receiving the most study is brass (Ref 2, 33-35). Copper-zinc (40 to 44% Zn) alloys decompose beneath an apparent $B_s$ temperature, according to separate cooling curve kinetics, to yield $\alpha_1$-phase plates characteristically formed in obtuse-angled V-shaped pairs (Fig. 26). Invariant plane-strain surface relief is observed (Fig. 3), and the plates have an irrational orientation relationship with the parent β' phase and irrational habit plane close to $\{2\ 11\ 12\}_{\beta'}$, both of which are equivalent to the lower temperature martensitic phase in the alloy.

The plates also show evidence of inhomogeneous shear by slip in the form of a regular array of stacking faults. Consequently, the transformation shows characteristics equivalent to a martensitic-type mechanism, but it remains unclear experimentally as to whether there is an initial composition change in the $\alpha_1$ plates during their immediate formation, although a subsequent progressive partitioning of copper and zinc occurs.

## REFERENCES

1. R.F. Hehemann, Ferrous and Non-Ferrous Bainitic Structures, in *Metals Handbook*, Vol 8, 8th ed., *Metallography, Structures and Phase Diagrams*, American Society for Metals, 1973, p 194-196
2. P.E.J. Flewitt and J.M. Towner, The Decomposition of Beta Prime in Copper-Zinc Alloys, *J. Inst. Met.*, Vol 95, 1967, p 273-280

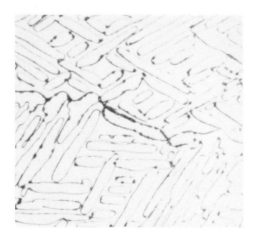

**Fig. 24** Plates of α phase in a matrix of retained β phase with $Ti_2Ni$ precipitation at the plate boundaries in a Ti-4.0Ni alloy, solution treated 1000 °C (1830 °F) for 20 min and isothermally transformed at 750 °C (1380 °F) for 1 h. 95% $H_2O$, 4% $HNO_3$, and 1% HF. 800×. (Ref 31)

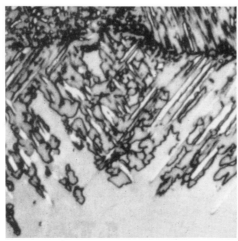

**Fig. 25** Laths of α phase with interlath precipitation in a Cu-27.0Sn alloy, solution treated and isothermally transformed at 500 °C (930 °F) for 1 min. No etchant given. 2000×. (Ref 32)

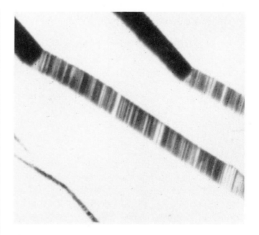

**Fig. 26** Thin-foil transmission electron micrograph of bainite plates in β brass (Cu-41.1Zn) that was solution treated, isothermally transformed at 250 °C (480 °F), and quenched. Diffraction conditions revealed crystal faults in one leg of each plate. 20 000×. (Ref 1)

3. J.M. Oblak and R.F. Hehemann, Structure and Growth of Widmanstätten Ferrite and Bainite, in *Transformation and Hardenability in Steels*, Climax Molybdenum Co., Ann Arbor, MI, 1967, p 15-30

4. F.B. Pickering, The Structure and Properties of Bainite in Steels, in *Transformation and Hardenability in Steels*, Climax Molybdenum Co., Ann Arbor, MI, 1967, p 109-129

5. G.V. Smith and R.F. Mehl, Lattice Relationships in Decomposition of Austenite to Pearlite, Bainite and Martensite, *Trans. AIME*, Vol 150, 1942, p 211-226

6. A.T. Davenport "The Crystallography of Upper Bainite," Republic Steel Corp. Research Center, Cleveland, Feb 1974

7. B.P.J. Sandvik, The Bainite Reaction in Fe-Si-C Alloys: The Primary Stage, *Met. Trans. A*, Vol 13, 1982, p 777-787

8. G. Kurdjumov and G. Sachs, *Z. Physik*, Vol 64, 1930, p 325-343

9. Z. Nishiyama, *Sci. Rep. Tôhoku Univ.*, Vol 23, 1934, p 637-664

10. G. Wassermann, *Arch. Eisenhüttenwes.*, Vol 6, 1933, p 347-351

11. Yu A. Bagaryatski, *Doklady Akad. Nauk SSSR*, Vol 73, 1950, p 1161-1164

12. I.V. Isaichev, *Z. Tekhn. Fiziki*, Vol 17, 1947, p 835-838

13. W. Pitsch, *Acta Metall.*, Vol 10, 1962, p 897-900

14. K.H. Jack, *J. Iron Steel Inst.*, Vol 169, 1951, p 26-36

15. Y. Ohmori, The Crystallography of the Lower Bainite Transformation in a Plain Carbon Steel, *Trans. Iron Steel Inst. Jpn.*, Vol 11, 1971, p 95-101

16. S. Hoekstra, A Check of the I.P.S. Theory with the Aid of an Accurate Determination of Habit Planes and Orientation Relationships in Bainitic Steels, *Acta Metall.*, Vol 28, 1980, p 507-517

17. H.K.D.H. Bhadeshia and D.V. Edmonds, Bainite Transformation in Silicon Steel, *Met. Trans. A*, Vol 10, 1979, p 895-907

18. V.T.T. Miihkinen, Mechanical Properties of High Strength Bainitic Steels Containing Retained Austenite, doctoral dissertation, University of Oxford, 1983

19. S. Cowley, private communication, University of Oxford, 1984

20. D.N. Shackleton and P.M. Kelly, The Crystallography of Cementite Precipitation in the Bainite Transformation, *Acta Metall.*, Vol 15, 1967, p 979-992

21. Y. Ohmori and R.W.K. Honeycombe, The Isothermal Transformation of Plain Carbon Austenite, *Trans. Iron Steel Inst. Jpn. (Suppl.)*, Vol 11, 1971, p 1160-1164

22. R.F. Mehl, The Physics of Hardenability—The Mechanism and the Rate of the Decomposition of Austenite, in *Hardenability of Alloy Steels*, American Society for Metals, 1939, p 1-54

23. H.K.D.H. Bhadeshia, The Lower Bainite Transformation and the Significance of Carbide Precipitation, *Acta Metall.*, Vol 28, 1980, p 1103-1114

24. G.R. Srinivasan and C.M. Wayman, The Crystallography of the Bainite Transformation, *Acta Metall.*, Vol 16, 1968, p 609-636

25. D.-H. Huang and G. Thomas, Metallography of Bainitic Transformation in Silicon Containing Steels, *Met. Trans. A*, Vol 8, 1977, p 1661-1674

26. M. Hillert, The Role of Interfacial Energy During Solid-State Phase Transformations, *Jernkontorets Ann.*, Vol 141, 1957, p 757-789

27. K.R. Kinsman and H.I. Aaronson, The Inverse Bainite Reaction in Hypereutectoid Fe-C Alloys, *Met. Trans.*, Vol 1, 1970, p 1485-1488

28. L.J. Habraken and M. Economopoulos, Bainitic Microstructures in Low-Carbon Alloy Steels and Their Mechanical Properties, in *Transformation and Hardenability in Steels*, Climax Molybdenum Co., Ann Arbor, MI, 1967, p 69-107

29. T.G. Nilan, Austenite Decomposition at High Pressure, in *Transformation and Hardenability in Steels*, Climax Molybdenum Co., Ann Arbor, MI, 1967, p 57-66

30. J.G. Spear, A Study of Solid-State Phase Transformations in Uranium Alloys, D. Phil. dissertation, University of Oxford, 1983

31. G.W. Franti, J.C. Williams, and H.I. Aaronson, A Survey of Eutectoid Decomposition in Ten Ti-X Sytems, *Met. Trans. A*, Vol 9, 1978, p 1641-1649

32. C.W. Spencer and D.J. Mack, Eutectoid Transformations in Non-Ferrous and Ferrous Alloy Systems, in *Decomposition of Austenite by Diffusional Processes*, V.F. Zackay and H.I. Aaronson, Ed., Interscience, 1962, p 549-603

33. R.D. Garwood, The Bainitic Transformation of the Beta Phase in Copper-Zinc Alloys, *J. Inst. Met.*, Vol 83, 1954-55, p 64-68

34. I. Cornelis and C.M. Wayman, Phase Transformations in Metastable $\beta'$ CuZn Alloys—II. Isothermal Transformations, *Acta Metall.*, Vol 22, 1974, p 301-311

35. P. Doig and P.E.J. Flewitt, Solute Redistribution During the Formation of $\alpha_1$ Bainite Plates in Cu-Zn and Cu-Au-Zn Alloys, in *Solid-Solid Phase Transformations*, H.I. Aaronson *et al.*, Ed., American Institute of Mining, Metallurgical, and Petroleum Engineers, New York, 1983, p 983-987

## SELECTED REFERENCES

- J.W. Christian, in *The Theory of Transformations in Metals and Alloys*, 1st ed., Pergamon Press, 1965, p 824-831
- R.F. Hehemann, The Bainite Transformation, in *Phase Transformations*, American Society for Metals, 1970, p 397-432
- R.F. Hehemann, K.R. Kinsman, and H.I. Aaronson, A Debate on the Bainite Reaction, *Met. Trans.*, Vol 3, 1972, p 1077-1094
- G.R. Purdy and M. Hillert, On the Nature of the Bainite Transformation in Steels, *Acta Metall.*, Vol 32, 1984, p 823-828
- J.W. Christian and D.V. Edmonds, The Bainite Transformation, in *Phase Transformations in Ferrous Alloys*, American Society for Metals, 1985

# Martensitic Structures

MARTENSITE is the generic term for microstructures formed by diffusionless phase transformation. The parent and product phases in a martensitic transformation have a specific crystallographic relationship. The movements of atoms during such a transformation are cooperative and change the shape of the transformed region or cause a surface upheaval (tilt) if the product phase intersects a free surface of the parent phase. The definition of martensitic transformation includes various resulting shapes, substructures, and crystal structures of martensitic units, all of which may vary with composition in a given material.

Martensitic transformations occur in steels and iron-base alloys as well as several nonferrous systems, such as Cu-Al and Au-Cd. Ceramists have also identified and termed displacive the characteristics of martensitic transformations in nonmetal systems, such as silica (Ref 1) and zirconia (Ref 2).

This article will discuss martensitic structures in ferrous and nonferrous alloys. Additional examples of martensitic structures can be found in the articles in the Section "Metallographic Techniques and Microstructures: Specific Metals and Alloys" in this Volume.

## Ferrous Martensitic Structures

By G.R. Speich
Professor and Chairman
Department of Metallurgy
    and Materials Engineering
Illinois Institute of Technology

Martensite usually is produced in steels or iron-base alloys by rapid quenching of austenite, the parent phase. Uninterrupted, rapid cooling is necessary to prevent decomposition of the austenite by diffusional processes, which would form such products as ferrite or pearlite. This mode of transformation kinetics is referred to as athermal (without thermal

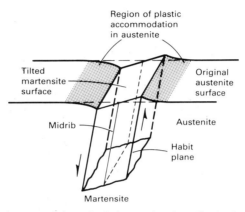

**Fig. 1** (Ref 3) Schematic of shear and surface tilt associated with formation of a martensite plate.

activation) to differentiate it from isothermal kinetics that characterize thermally activated diffusion-controlled transformations.

Martensite forms by a shear mechanism. Figure 1 shows several features of the shear or displacive transformation of austenite to martensite. The arrows indicate the directions of shear on opposite sides of the plane on which the transformation was initiated. The martensite crystal formed is displaced by the shear partly above and partly below the surface of the austenite. Therefore, the shear transformation rotates or tilts the originally horizontal surface of the parent phase into a new orientation. Surface tilting is an important characteristic of shear-type or martensitic transformation. The atom by atom transfer across interfaces by which diffusion-controlled transformations proceed does not produce tilting, but tends to produce surfaces of the product phase parallel to the surface of the parent phase (Ref 4).

Figure 1 also shows that considerable flow or elastic accommodation of the parent austenite must accompany the formation of a martensite crystal. The constraints of the parent phase eventually limit the width of a martensite volume, and further transformation can proceed only by the nucleation of new

volumes. If a parent austenite could not withstand the shape change produced by the martensitic shears, separation or cracking at the martensite/parent phase interface would occur. Austenite in steels normally has sufficient ductility to accommodate martensite formation. However, in many ceramic systems, the parent phase cannot adapt to the shape change, and displacive transformations must be avoided (Ref 4).

Martensite crystals ideally have planar interfaces with the parent austenite (see Fig. 1). The preferred crystal planes of the austenite on which the martensite crystals form are designated habit planes, which vary according to alloy composition. The midrib shown in Fig. 1 is generally considered to be the starting plane for the formation of a plate of martensite and may have a different fine structure than other parts of the plate (Ref 4).

An example of surface relief and its relationship to martensitic microstructure is shown in Fig. 2 to 5. Figure 2 shows the surface relief associated with the formation of hundreds of martensite crystals. The surface tilting is emphasized in some areas by the dark shadows present on surfaces tilted away from the light source. In Fig. 3, the surface relief has been almost polished away, and in Fig. 4, the surface shown in Fig. 3 has been etched. Lastly, Fig. 5 shows the microstructure after the surface has been polished to remove all relief and etched once again. Comparison of Fig. 4 and 5 with Fig. 2 reveals the direct correspondence of the surface relief with the martensitic units in the polished and etched microstructure. In polished and etched sections, the individual crystals of martensite appear long and thin and are very often acicular or needlelike. In three dimensions, however, the crystals have a lath or plate shape with flat interfaces, as shown in Fig. 1. Therefore, needlelike shapes visible on polished and etched surfaces are cross sections through laths or plates (Ref 4).

The temperature at which the martensitic transformation begins during continuous cooling is designated the martensitic start temperature ($M_s$). The $M_s$ reflects the amount

**Fig. 2** Surface tilting after quenching

**Fig. 3** Partially polished surface

**Fig. 4** Same area as in Fig. 3 after etching. See also Fig. 5

**Fig. 5** Same area as in Fig. 3 after polishing to remove all relief and re-etching

**Fig. 2 to 5** Surface tilting and its relationship to martensitic structure in an Fe-0.2C alloy. Nital. 175X. (Ref 4)

Martensites in steels generally contain more carbon or other alloying elements than can be contained in the ferrite phase under equilibrium conditions. In addition, martensite has a fine-scale substructure that consists of a high density of dislocations or internal twins.

The high strength of martensite can be attributed to (1) the high degree of supersaturation of carbon achieved in martensite (generally considered the most important factor), (2) the fine grain size and fine substructure of martensite (possibly of equal importance in low-carbon steels), and (3) the presence of substitutional alloying elements (usually of minor importance).

## Crystal Structure

In steels, the parent phase is usually austenite with a face-centered cubic (fcc) crystal structure, but the crystal structure of the product phase may be body-centered cubic (bcc), body-centered tetragonal (bct), or hexagonal close-packed (hcp). Under special conditions, steels undergo martensitic transformations in which the crystal structure of the product phase reverts to that of the parent. For example, high pressures applied dynamically by shock loading or statically may cause the bcc phase to revert to the fcc or hcp phase by a martensitic transformation. Moreover, with rapid heating of Fe-30Ni into the austenitic range, the bcc martensite may revert to fcc by a martensitic transformation.

Most medium-carbon and high-carbon steels form martensite with a bct crystal structure, because carbon atoms occupy only one of the three possible sets of octahedral interstitial positions. Low-carbon martensites do not exhibit this tetragonality, probably because of segregation of carbon atoms to dislocations during quenching. Iron-base martensites that contain only substitutional alloying elements, such as iron-nickel and iron-nickel-chromium, usually have bcc crystal structures, because the substitutional alloying elements are distributed at random on the lattice sites. However, tetragonality is observed in certain iron-nickel-titanium martensites because of the formation of $Ni_3Ti$ clusters in the austenite.

The high alloy content of some steels may result in martensitic crystal structures other than bcc or bct. Therefore, in iron-manganese alloys with more than 15% Mn and in some stainless steels, martensite forms with an hcp structure.

## Orientation Relation and Habit Plane

The parent austenite (fcc) and the product martensite (bcc, bct, or hcp) phases are in general related crystallographically; thus, close-packed rows and close-packed planes in

of thermodynamic driving force required to initiate the shear transformation of austenite to martensite. Figure 6 shows that the $M_s$ decreases significantly with increasing carbon content in iron-carbon alloys and carbon steels. Carbon in solid solution increases the strength or shear resistance of the austenite; therefore, greater undercooling or driving force is required to begin the shear for martensite formation in higher carbon alloys. Increasing alloy content also decreases the $M_s$. The $M_s$ temperatures of most carbon and low-alloy steels are between 500 and 200 °C (930 and 390 °F), but the $M_s$ temperatures of some high-alloy steels, such as stainless steels,

may be below room temperature.

The martensite finish temperature ($M_f$), the temperature at which the martensite transformation is complete in a given alloy, is approximately 120 °C (215 °F) below the $M_s$, although this difference varies with carbon content. A general feature of martensitic transformation is that the amount of martensite formed depends primarily on the temperature to which the specimen is cooled and not on the length of time at the transformation temperature. In certain high-alloy steels, however, substantial amounts of martensite may form isothermally at temperatures below zero.

the two phases are parallel. Therefore, in the fcc → bcc transformation, the Kurdjumov-Sachs (K-S) orientation relationship $\{111\}_A \parallel \{101\}_M$ and $\langle 110 \rangle_A \parallel \langle 111 \rangle_M$ is valid for high-carbon steels with $\{225\}_A$ habit planes. The K-S orientation relationship also holds for low-carbon steels with $\{557\}_A$ habit planes. The other orientation relationship, which is attributed to Nishiyama, is $\{111\}_A \parallel \{011\}_M$ and $\langle 112 \rangle_A \parallel \langle 011 \rangle_M$. This relationship is observed in alloys in which the martensite plates have $\{259\}_A$ habit planes. In the fcc → hcp transformation, the orientation relation $\{111\}_A \parallel \{00\bar{1}1\}_M$ and $\langle 110 \rangle_A \parallel \langle 11\bar{2}0 \rangle_M$ is always observed.

The martensite unit is flat, and it usually lies in a plane that is parallel to a crystallographic plane in the austenite, which is referred to as the habit plane (see Fig. 1). The habit plane of the martensite formed in the fcc → bcc transformation varies with alloy content of the iron or steel and precludes assignation of a simple Miller index. Low-car-

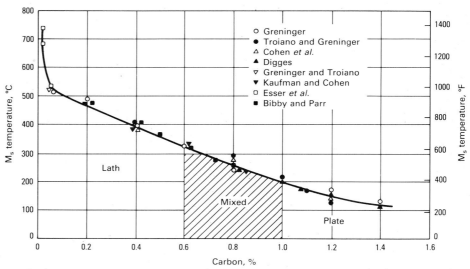

**Fig. 6** Martensite start ($M_s$) temperatures as a function of carbon content in steels. Composition ranges of lath and plate martensite in iron-carbon alloys are also shown. Investigations indicated are identified in Ref 5.

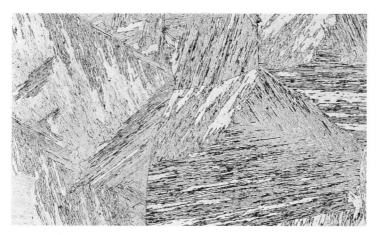

**Fig. 7** Lath martensite in a low-carbon alloy steel (0.03% C, 2% Mn). See also Fig. 9, which is a thin-foil electron micrograph of this same specimen. 2% nital. 100×

**Fig. 8** Lath martensite in an Fe-20Ni alloy. See also Fig. 10, which is a thin-foil electron micrograph of this structure in a similar alloy. 35% sodium thiosulfate. 200×. (A.R. Marder)

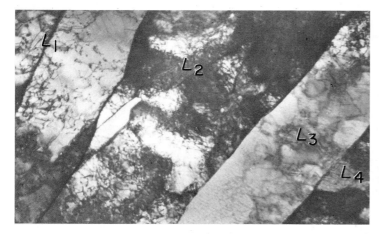

**Fig. 9** Thin-foil electron micrograph of the 0.03C-2Mn alloy steel specimen in Fig. 7 showing dislocation substructure in four of the martensite laths (marked $L_1$ to $L_4$). 26 000×

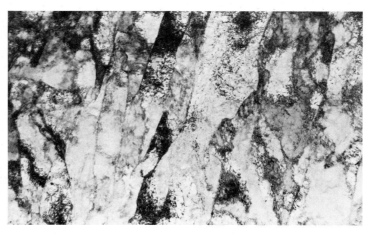

**Fig. 10** Thin-foil electron micrograph of lath martensite in Fe-16Ni showing dislocation substructure. See also Fig. 8, which shows lath martensite in a similar alloy. 20 000×

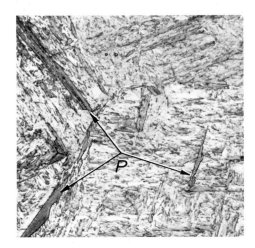

**Fig. 11** Plate martensite (marked *P*) and lath martensite in medium-carbon (0.57% C) steel. See also Fig. 12, which is a thin-foil electron micrograph of this specimen. 2% nital. 1000×

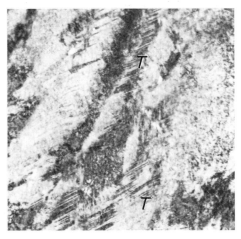

**Fig. 12** Thin-foil electron micrograph of one of the regions of plate martensite marked *P* in Fig. 11 showing twinned substructure (marked *T*). 26 000×

**Fig. 13** Lath martensite in iron, produced by shock loading to 15.5 GPa (2.25 × 10⁶ psi). Thin-foil electron micrograph showing substructure. 24 000×. (W.C. Leslie)

**Fig. 14** Plate martensite in a high-carbon (1.2% C) steel. Matrix is retained austenite. See also Fig. 15 and 16 for views of plate martensite in iron-nickel alloys. 2% nital. 1000×

**Fig. 15** Plate martensite and retained austenite (light) in an Fe-32Ni alloy. See also Fig. 16, which is a thin-foil electron micrograph of plate martensite in a similar alloy. 2% nital. 500×. (W.C. Leslie)

**Fig. 16** Plate martensite formed in an austenitic single crystal of an Fe-33.5Ni alloy by cooling to −196 °C (−321 °F). Plates are visible only because of surface relief generated by martensitic transformation. Etchant unknown. 200×. (Ref 4)

bon steels have a habit plane near $\{111\}_A$; high-carbon steels have a habit plane near $\{225\}_A$ or $\{259\}_A$. The habit plane of the martensite formed in the fcc → hcp transformation is always $\{111\}_A$.

## Morphology of Martensite

Martensite, once nucleated, propagates at nearly the velocity of an elastic wave in iron (~10⁵ cm/s, or 4 × 10⁴ in./s). Propagation in a direction lying in the plane of the martensite plate continues until a grain boundary, a twin boundary, or another martensite volume is encountered. Propagation in a direction perpendicular to the plane of the plate generally ceases when the cross section reaches a certain length-to-width ratio. This limit applies because of strain-energy effects or because the mobility of the interface between the austenite and martensite lattices is destroyed. Therefore, many martensitic transformations result in lath-shape or plate-shape martensite units.

The martensite units that form in the shape of laths are grouped into larger sheaves, or packets. This structure is generally called lath martensite, although it also has been called massive martensite or packet martensite. When the martensite units form as individual, lenticular, plate-shape units, the structure is called plate martensite. In certain high-alloy steels, the martensite units are formed as thin sheets called sheet martensite.

**Lath martensite,** the most common martensitic structure, is formed in all low-carbon and medium-carbon steels, maraging steels, and stainless steels (see Fig. 7 and 8). The crystal structure of lath martensite is usually bcc in low-carbon steels and substitutional iron-base alloys. The substructure of lath martensite consists of a high density of dislocations, some of which form laths or cells (see Fig. 9 and 10), a substructure similar to that of cold-worked iron. The martensite laths may be separated by small-angle or large-angle boundaries. In Fig. 9, the areas marked $L_1$ to $L_4$ are different laths.

In medium-carbon steels, although the principal form of martensite is lath martensite, some plate martensite also may be detected (Fig. 11). The substructure of the lath martensite is similar to that of other lath martensite (Fig. 10). The substructure of the plate martensite (regions marked *P* in Fig. 11) consists of fine, internal twins (see Fig. 12). Lath martensite can be produced in high-purity iron by extremely rapid quenching of thin sections or, as shown in Fig. 13, by shock loading at more than 13 GPa (1.89 × 10⁶ psi).

**Plate martensite** predominates in high-carbon steels (see Fig. 6 and 14) and in substitutional iron-base alloys with $M_s$ temperatures below room temperature (Fig. 15). Figure 16 shows plate martensite that was produced by cooling a single crystal of Fe-33.5Ni in liquid nitrogen (−196 °C, or −321 °F). Subzero cooling was required because

**Fig. 17** Sheet martensite in Fe-19Mn alloy. See Fig. 18, a thin-foil electron micrograph of this structure in a similar alloy. 2% nital. 1000×

**Fig. 18** Thin-foil electron micrograph of sheet martensite in Fe-15Mn alloy. Because of the thinness of the sheet, no substructure is detectable. See also Fig. 17. 27 500×

the high nickel content had lowered the $M_s$ to $-30$ °C ($-22$ °F).

The crystal structure of plate martensite may be bct (Fe-1.0C and Fe-30Ni-6Ti) or bcc (Fe-30Ni). The substructure of plate martensite consists of fine, internal twins with a spacing of 5 to 10 nm (50 to 100 Å). These twins usually do not extend to the sides of the plates, but degenerate into complex dislocation arrays near the periphery of the plate. Recent theories suggest that the twins provide a crystallographic shear that does not alter the crystal structure but that is required to

**Table 1  Characteristics of martensite in iron and steel**

| Shape and substructure of martensite | Change in crystal structure | Alloy system (and typical solute content, %) | $M_s$ temperature | |
|---|---|---|---|---|
| | | | °C | °F |
| Lath, dislocation cells . . . . . . . . fcc → bcc | | Fe | 750 | 1382 |
| | | Fe-C (<0.4C) | 550-360 | 1022-680 |
| | | Fe-Ni (4-20Ni) | 470-150 | 878-302 |
| | | Fe-Mn (4-10Mn) | 700-180 | 1292-356 |
| | bcc → hcp → bcc | Fe | (a) | . . . |
| Plate, internal twins . . . . . . . . . fcc → bcc | | Fe-Ni (28-32Ni) | −20 to −200 | −4 to −328 |
| | fcc → bct | Fe-C (>1.0C) | 150-20 | 302-68 |
| | | Fe-30-Ni-6Ti | −150 | −238 |
| | bcc → fcc | Fe-30Ni | (b) | . . . |
| | | Fe-32Ni | (c) | . . . |
| Sheet, no substructure . . . . . . . fcc → hcp | | Fe-Mn (>15Mn) | 150-0 | 302-32 |
| | | Fe, 11-19Cr, 7-17Ni | −50 to −150 | −58 to −238 |

(a) Produced by shock loading to more than 13 GPa (1.89 × 10⁶ psi) at 25 °C (75 °F). (b) Produced by rapidly heating to more than 300 °C (570 °F). (c) Produced by shock loading to 17 GPa (2.47 × 10⁶ psi) at 25 °C (75 °F)

make the habit plane a plane of no rotation and no distortion.

**Sheet martensite** is formed in iron-manganese alloys containing more than 15% Mn (Fig. 17), in austenitic manganese steel (Hadfield steels), and in certain stainless steels. The crystal structure of sheet martensite is always hcp, and it is formed parallel to {111} austenite planes because of the simple nature of the transformation, fcc → hcp. The sheets are so thin that little or no substructure can be detected (Fig. 18). Table 1 summarizes some of the important characteristics of martensite formed in steels and iron-base alloys.

# Nonferrous Martensitic Structures

By John F. Breedis
Supervisor—Alloy Research
Olin Corporation

Nonferrous martensitic structures, viewed using optical (light) microscopy, nearly always consist of plates that are very similar in appearance regardless of the metal or alloy in which they have formed. As a consequence of the transformation mechanism, a prepolished surface develops relief, which is a characteristic feature of martensite and can be used for recognition of martensitic transformation. A typical example of this surface relief is that which forms in β-brass, as shown in Fig. 19 (see also Fig. 2 to 5 in the section "Ferrous Martensitic Structures").

The internal microstructure of the martensite, however, varies greatly among different metals and alloys. This internal structure, which can be resolved by thin-foil transmission electron microscopy, results from the transformation mechanism or from accommodation deformation between the parent and martensite product phases during transformation. Table 2 shows composition ranges for martensitic transformation and changes in crystal structure that occur in martensitic transformation for selected nonferrous metals and alloy systems.

## Faulted Martensite

The martensite formed in all the copper-rich alloys in Table 2 has a plate shape identical to that of the martensite in the copper-zinc alloy shown in Fig. 19; when polished and viewed by polarized-light microscopy, it has the typical appearance of the martensite in copper-aluminum alloys, as shown in Fig. 20. This appearance is independent of (1) the crystal structure of the martensite phase, (2) whether the internal structure is twinned or faulted, and (3) the presence or absence of crystallographic order.

Because martensite formation is diffusionless, the order or disorder of the parent phase is transferred to the martensite. Disordered bcc copper-aluminum alloys (β) form disordered hcp martensite (β′); ordered cubic copper-aluminum alloys (β₁) and copper-tin alloys (β₁ or γ) form ordered orthorhombic martensite that is internally faulted (β′₁) or twinned (γ′). Growth of martensite plates is restricted by the grain boundaries of the parent phase and by previously formed plates.

The internally faulted structures in β′ and β′₁ martensite as well as the martensite in β-brass appear as closely spaced striations (Fig. 21). The faults usually extend across martensite plates, but occasionally terminate at partial dislocations. Not evident in the ordered β′₁ martensite shown in Fig. 21 is the antiphase domain structure. Under suitable diffraction-contrast conditions in an electron microscope, this structure appears in thin-foil electron micrographs as curved, dark boundaries that are separated by approximately 0.4 µm and that span faults and plate interfaces without apparent change in direction.

The faulted structures discussed above are believed to result from the transformation mechanism, but this is not true of all faulted structures. Martensite formed in cobalt and its alloys is fully coherent in that the lattice constants and crystal orientations are closely matched between the parent and martensite phases, and a mechanism-related substructure is not required. However, errors in atomic stacking do occur during transformation, and high densities of stacking faults develop that are associated with the habit plane

**Fig. 19** Metastable $\beta$-brass (Cu-39Zn) polished before martensitic transformation (achieved by cooling to $-232$ °C, or $-386$ °F) showing surface relief that resulted from the transformation. 400×. (D. Hull)

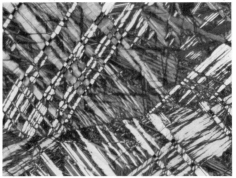

**Fig. 20** $\beta'_1$ martensite in Cu-12Al. This structure is typical of $\beta'$, $\beta'_1$, and $\gamma'$ martensites in copper-aluminum and copper-tin alloys. As-polished. Polarized light illumination. 500×. (I. Lefever and L. Delaey)

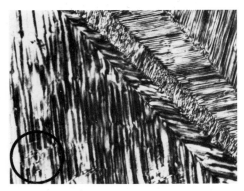

**Fig. 21** $\beta'_1$ martensite in Cu-12Al, with faults typical of those in copper-aluminum, copper-tin, and copper-zinc alloys. Some faults stop at dislocations (circled area). Thin-foil electron micrograph. 45 000×. (H. Warlimont)

of the martensite phase, which is parallel to the octahedral plane of the parent phase.

## Twinned Martensite

Fine-scale twin bands such as those found in $\gamma'$ martensite in copper-aluminum alloys

**Table 2 Martensitic transformations in selected nonferrous metals and alloy systems**

| Metal or alloy system | Composition range for transformation, % | Change in crystal structure; parent → martensite(a) |
|---|---|---|
| **Internally faulted structures** | | |
| Co . . . . . . . . . . . . . . . . . . . | . . . | fcc → hcp |
| Co-Fe . . . . . . . . . . . . . . | 0-3Fe | fcc → hcp |
| Co-Ni . . . . . . . . . . . . . . | 0-28Ni | fcc → hcp |
| Cu-Al . . . . . . . . . . . . . | 10-11Al | bcc → hcp |
| | 11-13Al | ord cu (cF 16) → ord ortho(b) |
| Cu-Sn . . . . . . . . . . . . . | 22-24Sn | ord cu (cF 16) → ord ortho(b) |
| Cu-Zn . . . . . . . . . . . . . | 38-41.5Zn | ord cu (cP2) → ord fcc |
| **Internally twinned structures** | | |
| Au-Cd . . . . . . . . . . . . . | 33-35Cd | ord cu (cP2) → ord ortho |
| Au-Mn . . . . . . . . . . . . | 74-78Au | ord cu (cP2) → ord tet |
| Cu-Al . . . . . . . . . . . . . | 13-14Al | ord cu (cF 16) → ord ortho(b) |
| Cu-Sn . . . . . . . . . . . . . | 24-26Sn | ord cu (cF 16) → ord ortho(b) |
| In-Tl . . . . . . . . . . . . . . | 28-33Tl | fcc → bct |
| Mn-Cu . . . . . . . . . . . . | 20-25Cu | fcc → bct |
| Ti . . . . . . . . . . . . . . . . . | . . . | bcc → hcp |
| Ti-Al-Mo-V . . . . . . . . | 8Al-1Mo-1V | bcc → hcp |
| Ti-Cb . . . . . . . . . . . . . . | 0-10Nb | bcc → hcp |
| | 10-14Hb | bcc → ortho |
| Ti-Cu . . . . . . . . . . . . . | 0-8Cu | bcc → hcp |
| Ti-Fe . . . . . . . . . . . . . | 0-3Fe | bcc → hcp |
| Ti-Mn . . . . . . . . . . . . | 0-5Mn | bcc → hcp |
| Ti-Mo . . . . . . . . . . . . | 0-4Mo | bcc → hcp |
| | 4-10Mo | bcc → ortho |
| Ti-O . . . . . . . . . . . . . . | 0.10 | bcc → hcp |
| Ti-V . . . . . . . . . . . . . . | 0-8V | bcc → hcp |

(a) The Pearson symbols are given parenthetically for ordered-cubic parent structures (see the article "Crystal Structure of Metals" in this Volume). ord cu, ordered cubic; ortho, orthorhombic; tet, tetragonal. (b) Crystal structure in doubt

are resolved only at high magnification by thin-foil transmission electron microscopy (Fig. 22). The twin bands within each plate are approximately 10 to 50 nm (100 to 500 Å) wide, are associated in general with one twinning system, and extend across each martensite plate. Close examination (circled area in Fig. 22) reveals that twin bands are subdivided by fine striations representing stacking faults and higher-order twin bands. Again, antiphase domain boundaries are evident only under suitable diffraction-contrast conditions and appear in $\gamma'$ martensite as curved, dark boundaries that extend indiscriminately across the interfaces of martensite plates but are discontinuous across twin boundaries.

Elastic constraints imposed by the parent phase on martensite formation are minimal in gold-cadmium, indium-tellurium, manganese-gold, and manganese-copper alloys, and an entire grain can transform to a single martensite crystal instead of to a number of small discrete plates. The martensites in these alloys are twinned on a scale usually visible by special optical microscopy techniques, as shown in Fig. 23, which was made using Nomarski interference contrast microscopy (for detailed information on the Nomarski technique, see the article "Color Metallography" in this Volume). Intersecting families of twin bands are observed when more than a single martensite plate is nucleated within a grain of a parent phase. Any given twin band has constant width but a range of apparent thicknesses of approximately 1 $\mu$m.

When viewed under an optical microscope, martensites in titanium alloys appear as fine, thin plates (see Fig. 24). However, using electron microscopy, these martensites display various internal structures. Martensitic structures in oxygen-containing titanium and in titanium-copper alloys with less than 4% Cu consist of random dislocations, stacking faults, and, depending on the alloy, some $\{10\bar{1}1\}$ or $\{10\bar{1}2\}$ twins. Martensites in all the following alloys exhibit $\{10\bar{1}1\}$ twins (Fig. 25): titanium-copper alloys containing 6 to 8% Cu, other binary alloys of titanium

**Fig. 22** $\gamma'$ martensite in Cu-14Al showing twin bands typical of those in martensite in copper-aluminum and copper-tin alloys. The bands contain fine striations (circled). A thin-foil electron micrograph. 40 000×. (H. Warlimont)

**Fig. 23** Twinned martensitic structure, in Au-34Cd, typical of martensites in gold-cadmium, indium-thallium, manganese-gold, and manganese-copper alloys. Nomarski interference contrast microscopy. As-polished. 400×. (R.S. Karz, M.A. Scherling, and D.S. Lieberman)

**Fig. 24** Martensitic structure, which consists of fine plates, in Ti-9Mo. Appearance is typical of martensites that form in unalloyed titanium and in Ti alloys. See also Fig. 25. 1% HF in glycerol. 200×

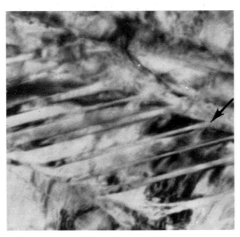

**Fig. 25** Twinned martensite in Ti-9Mo. The twin bands form serrations (arrow) where they intersect the edge of a martensite plate. A thin-foil electron micrograph. See also Fig. 24. 95 000×

with manganese, tantalum, or vanadium, and alloy Ti-8Al-1Mo-1V. The role of these twins has not been clearly established and, depending on the alloy, can be associated with the accommodation deformation or the transformation mechanism.

Many nonferrous martensitic structures exhibit shape memory effects. This holds for internally twinned and internally faulted martensites. Detailed information on the relationship between shape memory effect and martensitic transformation can be found in Ref 6.

## REFERENCES

1. W.D. Kingery, *Introduction to Ceramics*, John Wiley & Sons, 1960
2. G.K. Bansal and A.H. Heuer, On a Martensitic Phase Transformation in Zirconia ($ZrO_2$)—I. Metallographic Evidence, *Acta Metall.*, Vol 20, 1972, p 1281-1289
3. B.A. Bilby and J.W. Christian, The Crystallography of Martensite Transformations, *J. Iron Steel Inst.*, Vol 197, 1961, p 122-131
4. G. Krauss, *Principles of Heat Treatment of Steels*, American Society for Metals, 1980, p 43-75
5. A.R. Marder and G. Krauss, The Morphology of Martensite in Iron-Carbon Alloys, *Trans. ASM*, Vol 60, 1967, p 651-660
6. J. Perkins, Ed., *Shape Memory Effects in Alloys*, Plenum Press, 1975

# Peritectic Structures

By H.E. Exner and G. Petzow
Research Scientists
Max-Planck-Institut für Metallforschung
Institut für Werkstoffwissenschaften

PERITECTIC is a term that, in the science of heterogeneous equilibria, defines all reactions in which two or more phases (gas, liquid, solid) react at a defined temperature, $T_p$, to form a new phase that is stable below $T_p$. In this article, the term will be used in its usual sense for reactions in which a liquid phase reacts with at least one solid phase to form one new solid phase. This reaction is shown in a schematic binary phase diagram in Fig. 1(a). The liquid reacts with solid $\alpha$ at $T_p$ and $\beta$, which is not stable above $T_p$. This reaction can be written as $\alpha$ + liquid $\rightarrow \beta$. Furthermore, the term peritectoid denotes the special case of a phase equilibrium in which two or more solid phases are stable above the temperature $T_p$ and react at $T_p$ to form a new solid phase. In binary alloys, this reaction, which is also shown in Fig. 1(a), can be written as $\alpha + \beta \rightarrow \gamma$. The phases formed during a peritectic or peritectoid reaction are a solid solution of one of the components, an allotropic phase of one of the components, or an intermetallic phase.

Peritectic and peritectoid phase equilibria are very common in binary phase diagrams. Over 1000 reactions of this type have been registered in metallic systems, according to standard reference books on the contribution of binary alloys (Ref 1-3). In the majority of the 800 established phase diagrams involving peritectic phase equilibria, a congruently melting intermetallic or a high-melting component reacts with a melt and forms a new intermetallic phase. Several reactions often follow each other in a cascade (Fig. 1b and c). Systematic classifications of peritectic equilibria have been proposed in the literature (Ref 4, 5). Because published work on peritectic and peritectoid reactions in multiphase systems is virtually nonexistent, this article will focus on peritectic structure in binary alloys and the mechanisms of their formation.

## Mechanisms of Peritectic Reactions and Transformations

During solidification, a peritectic $\beta$ phase can form by at least three mechanisms: (1) The $\alpha$ phase reacts in contact with the melt to form $\beta$: $\alpha$ + liquid = $\beta$. This reaction can proceed only as long as $\alpha$ and liquid are in contact. Beta nucleates at the $\alpha$/liquid interface and readily forms a layer isolating $\alpha$ from the liquid, which is caused by the short-range diffusion mechanism shown in Fig. 2(a). (2) When $\beta$ isolates $\alpha$ from the liquid, long-range diffusion of A and B atoms through the $\alpha$ layer leads to formation of $\beta$ at the $\alpha/\beta$ and the $\beta$/liquid interfaces, respectively (Fig. 2b). The mechanism has been termed peritectic transformation in contrast to the direct peritectic reaction (Ref 5). These definitions are now generally accepted (Ref 6). (3) When the peritectic reaction or transformation is sluggish, which is nearly always the case, $\beta$ will precipitate directly from the melt when enough undercooling below the peritectic temperature occurs.

From the final microstructure, it is not apparent by which mechanism $\beta$ has formed. In any case, all three of the mechanisms require some undercooling, because the driving force is zero at the peritectic temperature. The time dependence is pronounced for the peritectic

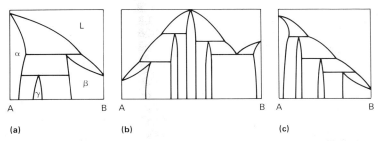

**Fig. 1** Typical peritectic phase diagrams. (a) Peritectic reaction $\alpha$ + liquid $\rightarrow \beta$ and peritectoid reaction $\alpha + \beta \rightarrow \gamma$. (b) Peritectic formation of intermetallic phases from a high-melting intermetallic. (c) Peritectic cascade between high- and low-melting components.

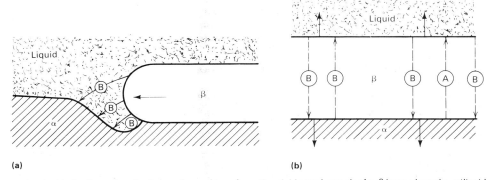

**Fig. 2** Mechanisms of peritectic reaction and transformation. (a) Lateral growth of a $\beta$ layer along the $\alpha$/liquid interface during peritectic reaction by liquid diffusion. (b) Thickening of a $\beta$ layer by solid-state diffusion during peritectic transformation. The solid arrows indicate growth direction of $\beta$; dashed arrows, the diffusion of the atomic species. (Ref 11)

**Fig. 3** Primary UAl₃ (gray) partially surrounded by peritectically formed UAl₄ (dark) in an Al-6U alloy that was cooled slowly from above liquidus to 760 °C (1400 °F) and held 10 min, then cooled to 670 °C (1240 °F) and held 15 min (peritectic temperature: 732 °C, or 1350 °F). The matrix is aluminum (white) with UAl₄ (dark) eutectic. This UAl₃ + Al → UAl₄ reaction leads to unfavorable rolling behavior. Electrolytically polished, etched in 50% HNO₃. 700×

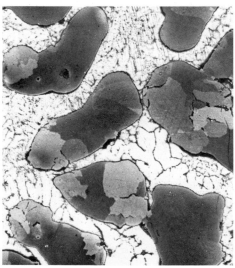

**Fig. 4** Local peritectic formation in a Zn-7Ni alloy that was cooled from above liquidus to 600 °C (1110 °F) and held 24 h, then cooled to 460 °C (860 °F) and held 15 min (peritectic temperature: 490 °C, or 914 °F). The primary NiZn₃ is dark, the peritectic δ phase is gray, and the matrix is zinc (white) with dark cell boundaries (δ/zinc eutectic). Mechanically polished, etched with CrO₃, contrasted with reactively sputtered interference layer. 200×

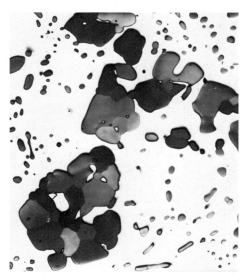

**Fig. 5** Peritectically formed UAl₄ in an Al-6U alloy that was cooled from above liquidus to 760 °C (1400 °F) and held 10 min, then cooled to 600 °C (1110 °F) and held 7 days (peritectic temperature: 732 °C, or 1350 °F; eutectic temperature: 640 °C, or 1184 °F). Note the rounded crystals and the necking between crystals of different orientation. The matrix is aluminum (white) with coarsened eutectic UAl₄ (dark). Electrolytically polished, etched in 50% HNO₃. 700×

transformation. Therefore, the amount of $\beta$ phase formed will depend on the cooling rate or on holding time if isothermal conditions are established. Quantitative expressions for describing peritectic reactions and transformations during continuous cooling are reviewed in Ref 6.

Localized nucleation of $\beta$ and shape changes of $\beta$ by solution reprecipitation, which is driven by surface energy through diffusion in the liquid, also influence the microstructure of peritectic alloys. Typical and specific microstructures will be discussed in the following sections. For demonstration purposes, results will be included from experimental alloys that were cooled rapidly from above the liquidus to a temperature above the peritectic equilibrium temperature $T_p$, held for some time to achieve large homogeneous primary $\alpha$ crystals, then cooled to a temperature below $T_p$ and held for extended times, inducing the formation of $\beta$ by peritectic reaction and transformation, rather than by direct precipitation from the melt.

## Nucleation-Controlled Peritectic Structures

The classical description of peritectic reactions postulates heterogeneous nucleation of $\beta$ at the $\alpha$/liquid interface at the peritectic equilibrium temperature $T_p$ (Ref 7). Undercoolings of up to 4% of $T_p$ are required for the systems investigated (Ref 8). If nucleation is limited to a few locations and lateral growth of the $\beta$ nuclei does not readily occur, no continuous layer of the peritectic phase is formed, as in Ni-Zn (Ref 4) and Al-U (Ref 9) systems. Typical microstructures are shown

in Fig. 3 and 4. Small crystals of the peritectic phase nucleate at the interface and grow into the primary crystals. After extended annealing below $T_p$, the reaction goes to completion (see Fig. 5 and 6). The original shape of the primary crystals is lost by decay into individual $\beta$ crystals that coarsen by Ostwald ripening during further annealing.

The peritectic reaction in the Al-U system was of special interest in the production of fuel elements for early nuclear reactors. The reaction UAl₃ + Al (liquid or solid) → UAl₄ is sluggish. In Fig. 3, this reaction could not be completely suppressed during the cooling cycles used, resulting in unfavorable rolling behavior. Additions of silicon or zirconium stabilize UAl₃, extending the UAl₃-Al equilibrium region below room temperature (Ref 10).

## Peritectic Reactions

In an ideal peritectic reaction, undercooling is rather low (up to a few degrees Kelvin), and a plateau is observed in the cooling curve, as in the Al-Ti system (Ref 5). Envelopes of the peritectic phase around the primary phase form by direct reaction in some systems—Cu-Sn and Ag-Sn, for example—through interrupted directional solidification experiments (Ref 6). Figures 7 and 8 depict microstructures of Cu-20Sn and Cu-70Sn alloys that demonstrate the onset of the peritectic reactions $\alpha$ + liquid → $\beta$ and $\varepsilon$ + liquid → $\eta$, respectively. Figure 9 shows, at a higher magnification, the homogeneous thickness of the $\beta$ layer around the $\alpha$ dendrites. The peritectic reaction can proceed very rapidly by liquid diffusion over a very short dis-

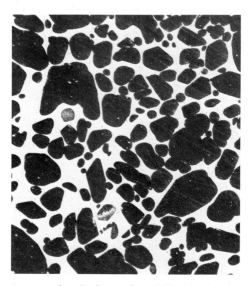

**Fig. 6** Completely transformed Zn-7Ni alloy that was cooled from above liquidus to 600 °C (1110 °F) and held 24 h, then cooled to 475 °C (885 °F) and held 3 h (peritectic temperature: 490 °C, or 914 °F). Note the small crystallite size of the peritectic δ phase compared to the large primary crystals in Fig. 4. The matrix is zinc (white). Mechanically polished, contrasted with reactively sputtered interference layer. 200×

tance in the lateral direction, as shown in Fig. 2(a). The thickness of the layers has been calculated with fairly good agreement to experimental results for copper-tin and silver-tin alloys on the basis of maximum growth rate or minimum undercooling from the laws derived for solidification at low undercoolings (Ref 6). The thickness depends to some extent on the cooling rate, but more strongly on the in-

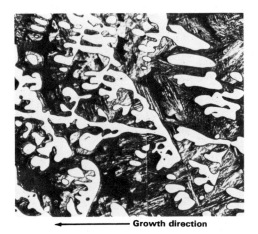

**Fig. 7** Start of the peritectic reaction in a directionally solidified Cu-20Sn alloy. Primary α dendrites (white) are covered by peritectically formed β layer (gray) shortly after the temperature reaches $T_p$. Matrix (dark) is a mixture of tin-rich phases. Mechanically polished, etched in $HNO_3$. 40×. (Ref 6)

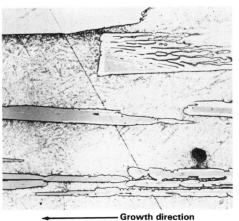

**Fig. 8** Start of the peritectic reaction in a directionally solidified Cu-70Sn alloy. The primary ε phase (dark) is covered by the peritectically formed η layer (white), which thickens with increasing undercooling below $T_p$. The matrix is the Sn-η eutectic. Mechanically polished, etched in $HNO_3$. 100×. (Ref 6)

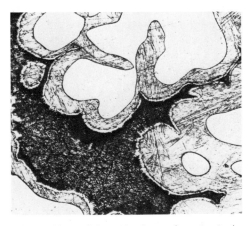

**Fig. 9** Start of the peritectic transformation in the same directionally solidified Cu-20Sn alloy shown in Fig. 7, but at higher magnification. Note the homogeneous thickness of the β layers (gray) around the primary α (white). The matrix (dark) is a mixture of tin-rich phases. Mechanically polished, etched in $HNO_3$. 160×. (Ref 6)

terfacial energies, σ, with $σ(liquid/β) + σ(α/β) - σ(liquid/α)$ as the determining factor.

## Peritectic Transformations

After isolation of primary α from the liquid by the β layer, the direct peritectic reaction can no longer take place. The growth rate of the layer follows the laws for diffusion through the β layer (Fig. 2b). During continuous cooling, this diffusional growth is affected by precipitation from the liquid and from the primary α or by dissolution of β, according to the slopes of the solubility limits in the phase diagram. Under simplifying conditions, the growth rates have been calculated numerically and found to be in reasonable agreement with the experimental findings in the Cu-Sn and Ag-Sn systems (Ref 6).

The kinetics of peritectic transformations can more easily be studied under isothermal conditions. Then, β is formed exclusively by diffusion of the two atomic species in the β layer at the α/β and the β/liquid interfaces. The thickness of the β layer, $L_β$, is given as a function of isothermal annealing time, $t$, by (Ref 11, 12):

$$L_β^2 = 2Dt \, Δc^β \frac{c^l - c^α}{(c^l - c^β)(c^β - c^α)} \quad \text{(Eq 1)}$$

where $D$ is the chemical diffusion coefficient in the β phase; $c^α$, $c^β$, and $c^l$ are the atomic concentrations in the α, β, and liquid phases; and $Δc^β$ is the concentration difference in the β phase at the α/β and the β/liquid interfaces, all at annealing temperature, $T$. At the peritectic equilibrium temperature, $T_p$, $Δc^β$ is zero and increases with increasing undercooling.

Because peritectic phases often have a very small range of homogeneity, $Δc^β$ is estimated from the chemical potential difference at the interfaces, yielding:

$$L_β^2 = 2Dt \frac{ΔS}{R} \cdot \frac{c^β(c^l - c^α)}{(c^l - c^β)(c^β - c^α)} \quad \text{(Eq 2)}$$

where $ΔS$ is the entropy of the reaction and $R$ is the gas constant. Because of the counteraction of the strongly temperature-dependent terms, the transformation has a maximum rate at a temperature $T_M$ given by:

$$T_M = T_p \cdot \frac{Q}{Q + RT_p} \quad \text{(Eq 3)}$$

where $Q$ is the activation energy of the chemical diffusion coefficient in the β phase.

For example, Fig. 10 shows the relevant portion of the Ni-Sb phase diagram and experimental results of the peritectic formation of $NiSb_2$. Figures 11 to 13 show typical microstructures that will be discussed below. Similar results have been obtained in the Cu-Sn system for the transformation ε + liquid → η (Ref 13) and for peritectic transforma-

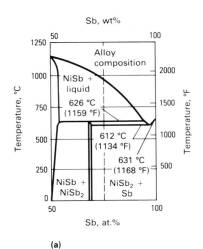

(a)

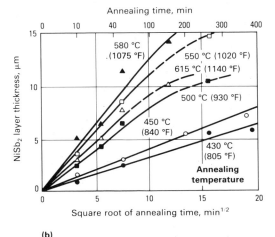

(b)

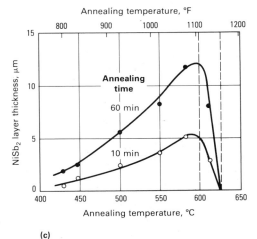

(c)

**Fig. 10** Peritectic transformation in the Ni-Sb system. (a) Relevant part of the phase diagram. (b) Growth of $NiSb_2$ layers around primary NiSb during the isothermal peritectic transformation NiSb + liquid → $NiSb_2$ at 615 °C (1140 °F) and NiSb + Sb (solid) → $NiSb_2$ at temperatures between 430 and 580 °C (805 and 1075 °F). (c) Temperature dependence $NiSb_2$ layer thickness after 10 and 60 min isothermal annealing. The curves are calculated from Eq 1 in the text. (Ref 4)

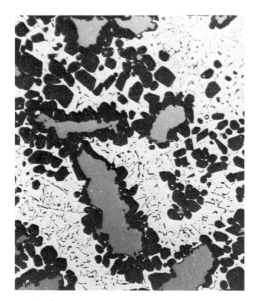

**Fig. 11** Peritectic transformation of a Sb-14Ni alloy that was slowly cooled to 650 °C (1200 °F) and held 1 h, then cooled to 615 °C (1140 °F) and held 10 min (peritectic temperature: 626 °C, or 1159 °F). An irregular layer of NiSb$_2$ crystals (dark) is formed around the coarse primary NiSb crystals. The matrix is the coarsened NiSb$_2$-Sb eutectic. Mechanically polished, contrasted by a reactively sputtered interference layer. 200×

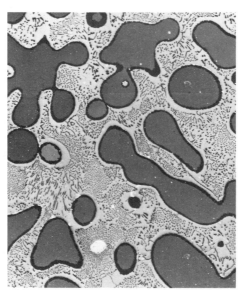

**Fig. 12** Transformation of a Sb-14Ni alloy below the eutectic temperature. The alloy was slowly cooled to 650 °C (1200 °F) and held 1 h, then cooled to 500 °C (930 °F) and held 10 min (peritectic temperature: 626 °C, or 1159 °F; eutectic temperature: 612 °C, or 1134 °F). Note the layer of fine NiSb$_2$ crystals (dark) on the single crystals of NiSb (gray). The matrix is slightly coarsened NiSb$_2$-Sb eutectic. Mechanically polished, reactively sputtered. 200×

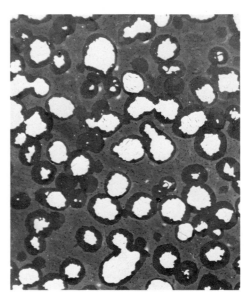

**Fig. 13** Same antimony-nickel alloy as illustrated in Fig. 12, but held 4 h at 500 °C (930 °F). Note the rather smooth outer interface and the wavy inner interface of coarse-grained NiSb$_2$ layer, which, depending on the ratio of interfacial and grain boundary energies, form after extended isothermal annealing times at low temperatures. Mechanically polished, contrasted by a reactively sputtered interference layer. 200×

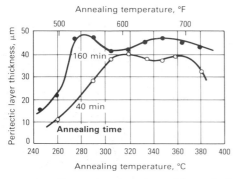

**Fig. 14** Temperature dependence of the peritectic transformation Cu$_5$Cd$_8$ + liquid → CuCd$_3$ in a Cd-10Cu alloy at 40 and 160 min isothermal annealing. (Ref 9)

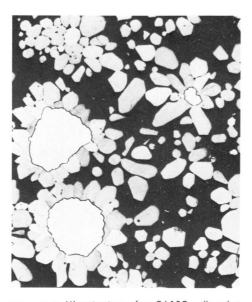

**Fig. 15** Microstructure of a Cd-10Cu alloy that was cooled to 410 °C (770 °F) and held 20 h, then cooled to 305 °C (580 °F) and held 160 min (peritectic temperature: 397 °C, or 747 °F). Note the faceted coarse crystals of the peritectically formed CuCd$_3$ envelopes (gray). The primary Cu$_5$Cd$_8$ crystals are white; the dark matrix is cadmium. Mechanically polished, etched in HNO$_3$. 100×

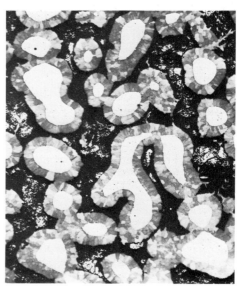

**Fig. 16** Same as Fig. 15, except alloy was cooled to 410 °C (770 °F) and held 20 h, then cooled to 275 °C (525 °F) and held 160 min (peritectic temperature: 397 °C, or 747 °F; eutectic temperature: 314 °C, or 597 °F). Note large number of grain boundaries in the peritectic CuCd$_3$ phase (gray) and its smooth interfaces with the primary Cu$_5$Cd$_8$ crystals (white) and the matrix Cd (dark). 100×

tions in the Co-Sn, Au-Bi, and Cr-Sb systems (Ref 4). In contrast, two maxima of the thickness of the peritectically formed CuCd$_3$ were observed in the Cu-Cd system, as shown in Fig. 14. The first maximum is attributed to the contribution of grain-boundary diffusion (Ref 7, 9), which is small for the faceted, large grains formed at high temperatures (Fig. 15) and large for the fine-grained, smooth layer formed below the eutectic temperature (Fig. 16).

In many binary systems, such as bronze and brass systems, the intermetallic phases form peritectic cascades (see Fig. 1c). In these cases, several envelopes can form. The individual thicknesses depend on the growth rate and the rate of consumption by other growing phases, that is, on the diffusivities and the molar volumes of the individual phases (Ref

14). An example of the tin-cobalt alloy microstructure developed in this manner is shown in Fig. 17. The cascade in the phase diagram for this alloy includes a peritectic and a peritectoid transformation. As shown in a detailed study of the Zr-Al system (Ref 15), peritectoid reactions and transformations follow the same principles as the peritectic ones. The theoretical analysis is confirmed by experimental results of the reaction Zr + Zr$_2$Al → Zr$_3$Al, with a parabolic growth dependence and a maximum growth rate approximately 100 K below the peritectoid temperature.

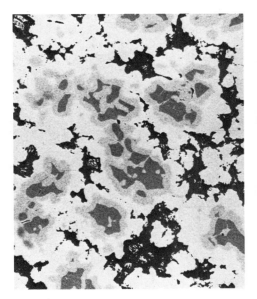

**Fig. 17** Microstructure of a Sn-17Co alloy that was cooled to 1000 °C (1830 °F) and held 2 h, then cooled to 225 °C (435 °F) and held 22 h. The primary γ phase has completely transformed and dissolved into relatively small CoSn crystals (compare with Fig. 19) that form the dark centers surrounded peritectically by CoSn₂ layers (gray), followed by a peritectoid envelope of the CoSn₃ phase that was not included in the phase diagram in Ref 1, but only found during a study of the peritectic transformation of CoSn (Ref 4). The temperatures of peritectic formation of CoSn and CoSn₂ are approximately 910 and 540 °C (1670 and 1005 °F), respectively; CoSn₃ forms peritectoidically at approximately 235 °C (455 °F). Scanning electron micrograph (backscattered electron image). 200×

## Morphology of Peritectic Microstructures

Smooth peritectic envelopes, according to the classical description of peritectic structures, usually develop only by a peritectic reaction or transformation during continuous cooling (see Fig. 7 to 9) or by isothermal peritectic transformations at a temperature where no liquid phase exists, that is, below the eutectic temperature (see Fig. 12 and 16). After extended isothermal annealing times at low temperatures, the peritectic envelope becomes coarse grained, and wavy interfaces develop, depending on the ratio of interfacial and grain boundary energies. A typical example is shown in Fig. 13.

In the normal temperature range of peritectic transformations, a liquid phase exists that allows rapid adjustment of the interface to minimal interfacial energies. As shown in Fig. 11 and 15, the interface between the two solid phases is again moderately structured, but the liquid/solid interface is highly irregular. Faceting of the grains in the envelope is often observed. Figure 18 shows highly faceted envelopes in a bismuth-gold alloy; Fig. 19, separation of peritectic crystals from the primary phase by the melt in a tin-cobalt alloy. Two highly faceted peritectic envelopes are illustrated in Fig. 20.

**Fig. 18** Peritectic envelope in a Bi-40Au alloy that was cooled to 450 °C (840 °F) and held 5 h, then cooled to 300 °C (570 °F) and held 2 h (peritectic temperature: 373 °C, or 703 °F). The morphology is entirely determined by the anisotropy of the interfacial energy of the face-centered cubic Au₂Bi crystals (gray). The primary crystals are gold (white); the matrix is the Au₂Bi-Bi eutectic. Mechanically polished, contrasted by reactively sputtered interference layer. 200×

By applying a large temperature gradient during directional solidification of a two-phase tin-cadmium alloy, it was speculated (Ref 16) that a planar solidification front with coupled (eutectic-like) precipitation of two solid phases involved in a peritectic transformation could be achieved to produce aligned microstructures. Although aligned microstructures were produced (Ref 16, 17), experimental results showed that coupled growth did not occur, and alternating bands of α (the high-temperature phase) and β (the low-temperature phase) were observed (Ref 16-19), a result that was explained by kinetic analysis (Ref 16) and later by thermodynamic analysis (Ref 11).

## Peritectic Structures in Iron-Base Alloys

From a technical point of view, the peritectic formation of austenite (γ) from primary ferrite (δ) is the most important peritectic reaction. Thermal analysis indicates that the reaction δ + liquid → γ proceeds to a great extent during continuous cooling (Ref 20), and δ-ferrite usually disappears completely upon cooling into the austenite region if not stabilized by alloying additions. Phase diagrams of iron with an austenite stabilizing element (carbon, nitrogen, nickel, manganese, and so on) always show a peritectic reaction. In most steels, austenite and ferrite stabilizing elements are present, as in stainless and high-speed steels for which peritectic formation of γ has been studied in detail (Ref

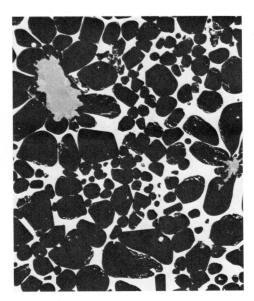

**Fig. 19** Microstructure of a Sn-17Co alloy that was cooled to 1000 °C (1830 °F) and held 2 h, then cooled to 570 °C (1060 °F) and held 3 h (peritectic temperature: 935 °C, or 1715 °F). The primary γ phase (gray) has transformed nearly completely. The peritectic CoSn crystals (dark) have elongated shapes when still connected to the peritectic envelope and are separated by long channels of the liquid. Most of the peritectically formed crystals are completely isolated from the primary phase by the melt and are slightly faceted or rounded. Mechanically polished, contrasted by reactively sputtered interference layer. 200×

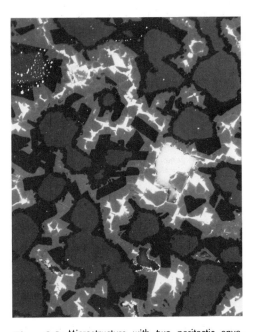

**Fig. 20** Microstructure with two peritectic envelopes in a Cd-25Ni alloy that was cooled to 730 °C (1345 °F) and held 24 h, cooled to 550 °C (1020 °F) and held 40 min, then cooled to 480 °C (895 °F) and held 10 min (peritectic temperatures: Ni + liquid → β at 695 °C, or 1283 °F; β + liquid → γ₁ at 510 °C, or 950 °F; γ₁ + liquid → γ at 490 °C, or 914 °F). Coarse nickel crystals (dark gray) with a faceted inner envelope of β (black) and a faceted outer γ envelope (gray). The matrix (white) is cadmium. γ₁ has not formed during this heat treatment. Mechanically polished, contrasted by reactively sputtered interference layer. 200×

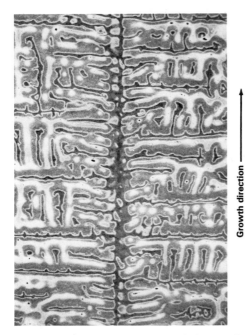

**Fig. 21** Longitudinal section through directionally solidified high-speed steel (AISI T1) that was cooled at 0.23 K/s from above liquidus. The peritectic envelopes of austenite (gray) around the highly branched dendrites of δ-ferrite (discontinuously transformed to austenite and carbide, dark) are clearly distinguishable. The matrix is fine ledeburite (white). Mechanically polished, Oberhoffer's etchant (1 g $CuCl_2$, 30 g $FeCl_3$, 0.5 g $SnCl_2$, 500 mL alcohol, 42 mL HCl, and 500 mL $H_2O$). 60×. (Ref 23)

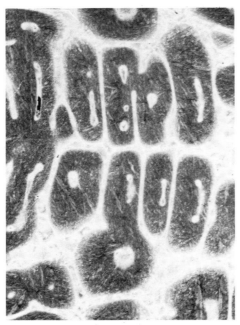

**Growth direction**

**Fig. 22** Longitudinal section through directionally solidified high-speed steel (AISI M2 with 1.12% C and 1% Nb) that was cooled at 0.1 K/s to approximately 1320 °C (2410 °F), that is, 20 K below the onset of the peritectic transformation. Note the thicker layers of peritectic austenite on the front faces of the secondary dendrites compared to the back. Mechanically polished, Oberhoffer's etchant. 100×

21-23). Quantitative treatments of the kinetics and the mechanisms of the transition from peritectic to eutectic solidification by the addition of ferrite stabilizers are now available. Detailed descriptions of the very complex solidification processes and microstructures in commercial high-speed steels with a thorough discussion of the peritectic transformation of δ ferrite to austenite (γ) have been given.

Figure 21 shows a directionally solidified high-speed steel with peritectic γ envelopes around the highly branched δ dendrites. Depicted in Fig. 22 is the varying thickness of the layers on the front and the back of the secondary dendrite arms. This is attributed to the wandering of the arms toward the tip of the dendrite, that is, in the solidification direction, during directional solidification due to temperature gradient zone melting (Ref 23). Under some cooling conditions, the layers appear to be partially missing on the back. This and other mechanisms related to the peritectic transformation complicate the interpretation of the microstructures found in high-speed steels and their weldments.

## Technical Relevance of Peritectic Structures

A thorough understanding of peritectic reactions and transformations is required for a concise interpretation of microstructures. In addition, some technical importance may be attributed to the possibility of producing metallic alloys with aligned fibers or plates (Ref 16-19) and of achieving grain refinement by means of peritectic decay of primary crystals (Ref 7, 24). Usually, however, peritectic structures are avoided due to their deteriorating effect on material properties. Up to the present time, controlled peritectic reactions and transformations have been rarely (if ever) used to optimize the microstructure of engineering materials.

## REFERENCES

1. M. Hansen and K. Anderko, in *Constitution of Binary Alloys*, McGraw-Hill, 1965
2. R.P. Elliott, in *Constitution of Binary Alloys*, McGraw-Hill, 1969
3. F.A. Shunk, in *Constitution of Binary Alloys*, McGraw-Hill, 1969
4. S. Uchida, Systematik und Kinetik peritektischer Umwandlungen, Ph.D. thesis, Technical University, Stuttgart, 1980
5. H.W. Kerr, J. Cisse, and G.F. Bolling, On Equilibrium and Non-Equilibrium Peritectic Transformations, *Acta Metall.*, Vol 22, 1974, p 677
6. H. Frederiksson and T. Nylén, Mechanism of Peritectic Reactions and Transformations, *Met. Sci.*, Vol 16, 1982, p 283-294
7. J.A. Sartell and D.J. Mack, The Mechanism of Peritectic Reactions, *J. Inst. Met.*, Vol 93, 1964, p 19-24
8. P.G. Boswell, G.A. Chadwick, R. Elliott, and F.R. Sale, Nucleation in Peritectic Systems, in *Solidification and Castings of Metals*, The Metals Society, London, 1979, p 175-178
9. G. Petzow and H.E. Exner, Zur Kenntnis peritektischer Unwandlungen, *Radex-Rundsch.*, Issue 3/4, 1967, p 534-539
10. H.E. Exner and G. Petzow, Untersuchungen zur Stabilisierung von $UAl_3$ in Aluminiumreichen Kernbrennstoffen, *Metall.*, Vol 23, 1969, p 220-225
11. M. Hillert, Keynote Address: Eutectic and Peritectic Solidification, in *Solidification and Castings of Metals*, The Metals Society, London, 1979, p 81-87
12. D.H. St. John and L.M. Hogan, The Peritectic Transformation, *Acta Metall.*, Vol 25, 1977, p 77-81
13. H. Baudisch, Mechanismus und Kinetik der peritektischer Umwandlung im System Kupfer-Zinn, Master's thesis, Technical University, Stuttgart, 1968
14. S.R. Shatynski, J.P. Hirth, and R.A. Rapp, A Theory of Multiphase Binary Diffusion, *Acta Metall.*, Vol 24, 1976, p 1071-1078
15. E.M. Schulson and D.B. Graham, The Peritectoid Transformation of Ordered $Zr_3Al$, *Acta Metall.*, Vol 24, 1976, p 615-625
16. W.J. Boettinger, The Structure of Directionally Solidified Two-Phase Sn-Cd Peritectic Alloys, *Metall. Trans. A*, Vol 5, 1974, p 2023-2031
17. H.D. Brody and S.A. David, Controlled Solidification of Peritectic Alloys, in *Solidification and Castings of Metals*, The Metals Society, London, 1979, p 144-151
18. A.P. Tichener and J.A. Spille, The Microstructure of Directionally Solidified Alloys That Undergo a Peritectic Transformation, *Acta Metall.*, Vol 23, 1975, p 497-502
19. A. Ostrowski and E.W. Langer, Unidirectional Solidification of Peritectic Alloy, in *Solidification and Castings of Metals*, The Metals Society, London, 1979, p 139-143
20. M.C. Flemings, Peritectic Solidification in Polyphase Alloys: Castings and Ingots, in *Solidification Processing*, McGraw Hill, NY, 1974, p 177-180
21. H. Frederiksson, The Mechanism of the Peritectic Reaction in Iron-Base Alloys, *Met. Sci.*, Vol 10, 1976, p 77-86
22. H. Frederiksson, Transition from Peritectic to Eutectic Reaction in Iron Base Alloys, in *Solidification and Castings of Metals*, The Metals Society, London, 1979, p 131-136
23. R. Riedl, Erstarrungsverlauf von Schnellarbeitsstrahlen, Ph.D. thesis, University of Leoben, Austria, 1984
24. I. Maxwell and A. Hellawell, An Analysis of the Peritectic Reaction with Particular Reference to Al-Ti Alloys, *Acta Metall.*, Vol 23, 1975, p 901-909

# Ordered Structures

By M.J. Marcinkowski
Professor
Department of Mechanical Engineering
University of Maryland

ORDERED STRUCTURES, often called "superlattices," result from the ability of the atoms within many alloy phases to arrange themselves into specific configurations. Table 1 lists several phases that have the more common types of ordered crystal structures, which are denoted by their prototype structures: AuCu I, AuCu₃, CsCl, BiF₃, Ni₃Sn, and AlCu₂Mn. Some typical unit cells associated with three of these structures are shown in Fig. 1 for the ordered AuCu₃, AlFe (CsCl), and AlFe₃ (BiF₃) phases. Gold atoms in the

AuCu₃ structure (Fig. 1a) never possess nearest-neighbor gold atoms, and aluminum atoms in the CsCl structure (Fig. 1b) never possess nearest-neighbor aluminum atoms. However, aluminum atoms in the BiF₃ structure (Fig. 1c) never have aluminum atoms as first or second nearest neighbors.

**Ordered Domains.** Most of the phases listed in Table 1 disorder at high temperatures, although regions of local order—that is, regions with dimensions of only a few interatomic distances—may persist. Ordering during cooling generally takes place independently in various portions of a crystal. When these ordered regions, or domains, grow, they impinge upon one another to form well-defined boundaries, termed antiphase boundaries (APBs), because the repeat patterns of atoms in adjacent ordered domains are out of step with one another.

**AuCu₃ Structures.** The domains in the ordered AuCu₃ phase (Fig. 2) can become out of step with one another in four ways, de-

pending on whether the gold atoms locate at corner sites or at the three distinct face-centered sites (see Fig. 1a). Two important features are associated with the AuCu₃ configu-

## Table 1 Selected alloy phases that possess superlattices with the structures indicated(a)

**AuCu I, tP4, P4/mmm**

AgTi, AlTi, AuCu I, CoPt, CrPd, Cu₃Pd, FePd, FePt, HgPd, HgPt, HgTi, HgZr, InMg, MgTl, MnNi, Mn₂Pd₃, MnPt, NiPt, PbZn, PtZn

**AuCu₃, cP4, Pm3m**

AgPt₃, Ag₃Pt, AlCo₃, AlNi₃, AlZr₃, AuCu₃ I, Au₃Pt, CaPb₃, CaSn₃, CdPt₃, CePb₃, CeSn₃, CoPt₃, Cr₂Pt, CuPd, Cu₃Pt, FeNi₃, FePt₃, Fe₃Pt, GeNi₃, HgTi₃, InMg₃, LaPb₃, LaSn₃, MnNi₃, MnPt₃, Mn₃Pt, NaPb₃, Ni₃Pt, PbPd₃, PbPt₃, Pt₃Sn, Pt₃Ti, Pt₃Zn, TiZn₃

**CsCl, cP2, Pm3m**

AgCd, AgCe, AgLa, AgLi, AgMg, AlCo, AlCu₂Zn, AlFe, AlNi, AuCd, AuMg, AuMn, AuZn, BeCo, BeCu, BeNi, CdCe, CeHg, CeMg, CeZn, CoFe, CoTi, CuPd, CuZn, CuZn₃, FeTi, HgLi₂Tl, HgMn, InNi, LaMg, LiPb, LiTl, MgPr, MgSr, MgTl, MnPt, NiTi, RuTa, TiZn

**BiF₃, cF16, Fm3m**

AlFe₃, BiLi₃, CeMg₃, Cu₃Sb, Fe₃Si, Mg₃Pr

**Ni₃Sn, hP8, P6₃/mmc**

CdMg₃, Co₃Mo, Co₃W, Fe₃Sn, Mn₁₁Sn₃, Ni₃Sn, PbTi₄, SiTa₄.₅, SnTi₃

**AlCu₂Mn, cF16, Fm3m**

AlCu₂Mn, AlNi₂Ti, Co₂MnSn, Cu₂FeSn, Cu₂InMn, Cu₂NiSn, MnNi₂Sb, MnNi₂Sn

(a) Prototype structure, Pearson symbol, and space group
Source: Ref 1

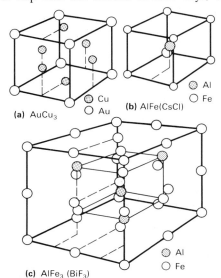

**Fig. 1** Unit cells of the superlattice (ordered) crystal structures of (a) AuCu₃, (b) AlFe, and (c) AlFe₃, (structure prototypes AuCu₃, CsCl, and BiF₃, respectively)

**Fig. 2** Configuration of atoms comprising the antiphase domain structure in ordered AuCu₃. Dashed lines represent antiphase boundaries. See also Fig. 3. (Ref 2)

**Fig. 3** Antiphase domain boundaries in ordered AuCu₃. Thin-foil electron micrograph. See also Fig. 2. 30 000×. (Ref 2)

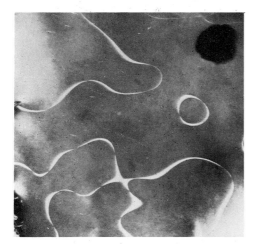

**Fig. 4** Antiphase domain boundaries in ordered AlFe alloy. Thin-foil electron micrograph. See also Fig. 5. 11 000×. (Ref 2)

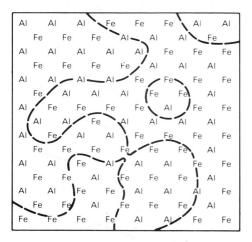

**Fig. 5** Configuration of atoms comprising the antiphase domain structure in ordered AlFe alloy. The dashed lines represent antiphase boundaries. See also Fig. 4.

ration, which is shown in Fig. 2: first, three or four antiphase boundaries can meet at a point so that a stable structure, the so-called foam structure, is obtained and, second, when the antiphase boundaries lie along horizontal or vertical planes, the high-energy nearest-neighbor Au-Au bonds frequently are absent, so that the antiphase boundaries are well defined.

Direct observation of antiphase boundaries is possible with thin-foil transmission electron microscopy (Ref 2). The electron waves comprising the microscope beam undergo a change in phase as they pass through the antiphase boundary. The resulting interference gives rise to contrast like that shown in Fig. 3, which depicts an antiphase boundary configuration similar to that in Fig. 2.

**CsCl Structures.** A typical antiphase boundary configuration associated with the CsCl structure is shown in the ordered AlFe phase in Fig. 4. The two features that characterize the antiphase boundary configuration of the AuCu₃ structure, shown in Fig. 3, are

absent in this structure. Specifically, the antiphase boundaries are curved and show no particular preference for any specific direction, and not more than two domains ever meet one another.

The actual atom configurations that comprise the domains in the AlFe superlattice are shown in Fig. 5. The antiphase boundaries (dashed lines) are characterized by wrong first nearest-neighbor aluminum and iron atom pairs. Only two distinct types of ordered domain are possible in the AlFe superlattice; the aluminum atom can locate at the body-centered site (Fig. 1b) or the corner site.

**BiF₃ Structures.** A more complex antiphase boundary configuration is exhibited by the BiF₃ superlattice. Figure 6 shows a typical example in the ordered AlFe₃ phase, in which atomic ordering occurs as a two-step process. Upon cooling, it first undergoes an ordering of the CsCl type; with further cooling, the CsCl ordering is converted to the BiF₃ type. These two types of ordering lead in turn to two types of antiphase boundaries, as shown

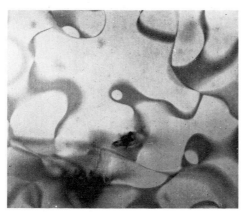

**Fig. 6** Antiphase domain boundaries in ordered AlFe₃ alloy. Thin-foil electron micrograph. Compare with the configuration shown in Fig. 7. 30 000×. (Ref 2)

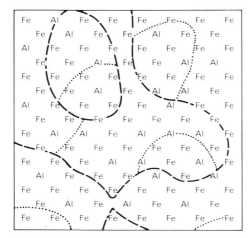

**Fig. 7** Configuration of atoms comprising the antiphase domain structure in ordered AlFe₃. Dashed lines represent antiphase boundaries that formed during CsCl ordering; dotted lines represent those that formed during later BiF₃ ordering. See also Fig. 6.

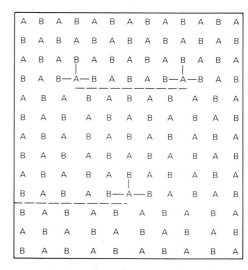

**Fig. 8** Schematic representation of two types of antiphase boundaries generated by edge dislocations in an ordered alloy. The lower boundary is terminated by a single dislocation; the upper boundary, by a pair of dislocations, forming a superlattice dislocation.

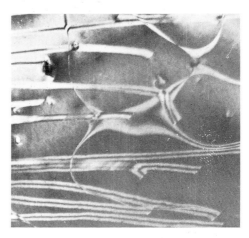

**Fig. 9** Dislocation-generated antiphase domain boundaries in ordered AlFe₃. Thin-foil electron micrograph. Compare with Fig. 6. 20 000×. (Ref 2)

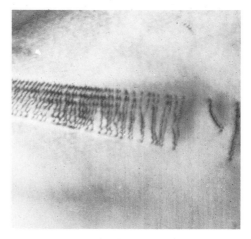

**Fig. 10** Group of edge-dislocation pairs, which are also termed superlattice dislocations, in ordered MnNi₃ alloy (AuCu₃ structure). Thin-foil electron micrograph. 60 000×. (Ref 2)

in Fig. 7. The antiphase boundary configuration in Fig. 7 resembles that in Fig. 6. The dashed lines in Fig. 7, which are associated with wrong nearest-neighbor aluminum atom pairs, correspond to the antiphase boundaries formed during CsCl ordering and resemble the antiphase boundaries shown in Fig. 5. The dotted lines in Fig. 7, which are associated with wrong second nearest-neighbor aluminum atom pairs, correspond to the antiphase boundaries formed during the conversion of the CsCl ordered configuration to the BiF$_3$ type. These antiphase boundaries always terminate on the CsCl type of antiphase boundaries formed earlier.

**Dislocation-Generated Antiphase Boundaries.** All the antiphase boundaries discussed thus far form when a phase is cooled from the disordered state. Antiphase boundaries are also generated by the motion of dislocations, as shown in Fig. 8. In the lower part of Fig. 8, a single edge dislocation is connected to an antiphase boundary, shown dashed. If a pair of such edge dislocations can be brought together, the extent of the antiphase boundary can be minimized, as shown in the upper part of Fig. 8. Because the total number of wrong atom bonds associated with the antiphase boundary is in turn also minimized, the dislocation configuration shown in the upper part of Fig. 8 represents a low-energy arrangement and has been termed a superlattice dislocation.

Both types of dislocations shown in Fig. 8 are frequently observed in ordered alloys. Figure 9 shows antiphase boundaries generated by moving dislocations in AlFe$_3$, and Fig. 10 shows dislocation pairs, or superlattice dislocations, in ordered MnNi$_3$, which has the AuCu$_3$ structure. The close association between antiphase boundaries and dislocations makes ordered phases useful for applications that require high strength at high temperatures (Ref 3).

**REFERENCES**

1. A. Taylor and B.J. Kagle, *Crystallographic Data on Metal and Alloy Structures*, Dover, 1963
2. M.J. Marcinkowski, in *Electron Microscopy and Strength of Crystals*, G. Thomas and J. Washburn, Ed., Interscience, 1963, p 333-439
3. B.H. Kear, C.T. Sims, N.S. Stoloff, and J.H. Westbrook, Ed., *Ordered Atoms—Structural Application and Physical Metallurgy*, Claitor's Publishing, 1970

# Plastic Deformation Structures

PLASTIC DEFORMATION of metals is commonly classified as cold work (no accompanying recrystallization) or as hot work (spontaneous recrystallization occurring simultaneously with, or soon after, deformation). Plastic deformation is accomplished by the motion of dislocations, by shearing processes such as twinning, and, in special circumstances, by the migration of vacant lattice sites. In deformed metals, the concentration of dislocations can be very high, typically changing from approximately $10^9/m^2$ in an annealed metal to $10^{13}$ to $10^{15}/m^2$ after heavy cold deformation. The dislocation density can be uniform or highly variable from point to point. The structures developed during plastic deformation depend on such factors as crystal structure, amount of deformation, composition, deformation mode, and deformation temperature and rate.

## Crystal Structure

The crystallographic planes on which dislocations move and the unit displacement of dislocations (Burgers vector) are determined by crystal structure. Slip has been reported in the body-centered cubic (bcc) lattice by glide of dislocations with Burgers vector of type $1/2 \langle 111 \rangle$ on $\{110\}$, $\{211\}$, and $\{321\}$ planes, totaling at least 48 possible slip systems. However, it is now considered that slip can occur on any plane containing a $\langle 111 \rangle$ slip direction (pencil glide).

In the face-centered cubic (fcc) lattice, slip occurs by movement of dislocations with Burgers vector of type $a/2 \langle 110 \rangle$ on $\{111\}$ planes, giving a total of 12 possible slip systems. In hexagonal close-packed (hcp) metals, the predominant Burgers vector is $1/3 \langle 11\bar{2}0 \rangle$ and the slip planes are usually the basal (0001) planes or $\{1\bar{1}00\}$ prismatic planes. In magnesium, $1/3 \langle 11\bar{2}0 \rangle$ slip on pyramidal $\{1\bar{1}01\}$ planes has been reported. Zinc and cadmium are reported to slip on $\{11\bar{2}2\}$ $\langle 11\bar{2}\bar{3} \rangle$ systems. In hcp metals, the number of slip systems and the twinning

shear are less than for cubic metals. Twinning is a common mode of deformation even at strains as small as 0.05.

## Amount of Deformation

Schematic tensile load-elongation curves illustrating the two types of yielding generally encountered at room temperature and at con-

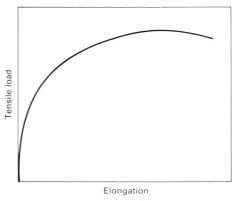

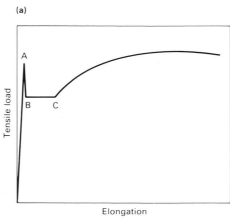

**Fig. 1** Idealized plots of tensile load versus elongation. (a) Continuous yielding. (b) Discontinuous yielding

ventional strain rates are presented in Fig. 1. As load is applied, the metal first deforms elastically, but the extent of such purely elastic deformation is severely limited. Dislocations begin to move at sites of stress concentration long before plastic deformation becomes apparent. In continuous yielding (Fig. 1a), plastic deformation is distributed uniformly throughout the specimen, at least on a macroscopic scale.

Abrupt, discontinuous yielding (Fig. 1b) requires:

- A low density of mobile dislocations in the metal before straining
- A mechanism for the rapid generation and multiplication of dislocations
- A small to moderate stress dependence of dislocation velocity

Discontinuous yielding is characterized by an upper yield point at A and yield elongation at essentially constant load from B to C (see Fig. 1b). The plastic deformation that occurs during yield elongation is heterogeneous in that one or more discrete deformation bands—known as Lüders lines, Lüders bands, or stretcher strains—propagate at various positions along the length of the tensile specimen (Fig. 2). These bands form at approximately 55° to the stress axis. Yield elongation continues at approximately constant load until, at point C (Fig. 1b), the bands have propagated to cover the entire length of the reduced section of the specimen.

The transition from undeformed to deformed material at the Lüders front can be seen at low magnification (Fig. 2). At higher magnification, optical microscopy can be used to monitor the transition by watching for the gradual fading out of slip lines on a polished surface or for the decrease in etch-pit density in alloys that etch pit readily, such as silicon iron.

A Lüders front in a low-carbon steel with a grain size of approximately 2 μm is shown in Fig. 3. This grain size was developed to increase the definition of the front for study by

Revised by William F. Hosford, Professor, Department of Materials and Metallurgical Engineering, University of Michigan; John J. Jonas, Professor, Department of Mining and Metallurgical Engineering, McGill University; and William C. Leslie, Professor Emeritus, Department of Materials and Metallurgical Engineering, University of Michigan

**Fig. 2** Lüders bands (roughened areas), which have propagated along the length of a specimen of annealed steel sheet that was tested in tension. Not polished, not etched. Actual size

**Fig. 3** A Lüders front in ultrafine-grained low-carbon steel. The front was moving to the left. Thin-foil transmission electron micrograph. 15 000×

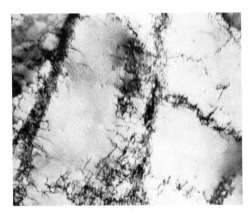

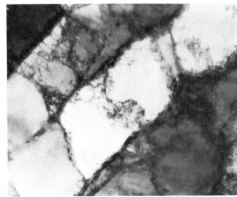

**Fig. 4, 5** Dense tangles of dislocations forming a cell structure in iron that was deformed at room temperature to 9% strain (Fig. 4) and to 20% strain (Fig. 5). Note that the average spacing between cell walls decreased as strain was increased. Thin-foil electron micrographs. 20 000×

thin-foil transmission electron microscopy. However, the features shown here are characteristic of those observed over a wide range of grain sizes. In the unyielded region ahead of the front, grain boundaries are sharp, and some of the grains display a low density of dislocations in somewhat regular arrays, indicating preyield microstrain. Grains within the front, which may be several grains wide, show a higher density of dislocations, some of which are still arranged regularly. Behind the front, grain boundaries contain a high density of dislocations, and dislocation tangles have begun to form within the grains.

As deformation proceeds beyond point C in Fig. 1(b) and into the workhardening stage, the density of dislocations increases and their distribution becomes less uniform. As shown in Fig. 4 and 5, dense tangles of dislocations are aligned, forming a cell structure of three-dimensional walls of dislocation tangles surrounding uniformly sized regions of nearly perfect lattice. These dislocation walls are frequently parallel to a slip plane. The average spacing between walls decreases as strain increases, up to a strain of approximately 0.10, then remains nearly constant at approximately 1.5 μm. The formation of cell walls requires cross-slip of dislocations. As

discussed later in this article, such cross-slip is difficult when stacking fault energy is low.

As deformation increases beyond a strain of approximately 0.2, dislocation glide, cell formation, and reduction in cell size can no longer describe the resulting microstructure. Moreover, deformation within individual grains becomes increasingly inhomogeneous, because each grain must conform to the macroscopic shape change. The microstructural features that appear after substantial deformation have been defined in Ref 1 as:

- *Deformation band*: A region of different orientation within a single grain
- *Transition band*: The boundary between two deformation bands, a region of continuous orientation change
- *Kink band*: A deformation band separating two regions of identical orientation
- *Microbands*: Long, straight bands of highly concentrated slip lying on the slip planes of individual grains. They are usually 0.1- to 0.2-μm thick, traverse an entire grain, and correspond to the slip bands seen on a polished surface.
- *Shear bands*: Bands of very high shear strain. During rolling, these form at ~±35° to the rolling plane, parallel to the

transverse direction. They are independent of grain orientation. At high strains of approximately 3.5, they traverse the entire thickness of the rolled sheet.

In metals that deform initially by slip, the sequence of processes is (1) slip by glide of dislocations, (2) microband formation, and (3) shear band formation. In this category are fcc metals of medium to high stacking-fault energy, such as copper and aluminum, and the bcc metals. However, at low temperatures and/or very high strain rates, these metals may deform by twinning as well.

Microbands are generally observed at strains exceeding 0.1. As deformation continues to strains generally greater than 1.0, shear bands appear. The first to appear are microscopic, often having the shear plane parallel to a twinning plane in the matrix and the shear direction parallel to the twinning direction. Figure 6 shows a shear band in iron rolled to a strain of 2.0. The aligned microbands have been incorporated into the shear band. Shear bands appear to operate only once, as indicated in Fig. 7. During continued rolling, a sheet specimen becomes nearly filled with microscopic shear bands, then macroscopic bands begin to cross the entire thickness of the sheet.

## Composition

Dislocation distribution can be altered by a change in composition and by the presence of a second phase. Generally, solutes that inhibit cross-slip at a given temperature and strain rate also inhibit cell formation, making the dislocation distribution more random. Closely spaced second-phase particles less than approximately 1 μm apart produce a more random distribution of dislocations; more widely spaced, larger particles act as nucleating sites for the cell structure.

Solutes can cause large changes in deformation structures in fcc alloys by altering the stacking-fault energy. When the stacking-fault energy is reduced, the unit slip dislocation, which has a Burgers vector of type $\frac{1}{2} \langle 110 \rangle$, may dissociate into two partial dislocations, each having a Burgers vector of type $\frac{1}{6} \langle 211 \rangle$. These partials separate, leaving a stacking fault between them. In transmission electron micrographs, these faults are indicated by a fringe pattern of alternate light and dark lines running parallel to the intersection of the fault with the foil surface (Fig. 8).

A low stacking-fault energy also inhibits cross slip and generally produces a uniform distribution of dislocations rather than the cell structure typical of alloys with high stacking-fault energies. Microbands are also absent. At strains as small as 0.05, very fine (~0.02 μm thick), closely spaced (~0.1 μm) deformation twins appear in cold-rolled 70-30 brass. With continued rolling, these are ro-

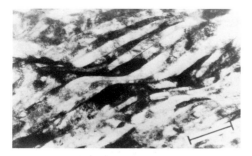

**Fig. 6** Longitudinal section showing a shear band in rolled iron. Rolling strain, $\varepsilon = 2$. Micron marker is parallel to the rolling direction. 12 000×. (D.J. Willis)

**Fig. 7** 70-30 brass, rolled 60%, etched, scratched parallel to rolling plane normal, and re-rolled 10%. Old shear bands do not operate in second rolling and are rotated; new shear bands displace scratch and produce relief. 410×. (M. Hatherly and A.S. Malin)

scale or the microscale arises because (1) stress gradients are produced by factors inherent in the method of load application (such as friction between tool and workpiece) or in the shape of the specimen (such as stress concentration at the roots of notches or cracks), (2) the mechanism of plastic yielding is dynamically unstable (as is the mechanism that causes the "yield point" in steel), (3) the initial structure is not homogeneous, but is a polycrystalline single-phase or multiphase aggregate, or (4) the fundamental deformation process (motion of an individual dislocation) is by its nature a localized event.

Macroscopic metallographic features, or features that are large in comparison with the grains of the material, include mechanical fibering, flow lines, strain markings, shear bands, and Lüders lines. Microscopic features, or features that are of a size comparable to that of the grains of the material, include curly grain structure, orange peel, slip lines, deformation twins, and kink bands.

**Mechanical fibering** refers to elongation and alignment of internal boundaries, second phases, and inclusions in particular directions corresponding to the directions of metal flow

**Fig. 8** Stacking faults (bands of closely spaced lines) and mechanical twins (the five dark, narrow bands) in 18Cr-8Ni stainless steel, deformed 5% at room temperature. Thin-foil electron micrograph. 10 000×

during deformation processing. If fibering is present, flow lines will often be visible on a macroetched section. Fibering often is associated with anisotropic mechanical properties. Figure 10 shows fibering in an Fe-2.5Si flat-rolled electrical sheet.

tated toward alignment with the rolling plane. At strains near 1.0, shear bands form.

The deformation ranges in which each of these processes operates in copper (high stacking-fault energy) and in α-brass (low stacking-fault energy) during rolling at room temperature are shown in Fig. 9. Slip and twinning are observed between the stacking-fault energies of copper ($\sim$60 mJ · m$^{-2}$) and copper-silicon alloys ($\sim$3 mJ · m$^{-2}$). In alloys that are metastable relative to a phase transformation, such as some austenitic stainless steels and the so-called transformation-induced plasticity (TRIP) steels, plastic deformation can trigger a martensitic transformation to a more stable phase.

## Deformation Modes

Metallographic investigation of deformation structures can be used to determine (1) the operative deformation mode (or modes) and (2) the kinds of crystal defects generated, as well as their concentration and distribution.

Metallographic identification of the common deformation modes is often based on the observed pattern of metal flow. Uniform homogeneous plastic straining of a metal is rarely achieved in practice and normally can only be approximated. Many important features exhibited by deformed structures are the result of nonuniform distribution of plastic strain. Nonuniform strain on the macro-

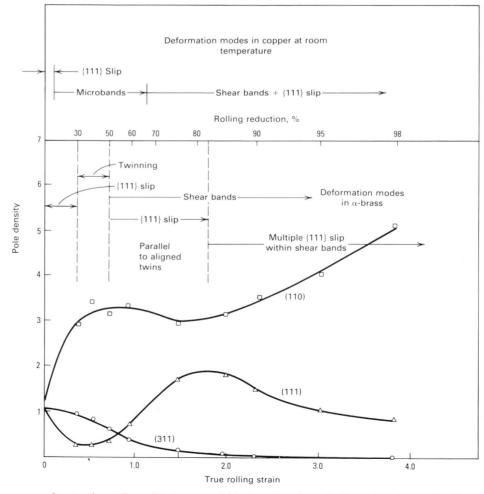

**Fig. 9** Density of crystallographic planes parallel to the rolling plane of α-brass after plane-strain rolling at room temperature. Microstructural deformation modes for α-brass and copper at room temperature, as a function of strain. (R.J. Asaro and A. Needleman)

**Flow lines** usually are revealed by deep etching cross sections of forgings; these lines form a pattern that suggests the direction and extent of metal movement during deformation. Figure 11 shows a closed-die forging in which flow, the configuration of which depends on that of the forging dies, is nonuniform.

**Strain markings** are lines that are visible on a surface that has been polished and etched after plastic flow. These lines define the traces of internal planes on which plastic shearing has occurred. They appear probably because of preferential etching attack at dislocations emerging at the sheared surfaces. The three macrographs in Fig. 12 show related views of the plastic zone near a crack tip. Dark-field illumination makes the heavily etched deformed regions appear white and the undeformed surrounding material appear dark.

**Shear bands** formed during rolling of sheet have been discussed above. Figure 13 shows shear bands in cold-reduced magnesium sheet.

**Lüders lines,** also called Lüders bands or stretcher strains, are commonly found in deep-drawn steel sheet. They are visible as surface markings, or surface roughening, caused by inhomogeneous (discontinuous) yielding during metal forming. Plastic yielding occurs within but not outside Lüders lines. Figure 14 shows a distinctive pattern of Lüders lines on the dome-shaped steel bottom of an aerosol can.

**Curly grain structure** is a phenomenon observed in transverse cross sections of heavily drawn bcc wires; it also occurs in fcc metals axisymmetrically compressed by large strains. Figures 15 and 16 show curly grain structure in a transverse section of iron wire in which neighboring grains are interlocked and convoluted. A curly lamellar structure in

**Fig. 10** Fibering in a 2.5% Si flat-rolled electrical sheet steel (M-36), as continuously cold rolled to 6-mm (0.25-in.) thickness—a 70% reduction. The structure consists of ferrite grains elongated in the rolling direction. 3% nital. 100×

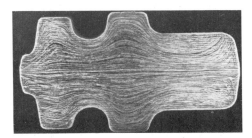

**Fig. 11** Flow lines in a closed-die forging of AISI 4340 alloy steel. Hot 50% HCl. Approx 0.75×

a drawn pearlitic steel wire is illustrated in Fig. 17. Curly grain structure originates in the ⟨110⟩ fiber texture developed in the early stages of deformation and in the resultant geometric relations of the operating slip systems.

**Orange peel,** or surface roughening on the scale of the grain size, is produced by plastic deformation of coarse-grained polycrystalline material; it is caused by differing patterns of flow resulting from orientation differences in neighboring grains. Orange peel is exemplified in Fig. 18, which depicts a Lüders-band boundary in a specimen that was polished before deformation. The polished surface was roughened by plastic straining in the yielded area (bottom). The smooth surface of the undeformed material (top) is shown for comparison. In specimens with large grain size, the orange-peel effect is visible without a microscope (see Fig. 5 in the article "Axial Compression Testing" in Volume 8 of the 9th Edition of *Metals Handbook*).

**Slip lines** are visible traces of slip planes on surfaces polished before deformation. The relative movement of material on opposite sides of a slip plane causes a surface step to appear. The term slip band is sometimes used to refer to a cluster of slip lines (Fig. 19). Planar slip refers to slip lines that are straight, indicating slip on a single plane. Wavy slip (Fig. 20) refers to slip lines that are irregular, indicating slip on two or more intersecting planes, such as that caused by repeated cross slip of a screw dislocation. Slip lines are more readily visible on specimens that have been polished prior to deformation.

**Deformation bands** are parts of a grain or a single crystal that have rotated in different directions during deformation, producing bands of different orientations within the crystal. In some instances, this rotation results from the operation of different sets of slip systems (Fig. 21).

**Deformation twins** are parts of crystals that have been deformed by homogeneous ("twinning") shear, which reorients the lattice in the twin into a mirror image of the parent

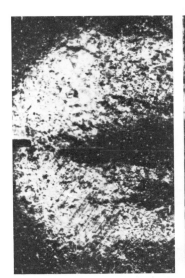

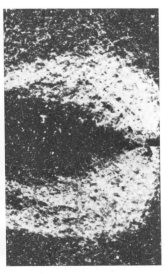

**Fig. 12** Three macrographs showing related views of strain markings (white regions) in the plastic zone near a crack tip in an Fe-3.25Si alloy sheet. The specimen was photographed under dark-field illumination. Morris's reagent: 25 g CrO₃, 133 mL acetic acid, 7 mL H₂O. 75×. (P.N. Mincer)

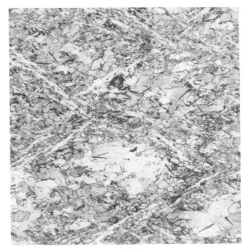

**Fig. 13** Shear bands (light streaks) in electrolytic magnesium cold rolled 50%, photographed with polarized light through a blue interference filter. Acetic-picral etchant (ASTM 127). 100×. (S.L. Couling)

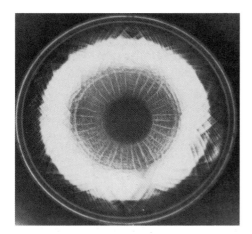

**Fig. 14** Lüders lines (stretcher strains) as they appear on the dome-shaped bottom of a deep drawn aerosol can made of low-carbon steel. Not polished, not etched. 0.67×. (M.J. Shemanski)

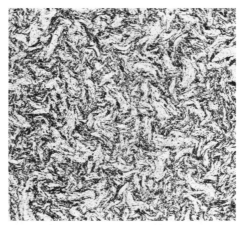

**Fig. 15** Curly grain structure in a transverse section of iron wire drawn to a true strain of 2.7. Longitudinal section of the same specimen is fibrous. 2% nital. 200×. (J.F. Peck and D.A. Thomas)

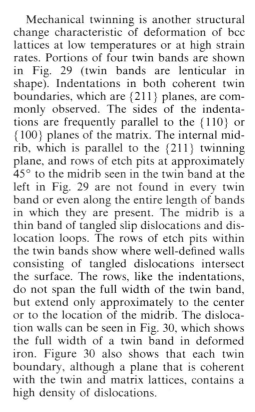

Mechanical twinning is another structural change characteristic of deformation of bcc lattices at low temperatures or at high strain rates. Portions of four twin bands are shown in Fig. 29 (twin bands are lenticular in shape). Indentations in both coherent twin boundaries, which are {211} planes, are commonly observed. The sides of the indentations are frequently parallel to the {110} or {100} planes of the matrix. The internal midrib, which is parallel to the {211} twinning plane, and rows of etch pits at approximately 45° to the midrib seen in the twin band at the left in Fig. 29 are not found in every twin band or even along the entire length of bands in which they are present. The midrib is a thin band of tangled slip dislocations and dislocation loops. The rows of etch pits within the twin bands show where well-defined walls consisting of tangled dislocations intersect the surface. The rows, like the indentations, do not span the full width of the twin band, but extend only approximately to the center or to the location of the midrib. The dislocation walls can be seen in Fig. 30, which shows the full width of a twin band in deformed iron. Figure 30 also shows that each twin boundary, although a plane that is coherent with the twin and matrix lattices, contains a high density of dislocations.

lattice. Deformation twins often are shaped like plates or lenses. Groups of fine twins (Fig. 22) may resemble bands of slip lines, making identification difficult by microscopy alone. Because they reveal the characteristic lattice rotation produced by twinning, x-ray and electron diffraction positively differentiate twins and slip lines (Fig. 23 and 24). Polarized light illumination is sometimes useful for identifying twins, especially in hcp metals.

**Kink bands** are identified by the abrupt change in lattice orientation that occurs across their boundaries (Fig. 25). Kink-band boundaries often lie roughly perpendicular to primary slip bands, a relationship attributable to the accumulation of primary dislocations of the same sign.

Dislocation-precipitate reactions are of two types. If particles are large (>1 μm) and strong, the particle-matrix interface, when stressed, can be a source of dislocations. If particles are small (<0.1 μm) and closely spaced, they obstruct dislocation glide. If the particles are weaker than the matrix, they may deform, producing a change in particle shape (Fig. 26) or an observable increase in

dislocation density within the particles or both. If the particles are strong and do not deform, the deformed matrix must accommodate a large strain gradient. Dislocation loops left around particles, as well as linear arrays of prismatic loops, indicate accommodation of the particles by flow in the matrix (Fig. 27).

## Low Temperature and High Strain Rate

Temperatures below ambient or high strain rates at ambient temperature produce distinctive deformation structures, especially in bcc metals such as iron. Decreasing the deformation temperature or increasing the strain rate results in a more uniform distribution of dislocations (Fig. 28), decreases the ability of screw dislocations to cross slip, and inhibits dynamic recovery. The dislocations in Fig. 28, which shows iron deformed at low temperature, are primarily screw dislocations; because cross slip is inhibited, they are longer and straighter than the dislocations in Fig. 3 to 5.

## Elevated Temperatures

When metals are plastically deformed at hot-working temperatures, the flow stress and the microstructure that develop depend largely on the temperature-strain-time history of the workpiece. Strain rate and temperature are complementary variables; an increase in strain rate and a reduction in temperature generally have equivalent effects. Both variables determine which deformation mechanisms will predominate and control the degree to which annealing processes occur simultaneously with, or following, the deformation process. The temperature at which deformation takes place ($T$) is usually evaluated

**Fig. 16** Thin-foil electron micrograph showing the cell structure in a transverse section of an iron wire drawn to 98% reduction. 12 000×. (R.C. Glenn)

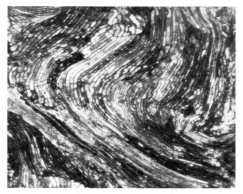

**Fig. 17** Curly lamellar structure in transverse section of a pearlitic steel wire drawn to a true strain of 3.2. Thin-foil electron micrograph. 20 000×

**Fig. 18** Orange peel (rough, yielded area in bottom half of micrograph) on the surface of mild steel that was polished and plastically deformed. 60×. (D.A. Chatfield)

**Fig. 19** Slip bands on two planes in a single crystal of Co-8Fe alloy that was polished, then plastically deformed. Compare with Fig. 20. 250×. (G.Y. Chin)

**Fig. 20** Wavy slip lines in a single crystal of aluminum that was polished, then plastically deformed. Compare with Fig. 19. 250×. (G.Y. Chin)

**Fig. 21** Deformation bands on (100) surface of a single crystal of Co-8Fe alloy deformed 44%, polished, and lightly deformed further. 250×. (G.Y. Chin)

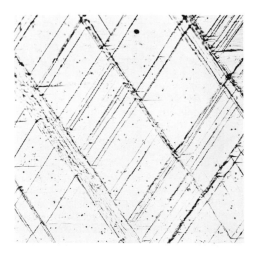

**Fig. 22** Groups of extremely fine twin bands in polished and plastically deformed titanium. Photographed with polarized light. See also Fig. 23. 200×. (N.E. Paton)

**Fig. 23** Twin band and surrounding matrix in deformed titanium shown in Fig. 22. Thin-foil electron micrograph; bright-field illumination. 44 000×. (N.E. Paton)

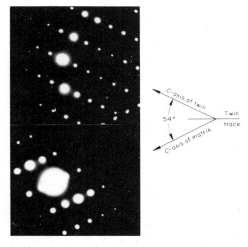

**Fig. 24** Electron diffraction patterns obtained from the twin band and the matrix in the deformed titanium in Fig. 23, showing mirror symmetry of spot patterns

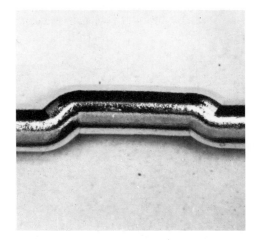

**Fig. 25** Double kink band produced in a single crystal of zinc by axial compression. As-polished and deformed. 3×. (J.J. Gilman)

**Fig. 26** Precipitate particles (light) in Ti-17Al alloy that was aged 48 h at 480 °C (895 °F), then plastically deformed. The deformation sheared the particles along the slip plane. Thin-foil transmission electron micrograph. 65 000×. (J. Williams)

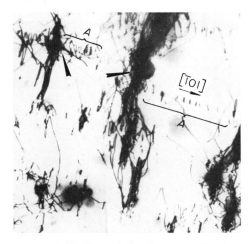

**Fig. 27** Thin-foil electron micrograph of a single copper crystal deformed 10%, showing arrays of prismatic dislocation loops (at *A*) and interaction of dislocations with spherical particles of silicon dioxide (at arrows). 6000×. (J. Humphries)

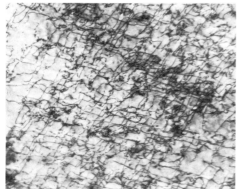

**Fig. 28** Uniform dislocation structure in iron deformed 14% at −195 °C (−320 °F). The dislocations are primarily of the screw type. Thin-foil electron micrograph. 40 000×

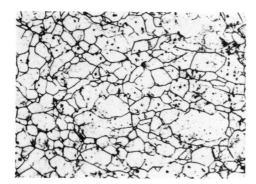

**Fig. 29** Mechanical twin bands in Fe-3Si alloy rolled 5% at −195 °C (−320 °F) showing indentations in twin-band boundaries. See also Fig. 30. Gorsuch reagent: 5 g picric acid, 8 g CuCl₂, 20 mL HCl, 6 mL HNO₃, and 200 mL 95% ethanol or 95% methanol. 250×

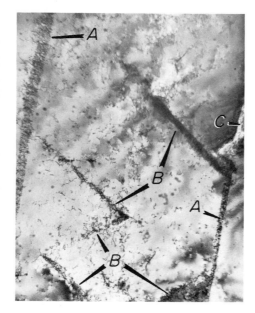

**Fig. 30** Thin-foil electron micrograph of a twin band in iron deformed 5% in tension at −195 °C (−320 °F) showing both of the boundaries (at A), several diagonal internal walls (at B), and a boundary indentation (at C). 6700×

in reference to the melting point of the metal ($T_M$) as $T/T_M$ (temperatures on absolute scale).

**Deformation at High Strain Rates.** During rapid hot working and during cold working, dislocation mechanisms of flow predominate. However, at elevated temperatures, the generation and storage of dislocations are largely offset by a concurrent, thermally activated rearrangement process known as dynamic recovery. The microstructural effect of dynamic recovery usually is the development of an intragranular subgrain structure. In this structure, micron-size subgrains are separated by small-angle boundaries, which can be revealed at high magnification by standard optical and electron microscopy (Fig. 31 to 33). When these same structures are viewed by low-magnification optical microscopy, they may resemble the distorted or fibered grain structure of cold-worked metals (see the streaked matrix in the extruded material shown in Fig. 34).

At large strains, in processes such as extrusion and planetary hot rolling, a second concurrent softening process known as dynamic recrystallization can be initiated. It occurs primarily in fcc metals (except aluminum) and leads to grain refinement by the dynamic nucleation and growth of fine grains along the original grain boundaries.

**Deformation at Low Strain Rates.** At low strain rates, the major mechanisms of elevated-temperature deformation are grain-boundary sliding (shearing), grain-boundary migration, and stress-induced atomic diffusion. Grain-boundary sliding is visible on a workpiece surface as shear offsets in scratches or in other surface irregularities that originally passed continuously across a grain boundary (Fig. 37).

In polycrystalline metals, grain-boundary sliding is constrained to small amounts by irregularities in the boundary plane and by adjacent grains that block each end of the shearing boundary. Large accumulated plastic strains are possible, however, if boundary sliding is also assisted by stress-induced diffusion, in which the atomic movements in each grain produce a change in the shape of the grain and of the entire piece of metal. For example, deformation resulting from tensile stress produces thickening of the grain along the direction of the imposed stress and thinning perpendicular to that direction. Metallographic evidence of this process can be observed in Fig. 38, which shows an alloy that contained immobile precipitate particles; the buildup of pure metal along the tension-loaded grain boundaries is shown by the precipitate-free regions along these boundaries.

**Static and Postdynamic Recrystallization.** The substructure that results from dynamic recovery effectively reflects an intermediate stage of annealing. After deformation has been completed, but before any significant drop in temperature, static recrystallization may occur by the usual processes of nu-

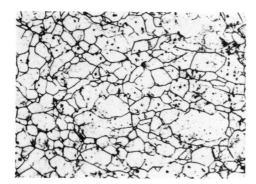

**Fig. 31** Subgrains separated by small-angle boundaries (black lines) in Fe-3.25Si alloy compressed at 1000 °C (1830 °F) and a strain rate of 0.15/s to a strain of 0.61, then quenched 1 s. Morris's reagent (see Fig. 12). 220×. (J.L. Uvira)

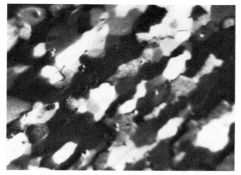

**Fig. 32** Longitudinal section of aluminum extruded at 400 °C (750 °F) showing subgrains revealed as patches of varying brightness by illumination of the electrolytically etched surface with polarized light. Barker's reagent. 375×. (W.A. Wong)

**Fig. 33** Longitudinal section of aluminum extruded at 250 °C (480 °F) and a strain rate of approximately 1/s to a strain of 0.975 showing subgrains (areas of varying brightness). Thin-foil transmission electron micrograph. 6500×. (H. McQueen)

**Fig. 34** Static recrystallization in aluminum extruded at 450 °C (840 °F). A longitudinal section, photographed with polarized light. Large, new grains of varying brightness have grown into the streaked matrix, which contains a very fine substructure. Barker's reagent. 40×. (W.A. Wong)

**Fig. 35** Static recrystallization in Fe-3.25Si alloy compressed at 910 °C (1670 °F) to 0.31 strain, held at temperature for 30 s. Large, defect-free grains have grown into the matrix, which contains a dense array of subboundaries. Morris's reagent (see Fig. 12). 1200×

**Fig. 36** Static recrystallization in oxygen-free copper rolled to 86% reduction in thickness in one pass (starting at 1000 °C, or 1830 °F; finishing at 600 °C, or 1110 °F), quenched 1 s. Composite of thin-foil electron micrographs showing new, dislocation-free grains that have grown into the matrix (upper right), which contains a fine substructure. 1000×. (H. McQueen)

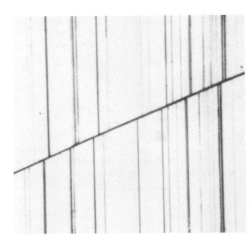

**Fig. 37** Al-1.91Mg alloy deformed 0.62% at 265 °C (510 °F) showing grain-boundary sliding. The sliding is revealed by the shear offsets of the surface scratches (vertical lines) at a grain boundary (diagonal line). Not polished, not etched. 250×. (A.W. Mullendore)

**Fig. 38** Mg-0.5Zr alloy deformed at 500 °C (930 °F) and a strain rate of 0.002/min to a strain of 0.5 (tensile direction, horizontal). Creep by atom diffusion is revealed by precipitate-free regions (light). Pepper's reagent: 5 g malic acid, 2 mL $HNO_3$, 0.5 mL HCl, and 97.5 mL ethanol. 500×. (Anwar-ul Karim)

cleation of new grains and the growth of those grains into the matrix of subgrains (Fig. 34 to 36). If dynamic recrystallization was initiated during straining, no incubation time is required for the nucleation of new grains upon unloading, and the resulting microstructural process, known as postdynamic recrystallization or metadynamic recrystalliza-tion, takes place considerably faster than conventional static recrystallization.

## REFERENCE

1. M. Hatherly, *Proceedings of the 6th International Conference on Strength of Metals and Alloys*, Melbourne, Pergamon Press, 1982, p 1181

## SELECTED REFERENCES

- W.A. Backofen, *Deformation Processing*, Addison-Wesley, 1972
- C.S. Barrett and T.B. Massalski, *Structure of Metals*, 3rd ed., McGraw-Hill, 1966
- R.W.K. Honeycombe, *The Plastic Deformation of Metals*, 2nd ed., E. Arnold, Ltd., 1968
- J.J. Jonas, C.M. Sellars, and W.F. McG. Tegart, *Met. Rev.*, No. 130, 1969, p 1-24
- A.S. Keh and S. Weissmann, *Electron Microscopy and the Strength of Crystals*, Interscience, 1953, p 231-300
- G. Krauss, Ed., *Deformation, Processing and Structure*, American Society for Metals, 1983
- R.J. McElroy and Z.C. Szkopiak, *Int. Met. Rev.*, Vol 17, 1972, p 175-202
- W. Rostoker and J.R. Dvorak, *Interpretation of Metallographic Structures*, Academic Press, 1965, p 12-25
- E. Schmid and W. Boas, *Plasticity of Crystals*, Chapman and Hall, 1968
- S.L. Semiatin and J.J. Jonas, *Formability and Workability of Metals: Plastic Instability and Flow Localization*, American Society for Metals, 1984
- Viewpoint Set on Shear Bands, *Scripta Met.*, Vol 18, 1984, p 421-458

# Recovery, Recrystallization, and Grain-Growth Structures

By Hsun Hu
Research Professor
Department of Metallurgical
and Materials Engineering
University of Pittsburgh

RECOVERY, RECRYSTALLIZATION, AND GRAIN GROWTH are the main stages of annealing when it is applied to a cold-worked metal. Such classification is approximate; some overlapping between the stages usually occurs because of microstructural nonhomogeneity of the specimen. To some extent, the annealing behavior of a metal may be different from metal to metal, and for the same metal of different purity, but the basic phenomena involved in the various annealing stages are similar.

When a metal is cold worked by plastic deformation, a small portion of the mechanical energy expended in deforming the metal is stored in the specimen. This stored energy resides in the crystals as point defects (vacancies and interstitials), dislocations, and stacking faults in various forms and combinations, depending on the metal. Therefore, a cold-worked specimen, being in a state of higher energy, is thermodynamically unstable. With thermal activation, such as provided by annealing, the cold-worked specimen tends to transform to states of lower energies through a sequence of processes with microstructural changes. Along with the microstructural changes, the properties of the specimen will change correspondingly. Deformation and annealing are important processing methods for producing desired properties of the material by controlling its microstructures.

## The Deformed State

For a better understanding of annealing, particularly recovery and recrystallization, a clear understanding of the deformed state is useful. Structures resulting from plastic deformation were presented and discussed in detail in the preceding article, "Plastic Deformation Structures." In addition, knowledge of the nature of the highly deformed structure and the mechanisms that are responsible for

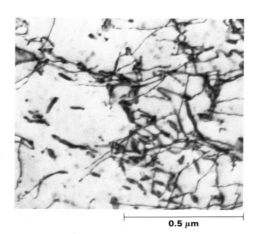

**Fig. 1** Fe-3Si single crystal, cold rolled 5% in the (111)[11$\bar{2}$] orientation. Trails of small dislocation loops, edge dislocation dipoles, and cusps on dislocation lines. Thin-foil TEM specimen prepared parallel to the rolling plane. 62 000×

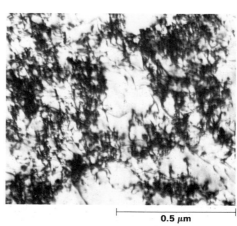

**Fig. 2** Fe-3Si single crystal, cold rolled 20% in the (111)[11$\bar{2}$] orientation showing increased density of dislocations and clusters of short dislocation loops. Thin-foil TEM specimen prepared parallel to the rolling plane. 62 000×

**Fig. 3** Type 304 stainless steel, cross rolled 90% at 200 °C (390 °F). Highly irregular cell structure and numerous microtwins and stacking faults. Thin-foil TEM specimen prepared parallel to the rolling plane. 30 000×. (Ref 1)

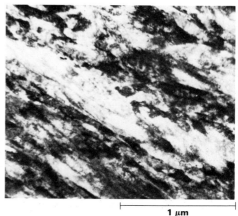

**Fig. 4** Same as Fig. 3. Deformation cells (resembling ribbons) of very small thicknesses lying parallel to the rolling plane of the sheet. Thin-foil TEM specimen prepared parallel to the longitudinal cross section. 30 000×. (Ref 1)

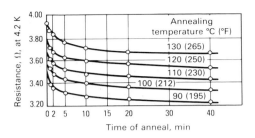

**Fig. 5** Change in electrical resistivity during isothermal recovery for copper deformed by torsion at 4.2 K. (Ref 2)

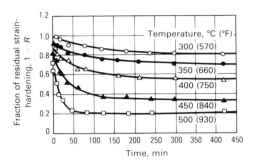

**Fig. 6** Change in residual strain hardening during isothermal recovery for zone-melted iron deformed 5% in tension at 0 °C (32 °F). The fraction of residual strain hardening, $1 - R = (\sigma - \sigma_0) \div (\sigma_m - \sigma_0)$, where $R$ is the fraction of recovery, $\sigma_0$ the flow stress of the fully annealed material, $\sigma_m$ the flow stress of the strain-hardened material at a predetermined constant strain, and $\sigma$ the initial flow stress after a recovery anneal. (Ref 3)

its development facilitates understanding the microstructural changes from a highly deformed to a fully annealed state.

Plastic deformation is achieved principally by passage of dislocations through the lattice. In the early stages of deformation, the dislocations are relatively long, straight, and few. With increasing deformation, more dislocations from other slip systems are produced, causing interactions among the various dislo-

cations. These dislocations and clusters of short loops tend to tangle and to align themselves roughly to broad boundaries. Small areas, or "cells," within which there are very few or no individual dislocations, are therefore outlined by these broad boundaries. This sequence of cell-structure development is depicted in Fig. 1 and 2. These thin-foil specimens were prepared parallel to the rolling plane of the strip for examination by transmission electron microscopy (TEM).

For polycrystalline specimens deformed to large strains, such as heavily cold-rolled sheet or strip, the dislocation density is very high, and the microstructure becomes extremely complex. For these materials, thin-foil specimens normally prepared parallel to the rolling plane of the sheet or strip show more diffuse structures (Fig. 3), because the cells are much thinner than the thin-foil specimen. A more clearly defined cell structure can be observed by using thin-foil specimens prepared parallel to the cross section of the sheet or strip (Fig. 4). The structural elements or deformation cells in a heavily cold-rolled sheet or strip are in the form of thin ribbons lying roughly parallel to the rolling plane of the sheet or strip. Optical micrographs will show the distorted grains and deformation bands within the grains only at moderate deformations. With increasing deformation, a strong preferred orientation or crystallographic texture is developed in the specimen, even when the initial grains are oriented at random (see the article "Textured Structures" in this Volume).

## Recovery

The earliest change in structure and properties that occurs upon annealing a cold-worked metal is considered the beginning of recovery. As recovery proceeds, a sequence of structural changes emerges: (1) the annealing out of point defects and their clusters, (2) the

annihilation and rearrangement of dislocations, (3) polygonization (subgrain formation and subgrain growth), and (4) the formation of recrystallization nuclei energetically capable of further growth. These structural changes do not involve high-angle boundary migration. Therefore, during this stage of annealing, the texture of the deformed metal essentially does not change.

**Changes in Properties.** During the early stages of recovery in which the annealing out of point defects and the annihilation and rearrangement of dislocations have occurred only to a limited extent, the change in microstructure may not be apparent in conventional optical or transmission electron micrographs. However, some physical or mechanical properties of the metal, such as electrical resistivity, x-ray line broadening, or strain-hardening parameters, may show the changes due to recovery with high sensitivities. Figures 5 and 6 show the changes in resistivity and residual strain hardening, respectively, during isothermal recovery annealing. These figures indicate that isothermal recovery of the various properties share the following features: (1) there is no incubation period; (2) the rate of change is highest at the beginning, decreasing with increasing time; and (3) at long times, the property approaches the equilibrium value very gradually. However, hardness is less sensitive to early stages of recovery in comparison with other properties, such as electrical resistivity, x-ray line broadening, strain hardening, and density.

**Changes in microstructure** during recovery become readily observable by transmission electron microscopy when the density of dislocations is considerably reduced and the appreciable rearrangement of the remaining dislocations has occurred. Figures 7 to 10 show the sequence of dislocation substructure changes for a single crystal of Fe-3Si (wt%), which was cold rolled 80% in the (001)[110]

  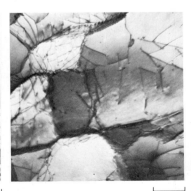 

**Fig. 7** High density of dislocations and no well-defined cell structure is revealed in the as-rolled condition.

**Fig. 8** Annealed at 400 °C (750 °F) for 1280 min. Reduced dislocation density and random arrays of dislocations are evident.

**Fig. 9** Annealed at 600 °C (1110 °F) for 1280 min. Well-defined subgrains resulting from polygonization are shown.

**Fig. 10** Annealed at 800 °C (1470 °F) for 5 min. Increased average diameter of the subgrains is due to subgrain growth.

**Fig. 7-10** Effect of annealing time and temperature on the microstructure of an Fe-3Si single crystal, cold rolled 80% in the (001)[110] orientation. Thin-foil TEM specimens prepared parallel to the rolling plane. All at 17 200×

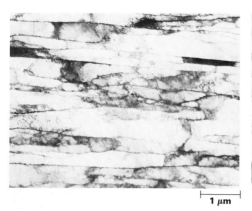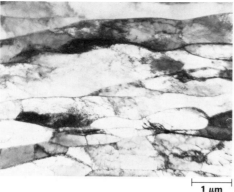

1 μm                    1 μm

**Fig. 11, 12** Electrolytic iron single crystal, cold rolled 70% in the (111)[1̄10] orientation. Fig. 11: thin, ribbon-like cells stacked up in the thickness dimension of the as-rolled crystal. Fig. 12: annealed at 550 °C (1020 °F) for 20 min. Increased cell thickness resulting from subgrain growth. Thin-foil TEM specimens prepared parallel to the transverse cross section. Both at 11 000×. (Ref 4)

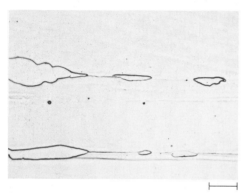

20 μm

**Fig. 13** Fe-3Si single crystal, cold rolled 80% in the (001)[100] orientation and annealed at 600 °C (1110 °F) for 25 min. Optical micrograph shows recrystallized grains formed at boundaries (microband region or transition bands) between the main deformation bands. See also Fig. 16. 5% nital. 400×

orientation and subsequently annealed at various temperatures. From a structure of random arrays of dislocations (Fig. 8) to that of well-defined subgrains (Fig. 9), the process is commonly referred to as polygonization. Further annealing may gradually increase the average size of the subgrains (Fig. 9 and 10).

When the microstructure of a heavily rolled crystal is revealed using thin-foil specimens parallel to the cross sections of the strip, the thin, ribbon-like deformation cells are readily observed. Figure 11 shows the dislocation substructure of an as-deformed iron crystal cold rolled in the (111)[110] orientation to 70% reduction (see also Fig. 4 for a much finer microstructure in a heavily rolled polycrystalline stainless steel). During recovery, the thickness of the ribbon-like subgrains increases, as shown in Fig. 12. Subgrain growth at these early stages cannot be clearly observed when thin-foil specimens parallel to the rolling plane are used for transmission electron microscopy examination. As mentioned earlier, this is because a clearly defined subgrain structure can be observed in a thin-foil specimen parallel to the rolling plane only when the thickness of the subgrains exceeds that of the foil.

## Recrystallization

Following recovery, recrystallization (or primary recrystallization) occurs by the nucleation and growth of new grains, which are essentially strain-free, at the expense of the polygonized matrix. During incubation, stable nuclei are formed by the coalescence of subgrains that leads to the formation of high-angle boundaries. From that time on, subsequent growth of new grains can proceed rapidly, because of the high mobility of the high-angle boundaries. The rate of recrystallization later decreases toward completion as concurrent recovery of the matrix occurs and more of the new grains impinge upon each other. Accordingly, isothermal recrystallization curves are typically sigmoidal (see Fig. 24 and 30). Because recrystallization is accomplished by high-angle boundary migration, a large change in the texture occurs.

Sufficient deformation and a sufficiently high temperature of annealing are required to initiate recrystallization following recovery. With a low degree of deformation and a low annealing temperature, the specimen may recover only without the occurrence of recrystallization. *In situ* recrystallization, or complete softening without the nucleation and growth of new grains at the expense of the polygonized matrix, is a process of recovery, not recrystallization, because it does not involve high-angle boundary migration. Consequently, there is no essential change in texture following *in situ* recrystallization.

**Nucleation Sites.** Because of the highly nonhomogeneous microstructure of a plastically cold-worked metal, recrystallization nuclei are formed at preferred sites. Examples of preferred nucleation sites include the original grain boundaries; the boundaries between deformation bands within a crystal or grain; the intersections of mechanical twins, such as Neumann bands in body-centered cubic crystals; the distorted twin-band boundaries; and the regions of shear bands. Limited recrystal-

lization may also occur by the growth of grains nucleated at large and hard inclusion particles.

In general, preferred nucleation sites are regions of relatively small volume where the lattice is highly distorted (having high lattice curvature). In such regions, the dimension of the substructure is fine, and the orientation gradient is high. Therefore, the critical size for a stable nucleus to form in these regions is relatively small and so can be attained more readily. Furthermore, the nucleus needs only to grow through a relatively short distance to form a high-angle boundary with the matrix.

Figure 13 shows recrystallized grains formed in the boundary region between two main deformation bands in a crystal of Fe-3Si that was cold rolled 80% in the (001)[100] orientation, then annealed at 600 °C (1110 °F) for 25 min. What appears as a thin-line boundary between main deformation bands in an optical micrograph (Fig. 13) actually contains a group of narrow, elongated, microband segments, among which nucleation occurs by the coalescence of the segments into a recrystallized grain (Fig. 14). Nucleation in such microband regions is also termed transition band nucleation, because the large orientation difference between the main deformation bands is accommodated in small steps by the microband segments. In heavily deformed polycrystalline specimens, such transition regions must exist between different deformation texture components, but they may not be as clearly defined and readily identified as in the similarly deformed specific single-crystal specimens.

Figures 15 and 16 show the nucleation of recrystallized grains in heavily rolled polycrystalline copper by the coalescence of subgrains in the microband regions. These micrographs, which were obtained from thin-foil specimens prepared parallel to the cross section of the sheet, show the evolution of the microstructure in nucleation. When thin-foil specimens prepared parallel to the rolling plane of the heavily rolled sheet are used for nucleation studies, the characteristics of the nucleation site cannot be defined with certainty (Fig. 17 and 18).

In moderately deformed samples with relatively coarse initial grains, the microstructure near the grain boundaries and the evolution of the microstructure during nucleation can be studied in considerable detail, even when thin-foil specimens parallel to the rolling plane are used for transmission electron microscopy examinations. Figure 19 shows the grain-boundary bands observed adjacent to an initial grain boundary in commercial-purity aluminum that was cold rolled 50%. The cumulative misorientations across the bands (16.5°), as shown in the inset, indicate similarity in feature between these grain-boundary bands and the transition bands described earlier. These grain-boundary bands obviously would not form at every grain boundary, but would depend on the relative orientations of the two adjacent grains.

**Fig. 14** Fe-3Si single crystal, cold rolled 80% in the (001)[100] orientation and annealed at 600 °C (1110 °F) for 125 min. Transmission electron micrograph showing a recrystallized grain grown from the microband region (transition bands). Thin-foil specimen prepared parallel to the rolling plane. Compare with Fig. 15. 14 740×

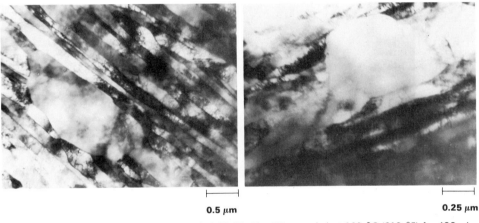

0.5 μm                                      0.25 μm

**Fig. 15, 16** Electrolytic copper, cold rolled 99.5%. Fig. 15: annealed at 100 °C (212 °F) for 625 min. Recrystallization nuclei formed among microbands are shown. 17 100×. Fig. 16: annealed at 100 °C (212 °F) for 25 min. Recrystallization nuclei formed among microbands by subgrain coalescence are shown. 34 200×. Both thin-foil TEM specimens prepared parallel to the transverse section

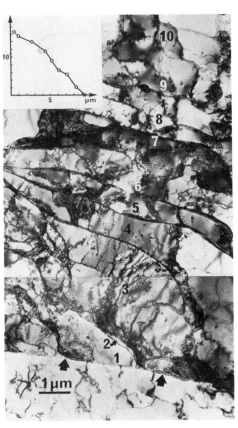

1 μm

**Fig. 19** Fine-grained commercial-purity aluminum, cold rolled 50%. A 9-μm wide grain boundary band consisting of elongated subgrains that was developed along an initial grain boundary marked by arrows. The inset shows the misorientations regarding the grain interior as a function of the distance from the grain boundary. Thin-foil TEM specimen prepared parallel to the rolling plane. 7300×. (Ref 6)

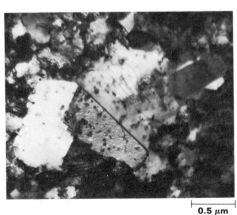

1 μm                              0.5 μm

2 μm

**Fig. 17** Low-carbon steel, cold rolled 70% and annealed at 450 °C (840 °F) for 260 h and 42 min. Well-developed recrystallized grains and recrystallization nuclei during their formation by subgrain coalescence in the recovered matrix still exhibit a "messy" substructure. Thin-foil TEM specimen prepared parallel to the rolling plane. 7020×

**Fig. 18** Type 304L stainless steel, cold rolled 90% at 25 °C (75 °F) and annealed at 600 °C (1110 °F) for 1 h. Early recrystallized grains with annealing twins in a highly "messy" matrix. Thin-foil TEM specimen prepared parallel to the rolling plane. 21 600×. (Ref 5)

**Fig. 20** Coarse-grained commercial-purity aluminum cold rolled 30% and annealed at 320 °C (610 °F) for 30 min. A recrystallization nucleus (denoted A) developed near arrow-marked FeAl₃ particles, and is shown straddling an initial grain boundary (marked by dotted line). Thin-foil TEM specimen prepared parallel to the rolling plane. 3650×. (Ref 6)

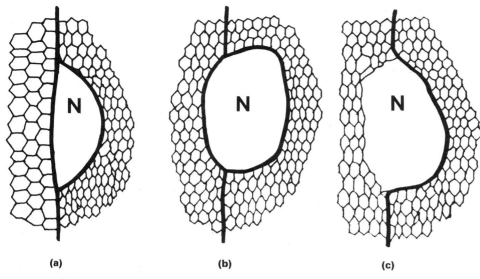

(a)       (b)       (c)

**Fig. 21** Schematic showing three types of grain-boundary nucleation and the growth of the nucleus (N) at the expense of the polygonized subgrains. See text for detailed explanation. (Ref 6)

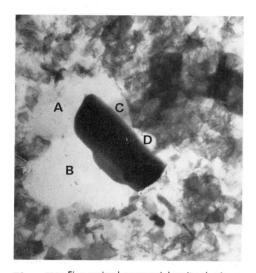

**Fig. 22** Fine-grained commercial-purity aluminum, cold rolled 90% and heated in a high-voltage electron microscope at 264 °C (507 °F) for 480 s. Recrystallized grains (denoted by letters) nucleated at a large FeAl₃ particle and grown into the polygonized matrix. Thin-foil TEM specimen prepared parallel to the rolling plane. 2810×. (Ref 6)

formed by subgrain growth to the right of the original grain boundary (Fig. 21a), by grain-boundary migration to the right and subgrain growth to the left forming a new high-angle boundary (Fig. 21b), and by grain-boundary migration to the right and subgrain growth to the left but without forming a new high-angle boundary (Fig. 21c).

When a polycrystalline specimen is deformed to a very small strain—less than 2 or 3%, for example—then annealed at a sufficiently high temperature, recrystallization occurs by strain-induced boundary migration of only a few grains. These few grains grow very

Grain-boundary nucleation by the "bulging out" of a section of an initial boundary from the region of a low dislocation content into a region of high dislocation content is frequently observed in large-grained materials deformed at low and medium strains. This bulging mechanism of nucleation for recrystallization is a consequence of the strain-induced boundary migration. Figure 20 shows a recrystallization nucleus that has formed by straddling a grain boundary in a coarse-grained aluminum that was cold rolled 30% and annealed at 320 °C (610 °F) for 30 min. Such grain-boundary nucleation was observed to have three types of structural detail. As shown in Fig. 21, the nucleus may be

large at the expense of the small matrix grains. The maximum level of strain below which such coarsening occurs is commonly termed critical strain. This behavior has been used to grow single crystals in the solid state by the so-called "strain-anneal" technique.

Figure 22 shows recrystallized grains nucleated and grown at a large and hard FeAl₃ inclusion particle in 90% cold-rolled aluminum after annealing in the high-voltage electron microscope at 264 °C (507 °F) for 480 s. Unless the volume fraction of the inclusion particles is substantially large, the contribution of particle-nucleated grains constitutes only a small fraction of the total recrystallization volume. From the above discussions on nucleation sites, it is easy to understand that the size of the recrystallized grains, as recrystallization is complete, decreases with increasing deformation, because the number of nuclei increases with increasing deformation.

**Growth of Nucleated Grains.** The growth of the newly formed strain-free grains at the expense of the polygonized matrix is accomplished by the migration of high-angle boundaries. Migration proceeds away from the center of boundary curvature. The driving force for recrystallization is the remaining strain energy in the matrix following recovery. This strain energy exists as dislocations mainly in the subgrain boundaries. Therefore, the various factors that influence the mobility of the high-angle boundary or the driving force for its migration will influence the kinetics of recrystallization. For example, impurities, solutes, or fine second-phase particles will inhibit boundary migration; therefore, their presence will retard recrystal-

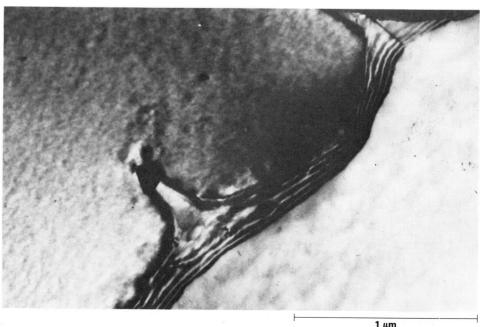

1 μm

**Fig. 23** Aluminum-aluminum oxide specimen, cold rolled and annealed. Shown is the pinning of a mobile low-angle boundary by a small Al₂O₃ particle during a recovery anneal. Thin-foil TEM specimen. 47 000×. (Ref 7)

lization. Figure 23 shows the pinning of a mobile low-angle boundary by a fine alumina ($Al_2O_3$) particle in an aluminum-alumina specimen during recovery. In connection with the driving force for recrystallization, a fine-subgrained matrix has a higher strain-energy content than does a coarse-subgrained matrix. Accordingly, recrystallization occurs faster in a fine-subgrained matrix than in a coarse-subgrained matrix. During recrystallization, continued recovery may occur in the matrix by subgrain growth, resulting in a reduction of the driving energy for recrystallization and therefore a decrease in the recrystallization rate. From driving energy considerations, it is understandable that the tendency for recrystallization is stronger in heavily deformed than in moderately or lightly deformed specimens. For a given de-

formation, the finer the original grain size the stronger the tendency for recrystallization. Figure 24 shows such effects in low-carbon steel.

## Grain Growth

After recrystallization is complete—that is, when the polygonized matrix is replaced by the new strain-free grains—further annealing increases the average size of the grains. The process, known as grain growth, is accomplished by the migration of grain boundaries. In contrast to recrystallization, the boundary moves toward its center of curvature. Some of the grains grow, but others shrink and vanish. Because the volume of the specimen is a con-

stant, the number of the grains decreases as a consequence of grain growth. The driving force for grain growth is the grain-boundary free-energy, which is substantially smaller in magnitude than the driving energy for recrystallization.

According to the growth behavior of the grains, grain growth can be further classified into two types: normal or continuous grain growth and abnormal or discontinuous grain growth. The latter has also been termed exaggerated grain growth, coarsening, or secondary recrystallization.

**Normal or continuous grain growth** occurs in pure metals and single-phase alloys. During isothermal growth, the increase in the average grain diameter obeys the empirical growth law, which can be expressed as $\bar{D} = Kt^n$, where $\bar{D}$ is the average grain diameter, $t$ is the annealing time, and $K$ and $n$ are parameters that depend on material and temperature. Therefore, when $\bar{D}$ and $t$ are plotted on a logarithmic scale, a straight line should be obtained, with $K$ as the intercept and $n$ the slope. The value of $n$, the time exponent in isothermal grain growth, is usually less than, or at most equal to, 0.5. A typical example for isothermal grain growth in zone-refined iron is shown in Fig. 25. The deviation from a straight-line relationship for very short annealing times at low temperatures is due to recrystallization, and that for long annealing times at high temperatures is due to the limiting effect of the sheet specimen thickness.

One of the structural characteristics during normal grain growth is that the grain size and grain-shape distributions are essentially invariant; that is, during normal grain growth, the average grain size increases, but the size and shape distributions of the grains remain essentially the same before and after the growth, differing only by a scale factor. Figures 26 and 27 show, respectively, the size and shape distributions of the grains in zone-refined iron after normal grain growth at 650 °C (923 K) for various lengths of time. The data points fit the same distribution curves. Therefore, to a first approximation, normal grain growth is equivalent to photographic enlargement.

During the normal grain growth, the change in texture is small and gradual. Assuming the initial grains are nearly random-oriented, after extensive normal grain growth some weak preferred orientations may be developed among the final grains, depending on such factors as the energies of the free surfaces of the grains. If the initial grains are strongly textured, normal grain growth may be inhibited as a consequence of low mobility of the matrix-grain boundaries (see the next section of this article). Figure 28 shows the grain aggregate of a zone-refined iron specimen after normal grain growth at 800 °C (1470 °F) for 12 min. The size and shape distributions of these grains are essentially the same as those of the much finer grains before growth.

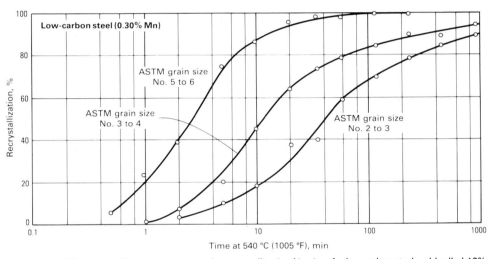

**Fig. 24** Effect of penultimate grain size on the recrystallization kinetics of a low-carbon steel, cold rolled 60% and annealed at 540 °C (1005 °F). Note the incubation time is shortened as the penultimate grain size before cold rolling is decreased. (Ref 8)

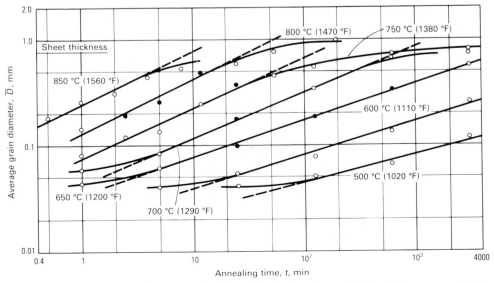

**Fig. 25** Normal grain growth in zone-refined iron during isothermal anneals. Closed circles represent specimens for which statistical analysis of grain-size and grain-shape distributions was conducted.

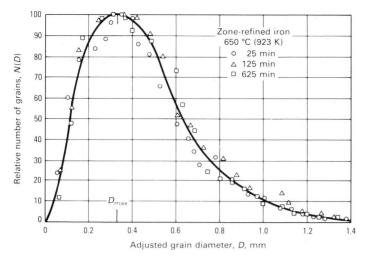

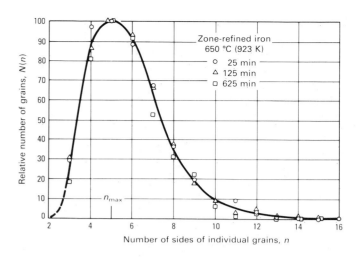

**Fig. 26** Grain-size distribution in zone-refined iron during isothermal grain growth at 650 °C (923 K), using a scalar-adjusted grain diameter for each specimen. The plot indicates that the grain-size distribution remains essentially unchanged during normal grain growth.

**Fig. 27** Grain-shape distribution in zone-refined iron during isothermal grain growth at 650 °C (923 K), using the number of sides of individual grains. The plot indicates that the grain-shape distribution remains essentially unchanged during normal grain growth.

**Abnormal grain growth,** or secondary recrystallization, occurs when normal growth of the matrix grains is inhibited and when the temperature is high enough to allow a few special grains to overcome the inhibiting force and to grow disproportionately. The commonly known conditions for inhibiting grain growth are a fine dispersion of second-phase particles, a strong single-orientation texture, and a stabilized two-dimensional grain structure imposed by sheet thickness. These conditions for inhibiting grain growth are readily understandable, because the fine particles exert a pinning force on the boundary motion, the matrix grain boundaries are predominantly low-angle boundaries, and therefore both low mobilities and the boundary grooving at the sheet surfaces retard boundary motion.

Figure 29 shows abnormal grain growth or secondary recrystallization in the cube-textured matrix of a type 304 stainless steel. The

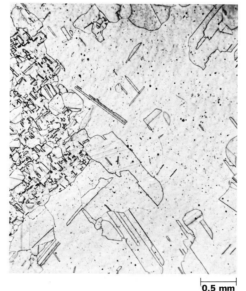

**Fig. 29** Type 304 stainless steel, rolled 90% at 800 °C (1470 °F) to produce a copper-type rolling texture, recrystallized to cube texture by annealing at 1000 °C (1830 °F) for 30 min, then annealed at 1000 °C (1830 °F) for 96 h to cause secondary recrystallization. Large secondary grains are shown in a cube-textured primary matrix. Rolling direction: left to right. Electrolytic etch. 20×. (Ref 5)

cube-textured matrix is characterized by the small grains; the twin traces within the cube grains are oriented at 45° to the rolling direction. This particular example of abnormal grain growth or secondary recrystallization in cube-textured type 304 stainless steel probably represents the combined effect of particle-inhibition and texture-inhibition on secondary recrystallization.

Like primary recrystallization, secondary recrystallization consists of nucleation and growth. Stable nuclei of the secondary grains are formed during incubation. In the case of

high-permeability, grain-oriented silicon steel, secondary recrystallization nuclei have been reported to form by the coalescence of the (110) oriented grains. Subsequent growth of the newly formed secondary grains is by the migration of high-angle boundaries. Consequently, a large change in texture results. Therefore, the characteristic features of primary and secondary recrystallizations are similar. However, the driving energy for secondary recrystallization, in contrast to the strain energy for primary recrystallization, is the grain-boundary energy of the primary grains, which is much smaller than the strain energy after recovery. Figure 30 shows the kinetics of secondary recrystallization in Fe-3Si for the formation of a cube-textured sheet by isothermal annealing at 1050 °C (1920 °F). Being similar to the kinetics of primary recrystallization, the curve is sigmoidal.

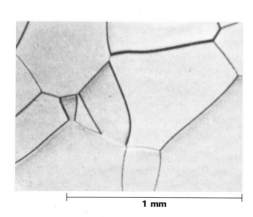

**Fig. 28** Zone-refined iron, cold rolled to a moderate reduction and annealed for recrystallization for several cycles to refine the penultimate grain size without introducing preferred orientation. Micrograph shows grain structure after normal grain growth at 800 °C (1470 °F) for 12 min. 2% nital. 45×

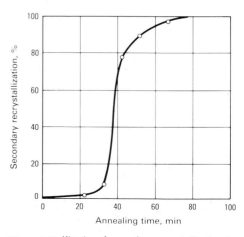

**Fig. 30** Kinetics of secondary recrystallization for cube texture formation in Fe-3Si during isothermal annealing at 1050 °C (1920 °F). The characteristics of this curve for secondary recrystallization are quite similar to those for primary recrystallization. (Ref 9)

## REFERENCES

1. R.S. Cline and H. Hu, *Abstract Bulletin*, TMS-AIME Fall Meeting, 1970, p 54
2. R.R. Eggleston, *J. Appl. Phys.*, Vol 23, 1952, p 1400
3. J.T. Michalak and H.W. Paxton, *Trans. AIME*, Vol 221, 1961, p 850
4. B.B. Rath and H. Hu, in *Proceedings of the 31st Annual Meeting of the Electron Microscopy Society of America*, San Francisco Press, 1973, p 160
5. S.R. Goodman and H. Hu, *Trans. Met. Soc. AIME*, Vol 233, 1965, p 103; Vol 236, 1966, p 710
6. B. Bay and N. Hansen, *Met. Trans. A*, Vol 10, 1979, p 279; Vol 15A, 1984, p 287
7. A.R. Jones and N. Hansen, in *Recrystallization and Grain Growth of Multiphase and Particle Containing Materials*, N. Hansen, A.R. Jones, and T. Leffers, Ed., Riso National Laboratory, Denmark, 1980, p 19
8. D.A. Witmer and G. Krauss, *Trans. ASM*, Vol 62, 1969, p 447
9. F. Assmus, K. Detert, and G. Ibe, *Z. Metallkd.*, Vol 48, 1957, p 344

## SELECTED REFERENCES

- H. Hu, *Can. Metall. Q.*, Vol 13, 1974, p 175
- H. Hu, in *Proceedings of the 5th International Conference on Textures of Materials*, Vol II, G. Gottstein and K. Lucke, Ed., Springer-Verlag, 1978, p 3
- H. Hu, in *Recovery and Recrystallization of Metals*, L. Himmel, Ed., Interscience, 1963, p 311
- H. Hu, in *Textures in Research and Practice*, J. Grewen and G. Wassermann, Ed., Springer-Verlag, 1969, p 200
- H. Hu, *Trans. Met. Soc. AIME*, Vol 230, 1964, p 572

# Textured Structures

By G.Y. Chin
Director, Materials Research Laboratory
AT&T Bell Laboratories

TEXTURE, or preferred orientation, describes a preferential alignment of the crystalline lattice of the various grains in a polycrystalline aggregate. Texture does not define the shape of grains; therefore, the presence or absence of texture cannot be inferred from the shape of the grains. For example, nonequiaxed grain shape is not a crystallographic texture, although the same process that develops a crystallographic texture in a metal may concurrently develop a nonequiaxed grain shape. Figures 1 and 2 illustrate two specimens that exhibit texture. The specimen shown in Fig. 1 exhibits an elongated grain shape, while the one in Fig. 2 exhibits an equiaxed grain shape.

In general, crystals are anisotropic with respect to properties; thus, control of texture is important, because it provides a means for optimizing desired properties in given directions in a polycrystalline metal. For example, a single crystal of iron is magnetized easily in the cube direction; that is, the [001] direction is parallel to the rolling direction. This phenomenon is important in the manufacture of iron-silicon transformer sheet.

Grain-oriented transformer sheet, in which the cube directions of the grains are closely aligned in the rolling direction (the direction of magnetization), exhibits magnetic properties that are superior to those of sheet with randomly oriented grains. However, the texture developed in transformer sheet is undesirable for drawing. When grain-oriented transformer sheet is drawn into the shape of a cup, unwanted "ears" are produced. These ears, which must be trimmed, form because the sheet is anisotropic with regard to mechanical as well as magnetic properties. Thus, the sheet is weaker or softer in given directions; when stressed in these directions greater metal flow occurs, causing the ears to form. Micrographs of grain-oriented silicon steels can be found in the article "Magnetic and Electrical Materials" in this Volume.

As shown in Table 1, several physical and mechanical properties are influenced by crystal direction. Consequently, in polycrystalline metals, the same properties are similarly affected by texture.

## Origins of Texture

Texture may develop in a metal during such processing operations as metal-film deposition, casting, plastic deformation, and annealing. Films prepared by sputtering, electrodeposition, or chemical vapor deposition frequently exhibit texture. The mechanisms of texture formation in metal films are complex and not well understood. In castings, the long grains of the columnar zone are usually textured, and the equiaxed grains in the central zone exhibit a more random orientation. A discussion of the origins of orientation in cast structures can be found in the article "Solidification Structures of Steel" in this Volume.

During plastic deformation of a cast ingot or a deformed and annealed metal specimen, the crystalline lattice rotates toward one or more stable (preferred) orientations, thus establishing a deformation texture. Lattice rotation occurs by slip or twinning (Fig. 3). The final deformation texture for a given specimen depends primarily on the initial grain orientation, the change in shape imposed on the specimen, and the temperature at which the specimen is deformed.

When a deformed metal is annealed, recovery or recrystallization occurs, depending on the annealing temperature. In general, annealing at low temperatures results in recovery, with little change in texture. At higher annealing temperatures, primary recrystallization occurs. The texture of the recrystallized structure is generally different from, but related to, the deformation texture.

At still higher annealing temperatures, some grains exhibit significant grain growth, thus consuming surrounding grains. This process, known as secondary recrystallization,

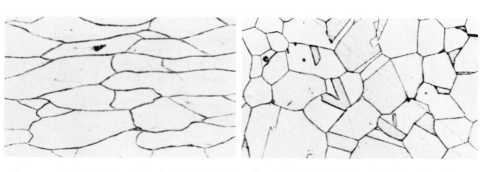

**Fig. 1, 2** Typical microstructures of 4-79 Moly Permalloy (4Mo-79Ni-17Fe). Fig. 1: Cold working has produced elongated grains and a textured structure. Fig. 2: Although annealing after working has produced equiaxed grains, this structure is also textured. Electrolytic etchant: $H_3PO_4$ saturated with $Cr_2O_3$. 85×

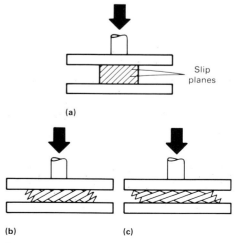

**Fig. 3** Schematic of lattice rotation during compression. Slip planes in specimen (a) are tilted toward compression plane (b and c).

**Table 1   Dependence of mechanical and physical properties on crystal direction**

| Property(a) | Metal | Crystal direction | Value of property |
|---|---|---|---|
| Young's modulus | Copper | $\langle 111 \rangle$ | 193 000 MPa (28 × 10⁶ psi) |
| | | $\langle 100 \rangle$ | 69 000 MPa (10 × 10⁶ psi) |
| Yield strength | Magnesium | c-axis 5° from tensile axis | 10 MPa (1450 psi) |
| | | c-axis 45° from tensile axis | 1.7 MPa (247 psi) |
| Thermal expansion | Uranium | a-axis | 33 × 10⁻⁶/K (59.4 × 10⁻⁶/°F) |
| | | b-axis | −6.5 × 10⁻⁶/K (−11.7 × 10⁻⁶/°F) |
| Electrical resistivity | Tellurium | c-axis | 6 × 10⁻⁴ Ωm (60 000 μΩ·cm) |
| | | 90° from c-axis | 15 × 10⁻⁴ Ωm (150 000 μΩ·cm) |
| Magnetic-flux density | Cobalt | c-axis | 1.8 T (18 000 G)(b) |
| | | 90° from c-axis | 0.6 T (6000 G)(b) |

(a) The following properties are anisotropic for cubic crystals: Young's modulus, Poisson's ratio, yield strength, tensile strength, elongation, coefficient of friction, magnetic-flux density (below saturation), magnetic permeability, magnetostriction. The following properties are isotropic for cubic crystals: coefficient of thermal expansion, thermal conductivity, electrical resistivity, dielectric constant, Thomson coefficient, Peltier coefficient, index of refraction. (b) At a magnetic field strength of 1.6 × 10⁵ A/m (2016 Oe)

reduces the grain-boundary surface area and therefore the energy of the workpiece. This results in the formation of still different textures.

## Types of Texture

**Fiber texture** exhibits rotational symmetry around an axis. Ideally, a single crystallographic direction in each grain is aligned parallel to a specimen direction called the fiber axis. The grains are randomly aligned in the plane normal to the fiber axis. The fiber axis may be the growth direction of columnar grains in a casting, the axial direction of a drawn wire, or the axis normal to the surface of a compressed (rolled) sheet. Figure 4(a) illustrates a $\langle 100 \rangle$ fiber texture in wire.

Generally, there is considerable scatter around the ideal orientation. Also, two or more directional components may appear; some grains may be aligned in a given direction parallel to the fiber axis, while others are aligned in a different direction.

**Sheet texture** exhibits three mutually perpendicular mirror planes of symmetry. Although commonly observed in rolled sheet, sheet texture is not restricted to sheet. Extruded tubing and flattened wire also exhibit sheet textures.

Two parameters are generally used to describe a sheet texture: a plane in the specimen that coincides with one of the symmetry planes and a symmetry direction in that plane. In rolled sheet, the rolling plane and the rolling direction have been adopted as reference parameters. Thus, the designation $\{110\}\langle 112 \rangle$ for a rolled sheet texture signifies that the grains have a $\{110\}$ plane parallel to the rolling plane and a $\langle 112 \rangle$ direction parallel to the rolling direction. This texture is illustrated in Fig. 4(b). In this specimen, all variants of a texture—(110)[1̄12] and (110)[11̄2]—are represented.

## Texture Control

The desirability of a specific texture depends on the desired properties, the directions in which these properties are optimum, and the direction of intended use for any given engineered material or alloy. Selection of a manufacturing process usually depends on several variables. Brittle materials cannot be deformed, and therefore the desired tex-

tures must be developed by casting, powder metallurgy techniques, or electrodeposition. Techniques of directional solidification can be used to enhance casting texture by favoring columnar grain growth.

Alnico permanent magnets are examples of alloys in which the desired texture is achieved by casting. In these alloys, the direction of intended use coincides with the optimum direction for the property involved. To ensure optimum matching of direction, it may be necessary to alter the direction of heat flow during solidification, to change the direction of growth by adding another element, or to employ seeding techniques using a properly oriented seed crystal.

Powder metallurgy techniques that incorporate conventional compaction and sintering usually do not produce textures. However, if some or all of the metal powders are magnetic, application of a magnetic field prior to and during compaction will orient the magnetic powder particles and cause a texture to develop. This magnetizing technique is applied commercially in the production of ferrite and Co₅Sm permanent magnets. The application of a uniaxial stress during compaction may also orient the particles mechanically to ensure texture.

Combining several types of deformation processing offers a means of developing various deformation textures. A narrow strip, for example, may be produced by conventional rolling followed by slitting or by wiredrawing followed by flattening. The textures developed by these two processing sequences usually are different. Intermediate annealing operations, normally performed to soften a workpiece for further deformation, can also be used for additional texture control similar to that obtained through recovery or recrystallization.

Random orientation in a casting can be obtained by chill casting or by ultrasonic vibration or mechanical stirring during solidification. Appreciable deformation textures in wrought products do not develop at strains of less than 50% and thus can be suppressed by appropriate cycles of straining and annealing at moderate temperatures.

## Characterization of Textures

Because physical and mechanical properties such as Young's modulus and magnetic

flux density are affected by crystal direction (see Table 1), texture can be investigated by measuring these properties. However, although the dependence of a property on direction often can be calculated if the texture is known, the reverse is generally not true. Furthermore, factors other than texture may be the cause of the observed dependence on direction. For example, properties that involve plastic deformation, such as tensile yield strength and elongation, are affected by alignment of second-phase particles (mechanical fibering) as well as by crystallographic texture.

Texture can be investigated directly by x-ray, electron, or neutron diffraction. Electron diffraction is generally limited to thin-film samples less than 100 nm (1000 Å) thick. Because of the much lower absorption coefficient for neutrons compared to x-rays, neutron diffraction can be used to study thick specimens (several millimeters) without a large absorption correction.

Nevertheless, x-ray diffraction is usually preferred because of the general availability of equipment. Also, specimens of convenient size can be examined in the laboratory. X-ray diffraction can be applied to thin samples in the transmission mode and thick samples in the reflection mode. The latter, however, samples only the surface grains.

**The Laue x-ray technique** of orienting single crystals is widely used, and the diffraction camera and other equipment used are readily available in x-ray diffraction laborato-

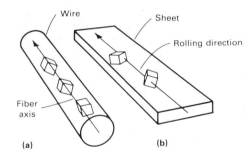

**Fig. 4** Schematic of (a) $\langle 100 \rangle$ fiber texture in wire and (b) $\{110\}\langle 112 \rangle$ sheet texture. Positions of unit cells in the wire and the sheet represent orientations of several grains.

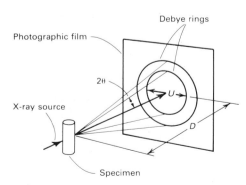

**Fig. 5** Schematic of pinhole photography. The diameter, U, of each Debye ring equals 2D tan 2θ, where D is the distance from the specimen to the film and 2θ is the diffracted angle.

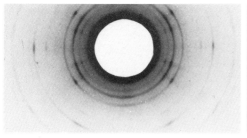
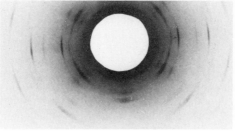

**Fig. 6, 7** Transmission pinhole photographs of iron-nickel alloy wires. The more uniform intensity of the Debye rings in Fig. 6 indicates a less textured structure than in Fig. 7.

ries. The Laue technique can be used to determine the orientation of individual grains in polycrystalline specimens by transmission (thin specimens) or by reflection (thick specimens). Generally, it is limited to relatively coarse grains (average dimension $\geq 1$ mm, or 0.04 in.). In the Laue camera, the size of the collimated beam required for smaller grains necessitates excessively long exposure times. This technique may be used for specimens deformed at small to moderate strains, but

Co₃.₄₅Fe₀.₂₅Cu₁.₃₅Sm compacted-powder
magnet alloy; CrKα radiation

**Fig. 8** Diffractometer traces of two compacted-powder specimens of permanent magnet alloy $Co_{3.45}Fe_{0.25}Cu_{1.35}Sm$. The Miller indices of the basal planes are marked on the graph. Note the high diffraction-line intensity of the basal planes in the specimen oriented in a magnetic field during compacting.

the Laue spots become diffuse after large strains.

**Pinhole photography** uses the same apparatus as the Laue technique. Instead of impinging white radiation on a single grain, as in the Laue technique, a pinhole photograph is obtained by impinging characteristic (monochromatic) radiation on a large number of grains. Again, both transmission and reflection modes are possible.

Figure 5 schematically illustrates transmission through a thin wire. The various crystallographic planes diffract to form concentric rings, called Debye rings, on the film. A uniform intensity of the Debye rings is indicative of random orientation, except when the x-ray beam coincides with the direction of the fiber axis in a specimen having a fiber texture. To ensure that random orientation is the cause of uniformly intense Debye rings, two or more pinhole photographs should be taken, each with the specimen tilted at a slightly different angle (10° variation, for example).

A nonuniform intensity of the Debye rings is an almost certain indication of texture, which can be analyzed quantitatively by examining the positions of the intensity maximums. Transmission pinhole photographs of iron-nickel alloy wires, made using zirconium-filtered Moκα radiation, are shown in Fig. 6 and 7.

**The diffractometer technique** for detecting texture involves the use of an x-ray dif-

fractometer. The intensities of the diffraction lines for a textured specimen can be compared with the intensity from a specimen with random orientation. The random intensity can be calculated by means of a standard formula, or it can be obtained experimentally using a specimen of densely compacted powder.

Figure 8 shows the intensities obtained from specimens of randomly oriented and textured material. Diffraction-line intensities determined by the diffractometer technique refer to crystal planes parallel to one plane of the specimen only (the surface of a sheet, for example). However, the most thorough investigation of texture requires pole-figure techniques.

**Pole-Figure Techniques.** A pole figure is a stereographic projection that shows the distribution of poles, or plane normals, of a specific crystalline plane, using specimen axes as reference axes. These techniques are widely used for examining sheet textures. For example, in examining a sheet specimen, all directions in the plane of the sheet (rolling plane) are projected as points on the circumference of the pole-figure circle (Fig. 9).

The rolling direction is usually located at the top, and the transverse direction is usually designated at the right of the pole figure. The center of the circle corresponds to the direction normal to the plane of the sheet (normal direction). Directions lying at angles between the normal direction and the rolling plane project as points inside the circle.

As a simple illustration, consider a unit cell of a single grain oriented in the sheet so that the (100) plane is parallel to the plane of the sheet and so that the two cube directions in the (100) plane—[010] and [001]—are aligned in the transverse and rolling directions, respectively. This is illustrated by the position of the unit cell in Fig. 9(a). The poles of the cube planes, which can be projected in the pole figure, are marked by arrows 1 to 5.

**Fig. 9** Schematic of pole-figure representation of crystal orientation. In (a) a crystal unit cell is aligned as shown. (b) and (c) are pole figures showing positions of poles in (a), represented by arrows emanating from the center of the unit cell. RD, rolling direction; TD, transverse direction; ND, normal direction

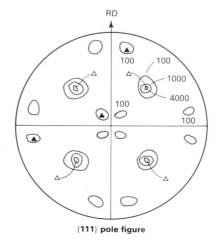

{111} pole figure

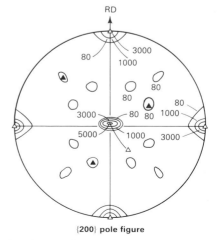

{200} pole figure

**Fig. 10** Actual {111} and {200} pole figures for electrolytic tough pitch copper that was rolled to 96% reduction in thickness and then annealed for 5 min at 200 °C (390 °F). Intensity values are given in arbitrary units. Positions of intensity maxima indicate cube texture plus twins of cube orientation, denoted by △, (100)[001], and by ▲, (122)[21̄2̄], respectively.

**Table 2 Summary of metal textures developed by various processing operations(a)**

| Crystal structure | Ideal texture(b) | Crystal structure | Ideal texture(b) |
|---|---|---|---|
| **Casting (fiber axis of columnar grains)** | | **Recrystallization after uniaxial compression or forging** | |
| fcc | ⟨100⟩ | fcc, Al, Cu, α-brass | ⟨110⟩ |
| bcc | ⟨100⟩ | bcc, Fe | ⟨111⟩ |
| hcp | | hcp, Mg | [0001] |
|    Cd, Zn | ⟨10Ī0⟩ ∥, (0001)⊥ | **Cold rolling** | |
|    Mg | ⟨2ĪĪ0⟩ ∥, {20Ī5}⊥ | | |
| hex, (Co,Cu)₅Sm, (Co,Cu)₅Ce | [0001] | fcc | |
| tet, β-Sn | ⟨110⟩ |    Al, Cu, Cu-Ni, Au, Ni, Ni-Fe, Pd, Th, Rh, Pb-0.26Ca {110}⟨Ī12⟩ + {112}⟨11Ī⟩ | |
| rhom, Bi | ⟨111⟩ |    Ag, Yb, Ni-15Mo, Ni-50Co, Co-10Fe, 18-8 stainless | |
| | |       steel, Cu alloys(d) {110} ⟨Ī12⟩ + spread around {110} to {110}⟨001⟩ | |
| **Film deposition** | | bcc {00Ī}⟨110⟩ + spread around ⟨110⟩ to {Ī12}⟨110⟩; also {11Ī} ⟨112⟩ | |
| fcc | ⟨111⟩ | hcp | |
| bcc | ⟨110⟩ |    Zn, Cd | [0001] at 20-25° from ND toward RD(e) |
| hcp | [0001] |    Mg, Co | [0001] ∥ ND(e) |
| | |    Ti-Al (>2% Al) | (0001) ⟨10Ī0⟩ |
| **Wiredrawing, swaging, extrusion** | |    Be, Hf, Zr, Ti, Ti-Nb, | |
| fcc | ⟨111⟩ + ⟨100⟩(c) |       Ti-Ta, Ti-Zr | [0001] at 20-40° from ND toward TD, ⟨10Ī0⟩ ∥ RD(e) |
| bcc | ⟨110⟩ | ortho | |
| hcp | |    U, <300-400°C (572-752 °F) | {103}⟨010⟩ |
|    Zn, small strain | [0001] |    U, >500°C (932 °F) | {1Ī6}⟨410⟩ + {103}⟨010⟩ |
|    Zn, large strain | [0001] 70° from wire axis | | |
|    Mg, <450°C (842°F); Be, Hf, Ti, Zr | ⟨10Ī0⟩ | **Recrystallization after cold rolling** | |
|    Mg, >450°C (842°F) | ⟨2ĪĪ0⟩ | | |
| ortho, U | ⟨010⟩ + ⟨410⟩ | fcc | |
| | |    Al, Au, Cu, Cu-Ni, Fe-Cu-Ni, Ni, Ni-Fe, Th | {100}⟨001⟩ |
| **Recrystallization after wiredrawing** | |    Ag, Ag-30Au, Ag-1Zn, Cu-(5-39Zn), Cu-(1-5Sn), | |
| fcc | ⟨111⟩ + ⟨100⟩; also ⟨112⟩ |       Cu-0.5 Be, Cu-0.5Cd, Cu-0.05P, Co-10Fe | {113}⟨21Ī⟩ |
| bcc | ⟨110⟩ | bcc | |
| hcp | |    Mo | Same as deformation texture |
|    Be | ⟨10Ī0⟩ |    Fe, Fe-Si, V {111}⟨2Ī1⟩, and {001} + {112} with ⟨Ī10⟩ 15° from RD(e) | |
|    Ti, Zr | ⟨11Ī0⟩ |    Fe-Si {110}⟨001⟩ after two-step rolling and annealing (Goss method); | |
| ortho, U | ⟨431⟩ + ⟨100⟩ |       also {110}⟨001⟩, {100}⟨001⟩ after high-temperature anneal (>1100°C, or | |
| | |       2012°F) | |
| **Uniaxial compression** | |    Ta | {111}⟨2Ī1⟩ |
| fcc | ⟨100⟩ |    W, <1800°C (3272 °F) | Same as deformation texture |
| bcc | ⟨111⟩ + ⟨110⟩ |    W, >1800°C (3272 °F) | {001}⟨Ī10⟩ 12° from RD(e) |
| hcp | | hcp | Same as deformation texture |
|    Mg, Co (?) | [0001] | ortho, U | {103}⟨010⟩ |
|    Hf, Ti | [0001] 10-30° from compression axis | | |

(a) This table summarizes the more prominent textures according to crystal structure. Gross variations among metals of a given crystal structure are listed separately. Alloy composition is in wt%. For more detailed information on individual metals and processing conditions, consult the Selected References at the end of this article. (b) The lattice direction parallel to the fiber axis is listed, except where directions both parallel (∥) and normal (⊥) to the axis are known. For sheet textures, both the lattice plane parallel to the rolling plane and the lattice direction parallel to the fiber axis are listed. Some textures comprise two superimposed components, forming a duplex texture. (c) Approximate percentage of ⟨100⟩ component: Al, Pb, Co-10Fe, Cu-8Al (<10%); Au (15%); Ni, 4Mo-79Ni-17Fe, Cu, Cu-2Al, Cu-4Al, Co-35Ni (25-35%); Co-40Ni (50%); Ag (>90%). (d) Binary Cu alloys containing more than 4% Al, 3.5% As, 5% Ge, 0.5% Mg, 4% Mn, 1% P, 3% Sb, 3% Sn, or 10% Zn. (e) ND, normal direction; RD, rolling direction; TD, transverse direction

A {100} pole figure, showing the positions of these poles, is illustrated in Fig. 9(b). The {111} poles of the same crystal are marked by arrows 6 to 9. The {111} pole figure then appears as shown in Fig. 9(c). Both pole figures indicate the same orientation of the unit cell; they appear different only because poles of different planes are used. A pole figure is always specified by the Miller indices of the poles.

Pole-figure construction by point plotting, as illustrated in Fig. 9, is useful for coarse-grained specimens, in which the orientation of each grain can be determined by Laue photography. For fine-grained material, the intensity data usually are presented as contours of equal value. Generally, the intensity value of each contour is expressed as the ratio of the value measured for a textured specimen to the value for a randomly oriented specimen.

Data are conveniently gathered with commercially available automatic pole-figure goniometers. With the diffraction angle fixed at the desired pole position, the pole-figure goniometer rotates the specimen to bring all specimen orientations to the diffracting position. Data are obtained by determining the

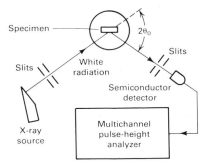

**Fig. 11** Schematic illustrating the principles of the x-ray energy-dispersive method

diffraction-line intensity of poles as a function of specimen orientation. The measured intensities can then be plotted as contour lines.

An example of {200} and {111} pole figures of a cube-textured sheet of annealed copper is shown in Fig. 10. From the positions of the intensity maximums, so-called ideal textures are often derived. These are summarized in Table 2 for textures developed in metals by various processing operations.

The technique described above for con-

structing pole figures using monochromatic beams from a characteristic radiation is generally referred to as angle-dispersive diffractometry. In recent years, pole figures have also been constructed using the technique of energy-dispersive diffractometry, in which a polychromatic beam is used and several Bragg reflections are recorded simultaneously as a function of the photon energy of the scattered x-rays.

The principle of energy-dispersive diffractometry is shown in Fig. 11. Usually, the continuous, or white, radiation of an x-ray tube is used. The entire spectrum of x-ray energy irradiates the sample. The diffracted intensity is measured with a semiconductor detector and registered in a multichannel analyzer. Figure 12 shows an example of the energy-dispersive diffraction patterns for iron. The data can then be analyzed to yield an inverse pole figure showing the distribution of pole densities along a specimen direction (Fig. 13). Normal pole figures such as those in Fig. 10 can also be generated. The principal advantage of the energy-dispersive method is that, with the specimen fixed at a given geometry and with rapid data acquisition, it is relatively easy to examine texture changes under

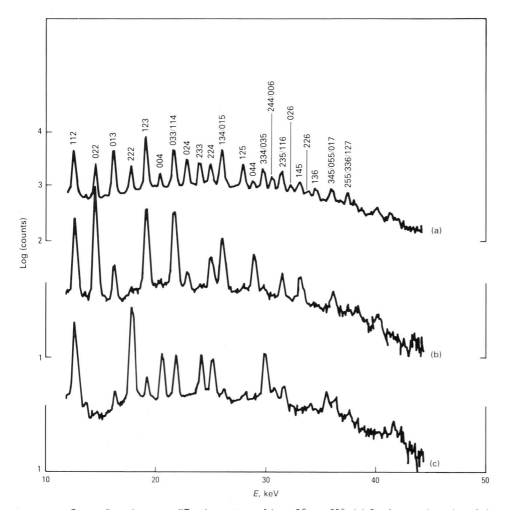

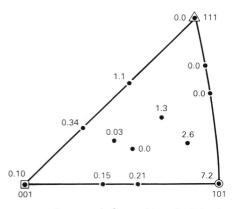

**Fig. 13** Inverse pole figure of iron sheet showing the distribution of pole densities along the rolling direction. (Ref 1)

**Fig. 12** Energy-dispersive x-ray diffraction pattern of iron. $2\theta_0 = 50°$. (a) Random specimen (powder). (b) Rolled sheet, rolling direction parallel to scattering vector. (c) Rolled sheet, surface normal parallel to scattering vector. (Ref 1)

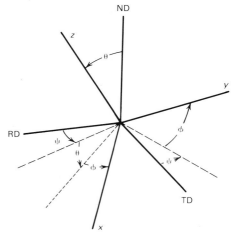

**Fig. 14** Euler angles $\psi$, $\theta$, $\phi$, relating the specimen axes, RD (rolling direction), TD (transverse direction), ND (normal direction), with the crystal axes, $x$, $y$, $z$. (Ref 2)

dynamic conditions, such as those encountered in recrystallization studies or tensile testing.

**The orientation distribution function** is a more quantitative description of texture beyond the idealized orientation of pole figures. This technique expresses the probability of a crystallite having an orientation described by the Euler angles that relate the specimen axes with the crystal axes (Fig. 14). This function can be expressed by a series expansion in generalized spherical harmonics. The coefficients of this series can be obtained from the pole distribution obtained from the pole figure, which is similarly expanded in a series of spherical harmonics. Greater precision is obtained using data from several pole figures.

The orientation distribution function can be plotted in two-dimensional sections using two of the Euler angles, as shown in Fig. 15. However, its usefulness lies in the quantitative comparison with the anisotropic properties of a textured specimen, such as Young's modulus, yield strength, and magnetocrystalline anisotropy energy. In these cases, the orientation dependence of a given property in a

polycrystalline sample is often expressed in terms of the coefficients of the series development of the crystallite orientation distribution. Additional information on orientation distribution functions can be found in Ref 3 and 4.

## REFERENCES

1. L. Gerward, S. Lehn, and G. Christiansen, *Texture*, Vol 2, 1976, p 95
2. J.S. Kelland and G.J. Davies, *Texture*, Vol 1, 1972, p 51
3. K. Lücke *et al.*, On the Problem of the Production of the True Orientation Distribution from Pole Figures, *Acta Metall.*, Vol 29, 1981, p 167-185
4. D.J. Willis, A Complete Description of Preferred Orientations, *Metals Forum*, Vol 1 (No. 2), June 1978, p 79-94

## SELECTED REFERENCES

- L.V. Azaroff, *Elements of X-ray Crystallography*, McGraw-Hill, 1968
- C.S. Barrett and T.B. Massalski, *Structure of Metals*, 3rd ed., McGraw-Hill, 1966
- K.L. Chopra, *Thin Film Phenomena*, McGraw-Hill, 1969
- P. Coulomb, *Les Textures dans Les Métaux de Réseau Cubique*, Dunrod, 1972
- B.D. Cullity, *Elements of X-ray Diffraction*, Addison-Wesley, 1956
- G.J. Davies, Texture Analysis and Anisotropy in Metals, *J. Metals*, July 1976, p 21-28
- I.L. Dillamore and W.T. Roberts, Preferred Orientation in Wrought and Annealed Metals, *Met. Rev.*, Vol 10, 1965, p 271-380
- M.H. Francombe and H. Sato, Ed., *Single Crystal Films*, Pergamon Press, 1964
- J. Grewen and G. Wassermann, Ed., *Textures in Research and Practice*, Springer-Verlag, 1969
- M. Hatherly and I.L. Dillamore, Theories of Texture Development, *J. Austral. Inst. Met.*, Vol 20 (No. 2). June 1975, p 71-84
- H. Hu, Texture of Metals, *Texture*, Vol 1, 1974, p 233
- "Preparing Quantitative Pole Figures of

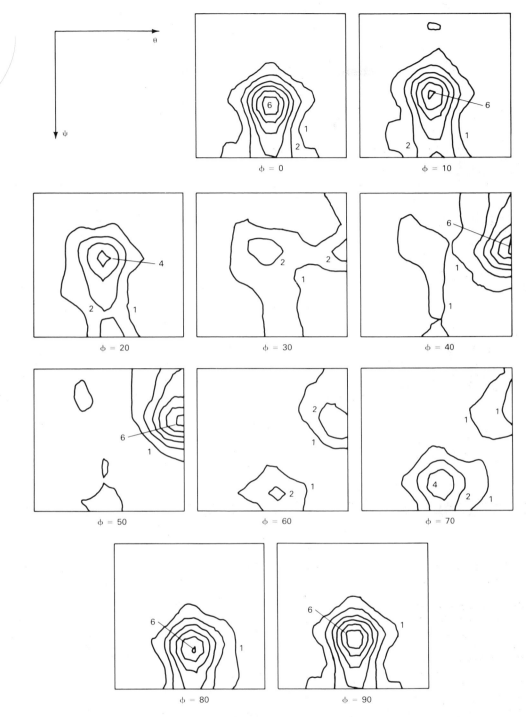

**Fig. 15** The crystallite orientation distribution function for cold-rolled Cu-30Zn after 90% reduction. Numbers indicate the orientation points per unit volume. (Ref 2)

Metals," ASTM E 81, *Annual Book of ASTM Standards,* Vol 03.03, ASTM, Philadelphia, 1984, p 77-81
- *Recrystallization, Grain Growth and Textures,* American Society for Metals, 1966
- E. Schmid and W. Boas, *Plasticity of Crystals,* Chapman & Hall, 1968
- R. Sowerby and W. Johnson, A Review of Texture and Anisotropy in Relation to Metal Forming, *Mat. Sci. Eng.,* Vol 20,

1975, p 101-111
- J. Szpunar, Geometry of Texture Measurements for Dispersive Methods. *Texture of Crystalline Solids,* Vol 4, 1981, p 171
- J. Szpunar and L. Gerward, Energy-Dispersive X-Ray Diffraction Studies of the Texture in Cold-Rolled Alpha-Beta Brass, *J. Mat. Sci.,* Vol 15, 1980, p 469-476
- T.R. Thomson and J.M. Baker, Considerations of Texture and Anisotropy in Metal

Forming, *J. Austral. Inst. Met.,* Vol 14 (No. 2), May 1969, p 84-91
- F.A. Underwood, *Textures in Metal Sheets,* MacDonald, 1961
- G. Wassermann and J. Grewen, *Textures of Metallic Materials,* 2nd ed., Springer-Verlag, 1962 (in German)
- D.V. Wilson, Controlled Directionality of Mechanical Properties in Sheet Metals, *Metall. Rev.,* Vol 3, 1969, p 175-188

# Crystal Structure of Metals

By C.S. Barrett
Professor of Metallurgy
University of Denver

THE CRYSTAL STRUCTURES presented in this article are those that have been widely studied and are of most importance to metallurgists. More complete coverage is given in the references listed at the end of this article.

## Crystallographic Terms and Concepts

The terms and concepts defined and explained in this section are basic to an understanding of the descriptions and illustrations of crystal structures presented in the next section of this article.

**Crystal structure** is the arrangement of atoms in the interior of a crystal. A fundamental unit of the arrangement repeats itself at regular intervals in three dimensions throughout the interior of the crystal.

**A unit cell** is a parallelepiped whose edges form the axes of a crystal. A unit cell is the smallest pattern of atomic arrangement. A crystal consists of unit cells stacked tightly together, each identical in size, shape, and orientation with all others. The choice of the boundaries of a unit cell is somewhat arbitrary, being conditioned by symmetry considerations and by convenience.

**Crystal Systems.** Crystallography uses seven different systems of axes, each with a specified equality or inequality to others of axial lengths and interaxial angles. These are the basis of the following crystal systems—triclinic (anorthic), monoclinic, orthorhombic, tetragonal, hexagonal, rhombohedral (trigonal), and cubic—employed in the classification of crystals.

The edge lengths $a$, $b$, and $c$ (along the corresponding crystal axes) of unit cells are expressed in angstroms (1 Å = 0.1 nm, or $10^{-10}$ m). Faces of unit cells are identified by the capital letter $A$, $B$, or $C$, when the faces contain axes $b$ and $c$, $c$ and $a$, or $a$ and $b$, respectively.

Angles between the axes are expressed in degrees, with the angle in the $A$ face denoted $\alpha$, the angle in the $B$ face $\beta$, and the angle in the $C$ face $\gamma$. Table 1 shows the relationships of the edge lengths along the crystal axes, and of the interaxial angles, for each of the seven crystal systems. The edge lengths and angles are sometimes referred to as the lattice parameters, lattice spacings, or lattice constants for a unit cell.

**A lattice** (space lattice or Bravais lattice) is a regular, periodic array of points (lattice points) in space, at each of which is located the same kind of atom or a group of atoms of identical composition, arrangement, and orientation in a perfect crystal (at least, on a time-average basis).

There are five (actually, four plus rhombohedral) basic arrangements for lattice points within a unit cell, and each is identified by a Hermann-Mauguin letter symbol in a space-lattice notation. These letter symbols and the arrangements they identify are $P$, for primitive (simple), with lattice points only at cell corners; $C$, for base-face centered (end-centered), with lattice points centered on the $C$ faces or ends of the crystal; $F$, for all-face centered, with lattice points centered on all faces; and $I$, for innercentered, with lattice points at the center of volume of the unit cell (body-centered). The rhombohedral cell, also primitive, has $R$ as its symbol.

The face having the base-face centered lattice point may be designated the $C$ face, because the choice of axes is arbitrary and does not alter the atom positions in the space lattice. Rhombohedral crystals can be considered as having either a rhombohedral cell or a primitive hexagonal cell.

The above letter symbols and definitions apply only to basic arrangement of atoms and do not limit the number of atoms in a unit cell. Atoms may be found at each corner of a base-centered, face-centered, or innercentered cell and in some crystals also at other positions on the cell faces or within the cell.

There are 14 kinds of space lattices, derived from all the combinations of equality and inequality of lengths of axes and interaxial angles. They are listed in Table 2, along with Hermann-Mauguin and Pearson symbols. The Pearson symbols (Ref 1) consist of Hermann-Mauguin space-lattice letters preceded by $a$, $m$, $o$, $t$, $h$, and $c$ to denote, respectively, six crystal systems: triclinic (anorthic), monoclinic, orthorhombic, tetragonal, hexagonal, and cubic.

**Structure symbols** are arbitrary symbols that designate the type of crystal structure. The Strukturbericht symbols (Ref 2) were widely used in the past and are still used today, but this system of naming structure types has been overwhelmed by the number and complexity of types that are now recognized. Furthermore, the final publication of Strukturbericht was in 1939.

Today, the accepted system of naming the types of crystal structures that metals and alloys adopt is to select arbitrarily the formula of a phase with the structure type (that is, a prototype), followed by the Pearson symbol

**Table 1 Relationships of edge lengths and of interaxial angles for the seven crystal systems**

| Crystal system | Edge lengths | Interaxial angles | Examples |
|---|---|---|---|
| Triclinic (anorthic) | $a \neq b \neq c$ | $\alpha \neq \beta \neq \gamma \neq 90°$ | HgK |
| Monoclinic | $a \neq b \neq c$ | $\alpha = \gamma = 90° \neq \beta$ | $\beta$-S; $CoSb_2$ |
| Orthorhombic | $a \neq b \neq c$ | $\alpha = \beta = \gamma = 90°$ | $\alpha$-S; Ga; $Fe_3C$ (cementite) |
| Tetragonal | $a = b \neq c$ | $\alpha = \beta = \gamma = 90°$ | $\beta$-Sn (white); $TiO_2$ |
| Hexagonal | $a = b \neq c$ | $\alpha = \beta = 90°$; $\gamma = 120°$ | Zn; Cd; NiAs |
| Rhombohedral(a) | $a = b = c$ | $\alpha = \beta = \gamma \neq 90°$ | As; Sb; Bi; calcite |
| Cubic | $a = b = c$ | $\alpha = \beta = \gamma = 90°$ | Cu; Ag; Au; Fe; NaCl |

(a) Rhombohedral crystals (sometimes called trigonal) can also be described by using hexagonal axes (rhombohedral-hexagonal).

The structure-type nomenclature used in this article was supplied by W.B. Pearson, Department of Physics, University of Waterloo.

for the Bravais lattice of the structure, then the number of atoms in the conventionally chosen unit cell. Therefore, the nickel-arsenide structure is referred to as the NiAs $hP4$ type (meaning hexagonal, primitive, 4 atoms per unit cell) and rock salt as the NaCl $cF8$ type. The arbitrariness in the system does not appear to be a problem, because norms become established by common usage. Therefore, the ordered AuCu structure should properly be described as AuCu $tP2$, according to the smallest primitive cell, but due to association of the structure with ordering from a face-centered cubic solid solution ($cF4$), it is typically referred to as AuCu $cF4$.

The advantage of this way of naming structure types is that it is open ended, that is, not limited in use by future discoveries of new crystal-structure types. Secondly, compared to using only a formula name, it is crystallographically informative due to the addition of the Pearson symbol and thus amenable to classification. Therefore, upon discovering a new intermetallic phase and es-

**Table 2 The 14 space (Bravais) lattices and their Hermann-Mauguin and Pearson symbols**

| System | Space lattice | Hermann-Mauguin symbol | Pearson symbol |
|---|---|---|---|
| Triclinic (anorthic) ...... | Primitive | $P$ | $aP$ |
| Monoclinic ...... | Primitive | $P$ | $mP$ |
| | Base-centered(a) | $C$ | $mC$ |
| Orthorhombic .... | Primitive | $P$ | $oP$ |
| | Base-centered(a) | $C$ | $oC$ |
| | Face-centered | $F$ | $oF$ |
| | Body-centered | $I$ | $oI$ |
| Tetragonal ....... | Primitive | $P$ | $tP$ |
| | Body-centered | $I$ | $tI$ |
| Hexagonal ....... | Primitive | $R$(b) | $hP$ |
| Rhombohedral ... | Primitive | $R$ | $hR$ |
| Cubic .......... | Primitive | $P$ | $cP$ |
| | Face-centered | $F$ | $cF$ |
| | Body-centered | $I$ | $cI$ |

(a) The face that has a lattice point at its center may be chosen as the c face (the xy plane), denoted by the symbol C, or as the a or b face, denoted by A or B, because the choice of axes is arbitrary and does not alter the actual translations of the lattice. (b) The symbol C may be used for hexagonal crystals, because hexagonal crystals may be regarded as base-centered orthorhombic.

tablishing for it preliminary crystallographic information (the space lattice and the number of atoms in the unit cell), a table of known structure types, classified by Pearson symbols, can be consulted to determine what already characterized types may resemble the newly discovered phase. For convenience, Table 3 lists Strukturbericht structure symbols, prototype names, and the corresponding Pearson symbols.

**Space-group notation** is a symbolic description of the space lattice and the symmetry of a crystal. The notation for a space group consists of the symbol for a space lattice followed by letters and numbers describing the symmetry of the crystal. These symmetry designations are not discussed here, but are described in various textbooks and are tabulated in the International Tables for Crystallography (Ref 4).

**Structure Prototype.** To assist in classification and identification, each structure type has been given the name of a representative substance (an element or phase) having that

**Table 3 Conversion of Strukturbericht to Pearson symbol**

| Strukturbericht designation | Structure prototype | Pearson symbol | Strukturbericht designation | Structure prototype | Pearson symbol | Strukturbericht designation | Structure prototype | Pearson symbol |
|---|---|---|---|---|---|---|---|---|
| $A1$ ............. | Cu | $cF4$ | $C11_b$ ........... | $MoSi_2$ | $tI6$ | $D5_1$ ............. | $\alpha\text{-}Al_2O_3$ | $hR10$ |
| $A2$ ............. | W | $cI2$ | $C12$ ............. | $CaSi_2$ | $hR6$ | $D5_2$ ............. | $La_2O_3$ | $hP5$ |
| $A3$ ............. | Mg | $hP2$ | $C14$ ............. | $MgZn_2$ | $hP12$ | $D5_3$ ............. | $Mn_2O_3$ | $cI80$ |
| $A4$ ............. | C | $cF8$ | $C15$ ............. | $Cu_2Mg$ | $cF24$ | $D5_8$ ............. | $S_3Sb_2$ | $oP20$ |
| $A5$ ............. | Sn | $tF4$ | $C15_b$ ........... | $AuBe_5$ | $cF24$ | $D5_9$ ............. | $P_2Zn_3$ | $tP40$ |
| $A6$ ............. | In | $tI2$ | $C16$ ............. | $Al_2Cu$ | $tI12$ | $D5_{10}$ ............. | $Cr_3C_2$ | $oP20$ |
| $A7$ ............. | As | $hR2$ | $C18$ ............. | $FeS_2$ | $oP6$ | $D5_{13}$ ............. | $Al_3Ni_2$ | $hP5$ |
| $A8$ ............. | Se | $hP3$ | $C19$ ............. | $CdCl_2$ | $hR3$ | $D5_a$ ............. | $Si_2U_3$ | $tP10$ |
| $A10$ ............. | Hg | $hR1$ | $C22$ ............. | $Fe_2P$ | $hP9$ | $D5_c$ ............. | $C_3Pu_2$ | $cI40$ |
| $A11$ ............. | Ga | $oC8$ | $C23$ ............. | $PbCl_2$ | $oP12$ | $D7_1$ ............. | $Al_4C_3$ | $hR7$ |
| $A12$ ............. | $\alpha$-Mn | $cI58$ | $C32$ ............. | $AlB_2$ | $hP3$ | $D7_3$ ............. | $P_4Th_3$ | $cI28$ |
| $A13$ ............. | $\beta$-Mn | $cP20$ | $C33$ ............. | $Bi_2STe_2$ | $hR5$ | $D7_b$ ............. | $Ta_3B_4$ | $oI14$ |
| $A15$ ............. | $W_3O$ | $cP8$ | $C34$ ............. | $AuTe_2$ | $mC6$ | $D8_1$ ............. | $Fe_3Zn_{10}$ | $cI52$ |
| $A20$ ............. | $\alpha$-U | $oC4$ | $C36$ ............. | $MgNi_2$ | $hP24$ | $D8_2$ ............. | $Cu_3Zn_8$ | $cI52$ |
| $B1$ ............. | NaCl | $cF8$ | $C38$ ............. | $Cu_2Sb$ | $tP6$ | $D8_3$ ............. | $Al_4Cu_9$ | $cP52$ |
| $B2$ ............. | CsCl | $cP2$ | $C40$ ............. | $CrSi_2$ | $hP9$ | $D8_4$ ............. | $Cr_{23}C_6$ | $cF116$ |
| $B3$ ............. | ZnS | $cF8$ | $C44$ ............. | $GeS_2$ | $oF72$ | $D8_5$ ............. | $Fe_7W_6$ | $hR13$ |
| $B4$ ............. | ZnS | $hP4$ | $C46$ ............. | $AuTe_2$ | $oP24$ | $D8_6$ ............. | $Cu_{15}Si_4$ | $cI76$ |
| $B8_1$ ............. | AsNi | $hP4$ | $C49$ ............. | $Si_2Zr$ | $oC12$ | $D8_8$ ............. | $Mn_5Si_3$ | $hP16$ |
| $B8_2$ ............. | $InNi_2$ | $hP6$ | $C54$ ............. | $Si_2Ti$ | $oF24$ | $D8_9$ ............. | $Co_9S_8$ | $cF68$ |
| $B9$ ............. | HgS | $hP6$ | $C_c$ ............. | $Si_2Th$ | $tI12$ | $D8_{10}$ ............. | $Al_8Cr_5$ | $hR26$ |
| $B10$ ............. | PbO | $tP4$ | $C_e$ ............. | $CoGe_2$ | $oC23$ | $D8_{11}$ ............. | $Al_5Co_2$ | $hP28$ |
| $B11$ ............. | $\gamma$-CuTi | $tP4$ | $D0_2$ ............. | $As_3Co$ | $cI32$ | $D8_a$ ............. | $Mn_{23}Th_6$ | $cF116$ |
| $B13$ ............. | $\alpha$-NiS | $hR6$ | $D0_3$ ............. | $BiF_3$ | $cF16$ | $D8_b$ ............. | $\sigma$-phase (CrFe) | $tP30$ |
| $B16$ ............. | GeS | $oP8$ | $D0_9$ ............. | $O_3Re$ | $cP4$ | $D8_f$ ............. | $Ge_7Ir_3$ | $cI40$ |
| $B17$ ............. | PtS | $tP4$ | $D0_{11}$ ............. | $Fe_3C$ | $oP16$ | $D8_i$ ............. | $B_4Mo_2$ | $hR7$ |
| $B18$ ............. | CuS | $hP12$ | $D0_{18}$ ............. | $AsNa_3$ | $hP8$ | $D8_h$ ............. | $B_5W_2$ | $hP14$ |
| $B19$ ............. | $\beta'$-AuCd | $oP4$ | $D0_{19}$ ............. | $Ni_3Sn$ | $hP8$ | $D8_l$ ............. | $Cr_5B_3$ | $tI32$ |
| $B20$ ............. | FeSi | $cP8$ | $D0_{20}$ ............. | $Al_3Ni$ | $oP16$ | $D8_m$ ............. | $Si_3W_5$ | $tI32$ |
| $B27$ ............. | BFe | $oP8$ | $D0_{21}$ ............. | $Cu_3P$ | $hP24$ | $D10_1$ ............. | $Cr_7C_3$ | $hP80$ |
| $B31$ ............. | MnP | $oP8$ | $D0_{22}$ ............. | $Al_3Ti$ | $tI8$ | $D10_2$ ............. | $Fe_3Th_7$ | $hP20$ |
| $B32$ ............. | NaTl | $cF16$ | $D0_{23}$ ............. | $Al_3Zr$ | $tI16$ | $E0_1$ ............. | ClFPb | $tP6$ |
| $B34$ ............. | PdS | $tP16$ | $D0_{24}$ ............. | $Ni_3Ti$ | $hP16$ | $E1_1$ ............. | $CuFeS_2$ | $tI16$ |
| $B35$ ............. | CoSn | $hP6$ | $D0_c$ ............. | $SiU_3$ | $tI16$ | $E2_1$ ............. | $CaO_3Ti$ | $cP5$ |
| $B37$ ............. | SeTl | $tI16$ | $D0_e$ ............. | $Ni_3P$ | $tI32$ | $E3$ ............. | $Al_2CdS_4$ | $tI14$ |
| $B_e$ ............. | CdSb | $oP16$ | $D1_3$ ............. | $Al_4Ba$ | $tI10$ | $E9_3$ ............. | $Fe_3W_3C$ | $cF112$ |
| $B_f$ $(B33)$ ........ | $\zeta$-CrB | $oC8$ | $D1_a$ ............. | $MoNi_4$ | $tI10$ | $E9_a$ ............. | $Al_7Cu_2Fe$ | $tP40$ |
| $B_g$ ............. | BMo | $tI16$ | $D1_b$ ............. | $Al_4U$ | $oI20$ | $E9_b$ ............. | $AlLi_3N_2$ | $cI96$ |
| $B_h$ ............. | WC | $hP2$ | $D1_c$ ............. | $PtSn_4$ | $oC20$ | $F0_1$ ............. | NiSSb | $cP12$ |
| $B_i$ ............. | $\gamma'$-CMo (AsTi) | $hP8$ | $D1_e$ ............. | $B_4Th$ | $tP20$ | $F5_1$ ............. | $CrNaS_2$ | $hR4$ |
| $C1$ ............. | $CaF_2$ | $cF12$ | $D1_f$ ............. | $BMn_4$ | $oF40$ | $H1_1$ ............. | $Al_2MgO_4$ | $cF56$ |
| $C1_b$ ............. | AgAsMg | $cF12$ | $D2_1$ ............. | $B_6Ca$ | $cP7$ | $H2_4$ ............. | $Cu_3S_4V$ | $cP8$ |
| $C2$ ............. | $FeS_2$ | $cP12$ | $D2_3$ ............. | $NaZn_{13}$ | $cF112$ | $L1_0$ ............. | AuCuI | $tP4$ |
| $C3$ ............. | $Cu_2O$ | $cP6$ | $D2_b$ ............. | $Mn_{12}Th$ | $tI26$ | $L1_2$ ............. | $AuCu_3$ | $cP4$ |
| $C4$ ............. | $TiO_2$ | $tP6$ | $D2_c$ ............. | $MnU_6$ | $tI28$ | $L2_1$ ............. | $AlCu_2Mn$ | $cF16$ |
| $C6$ ............. | $CdI_2$ | $hP3$ | $D2_d$ ............. | $CaCu_5$ | $hP6$ | $L'2_b$ ............. | $H_2Th$ | $tI6$ |
| $C7$ ............. | $MoS_2$ | $hP6$ | $D2_f$ ............. | $UB_{12}$ | $cF52$ | $L'3$ ............. | $Fe_2N$ | $hP3$ |
| $C11_a$ ........... | $CaC_2$ | $tI6$ | $D2_h$ ............. | $Al_6Mn$ | $oC28$ | $L6_0$ ............. | $CuTi_3$ | $tP4$ |

Source: Ref 3

structure. Unit cells with the same structure type generally do not have dimensions identical to the prototype or to each other, because different materials with the same type of atomic arrangement have atoms that differ in size, causing the lengths of the $a$, $b$, and $c$ edges to differ. Similarly, the atom-position coordinates $x$, $y$, and $z$ vary among different materials.

**Atom Positions.** The position of an atom, or the lattice point, in a unit cell is expressed by three coordinates (Ref 5)—the three distances parallel to the $a$, $b$, and $c$ axes, respectively, from the origin at one corner of the cell to the atom in question. These distances are expressed in fractions of the edge lengths $a$, $b$, and $c$, respectively, rather than in angstroms. Therefore, $1/2,0,0$ is the midpoint of the $a$ edge, $1/2,1/2,0$ is at the center of the $C$ face, and $1/2,1/2,1/2$ is at the center of the volume of the unit cell. The letters $x$, $y$, and $z$ are used for the coordinates that are not convenient fractions or that differ in different phases.

A primitive (simple) unit cell has lattice points at its corners only, that is at $0,0,0$. A body-centered unit cell has lattice points at the corners (at $0,0,0$) and also at the center of volume (at $1/2,1/2,1/2$). A face-centered unit cell has lattice points at the corners and at the center of all six faces. The lattice points are at $0,0,0$; $0,1/2,1/2$; $1/2,1/2,0$ and $1/2,0,1/2$. A negative value for a coordinate is indicated by placing a bar over the letter—for example, $\bar{x}$.

**Point Groups.** A structure described by a specific space lattice (for example, $cP$) may not have any atoms lying at the (space) lattice points; instead, groups of atoms with specific so-called point symmetries may be clustered identically about each of the space-lattice points. Nevertheless, the same space-lattice symmetry ($cP$) still pertains to the crystal structure. Thus, for example in the close-packed-hexagonal structure Mg $hP2$, the primitive space-lattice points are vacant, and the two magnesium atoms are located within the unit cell at $1/3$, $2/3$ and $1/4$, and at $2/3$, $1/3$, $3/4$. The structure type $hP1$, where only the primitive hexagonal space-lattice points are occupied, does not exist.

Alternatively, the space-lattice points may be occupied by atoms, and, in addition, there may be groups of other atoms with various point-group symmetries surrounding the atoms on the space-lattice points, as in the $CaF_2$ $cF12$ structure, where calcium occupies the face-centered cubic space-lattice sites; the fluorine atoms surround these sites.

**Equivalent Positions.** In each unit cell, there are positions that are equivalent because of crystal symmetry. This is often true of atoms at special positions (such as $1/2,0,0$) and also of atoms at $x$, $y$, and $z$, where the coordinates may have specific values. At each point of a set of equivalent positions in a unit cell, the same kind of atom will be found (if the crystal if perfect), and all of the cells will be identical. The coordinates listed for each kind of atom in the descriptions of crystal

structure in Table 4 are thus coordinates of sets of equivalent positions.

The more complete tables, such as those in the International Tables for Crystallography (Ref 4), show clearly the number of equivalent points belonging to each set (the multiplicity of the set) and therefore the number of atoms that could be located at the equivalent points of each set in a crystal. To save space in tabulating all these sets of equivalent points in Ref 4, the coordinates of certain special points are given at the top of the list and these coordinates must be added to each of the coordinates listed below them.

As an example, for arsenic, $hR2$, in the cell based on hexagonal axes, the equivalent points are $(0,0,0; 1/3,2/3,2/3; 2/3,1/3,1/3)$ with coordinates $0,0,z$; $0,0,\bar{z}$ to be added. The full list for the six atoms in the unit cell, obtained by addition of coordinates, is thus $0,0,z$; $1/3,2/3,2/3 + z$; $2/3,1/3,1/3 + z$; $0,0,\bar{z}$; $1/3,2/3,2/3 - z$; $2/3,1/3,1/3 - z$.

**Effect of Alloy Composition.** Structures are described by giving a prototype structure, as if they were compounds of unvarying stoichiometric composition; in general composition can vary and unit cell edges vary in length somewhat without changing the type of structure. Interaxial angles other than 90° or 120° may also change slightly.

The special atom-coordinate values, such as $0$, $1/8$, $1/4$, $1/2$, and $1/3$, often do not change, but $x$, $y$, and $z$ values, which are variable, generally change with composition across a single-phase region of a phase diagram.

**Disordered Versus Ordered Superstructures.** Solid solutions may have more than one kind of atom at a set of equivalent positions. In an alloy of A and B atoms, the probability of finding an A atom (or a B atom) at a given atomic position is a function of the alloy composition and, in simple alloys, is equal to the atomic percentage of A atoms (or B atoms) in the alloy. If occupation of the individual sites by A or B atoms is random, or nearly so, the solid solution is said to be disordered; if A atoms occupy one set of positions and B atoms the other set, the solution is said to be ordered. A solid solution is most likely to be disordered at high temperatures.

At lower temperatures the tendency for A atoms to locate at some positions and B atoms at others may overcome the randomizing action of thermal agitation and produce partial or complete order. When this occurs, the unit cell may be larger than that for the disordered state (usually with one, two, or all three edges doubling in length), the number of atoms per unit cell is proportionately larger, and the crystal is said to be an ordered superstructure or superlattice.

Alternatively, the ordering of atoms that have previously been randomly distributed in a solid solution may occur with a lowering of the crystal symmetry of the structure, but without multiplication of the length of any of the unit-cell edges. An example of this is $\beta$ brass, which has a disordered body-centered cubic structure (W $cI2$) at high temperatures

and is designated $\beta$ Cu-Zn but which upon cooling acquires an ordered (CsCl $cP2$) structure designated $\beta'$ Cu-Zn, in which copper atoms are chiefly at positions $0,0,0$, and zinc atoms are chiefly at positions $1/2,1/2,1/2$ or conversely.

**Number of Atoms per Cell: Calculated Density.** Calculation of the number of atoms in a unit cell requires inspecting the cell to determine those atoms that are shared by other unit cells, the number of cells that share each of these atoms, and those atoms that are entirely within the cell. The atoms at each of the eight corners of a unit cell are shared by the eight cells that share that corner and thus count as only one atom per cell ($1/8 \times 8$). In a face-centered cell (such as that of Cu $cF4$), there is, in addition, an atom in each of the six faces; each of these atoms is shared by two cells, and therefore, an atom in a face counts as one half an atom per cell. With six faces, there are three ($1/2 \times 6$) atoms per cell in the faces; therefore, a face-centered cell has a total of four atoms. In a body-centered cell (such as that of W $cI2$), there is one atom at the corners plus one atom in the center of the volume, totaling two atoms per body-centered cell. The calculated density, $\rho$, of a crystal is given by $\rho = n\bar{A}/VN$, where $n$ is the total number of atoms in the unit cell, $\bar{A}$ is their mean atomic weight (calculated with atomic percentages), $V$ is the volume of the unit cell, and $N$ is Avogadro's number ($6.022 \times 10^{23}$).

**Miller Indices for Planes and Direction.** Miller indices used for designating planes within a crystal are based on the intercepts of the plane with the crystal axes. If the unit-cell edges are of lengths $a$, $b$, and $c$ and if a plane intersects these edges at $a/h$, $b/k$, and $c/l$, the fractional intercepts are $1/h$, $1/k$, and $1/l$. The reciprocals of these fractional intercepts, when reduced to the smallest common denominator, are the Miller indices of the plane. They are written in parentheses—for example, $(hkl)$. A negative intercept is indicated using an overbar; for example, $(hk\bar{l})$ indicates a negative intercept along the $c$ axis. Integers enclosed by braces designate all the equivalent nonparallel planes of a crystal; for example, the entire set of cube faces of a cubic crystal is designated $\{100\}$.

In Miller indices specifying directions in a crystal, the notation $[uvw]$ is used to indicate the direction of a line from the origin to a point whose coordinates are $u$, $v$, and $w$. It is customary to use square brackets, to avoid fractional coordinates, and to use the smallest integers that will locate a point on the line. Negative indices are indicated using overbars. Because of symmetry, various directions in a crystal are equivalent. A full set of equivalent directions (directions of a form) is enclosed by carets, as in $\langle uvw \rangle$. For additional information, see Ref 6 to 8.

**Miller-Bravais indices,** instead of Miller indices, are used for hexagonal crystals. These crystals have three equal axes in the basal plane of the unit cell: $a_1$, $a_2$, and $a_3$. If

## Table 4   Crystal structures of the elements

| Element | Phase(a) | Structure type | Ref |
|---|---|---|---|
| Ac (actinium) ........... | | Cu cF4 | 1 |
| Ag (silver) ............. | | Cu cF4 | 1 |
| Al (aluminum) .......... | | Cu cF4 | 1 |
| Am (americium) ....... α (RT) | La hP4 | 9 |
| | β (HT) | Cu cF4 | 1 |
| Ar (argon) ............. | | Cu cF4 | 9 |
| As (arsenic) .......... α | As hR2 | 1 |
| | β | P oC8 | 1 |
| At (astatine) ........... | | ... | ... |
| Au (gold) .............. | | Cu cF4 | 1 |
| B (boron) .............. α | B hR12 | 9 |
| | β | B hR105 | 16 |
| | γ | B tP190 | 9 |
| Ba (barium) ............ | | W cI2 | 1 |
| | Ba II (62 kbar; RT) | Mg hP2 | 1 |
| Be (beryllium) ........ α | Mg hP2 | 1 |
| | β (HT) | W cI2 | 1 |
| Bi (bismuth) .......... α (RT) | As hR2 | 1 |
| | HP phases uncertain | ... | 16 |
| Bk (berkelium) ....... α (RT) | La hP4 | 10 |
| | β (HT) | Cu cF4 | 10 |
| C (carbon) ........... Graphite | C hP4 | 9 |
| | Rhombohedral graphite | C hR2 | 16 |
| | Diamond | C cF8 | 1 |
| | Hexagonal diamond | C hP4 | 16 |
| Ca (calcium) ......... α (RT) | Cu cF4 | 1 |
| | β (HT) | W cI2 | 1 |
| Cd (cadmium) .......... | | Mg hP2 | 1 |
| | Cd II (HP: above about 100 kbar) | La hP4 (?) | 14, 15 |
| Ce (cerium) .......... α (RT) | Cu cF4 | 9 |
| | β (<250 K) | La hP4 | 9 |
| | γ (<110 K) | Cu CF4 | 9 |
| | δ (HT) | W cI2 | 9 |
| Cm (curium) ......... α (LT) | La hP4 | 11 |
| | β (HT?) | Cu cF4 | 11 |
| Co (cobalt) .......... α | Mg hP2 | 1 |
| | β | Cu cF4 | 1 |
| Cr (chromium) ........ | | W cI2 | 1 |
| Cs (cesium) .......... | | W cI2 | 1 |
| Cu (copper) .......... | | Cu cF4 | 1 |
| Dy (dysprosium) ...... α (RT) | Mg hP2 | 1 |
| | β (HT) | W cI2 | 1 |
| | γ (<86 K) | Tb oC4 | 1, 16 |
| | δ (at 75 kbar and RT) | Sm hR3 | 16 |
| Er (erbium) .......... α (RT) | Mg hP2 | 1 |
| Es (einsteinium) ......... | | ... | ... |
| Eu (europium) .......... | | W cI2 | 1 |
| F (fluorine) .......... α (<45.6 K) | Monoclinic | 18 |
| | β (>45.6 K) | Cubic | 18 |
| Fe (iron) ............. α (RT) | W cI2 | 1 |
| | β (910-1390 °C, or 1670-2535 °F) | Cu cF4 | 1, 16 |
| | δ (>1390 °C, or 2535 °F) | W cI2 | 1, 16 |
| | Fe II (≳130 kbar) | Mg hP2 | 1 |
| Fm (fermium) .......... | | ... | ... |
| Fr (francium) .......... | | ... | ... |
| Ga (gallium) ......... α (RT) | Ga oC8 | 1 |
| | β (metastable, but stable above about 15 kbar at 0 °C, or 32°F) | Ga mC4 | 1 |
| | (metastable or stable above 30 kbar at 50-70 °C, or 120-160 °F) | Ga oC40 | 1 |
| Gd (gadolinium) ...... α (RT) | Mg hP2 | 1 |
| | β (HT) | W cI2 | 1 |
| | Gd II (formed at 400 °C, or 750 °F, and 40 kbar, retained at normal T and P) | Sm hR3 | 1 |
| Ge (germanium) ...... RT | C cF8 | 1 |
| | Ge II (RT; 120 kbar) | SN tI4 | 1 |
| | Ge III (formed above 120 kbar, retained when pressure removed) | Ge tP2 | 1 |
| H (hydrogen) ........ α | Mg hP2(?) | 9 |
| | β | fcc | 9 |

| Element | Phase(a) | Structure type | Ref |
|---|---|---|---|
| He (helium) .......... α | Mg hP2 | 9 |
| | β | Cu cF4 | 9 |
| | γ | W cI2 | 9 |
| Hf (hafnium) ......... α (RT) | Mg hP2 | 1 |
| | β (HT) | W cI2 | 1 |
| Hg (mercury) ........ Below RT | Hg hR1 | 1 |
| | Hg II (formed at HP, retained at 77 K when pressure removed) | Pa tI2 | 1 |
| Ho (holmium) ........ α (RT) | Mg hP2 | 1 |
| | Ho II (>75 kbar at RT) | Sm hR3 | 16 |
| In (indium) ............. | | In tF4 | 1 |
| Ir (iridium) ............. | | Cu cF4 | 1 |
| K (potassium) ........... | | W cI2 | 1 |
| Kr (krypton) ........... | | Cu cF4 | 9 |
| La (lanthanum) ....... α (RT) | La hP4 | 1 |
| | β | Cu cF4 | 1 |
| | γ (HT) | W cI2 | 1 |
| Li (lithium) .......... α (RT) | W cI2 | 9 |
| | β (LT: 78 K) | Mg hP2 | 9 |
| | γ (LT; strain induced at 20 K) | Cu cF4 | 1 |
| Lr (lawrencium) .......... | | ... | ... |
| Lu (lutetium) ......... α (RT) | Mg hP2 | 1 |
| Md (mendelevium) ....... | | ... | ... |
| Mg (magnesium) .......... | | Mg hP2 | 1 |
| Mn (manganese) ....... α (RT) | Mn cI58 | 1 |
| | β (HT: >727 °C, or 1341 °F) | Mn cP20 | 1, 16 |
| | γ (HT: >1095 °C, or 2003 °F) | Cu cF4 | 1, 16 |
| | δ (HT: >1133 °C, or 2071 °F) | W cI2 | 1, 16 |
| Mo (molybdenum) ....... | | W cI2 | 1 |
| N (nitrogen) .......... α | Cubic | 9 |
| | γ (HP) | Tetragonal | 19 |
| | β | Hexagonal | 9 |
| Na (sodium) .......... α (RT) | W cI2 | 1 |
| | β (LT) | Mg hP2 | 1 |
| Nb (niobium) .......... | | W cI2 | 1 |
| Nd (neodymium) ...... α (RT) | La hP4 | 1 |
| | β (HT) | W cI2 | 1 |
| | Nd II (RT; 50 kbar) | Cu cF4 | 16 |
| Ne (neon) ............. | | Cu cF4 | 9 |
| Ni (nickel) ............. | | Cu cF4 | 1 |
| No (nobelium) .......... | | ... | ... |
| Np (neptunium) ....... α (RT) | Np oP8 | 1 |
| | β (HT: >280 °C, or 535 °F) | Np tP4 | 1,16 |
| | γ (HT: >577 °C, or 1071 °F) | W cI2 | 1,16 |
| O (oxygen) .......... α | Monoclinic | 17 |
| | β | Hexagonal | 9 |
| | γ | Cubic | 9 |
| Os (osmium) ............. | | Mg hP2 | 1 |
| P (phosphorus) ........ White | Cubic | 1, 9 |
| | Black | P oC8 | 1, 9 |
| | Red | P c-66 | 1, 9 |
| | Hittorf's | P mP84 | 16 |
| | P II (RT; 50-83 kbar) | As hR2 | 1 |
| | P III (RT; 120 kbar) | Po cP1 | 1 |
| Pa (protactinium) ......... | | Pa tI2 | 1 |
| Pb (lead) ............. RT | Cu cF4 | 1 |
| | Pb II (RT; 130 kbar) | Mg hP2 | 16 |
| Pd (palladium) .......... | | Cu cF4 | 1 |
| Pm (promethium) ...... α (RT) | La hP4 | 12 |
| | β (HT) | W cI2 | ... |
| Po (polonium) ........ α (10 °C, or 50 °F) | Po cP1 | 1 |
| | β (75 °C, or 167 °F) | Hg hR1 | 1 |
| Pr (praseodymium) .... α (RT) | La hP4 | 1 |
| | β (HT) | W cI2 | 1 |
| | Pr II (RT; 40 kbar) | Cu cF4 | 1 |
| Pt (platinum) ........... | | Cu cF4 | 1 |
| Pu (plutonium) ........ α (RT) | Pu mP16 | 9, 16 |
| | β (>122 °C, or 252 °F) | Pu mI32 | 9, 16 |
| | γ (>206 °C, or 403 °F) | Pu oF8 | 9, 16 |
| | δ (>319 °C, or 606 °F) | Cu cF4 | 9, 16 |
| | δ' (>451 °C, or 844 °F) | In tF4 | 9, 16 |
| | ε (>476 °C, or 889 °F) | W cI2 | 9, 16 |
| Ra (radium) ............. | | W cI2 | 13 |

(continued)

**Table 4** (continued)

| Element | Phase(a) | Structure type | Ref | Element | Phase(a) | Structure type | Ref |
|---|---|---|---|---|---|---|---|
| Rb (rubidium) .......... ··· | | W cI2 | 1 | Tc (technetium) ......... ··· | | Mg hP2 | 1 |
| Re (rhenium) .......... ··· | | Mg hP2 | 1 | Te (tellurium) .......... ··· | | Se hP3 | 1 |
| Rh (rhodium) .......... ··· | | Cu cF4 | 1 | | Te II (>15 kbar) | As hR2 (?) | 1 |
| Rn (radon) ............. ··· | | ··· | ··· | | Te II (>70 kbar) | Hg hR1 | 16 |
| Ru (ruthenium) ......... ··· | | Mg hP2 | 1 | Th (thorium) ......... α (RT) | | Cu cF4 | 1 |
| S (sulfur) ............. α (RT) | | S oF128 | 9 | | β (HT) | W cI2 | 1 |
| | β (RT) | S mP48 | 9 | Ti (titanium) ......... α (RT) | | Mg hP2 | 1 |
| | γ (RT) | S hR6 | 9 | | β (HT) | W cI2 | 1 |
| Sb (antimony) ........ α (RT) | | As hR2 | 1 | | Ti II (HP; retained when pressure removed) | Ti hP3 (ω phase) | 1 |
| | Sb II (RT; 50-70 kbar) | Po cP1 | 1 | Tl (thallium) ......... α (RT) | | Mg hP2 | 1 |
| | Sb III (RT; 90 kbar) | Mg hP2 | 1 | | β (HT) | W cI2 | 1 |
| Sc (scandium) ........ α (RT) | | Mg hP2 | 1 | | γ (HP: >40 kbar) | Cu cF4 (?) | 16 |
| | β (HT) | W cI2 | 1 | Tm (thulium) ......... α (RT) | | Mg hP2 | 1 |
| Se (selenium) ......... α (RT) | | Se(1) mP32 | 1 | U (uranium) ......... α (RT) | | U oC4 | 1 |
| | β (RT) | Se(2) mP32 | 1 | | β (HT: 720 °C, or 1328 °F) | CrFe tP30 (σ phase) | 1 |
| | γ (RT) | Se hP3 | 1 | | γ (HT: 805 °C, or 1481 °F) | W cI2 | 1 |
| Si (silicon) ............. ··· | | C cF8 | 1 | | | | |
| | Si II (RT; 195 kbar) | Sn tI4 | 1 | V (vanadium) ........... ··· | | W cI2 | 1 |
| | Si III (110-160 kbar; retained when pressure removed) | Si cI16 | 1 | W (tungsten) ............ ··· | | W cI2 | 1 |
| | | | | Xe (xenon) ............. ··· | | Cu cF4 | 9 |
| Sm (samarium) ....... α (RT) | | Sm hR3 | 1 | Y (yttrium) .......... α (RT) | | Mg hP2 | 9 |
| | β (HT) | W cI2 | 9 | | β (HT) | W cI2 | 9 |
| | Sm II (300 °C, or 572 °F; 40 kbar) | La hP4 | 16 | Yb (ytterbium) ........ α (RT) | | Cu cF4 | 9 |
| Sn (tin) ........ α (gray; LT) | | C cF8 | 1 | | β (HT; also at RT and 40 kbar) | W cI2 | 9 |
| | β (white) | Sn tI4 | 1 | | γ (LT: <270 K) | Mg hP2 | 16 |
| | Sn II (314 °C, or 597 °F; 39 kbar) | Pa tI2 | 1 | Zn (zinc) .............. ··· | | Mg hP2 | 1 |
| | Sn III (RT; 110 kbar) | Cubic (?) | 1 | | Zn II (HP: above about 40 kbar) | La hP4 (?) | 14, 15 |
| Sr (strontium) ........ α (RT) | | Cu cF4 | 9 | Zr (zirconium) ........ α (RT) | | Mg hP2 | 1 |
| | β (HT) | W cI2 | 9 | | β (HT) | W cI2 | 1 |
| | Sr II (RT; 35 kbar) | W cI2 | 1 | | Zr II (HP; retained when pressure removed) | Ti hP3 | 1 |
| Ta (tantalum) .......... ··· | | W cI2 | 1 | | | | |
| Tb (terbium) ......... α (RT) | | Mg hP2 | 1 | | | | |
| | β (HT) | W cI2 | 1 | | | | |
| | γ (<220 K) | Tb oC4 | 1, 16 | | | | |
| | δ (60 kbar at RT) | Sm hR3 | 16 | | | | |

Note: 1 kbar = 100 MPa.
(a) RT, room temperature; HT, high temperature; LT, low temperature; HP, high pressure; phases formed under high-pressure conditions are designated by roman numerals—e.g., Ge II, Ge III.

the fractional intercepts on these three axes are $1/h$, $1/k$, and $1/i$ and the intercept on the $c$ axis is $1/l$, the Miller-Bravais indices of the plane are $(hki l)$.

**Crystal Zone and Zone Axes.** A crystal zone is that set of nonparallel faces that intersect each other in a series of parallel straight lines. Crystal faces belonging to a zone lie parallel to a line that is called the zone axis and that defines a specific direction in the crystal. A line passing through the lattice point defined as the origin $(0,0,0)$ and through a neighboring lattice point whose coordinates are $u$, $v$, and $w$ in terms of the axial lengths $a$, $b$, and $c$, respectively, defines the direction of the zone axis or line and is designated by the indices $[uvw]$. Two intersecting zone axes define a plane and thus a possible crystal face or face of a unit cell.

## Metallurgically Important Crystal Types

Table 4 gives the crystal structures of the elements. These are described by the Pearson symbols for crystal system ($c$, $h$, $o$, $t$, $m$ or $a$), space lattice ($P$, $F$, $I$, $C$ or $R$; see Table 2), and the total number of atoms per unit cell, and by the prototype structure.
Table 5 describes the crystal structures of selected phases of special interest to metallurgists. This table also uses Pearson symbols

for crystal system, space lattice, and the total number of atoms per unit cell. The prototype formula name, as well as the space group, is given. The last column gives atom positions (for the simpler structures) in the prototype structure; interaxial angles are mentioned only when they differ from 90° (or 120° in hexagonal crystals). Several of the listed phases have the same prototype.

Figure 1 illustrates many of the crystals described in this article; the illustrations include perspective drawings of unit cells and projections onto cell faces. Small circles indicate the position of atom centers, without implying that the atoms are as small and as widely separated as the circles. Included in Fig. 1 are views in which the atoms are projected onto the (001) face of the unit cell, the face containing the origin and the axes $a$ and $b$. The circles represent atom positions; the numbers adjacent to the circles indicate the distance from the atom to that face in terms of fractions (or decimal equivalents of fractions) of the length of the unit-cell edge extending up from that face. The edge lengths and interaxial angles shown are those that apply to the structure prototype. Cell dimensions for other element or alloy phases with the same structure prototype vary according to phase and composition, as discussed in the section "Effect of Alloy Composition" in this article.

**Long-Period Superlattices.** Some alloys in the ordered state have periodic structures with unit cells many times larger than in the disordered state; the long period may be along one axis, as in Fig. 2, along two axes, as in Fig. 3, or along three axes. The superperiods, which have different values in different alloy systems and which differ with composition, are known to depend on the average number of valence electrons per atom. Figure 2 shows an AuCu II structure with a one-dimensional long-range superlattice, with antiphase boundaries at intervals of five unit cells of the disordered state. It is orthorhombic when ordered and face-centered cubic when disordered. Figure 3 shows a two-dimensional long-period superlattice as in certain $AB_3$ alloys (Cu-Pd, Au-Zn, Au-Mn), with antiphase boundaries spaced at intervals $M_1$ and $M_2$ and unit cell dimensions $a$, $b$, and $c$ in the ordered state. This superlattice is orthorhombic when ordered and face-centered cubic when disordered.

## Crystal Defects

Crystal defects are important features in all real crystals. Some of the most significant defects are described in the following paragraphs. Additional information on defects, slip, twinning, and cleavage can be found in Ref 6 to 8.

**Table 5  Assorted structure types of metallurgical interest arranged according to Pearson symbol**

| Pearson symbol | Prototype | Space group | Unit-cell description | Pearson symbol | Prototype | Space group | Unit-cell description |
|---|---|---|---|---|---|---|---|
| cP1 | α-Po | Pm3m | One atom per cell, at 0,0,0. For α-Po, $a = 3.34$ Å. See Fig. 1. **Examples:** Ag-Te (metastable), Au-Te (metastable), α-Po, Sb II (high pressure) | cF8 | ZnS | F43m | Sphalerite. Four zinc atoms at 0,0,0; 0,1/2,1/2; 1/2,0,1/2; and 1/2,1/2,0; four sulfur atoms at 1/4,1/4,1/4; 1/4,3/4,3/4; 3/4,1/4,3/4; and 3/4,3/4,1/4. For ZnS (sphalerite), $a = 5.42$ Å. See Fig. 1. **Examples:** CdS, CdSe, CdTe, CuFeS₂ (high temperature), GaP, GaSb, InAs, InP, InSb, β MnS, β SiC, ZnO, ZnS (sphalerite), ZnSe |
| cP2 | CsCl | Pm3m | One cesium atom at 0,0,0, and one chlorine atom at 1/2,1/2,1/2. For CsCl, $a = 4.11$ Å. See Fig. 1. **Examples:** AgCd, CoTi, CsCl, FeAl, FeCo, FeTi, FeV, β NiAl, β NiGa, δ NiIn, NiTi, β′ Cu-Zn | | NaCl, rocksalt | Fm3m | Four sodium atoms at 0,0,0; 0,1/2,1/2; 1/2,0,1/2; and 1/2,1/2,0; four chlorine atoms at 1/2,1/2,1/2; 1/2,0,0; 0,1/2,0; and 0,0,1/2. For NaCl, $a = 5.64$ Å. See Fig. 1. **Examples:** BaS, CdO, CdS, CrN, HfC, HfN, NaCl, NiO (high temperature), PbS, PbSe, TiO, UC, UO, UP, US, VO, ZrO |
| cP4 | AuCu₃ | Pm3m | One gold atom at 0,0,0; three copper atoms at 0,1/2,1/2; 1/2,0,1/2; and 1/2,1/2,0. For AuCu₃, $a = 3.74$ Å. See Fig. 1. **Examples:** α′ AlNi₃, AlZr₃, Au₃Cu, AuCu₃ I, CoPt₃, Cr₃Pt, Fe₃Ga, FePd₃, Ni₃Fe, Ni₃Mn, Sn₃U | | C | Fd3m | Diamond. Eight atoms per cell, at 0,0,0; 0,1/2,1/2; 1/2,0,1/2; 1/2,1/2,0; 1/4,1/4,1/4; 1/4,3/4,3/4; 3/4,1/4,3/4; and 3/4,3/4,1/4. For C (diamond), $a = 3.57$ Å. See Fig. 1. **Examples:** C (diamond), Ge, Si, α-Sn |
| cP5 | CaTiO₃ | Pm3m | Perovskite. One calcium atom at 0,0,0; one titanium atom at 1/2,1/2,1/2; three oxygen atoms at 0,1/2,1/2; 1/2,0,1/2; and 1/2,1/2,0. **Examples:** AlCFe₃, AlCMn₃, AlCTi₃, CaTiO₃, Fe₃CₓIn, Fe₃NNi, Fe₃NPd, Fe₃NSn | cF12 | AgAsMg | F43m | Ternary version of fluorite. For AgAsMg, $a = 6.25$ Å. **Examples:** AlBBe, CdCuSb, CuMnSb, NiSbV |
| cP7 | B₆Ca | Pm3m | One calcium atom at 0,0,0; six boron atoms at $x$,1/2,1/2; 1/2,$x$,1/2; 1/2,1/2,$x$; $\bar{x}$,1/2,1/2; 1/2,$\bar{x}$,1/2; 1/2,1/2,$\bar{x}$ with $x = 0.207$. For B₆Ca, $a = 4.15$ Å. **Examples:** B₆Ba, B₆Gd, B₆Sc, B₆Th, B₆Yb | | CaF₂ | Fm3m | Fluorite. Four calcium atoms at 0,0,0; 0,1/2,1/2; 1/2,0,1/2; and 1/2,1/2,0; eight fluorine atoms at 1/4,1/4,1/4; 1/4,3/4,3/4; 3/4,1/4,3/4; 3/4,3/4,1/4; 3/4,1/4,1/4; 1/4,3/4,1/4; and 1/4,1/4,3/4. For CaF₂, $a = 5.46$ Å. See Fig. 1. **Examples:** Be₂B, Be₂C, CaF₂, CoSi₂, rare-earth hydrides, K₂O, K₂S, Mg₂Pb, Mg₂Si, ζ NiSi₂, UN₂, UO₂ |
| cP8 | FeSi | P2₁3 | Four iron atoms at $x,x,x$; $1/2 + x, 1/2 - x, \bar{x}$; $\bar{x}, 1/2 + x, 1/2 - x$; and $1/2 - x, \bar{x}, 1/2 + x$ (with $x = 0.137$); four silicon atoms at $x,x,x$; $1/2 + x, 1/2 - x, \bar{x}$; $\bar{x}, 1/2 + x, 1/2 - x$; and $1/2 - x, \bar{x}, 1/2 + x$, (with $x = 0.842$). For FeSi, $a = 4.49$ Å. **Examples:** CoSi, FeSi, MnSi | cF16 | AlCu₂Mn | Fm3m | Heusler alloy. For AlCu₂Mn, $a = 5.95$ Å. **Examples:** AgAuCd₂, AlNi₂Ta, Co₂GaTi, CsK₂Sb |
| | W₃O or Cr₃Si | Pm3n | Atom I, two at 0,0,0; and 1/2,1/2,1/2; atom II, six at 1/4,0,1/2; 1/2,1/4,0; 0,1/2,1/4; 3/4,0,1/2; 1/2,3/4,0; and 0,1/2,3/4. For W₃O, $a = 5.04$ Å. See Fig. 1. The prototype structure originally was attributed to β-W. This has since been shown to be the oxide, W₃O, having random distribution of atoms. **Examples:** AlV₃, AuTi₃, CoV₃, Cr₃O, Cr₃Si, Mo₃O, V₃Si, W₃O, W₃Si | | BiF₃ or BiLi₃ | Fm3m | Four bismuth atoms at 0,0,0; 0,1/2,1/2; 1/2,0,1/2; and 1/2,1/2,0; 12 fluorine (or lithium) atoms at 1/2,1/2,1/2; 1/2,0,0; 0,1/2,0; 0,0,1/2; 1/4,1/4,1/4; 1/4,3/4,3/4; 3/4,1/4,3/4; 3/4,3/4,1/4; 3/4,1/4,1/4; 1/4,3/4,1/4; and 1/4,1/4,3/4. For BiLi₃, $a = 6.71$ Å. See Fig. 1. **Examples:** BiF₃, BiLi₃, Fe₃Al, γ Cu₃Sn (high temperature), α Fe₃Si, Mn₃Si, Ni₃Sn (high temperature) |
| cP12 | NiSSb | P2₁3 | For NiSSb, $\alpha = 5.88$ Å. **Examples:** AsPdSe, BiPtTe, IrSbSe, RhSSb | | NaTl | Fd3m | For NaTl, $a = 7.49$ Å. **Examples:** AlLi, CdLi, GaLi, InNa, LiZn |
| | FeS₂ | Pa3 | Pyrite. Four iron atoms at 0,0,0; 0,1/2,1/2; 1/2,0,1/2; and 1/2,1/2,0; eight sulfur atoms at $x,x,x$; $1/2 + x, 1/2 - x, \bar{x}$; $\bar{x}, 1/2 + x, 1/2 - x$; $1/2 - x, \bar{x}, 1/2 + x$; $\bar{x},\bar{x},\bar{x}$; $1/2 - x, 1/2 + x, x$; $x, 1/2 - x, 1/2 + x$; and $1/2 + x, x, 1/2 - x$. For FeS₂ (pyrite), $x = 0.386$ and $a = 5.42$ Å. **Examples:** CoPS, CoS₂, CoSe₂, FeS₂ (pyrite), MnS₂, MnTe₂, NiS₂₊ₓ, NiSe₂ | cF24 | AuBe₃ | F43m or F23 | For AuBe₅, $a = 6.70$ Å. **Examples:** Au₅Ca, Be₅Pd, HfNi₅, Ni₅U |
| cP20 | β-Mn | P4₁32 | For β-Mn, $a = 6.13$ Å. **Examples:** Ag₃Al, Au₉Nb₁₁, T C-Cr-Fe-W, γ Cu₃Si | | Cu₂Mg | Fd3m | Eight magnesium atoms at 0,0,0; 0,1/2,1/2; 1/2,0,1/2; 1/2,1/2,0; 1/4,1/4,1/4; 1/4,3/4,3/4; 3/4,1/4,3/4; and 3/4,3/4,1/4; 16 copper atoms at 5/8,5/8,5/8; 5/8,1/8,1/8; 1/8,5/8,1/8; 1/8,1/8,5/8; 5/8,7/8,7/8; 5/8,3/8,3/8; 1/8,7/8,3/8; 1/8,3/8,7/8; 7/8,5/8,7/8; 7/8,1/8,3/8; 3/8,5/8,3/8; 3/8,1/8,7/8; 7/8,7/8,5/8; 7/8,3/8,1/8; 3/8,7/8,1/8; and 3/8,3/8,5/8. For Cu₂Mg, $a = 7.05$ Å. **Examples:** Al₂Ca, Al₂U, CdCuZn, Co₂U, Co₂Zr, Cr₂Ti, Cu₂Mg, FeNiTa, Fe₂U, Fe₂Zr, MgNiZn, α TiCo₂, ZrW₂ |
| cP36 | BaHg₁₁ | Pm3m | For BaHg₁₁, $a = 9.59$ Å. **Examples:** Cd₁₁Ce, Hg₁₁K, Hg₁₁Sr | | | | |
| cP52 | Al₄Cu₉ | P43m | γ brass. For Al₄Cu₉, $a = 8.70$ Å. **Example:** Ga₄Cu₉ | cF52 | UB₁₂ | Fm3m | For UB₁₂, $a = 7.48$ Å. **Examples:** DyB12, ScB₁₂, ZrB₁₂ |
| cF4 | Cu | Fm3m | Four atoms at 0,0,0; 1/2,0,1/2; 0,1/2,1/2; and 1/2,1/2,0. For Cu, $a = 3.61$ Å. See Fig. 1. **Examples:** Ag, Al, Au, α-Ca, α-Ce, β-Co, Cu, γ-Fe, Ir, Ni, Pb, Pd, Pt, Rh, α-Sr, α-Th | cF56 | Al₂MgO₄ | Fd3m | Spinel. **Examples:** Al₂CrS₄, Al₂MgO₄, Co₂NiS₄, Co₃O₄, Co₃S₄, CuS₄Ti₂, FeNi₂S₄, Fe₃O₄, Fe₃S₄ (greigite), Ni₃S₄ (low temperature) |

(continued)

**Table 5 (continued)**

| Pearson symbol | Prototype | Space group | Unit-cell description |
|---|---|---|---|
| $cF112$ | $NaZn_{13}$ | $Fm3c$ | For $NaZn_{13}$, $a = 12.28$ Å. **Examples:** $AmBe_{13}$, $Be_{13}Ho$, $Be_{13}Zr$, $Cd_{13}Cs$, $KZn_{13}$ |
| | $Fe_3W_3C$ | $Fd3m$ | η-carbide. For $Fe_3W_3C$, $a = 11.06$ Å. **Examples:** $CoNb_2(C, N, O)_x$, $Co_2Mo_4C$, $Cr_3Nb_3C$, η $Fe_2Nb_3$, $Fe_3Mo_3C$, $Fe_3Mo_3N$, $Fe_3W_3C$, $Mn_3Mo_3C$, $Mo_3Ni_3C$, $NiTi_2$, $Ni_3W_3C$ |
| $cF116$ | $Cr_{23}C_6$ | $Fm3m$ | For $Cr_{23}C_6$, $a = 10.66$ Å. **Examples:** $Mn_{23}C_6$, $Fe_{21}Mo_2C_6$ |
| | $Mn_{23}Th_6$ ($Cu_{16}Mg_6Si_7$) | $Fm3m$ | For $Mn_{23}Th_6$, $a = 12.52$ Å. **Examples:** $Dy_6Mn_{23}$, $Mg_{23}Sr_6$, $Co_{16}Hf_6Si_7$, $Mn_6Ni_{16}Si_7$ |
| $cI2$ | W | $Im3m$ | Two atoms at 0,0,0 and 1/2,1/2,1/2. For W, $a = 3.16$ Å. See Fig. 1. **Examples:** Ba, Nb, Cr, Cs, β Cu-Zn (high temperature), α-Fe, δ-Fe, K, β-Li, Mo, β-Na, Rb, Ta, V, W |
| $cI26$ | $Al_{12}W$ | $Im3$ | For $Al_{12}W$, $a = 7.58$ Å. **Examples:** $Al_{12}Mo$, $Al_{12}Re$, $Al_{12}Tc$ |
| $cI28$ | $P_4Th_3$ | $I\bar{4}3d$ | For $P_4Th_3$, $a = 8.62$ Å. **Examples:** $As_4Th_3$, $BaLa_2S_4$, $Bi_4U_3$, $Gd_2Se_4Sr$, $Se_4U_3$ |
| $cI32$ | $As_3Co$ | $Im3$ | For $As_3Co$, $a = 8.20$ Å. **Examples:** $As_3Ir$, $CoSb_3$, $IrP_3$, $RhSb_3$ |
| $cI40$ | $C_3Pu_2$ | $I\bar{4}3d$ | For $C_3Pu_2$, $a = 8.13$ Å. **Examples:** $C_3Ce_2$, $C_3Pr_2$, $C_3U_2$ |
| $cI52$ | $Cu_5Zn_8$ | $I\bar{4}3m$ | γ brass. For $Cu_5Zn_8$, $a = 8.86$ Å. **Examples:** $Ag_5Cd_8$, $Ag_5Zn_8$, $Al_8V_5$, $Cd_8Cu_5$ |
| $cI58$ | α-Mn | $I\bar{4}3m$ | α-Mn appears to be an ordered array of two or three physically distinguishable types of manganese atoms located on four crystallographically different sets of positions, which have an ordered array of atoms in the chi-phase structure ($Fe_{36}Cr_{12}Mo_{12}$ and $Al_{12}Mg_{17}$). For α-Mn, $a = 8.91$ Å. Other closely related structures are the μ-, P-, R-, and δ-phases (see Ref 5-7). **Examples:** γ $Al_{12}Mg_{17}$, χ $Co_5Cr_3Si_2$, $CrMn_2$, $Fe_{36}Cr_{12}Mo_{12}$, $Fe_5Si_2V_3$, α-Mn |
| $cI80$ | β $Mn_2O_3$ | $Ia3$ | Type C. For $Mn_2O_3$, $a = 9.41$ Å. **Examples:** $Am_2O_3$, $Be_3P_2$, $Cd_3N_2$, $N_2Zn_3$, $O_3Y_2$ |
| $hP2$ | WC | $P\bar{6}m2$ | One tungsten atom at 0,0,0; one carbon atom at 1/3,2/3,1/2 or at 2/3,1/3,1/2. For WC, $a = 2.91$ Å and $c = 2.84$ Å. **Examples:** γ MoC, TiS, WC, WN, $Zr_3S_2$ |
| | Mg | $P6_3/mmc$ | Hexagonal close-packed. Atoms at 1/3,2/3,1/4; 2/3,1/3,3/4. These are the positions of the In atoms of the $Ni_2In$ structure shown in Fig. 1. For Mg, $a = 3.21$ Å, $c = 5.20$ Å. **Examples:** α-Be, Cd, α-Co, Mg, α-Ti, Zn, α-Zr |
| $hP3$ | $CdI_2$ | $P\bar{3}m1$ | One cadmium atom at 0,0,0; two iodine atoms at 1/3,2/3,$z$; 2/3,1/3,$\bar{z}$, with $z = 1/4$. For $SnS_2$, $a = 3.65$ Å, $c = 5.88$ Å. **Examples:** $HfS_2$, $PdTe_2$, $S_2Ta$, $Se_2V$, $Te_2Zr$ |
| | $Fe_2N$ or $W_2C$ | $P6_3/mmc$ | Two iron atoms at 1/3,2/3,1/4 and 2/3,1/3,3/4; one nitrogen atom at 0,0,0 or 0,0,1/2. See Fig. 1. **Examples:** $Fe_2N$, ζ $Mn_2N$, β $Ta_2C$, $Ta_{\sim2}N$, $V_2C$, $W_2C$ |
| | Se | $P3_121$ or $P3_221$ | Three atoms at $x$,0,1/3; 0,$x$,2/3; and $\bar{x}$,$\bar{x}$,0 (or at $x$,0,2/3; 0,$x$,1/3; and $\bar{x}$,$\bar{x}$,0). For Se, $a = 4.36$ Å, $c = 4.96$ Å and $x = 0.217$. **Example:** γ-Se |
| | $AlB_2$ | $P6/mmm$ | One aluminum atom at 0,0,0; two boron atoms at 1/3,2/3,1/2; 2/3,1/3,1/2. For $AlB_2$, $a = 3.01$ Å, $c = 3.26$ Å. **Examples:** $Al_2Th$, $B_2Lu$, $B_2Mg$, $Ga_2Ho$, $Hg_2U$, $PuZr_2$ |
| $hP4$ | AsNi | $P6_3/mmc$ | Two nickel atoms at 0,0,0 and 0,0,1/2; two arsenic atoms at 1/3,2/3,1/4 and 2/3,1/3,3/4. For AsNi, $a = 3.62$ Å, $c = 5.03$ Å. **Examples:** CoSb, CoSe, CoTe, CrH, CrSe, α″ FeS, MnSb, NiAs, NiSb, NiTe, TiS, VS, VSb |
| | C | $P6_3/mmc$ | Graphite. Two carbon(1) atoms at 0,0,1/4; 0,0,3/4. Two carbon(2) atoms at 2/3,1/3, 1/4; 1/3,2/3,3/4. For hexagonal graphite, $a = 2.46$ Å, $c = 6.71$ Å. See Fig. 1. |
| | La | $P6_3mmc$ | Two lanthanum(1) atoms at 0,0,0; 0,0,1/2; two lanthanum(2) at 1/3,2/3,1/4; 2/3,1/3,3/4. For La, $a = 3.77$ Å, $c = 12.16$ Å. **Examples:** Am, α-Nd, α-Pr, α-Pm |
| | ZnS | $P6_3mc$ | Würtzite. Two zinc atoms at 1/3,2/3,$z$ and 2/3,1/3,1/2 + $z$ (with $z = 0$); two sulfur atoms at 1/3,2/3,$z$ and 2/3,1/3,1/2 + $z$ (with $z = 0.371$). For ZnS (würtzite), $a = 3.82$ Å and $c = 6.26$ Å. See Fig. 1. **Examples:** AlN, BeO, CdS, CdSe, CuH, InN, InSb, γ MnS, ZnO, ZnS (würtzite), ZnSe |
| $hP5$ | $Al_3Ni_2$ | $P\bar{3}m1$ | One aluminum(1) atom at 0,0,0; two aluminum(2) at 1/3,2/3,$z$; 2/3,1/3, $\bar{z}$; with $z = 0.648$. Two nickel atoms as Al(2) with $z = 0.149$. For $Al_3Ni_2$, $a = 4.04$ Å, $c = 4.90$ Å. **Examples:** $Al_3Pd_2$, $Al_3Ru_2$, $Ga_3Ni_2$, $In_3Pt_2$ |
| | $La_2O_3$ | $P\bar{3}m1$ | Type A. One oxygen(1) atom at 0,0,0; two oxygen(2) atoms at positions of Al(2) in $Al_3Ni_2$ $hP5$, with $z = 0.63$, La similarly with $z = 0.235$. For $La_2O_3$, $a = 3.94$ Å, $c = 6.13$ Å. **Examples:** $Ce_2O_3$, $N_3Th_2$, $N_3U_2$, $O_3Pu_2$ |
| $hP6$ | $CaCu_5$ | $P6/mmm$ | One calcium atom at 0,0,0; two copper(1) atoms at 1/3,2/3,0; 2/3,1/3,0; three copper(2) at 1/2,0,1/2; 0,1/2,1/2; 1/2,1/2,1/2. For $CaCu_5$, $a = 5.09$ Å, $c = 4.09$ Å. **Examples:** $Ag_5Ba$, $Be_5Sc$, $CeNi_5$, $Cu_5Y$, $LaNi_5$, $Pt_5Sr$ |
| | CoSn | $P6/mmm$ | For CoSn, $a = 5.28$ Å, $c = 4.26$ Å. **Examples:** FeGe, FeSn, InNi, PtTl |
| | $CaIn_2$ | $P6_3/mmc$ | Two calcium atoms at 0,0,1/4; 0,0,3/4; four indium atoms at 1/3,2/3,$z$; 2/3,1/3,1/2 + $z$; 2/3,1/3,$\bar{z}$; 1/3,2/3,1/2 − $z$; with $z = 0.455$. For CaIn1/2, $a = 4.90$ Å, $c = 7.75$ Å. **Examples:** $EuIn_2$, $Ga_2Y$, $In_2Sr$, $SrTl_2$ |
| | $InNi_2$ | $P6_3/mmc$ | Two nickel atoms at 0,0,0 and 0,0,1/2; two nickel atoms at 1/3,2/3,3/4 and 2/3,1/3,1/4; two indium atoms at 1/3,2/3,1/4 and 2/3,1/3,3/4. For $InNi_2$, $a = 4.18$ Å and $c = 5.13$ Å. See Fig. 1. **Examples:** $AlZr_2$, CoNiSn, $Cu_2In$, $In_2Bi$, $Ni_2In$, $Ni_{1.4}Sn$, $Ti_2Sn$ |
| $hP8$ | H-$AlCCr_2$ | $P6_3/mmc$ | Two aluminum atoms at 1/3,2/3,3/4; 2/3,1/3,1/4; two carbon atoms at 0,0,0; 0,0,1/2; four chromium atoms at 1/3,2/3,$\bar{z}$; 2/3,1/3,$z$; 2/3,1/3,1/2 + $z$; 1/3,2/3,1/2 − $z$; with $z = 0.086$. For $AlCCr_2$, $a = 2.86$ Å, $c = 12.82$ Å. **Examples:** $AlCNb_2$, $CCdTi_2$, $CGeV_2$, $InNTi_2$ |
| | $AsNa_3$ | $P6_3/mmc$ | For $AsNa_3$, $a = 5.10$ Å, $c = 9.00$ Å. **Examples:** $AuMg_3$, $K_3P$, $Li_3Sb$, $Mg_3Pt$ |

(continued)

**Table 5 (continued)**

| Pearson symbol | Prototype | Space group | Unit-cell description |
|---|---|---|---|
| $hP8$ .......... | Ni$_3$Sn | $P6_3/mmc$ | Two tin atoms at $1/3,2/3,1/4$ and $2/3,1/3,3/4$; six nickel atoms at $x,2x,1/4$; $2\bar{x},\bar{x},1/4$; $x,\bar{x},1/4$; $\bar{x},2\bar{x},3/4$; $2x,x,3/4$; and $\bar{x},x,3/4$ (with $x = 0.833$). For Ni$_3$Sn, $a = 5.29$ Å and $c = 4.24$ Å. See Fig. 1. **Examples:** AlTi$_{2-3}$, Cd$_3$Mg, CdMg$_3$, Co$_3$Mo, Co$_3$W, $\beta''$ Fe$_3$Sn, $\gamma$ Ni$_3$In, Ni$_3$Sn, Ti$_4$Pb |
| $hP9$ .......... | Fe$_2$P | $P\bar{6}2m$ | Three iron atoms at $x,0,0$; $0,x,0$ and $\bar{x},\bar{x},0$ (with $x = 0.256$); three iron atoms at $x,0,1/2$; $0,x,1/2$; and $\bar{x},\bar{x},1/2$ (with $x = 0.594$); three phosphorus atoms at $0,0,1/2$; $1/3,2/3,0$; and $2/3,1/3,0$. For Fe$_2$P, $a = 5.93$ Å and $c = 3.45$ Å. See Fig. 1 **Examples:** Fe$_2$P, Mn$_2$P, Ni$_2$P, Pt$_2$Si (high temperature) |
| $hP12$ ........ | MgZn$_2$ | $P6_3/mmc$ | Four magnesium atoms at $1/3,2/3,z$; $2/3,1/3,\bar{z}$; $2/3,1/3,1/2 + z$; and $1/3,2/3,1/2 - z$ (with $z = 0.062$); two zinc atoms at $0,0,0$ and $0,0,1/2$; six zinc atoms at $x,2x,1/4$; $2\bar{x},\bar{x},1/4$; $x,\bar{x},1/4$; $\bar{x},2\bar{x},3/4$; $2x,x,3/4$; and $\bar{x},x,3/4$ (with $x = 0.83$). For MgZn$_2$, $a = 5.18$ Å and $c = 8.52$ Å. See Fig. 1. **Examples:** Al$_2$Zr, Be$_2$Mo, CaCd$_2$, CaMg$_2$, CdCu$_2$, Fe$_2$Mo, FeSiW, Fe$_2$Ta, Fe$_2$Ti, Fe$_2$W, MgZn$_2$, TiZn$_2$ |
| $hP16$ ......... | Mn$_5$Si$_3$ | $P6_3/mcm$ | For Mn$_5$Si$_3$, $a = 6.91$ Å, $c = 4.81$ Å. **Examples:** Al$_3$Zr$_5$, Dy$_5$Ge$_3$, Ga$_3$Y$_5$, P$_3$Ti$_5$, Sn$_3$Zr$_5$ |
|  | Ni$_3$Ti | $P6_3/mmc$ | Four titanium atoms at $0,0,0$; $0,0,1/2$; $1/3,2/3,1/4$; and $2/3,1/3,3/4$; 12 nickel atoms at $1/2,0,0$; $0,1/2,0$; $1/2,1/2,0$; $1/2,0,1/2$; $0,1/2,1/2$; $1/2,1/2,1/2$; $x,2x,1/4$; $2\bar{x},\bar{x},1/4$; $x,\bar{x},1/4$; $\bar{x},2\bar{x},3/4$; $2x,x,3/4$; and $\bar{x},x,3/4$ (with $x = 0.833$). For Ni$_3$Ti, $a = 2.55$ Å and $c = 8.31$ Å. **Examples:** Co$_3$Ti, Ni$_3$Ti, Pd$_3$Ti |
| $hP20$ ......... | Fe$_3$Th$_7$ | $P6_3/mc$ | For Fe$_3$Th$_7$, $a = 9.85$ Å, $c = 6.15$ Å. **Examples:** B$_3$Re$_7$, C$_3$Fe$_7$, Co$_3$Th$_7$, Ru$_3$Th$_7$ |
| $hP24$ ......... | HoH$_3$ | $P\bar{3}c1$ | For HoH$_3$, $a = 6.31$ Å, $c = 6.56$ Å. **Examples:** DyH$_3$, LuH$_3$, YH$_3$ |
|  | MgNi$_2$ | $P6_3/mmc$ | For MgNi$_2$, $a = 4.82$ Å, $c = 15.80$ Å. **Examples:** CdCu$_2$, Cr$_2$Hf, Fe$_2$Sc, NbZn$_2$ |
| $hR1$ .......... | Hg | $R\bar{3}m$ | One atom per cell, at $0,0,0$. For Hg, $a = 3.005$ Å and $\alpha = 70°$ 32'. A hexagonal cell, where $a = 3.47$ Å and $c = 6.74$ Å, has three atoms per cell, at $0,0,0$; $1/3,2/3,2/3$; and $2/3,1/3,1/3$. **Example:** Hg |
| $hR2$ .......... | As | $R\bar{3}m$ | In the cell based on hexagonal axes, there are six atoms, at $0,0,z$; $1/3,2/3,2/3 + z$; $2/3,1/3,1/3 + z$; $0,0,\bar{z}$; $1/3,2/3,2/3 - z$; and $2/3,1/3,1/3 - z$; where $z = 0.226$, $a = 3.76$ Å and $c = 10.55$ Å for $\alpha$-As. The cell based on rhombohedral axes contains two atoms, at $x,x,x$ and $\bar{x},\bar{x},\bar{x}$; where $x = 0.276$, $a = 4.13$ Å and $\alpha = 54°$ 8' for $\alpha$-As. **Examples:** $\alpha$-As, Bi, Sb |
| $hR3$ .......... | Sm | $R\bar{3}m$ | In a cell based on a hexagonal axis, there are nine atoms per cell, at $0,0,0$; $1/3,2/3^32/3$; $2/3,1/3,1/3$; $0,0,z$; $0,0,\bar{z}$; $1/3,2/3,2/3 + z$; $1/3,2/3,2/3 - z$; $2/3,1/3,1/3 + z$; and $2/3,1/3,1/3 - z$. For $\alpha$-Sm, $a = 3.621$ Å, $c = 26.25$ Å and $z = 2/9$. The cell based on rhombohedral axes contains three atoms per cell, at $0,0,0$; $x,x,x$; and $\bar{x},\bar{x},\bar{x}$; with $a = 9.00$ Å, $\alpha = 23°$ 19' and $x = 2/9$. **Examples:** $\alpha$-Sm, Ce-Y, $\delta$ Nd-Tm, $\delta$ Pr-Y |
| $hR5$ .......... | Bi$_2$STe$_2$ | $R\bar{3}m$ | One sulfur atom at $0,0,0$; two bismuth atoms at $x,x,x$; $\bar{x},\bar{x},\bar{x}$ with $x = 0.392$. Tellurium atoms similarly with $x = 0.788$. For Bi$_2$STe$_2$, $a = 10.33$ Å, $\alpha = 24°$ 10'. **Examples:** Bi$_2$Se$_3$ Bi$_2$SeTe$_2$, Sb$_2$Te$_3$ |
| $hR10$ .......... | $\alpha$ Al$_2$O$_3$ | $R\bar{3}c$ | Ten atoms per unit rhombohedral cell or 30 atoms per unit hexagonal cell. There are also other structures of Al$_2$O$_3$ (alumina). **Examples:** $\alpha$ Al$_2$O$_3$, $\alpha$ Fe$_2$O$_3$, Rh$_2$O$_3$, Ti$_2$O$_3$, V$_2$O$_3$ (high temperature) |
| $hR13$ .......... | Fe$_7$W$_6$ | $R\bar{3}m$ | $\mu$-phase. For Fe$_7$W$_6$, $a = 9.04$ Å, $\alpha = 30°$ 30'. **Examples:** Co$_7$Mo$_6$, Fe$_7$Mo$_6$, (Fe,Si)$_7$Re$_6$ |
| $hR19$ .......... | Th$_2$Zn$_{17}$ | $R\bar{3}m$ | For Th$_2$Zn$_{17}$ in the hexagonal cell containing 57 atoms, $a = 9.03$ Å, $c = 13.20$ Å. **Examples:** Ba$_2$Mg$_{17}$, Ce$_2$Fe$_{17}$, U$_2$Zn$_{17}$ |
| $hR26$ .......... | Al$_8$Cr$_5$ | $R3m$ | Rhombohedrally distorted $\gamma$ brass: For Al$_8$Cr$_5$, $a = 7.80$ Å, $\alpha = 109°$. **Examples:** Fe-Ga, Ga-Mn |
| $hR53$ .......... | $R$ Co-Cr-Mo | $R\bar{3}$ | $R$-phase. For $R$ Co-Cr-Mo, $a = 9.01$ Å, $\alpha = 74°$ 27'. See $\alpha$-Mn $cI58$ type, above; and Ref 6-8. **Examples:** $R$-(Co-Cr-Mo), Co$_3$Cr$_3$Si$_2$, $R$-(Co-Mn-,Mo), $R$-Fe$_{52}$Mn$_{16}$Mo$_{32}$, Fe$_2$SiV$_2$, Mn$_{78}$Mo$_3$Si$_{19}$, Mn$_6$Si, Ni$_3$SrV$_6$ |
| $tP4$ ($tP2$) ....... | AuCu | $P4/mmm$ | Two gold atoms at $0,0,0$ and $1/2,1/2,0$; two copper atoms at $0,1/2,1/2$ and $1/2,0,1/2$. For AuCu, $a = 3.97$ Å, $c = 3.67$ Å. A smaller cell can also be taken with $a/\sqrt{2}$ and Au and Cu atoms at $0,0,0$ and $1/2,1/2,1/2$, respectively. See Fig. 1. **Examples:** AgTi, AlTi, AuCu I, $\theta$ CdPt, FePd, $\gamma''$ FePt, $\theta$ MnNi, NiPt |
|  | CuTi$_3$ | $P4/mmm$ | One copper atom at $0,0,0$; one titanium(1) atom at $1/2,1/2,0$; two titanium(2) atoms at $0,1/2,1/2$; $1/2,0,1/2$. For CuTi$_3$, $a = 4.16$ Å, $c = 3.59$ Å. **Examples:** AgZr$_3$, BaBi$_3$, DyIn$_3$, Pc$_3$Tl |
|  | $\gamma$ CuTi | $P4/nmm$ | Two copper atoms at $0,1/2,z$ and $1/2,0,\bar{z}$ (with $z = 0.10$); two titanium atoms at $0,1/2,z$ and $1/2,0,\bar{z}$ (with $z = 0.65$). For $\gamma$ CuTi, $a = 3.12$ Å and $c = 5.92$ Å. See Fig. 1. **Examples:** AgZr, AuTi (low temperature), $\gamma$ CuTi |
|  | PbO | $P4/nmm$ | Two oxygen atoms at $0,0,0$ and $1/2,1/2,0$; two lead atoms at $0,1/2,z$ and $1/2,0,\bar{z}$ (with $z = 0.237$). For PbO, $a = 3.97$ Å, $c = 5.02$ Å. See Fig. 1. **Examples:** FeS, $\beta$ FeTe$_{0.9}$, PbO, SnO |
| $tP6$ ........... | Cu$_2$Sb (GeSeZr) | $P4/nmm$ | Two copper atoms at $0,0,0$; $1/2,1/2,0$; two at $0,1/2,z$ and $1/2,0,\bar{z}$ (with $z = 0.27$); two antimony atoms at $0,1/2,z$ and $1/2,0,\bar{z}$ (with $z = 0.70$). Thus, ordered ternary phases also take the structure. For Cu$_2$Sb, $a = 3.99$ Å and $c = 6.09$ Å. See Fig. 1 **Examples:** AlNaSi$_4$, AsCr$_2$, AsMn$_2$, Bi$_2$U, Cu$_2$Sb, Mn$_2$Sb, Pu$_2$Sb, Sb$_2$U |
|  | TiO$_2$ | $P4_2/mnm$ | Rutile. Two titanium atoms at $0,0,0$ and $1/2,1/2,1/2$; four oxygen atoms at $x,x,0$; $\bar{x},\bar{x},0$; $1/2 + x, 1/2 - x, 1/2$; and $1/2 - x, 1/2 + x, 1/2$. For TiO$_2$, $x = 0.3056$, $a = 4.59$ Å and $c = 2.96$ Å. See Fig. 1. **Examples:** CrO$_2$, $\beta$ MnO$_2$, PbO$_2$, SnO$_2$, TaO$_2$, TeO$_2$, TiO$_2$ (rutile), VO$_2$ (high temperature), WO$_2$ |

(continued)

**Table 5 (continued)**

| Pearson symbol | Prototype | Space group | Unit-cell description |
|---|---|---|---|
| $tP10$ ......... $Si_2U_3$ | | $P4/mbm$ | For $Si_2U_3$, $a = 7.33$ Å, $c = 3.90$ Å. **Examples:** $Al_2Th_3$, $B_2V_3$, $Be_2Ta_3$, $Ga_2Ta_3$, $Si_2Zr_3$ |
| $tP16$ ......... $CoGa_3$ | | $P\bar{4}n2$ | For $CoGa_3$, $a = 6.26$ Å, $c = 6.48$ Å. **Examples:** $FeGa_3$, $Ga_3Os$, $In_3Ir$, $In_3Rh$ |
| $tP20$ ......... $B_4Th$ | | $P4/mbm$ | For $B_4Th$, $a = 7.26$ Å, $c = 4.11$ Å. **Examples:** $B_4Ce$, $B_4Ho$, $B_4Pu$, $B_4U$, $B_4Y$ |
| $tP30$ ......... $CrFe$ ($\sigma$-phase) | | $P4_2/mnm$ | This is a complex structure formed by transition-metal alloys in which the metal atoms occupy five independent site-sets. For CrFe, $a = 8.80$ Å, $c = 4.54$ Å. **Examples:** $AlNb_2$, $CoCr$, $Co_2Mo_3$, $Cr_2Os$, $Cr_2Ru$, $FeMo$, $FeV$, $MoTc_3$, $Ni_2V_3$, $Re_3Ta_2$ |
| $tI2$ ......... In | | $I4/mmm$ | Two atoms per cell, at $0,0,0$ and $1/2,1/2,1/2$. It is conventional also to use the cell that has four atoms, at $0,0,0$; $0,1/2,1/2$; $1/2,0,1/2$; and $1/2,1/2,0$. For In, $a = b = 4.60$ Å and $c = 4.95$ Å. At room temperature, the unit cell resembles that of Cu, which is shown in Fig. 1. **Examples:** $\delta$ $GaNi_2$, In, $InPd_3$ |
| | Pa | $I4/mmm$ | Atom positions as for In $tI2$, but $c/a < 1$. For Pa, $a = 3.93$ Å, $c = 3.24$ Å |
| $tI4$-$x$ ......... Fe-C | | $I4/mmm$ | Martensite. In the unit cell there are iron atoms at $0,0,0$ and $1/2,1/2,1/2$; the carbon atoms are random, at $1/2,1/2,0$ and/or $0,0,1/2$, to provide two iron atoms and up to 0.12 carbon atoms per cell. **Examples:** Fe-C martensite, $\alpha'$ Fe-N martensite |
| $tI4$ ......... Sn | | $I4_1/amd$ | White Sn. Four atoms per cell, at $0,0,0$; $1/2,1/2,1/2$; $0,1/2,1/4$; and $1/2,0,3/4$. For $\beta$-Sn, $a = 5.83$ Å and $c = 3.18$ Å. See Fig. 1. **Examples:** AlSb II (high pressure). InSb II (high pressure), $\beta$-Sn (white) |
| $tI6$ ......... $CaC_2$ | | $I4/mmm$ | Two calcium atoms at $0,0,0$; $1/2,1/2,1/2$. Four carbon atoms at $0,0,z$; $0,0,\bar{z}$; $1/2,1/2,1/2 + z$; $1/2,1/2,1/2 - z$ with $z = 0.407$, form dumbbells along [001]. For $CaC_2$, $a = 3.88$ Å, $c = 6.37$ Å. **Examples:** $BaC_2$, $ErC_2$, $NDC_2$, $UC_2$, $SrO_2$ |
| | $MoSi_2$ | $I4/mmm$ | Two molybdenum atoms at $0,0,0$ and $1/2,1/2,1/2$; four silicon atoms at $0,0,z$; $0,0,\bar{z}$; $1/2,1/2,1/2 + z$; and $1/2,1/2,1/2 - z$ (with $z = 0.333$). For $MoSi_2$, $a = 3.20$ Å and $c = 7.86$ Å. See Fig. 1. **Examples:** $AgZr_2$, $AlCr_2$, $Au_2Be$, $Au_2Mn$, $CuTi_2$, $Hg_2Mg$, $MoSi_2$, $Ni_2Ta$, $Si_2W$ |
| $tI8$ ......... $Al_3Ti$ | | $I4/mmm$ | Two titanium atoms at $0,0,0$; $1/2,1/2,1/2$. Two aluminum(1) atoms at $0,0,1/2$; $1/2,1/2,0$. Four aluminum(2) atoms at $0,1/2,1/4$; $1/2,0,1/4$; $1/2,0,3/4$; $0,1/2,3/4$. For $Al_3Ti$, $a = 3.85$ Å, $c = 8.60$ Å. **Examples:** $Al_3Nb$, $Ga_3Ti$, $Ni_3Ta$, $Pd_3V$, $Pt_3V$ |
| $tI10$ ......... $MoNi_4$ | | $I4/m$ | For $MoNi_4$, $a = 5.73$ Å, $c = 3.57$ Å. **Examples:** $Au_4Cr$, $Au_4Ti$, $Ni_4W$ |
| $tI10$ ......... $Al_4Ba$ ($Cu_2Si_2Th$) | | $I4/mmm$ | Two barium atoms at $0,0,0$; $1/2,1/2,1/2$. Four aluminum(1) atoms at $0,1/2,1/4$; $1/2,0,1/4$; $1/2,0,3/4$; $0,1/2,3/4$. Four aluminum(2) atoms at $0,0,z$; $0,0,\bar{z}$; $1/2,1/2,1/2 + z$; $1/2,1/2,1/2 - z$, with $z = 0.380$. The three atom-sites allow the formation of ordered ternary phases. For $Al_4Ba$, $a = 4.57$ Å, $c = 11.25$ Å. **Examples:** $BaGa_4$, $ThZn_4$, $B_2Co_2Nd$, $Au_2GdSi_2$. N.B. There are more recognized phases with this structure type than with any other structure of metallurgical interest. |
| $tI12$ ......... $Al_2Cu$ | | $I4/mcm$ | Four copper atoms at $0,0,1/4$; $1/2,1/2,3/4$; $0,0,3/4$; and $1/2,1/2,1/4$; eight aluminum atoms at $x,1/2 + x,0$; $\bar{x},1/2 - x,0$; $1/2 + x,\bar{x},0$; $1/2 - x,x,0$; $1/2 + x,x,1/2$; $1/2 - x,\bar{x},1/2$; $x,1/2 - x,1/2$; and $\bar{x},1/2 + x,1/2$ (with $x = 0.158$). For $Al_2Cu$, $a = 6.07$ Å and $c = 4.87$ Å. **Examples:** $Co_2B$, $Cr_2B$, $\theta$ $CuAl_2$, $Fe_2B$, $FeSn_2$, $Mo_2B$, $Ni_2B$, $W_2B$ |
| | $Si_2Th$ | $I4_1/amd$ | For $Si_2Th$, $a = 4.14$ Å, $c = 14.38$ Å. **Examples:** $CeGe_2$, $DySi_{1.4}$, $Ga_2Th$, $LaSi_2$ |
| $tI16$ ......... $CuFeS_2$ | | $I\bar{4}2d$ | Chalcopyrite. For $CuFeS_2$, $a = 5.25$ Å, $c = 10.32$ Å. **Examples:** $AgAlS_2$, $AlCuSe_2$, $GeP_2Zn$, $CuS_2Tl$ |
| | $Al_3Zr$ | $I4/mmm$ | For $Al_3Zr$, $a = 4.01$ Å, $c = 17.32$ Å. **Examples:** $Al_3Hf$, $Ga_3Zr$ |
| | $SiU_3$ | $I4/mcm$ | For $SiU_3$, $a = 6.03$ Å, $= 8.70$ Å. **Examples:** $Ir_3Si$, $Pt_3Si$ |
| | SeTl | $I4/mcm$ | For SeTl, $a = 8.04$ Å, $c = 7.01$ Å. **Examples:** InTe, STl |
| $tI18$ ......... $Te_4Ti_5$ | | $I4/m$ | For $Te_4Ti_5$, $a = 10.16$ Å, $c = 3.77$ Å. **Examples:** $Nb_5Sb_4$, $Nb_5Te_4$, $Sb_4Ta_5$ |
| $tI26$ ......... $Mn_{12}Th$ | | $I4/mmm$ | For $Mn_{12}Th$, $a = 8.74$ Å, $c = 4.95$ Å. **Examples:** $AgBe_{12}$, $Al_8CeMn_4$, $Mg_{12}Nd$, $Mn_{12}Y$ |
| $tI28$ ......... $MnU_6$ | | $I4/mcm$ | For $MnU_6$, $a = 10.29$ Å, $c = 5.24$ Å. **Examples:** $CoU_6$, $FePu_6$, $NiU_6$ |
| $tI32$ ......... $Ni_3P$ | | $I\bar{4}$ | For $Ni_3P$, $a = 8.95$ Å, $c = 4.39$ Å. **Examples:** $Cr_3P$, $Fe_3P$, $Mo_3P$ |
| | $B_3Cr_5$ | $I4/mcm$ | For $B_3Cr_5$, $a = 5.46$ Å, $c = 10.64$ Å. **Examples:** $Ag_3Ca_5$, $B_2Co_5P$, $Ba_5Pb_3$, $Si_3Ta_5$ |
| | $Si_3W_5$ | $I4/mcm$ | For $Si_3W_5$, $a = 9.61$ Å, $c = 4.96$ Å. **Examples:** $CeCo_3Pu_4$, $Cr_5Ge_3$, $Ga_3Ti_5$, $Re_5Si_3$ |
| $tI48$ ......... $BaCd_{11}$ | | $I4_1/amd$ | For $BaCd_{11}$, $a = 12.02$ Å, $c = 7.74$ Å. **Examples:** $Cd_{11}Eu$, $LaZn_{11}$, $PrZn_{11}$ |
| $tI64$ ......... NaPb | | $I4_1/acd$ | For NaPb, $a = 10.58$ Å, $c = 17.75$ Å. **Examples:** CsPb, KSn, PbRb, RbSn |
| $oP4$ ......... AuCd | | $Pmma$ | Two gold atoms at $1/4,1/2,z$ and $3/4,1/2,\bar{z}$ (with $z = 0.812$); two cadmium atoms at $1/4,0,z$ and $3/4,0,\bar{z}$ (with $z = 0.313$). For $\beta'$ AuCd, $a = 4.76$ Å, $b = 3.15$ Å and $c = 4.86$ Å. See Fig. 1. **Examples:** $\beta''$ AgCd, $\beta'$ AuCd, CdMg, IrMo, IrW |
| $oP6$ ......... $FeS_2$ | | $Pnnm$ | Marcasite. Two iron atoms at $0,0,0$ and $1/2,1/2,1/2$; four sulfur atoms at $x,y,0$; $\bar{x}\bar{y},0$; $1/2 + x,1/2 - y,1/2$; and $1/2 - x,1/2 + y,1/2$ (with $x = 0.200$ and $y = 0.378$). For $FeS_2$ (marcasite), $a = 4.44$ Å, $b = 5.42$ Å and $c = 3.39$ Å. See Fig. 1. **Examples:** $\gamma$ $CrSb_2$, $FeP_2$, $FeS_2$ (marcasite), $FeSe_2$, $FeTe_2$, $NiSb_2$ |

(continued)

**Table 5   (continued)**

| Pearson symbol | Prototype | Space group | Unit-cell description |
|---|---|---|---|
| $oP8$ .......... | $\beta$ Cu$_3$Ti | $Pmmn$ | For Cu$_3$Ti, $a = 5.16$ Å, $b = 4.35$ Å, $c = 4.53$ Å. **Examples:** Au$_3$Hf, MoNi$_3$, Ni$_3$Sb, Pt$_3$Ta |
| | FeB | $Pnma$ | For FeB, $a = 5.51$ Å, $b = 2.95$ Å, $c = 4.06$ Å. **Examples:** CoB, MnB, DyNi, LuPt, SiTi |
| | GeS | $Pnma$ | For GeS, $a = 10.44$ Å, $b = 3.65$ Å, $c = 4.30$ Å. **Examples:** GeSe, PbSe II, SnS, SnTe II |
| | MnP | $Pnma$ | Four manganese atoms at $x,\frac{1}{4},z$; $\bar{x},\frac{3}{4},\bar{z}$; $\frac{1}{2} - x,\frac{3}{4},\frac{1}{2} + z$ and $\frac{1}{2} + x,\frac{1}{4},\frac{1}{2} - z$ (with $x = 0.20$ and $z = 0.005$); four phosphorus atoms at $x,\frac{1}{4},z$; $\bar{x},\frac{3}{4},\bar{z}$; $\frac{1}{2} - x,\frac{3}{4},\frac{1}{2} + z$; and $\frac{1}{2} + x,\frac{1}{4},\frac{1}{2} - z$ (with $x = 0.57$ and $z = 0.19$). For MnP, $a = 5.26$ Å, $b = 3.17$ Å, $c = 5.92$ Å. **Examples:** CoP, CrP, FeP, MnP, WP |
| $oP12$ .......... | PbCl$_2$ (NiSiTi) | $Pnma$ | The atoms occupy three independent site-sets, so that ordered ternary phases occur with this structure. For AlPd$_2$, $a = 5.41$ Å, $b = 4.06$ Å, $c = 7.77$ Å. **Examples:** AlPd$_2$, As$_2$Zr, CoMnSi, CoGeV, NiSiZr |
| $oP16$ .......... | AlEr | $Pmma$ | For AlEr, $a = 5.57$ Å, $b = 5.80$ Å, $c = 11.27$ Å. **Examples:** AlDy, AlHo, AlTb |
| | Ge$_3$Rh$_5$ | $Pbam$ | For Ge$_3$Rh$_5$, $a = 5.42$ Å, $b = 10.32$ Å, $c = 3.96$ Å. **Examples:** Al$_3$Pd$_5$, Ge$_3$Rh$_5$, In$_3$Pd$_5$, Rh$_5$Si$_3$ |
| | Fe$_3$C | $Pnma$ | Cementite. For Fe$_3$C, $a = 5.09$ Å, $b = 6.74$ Å, $c = 4.52$ Å. **Examples:** Co$_3$B, Co$_3$C, Ni$_3$C, Pd$_3$P |
| $oP20$ .......... | Sb$_2$S$_3$ | $Pbnm$ | For Sb$_2$S$_3$, $a = 11.25$ Å, $b = 11.33$ Å, $c = 3.84$ Å. **Examples:** Bi$_2$S$_3$, Dy$_2$Se$_3$, Np$_2$S$_3$, U$_2$Se$_3$ |
| $oP56$ .......... | $P$-Cr$_{18}$Mo$_{42}$Ni$_{40}$ | $Pbnm$ | $P$-phase. For Cr$_{18}$Mo$_{42}$Ni$_{40}$, $a = 9.07$ Å, $b = 16.98$ Å, $c = 4.75$ Å. See $\alpha$-Mn $cI58$ type, above, and Ref 6-8. **Examples:** $P$-Cr$_{18}$Mo$_{42}$Ni$_{40}$, $P$-(Mo-Fe-Ni), $P$-(Mo-Mn-Co) |
| $oC4$ .......... | $\alpha$-U | $Cmcm$ | Four atoms at $0,y,\frac{1}{4}$; $0,\bar{y},\frac{3}{4}$; $\frac{1}{2},\frac{1}{2} + y,\frac{1}{4}$; and $\frac{1}{2},\frac{1}{2} - y,\frac{3}{4}$. For $\alpha$-U, $a = 2.85$ Å, $b = 5.87$ Å, $c = 4.95$ Å, and $y = 0.1024$ |
| $oC8$ .......... | CrB | $Cmcm$ | Four chromium atoms at $0,y,\frac{1}{4}$; $0,\bar{y},\frac{3}{4}$; $\frac{1}{2},\frac{1}{2} + y,\frac{1}{4}$; $\frac{1}{2},\frac{1}{2} - y,\frac{3}{4}$; with $y = 0.146$. Four boron atoms at similar positions with $y = 0.440$. For CrB, $a = 2.97$ Å, $b = 7.86$ Å, $c = 2.93$ Å. **Examples:** AgCa, NiB, CeNi, HfNi, NdRh, RuTh |
| | Ga | $Cmca$ | Eight atoms at $0,y,z$; $0,\bar{y},\bar{z}$; $\frac{1}{2},y,\frac{1}{2} - z$; $\frac{1}{2},\bar{y},\frac{1}{2} + z$; $\frac{1}{2},\frac{1}{2} + y,z$; $\frac{1}{2},\frac{1}{2} - y,\bar{z}$; $0,\frac{1}{2} + y,\frac{1}{2} - z$; and $0,\frac{1}{2} - y,\frac{1}{2} + z$. For Ga, $a = 2.90$ Å, $b = 8.13$ Å, $c = 3.17$ Å, $y = 0.1549$, and $z = 0.081$ |
| $oC12$ .......... | Si$_2$Zr | $Cmcm$ | All atoms at the same sites as for BCr $oC8$ with Zr: $y = 0.102$; Si(1): $y = 0.752$; Si(2): $y = 0.447$. For Si$_2$Zr, $a = 3.72$ Å, $b = 14.68$ Å, $c = 3.68$ Å. **Examples:** Ge$_2$Hf, Ge$_2$U, Si$_2$Ti |
| $oC28$ .......... | Al$_6$Mn | $Cmcm$ | For Al$_6$Mn, $a = 7.55$ Å, $b = 6.50$ Å, $c = 8.87$ Å. **Examples:** Al$_6$Fe, Al$_6$Re, Al$_6$Tc |
| $oF24$ .......... | Si$_2$Ti | $Fddd$ | For Si$_2$Ti, $a = 8.25$ Å, $b = 4.78$ Å, $c = 8.54$ Å. **Examples:** Al$_2$Ru, Ga$_2$Ru, Ge$_2$Ti, Sn$_2$Zr |
| $oI6$ .......... | MoPt$_2$ | $Immm$ | Two molybdenum atoms at $0,0,0$; $\frac{1}{2},\frac{1}{2},\frac{1}{2}$. Four platinum atoms at $0,y,0$; $0,\bar{y},0$; $\frac{1}{2},\frac{1}{2} + y,\frac{1}{2}$; $\frac{1}{2},\frac{1}{2} - y,\frac{1}{2}$, with $y = 0.353$. For MoPt$_2$, $a = 2.75$ Å, $b = 8.24$ Å, $c = 3.92$ Å. **Examples:** NbPd$_2$, Ni$_2$V, Pd$_2$V, Pt$_2$V |
| $oI12$ .......... | CeCu$_2$ | $Imma$ | For CeCu$_2$, $a = 4.43$ Å, $b = 7.06$ Å. $c = 7.48$ Å. **Examples:** Ag$_2$Ca, Cu$_2$Dy, Cu$_2$Pr, Hg$_2$K, SrZn$_2$ |
| | GdSi$_2$ (GdSi$_{1.4}$) | $Imma$ | Atoms at $0,\frac{1}{4},z$; $0,\frac{3}{4},\bar{z}$; $\frac{1}{2},\frac{3}{4},\frac{1}{2} + z$; $\frac{1}{2},\frac{1}{4},\frac{1}{2} - z$ with Gd: $z = 0.375$; Si(1): $z = 0.786$; Si(2): $z = 0.964$. For GdSi$_{14}$, $a = 4.09$ Å, $b = 4.01$ Å, $c = 13.44$ Å. **Examples:** CeGe$_2$, DySi$_{1.4}$, HoSi$_2$, PrSi$_{1.4}$ |
| $oI14$ .......... | B$_4$Ta$_3$ | $Immm$ | For B$_4$Ta$_3$, $a = 3.28$ Å, $b = 13.38$ Å, $c = 3.13$ Å. **Examples:** B$_4$Cr$_3$, B$_4$Cr$_2$Ni, B$_4$Mn$_3$, B$_4$V$_3$ |
| $oI20$ .......... | Al$_4$U | $Imma$ | For Al$_4$U, $a = 4.41$ Å, $b = 6.27$ Å, $c = 13.71$ Å. **Examples:** Al$_4$Np, Al$_4$Pu |
| $mP8$ .......... | Se$_3$Zr | $P2_1/m$ | For Se$_3$Zr, $a = 5.42$ Å, $b = 3.76$ Å, $c = 19.0$ Å, $\beta = 97.6°$. **Examples:** HfS$_3$, HfSe$_3$, TiS$_3$ |
| $mP12$ .......... | CoSb$_2$ | $P2_1/c$ | For CoSb$_2$, $a = 6.52$ Å, $b = 6.38$ Å, $c = 6.55$ Å. $\beta = 118.2°$. As the atoms occupy three different site-sets, ordered ternary phases with the structure occur. **Examples:** As$_2$Co, As$_2$Ir, IrP$_2$, RhSb$_2$, AS$_{1.1}$FeS$_{0.9}$, AsOsS, AsOsTe, RuSbTe |
| $mP16$ .......... | AsLi | $P2_1/c$ | For AsLi, $a = 5.79$ Å, $b = 5.24$ Å, $c = 10.70$ Å, $\beta = 117.4°$ **Examples:** KSb, NaSb |
| $mC12$ .......... | As$_2$Nb | $C2$ | For As$_2$Nb, $a = 9.36$ Å, $b = 3.38$ Å, $c = 7.79$ Å, $\beta = 119.5°$. **Examples:** As$_2$Mo, NbSb$_2$, Sb$_2$Ta |
| $mC14$ .......... | Cr$_3$S$_4$ | $C2/m$ | For Cr$_3$S$_4$, $a = 5.97$ Å, $b = 3.43$ Å, $c = 11.36$ Å, $\beta = 91.2°$. **Examples:** Cr$_3$Se$_4$, Fe$_3$Se$_4$, CoCr$_2$Se$_4$ |
| $mC28$ .......... | CoZn$_{13}$ | $C2/m$ | For CoZn$_{13}$, $a = 13.31$ Å, $b = 7.54$ Å, $c = 4.99$ Å, $\beta = 126.8°$. **Examples:** CrZn$_{13}$, FeZn$_{13}$ |
| | Mn$_5$C$_2$ | $C2/c$ | For Mn$_5$C$_2$, $a = 5.09$ Å, $b = 4.57$ Å, $c = 11.66$ Å, $\beta = 97.7°$. **Examples:** Pd$_5$B$_2$, Fe$_5$C$_2$ |
| $aP8$ .......... | HgK | $P\bar{1}$ | For HgK, $a = 6.59$ Å, $b = 6.76$ Å, $c = 7.06$ Å, $\alpha = 106°$, $\beta = 102°$, $\gamma = 93°$ |
| $aP12$ .......... | ReSe$_2$ | $P\bar{1}$ | For ReSe$_2$, $a = 6.73$ Å, $b = 6.61$ Å, $c = 6.72$ Å, $\alpha = 119°$, $\beta = 92°$, $\gamma = 105°$ |

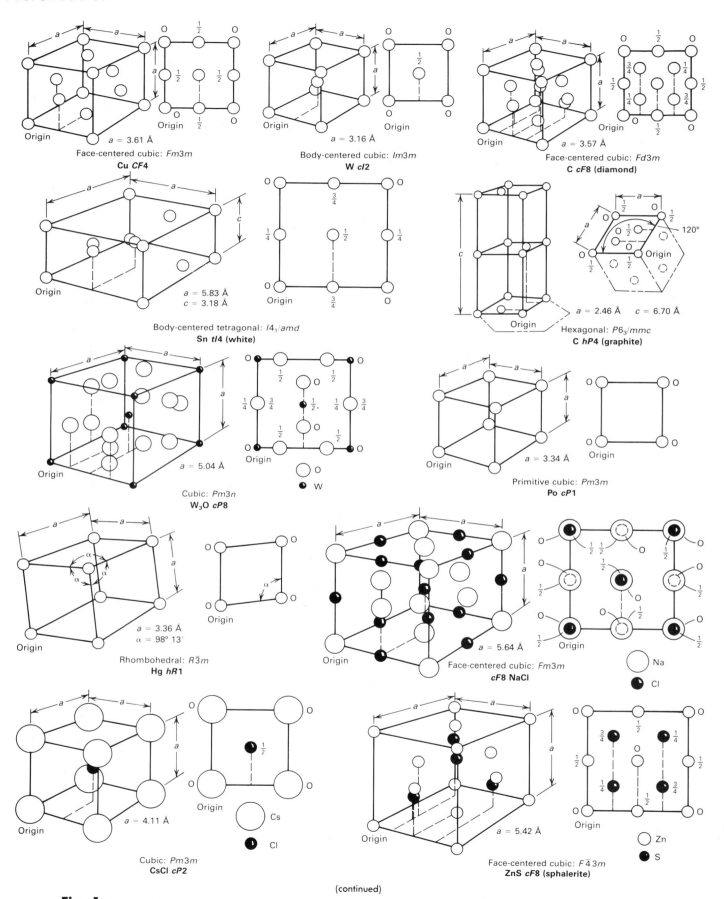

**Fig. 1** Atom positions, prototypes, structure symbols, space-group notations, and lattice parameters for some of the simple metallic crystals

(continued)

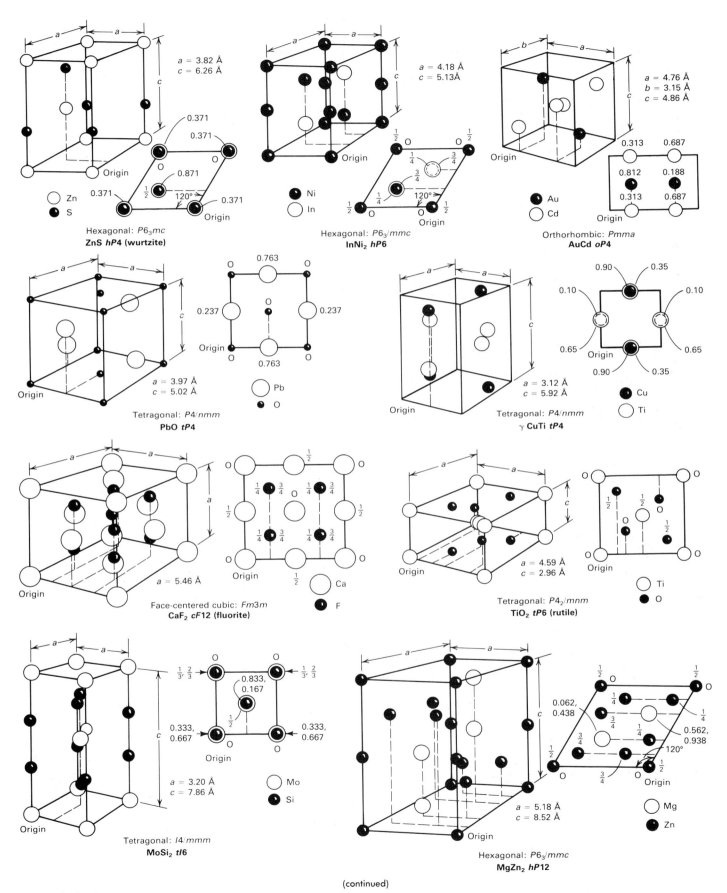

**Fig. 1** Atom positions, prototypes, structure symbols, space-group notations, and lattice parameters for some of the simple metallic crystals

(continued)

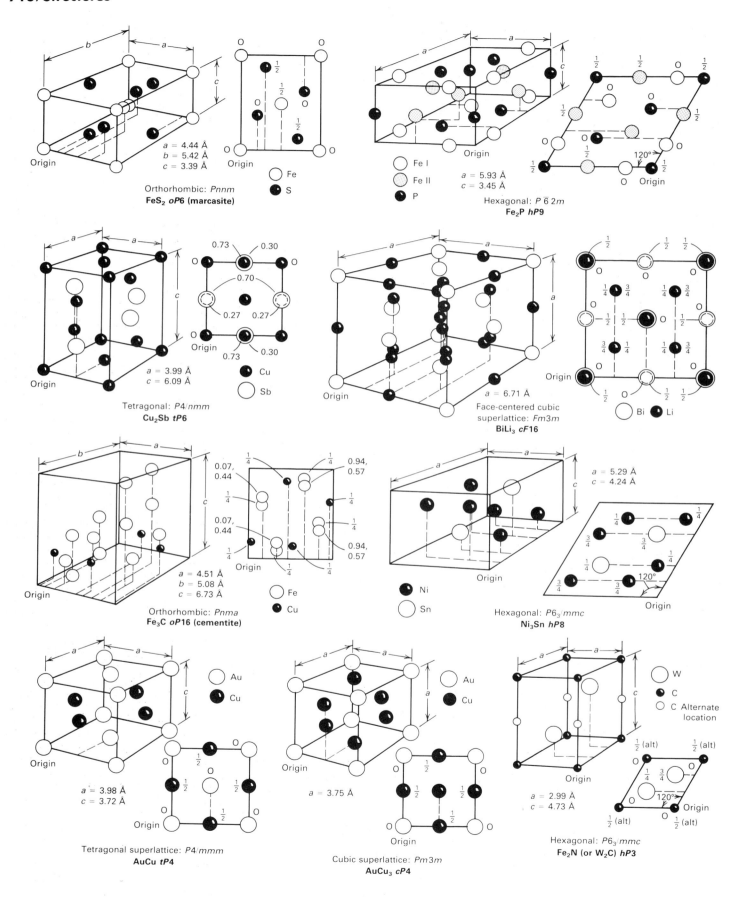

**Fig. 1** Atom positions, prototypes, structure symbols, space-group notations, and lattice parameters for some of the simple metallic crystals

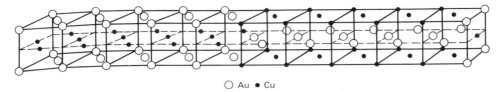

○ Au    ● Cu

**Fig. 2** AuCu II structure: a one-dimensional, long-period superlattice, with antiphase boundaries at intervals of five unit cells of the disordered state

**Point defects** include vacant atom positions that are occupied in perfect crystals. These vacancies increase in number as temperature is increased, and by jumping about from one lattice site to another, they cause diffusion.

Interstitial atoms are those located between the atoms of the normal, perfect-crystal array; therefore, the carbon atoms in body-centered cubic ferrite are interstitials in that they fit between the iron atoms of its body-centered cubic structure, which is similar to the W *cI2* type illustrated in Fig. 1. Substitutional atoms are those located at atom positions normally occupied by the atoms of the host crystal, and thus "substitute" for host atoms. There are also many close pairs and clusters of point defects, such as divacancies, trivacancies, and interstitial-vacancy pairs.

**Line Defects.** Dislocations are line defects that exist in nearly all real crystals. An edge dislocation, which is the edge of an incomplete plane of atoms within a crystal, is represented in cross section in Fig. 4. In this illustration, the incomplete plane extends partway through the crystal from the top down, and the edge dislocation (indicated by the standard symbol ⊥) is its lower edge.

If forces, as indicated by the arrows in Fig. 5, are applied to a crystal, such as the perfect crystal shown in Fig. 5(a), one part of the crystal will slip. The edge of the slipped region, shown as a dashed line in Fig. 5(b), is a dislocation. The portion of this line at the left

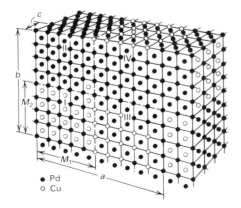

**Fig. 3** Two-dimensional, long-period superlattice (as in Cu-Pd), with antiphase boundaries spaced at intervals $M_1$ and $M_2$ and unit-cell dimensions $a$, $b$, and $c$ in the ordered state. The palladium atom has different positions in the small cubes in domains I, II, III, and IV.

● Pd
○ Cu

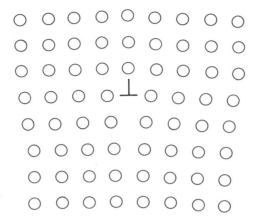

**Fig. 4** Schematic representation of a section through an edge dislocation, which is perpendicular to the plane of the illustration and is indicated by the symbol ⊥

near the front of the crystal and perpendicular to the arrows, in Fig. 5(b), is an edge dislocation, because the displacement involved is perpendicular to the dislocation.

The slip deformation in Fig. 5(b) has also formed another type of dislocation. The part of the slipped region near the right side, where the displacement is parallel to the dislocation, is termed a screw dislocation. In this part, the crystal no longer is made of parallel planes of atoms, but instead consists of a single plane in the form of a helical ramp (screw).

As the slipped region spread across the slip plane, the edge-type portion of the dislocation moved out of the crystal, leaving the screw-type portion still embedded, as shown in Fig. 5(c). When all of the dislocation finally emerged from the crystal, the crystal was again perfect but with the upper part displaced one unit from the lower part, as shown in Fig. 5(d). Therefore, Fig. 5 illustrates the mechanism of plastic flow by the slip process, which is actually produced by dislocation movement.

The displacement that occurs when a dislocation passes a point is described by a vector, known as the Burgers vector. The fundamental characteristics of a dislocation are the direction of the vector with respect to the dislocation line, and the length of the vector with respect to the identity distance in the direction of the vector. The perfection of a crystal lattice is restored after the passage of a dislocation, as indicated in Fig. 5(d), provided that no additional defects are generated in the process.

Each dislocation in a crystal is the source of local stresses. The nature of these microstresses is indicated by the arrows in Fig. 6, which represent (qualitatively) the stresses acting on small volumes at different positions around the dislocation at the lower edge of the incomplete plane of atoms. Interstitial atoms usually cluster in regions where tensile strains and stresses make more room for them, as in the lower central part of Fig. 6.

In addition to the large-angle boundaries that separate crystal grains, which have different lattice orientations, the individual grains are separated by small-angle boundaries (subboundaries) into subgrains that differ very little in orientation. These subboundaries may be considered as arrays of dislocations; tilt boundaries are arrays of edge dislocations, and twist boundaries are arrays of screw dislocations. A tilt boundary is represented in Fig. 7 by the series of edge dislocations in a vertical row. Compared with large-angle boundaries, small-angle boundaries are less severe defects, obstruct plastic flow less, and are less effective as regions for chemical attack and segregation of alloying constituents. In general, mixed types of grain-boundary defects are common. All grain boundaries are sinks into which vacancies and dislocations can disappear and may also serve as sources of these defects; they are important factors in creep deformation.

**Stacking faults** are two-dimensional defects that are planes where there is an error in the normal sequence of stacking of atom layers. Stacking faults may be formed during the growth of a crystal. They may also result from motion of partial dislocations. Unlike a full dislocation, which produces a displacement of a full distance between the lattice points, a partial dislocation produces a movement that is less than a full distance.

**Twins** are portions of a crystal that have certain specific orientations with respect to each other. The twin relationship may be such that the lattice of one part is the mirror image of that of the other, or one part may be related to the other by a rotation about a specific crystallographic axis. Growth twins may occur frequently during crystallization from the liquid or the vapor state by growth during annealing (by recrystallization or by grain-growth processes) or by the movement between different solid phases, such as during phase transformation. Plastic deformation by shear may produce deformation (mechanical) twins. Twin boundaries generally are very flat, appearing as straight lines in micrographs, and are two-dimensional defects of lower energy than large-angle grain boundaries. Twin boundaries, therefore, are less effective as sources, and sinks, of other defects and are less active in deformation and corrosion than are ordinary grain boundaries. Textbooks and reference books, such as Ref 6, 7, and 8 list the indices of twinning planes (shear planes) and the directions of shear that occur when deformation twins are formed.

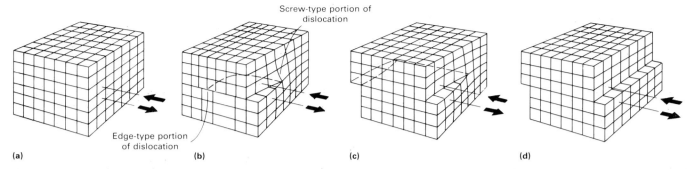

**Fig. 5** Schematic representation of four stages of slip deformation by formation and movement of a dislocation (dashed line) through a crystal. (a) Crystal before displacement. (b) Crystal after some displacement. (c) Complete displacement across part of crystal. (d) Complete displacement across entire crystal

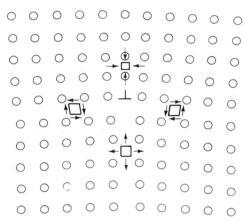

**Fig. 6** Schematic representation of a crystal containing an edge dislocation, indicating qualitatively the stresses (shown by direction of arrows) at four positions around the dislocation

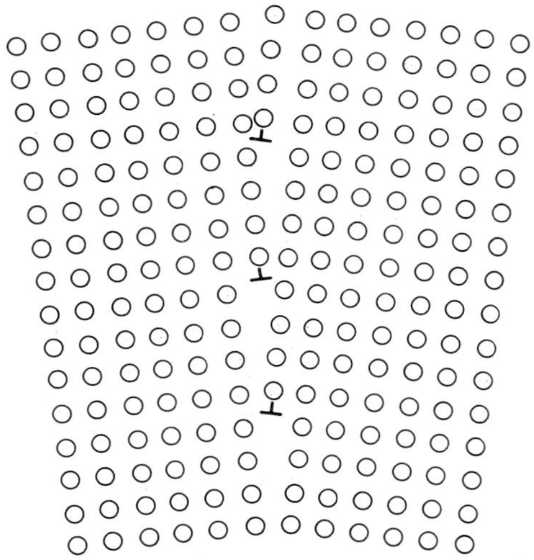

**Fig. 7** Small-angle boundary (subboundary) of the tilt type, which consists of a vertical array of edge dislocations

## REFERENCES

1. W.B. Pearson, *A Handbook of Lattice Spacings and Structures of Metals and Alloys*, Pergamon Press, Vol 1, 1958; Vol 2, 1967
2. *Strukturbericht*, Akademische Verlagsgesellschaft m.b.H., Leipzig, Germany, 1913-1939; continued as *Structure Reports*, International Union of Crystallography, 1940 to the present
3. C.R. Hubbard and L.D. Calvert, *Bulletin of Alloy Phase Diagrams*, Vol 2, 1981, p 153-156
4. T. Hahn, Ed., *International Tables for Crystallography*, Vol A, International Union of Crystallography, D. Reidel Publishing, 1983

5. R.W.G. Wyckoff, *Crystal Structures*, Interscience, Vol 1, 1963; Vol 2, 1964; Vol 3, 1965
6. C.S. Barrett and T.B. Massalski, *Structure of Metals*, 3rd ed., Pergamon Press, 1980
7. A.G. Guy, *Elements of Physical Metallurgy*, Addison-Wesley, 1959
8. L.H. Van Vlack, *Elements of Materials Science*, Addison-Wesley, 1964
9. R. Hultgren *et al.*, *Selected Values of the Thermodynamic Properties of the Elements*, American Society for Metals, 1973
10. J.R. Peterson, J.A. Fahey, and R.D. Baybarz, *J. Inorg. Nucl. Chem.*, Vol 33, 1971, p 3345-3351
11. P.K. Smith, W.H. Hale, and M.C. Thompson, *J. Chem. Phys.*, Vol 50, 1969, p 5066-5076
12. P.G. Pallmer and T.D. Chikalla, *J. Less-Common Metals*, Vol 24, 1971, p 233-236
13. F. Weigel and A. Trinkl, *Radiochim. Acta*, Vol 10, 1967, p 78-82
14. R.W. Lynch and H.G. Drickamer, *J. Phys. Chem. Solids*, Vol 26, 1965, p 63
15. E.A. Perez-Albuerne *et al.*, *Phys. Rev.*, Vol 142, 1966, p 392
16. J. Donohue, *The Structures of the Elements*, Wiley-Interscience, 1974
17. C.S. Barrett and L. Meyer, *Phys. Rev.*, Vol 160, 1967, p 694
18. L. Pauling *et al.*, *J. Solid State Chem.*, Vol Z, 1970, p 225
19. A.F. Schach and R.L. Mills, *J. Chem. Phys.*, Vol 1 (No. 52), 1970, p 6000

## SELECTED REFERENCES

- J.D.H. Donnay, *Crystal Data*, American Crystallographic Assn., 1963
- M. Hansen with K. Anderko, Constitution of Binary Alloys, McGraw-Hill, 1958; First Supplement, P.P. Elliott, 1965; Second Supplement, F.A. Shunk, 1969
- "Powder Diffraction Data File," International Center for Diffraction Data, Swarthmore, PA
- C.J. Smithells, *Metals Reference Book*, 4th ed., Vol 1, Plenum Press, 1967
- J.H. Westbrook, Ed., *Intermetallic Compounds*, John Wiley & Sons, 1967

# Metric Conversion Guide

This Section is intended as a guide for expressing weights and measures in the Système International d'Unités (SI). The purpose of SI units, developed and maintained by the General Conference of Weights and Measures, is to provide a basis for world-wide standardization of units and measure. For more information on metric conversions, the reader should consult the following references:

- "Standard for Metric Practice," E 380, *Annual Book of ASTM Standards*, 1984, ASTM, 1916 Race Street, Philadelphia, PA 19103
- "Metric Practice," ANSI/IEEE 268–1982, American National Standards Institute, 1430 Broadway, New York, NY 10018
- *Metric Practice Guide—Units and Conversion Factors for the Steel Industry*, 1978, American Iron and Steel Institute, 1000 16th Street NW, Washington, DC 20036
- *The International System of Units*, SP 330, 1981, National Bureau of Standards. Order from Superintendent of Documents, U.S. Government Printing Office, Washington, DC 20402
- *Metric Editorial Guide*, 5th ed., 1985, American National Metric Council, 1010 Vermont Ave. NW, Suite 320, Washington, DC 20005
- *ASME Orientation and Guide for Use of SI (Metric) Units*, ASME Guide SI 1, 9th ed., 1982, The American Society of Mechanical Engineers, 22 Law Drive, Fairfield, NJ, 07007

## Base, supplementary, and derived SI units

| Measure | Unit | Symbol | Measure | Unit | Symbol |
|---|---|---|---|---|---|
| **Base units** | | | Entropy | joule per kelvin | J/K |
| | | | Force | newton | N |
| Amount of substance | mole | mol | Frequency | hertz | Hz |
| Electric current | ampere | A | Heat capacity | joule per kelvin | J/K |
| Length | meter | m | Heat flux density | watt per square meter | W/m² |
| Luminous intensity | candela | cd | Illuminance | lux | lx |
| Mass | kilogram | kg | Inductance | henry | H |
| Thermodynamic temperature | kelvin | K | Irradiance | watt per square meter | W/m² |
| Time | second | s | Luminance | candela per square meter | cd/m² |
| | | | Luminous flux | lumen | lm |
| **Supplementary units** | | | Magnetic field strength | ampere per meter | A/m |
| | | | Magnetic flux | weber | WB |
| Plane angle | radian | rad | Magnetic flux density | tesla | T |
| Solid angle | steradian | sr | Molar energy | joule per mole | J/mol |
| | | | Molar entropy | joule per mole kelvin | J/mol · K |
| **Derived units** | | | Molar heat capacity | joule per mole kelvin | J/mol · K |
| | | | Moment of force | newton meter | N · m |
| Absorbed dose | gray | Gy | Permeability | henry per meter | H/m |
| Acceleration | meter per second squared | m/s² | Permittivity | farad per meter | F/m |
| Activity (of radionuclides) | becquerel | Bq | Power, radiant flux | watt | W |
| Angular acceleration | radian per second squared | rad/s² | Pressure, stress | pascal | Pa |
| Angular velocity | radian per second | rad/s | Quantity of electricity, electric charge | coulomb | C |
| Area | square meter | m² | Radiance | watt per square meter steradian | W/m² · sr |
| Capacitance | farad | F | | | |
| Concentration (of amount of substance) | mole per cubic meter | mol/m³ | Radiant intensity | watt per steradian | W/sr |
| Conductance | siemens | S | Specific heat capacity | joule per kilogram kelvin | J/kg · K |
| Current density | ampere per square meter | A/m² | Specific energy | joule per kilogram | J/kg |
| Density, mass | kilogram per cubic meter | kg/m³ | Specific entropy | joule per kilogram kelvin | J/kg · K |
| Electric charge density | coulomb per cubic meter | C/m³ | Specific volume | cubic meter per kilogram | m³/kg |
| Electric field strength | volt per meter | V/m | Surface tension | newton per meter | N/m |
| Electric flux density | coulomb per square meter | C/m² | Thermal conductivity | watt per meter kelvin | W/m · K |
| Electric potential, potential difference, electromotive force | volt | V | Velocity | meter per second | m/s |
| | | | Viscosity, dynamic | pascal second | Pa · s |
| Electric resistance | ohm | Ω | Viscosity, kinematic | square meter per second | m²/s |
| Energy, work, quantity of heat | joule | J | Volume | cubic meter | m³ |
| Energy density | joule per cubic meter | J/m³ | Wavenumber | 1 per meter | 1/m |

## Conversion factors

| To convert from | to | multiply by | To convert from | to | multiply by | To convert from | to | multiply by |
|---|---|---|---|---|---|---|---|---|
| **Angle** | | | **Heat input** | | | **Specific heat** | | |
| degree | rad | 1.745 329 E − 02 | J/in. | J/m | 3.937 008 E + 01 | Btu/lb · °F | J/kg · K | 4.186 800 E + 03 |
| | | | kJ/in. | kJ/m | 3.937 008 E + 01 | cal/g · °C | J/kg · K | 4.186 800 E + 03 |
| **Area** | | | | | | | | |
| in.² | mm² | 6.451 600 E + 02 | **Length** | | | **Stress (force per unit area)** | | |
| in.² | cm² | 6.451 600 E + 00 | Å | nm | 1.000 000 E − 01 | tonf/in.² (tsi) | MPa | 1.378 951 E + 01 |
| in.² | m² | 6.451 600 E − 04 | μin. | μm | 2.540 000 E − 02 | kgf/mm² | MPa | 9.806 650 E + 00 |
| ft² | m² | 9.290 304 E − 02 | mil | μm | 2.540 000 E + 01 | ksi | MPa | 6.894 757 E + 00 |
| | | | in. | mm | 2.540 000 E + 01 | lbf/in.² (psi) | MPa | 6.894 757 E − 03 |
| **Bending moment or torque** | | | in. | cm | 2.540 000 E + 00 | MN/m² | MPa | 1.000 000 E + 00 |
| lbf · in. | N · m | 1.129 848 E − 01 | ft | m | 3.048 000 E − 01 | | | |
| lbf · ft | N · m | 1.355 818 E + 00 | yd | m | 9.144 000 E − 01 | **Temperature** | | |
| kgf · m | N · m | 9.806 650 E + 00 | mile | km | 1.609 300 E + 00 | °F | °C | 5/9 · (°F − 32) |
| ozf · in. | N · m | 7.061 552 E − 03 | | | | °R | °K | 5/9 |
| | | | **Mass** | | | | | |
| **Bending moment or torque per unit length** | | | oz | kg | 2.834 952 E − 02 | **Temperature interval** | | |
| lbf · in./in. | N · m/m | 4.448 222 E + 00 | lb | kg | 4.535 924 E − 01 | °F | °C | 5/9 |
| lbf · ft/in. | N · m/m | 5.337 866 E + 01 | ton (short, 2000 lb) | kg | 9.071 847 E + 02 | | | |
| | | | ton (short, 2000 lb) | kg × 10³(a) | 9.071 847 E − 01 | **Thermal conductivity** | | |
| **Current density** | | | ton (long, 2240 lb) | kg | 1.016 047 E + 03 | Btu · in./s · ft² · °F | W/m · K | 5.192 204 E + 02 |
| A/in.² | A/cm² | 1.550 003 E − 01 | | | | Btu/ft · h · °F | W/m · K | 1.730 735 E + 00 |
| A/in.² | A/mm² | 1.550 003 E − 03 | **Mass per unit area** | | | Btu · in./h · ft² · °F | W/m · K | 1.442 279 E − 01 |
| A/ft² | A/m² | 1.076 400 E + 01 | oz/in.² | kg/m² | 4.395 000 E + 01 | cal/cm · s · °C | W/m · K | 4.184 000 E + 02 |
| | | | oz/ft² | kg/m² | 3.051 517 E − 01 | | | |
| **Electricity and magnetism** | | | oz/yd² | kg/m² | 3.390 575 E − 02 | **Thermal expansion** | | |
| gauss | T | 1.000 000 E − 04 | lb/ft² | kg/m² | 4.882 428 E + 00 | in./in. · °C | m/m · K | 1.000 000 E + 00 |
| maxwell | μWb | 1.000 000 E − 02 | | | | in./in. · °F | m/m · K | 1.800 000 E + 00 |
| mho | S | 1.000 000 E + 00 | **Mass per unit length** | | | | | |
| Oersted | A/m | 7.957 700 E + 01 | lb/ft | kg/m | 1.488 164 E + 00 | **Velocity** | | |
| Ω · cm | Ω · m | 1.000 000 E − 02 | lb/in. | kg/m | 1.785 797 E + 01 | ft/h | m/s | 8.466 667 E − 05 |
| Ω circular-mil/ft | μΩ · m | 1.662 426 E − 03 | | | | ft/min | m/s | 5.080 000 E − 03 |
| | | | **Mass per unit time** | | | ft/s | m/s | 3.048 000 E − 01 |
| **Energy (impact, other)** | | | lb/h | kg/s | 1.259 979 E − 04 | in./s | m/s | 2.540 000 E − 02 |
| ft · lbf | J | 1.355 818 E + 00 | lb/min | kg/s | 7.559 873 E − 03 | km/h | m/s | 2.777 778 E − 01 |
| Btu (thermochemical) | J | 1.054 350 E + 03 | lb/s | kg/s | 4.535 924 E − 01 | mph | km/h | 1.609 344 E + 00 |
| cal (thermochemical) | J | 4.184 000 E + 00 | | | | | | |
| kW · h | J | 3.600 000 E + 06 | **Mass per unit volume (includes density)** | | | **Velocity of rotation** | | |
| W · h | J | 3.600 000 E + 03 | g/cm³ | kg/m³ | 1.000 000 E + 03 | rev/min (rpm) | rad/s | 1.047 164 E − 01 |
| | | | lb/ft³ | g/cm³ | 1.601 846 E − 02 | rev/s | rad/s | 6.283 185 E + 00 |
| **Flow rate** | | | lb/ft³ | kg/m³ | 1.601 846 E + 01 | | | |
| ft³/h | L/min | 4.719 475 E − 01 | lb/in.³ | g/cm³ | 2.767 990 E + 01 | **Viscosity** | | |
| ft³/min | L/min | 2.831 000 E + 01 | lb/in.³ | kg/m³ | 2.767 990 E + 04 | poise | Pa · s | 1.000 000 E + 01 |
| gal/h | L/min | 6.309 020 E − 02 | | | | strokes | m²/s | 1.000 000 E − 04 |
| gal/min | L/min | 3.785 412 E + 00 | **Power** | | | ft²/s | m²/s | 9.290 304 E − 02 |
| | | | Btu/s | kW | 1.055 056 E + 00 | in.²/s | mm²/s | 6.451 600 E + 02 |
| **Force** | | | Btu/min | kW | 1.758 426 E − 02 | | | |
| lbf | N | 4.448 222 E + 00 | Btu/h | W | 2.928 751 E − 01 | **Volume** | | |
| kip (1000 lbf) | N | 4.448 222 E + 03 | erg/s | W | 1.000 000 E − 07 | in.³ | m³ | 1.638 706 E − 05 |
| tonf | kN | 8.896 443 E + 00 | ft · lbf/s | W | 1.355 818 E + 00 | ft³ | m³ | 2.831 685 E − 02 |
| kgf | N | 9.806 650 E + 00 | ft · lbf/min | W | 2.259 697 E − 02 | fluid oz | m³ | 2.957 353 E − 05 |
| | | | ft · lbf/h | W | 3.766 161 E − 04 | gal (U.S. liquid) | m³ | 3.785 412 E − 03 |
| **Force per unit length** | | | hp (550 ft · lbf/s) | kW | 7.456 999 E − 01 | | | |
| lbf/ft | N/m | 1.459 390 E + 01 | hp (electric) | kW | 7.460 000 E − 01 | **Volume per unit time** | | |
| lbf/in. | N/m | 1.751 268 E + 02 | | | | ft³/min | m³/s | 4.719 474 E − 04 |
| | | | **Power density** | | | ft³/s | m³/s | 2.831 685 E − 02 |
| **Fracture toughness** | | | W/in.² | W/m² | 1.550 003 E + 03 | in.³/min | m³/s | 2.731 177 E − 07 |
| ksi√in. | MPa√m | 1.098 800 E + 00 | | | | | | |
| | | | **Pressure (fluid)** | | | **Wavelength** | | |
| **Heat content** | | | atm (standard) | Pa | 1.013 250 E + 05 | Å | nm | 1.000 000 E − 01 |
| | | | bar | Pa | 1.000 000 E + 05 | | | |
| Btu/lb | kJ/kg | 2.326 000 E + 00 | in.Hg (32 °F) | Pa | 3.386 380 E + 03 | | | |
| cal/g | kJ/kg | 4.186 800 E + 00 | in.Hg (60 °F) | Pa | 3.376 850 E + 03 | | | |
| | | | lbf/in.² (psi) | Pa | 6.894 757 E + 03 | | | |
| | | | torr (mmHg, 0 °C) | Pa | 1.333 220 E + 02 | | | |

(a) kg × 10³ = 1 metric ton

**SI prefixes—names and symbols**

| Exponential expression | Multiplication factor | Prefix | Symbol |
|---|---|---|---|
| $10^{18}$ | 1 000 000 000 000 000 000 | exa | E |
| $10^{15}$ | 1 000 000 000 000 000 | peta | P |
| $10^{12}$ | 1 000 000 000 000 | tera | T |
| $10^{9}$ | 1 000 000 000 | giga | G |
| $10^{6}$ | 1 000 000 | mega | M |
| $10^{3}$ | 1 000 | kilo | K |
| $10^{2}$ | 100 | hecto(a) | h |
| $10^{1}$ | 10 | deka(a) | da |
| $10^{0}$ | 1 | BASE UNIT | |
| $10^{-1}$ | 0.1 | deci(a) | d |
| $10^{-2}$ | 0.01 | centi(a) | c |
| $10^{-3}$ | 0.001 | milli | m |
| $10^{-6}$ | 0.000 001 | micro | $\mu$ |
| $10^{-9}$ | 0.000 000 001 | nano | n |
| $10^{-12}$ | 0.000 000 000 001 | pico | p |
| $10^{-15}$ | 0.000 000 000 000 001 | femto | f |
| $10^{-18}$ | 0.000 000 000 000 000 001 | atto | a |

(a) Nonpreferred. Prefixes should be selected in steps of $10^3$ so that the resultant number before the prefix is between 0.1 and 1000. These prefixes should not be used for units of linear measurement, but may be used for higher order units. For example, the linear measurement, decimeter, is nonpreferred, but square decimeter is acceptable.

# Abbreviations and Symbols

*a* crystal lattice length along the *a* axis

**A** ampere

**Å** angstrom

**AA** Aluminum Association

**ac** alternating current

**Ac$_{cm}$** in hypereutectoid steel, the temperature at which solution of cementite in austenite is completed during heating

**Ac$_1$** the temperature at which austenite begins to form during heating

**Ac$_3$** the temperature at which the transformation of ferrite to austenite is completed during heating

**Ac$_4$** the temperature at which austenite transforms to δ-ferrite during heating

**ACI** Alloy Casting Institute

**Ae$_{cm}$, Ae$_1$, Ae$_3$, Ae$_4$** the temperatures of phase transformations at equilibrium

**AFS** American Foundrymen's Society

**AIME** American Institute of Mining, Metallurgical and Petroleum Engineers

**AIP** American Institute of Physics

**AISI** American Iron and Steel Institute

**AMS** Aerospace Material Specification

**ANSI** American National Standards Institute

**APB** antiphase boundary

**API** American Petroleum Institute

**Ar$_{cm}$** in hypereutectoid steel, the temperature at which precipitation of cementite starts during cooling

**Ar$_1$** the temperature at which transformation of austenite to ferrite or to ferrite plus cementite is completed during cooling

**Ar$_3$** the temperature at which austenite begins to transform to ferrite during cooling

**Ar$_4$** the temperature at which δ-ferrite transforms to austenite during cooling

**ASM** American Society for Metals

**ASME** American Society of Mechanical Engineers

**ASTM** American Society for Testing and Materials

**at.%** atomic percent

**atm** atmosphere

**AWS** American Welding Society

*b* crystal lattice length along the *b* axis

**b** barn (unit of nuclear cross section); Burgers vector

**bal** balance or remainder

**bcc** body-centered cubic

**bct** body-centered tetragonal

**BE** backscattered electron

**BF** bright-field (illumination)

**Btu** British thermal unit

***Blc** crystal lattice length along the *c* axis

**C** coulomb

**cal** calorie

**CCT** continuous cooling transformation (diagram)

**CDA** Copper Development Association

**cm** centimeter

**COE** cube-on-edge

**conc** concentrated

**CRT** cathode ray tube

**dc** direct current

**DF** dark-field (illumination)

**diam** diameter

**DIC** differential interference contrast (illumination)

**DPH** diamond pyramid hardness (Vickers hardness)

**e** natural log base, 2.71828 . . .

**ECM** electrochemical machining

**EDM** electrical discharge machining

**EDS** energy dispersive spectroscopy

**EDXA** energy dispersive x-ray analysis

**EMC** electromagnetic casting

**EMPA** electron microprobe analysis

**Eq** equation

*et al.* and others

**ETP** electrolytic tough pitch (copper)

**eV** electron volt

**F** farad

**fcc** face-centered cubic

**Fig.** figure

**FRTP** fire-refined tough pitch (copper)

**ft** foot

**g** gram; diffraction vector

**G** gauss

**gcp** geometrically close-packed

**GdIG** gadolinium-iron garnet

**GP** Guinier-Preston (zone)

**Gy** gray

**h** hour

**HAD** high aluminum defect

**HAZ** heat-affected zone

**HB** Brinell hardness

**hcp** hexagonal close-packed

**HID** high interstitial defect

**HK** Knoop hardness

**HR** Rockwell hardness (requires designation such as HRC for Rockwell C hardness)

**HSLA** high-strength low-alloy

**HV** Vickers hardness (diamond pyramid hardness)

**Hz** hertz

**ID** inside diameter

**in.** inch

**INCRA** International Copper Research Association

**ISO** International Organization for Standardization

**J** joule

**k** wave vector

**K** Kelvin

**kbar** kilobar (pressure)

**kg** kilogram

**kPa** kilopascal

**ksi** kips per square inch (1000 pounds per square inch)

**kV** kilovolt

**L** liter

**lb** pound

**log** common logarithm (base 10)

**ln** natural logarithm (base e)

**m** meter

**mA** milliampere

**max** maximum

**M$_f$** the temperature at which martensite formation finishes during cooling

**min** minimum; minute

**MJ** megajoule

**mL** milliliter

**mm** millimeter

**MPa** megapascal

**MPIF** Metal Powder Industries Federation

**ms** millisecond

**M$_s$** the temperature at which martensite starts to form from austenite upon cooling

*n* refractive index

**N** Newton

*N* normal (solution)

**NA** numerical aperture

**NACE** National Association of Corrosion Engineers

**NASA** National Aeronautics and Space Administration

**NBS** National Bureau of Standards

**nm** nanometer

**No.** number

**NRC** Nuclear Regulatory Commission

**ns** nanosecond

**OD** outside diameter

**OFE** oxygen-free electronic (copper)

**OFHC** oxygen-free high-conductivity (copper)

**ORNL** Oak Ridge National Laboratory

**OSHA** Occupational Safety and Health Administration

**oz** ounce

**p** page

**Pa** pascal

**pH** negative logarithm of hydrogen-ion activity

**PH** precipitation-hardenable

**pixel** picture element

**P/M** powder metallurgy

**ppm** parts per million

**psi** pounds per square inch

**PVC** polyvinyl chloride

**R** roentgen

**RE** rare earth (elements)

**Ref** reference

**REG** rare-earth garnet

**rem** roentgen equivalent man; remainder or balance

**rpm** revolutions per minute

**s** second

**SAE** Society of Automotive Engineers

**SCE** saturated calomel electrode

**SE** secondary electrons

**SEM** scanning electron microscopy

**SHE** standard hydrogen electrode

**SI** Système International d' Unités

**SME** Society of Manufacturing Engineers

**STEM** scanning transmission electron microscopy

*t* time; thickness

**T** tesla

**tcp** topologically close-packed

**TEM** transmission electron microscopy

**TTT** time-temperature transformation (diagram)

**UNS** Unified Numbering System (ASTM-SAE)

**V** volt

**vol** volume

**vol%** volume percent

**W** watt

**wt%** weight percent

**YIG** yttrium-iron garnet

**yr** year

° degree; angular measure

°C degree Celsius (centigrade)

°F degree Fahrenheit

⇌ direction of reaction

÷ divided by

= equals

≈ approximately equals

≠ not equal to

≡ identical with

> greater than

≫ much greater than

≥ greater than or equal to

∫ integral of

∞ infinity

∝ varies as; is proportional to

< less than

≪ much less than

≤ less than or equal to

± maximum deviation

− minus; negative ion charge

× multiplied by; diameters (magnification)

· multiplied by

/ per

% percent

+ plus; in addition to; positive ion charge

√ surface roughness

√ square root of

∼ similar to; approximately

μF microfarad

μin. micro-inch

μm micron (micrometer)

μs microsecond

# Greek Alphabet

| | | |
|---|---|---|
| A, $\alpha$ alpha | I, $\iota$ iota | P, $\rho$ rho |
| B, $\beta$ beta | K, $\kappa$ kappa | $\Sigma$, $\sigma$ sigma |
| $\Gamma$, $\gamma$ gamma | $\Lambda$, $\lambda$ lambda | T, $\tau$ tau |
| $\Delta$, $\delta$ delta | M, $\mu$ mu | $\Upsilon$, $\upsilon$ upsilon |
| E, $\epsilon$ epsilon | N, $\nu$ nu | $\Phi$, $\phi$ phi |
| Z, $\zeta$ zeta | $\Xi$, $\xi$ xi | X, $\chi$ chi |
| H, $\eta$ eta | O, $o$ omicron | $\Psi$, $\psi$ psi |
| $\Theta$, $\theta$ theta | $\Pi$, $\pi$ pi | $\Omega$, $\omega$ omega |

# Index

The word "microstructure" in this index refers to text discussions of microstructure. Micrographs of specific alloys are usually referenced under the "alloys, specific types" headings.